The
EQUITABLE
· SCHOOLS BOOK ·
1992

The
EQUITABLE
· *SCHOOLS BOOK* ·
1992

**THE DISCRIMINATING PARENTS'
GUIDE TO INDEPENDENT SECONDARY SCHOOLS**

Editors
**KLAUS BOEHM
JENNY LEES-SPALDING**

BLOOMSBURY

This edition published in 1991 by Bloomsbury Publishing Limited,
2 Soho Square, London W1V 5DE

The moral right of the author has been asserted

Copyright © Klaus Boehm Publications Ltd,
Klaus Boehm, Jenny Lees-Spalding 1988, 1989, 1990, 1991

**This edition has been supported by
THE EQUITABLE LIFE ASSURANCE SOCIETY**

Publisher's note
The information in this book was correct to the best of the Editors'
and Publishers' belief at the time of going to press.
While no responsibility can be accepted for errors and omissions,
the Editors and Publisher would welcome corrections and suggestions
for inclusion in future editions of this title.

A copy of the CIP entry for this book is available from
the British Library

ISBN 0 7475 1001 6

Designed by Geoff Green
Typeset by Florencetype Ltd, Kewstoke, Avon
Printed in England by Clays Ltd, St Ives plc

· *Contents* ·

· *Foreword* ·

This is a consumer book. To be precise it is a book for the parents of children who may become pupils in independent secondary schools. Its premise is that just as there are horses for courses, a child will flourish in some schools and flop in others because no school can do equally well for all types of children.

1992 complicates your choice. By the time your children complete their education, the single European market will be up and running and they will almost certainly work within it. To help them *now*, you can make sure they pick up European language skills at school. It is not safe to rely on university or college courses to make good earlier gaps; they are not (and probably will not be) equipped to do so.

For this, the 1992 edition, well over 90% of the schools have provided us with basic indicators of their own European activities and we are deeply indebted to them. We have been able to provide a snapshot of what is going on but things are moving fast and it is worth checking developments in detail before you choose.

As always, the range is enormous. Some schools offer French only, some offer up to eight EC languages. In some, very few pupils take GCSE in more than one European language, in others the majority do and in a few all pupils continue with European languages throughout their time in the school. The majority encourage pupils from other EC countries to attend their school; an increasing number run regular exchanges to the countries whose languages they offer. Many run educational or cultural visits to one or more countries. A few are involved in the European Youth Parliament, run special European events, teach European languages to parents, send pupils to work experience places in the EC or even take a whole class to France to be taught all their GCSE subjects in French.

This book aims to help you shortlist schools. It is no substitute for your own enquiries, your own scrutiny of school prospectuses, your own school visits and the exercise of your own judgement on behalf of your child. You pay, you choose. We will do neither for you.

Klaus Boehm
Jenny Lees-Spalding
June 1991

· *How to use the book* ·

The book is arranged in three unequal sections:

- How to go about it A–Z
- Schools A–Z
- School Spotter

· How to go about it A–Z ·

Everything we think you'll need to know about the independent secondary school system, arranged alphabetically – from *Abbreviations* to *Language Skills* and *Young Enterprise*.

· Schools A–Z ·

Descriptions of over 530 independent secondary schools, arranged alphabetically. Most are based on a questionnaire, with specific questions, completed by the school and returned to Heads for checking. Where a school has a junior department, this is indicated in the age range. There is no further attempt to cover the junior department eg boarding may not be available for younger children and we have not given IAPS affiliation.

All school descriptions include, at the top, key facts such as overall size: boys/girls, day/boarding; senior pupils' fees for day, boarding and weekly boarding; size of the upper sixth (ie A-level year); and affiliations, either the Head's (eg HMC) or the school's (eg Woodard); those of the governing body, bursars etc are not included. Other sections are.

What it's like
Our view of what the school is like.

School profile
Hard facts about the school. These are intended to be indicative not definitive. Some figures are presented as percentages, some as actual numbers; some are for a specific year, some are an average over three years; many are approximations; percentages will not necessarily add up to 100. But the numbers given should give you a fair picture of the school.

Pupils
Total numbers of pupils, also broken down into day/boarding and boys/girls. Where the school take pupils below secondary school age, the size and age range of the senior department is also given. It gives the proportion of the school's intake which has come from state schools. Sometimes the proportion coming to the sixth is very high but the total intake at that stage may be very small.

Entrance
How the school selects and what financial assistance is available.

Parents
Where they live and what they do.

Staff
Who's the head; staff numbers and turnover.

Academic work
Public exams taken; the number of subjects offered (including whether or not A-level general studies is offered, which is sometimes taken as an extra A-level); any subjects that are unusual; and passes per pupil – not pass rates. So you can see, for example, if all pupils pass 2 A-levels or some pass 4, some 1.

If you are not familiar with the Scottish exam system but are interested in Scottish schools, please look up *Scotland* in How To Go About It before looking up the individual Scottish schools. The school examinations are different to those in England and a whole cohort does not necessarily take each exam.

European Community
EC languages offered, proportion of pupils taking 2 or more at GCSE. The regular exchanges run and any other initiatives.

Senior pupils' non-academic activities
Usually concentrates on pupils in the upper fifth and above. It won't give a complete picture of all that happens in a school but does give some comparative information by which to judge how much is going on other than passing A-levels. In some day schools, pupils may do eg music without the involvement of the school.

Careers
Revised this year, this gives a profile of what leavers go on to do. Look carefully – where there is a large drop between the number of upper fifth and upper sixth pupils, some schools have given information on all their leavers, some for sixth form leavers only.

Uniform/Houses/Prefects/Religion/Social
To help you judge the flavour of the school.

Discipline
A very sensitive area. We felt it was important to know what a school's attitude was to discipline. Whilst it is obvious that each case must be judged individually, we asked schools what they would *expect* by way of punishment in two cases – a relatively minor incident (failure to produce homework on a single occasion) and an obviously serious offence (smoking cannabis). We must emphasise that, in this latter case, we asked for punishment *other than* any police involvement and that schools answered the question hypothetically. Do not assume that a school has a drugs problem simply because it has considered what its reaction would be if one should arise.

Boarding
The way boarding is organised and when pupils are allowed out.

Alumni Association
How to get in touch with the person who runs the old boys'/girls' association.

Former pupils
Names selected by the school.

This is a search index listing all the schools by country, county and city based on the full description in the *Schools A–Z*, in particular –

Termly fees
If the fees for full and weekly boarding are the same, only one figure is given.

Financial help
Asst places = assisted places; Schols = scholarships; and LEA or MoD mean that the Local Education Authority or the Ministry of Defence offer grants to eligible pupils.

Religion
That which predominates, not necessarily that from which pupils are exclusively drawn.

Special strengths
Non-academic activities in which the school is strong eg music, which does not imply that the school is a specialised music school.

Special provisions
Provision for, say, dyslexic pupils; it should not be supposed the school specialises in pupils with difficulties.

NB Schools are grouped in areas defined by their postal address. In London, schools with, eg SW post codes are in South London, EC post codes in East London. Please be sure to read the full descriptions of the schools in which you are interested in the *Schools A–Z*.

· *How to go about it A–Z* ·

· *How to go about it* ·

· *Abbreviations* ·

AAA	Amateur Athletic Association
ABRSM	Associated Board of the Royal Schools of Music
ACE	Advisory Centre for Education
A-level	Advanced level examination
Alumni	Latin term for old boys/girls of a school
APS	Assisted Places Scheme
ARCM	Associate of the Royal College of Music
ARCO	Associate of the Royal College of Organists
ASA	Amateur Swimming Association
AS-level	Advanced Supplementary level
ATC	Air Training Corps
ATI	Association of Tutors Incorporated
BA	Bachelor of Arts degree
BAGA	British Amateur Gymnastics Association
BAYS	British Association of Young Scientists
BBC	British Broadcasting Corporation
BEd	Bachelor of Education
BSc	Bachelor of Science
BTEC	Business and Technical Education Council
c/ca	circa (Latin for approximate)
Cantab	abbreviated Latin term for Cambridge University
CCF	Combined Cadet Force
CCSS	Conference of Catholic Secondary Schools
CDT	Craft Design Technology
CE	Common Entrance exam
CEE	Certificate of Extended Education; can also mean Common entrance exam
CERN	*Conseil Européen pour la Recherche Nucléaire* (European Organization for Nuclear Research)
Cert Ed	Certificate of Education
CHE	College of Higher Education
CIFE	Conference for Independent Further Education
CNAA	Council for National Academic Awards
C of E	Church of England
CPVE	Certificate of Pre-vocational Education
CSCL	Church Schools Company Ltd
CSV	Community Service Volunteers
CSYS	Certificate of Sixth-year Studies Examination
CTF	Catholic Teachers Federation
CV	Curriculum vitae
DES	Department of Education and Science
DipEd	Diploma of Education
D of E	Duke of Edinburgh's Award Scheme
ECIS	European Council of International Studies
EFL	English as a Foreign Language
ERASMUS	European Community Action Scheme for the mobility of University Students
ESB	English Speaking Board

ESHA	European Secondary Heads Association
ESL	English as a Second Language
ESU	English Speaking Union
FCA	Fellow of the Institute of Chartered Accountants
FLIC	Foreign Languages for Industry & Commerce
FLAW	Foreign Languages at work
FT/PT	Full Time/Part Time
GAP	Gap Activity Projects (or Government Assisted Places)
GBA	Governing Bodies Association
GBGSA	Governing Bodies of Girls' Schools Association
GCSE	General Certificate of Secondary Education
GNSM	Graduate of Northern School of Music
GPDST	Girls' Public Day School Trust
GSA	Girls' Schools Association
HAS	Headteachers Association in Scotland
HMC	Headmasters' Conference
Hons	Honours degree
IAPS	Incorporated Association of Preparatory Schools
IB	International Baccalaureat
i/c	In charge
IQ	Intelligence quotient
ISAI	Independent Schools Association Incorporated
ISBA	Independent Schools Bursars' Association
ISCO	Independent Schools Careers Organisation
ISIS	Independent Schools Information Service
ISJC	Independent Schools Joint Council
LAMDA	London Academy of Music and Dramatic Art
LATE	Looking at the Environment
LEA	Local Education Authority
LINGUA	Community Action Programme to Promote Foreign Language Conferences in the European Community
LRAM	Licentiate of the Royal Academy of Music
LSE	London School of Economics
MA	Master of Arts
N/A	Not applicable
NACCW	National Advisory Centre on Careers for Women
NFER	National Foundation for Educational Research in England and Wales
NVQ	National Vocational Qualification
OB	Old Boys
OG	Old Girls
O-grade	Ordinary grade examination
Oxbridge	Oxford and Cambridge Universities
Oxon	Abbreviated Latin term for Oxford University
pa	per annum
PE	Physical Education
PGCE	Postgraduate Certificate of Education
PRISM	Peace and Reconciliation Inter-Schools Movement
PT	Physical Training
RAD	Royal Academy of Dance
RADA	Royal Academy of Dramatic Art
RC	Roman Catholic
RE/RI/RS	Religious Education/Religious Instruction/Religious Studies
RLSS	Royal Life Saving Society

RNIB	Royal National Institute for the Blind
RSA	Royal Society of Arts
SAT	Stanford Achievement Tests
SCE	Scottish Certificate of Education
SCIS	Scottish Council for Independent Schools
S-grade	Standard grade examination
SHA	Secondary Heads' Association
SHMIS	Society of Headmasters of Independent Schools
SLD	Special Learning Difficulties
SRN	State Registered Nurse
Steiner schools	Schools founded by Rudolf Steiner
STEP	Sixth Term Exam Paper (entrance exam for Cambridge University)
UKCPU	United Kingdom College, Polytechnic or University
V, VI	Roman numerals five and six (sometimes used to mean fifth and sixth forms)
VDU	Visual Display Unit
VSO	Voluntary Service Overseas
wef	with effect from
Woodard schools	Group of schools administered by the Woodard Corporation

· Academic results ·

Many parents assume that by going independent their children's academic chances will be optimised. Raw educational statistics suggest they are right: in England, of all those getting one or more A-levels, only 17% come from the maintained sector while 67% are from independent schools, a colossally skewed result when you remember that more than 90% of all children attend maintained schools. Providing you choose a school to match your child, then other things being equal it is likely that:

Independent education + effort = a good university place.

But beware. Some schools emphasise their academic results at the expense of all else – apparently a reflection of parents' concerns. Some children will thrive in academic hot houses where the principal aim is to get the maximum number of pupils through 3 or more A-levels; many will not. If a child feels seriously pressurised the results can be frightening – anorexia, depression and, in rare cases, even suicide.

If your child is likely to go on to a degree course, two or three A-levels are needed as well as a respectable clutch of GCSE passes; but achieving this is not of itself a good gauge of a good education. Many schools are keen to advertise their percentage pass rates (number of passes per 100 entries). This of course allows a school to show a 100% pass rate having put one successful candidate in for one exam. In *The Equitable Schools Book* we give the number of passes per child (GCSE in upper fifth, A-levels in upper sixth); we hope the discerning parent will not look only at those figures in the school profiles. A school may have done a better job getting a marginal candidate through any exams at all, than a bright pupil through 4 A-levels at grade A.

It's worth getting academic results into perspective. You don't necessarily have to achieve them to succeed viz – Mr John Major and the Archbishop of Canterbury. Nevertheless in many careers they are a necessary qualification and in many others they are the most obvious path to success.

· Aegrotat ·

Latin term for 'is sick'. In schools this means permission, usually in writing, for a pupil to be excused from a class or sporting activity on grounds of illness or injury.

· Affiliation ·

Nearly all of the schools in *The Equitable Schools Book* are affiliated to some sort of association. It isn't always clear exactly what such affiliation entails but a school or head will probably have been vetted before being accepted, so a degree of quality control and uniformity of aims is indicated. In some cases affiliation is through the Head (eg HMC); in others (eg Steiner) it indicates a particular educational philosophy. We do not itemise the junior school affiliations or those that relate to eg the bursar or the Governing Body.

· After school ·

Most independent school-leavers go on to higher education. *The Equitable Schools Book* profiles give some idea of where pupils go on to. Most schools have good liaison with universities and polytechnics; hold copies of their prospectuses; and give advice about degree courses and the best A-levels to do. Schools can prepare their pupils for life after school or university in a variety of ways:

- Liaison with business and industry through visiting lecturers and work experience or work shadowing.
- Responsibilities while at school: as prefects; on school magazines; running clubs and societies.
- Courses in life skills, such as car maintenance, word processing, cookery.
- Year off between school and a degree: GAP, CSV.

· Age at joining ·

The Equitable Schools Book is about secondary schools. Many of them have their own junior or prep departments so you may be able to find a school that will suit your child from the age of 5 to 18 (so long as you don't feel 13 years in the same school is too long.

You need to consider:
- How many years of school fees do you want to pay?
- When does the school have intakes (usually at 5, 7–8, 11–13 and into the sixth)? It's easier not to be the only new kid in the class.
- Moves during GCSE or A-level courses should be avoided.
- Whether you want to keep your child in a State primary school, in which case you either move at 11 or into the sixth form.

· Aided pupils scheme ·

This is a government funded scheme, under which a proportion of the fees are paid for pupils at specialist music and ballet schools. Like the assisted places, the proportion is linked to family income; it differs both in the size of the contribution and by covering boarding fees as well as tuition fees. The Aided Pupils Scheme is open to pupils at five schools in *The Equitable Schools Book* – Chetham's, Purcell, Royal Ballet, Wells Cathedral and Yehudi Menuhin.

· A-levels ·

A-levels matter. Three, with good grades, are needed to get into the top university or polytechnic courses; 2 for others and for direct entry into professions like accountancy and the army. The A-level course is designed to take 2 years to complete – usually between the ages of 16 and 18. Some schools may allow their more academic pupils to take one (and maybe some AS-levels) after one year. Most schools help match A-level choices with what your child wants to do after school. Some A-levels (eg, general studies and art) aren't always acceptable for entrance to degree courses. Find out which subjects and – most important – combinations of subjects are available; some schools have an arts or science bias. Ask to look at results for the past few years (ask for results by subject and/or by pupil; be suspicious of pass rates).

· Allied schools ·

This is a group of 7 Church of England schools (3 for boys, 4 for girls) established during the 1920s.

· Alumni ·

Latin for 'foster children', this means former pupils of a school. *The Equitable Schools Book* includes famous alumni listed by the schools – the range of these shows something of the ethos of the school even if it doesn't necessarily imply that it'll turn your child into a great rugby player, writer or spy.

Some girls' schools use the feminine form – alumnae.

· Art ·

Often part of the curriculum for the first few years of secondary school. Most schools teach it up to A-level although some academic ones don't regard it as a suitable A-level for brighter pupils to do (it isn't an acceptable A-level for some degree courses). Schools often offer it as a non-examined interest subject during A-level courses or as an extra A-level (third or fourth). Some schools make art facilities (often very extensive – including screen printing, pottery, dyeing) available to pupils at lunch-time and after school; in other schools the facilities are closed to non-examinees – you can get some idea from the number of pupils taking non-examined art in the school profiles.

· AS-levels ·

The first Advanced Supplementary level exams were in 1989. They're designed to broaden the sixth-form syllabus. Two AS-levels are equivalent to 1 A-level and pupils can opt to replace 1 or more A-levels with AS-levels, either to complement their specialisation (eg, a language with sciences) or to broaden it (eg, maths for biologists). Are being used by schools as an *EXTRA* to A-levels i.e. nobody is reducing the number of A-levels, just adding on. This is because admissions tutors are not used to equating 2=1 A-level.

· Assisted Places Scheme ·

Under this scheme the government pays a proportion of the school fees of children whose parents can't afford them. Means-tested help is available for children from the age of 11 or in the sixth form, regardless of their current school. But remember, a Labour government would put this scheme in jeopardy.

There are over 36,000 government-assisted places at over 350 schools in England, Scotland and Wales. These account for about $8^1/_2$% of the total independent school population. What you pay this year depends on your family income last year. Check the small print but use this table as a rough guide.

8

ASSISTED PLACES: ROUGH GUIDE		
1990/91 INCOME (income after allowances for dependents)	PARENTS' CONTRIBUTION TO FEES	
	One assisted place holder	For each of two assisted place holders
8,714	0	0
8,750	15	9
10,000	147	108
12,000	471	354
14,000	897	672
16,000	1,377	1,032
18,000	1,956	1,464
20,000	2,616	1,959
22,000	3,276	2,454
24,000	3,936	2,949
27,000	4,926	3,693
30,000	5,769	4,434
35,000	–	5,673

Each school in the scheme has a limited number of assisted places which it fills using its own method of selection. Government-assisted places don't include boarding fees but some of the schools participating run their own schemes for boarding pupils. Apply directly to the school of your choice. Further information and lists of participating school from:

- **England**: Assisted Places Scheme, Department of Education and Science, Mowden Hall, Darlington, Co Durham DL3 9BG (tel: 0325 392156).
- **Wales**: Welsh Office Education Department, Phase II, Government Buildings, Tŷ Glas Road, Llanishen, Cardiff CF4 5WE (tel: 0222 761456).
- **Scotland**: Scottish Education Department, Room 4/08, New St Andrew's House, Edinburgh ED1 3SY (tel: 031 244 5521).

· Boarding schools ·

These range from day schools with perhaps the odd boarder to boarding schools with the occasional day pupil. One head tells parents that boarding is unnatural and yet he will not allow weekly boarding as weekends reinforce the community feeling of the school and are the major periods for extra-curricular activities. But a number of schools do now offer weekly boarding as a half-way house.

Less popular than it used to be, boarding makes especially good sense to parents if there are no suitable day schools within reach, you are likely to move during critical periods of your child's school career or your work makes it difficult to deal with children at day schools. From the child's standpoint, you need to make sure your child is happy with the idea, particularly if there are problems at home. Some independent children will flourish in a boarding school; others may be homesick, feel rejected and become demotivated.

It's worth thinking about:

- Distance: most parents choose a boarding school that's within about $1\frac{1}{2}$ hours' travelling time of home; if that's impossible, is there one close to grandparents, friends or relations?

- Schedule and extra-curricular activities: what's available, especially at weekends; how much of the day is scheduled and organised? Is it geared to boarders or day pupils? Are children free to pursue their own interests as well as those that the school regards as appropriate. What sort of contact is there with the local community or other schools? Are they allowed into the local town – accompanied or unaccompanied?
- Food: more important for boarders who can't rely on daily supplements from home. What other food can they buy or keep?
- Meet the house staff and find out about the routine in the boarding houses. Are children expected to help with table-laying? What are dormitories and other rooms like? How much privacy do pupils have? Are they allowed into dormitories/bedrooms during the day? Do bed-times make sense?
- Exeats: how many and for how long? Are they fixed or flexible? What if you want to take your child out of school at short notice, or before the end of term? Is weekly boarding available and how prevalent is it?
- What provision is there for ill children? Is there a nurse on the premises and a nearby doctor on call?

· Boys' schools ·

Some boys' secondary schools take boys from 11, some from 13. The traditional public schools start at 13 although a few have small junior departments for boys of 11 and 12 and many have associated prep schools taking boys from 5 or 8.

The drawbacks of all-male schools are notorious, from mild unease with women to rampant misogyny or homosexuality. These are exaggerated; attempts are made to counteract them, such as mixed activities with local girls' schools and female teaching staff. Many boys' schools take girls into the sixth; an increasing number are becoming co-ed throughout.

· Bullying ·

It happens. It is inherent in institutional life; never believe the contrary. Good schools try hard to eradicate it; poor schools pretend it does not exist. There are many causes. You may find heads' attitudes illuminating.

Remember your child can either be the bully or the one who is bullied. If you think your child is being bullied, tell the head or housemaster/mistress. The problem may not be immediately soluble but a good head will find out what's going on and can advise you and your child on how to deal with it. If you get no help, or if your child continues to be unhappy at school, investigate further: you might have chosen the wrong school.

· Burning out ·

It shouldn't happen but if it does there is very little you can do about it except keep your fingers crossed and rely on time the great healer. Why? Because it results from having let/encouraged/forced a child's academic development so that it races ahead of personal and emotional maturation. If you are lucky the two paths may still converge; if not, your achieving, prize-winning child may have been transformed into one more demotivated dropout. Better not to let it happen.

· Bursaries ·

These are means-tested awards made by some schools to the children of parents who can't afford to pay full fees. If you fall on hard times after your child has started at the school you may be able to get a bursary on the strength of the child's school record. Bursaries for new pupils can be more difficult, although some schools offer fee reductions for the children of clergymen, service personnel or alumni, or for second and subsequent siblings.

· Careers ·

Most schools concentrate on getting their pupils into higher education, leaving most decisions about occupational choice for the future. Careers advice is more or less synonymous with higher education advice. It can include:

- A careers library, with university and polytechnic prospectuses.
- At least one adviser to point pupils towards the next step if they know what they want to do, and towards some books if they don't.
- Arranging attendance at higher education and careers fairs arranged for several schools.
- Films and talks about careers options: the services, industry or, depending on the head's friends, careers in falconry or bookmaking. Parents are often used for careers talks as well.
- Some schools do not send the bulk of their pupils on to higher education. Here occupational information and advice is more important and check what is provided, especially if your child is not very academic.
- Valuable work experience can be gained in some schools – pupils sent on short-term job placements with local industry during the holidays or after exams; running miniature companies selling tuck or stationery; or running a school bank; writing; designing, editing and producing their own magazine.

Look at the careers room when you visit; ask the head about careers advice and counselling; when does it start? who visits? what do pupils do immediately after they leave school? School magazines with their lists of leavers' destinations (or intended destinations – often those given are dependent on A-level results) are useful reading. Some schools turn out generation after generation of successful local professionals – good secure establishment stuff but is this right for your child?

· CCF ·

The modern Combined Cadet Force was formed in 1948, from the OTC (Officers' Training Corps) and ATC (Air Training Corps) to provide military training units in schools and universities.

A large number of schools run a CCF (boys and girls), often only one section (Army, Navy, RAF or Royal Marines), sometimes 2 or even 3. In some schools it may be compulsory for a period. Many CCFs have a band (drums, brass; in Scotland, bagpipes).

Basic training will include foot drill, arms drill, tactics, weapon training, shooting (with .22 rifles), aircraft recognition, map-reading, camping, first aid, radio communications, signals, assault courses, survival techniques and so on. Some schools have commando and SAS-type exercises (including yomping). Most CCFs have an annual camp which is based on some form of military installation. There are also manoeuvres (sometimes in conjunction with other schools) and there is usually an annual inspection by somebody suitably distinguished in the services.

Membership of the CCF appeals to those who enjoy teamwork, team spirit, discipline and self-discipline, physical and mental challenge and an element of adventure accompanied by some hazard. There are agreeable perks, too, such as visits to naval bases (perhaps a guided tour of a warship), to RAF bases where you may get a flight, and to army depots where you may sample the full hardware of modern warfare.

· Checklists ·

There are thousands of points to consider when you're choosing a school. Make your own checklist; here are a few points you might like to include:

- area and distance from home;
- town/country;
- single sex/co-ed/mixed sixth;
- boarding/weekly, boarding/day;
- size of school/size of sixth;
- facilities for your child's interests/abilities;
- special provisions for dyslexia etc;
- fees and extras – what you can afford;
- intake age; junior/prep school attached;
- good academic/musical/sporting record etc;
- religious policy, if necessary;
- a head you can trust.

· Child Abuse ·

Schools, and boarding schools in particular, are not immune from the predatory sexual proclivities of evil adults placed in a position of authority over vulnerable children. While child abuse is rare, there have been a number of convictions and the Department of Education and Science and the Independent Schools Joint Council therefore funded a brief experiment to establish needs which was called The Boarding Schools Helpline and was operated by the child abuse charity, ChildLine. Pupils can now get advice from an experienced counsellor by telephoning HelpLine direct on:– 0800 1111.

· Child psychologist ·

If your child has an emotional, social or learning problem, this may be helped by a child psychologist. The school may be able to refer one; otherwise consult the register of chartered psychologists in your public library or through the British Psychological Society, St Andrew's House, 48 Prince's Road East, Leicester LE1 7DR (tel: 0533 549568).

· Choir schools ·

There are over 35 choir schools in the UK attached to, and providing choristers for, churches, cathedrals and college chapels. Of these, about 14 teach up to A-level, the rest are prep schools only. Although some of the schools accept girls, the choirs do not. If your son is good at singing and enjoys it enough to spend a lot of his time singing at church services, he may be able to get part or all of his fees paid as a chorister. This usually means passing a voice trial some time between the ages of 7 and 10.

Further information is available from the Choir Schools Association, Kings School, College Green, Worcester, WR1 2LH (tel: 0905–23016).

· Choosing ·

Choosing a school means finding the right school for your child. Dip into *The Equitable Schools Book* for a feel of what to expect from independent schools. You, the child and the school have to make the decisions. First work out a strategy. For example, if you've encouraged independence of thought, don't go for a school with tight rules and an urge to train children in a particular mould; if your child enjoys art but is not talented, beware the school with an art department closed to all but examinees; try and find a school that suits your child's academic ability, not the other way round.

- Draw up your basic criteria: location; fees; co-ed/single sex; day/boarding; intake age; range of curricular and extra-curricular activities.
- Find out which schools fit. If your child is at a good prep school, the head should know the local schools and help you shortlist. Include any that you think may be interesting even if they don't adhere absolutely to your expectations of what the right school is.
- Get the prospectuses and magazines from these schools. Mention your child's age, sex, the intended year of entry and any special needs.
- Draw up a shortlist of schools to visit.
- Arrange to go to at least 3 day (5 boarding schools). Unless you *and* your child are adamant about the type of school, visit a range – co-ed, single sex; town, country, suburban; with or without boarding.
- Prepare for the visit, arrange to speak to the teaching staff, housemasters/ mistresses; draw up a list of points to investigate and questions to ask.
- After the visit, shortlist again and take your child on a second visit to 1 or 2 schools.
- Register your child for the right school; if this is a very competitive one, have a fall-back in mind. If you register your child early, keep a range of options; the child may not meet your expectations or may exceed them.
- Prepare your child for the admissions procedure, common entrance, exams, special subjects, etc.
- Keep your child involved with the process – children who have been involved in their choice of secondary schools settle in more easily.
- Remember. Your view is almost always going to be coloured by your own educational experience so don't set out to win your old battles.

· Classroom discipline ·

Most schools now realise that interesting presentation is a far more successful way of teaching than is rigorous discipline. However, there are still a few teachers (and schools) that follow the speak-only-when-I-tell-you-to-and-stand-up-when-I-enter-the-room approach, just as there are some whose classes regularly turn into brawls. Either is equally frustrating for anybody with an interest in the subject. Find out what the school's general policy is on classroom discipline when you visit. Pick up as much as you can from pupils and parents about what individual teachers are like. How are disruptive pupils dealt with? Whose classes are the most interesting; most chaotic? etc.

· Co-ed schools ·

Co-educational schools admit girls and boys. More and more schools are becoming co-educational as many single-sex schools (particularly boys' schools) are letting in the opposite sex or merging with a brother/sister school. Much of this is in response to market demand but some schools believe there is no longer any justification for educating the sexes separately in a world where they will work together.

Some heads opt for a specific male:female ratio, others let one evolve. In schools that have always been co-ed, this tends to be about 50:50. Schools that used to be single sex are usually still dominated by that sex and its ethos. If you are looking at a school that has recently become co-ed, you may like to check the following –

- the prospectus, for what's between the lines. If girls have not been integrated into a boys' school's prospectus, they're unlikely to be integrated into the school. (eg schools with a strong house structure where girls board with staff).
- how many boys, how many girls are in positions of authority, eg prefects?
- how many men and women are in the staff common room?
- the house system – if the school has competitive houses, how has it integrated co-education eg mixed houses or twinned single sex houses?

Co-ed schools often have a wider range of activities because they are less affected by generalised beliefs such as boys don't sew and girls don't like electronics. Conversely, some research suggests that girls do better academically in girls' schools, particularly in science. If you are not sure you want a full co-ed school for your child, you can consider brother/sister schools.

· Commitment ·

This works both ways. You should check that the school you choose is committed to doing the best for your child – and does not shed the less bright in favour of the more academic to keep its final results looking good and glossy for the next prospectus.

Conversely, you need to be sufficiently thorough in your job of selecting a school that you feel committed to it too. Don't treat schools like products on a supermarket shelf. Some heads complain of parents finding a school doesn't look quite right after a week or so, and trying to move their child to a different one – no good for the school or the pupil. Do your homework well; make sure your child is involved with the choice (there are fewer problems settling in children who have been involved), and then commit yourself to making it work. If, after all that, it really doesn't, you will obviously have to arrange a move (although a few schools demand curious undertakings from parents that they keep their children in the school until they are 16 or even 18).

· Common Entrance ·

Many independent secondary schools use the same entrance exam, called Common Entrance (CE). This can be taken by girls aged 11, 12 or 13; boys take it at 13, traditionally girls transfer to secondary school at a younger age. Prep schools prepare pupils for CE. If your child's school doesn't, contact the Examination Officer, Common Entrance Examination Board, Ashley Lane, Lymington, Hampshire SO4 9YR (tel: 0590 675947). You should do this at least 10 weeks before the exam, and ideally a lot earlier to allow time to prepare for the exam. Pupils are tested in English, maths, French, science, history, geography and RE; Latin and Greek are optional extras. All syllabuses are being reviewed in the light of the National Curriculum and some have already been revised. The exam is currently being reformed. The CE Exam Board can provide past papers; order by ringing 0590 679554.

Common Entrance is centrally set and administered but is marked by the participating schools. Each school sets its own pass mark which reflects the demand for places; thus the pass mark for one school may be 70%, for another 45%. You can ask to have the scripts sent on to another school if your child doesn't get into your first choice.

CE isn't always necessary. Lots of schools have their own entrance exam or test – either instead of, or as an alternative to, Common Entrance.

· Community service ·

Some schools organise their pupils to help in the community outside the school. This is often offered as an alternative to sport for senior pupils – very occasionally it is compulsory.

In practice, school community service usually means visiting old people; talking to them; entertaining them and doing odd jobs for them like decorating and gardening. It may also involve work with children or the mentally handicapped. Some schools, especially rural ones, take the notion of community service several steps further and organise local services such as mountain rescue and fire-fighting.

· Computing ·

It's going to be increasingly difficult to get through life without some computer competence and schools with no computing facilities are rare. Most integrate the use of computers with the teaching of a wide range of other subjects such as sciences, geography and maths, as well as offering it as a subject in its own right. Lists of computing equipment may mean little to you, but you can still find out how much help pupils are given with learning how and when to use them.

· Corporal punishment ·

Still a delicate matter. It has long been banished from the maintained sector and only exists (at any rate officially) in some dozen independent secondary schools. The vast majority of heads stress emphatically that it is never used. Nowadays it is more likely that teachers will suffer corporal punishment in the form of assault (with or without weapons) by a pupil or pupils. Recently, a London headmaster told his staff: 'You must not hit the boys.' Then he added: 'And the boys must not hit you.' Quite right.

· CSV ·

Community Service Volunteers will arrange community work in the UK for anybody aged 16 to 35. This is full-time, somewhere in the UK but away from home, and is for periods of 4 months to a year. This makes it an option for students after A-levels. Volunteers get food, accommodation plus £18.50 a week. Details from CSV, 237 Pentonville Road, London N1 9NJ (tel: 071–278 6601).

· CSYS ·

Certificates of Sixth Year Studies are Scottish exams which some pupils sit the year after Highers. They are very roughly comparable with A-levels but are often not recognised as such, especially south of the border. Results in Highers or A-levels are more normally used for university entrance.

· Curriculum ·

Latin term for 'career' – the course of study taught at school. For the first few years at secondary school, most pupils follow roughly the same curriculum: English, maths, at least one modern language (usually French), history, geography, some science, Latin (sometimes), art/craft, music and physical education. Most heads of independent schools believe they cover the national curriculum and more.

At 14, they choose 7 or 8 GCSE or S-Grade subjects; the exams are normally taken at 16. By the time they come to decide which A-levels to do, they'll have to limit themselves to taking 2 to 4 subjects seriously (5 or 6 if they're doing Highers or AS-levels). A-level courses last 2 years, the exams normally taken at 18.

· CV game ·

Your child can use the time in education to build a CV (curriculum vitae, ie 'course of life') to impress future employers. Evidence of a full school career (involvement in, say, sports teams, orchestra and community service as well as exams) is as useful as the individual positions. They can get some useful CV building bricks at school from:
- holding positions of responsibility such as being a prefect;
- organising and managing school clubs, societies and events;
- involvement with magazines, drama productions, school music and sports etc;
- voluntary or community work;
- Duke of Edinburgh's Awards or CCF;
- work experience during holidays or at weekends (if it doesn't conflict with school work).

· Dance ·

Most people with a future as professional dancers start very young. Ballet dancers have to begin intensive training at the age of 11. The Royal Ballet School is a specialist ballet school; others such as the Arts Educational Schools and Italia Conti concentrate on dance with drama.

Otherwise it tends to be part of physical education. Some, especially boys' schools, don't bother with it at all while others offer a wide range including folk, modern, ballet, ballroom. Some emphasise free movement while others still regard dancing as a social accomplishment.

· Day schools ·

Day schools are becoming more popular but there are a number of special factors you'll need to consider as well as finding a school that suits your child academically and socially. Your choice of day school is limited by the time it takes to travel to school and back home again. Make sure that you calculate this time in terms of the transport your child will use to get to school. Some parents make the mistake of driving to the school and assuming that the driving time equals the time spent on public transport. It seldom does. Find out what time your child will leave school at the end of the day and whether they are expected to be there at weekends. If the school has a proportion of boarders, the hours may be longer than you expect. At some boarding schools day pupils are regarded as second-class citizens; check how well they are integrated.

· Direct grant schools ·

Until 1975 when the scheme was phased out in England and Wales, direct grant schools offered free or subsidised education to a proportion of their pupils in exchange for a grant from the Department of Education and Science. Those schools are now either fully independent or fully maintained by their LEAs. GPDST and many grammar schools fell into this category.

· Distance ·

Choose a day school that's close enough to home to allow your child to take part in after-school activities, and accessible by public transport: you may not mind driving a 7-year-old to school every day but what about a 16-year old?

More means worse: if you have four children at four different day schools you can be on a perpetual school run. Boarders now tend to live within $1\frac{1}{2}$ hours' travelling distance from home. This makes it easier for you to get to each other and also increases the likelihood of your child having at least a few schoolfriends within reach for holidays and weekends.

· Divorce and separation ·

Let the school know what's going on. This is probably not the time to change your child's school unless absolutely unavoidable. If your child is at boarding school this may be an advantage as it can provide valuable continuity – but make sure that you keep in closer touch than usual. Don't expect your children to do anything to make life easier for you. If they *have* any sympathy with, or understanding of, what's going on they may do their best to hide it.

· Drama ·

There are schools which specialise in drama (many of which also supply young actors for TV, West End and local theatre). But professional actors emerge from many non-specialist schools, even though drama often isn't taught as a curriculum subject beyond the age of about 14. Many schools have theatres equipped to professional standards; most schools put on dramatic productions every year. Find out how many of these there are, who and how many participate, what sort of drama it is (Shakespeare, musical, comedy, Greek tragedy, etc). Are pupils involved as scene builders, wardrobe people, with publicity? Are there any drama clubs?

· Drinking ·

Adults are *expected* to drink in moderation and, while buying alcohol in pubs or shops is illegal for under-18s, most children have the occasional drink long before this. Many schools do not allow drinking of any kind, which leaves young people to find out about drinking in the holidays or after they leave school. Spirits are almost always prohibited in schools but several boarding schools allow limited drinking of beer and wine in sixth-form clubs and bars. Although this stops alcohol from having quite the illicit appeal that drugs and cigarettes enjoy, it doesn't stop massive amounts of cheap wine and strange spirits being consumed at any opportunity. If your child does occasionally appear to have had too much to drink with friends, the biggest problem is probably the next day's hangover.

However, habitual heavy drinking is far worse for adolescents than for adults. Their bodies are less able to cope with quantities of alcohol and there is an increased likelihood of dependence. If teenagers are drinking heavily and regularly (especially if they're drinking alone) it could be a symptom of other problems. You should speak to your GP or consult Alcoholics Anonymous (local address in the telephone directory).

· Drugs ·

On the whole, cannabis is the only illegal drug that schoolchildren are likely to come across. Experimenting with the occasional joint is now a common part of growing up and you have to take a lot of cannabis before it will do any harm. For schoolchildren, the greatest risk isn't so much the damage that it might be doing to their bodies as the damage that it might do to their futures if they're caught. Expulsion is probable (although not always automatic) and police involvement could be serious. Because of the excellent airport security in Northern Ireland, drugs have never found their way into NI boarding schools.

Hard drugs are a different story, although they are far less prevalent in schools. Their effects on the brain are more dramatic and less predictable; any use of hypodermic needles carries the added risk of infection including hepatitis and AIDS. It can be difficult to tell if a teenager is on drugs because many of the classic symptoms of hard-drug users – dramatic mood swings, listlessness, unhealthy complexion, lack of money, etc – are exhibited by normal, undrugged teenagers. There are lots of sources of help and counselling for people who are having problems with drugs (often drugs misuse is a symptom of another underlying problem). If you're worried, speak to a sympathetic doctor or contact Families Anonymous, 310 Finchley Road, London NW3 7AG (tel: 071–431–3537).

All schools take drug abuse very seriously (at least one school has the overwhelming support of parents to conduct random drugs tests in order to stamp it out). You can help by not making drugs an unmentionable horror; make sure that your children are aware of the legal and health risks involved; and remain approachable. You want to know as soon as possible if your child is in difficulty because of drugs – either legal, such as alcohol, tobacco, caffeine, or illegal, such as cannabis, cocaine, heroin.

· Duke of Edinburgh's Award Scheme ·

'Designed as an introduction to leisure-time activities, a challenge to the individual to personal achievement, and as a guide to those people and organisations who are concerned about the development of our future citizens' (HRH the Duke of Edinburgh).

Duke of Edinburgh's Awards can be taken outside school or as an extra-curricular activity within the school. There are 3 levels: bronze (taken from the age of 14+), silver (15+) and gold (16+). Awards are made on successful completion of a programme of community service, sport, adventure training and practical skills. Courses must be finished by the age of 24.

Further information from the scheme's headquarters at: Gulliver House, Madeira Walk, Windsor, Berks SL4 1EU (tel: 0753 810 753).

· Dyslexia ·

This is a condition in which you have difficulty organising letters, numbers, words and ideas; this leads to problems with reading, writing and learning and holds sufferers back. Eileen Simpson has described her experience of dyslexia in *Reversals* (Gollancz, 1980).

A number of the schools in *The Equitable Schools Book* give extra help to dyslexic children. This varies a lot in frequency and intensity; make sure the dyslexia provision is suitable for your child's needs. You can contact the British Dyslexia Association, 98 London Road, Reading RG1 5AU (tel: 0734 668271), or the Dyslexia Institute, 133 Gresham Road, Staines, Middlesex TW18 2AJ (tel: 0784 463851). You may also find a child psychologist helpful.

· Educational change ·

The chances are that, whether you are paying fees or not, your child's schooldays will be affected at some stage by the introduction of new examinations/educational legislation. Policies that are designed to bring about long-term changes can be disruptive during their first years and many disorientate pupils, parents and teachers, making them feel as though they are guinea pigs performing capricious tasks at the whim of the Secretary of State for Education.

Although the final aim of the change *may* be good, it isn't necessarily a comfort to know that all of your child's contemporaries are putting up with the same disruption, nor do many parents take kindly to educational changes which are designed to benefit future generations when their own children's education may be jeopardised by the stresses of initial confusion. The National Curriculum is the current novelty, and looks set to run and run.

· EFL ·

English as a Foreign Language is taught at some boarding and a few day schools (sometimes taught as ESL, English as a Second Language). Such schools may be better geared all round to the needs of children for whom English is a foreign language, or whose parents live abroad.

· Entrance exams ·

Schools that don't use common entrance usually set their own exams; and many schools that do use common entrance also have their own exams for children for whom the CE is inappropriate eg non-standard age or children from state schools. Exams are often held early in the academic year prior to entry, so approach the school well in advance. You may be able to get hold of some past papers – and each school's will be different.

Too many entrance exams is not a good idea. In places like London, where competition is fierce, some schools have formed consortia, each setting a single paper. Try not to enter your child for more than 2 or 3; that means applying to schools that really are right and, perhaps, choosing one that's less competitive than the others.

· Equipment ·

Depending on the school and the child, you'll have to buy a variety of equipment from pencils to bagpipes. You can expect to have to provide things like a calculator, a dictionary (even if you aren't expected to buy other books), various bits and pieces for sport and any optional extras. Boarders will need more – their own clothes, suitcases, towels, duvet, clock, lamp, games and hobbies stuff.

· Exeat ·

Exeat is a Latin word meaning 'let him escape'. At school (especially boarding school) it is used to mean permitted time spent away from school during term. Most schools have a policy of allowing a certain number of overnight or weekend exeats a term – this can vary from any weekend to only one break at half-term or even none at all. You'll have to decide which is the most appropriate for your family; if you live abroad, your child may be happier at a school that doesn't empty at weekends, whereas if you live within easy travelling distance of the school, weekly boarding may be possible.

· Expulsion ·

The ultimate deterrent at most schools. Although used rarely, it is more common in the independent than the maintained sector. It's not the end of the world. It goes on to your child's academic record and may be picked up in the future, but it needn't blight any careers. The immediate problem may be finding another school; the present school might be willing to help with this (depending on the reason for expelling your child in the first place). Some schools expel more readily than others and it's worth finding out something of the school's policy from the head when you visit.

· Extra-curricular activities ·

A vital part of education, giving children the opportunity to try out a range of activities, outside the formal curriculum. This is particularly important if your child is not particular academic but can pick up a large range of skills and interests while at school.

Many schools in *The Equitable Schools Book* offer a wide range of indoor and outdoor pursuits to a high standard eg Highland Cattle Society, Young Enterprise groups, BAYS, bedsit cookery, computer clubs, fencing, curling, Duke of Edinburgh's Award Scheme, CCF. Check the school profiles.

Find out the range available and the timetable. You can find out a good deal by looking at pupils' almanac/calendar/diary if the school issues one (if it doesn't, ask how pupils find out what is available and when). Try also to get some idea of numbers involved, especially in optional activities. Apathetic peers can be just as pressurising as active ones.

· Extras ·

As well as fees, most schools charge extras, normally some £300 pa, often much, much more. Parents are usually charged extra for eg instrumental tuition, sports coaching and excursions, including those that are compulsory; less often for eg team transport to away matches, lunch for day pupils laundry for boarders, and exam fees. Ask what's included in school fees and what you should expect to pay on top of that.

· Fagging ·

It's unlikely that you'll find a school that still has a policy of allowing seniors to use younger pupils as unpaid skivvies and lavatory-seat warmers on cold days. Fagging has been replaced at many schools with a sort of school community service. This is more common in boarding schools where all pupils may be expected to help with, say, keeping dormitories and dining rooms tidy.

· Fee levels ·

Most schools state their termly fees. Annual figures, although far more relevant, look horrific (the first schools have broken the £10,000 barrier). Fees range from about £700–£2000+ per term for day pupils and about £1900–£3000+ for boarding (plus extras). They rise by some 10% annually. (For comparison – the guide price for a computer science degree course if £3500 per year.)

The heavily-endowed schools still tend to charge very high fees but pay their staff well, have good facilities and a lot of scholarships. Schools charging very low fees may be constrained by low income.

· Fees – paying them ·

There are ways of alleviating the burden of fees, even if you are not eligible for any financial assistance eg government assisted place. Here are some:

If you are lucky enough to be able to pay fees out of capital, you can greatly reduce the costs by paying into an educational trust. These offer considerable advantages by utilising their charitable status. Many independent schools offer them together with a reduction in fees for parents paying in this way. Typically, you can save up to 15% of fees if you pay a lump sum when your child starts school.

One general misconception is that all educational trusts are inflexible, that because the proceeds of the trust have to be used to fund school fees and the trust is run by an individual school, you are locked into sending your child to that school. But a few insurance companies run their own educational trusts, with charitable status. Your choice of school does not have to be made until a month or so before the child starts, and you can pay a lump sum or through regular savings out of your income.

There are advantages in using a charitable trust; they may give what amounts to a postponement of basic income tax; there is an absence of higher rate tax; they are expense-free to you since the trustees, who take an allowance approximate to basic rate tax, pay all their expenses from that.

If, like most parents, you cannot pay fees out of capital, then you may find that the only practical method of ensuring funds are available at the right time is regular saving from income.

The most popular way of saving for school fees used to be to take out a series of life assurance endowment policies. Since the removal of tax relief on life assurance premiums in 1984, this method has lost some of its appeal but is still regarded by many parents as one of the cheapest and least risky ways of saving for school fees. It involves parents taking out a policy a year over, say, seven years. As each matures, the lump sum it pays out will provide that year's school fees. The ideal time to start is before your child's first birthday, so that the endowments can run a full ten years before you need to pay secondary school fees, thus maintaining the qualifying status of the policy.

There are drawbacks. Although in the first year you pay a reasonably affordable sum into only one policy, by the time your savings plan is in full swing you can be pretty stretched to fund the lot. Say you commit yourself to £40.00 per month in the first year, by year seven you will be paying £280.00 per month if you are putting the same amount into each policy. If you can easily save £3,000 a year out of your income, you may get a better return from other forms of investment.

Hence the growing popularity of other forms of savings, with greater growth potential, for school fees – eg unit trust savings schemes, PEPs, or, if you are of an age where you may be eligible to take early retirement, personal pension plans.

As with all savings, there is a lot on offer and it's up to you to choose where you want to place your money, taking into account the level of risk you want to take between, say, the safer with-profits type endowment policies, their unit-linked counterparts, various forms of direct equity investment or speculating on the commodity markets.

A straightforward loan or overdraft is a very expensive way of funding school fees. If you are a homeowner, you may be able to use a home equity release scheme (sometimes called a capital drawdown plan). These schemes allow you to borrow usually 60–80% of the current value of your house, less any outstanding mortgage.

You may be eligible for a grant from the Ministry of Defence, the Foreign Office or your firm. Finally, some schools give reductions in fees for second and subsequent children or the children of, for example, the clergy or old pupils.

You should not expect your children to move schools if you fall ill, on hard times or – heaven forbid – you die. You can insure against your inability to pay through death, illness or redundancy. Some school fees remission schemes may also reimburse you if your child is absent from school through illness for a long time. Ask your insurance broker, ISIS or the British Insurance Brokers Association, 14 Bevis Marks, London EC3A 7NT (tel: 071–623 9043). Some schools have their own support schemes for parents who fall on hard times. Investigate these in advance.

Payment of fees is, for most people, a heavy financial burden and mistakes are expensive. Consult ISIS.

· Food ·

Although children are unlikely to starve, many schools continue to serve up overcooked vegetables and stodgy puddings although there is usually a choice these days. Dynamic heads are unlikely to throw their energy into dietary improvements while they've got things like exam results and discipline to sort out. But several schools have food committees. When you visit a school try to find out about the food. This is especially important for boarders who can't top up the school's diet at home. Find out what other food is available (tuck shops, etc). Some day schools allow packed lunches; and senior boarders may have some cooking facilities. Most schools will cater for children with special diets.

· Friends' schools ·

These are schools run by Quakers (Society of Friends). They hold regular Quaker religious meetings which pupils may or may not have to attend and emphasise the importance of tolerance of other people and of responsibility to the community. Friends' schools accept non-Quaker pupils. Further information from the Friends' Schools Joint Council, Friends House, Euston Road, London NW1 2BJ (tel: 071–387 3601).

· Froebel method ·

An educational method associated with Friedrich Froebel (1782–1852) who adapted the child-centred ideals and principles of Rousseau and Johann Pestalozzi to the education of infants in Germany. It was Froebel who founded the *Kindergarten* and thus established the kind of infant and nursery schools which are now common and in which children explore and discover the world through play, games, toys, shapes, music, stories, drawing and so on. He had a considerable influence on Montessori and his long-term influence has been profoundly beneficial.

· Gap year ·

The gap year is the year after leaving school, before taking up a degree course or a career. This is a good opportunity to do something completely different, either on the person's own initiative or through GAP Activity Projects Ltd. GAP Ltd provides about 6 months' overseas voluntary work in schools, farms, hospitals and businesses for young people in part of their gap year. Not all schools are members of GAP Ltd, but anyone can apply; contact the Secretary, GAP Activity Projects (GAP) Limited, 44 Queens Road, Reading, Berkshire RG1 4BB (tel: 0734 594914).

· GBA ·

The Governing Bodies Association is a co-ordinating organisation for representatives from the governing boards of independent boys' or co-ed schools. Many of them are HMC or SHMIS schools.

· GBGSA ·

The Governing Bodies of Girls' Schools Association is a co-ordinating organisation for representatives from the governing bodies of independent girls' schools – many of these are GSA schools.

· GCSE ·

Taken at 15 or 16, GCSE (General Certificate of Secondary Education) is designed to provide a single system of examination across the whole ability range and to enable candidates at all levels to demonstrate their knowledge, abilities and achievements; it includes considerable amounts of in-course assessment as well as exams. It aims to test the ability to apply what is learned to practical situations rather than merely the ability to remember and re-present factual knowledge which has been acquired in the classroom. GCSEs may be taken in a variety of subjects including physical education and arts options. Because it replaced O-levels and CSEs the general standards achieved in independent schools look higher than those for O-levels.

· Getting in ·

Once you've found a school that's right, your child has to get through an admission procedure. This will probably involve:

- an entry test (the school's own or common entrance);
- possibly additional tests for scholarships, bursaries or government-assisted places;
- a report from your child's current school;
- an interview.

Find out which of these apply and make sure your child knows about the requirements and is reasonably prepared. Many schools have traditional feeder schools (eg their own junior school, local prep schools); your child's chances may be improved by starting there.

Some problems arise from the different times schools you apply to make you an offer: you may get a firm offer (to which you must give a reply by a specified date) from your second choice before you hear from your first choice.

· Gifted children ·

Gifted children may be held back and frustrated by their less able contemporaries. If your child is gifted in one or more areas – music, maths, painting, etc – contact the National Association for Gifted Children, Nene College, Moulton Park, Boughton Green Road, Northampton NN2 7AL (tel: 0604 792300).

· Girls' schools ·

Girls' secondary schools usually take pupils from the age of 11. Many have their own prep or junior schools, which may be co-ed; a very few take boys into the sixth.

There is some evidence that girls do better in the more protected environment of a single sex school where there is not, for example, the gender-typing pressure to steer away from hard sciences and exam results are better. This evidence is hotly disputed by heads of co-ed schools and the truth is that some girls doubtless flourish in girls' schools and others respond to the greater competitiveness of a co-ed.

Girls' schools are changing. The cold wind that blew round their sixth forms, when the fashion was for girls to move at 16 to a school with a mixed sixth, has changed direction. Many of the boys schools that experimented with mixed sixths are now completely co-ed, so there is an overall drain on girls schools at 13. Some schools are feeling this keenly; others are finding their enrolments are high, the girls now stay on for their A-levels and they have expanding and flourishing sixth forms. Find out which way your shortlisted schools are moving, starting with the profiles in *The Equitable Schools Book.*

Some girls' schools are also good at providing the non-academic pupils with a good grounding for moving straight into a career. There are some lively one-year courses (including languages, financial skills etc) run for pupils who want to stay on after GCSE but who are not interested/advised to take A-levels. Such courses are by no means universal – some girls still leave school at 16 with very little.

Many girls' schools have brother schools; most share activities, events and sometimes classes with local boys' schools; a few remain socially isolated. Many girls' schools have now appointed headmasters.

· Governors ·

These are the people who sit on a board and are responsible for the school's success as a business. Their main job is to ensure that there's enough money to run the school (a large, well-endowed boarding school has an annual turnover of some £5 million); they also usually appoint new heads.

Governors often air their views on the day-to-day running of the school (eg discipline, or even the appointment of prefects) – in the stated belief this will improve the school's marketability. Governors can be the bane of heads' lives. Some forward-looking heads may be held back by boards of governors. Recent books by distinguished heads, John Rae (*Letters from School*) and John Thorn (*Road to Winchester*), are illuminating.

· GPDST ·

Founded in 1872. Until 1975 the schools in the Girls' Public Day School Trust were direct grant grammar schools. Currently there are 26 member schools providing education for day girls of 5–18. Further information from GPDST, 26 Queen Anne's Gate, London SW1H 9AN (tel: 071–222 9595).

· Grant-maintained schools ·

These are self-governing and receive funding direct from the Department of Education and Science. They are not covered in *The Equitable Schools Book.*

· Grapevines ·

Schools change frequently. Heads move every 5–10 years on average and there's a complete change of pupils every 6 years or so; gossip about schools dates quickly and reputations live long ('That's the school where the first eleven burnt down the cricket pavilion after losing a home match').

A parent with a child already at the school will be best able to give you the low-down on pupils/staff and parent/staff relations. Is that dynamic head really as active as you may have been led to believe? Are pupils with your child's particular interests and abilities encouraged? Parents may also give you and your child the chance to meet some other pupils and to decide what you think of them. But don't forget parents' views of a school will be coloured by the very particular experience of their child, which may or may not be relevant. The low-down that prep school heads have should be up-to-date and objective, if you are interested in schools they feed.

· GSA ·

The Girls' School Association is a club for the heads of over 240 girls' secondary schools. It is roughly the female equivalent of the HMC, regarding itself as representing the élite. It brings out an annual reference book, *The Independent Schools Yearbook: Girls' Schools* (A & C Black); meets to discuss educational issues affecting its schools; and keeps information flowing between them.

· Guardians ·

Guardians step in for half-terms, at school events or in emergencies if you can't yourself. Your child will need a guardian if you live overseas or a long way from school. You can get help with finding a guardian through the school or ISIS, but it's better to find someone your child knows and likes.

· Handicaps ·

A mildly handicapped child, especially an intelligent one, may do better at an ordinary school than a special one. Speak to the head about this. Possible problems include:

- Mobility: most schools aren't built to be easy to get around for people with a mobility or visual handicap.
- Teaching which is geared towards pupils who can hear well.
- A mildly handicapped pupil will have to cope with being noticeably different from everybody else.

For those with more serious handicaps contact:

- **England**: Department of Education and Science, Schools Branch 2 Division B, (Special Education), Elizabeth House, 39 York Road, London SE1 7PH (tel: 071–934 9000).
- **Wales**: Welsh Office Education Department, Schools Administration Branch 3, Phase 2 Government Buildings, Tŷ Glas Road, Llanishen, Cardiff CF4 5WE (tel: 0222 761456).

- **Scotland**: Scottish Education Department (Special Schools), New St Andrew's House, St James Centre, Edinburgh EH1 3SY (tel: 031 556 8400).

- **Northern Ireland**: Department of Education for Northern Ireland, Schools Division, Rathgael House, Balloo Road, Bangor, Northern Ireland BT19 2PR (tel: 0247 270077).

· Heads ·

Choosing a school means choosing a head. Heads tend to move on their own career paths so they last (on average) only 8 years at each school. They have a terrific influence while they're there, so find out as much as you can about the head's policies, principles and obsessions.

A lot of the business of choosing a head falls back on instinct, but while you're visiting schools and talking to heads consider:

- how well would you trust their judgement?
- how approachable are they?
- how compatible are their special interests and concerns with your child's interests and needs?
- do they seem willing to admit to problems and to be capable of doing something about them?

Heads usually have a lot of experience of teaching and children. This doesn't mean that they are infallible. Don't hesitate to let your child's head know if you honestly think that they are wrong. Cultivating an aura of authority is part of the job. Don't be put off. But remember that the head is running an enterprise of maybe 1000+ people and £5 million.

Read *Letters from School* by John Rae (Collins, 1987) and *Road to Winchester* by John Thorn (Weidenfeld and Nicolson, 1989) to remind yourself that heads are human.

· Head boy/girl ·

This is a responsible position and can be a strain – the entire school knows who they are and they're expected to behave like paragons (hell breaks loose if they don't). The pay-off might come when they start applying for some universities and jobs where head boy/girl experience may be useful on a CV. Some head boys/girls are appointed by the head; others are elected by the pupils.

· Highers ·

These are exams taken in Scotland at the age of 16 or 17. Four or five good Higher grades are needed for a place at university in Scotland. Highers are sat the year after S-grades, so students go to university a year earlier than they do in England (this practice is decreasingly popular). Universities and polytechnics south of the border still find Highers confusing. Many Scottish schools offer A-level syllabuses as well as Highers – possibly a better bet for sixth-formers who want to go south.

· HMC ·

The Headmasters' Conference started in 1869 as a club for headmasters; it now has some 200 members (plus associate members). It regards itself as representing the élite of the independent boys' schools. The heads of some schools become members automatically; otherwise they have to apply. It is now a professional organisation keeping its members informed and generating discussion on educational issues affecting their schools.

There is an annual book giving details of schools run by members of the HMC, *The Independent Schools Yearbook: Boys' Schools* (A & C Black).

· Homosexuality ·

Not as prevalent in schools as it is supposed to have been in the past. This is probably mainly due to the less monastic or nunnish existence of most schoolchildren nowadays and to a more open attitude towards sexuality in general. Children in single-sex schools are far more likely to fear the possibility of being homosexual than to feel encouraged to be so. Nowadays, if somebody is homosexual, it is unlikely to be because that is the norm at school.

· Housemasters/mistresses ·

Usually a member of the teaching staff. This is a prestigious position in boarding schools; the housemaster or housemistress is *in loco parentis*. Make sure you trust them and that they'll get on well with your child. While the head has a massive influence on the school, houses within a school can vary a lot according to the personality of the housemaster/mistress in charge.

This is usually the first person you should contact if you're worried about your child's happiness or health.

· Houses ·

A lot of schools separate their pupils into different 'houses' for competitive and/or pastoral purposes. These usually have roughly equal numbers from each year and, depending on how seriously the school takes the house system, they may have a senior pupil as head of house, distinguishing ties or badges, etc. Sometimes houses represent all age groups and are competitive (sometimes described as vertical); in other schools, membership of houses is according to age group (sometimes described as horizontal).

Pupils at most boarding schools sleep in separate houses – which may be the same as the competitive houses. The sixth or upper sixth are often separated. The boarding house is in the charge of a housemaster or mistress (usually a member of the teaching staff) and some assistants. The pupils may eat in the house or in a central dining room shared with the rest of the school.

In co-ed schools, the boarding houses are sometimes mixed and sometimes single sex. Where houses are also competitive, it is not always clear how eg a single girls' house fits into the system. In some cases, boys' and girls' houses may be twinned for competitive purposes.

· Independent schools ·

These are schools that are not maintained by local or national government and are financed by fees and endowments. They include so-called public schools and private schools and are theoretically more free than maintained ones to decide their own policies and priorities. It is this element of choice that makes independent schools increasingly attractive to parents.

More than 7% (approximately 600,000) of schoolchildren in the UK are educated at independent schools – 20% of the 16–18 age-group. The numbers are increasing in spite of a decrease in school-age population. Approximately 57% are boys. 40% of the parents of these children were not, themselves, educated at independent schools.

· Insurance ·

You may want the following:

- school fees insurance, if you can't pay;
- life insurance – yours and your child's;
- health insurance (yours and your child's – you'll still pay a term's fees if your child can't attend).
- accident disability insurance;
- your child's personal property insurance.

Check what your school offers – eg for riding/rugby injuries.

· International Baccalaureate ·

This is taken in the sixth form and is accepted as an entrance qualification for degree courses throughout the world. It is offered at some 300 schools worldwide but only in a handful of independent schools in the UK, sometimes in place of A-levels, sometimes as an alternative. Only four schools in *The Equitable Schools Book* offer the IB at present – Atlantic College, Marymount, Sevenoaks and Southbank.

Teaching for the IB is in English in this country. 6 subjects are studied (3 to higher level and 3 as subsidiaries), including mother tongue plus 1 language, maths, 1 human science, 1 exact science and 1 subject of the candidate's choice.

The International Baccalaureate Office in the UK is at 18 Woburn Square, London WC1H 0NS (tel: 071–637 1682).

· Interviews ·

These always form part of the school selective procedure. They should be a two-way process, allowing you, your child and the head to decide if this is the right choice of school. Interviews aren't necessarily designed to find out how much Latin children know, nor how well they cope under pressure. Don't worry if your normally self-assured child dries up – heads should be used to that sort of thing and the interview will probably go much better when you aren't in the room.

· ISAI ·

The Independent Schools Association Incorporated, founded in 1895, is a club for the heads of a variety of schools (co-ed, single sex, day, boarding).

· ISCO ·

The Independent Schools Careers Organisation provides training, advice and resources for careers advisers and pupils at its 360 member schools. Contact ISCO, 12a–18a Princess Way, Camberley, Surrey GU15 3SP (tel: 0276 21188) for further information.

· ISIS ·

The Independent Schools Information Service acts as a useful intermediary for its 1300 prep and secondary member schools and parents who are trying to find a school. It also provides advice on financing school fees, and how to choose a school; ISIS itself doesn't recommend individual schools but it does provide consultancy and placement services. There are regional offices; details from the central office at 56 Buckingham Gate, London SW1E 6AG (tel: 071–630 8793). We strongly recommend contacting ISIS if you need information on any aspect of independent education and consulting its useful annual guide *Choosing Your Independent School*.

· ISJC ·

The Independent Schools Joint Council is an umbrella organisation that represents nine other independent school associations: HMC, SHMIS, GBA, GBGSA, GSA, IAPS, ISAI, ISIS and ISBA.

· Language skills ·

As an academic discipline the study of modern European languages has a distinguished tradition in British schools but the needs of non-specialists have been less adequately met. Now, with the advent of the single European market, parents, teachers and young people know that they cannot rely on English as lingua franca so new language courses have been introduced into many schools to develop spoken and written (rather than literary) skills.

There is one golden rule for all non-specialists – if possible acquire your language skills at school. Do not assume that you can leave it until you go up to university or polytechnic.

Schools offer a number of practical language qualifications. The major ones are Flic (Foreign Languages for Industry and Commerce) and Flaw (Foreign Languages at Work), both organised by the London Chamber of Commerce; and the qualifications of the Institute of Linguists. Both Flic and some of the Institute of Linguists exams are oral only; none covers the literature of the language and all are highly practical and applied.

Very many schools take their own initiatives eg transplanting an entire GCSE form to France (teaching all subjects in French); providing regular exchange arrangements; arranging European sports fixtures; acquiring a school chateau; deliberately recruiting large numbers of European pupils into the school itself.

· Late developers ·

Children develop at different rates; education systems don't always cater for this. If your child seems to be having problems keeping up with the rest of the class, investigate the possibility of learning difficulties. You may be better finding a school that caters for a wide range of ability; children often do better once they're out of an environment where they're always at the bottom of the class. Some slow starters have turned out to be high-fliers (Einstein, for example).

· Latin ·

Still taught in some schools despite pressure to replace it with a second (or more) modern European language as we move towards 1992. Latin is widely regarded as a useful training and intellectual discipline, especially in the learning of logical and precise expression, in sound grammatical usage, and also in the development of vocabulary. Much scientific nomenclature *is* Latin. Tens of thousands of words in the English0 language derive from Latin; children with a sound knowledge of the language have a richer vocabulary.

The teaching of Latin has been revolutionised to make the language more accessible and entertaining. However, it remains a bugbear for many children who find it difficult, and therefore find it involves hard work. In actuality it is no more difficult than modern languages such as Serbian, and very much easier than, say Finnish, Hungarian, Turkish and Chinese.

· Learning difficulties ·

Intelligent parents often find it difficult to admit that their children have learning problems. However, some children do. Reading problems are often the first to be noticed. If your child does seem to be having problems, speak to the school or an educational or child psychologist. You can also get help, if appropriate, from the Dyslexia Institute, 133 Gresham Road, Staines, Middlesex TW18 2AJ (tel: 0784 463851). Look at the *School Spotter* for schools with special provision for children with learning difficulties. Many academic failures from strongly academic schools flourish in other schools where they are more fully exposed to practical or creative subjects (gardening, mechanics, music, sports, drama). Find something that your child enjoys doing and is reasonably good at.

· Maintained schools ·

Nearly ninety-three per cent of schoolchildren in the UK go to maintained schools. These are schools where parents don't have to pay fees because the school is fully funded by local or national government. They are not included in *The Schools Book*. Children can transfer from maintained schools to independent schools.

· Matching ·

Finding the right school for your child involves matching your child's needs with the education and ethos provided by the school at an affordable price. No school can be equally successful with every kind of child and most schools will admit this. Also, it

31

does not follow that a school which was right for you or your elder child will suit your younger child. Your main considerations should be:

- Academic: your child will probably be best suited to a school where he or she is slightly above average but won't be bored by too slow a pace; where the range of subjects seems to match the child's existing interests while allowing for new ones to develop.
- Social: what are the other children like? What are the most popular curricular and extra-curricular activities? What about other parents – do you think they may share some of your values?
- Discipline: match this roughly to what your child is used to and can cope with. Find a regime that isn't going to conflict too strongly with the one at home. Children ought to be given more autonomy as they get older.
- Extra-curricular activities: particularly important at boarding school. Are there facilities for your child's existing interests with room for variety: Duke of Edinburgh's Award, philosophy, pottery, fencing, reptiles, public speaking, music etc? Are pupils given time to pursue interests other than those offered by the school?
- Routine: again, especially important at boarding school where school-enforced routine lasts 24 hours a day. An impressive array of organised weekend activities might mean that children have no time to themselves.

· Mixed sixths ·

Many boys' schools take girls into their sixth forms for A-levels (a very few girls' schools do the same for boys). Roughly speaking, the benefits are thought to be that, while girls are given access to better facilities and teaching, boys are stimulated by the influx of ambitious, intelligent females. For boys and girls it can make a sensible stepping stone between single sex education and the hurly-burly of life on a degree course. Some brother/sister schools run joint sixth forms.

However, most girls entering a boys' school should have both a sense of humour and a robust character as the first few weeks can be difficult. Both sexes are defensive as they survey the new set-up, and the boys can be unkind while they get used to their new colleagues. Once the dust settles, it can be a positive experience in a well run school. Check that your child will be properly integrated in the school; start with the prospectus ('The word boys refers also to sixth form girls unless obviously inappropriate').

· Montessori schools ·

An educational method associated with Maria Montessori (1870–1952), Italy's first woman doctor. Initially she worked in Rome with feeble-minded children and later with normal children (aged 3–7). She invented auto-didactic furniture and apparatus to exercise children's physical mechanisms and extend their capacity to assess length, size, weight, shape, colour and texture. The method was championed by progressive educationalists and is still widely used, though it is not so popular in Britain where the Froebel method is preferred. The Dottoressa's methods and doctrines can be applied until the age of 18, but most Montessori schools are nursery with a few taking pupils to the age of 10.

· Music ·

Provisions for music vary greatly in the independent sector. A handful of schools have virtually none; others have a massive commitment which involves some two-thirds of the pupils learning an instrument; and there are specialist music schools. The vast majority of schools have a certain amount of music as an integral part of the curriculum. Most schools have a choir and some sort of orchestra. A lot of schools have more than one choir and orchestra, plus wind and brass ensembles, madrigal groups, brass and jazz groups etc. Many have music scholarships on entrance, send pupils to Music School and have an impressive collection of musicians among their alumni (see school profiles). Much depends on the enthusiasm and dedication of the director of music and the staff and also, of course, on the policy and interests of the head. Most schools have full-time music staff and visiting instrumental teachers (in some instances a dozen or more). Choir schools and others closely associated with cathedrals tend to provide a lot of music and choristers who sing in the cathedral.

Many schools make excellent provision for individual tuition (at a price) in a variety of instruments. This may include the opportunity to hire instruments. Lessons at school may be more convenient and are often fitted into the school day on a rota. Many school choirs, orchestras, pop groups and other groups give regular performances; choirs and orchestras go on tour in Britain and overseas; there are numerous links with national youth orchestras, choirs and music schools.

Specialist music schools cater specifically for the needs of musically gifted children who have a future as professional musicians. Although some also have a wide range of A-level options the vast majority of leavers go on to Music School. Children at music schools tend to spend most of their free time in musical activities and may have a limit (often 2) on the number of A-levels they can take. Special government assistance is available to pupils at specialist music schools, in the form of the aided pupil scheme.

· Narrowing down ·

Choosing the right school is a process of elimination; start wide, with plenty of time. This may get harder as the field narrows and you have to make decisions that are more and more specific – a wide range of extra-curricular activities versus strong ties with a school in France? You'll end up with one school eventually.

· National Curriculum ·

If you are confused by the National Curriculum, you are not alone.

Independent schools are excluded from the requirement to implement the NC and have complete freedom to teach what they like. That is the formal position.

But life is not that simple. Most heads seem to believe that their schools are already broadly in line with the NC; where they are not, heads accept they will have to take it on board since it will dictate the general educational environment in which independent schools operate. This attitude is encouraged by ministers; HM inspectors will doubtless see how this is translated into action on their periodic visits to each independent school (they look at the curriculum among other things).

The NC is obviously going to take some time to feed into independent secondary schools. At present, parents are trying to comprehend the gnomic nomenclature with which the NC is littered; staff in state schools are wrestling to keep up with and teach the subjects where the content has been dictated; and committees are still discussing the content of other subjects. What it will mean in the end is that all pupils will cover three core subjects (English, maths, science) and seven other foundation subjects (technology, history, geography, music, art, physical education and a modern language). Many heads have commented that the introduction of the NC will ease the transfer of pupils between the state and independent schools. And then there is assessment. One of the assessment ages dictated by the NC is 16+ and it is far from clear how this will relate to GCSEs, also taken at 16. Time alone will tell whether the NC 16+ assessment replaces GCSE or not.

· Objectives ·

Like any business, schools advertise their aims and objectives – often in a few succinct words in the prospectus about realisation of the individual's potential. Although there seems to be little to take exception to in this, a neatly stated objective should be treated with caution: what happens to those who don't fit the mould (ie, artists at a highly academic school)? Is the school actually meeting its objectives? How does it achieve them?

It is helpful to have an idea of the school's priorities. Although children's determination will probably allow them to succeed anyway, it's easier if there's some support from school for their chosen field. Reading between the lines of prospectuses, magazines and *The Equitable Schools Book* can give you some clue as to what the school actually achieves. Look at school-leavers' first destinations; range of non-academic activities; exam results; approach to discipline; social activities. Has the school listed any traditional careers? Does all this match what you think your child needs from school?

· O-Grades ·

Roughly speaking, the Scottish equivalent of O-level; they will be replaced by S-grades by 1992.

· Old pupils ·

Most schools have associations of ex-pupils who keep in touch with each other and the school. Past pupils are called old boys/girls or alumni (alumnae at more classically minded girls' schools). They can be useful to the school when it needs to raise cash for new facilities or wants somebody to talk to the sixth about careers. Pupils who have just left school may be a useful source of inside information on the school.

They could have joined the alumni association for a variety of reasons:

- Old school tie: the school has some useful old pupils to tap in the careers market.
- They enjoyed their schooldays.
- Many alumni associations exist because of sporting ties.
- They don't have much else going on in their lives.
- They are professional old boys whose alma-maternal/umbilical cords are never severed.

· O-levels ·

These have now been replaced by GCSEs.

· Open days ·

Most schools have open days when prospective parents can visit and see what the school and some of the staff look like and talk to pupils. A bit like a living prospectus, open days give you the opportunity to see the facilities for science, sports, art, music, eating, sleeping, etc and to look at classrooms (at their best) and noticeboards. You may be able to have a few words with a member of staff or to ask a few general questions. Open days are helpful; make full use of them both to find out about the individual school and to build up a general impression of the range of what independent schools have to offer.

· Outings ·

Most schools arrange some; often related to coursework. Visits to museums, factories, nature reserves, theatre productions and trips abroad are usually a stimulating addition to normal school routine. Other outings are recreational; some schools have their own outdoor-pursuit centres, arrange ski-ing holidays, sailing, riding, community service, giving children the chance to develop new interests. Find out what outings the school arranges; school magazines often publish pupils' accounts of these.

· Outward Bound ·

Many schools offer Outward Bound opportunities. The Outward Bound Trust is an outdoor personal development organisation which runs a variety of programmes (not only for young people) in its own centres. Its philosophy is based on two simple beliefs – that everyone is capable of achieving more than they might realise and that few people have a real appreciation of what can be achieved by teamwork. Financial aid to young people is available. Discuss with your school or contact: Outward Bound Trust, Chestnut Field, Regent Place, Rugby CV21 2PJ (Tel. 0788 560423).

· Overseas parents ·

If you live overseas and are sending your child to school in Britain:

- You'll have to appoint a guardian. This can be a friend or relation with whom the child can stay at half-terms and for exeats; who is on call for emergencies and who can help to arrange travel home for holidays. Choose someone your child knows and likes, who is responsible and fun, and who lives within easy travelling distance of school. If you can't come up with anyone yourself, some schools help with lists of suitable guardians or contact ISIS.
- If English isn't your child's first language, arrange for some initial coaching. Survival at school requires very fluent English but many school-age children are able to pick it up quickly once they're there, regardless of the amount of help they're given. Schools with their own EFL provisions may be better able to deal with non-native English speakers (see the *School Spotter*).

- Choose a school where there are other pupils with parents overseas. What provisions are made at weekends and over half-term for those who can't go home? What transport to the airport does the school arrange? Will it arrange any necessary immunisation?

· Parents ·

Perhaps the most difficult thing for parents is to be objective about their child's abilities, whether sporting, academic, musical etc. Your success may be a handicap to your child. One head told us 'untold damage is done to children by their parents' aspirations'. Another told us that daughters particularly suffered from the weight of parental aspirations placed on them where there were no brothers. Remember, it's your child's life not yours. There are hairy tales of children being packed off to psychologists because they are not achieving the 'correct' academic level at the right time; some children even suffer from stress and depression aged eight.

· Parents' associations ·

Increasingly important, the role of parents' associations varies. A lot depends on how much parental involvement the head can cope with but, on the whole, there is a move towards allowing and encouraging more. School parents' associations may:

- have representatives on the board of governors;
- act as a sounding board for the head; presenting complaints or suggestions; giving reactions to proposed changes;
- help with fund-raising, selling second-hand uniform, books, etc.
- provide a useful source of careers information.

They're more likely to be effective if the head and parents get on with one another.

· Parents' meetings ·

These are when you meet your child's teachers for a progress report. Most schools arrange at least one a year; at boarding schools this is often at the end of term or fixed exeat when you are likely to be at the school anyway. This provides a chance for you to assess the teachers and to raise any minor questions or concerns. For anything pressing, don't wait; make an appointment immediately to speak to the teacher, housemaster/mistress or the head.

· Pass rates ·

These are impressive-looking statistics often presented by schools. Good pass rates tell you very litle, other than that the school is good at judging a pupil's chances of success before entering them for exams – and only enter the pupils they think will pass. (Put one successful pupil in for an exam and, bingo! – 100% pass rate.) If your child is marginal, you may prefer a school which will simply let them have a go – in which case the school will not sport well polished pass rates.

To really find out what goes on, find out the number of GCSEs and A-levels passed by real pupils (start with *The Equitable Schools Book* profiles). Also looking at a school's passes in individual subjects may be revealing although you should judge these against the national spread of grades in the subjects (eg most children taking GCSE Greek get grade A, because only reasonably academic children tend to take Greek unlike, say, English which nearly all children take).

· Prefects ·

These are senior pupils whose responsibilities and method of selection vary from school to school. Some are chosen by the staff and head, sometimes after consultation with pupils; others are elected. Prefects can be responsible for:

- organising inter-house and inter-school games calendars;
- helping with crowd control at school functions;
- showing prospective parents around or organising others to do so;
- keeping an eye on younger pupils, especially in boarding houses.

In some areas of employment and higher education, prefect experience is a useful item for a school-leaver's CV.

Increasingly, the system emphasies responsibility rather than superiority. Although prefects no longer expect to be allowed to beat younger pupils as they may have been in the past, they are usually given privileges and badges of office in recognition of their service to the school.

· Prep schools ·

Prep schools are in business to prepare pupils for Common Entrance. Traditional prep (preparatory) schools take day or boarding pupils from the age of 7 or 8 until they start at secondary school (usually 11 for girls, 13 for boys). Prep schools are the right starting point if you want your child prepared for the common entrance exam; heads of good prep schools will act as useful guides to the schools which use CE and are usually very experienced at matching their pupils with these secondary schools in their area which use Common Entrance. Some have links with, or are prep departments of, specific secondary schools.

· Private schools ·

These are strictly privately-owned schools; there are very few of them. The term is often used to describe those independent schools that are not regarded as public schools.

· Progressive schools ·

Many of the practices and theories initiated by progressive schools from the end of the last century onwards have been adopted by others, so don't expect anything too revolutionary or liberal. Progressive schools tended to put the emphasis on community atmosphere and were less affected by the hangovers of Victorian public school values (such as unquestioning deference to authority and the status quo) than were many other schools. Now most of them are co-ed and many offer a wide range of non-academic activities including farming, gardening, adventure training and community service. Schools that have been regarded as progressive include Abbotsholme, Bedales and St Christopher's (Letchworth) Friends' and Round Square Conference schools.

· Prospectuses ·

It is pretty well essential to get a prospectus. These vary enormously, from being totally inadequate 4-page leaflets which look as if they've been cobbled together by the school's media research officer, to 60-page brochures, with elegant text, beautiful photographs and maybe an accompanying video, created by highly professional PR firms and first-class printers. There is often a correspondence between the quality of a prospectus and the quality/reputation of a school. Crummy provincial schools that nobody's ever heard of provide crummy prospectuses; most good schools provide high-gloss, detailed brochures; a handful of the most distinguished make no attempt to sell themselves at all.

Prospectuses should be perused thoroughly and with caution. Not infrequently they are out-of-date. In any case, their aim is to present all or most of the best features of a school. They are *advertisements*. They do not, therefore, dwell on emetic food, pederastic staff, the nymphomaniac matron, or cannabis behind the cricket pavilion – or indeed any of the other shortcomings which, from time to time, surface even in the best-run establishments.

An original prospectus is rare for the very good reason that it is extremely difficult to produce a truthful and persuasive portrait of so complex a microcosm as a school. Too often they contain standard and cliché-ridden waffle about developing potential and producing well-rounded individuals in a caring environment. Nevertheless, a close study of a prospectus (including the essential reading between the lines) can be rewarding and provide a lot of information. Be suspicious, for example, of the school which dismisses the curriculum in one paragraph but requires a whole page of the prospectus to deal with fees in lieu of notice. The prospectus has to be considered in conjunction with the obligatory visit to the school.

· Public schools ·

The exact definition of a public school is unclear. Usually it is used to refer to schools with heads who are members of the HMC or GSA. Some boys' public schools are enormously well endowed and can afford outstanding facilities. Public schools are subdivided into major and minor, depending on the viewpoint and the alma mater of whoever is using the expression.

· Punishments ·

Although some of the archaic, petty, time-wasting punishments such as writing lines have been dropped at most schools, nearly all have some sort of penal code for dealing with nonconforming and unruly pupils. A few still regard beating children as defensible as a last resort if it is done by a head or housemaster. Find out the scale of punishments (some schools are cagey about this). How often are they meted out and why? Many punishments involve deprivation of free time in detention, manual work (sweeping leaves, picking up litter, sometimes referred to as hard labour) or, at boarding schools, a system of gating. For more serious offences many schools suspend pupils for a period; this could punish you more than your child if your schedule is built round not having children at home. For dire offences, most will resort to expulsion, in which case you start the whole process of finding a school all over again. Heads of the expelling school may help place the child.

· Pupils ·

When you visit a school observe the relationship between the pupils with one another and with you. Do they reflect the impression you have of the school? Are they interested in all those extra-curricular activities or is high attendance at clubs and societies a result of coercion? No matter how impressed you may be by their beautiful behaviour and smart appearance, ask yourself how well would your child get on with them?

Pupils can also be a valuable source of information about the school. Find out what they like or don't like about the school. What would they change if they could? You could try showing them the prospectus and see what comments it provokes.

· Pupil/staff relations ·

Education is essentially about people – in the first place the pupils in the school and those who teach them. It is the relationships between the pupils themselves, between the pupils and their teachers and between the individual teachers which largely determine the character and success of a school. Much can be learned by watching pupils and teachers as they move about the school. You may be able to see some classes in action when you visit. What's the atmosphere like? Better still, how do pupils and staff treat each other at school sports days and plays, when they're out of the formal setting of school? Do they seem to like each other? Do the staff treat the senior pupils as adults and is there any forum (eg staff/sixth form bar) in which they can meet as equal adults?

· Questions ·

Write down all the questions that occur to you about the schools on your shortlist, from how many pupils go on to Oxbridge to how often they can change their socks. Try to gather as many of the answers as possible from prospectuses, school magazines, the pupils and parents you meet, and observation when you visit. Keeping direct questioning of the staff and head to a minimum gives you more time to concentrate on summing them up. However, some things need to be asked outright. An evasive response can often answer a question just as well as a straightforward reply.

· Range of schools ·

Investigate a range of schools to test your assumptions; you might find that a school of 1,000 provides more individual attention than one of 200 or that the nearest girls' school has the best science facilities in the area.

Go to as many open days as possible (at least 4 or 5) and get a good background on which to base decisions about what's right for your child. Investigate:

- co-ed and single-sex schools;
- town, suburban, country;
- long-established and new;
- big and small.

· Reception ·

Joining a secondary school can be traumatic; find out the school's approach – does it encourage pupils to come into the school and familiarise themselves with the place before they join? Does it start term for the new intake early?

· Registration ·

Once you've found the right school you'll have to register your child for entrance tests and interviews. The school's prospectus will tell you how. Usually it means filling in a form with details of your child's name, age, address and current school. You may have to pay a non-returnable registration fee.

Some schools are so over-subscribed that you're recommended to register your child several years before entry (for a tiny handful, you must do this before they are out of nappies); investigate well in advance. It's difficult to match a secondary school to a new-born baby and the child will still have to pass through the school's entry procedure; early registration is no guarantee of acceptance. So have back-up choices up your sleeve and make absolutely sure that it *is* the right school before automatically embarking on the selection procedure.

· Religion ·

The majority of independent schools have a declared religious persuasion and are often a religious, usually a Christian foundation. During the last 25 years the ecumenical movement has had considerable and beneficial effects, as has racial integration. There is much less bigotry, much more tolerance. Nowadays most schools are ecumenically disposed towards a miscellany of faiths and members of minority sects or those of no particular persuasion, although it is unusual to find a specific attitude towards, say, agnostics, gnostics, atheists and heretics.

Provisions for religious instruction and worship vary greatly. Schools with a clearly prescribed policy make it clear if they are willing to accept pupils of any persuasion or none; and Muslims, Hindus, Jews et al are often allowed to opt out from any arrangements for Christians and are able to follow their own religious practices.

Nearly all schools have religious education of *some* kind on the curriculum. This often includes a study of world religions so children develop an idea of what inspires people of different faiths, and learn their practices, customs, laws, conventions and traditions.

A large number of schools are Church of England foundations and follow, to varying degrees, Protestant/Anglican practice. Some make a token subscription in the form of a prayer and perhaps a hymn at assembly, and occasional attendance at chapel; others make a certain amount of worship compulsory. Candidates are often prepared for confirmation.

Methodist, Quaker and Presbyterian schools tend to have a clearly defined policy and give considerable attention to religious worship and instruction.

The Roman Catholic schools, administered by the Benedictines, the Christian Brothers and other Orders, and by various teaching Orders of nuns, have very clear and comprehensive policies to educate and nurture children in the Faith so that they become devout and mature Christians. There is considerable stress on religious instruction and on worship according to the liturgy of the Church, regular attendance at high and low Mass on Sundays and Holidays of Obligation, the taking of the sacraments, attendance at prayers, benediction, vespers, saying the Angelus, and so on. For a list of Catholic schools contact the Catholic Education Council for England and Wales, 41 Cromwell Road, London SW7 2DJ (tel: 071–584 7491).

In an overwhelmingly secular adult society in which religious observance plays a very small part, many people still think that it is not a bad thing for their children to be brought up according to *some* religious doctrine and set of beliefs. If it does matter to you that your child receives definite religious instruction and has the opportunity of worship and cultivating a spiritual life you will find that very many independent schools agree with you.

· Reports ·

Reports come in a wide variety of formats; virtually every school has its own. They are usually sent 2 or 3 times a year. Basically a report comprises a grade mark on each taught subject. In addition there will probably be a comment from any or all of the following: head teacher, housemaster/mistress, tutor, form teacher, deputy head, games teacher. Some schools provide commodious reports in which there is much detail. Quite often there is so little space allotted to each subject that only 10–15 words of comment are possible. Reports which bear subject comments such as 'satis.', 'more effort needed', 'a good term's work', 'could work harder' *and nothing else* are the product of inefficiency, ignorance or laziness (or, conceivably, mere weariness). Whatever the reason, they should not be accepted. Remember that you are paying a large sum of money for your child's education and you are entitled, at the very least, to a thorough report. In other words – complain. Make sure you get your money's worth with a detailed report which goes into you child's merits and shortcomings. Teaching staff should always be prepared to answer any questions and discuss any problems you may have.

· Right school for your child ·

This will not necessarily be the one you wish *you'd* gone to, nor the one that's right for your other children, or the most prestigious that you can afford. The right school will be the one your child fits into most easily without having to be forced into a mould, and will provide:

- good teaching in your child's best subjects;
- a range of subject combinations at GCSE and A-level from which your child will benefit;
- motivation to develop extra-curricular interests;
- an environment in which your child will feel at home.

The strengths and interests of an 11–18 year-old aren't always obvious when the child is 5, 7 or even 9. Selecting is a process of elimination. Reject those schools that are obviously wrong for your child – too academic, too traditional, not enough music, too disciplinarian – before looking more carefully at the possible ones.

· Round Square Conference ·

Named after the Round Square, one of the buildings at Gordonstoun where this association started. There are some 15 member schools all over the world which follow the educational theories and methods of Kurt Hahn, the founder of Gordonstoun, who placed much importance on the value of outward bound and community service activities.

· Routine ·

Anybody who is trying to co-ordinate the movements of hundreds of children and teenagers, with the demands of a curriculum that requires their attendance at classes, has to work to a rigid schedule. School days are timetabled to the minute. In an attempt to make this less stultifying, some schools operate a timetable over a 6- or 7-day cycle so that Monday doesn't always start with double maths. Senior pupils may be granted some autonomy in private study periods.

At boarding schools routine can stretch throughout the day, ending with set supper and bed-times and baths according to a rota – and even into the weekend with organised trips to the local town on Saturday afternoons after playing sport for the school in the morning. This sort of routine is far more restricting than any they will encounter in adult life; it won't necessarily foster self-motivation or the ability to use time properly when they leave school and find that timetables are not externally enforced. Many children need to have some time to themselves, for reading, talking to friends, playing tennis, painting, catching up on homework – or doing nothing. Your child may be better off at a school with a range of really optional extras than at one where every hour is filled from a list of permissible options.

· Rules ·

There will be a set of rules for you and a set for the pupils. Yours may look like a particularly repressive contract of employment, with strict instructions to inform the school of the least departure from your child's normal routine, and so on. But ask to see a copy of the pupils' school rules. These indicate how much restriction the school places on its pupils and show how important traditions are, eg perhaps only sixth-formers may walk on the grass. How much control does the school try to exert over its pupils when they aren't in school? How difficult would it be to take your child out of school for a few days for a family occasion? A lot of schools don't publicise their policies on issues like smoking, drinking and drugs because they believe parents will assume that by mentioning them there is a real smoking/ drinking/drugs problem in the school.

Some children flourish in a fairly regimented environment, others find it a strain to be constantly bumping up against authority. Find a school where the level of insistence on conforming to rules matches what you think is your child's instinct and family experience.

· Scholarships and exhibitions ·

Some pupils can have all or a proportion of their fees paid by a scholarship or exhibition. The well-endowed schools often have scores of scholarships; most have at least a handful. They are awarded, by the school, on the strength of the pupil's potential, usually judged by exam or test. Depending on the school, scholarships may be given for academic ability or for music, prowess at sport etc and at various ages. They are sometimes awarded irrespective of parental income, sometimes means tested.

· School consultants ·

These are people who give advice on suitable schools for your child. They may be worth considering if you really don't know where to begin in matching school and child (and if you're sure that your child needs an independent school). Consultants are sometimes paid a retainer by schools who want to be recommended. Get advice about reputable consultants from ISIS.

· School councils ·

The idea is that pupil representatives from every form, or perhaps just senior forms, should meet the staff to discuss issues such as food, discipline, school outings, and to air grievances. Some heads and staff at independent schools do not warm to this democratisation.

· School magazines ·

Many schools will send you one if asked. Like prospectuses, magazines are geared towards creating a good impression; they vary a lot in size and quality of production but most give you *some* idea of what's going on in the school. How much involvement do the pupils have in the magazine contents and production? How many trips and excursions are reported? What are the leavers going to do and where? Leavers' first destinations are important. (News of alumni may not be quite as relevant – many people lose touch with their schools.) What sort of drama, music and sport are the pupils doing? Do only one or two members of staff seem to be arranging all the extra-curricular activities? Does one pupil seem to excel at everything, making you wonder what the others are up to?

The pupils of some schools bring out their own, unofficial, magazine; these aren't usually written to impress parents and can be difficult to get hold of through official channels. If you track one down, it should give an impression of the concerns of the more vociferous (and critical?) pupils, and makes a good counterbalance to the official version.

· Scotland ·

The educational system in Scottish maintained schools is subtly different. Some Scottish independent schools follow the Scottish system, others stick to the English one, and others are a hybrid of the two.

Firstly, secondary schooling in Scotland starts at 12, rather than 11. Then, while English and Welsh pupils are doing GCSEs, Scots are doing S-grades (standard grade) which are replacing O-grades by 1992; these are followed a year later by Highers; and CSYS a year after that. For further information, contact Scottish Examination Board, Ironmills Road, Dalkeith, Midlothian EH22 1LE; tel: 031–663 6601.

Many pupils by-pass S-grades in subjects they intend to sit as Highers. You are prohibited from taking a subject in CSYS until you have passed it as a Higher; but many independent schools take Highers and A-levels together. Traditionally,

Scottish students went on to degree courses after Highers when they were 17; some still do. But they usually stay into the sixth, particularly if they want to move south of the border, which they often do not. There is a strong tradition in Scottish schools *not* to head for Oxbridge. And Glasgow schools often lead pupils to Glycom universities.

· Service children ·

The Ministry of Defence may give grants towards the day or boarding fees of the children of armed service personnel. You can find out more from your local Service Education Unit or from MOD, Service Children's Education Authority, Court Road, Eltham, London SE9 5NR (tel: 081–854 2242, x4277).

· Setting ·

Some schools split children into teaching groups for particular subjects according to ability judged on performance in exams and class. Setting is distinct from streaming, where pupils are assigned to their basic class by ability, age etc.

The advantages of setting are that groups of similar ability are easier to teach, prevent quick learners from being held back and allow slower ones to move at a less pressured pace.

The disadvantages are that children can be held back by being wrongly setted and that often the best teachers and facilities may automatically go to the more able sets.

· Sex ·

Most schoolchildren don't have the opportunity to indulge in active sex lives, but they do think and talk about sex a lot. (It was once claimed that sixth-form boys thought, albeit fleetingly, about sex an average of eight times an hour.) *The Equitable Schools Book* doesn't attempt to assess the sex education provision of individual schools. A straightforward account of human copulation and reproduction, as provided in many school sex education classes, isn't necessarily the most relevant way of finding out about sex – it can confuse rather than clarify. Also, it's difficult to measure sex education as it crops up in other subjects and classroom discussions.

Many parents find it difficult to think of their children as being sexually active and adolescents sometimes resent what they see as parental interference in their personal lives. However, it's worth braving the mutual embarrassment; while the repercussions of an unplanned pregnancy are as traumatic and lasting as ever, AIDS has made ignorance an even greater danger than it was before. There are lots of books about sex around; you might learn as much as your child from *Sex with Paula Yates* (Sphere, 1987); or you can start basic with *Clare Rayner's Body Book* (Deutsch, 1982) and *Where Did I Come From?* and *What's Happening to Me?* (both Macmillan).

In the meantime, you can find out about the school's attitude towards sex – relationships between pupils of the same or different ages; homosexuality. At boarding schools you may also want to find out whether girls and boys are allowed into each other's bedrooms; are they discouraged from forming close relationships?

· S-grades ·

These are replacing O-grades in Scotland.

The exams are designed to test a wider range of ability than O-grades – subjects are broken down into different elements such as application and understanding, and assessment is based on exams and set classwork during the course.

Scottish pupils often sit S-grades only in those subjects that they aren't going to continue to Higher or A-level. This means that some of the ablest Scottish pupils will have only 3 or 4 S-grades. Bear that in mind when you read Scottish school profiles in *The Equitable Schools Book*.

· SHA ·

The Secondary Heads Association is a club for the majority of heads and deputies of secondary schools. It provides a rare forum for heads of state and independent schools to discuss general educational matters common to both sectors.

· SHMIS ·

The Society of Headmasters and Headmistresses of Independent Schools is a club for heads – mostly of smaller independent schools. It was established in 1961 to provide a forum for the exchange of ideas, because membership of the HMC was full. Some headmasters are members of both.

· Siblings ·

Very often siblings are automatically sent to the same school. This has advantages; younger siblings have a familiar face around from day one, it's convenient for them to have roughly the same daily and holiday routine, and some schools reduce the fees for second and subsequent children. However, siblings can have very different educational needs and may flourish in very different schools. Where children scrape into a school attended by an elder sibling, especially under family pressure, there is a strong risk of future disaster.

· Sickness ·

If you keep your child away from school due to illness, inform the school at once and let them know what's wrong; this is especially important if it's infectious or will curtail your child's activities after going back to school.

School isn't necessarily any more dangerous than home but accidents happen. You should leave home and office telephone numbers with the school and be very specific about when and where you can be contacted; this can save much anxiety to frantic teachers. If for any reason you can't be contacted, arrange to have a friend standing by to step in if your child is ill or has an accident at school.

Find out what facilities for sick or injured children there are on the premises. Is there a resident nurse and a sick-room (especially relevant for boarding schools)? How far away is the nearest hospital?

You can insure school fees against long absences from school due to illness; speak to an insurance broker about this or contact ISIS.

· Single-sex schools ·

Although it may be an artificial environment, some children are happier in all girls' or all boys' schools. A lot of the heavyweight schools (academically and socially) have remained single sex; although many boys' schools have now gone co-ed or take girls into the sixth (mixed sixth) and a handful of girls' schools have done the same. Academically, girls from single-sex schools appear to get better exam results than those from co-ed schools. The reverse is true of boys.

Most schools make some attempt to introduce the opposite sex at some stage. Many team up with other schools (particularly if there is a brother/sister school) and share activities, productions and outings. Some may also have joint facilities, join forces for A-levels or in the prep/junior department. A few remain socially isolated.

· Sixth form ·

A pathetically small proportion of British pupils stay on at school after they take GCSE at 16, but the majority of independent schoolchildren do. Of the 16–18 age group at school, 20% is at independent school as against 7% overall.

The sixth form lasts for two years (lower and upper). Some pupils stay for only one year in the sixth, having done additional GCSEs or other qualifications (secretarial, City and Guilds, Certificate of Further Studies etc); most stay for two, doing A-level courses. Schools usually give the size of their whole sixth forms (they look bigger then); *The Schools Book* gives the size of the upper sixth – that is the number of A-level candidates in a year.

The recruitment of girls into sixth forms at boys' schools, together with the development of sixth form colleges, has created some enthusiasm for moving children after GCSE. In some cases, this is the right thing; some 16-year-olds can need somewhere new and challenging. But in the opinion of at least one head, this can reduce the effective A-level course from 5 terms to 4 terms, by the time the pupil has settled in. Good schools will take the trouble to assess how easily a child will settle into their school, as well as looking at academic ability.

· Size of school ·

Independent secondary schools range in size from about 120 pupils to over 2,000. Just as some people are happier in the bustle of large cities than they are in small towns, some children prefer a certain size of school. Consider the facilities and subjects offered; there may be more going on at a large school and possibly better, newer facilities, but there isn't always a bigger range. Large schools can often give pupils some of the advantages of small schools by breaking down the whole school into houses with a life of their own. It does not necessarily follow that small schools can provide a more caring environment, although it is obvious sometimes they care that they do.

· Smoking ·

Still prevalent in schools in spite of massive anti-smoking campaigns from heads and the government. Most schools prohibit smoking, many expel those caught. In general, if children get through school without smoking they'll probably never start but peer pressure and the need to flaunt authority makes this difficult. Many of those who don't smoke have parents who do. Girls appear more inclined to smoke than boys.

Making children aware of the dangers doesn't seem to stop them; teenagers regard themselves as immortal and don't appreciate how difficult giving up can be. One head recommends massive parental bribes for not smoking before they are 21 (at least £1,000 to be worth considering). Schools with an 'expulsion for smoking' policy have been known to have to step down when the entire sixth form is caught. There is a lot of anti-smoking information from pressure groups such as ASH (Action on Smoking and Health), 5–11 Mortimer Street, London W1N 7RH (tel: 071–637 9843).

· Special needs ·

Some schools in *The Equitable Schools Book* make provision for children with special needs due to, for example, mild handicap, learning or language difficulties. Some of these are listed in the *School Spotter*.

For listings of specialist schools contact:

- **England**: Department of Education and Science, Schools Branch 2, Division B (Special Education), Elizabeth House, 39 York Road, London SE1 7PH (tel: 071–934 9000).
- **Wales**: Welsh Office Education Department, Schools Administration Branch 3, Phase 2 Government Buildings, Tŷ Glas Road, Llanishen, Cardiff CF4 5WE (tel: 0222 761456).
- **Scotland**: Scottish Education Department (Special Schools), New St Andrew's House, St James Centre, Edinburgh EH1 3SY (tel: 031 556 8400).
- **Northern Ireland**: Department of Education for Northern Ireland, Schools I Division, Rathgael House, Balloo Road, Bangor, Northern Ireland BT19 2PR (tel: 0247 270077).

· Sports and games ·

There is still much emphasis on sports and games in independent schools and still pressure to play *the* team sport of the term in traditional schools eg rugby (autumn), hockey (spring), cricket (summer). In many, 5 or 6 afternoons a week (plus other times) are devoted to them and most schools have excellent facilities on site or nearby (including an increasing number of sports halls). Even so, performances at national and international level remain poor and the facilities that are provided in schools are inferior to those available in many other countries.

Many schools run sports and games on a voluntary basis and nowadays it is comparatively rare to find a school which insists on everyone taking part in official sports and games regardless of ability, physique and inclination.

The principal and most popular field games are: rugby union, cricket, hockey, soccer, lacrosse, handball, softball, rounders and forms of baseball. Some Irish schools provide hurling and Gaelic football. The main court games are: lawn tennis, hard-court tennis, badminton, basketball, squash, rackets, volleyball, and croquet; plus Eton fives and Rugby fives. A few schools provide real tennis.

Of the course games, golf is easily the most popular. Quite a lot of schools have 9-hole courses on their estates, or have access to courses nearby.

Athletics are very popular and most schools can provide a full range of field and track events (not a few schools have all-weather running tracks). Cross-country running is very popular.

Some martial arts are also common and popular and include judo, karate, kendo and kung-fu. Fencing is also popular, but boxing appears to be a thing of the past.

Target sports (eg, archery, clay-pigeon shooting, rifle-shooting – small and full-bore – and pistol-shooting) are available in quite a lot of schools and are linked with activities in the CCF.

Water sports (especially water polo, surfing, canoeing, sailing, rowing and diving) are always popular. Schools situated near the sea, a river or lake tend to make good use of water.

Gymnastic sports are extremely popular and most schools have good facilities for these.

Some schools (particularly girls' schools) can provide riding and some show-jumping.

Outdoor pursuits are often closely associated with sport (or are sports in their own right), and include sailing, canoeing, ski-ing, rock-climbing, fell-walking, cliff-scaling, gliding and parachuting. A few schools even manage to have their own packs of beagles. Country schools (especially those in Scotland and the North of England) have a very full range of outdoor pursuits/sports including outdoor-pursuit centres which pupils can visit for a few days at a time. Such activities have links with various enterprises in the Duke of Edinburgh's Award Scheme. The *mens sana in corpore sano* philosophy – no doubt a continuation of the Victorian cult of athletic prowess and muscle-bound Christianity – is still widespread and many schools see team and individual sports and games as valuable character-building influences. Most schools have a hard core of dedicated sports/games enthusiasts on the staff (some headmasters are fanatics) who are qualified to coach, referee and umpire and who are prepared to devote an enormous amount of time and effort to their chosen activity. The majority of schools run sports and games on a competitive basis, with inter-house competitions and numerous fixtures with other schools.

Whether or not all this is a good thing is another issue. The amount of time and effort given to sports and games is often a matter of contention among school staffs. Clashes of interest are frequent. You are well advised to think carefully about what you want your child to be exposed to – or deprived of.

· Staff ·

You'll probably get a list of staff and their credentials with the prospectus. You can investigate them further when you visit. What is the male:female ratio? Which departments have the largest teaching staff? How old are they (or do they seem)? The average pupil:staff ratio is about 11:1 or 12:1, but this varies a lot and you're probably more interested in the teaching groups. What do you think your child will make of the staff, and how interesting would *you* find them? Can you find out how long they've served? Most profiles in *The Equitable Schools Book* give the annual staff turnover – usually about 5–10% which gives a reasonable influx of new blood to the staff. When turnover is low, is this because the staff are good, happy teachers or because they are inert?

· Starting out ·

Before your child's first day at a new school, check:

- whether there are other new pupils in the class;
- what time the new pupils are expected to get there;
- what time the day ends; or, at a boarding school, when the first exeat is;
- that you've got all the necessary equipment and uniform.

Try to introduce your child to some of the other pupils in the class so that there'll be someone familiar on the first day.

· Stealing ·

Theft is inherent and pretty well inevitable in all institutional life. In any school, at any given moment, there is likely to be a thief or two about. Petty pilfering (of pens, watches, calculators, cash and items of clothing) is especially frequent in day schools (the swag can be got away easily). Life is often easy for the petty thief because pupils are so careless about their belongings, especially on games days; changing-rooms are easy targets. (In many schools, easily portable valuables are collected before games, but many pupils forget to hand them in.) Naming children's property can help schools reduce the scale of the problem; mark everything that can be marked.

Don't send your child to school with large amounts of cash or other valuables; if this can't be avoided, make sure it is handed to a member of staff for safekeeping (make sure your child knows which one). Find out what locker and other facilities for protection there are, where bikes can be stored and so on. If you think your child has had something stolen you should immediately contact the head or the child's teacher.

· Steiner schools ·

Schools whose teaching follows the philosophy of Rudolf Steiner who placed great emphasis on the development of the individual and believed that spiritual truth was human rather than in some way divine. The first Steiner school opened in Germany in 1914; they were closed by the Nazis in 1938. Currently there are about 200 worldwide. Many of them are prep only but a few (included in *The Equitable Schools Book*) teach up to A-level.

Further details from the Secretary, Steiner Schools Fellowship, c/o Michael Hall Rudolph Steiner School, Kidbrooke Park, Forest Row, East Sussex RH18 5JB (tel: 0342 822275).

· Streaming ·

A form of internal organisation in which pupils are grouped across the curriculum by such criteria as age, intelligence, ability and aptitude (or a combination of two or more of these). It is largely based on achievement in the three Rs. It starts in primary schools and extends into selective secondary education. An alternative pattern in mixed ability exists in many schools. Streaming is to be distinguished from setting, a system by which pupils are grouped for particular subjects (eg, maths, modern languages) according to ability.

· Subjects offered ·

Check what GCSE and A-level subjects the school offers. Even more important, what subject combinations are possible? Because of the early specialisation demanded by A-levels, pupils may still have to opt for an exclusively arts or science bias at the age of 16. This varies by school. The school profiles give the number of pupils combining arts and sciences at A-level. Some schools don't have the facilities to offer teaching in a combination of both areas.

· Transfer from the state system ·

Nearly half the pupils in independent secondary schools have not attended an independent junior school but there are huge variations – from 1%–100% – in the proportion of children each independent school recruits from the state sector.

For parents the good news is that the majority of secondary heads see no problem in transferring from a state school. Many are more positive ('. . . they should try it'; 'nicely spontaneous'; 'they take to us like ducks to water'; 'tends to be a very stimulating move').

And the bad news?

Very little, but you'll need to concentrate on:

(a) the age you want to make the transfer
(b) the entrance examination
(c) settling in

Transfer age

You should presume that, broadly, transfer at the end of state primary school or into the sixth form works well; at other ages it's more tricky. Schools that recruit at 13, two years after the end of most state primary education, are the main difficulty; usually boys' schools using the common entrance, they have few state entrants. Schools that recruit at 11 (or 12 in Scotland) take many more; some expect their pupils to come from local primary schools (mainly former direct grant grammar schools).

Entrance examination

Almost all independent secondary schools have one; former direct grant grammar schools often have something like the 11+. You may find it necessary to get a private tutor to help your child through. Most entrance exams are quite suited to state pupils but the common entrance examination is not – at least at present, although its curriculum is being tailored to the requirements of the National Curriculum so there could be some convergence in the future.

Settling in

At 11, Heads report few problems apart from the fact that state primary schools do not teach languages, in contrast to independent schools where pupils will certainly have studied at least one. The most frequently mentioned problems are discipline (academic and personal); hard work, homework and commitment ('inability to hide poor homework'; 'regular assignments collected by a deadline and marked promptly'; 'adjustment to small classes and consequent need to concentrate through the whole lesson'; 'six day week'; 'different attitude to out of work activities eg games').

At 16 and after GCSE there could be a difficulty on the science side for state pupils transferring into an independent science sixth form – they may have to switch from integrated science to individual sciences; also they may find that they are not ready for an A-level maths course. Neither is a real barrier to those prepared to work hard.

Problems of social integration at either 11 or 16 are reported to be very rare. What may disconcert a child might seem trivial to an adult – classroom silence after the hubbub of their primary school classroom; weekly tests in different subjects; standing up when the teacher comes into the room; remembering on no account to call her 'Miss'. The problems children encounter are common to any transfer from one school to another, not normally to any incompatibility between the state and independent systems.

· Tutorial colleges ·

Sometimes called crammers, they can be day or boarding and are nearly always co-ed. Tutorial colleges usually take students from the age of 16 for A-levels or additional GCSEs; many also coach for other exams: International Baccalaureat, Royal Society of Arts, Ordinary National Diploma. Fees are often charged according to the number of subjects studied. Because their youngest students are the age of a school's oldest pupils, tutorial colleges tend to have fewer rules, making them a good option for sixth-formers who have had enough of school discipline and tradition. Tutorial colleges are not included in *The Equitable Schools Book*; you can get lists of qualified tutorial colleges from CIFE, Buckhall Farm, Bull Lane, Bettersden, Ashford, Kent TN26 3HB (tel: 0233 82797) or ATI, 27 Radburn Court, Dunstable, Bedfordshire, LU6 1HW (tel: 0582 605920).

· Tutors ·

Tutors working as individuals (not as members of a tutorial college) can provide one-to-one teaching to help children overcome their learning difficulties or prepare for an examination. They are often useful when children are about to transfer from a state primary school to an independent secondary school. You usually find them by personal recommendation from a satisfied parent/child or from your child's current school.

If you want to check up on the bona fides of a tutor you could try asking whether they are a member of their professional body, The Association of Professional Tutors (27 Radbourne Court, Dunstable, Beds LU6 1HW tel: 0582 605920). Not all good tutors are members. The APT checks the credentials of its prospective members and is also a holder of the DES List 99, the official list of persons no longer permitted to hold a teaching post.

· Uniform ·

Most independent schools have a uniform. Often it won't have changed for a long time. This usually means buying a special tie and blazer; skirts/trousers, shirts, shoes, jumpers, even knickers, in the right colour. In addition you may need to buy special sports equipment and clothes, school colours for sports teams, summer clothes, formal dress (kilts if it's a Scottish school), coats, macs, smocks for art, etc. Schools will let you know where to buy the uniform, including any second-hand sources, before your child joins. Some are more demanding than others about what will or will not do. Uniforms can set you back by hundreds of pounds.

Many schools allow pupils to wear clothes of their own choice in their 'off duty' times (evenings, half holidays and at weekends). In the sixth form, uniform may be waived completely or replaced by a dress code; where the sixth is mixed this sometimes applies to the girls, not the boys. Check this with the school.

· Value for money ·

As more and more parents opt for independent education, often at the expense of family holidays, costs continue to rise at a rate higher than inflation (at least 10% a year). So, assuming day fees of £1,000 a term when your child is 13, they will be over £1,400 per term by the end – more than £18,000 for five years. With boarding fees of say £2,000 a term, five years will cost you over £36,000. So make sure that you're getting what you and your child want and need for this. If your child goes on to a degree course, you may find the government does not pay the full tuition fees by the late 1990s, as they do at the moment – so the costs go on; although even the full cost of a degree course is often less than school fees – from £2,800 for social studies courses.

· Visiting the school ·

You'll find out a lot about a school from observation when you visit.

- Go during term time.
- You can learn a lot from the attitude of the first person you meet – whether pupil, teacher or administrator.
- Observe the pupils. What do they look like? How do they react to what you ask (even if it's just 'Where's the head's study?')? Do they seem friendly, alert, interested?
- What about staff? what age range? how interested and interesting do they seem?
- Look at noticeboards. What's going on; who's involved? Sports, drama, talks, films, out-of-school visits, volunteers for community work or to help with school events? Are pupils honoured for achievements or are there lists of the latest suspensions?
- Look at classroom displays. Do they cover a range of interests and are they stimulating? Have the pupils done them themselves or do they look as though they've been pinned there in the vague hope that someone will look at them?
- Buildings: how impressive are they? How comfortable are they to work and live in? What are the facilities like? How consistently good or bad are they? (Your child may not be among those using the new physics lab.)
- Boarding accommodation: how stark, over-crowded or otherwise, are the dormitories and bathrooms? Can you believe that normal children live here happily?
- Don't be put off by discreet graffiti in pupils' lavatories and on desks – that's universal; spray paint on the swimming-pool wall isn't.

· Voluntary-aided schools ·

These are voluntary in so far as they have been founded by a voluntary religious body (eg the Church of England or the Roman Catholic Church) and aided in that they are supported by public funds. The LEA meets the running costs; repairs and three-quarters of improvements are paid for out of national funds; the rest is covered by the religious body. The voluntary body has the right to choose staff and decide on what religious education may be given. There are not many voluntary-aided schools today and most of them are church schools.

· Woodard schools ·

Nathaniel Woodard founded 7 schools starting with Lancing in 1848. The Woodard Corporation now maintains 23 schools throughout the country and a further 10 are associated with it, some from overseas. All have an Anglican foundation and together form the largest group of church schools in England and Wales.

· Young Enterprise ·

Young Enterprise helps young people (aged 15–19) form and run their own companies. This offers them a way of developing their enterprise skills and smoothing the difficult transition from school to work. Business consultants advise each company. There is a one-term course devised to meet many of the requirements of the National Curriculum for economic and environmental awareness and an examination (run by the Oxford board). Many schools participate in the scheme. You can find out more from Young Enterprise, Ewert Place, Summertown, Oxford OX2 7BZ (tel: 0865 311180).

· Schools A–Z ·

B L O O M S B U R Y

SCHOOL LEAVER'S HANDBOOK
Ed Stephen Adamson
No jargon, no preaching, no waffle - just the facts of real life for all school leavers, especially the things they don't teach you at school, such as leaving home, sex, relationships and health.

ISBN 0 7475 0681 7   .   £4.99

TIME OUT NUS STUDENT GUIDE
The essential guide to college life, compiled by the experts at the NUS and *Time Out*. Comprehensive, lively and opinionated, it contains in-depth and invaluable advice on all aspects of college life.

ISBN 0 7475 0916 6   £7.99

INDEPENDENT CAREERS GUIDE
Klaus Boehm & Jenny Lees-Spalding
Independent Careers is invaluable reading for anyone wanting to work for themselves. The fourth edition of this authoritative guide has been updated with the coming of the single European market in mind.

ISBN 0 7475 1002 4   £12.99

FAMILY TRAVEL HANDBOOK
A godsend to those with babies, toddlers and infants, this thoroughly-researched handbook is essential to anyone
travelling with children at home or abroad.
No family can afford to leave home without it.

ISBN 0 7475 0744 9   £9.99

Send orders to:
Sales Dept, Bloomsbury Publishing,
2 Soho Square, London WC1V 5DE
Telephone 071 494 2111

a

· *Abbotsholme* ·

Abbotsholme School
Rocester
Uttoxeter
Staffordshire
ST14 5BS
Tel 0889 590217

- Pupils 245
- Boys 11–18
  (Day/Board)
- Girls 11–18
  (Day/Board)
- Upper sixth 31

- Termli fees
  £1860 (Day)
  £2790 (Board/
  Weekly)
- HMC, SHMIS,
  Round Square
  Enquiries/application to
  the Headmaster

What it's like

Founded in 1889 by Dr Cecil Reddie, it was the first of a series of new schools which had considerable influence in Britain and on the continent. He was the originator of a movement which embraced the Lietz Schule in Germany and led to the foundation of Bedales, Gordonstoun and many others. The methods pioneered by Abbotsholme have been adopted in many schools and it was one of the first boys' schools to become fully co-educational (in 1969). Its handsome and well-equipped buildings lie in 140 acres of splendid private grounds in some of the most beautiful countryside in England, at the edge of the Peak District National Park. The main buildings include a fine chapel, music and art blocks and engineering workshops. Recent additions comprise a girls' boarding house, a computer laboratory, and a capacious science block. There is also a huge and superbly-equipped sports centre. Abbotsholme has all the advantages of a small school; the emphasis is on informality, a friendly and relaxed atmosphere and the creation of a strong community spirit. Parental involvement is encouraged to an unusual degree. Careful attention is given to religious education and all pupils attend a chapel service each day. A very favourable staff:pupil ratio of 1:9 permits small sets and classes and much individual attention. Academic standards are high and results most creditable. A high proportion of the sixth form goes on to degree courses, some to Oxbridge. But the academically less able are also well catered for. Music, drama and art are all vigorously supported. A feature of the school is the Arts Society (open to the public by subscription) which has an international reputation for its programmes. A dozen or more recitals/concerts are held each year at which musicians of international renown perform. Twenty acres of excellent playing fields provide for a standard range of sports and games. A large number of clubs and societies cater for a wide range of extra-curricular activity. There is much emphasis on open-air pursuits and outdoor education is an integral part of the school's programme. The pursuits include ski-ing, caving, canoeing, camping, mountaineering and rock-climbing. Many pupils take part successfully in the Duke of Edinburgh's Award Scheme. An important feature of the school is the 70-acre farm, also an integral part of school life (pupils are responsible for feeding, lambing, harvesting etc). There is also a big commitment to highly-organised local community services.

School profile

Pupils Age range 11–18; 245 pupils, 33 day (16 boys, 17 girls), 212 boarding (144 boys, 68 girls). Main entry ages, 11, 12, 13 and into sixth. 5% are children of former pupils. *Transfer from maintained schools:* 25% main intake, plus 50% to sixth.

Entrance Common entrance and own exam used. Not oversubscribed. No special skills or religious requirements. Parents not expected to buy text books. No compulsory extras – charges vary. Up to 8 scholarships/bursaries pa, 50–33% fees.

Parents 15+% from industry/commerce. 10–30% live within 30 miles, 10–30% live overseas.

Staff Headmaster Darrell J Farrant, in post for 7 years. 28 full time staff, 4 part time. Annual turnover 2%. Average age 42.

Academic work GCSE and A-levels. 22 subjects at GCSE; 16 at A-level (including history of art and general studies). In 1990, 52 pupils in upper fifth, 31 in upper sixth. *GCSE:* in 1990, 27% upper fifth gained at least grade C in 8+ subjects; 29% in 5–7; and 44% in 1–4 subjects. *A-levels:* 25% upper sixth passed in 4+ subjects; 22% in 3; 32% in 2; and 21% in 1 subject. 38% took science A-levels; 35% arts/humanities; 26% both. *Computing facilities:* Econet system running BBC 'B's, and stand-alone machines in most departments. *Special provision:* Specialist teachers for both dyslexia and EFL.

European Community *Languages:* French offered: to age 14; GCSE; AS-level; A-level. German offered: to age 14; GCSE; AS-level; A-level. 10–25% take GCSE in more than 1 EC language. *Exchanges:* Regular exchanges for pupils aged 14–18 to France and Germany. *Other:* Number of students from European countries for short periods. Regularly participates in joint ventures with European schools for community service overseas.

Senior pupils' non-academic activities *Music:* 120 learn a musical instrument, 10 up to Grade 6; 35 in school orchestra, 40 in school choir, 6 in pop group. *Drama and dance:* 30 in school productions; 40 LAMDA Grades 1–8; 20 above Grade 6; 6 bronze, silver and gold medals; 15 enter speech and drama festivals. *Art:* 15–20 take GCSE art; 5–8 A-level art; 5–8 history of art; 2–3 accepted for Art School. *Sport:* Boys: rugby, soccer, hockey, cricket. Girls: hockey, netball, rounders. Other sports available: swimming, tennis, badminton, squash, cross country, athletics, riding, volleyball, basketball, canoeing, windsurfing, clay-pigeon shooting, fitness, 5-a-side football, table tennis. 100 take non-compulsory sport. 20 take exams. 6 represent county/country (hockey, rugby, cricket, athletics). *Other:* 55 take part in local community schemes. 35 have bronze Duke of Edinburgh's Award, 25 silver and 15 gold. Many other activities including music, stage lighting, rock-climbing, windsurfing, caving, orienteering, animal husbandry, aikido, computers, fishing, model railway, young enterprise.

Careers In 1990, 46% leavers went on to degree courses; 6% to art/drama/music colleges; 16% to non-degree courses; 10% straight into careers; 10% other. Of those going on to degree courses, 5% went to Oxbridge; 47% to other universities; 47% to poly/colleges. 11% those going on to higher education went to courses in practical art; 35% in humanities/social sciences and 53% in science/engineering.

Uniform School uniform worn throughout.

Houses/prefects Competitive houses. Head boy/girl, prefects, head of house and house prefects, appointed by the head and elected by the school.

Religion Attendance at religious worship compulsory.

Social Academic lectures, university visits, general knowledge competitions, outdoor expeditions joint with other schools. Annual French trip (forms 1–3), Round Square exchange students (Germany) and international service projects.

Pupils allowed to bring own bike/horse. Meals self-service. School shop. No tobacco/alcohol allowed.

Discipline No corporal punishment. Pupils failing to produce homework once could expect work to be re-done under supervision on a half-holiday; those caught smoking cannabis on the premises could expect expulsion.

Boarding 10% have own study bedrooms; 60% share with 1–3 others. 30% in dormitories of 6+. Single sex houses, approx 13–35, same as competitive houses. Resident qualified nurse. Pupils can provide and cook own food. 3 weekend exeats a term plus 2 days. Visits to the local town allowed twice a week for all ages – younger ones only in a group.

Alumni association is run by Mr P Powell, Girsby Thickets, Girsby, Burgh-on-Bain, Lincoln LN3 6LA.

· *Abingdon* ·

Abingdon School
Abingdon
Oxfordshire
OX14 1DE
Tel 0235 21563

- Pupils 750
- Boys 11–18
  (Day/Board)
- Girls None
- Upper sixth 117

- Termly fees
  £1277 (Day)
  £2426
  (Board/Weekly)
- HMC
  Enquiries/application to
  the Registrar

What it's like

Founded in 1256, re-endowed in 1563, it was rebuilt on its present site in 1870. This is a most agreeable site of some 30 acres of grounds and handsome buildings a few hundred yards from the centre of the old and attractive market town of Abingdon, six miles from Oxford. Since 1945 there has been steady expansion of buildings which provide good facilities and comfortable boarding accommodation (weekly boarding has become a deliberate policy). Recent acquisitions include a fine sports hall and technology centre. The school is Anglican by tradition and the chapel is a focus of its corporate life. Attendance at religious worship is compulsory unless dispensation has been granted before entry. It has the reputation of being a versatile and well-run school which provides a successful all-round education. Somewhat anti-specialist and there is a wide range of non-specialist studies. A most favourable staff:pupil ratio of 1:11 ensures high academic standards and results are impressive. Very many leavers proceed to degree courses, many to Oxbridge. French and German on offer to A-level, Italian and Spanish to GCSE. A high proportion of boys takes GCSE in more than one European language. Music is particularly strong. A very large number of pupils learn a musical instrument; orchestras and choirs have vigorous support, as do other music-making groups. Drama is pretty strong, too. Facilities for sports and games are first rate. A standard range is available, plus rowing, shooting, rugby fives and golf. High standards are attained (a fair number of representatives at county level). Numerous clubs and societies exist. An enterprising variety of overseas trips is organised annually. Many pupils are involved in local community services and the Duke of Edinburgh's Award Scheme has been well supported. A CCF flourishes and this works in conjunction with community services and the Award Scheme. There are close connections with the local community and region.

School profile

Pupils Age range 11–18; 750 pupils (600 day, 150 boarding). Main entry ages, 11, 13 and into sixth. 4% are children of former pupils. *Transfer from maintained schools:* 65% main intake, five a year to sixth.

Entrance Common entrance and own exam used. Oversubscribed, especially for day places. No special skills or religious requirements. Parents not expected to buy text books. Average extras, £10 or less. 20 assisted places pa. 15 scholarships/bursaries pa including music and technology, full fees to one-eighth fees.

Parents 15+% are doctors, lawyers etc; 15+% in industry/commerce. 60+% live within 30 miles, less than 10% live overseas.

Staff Headmaster M St John Parker. 64 full time staff, 26 part time – mainly music. Annual turnover 8%. Average age 40 approx.

Academic work GCSE, AS and A-levels. 28 subjects offered (including Greek but not A-level general studies), 7 to AS-level. In 1990, 118 pupils in fifth, 117 in upper sixth. *GCSE:* in 1990, 103 upper fifth gained at least grade C in 8+ subjects; 11 in 5–7; and 1 in 1–4 subjects. *A-levels:* 13 upper sixth passed in 4+ subjects; 91 in 3; 11 in 2; and 3 in 1 subject. 25% took science A-levels; 32% arts/humanities; 43% both. *Computing facilities:* Apple Macintoshes and laser printers in IT centre and in classrooms. Use of computers across curriculum in music, technology, modern languages etc. *Special provision:* Ad hoc arrangements for intelligent dyslexics. Additional English for non-native English speakers.

European Community *Languages:* French offered: to age 14; GCSE; AS-level; A-level; as non-examined subject. German offered: to age 14; GCSE; AS-level; A-level. Italian and Spanish offered to GCSE. 35–60% take GCSE in more than 1 EC language. *Exchanges:* Regular exchanges for pupils aged 11–16 to France and Germany. *Other:* Fifth form study the FLAW (Foreign Languages at Work) course in French. Bright pupils can take French GCSE early; language diversification in years 1 and 2, one form does French, another German, another Russian. Satellite link for French and German TV programmes and computer link with French schools.

Senior pupils' non-academic activities *Music:* 330 learn a musical instrument, 46 up to Grade 6; 120 in school orchestra, 110 in school choir, 25 in pop group, 80 in other bands. 15 in Thames Vale Youth Orchestra, 2 in Oxford Youth Chamber Orchestra, 2 in National Youth Big Band, 5 in Oxon Youth Orchestra. 3 go on to degree course in music. *Drama and dance:* 120 in school productions; 1 accepted for Drama/Dance School. *Art:* 30 take art as non-examined subject within general studies, 25 take GCSE art; 18 A-level art; 6 AS-level ceramics; 7 A-level art history. 4 accepted for Art School; 1 to Courtauld; 4 to architecture school. *Sport:* Rugby, cricket, hockey, rowing, tennis, badminton, shooting, golf, fencing, rugby fives, table tennis, volleyball, sailing, soccer available. 150 take part in non-compulsory sport. 14 represent county (badminton, rugby, cricket). *Other:* 40 take part in local community schemes. 25 have bronze Duke of Edinburgh's Award, 7 silver and 1 has gold. Other activities include chess club (40 players, 25 matches a year). IT flourishes outside lesson time. Recent successes in chess, national general knowledge competitions, junior European parliament debating.

Careers In 1990, 80% leavers went on to degree courses; 2% to art/drama/music colleges; 2% straight into careers; 16% other. Of those going on to degree courses, 18% went to Oxbridge; 71% to other universities; 11% to poly/colleges. 2% those going on to higher education went to courses in practical art; 1% in drama/acting; 2% in music; 53% in humanities/social sciences; 3% in medicine; and 39% in science/engineering.

Uniform Simple school uniform worn throughout.

Houses/prefects Moderately competitive houses. Head boy, prefects, head of house and house prefects.

Religion Attendance at religious worship compulsory (unless dispensation granted before entry).

Social Joint debates; mixed casts for drama productions (local girls schools); careers evenings; some joint choral work with other local schools. Abingdon inter-sixth form society. Some sixth form joint teaching (German, Greek, Russian, Spanish, Italian, Japanese, Economics). Annual cultural visits to eg Turkey, Egypt, Italy; ski trips; language exchanges to Russia, Germany and France. Pupils allowed to bring own car/bike/motorbike. Meals occasionally formal, usually self-service. School shop. No tobacco/alcohol allowed.

Discipline No corporal punishment. Response to misdemeanours depends on age and past record but if a piece of homework is not produced with no plausible excuse, the work must be done in a special work detention. Those caught smoking cannabis on the premises might expect expulsion.

Boarding 5% have own study bedrooms; 75% share with 1–3 others. 20% in dormitories of 6+. Houses, of 10–50, same as competitive houses. Resident qualified nurse; doctor attends frequently. Pupils can provide and cook own food. One (one Saturday morning) exeat for full boarders; weekly boarders leave each weekend. Visits to the local town allowed at housemaster's discretion.

Alumni association is run by The Secretary, The Old Abingdonian Club, c/o The School.

Former pupils Robert Hayward MP, Francis Maude MP, David Bobin (Channel 4 sports commentator), Tom Kempinski (playwright), Robin Kermode (actor).

· Ackworth ·

Ackworth School
Ackworth
Pontefract
West Yorkshire
WF7 7LT
Tel 0977 611401

- Pupils 520
- Boys 7–18 (Day/Board)
- Girls 7–18 (Day/Board)
- Upper sixth 45

- Termly fees £1232 (Day) £2193 (Board)
- SHMIS
Enquiries/application to the Head

What it's like

Founded in 1779 in the village of Ackworth (4 miles from Pontefract). It is blessed with an estate of 270 acres, including a magnificent Grade I listed Georgian block, spacious gardens and playing fields. There are many modern facilities and new buildings including a sports hall and computer centre; the first phase of a new technology centre is complete. Through a school council, the pupils play a part in the running of the school and there are strong bonds with the local community. As it is a Quaker foundation the pattern of life has as its basis the belief that religion and life are one. It stresses the traditional values of 'courtesy, service and academic rigour'. It being a small school, a 'family' atmosphere prevails and this is much encouraged. Many sixth form leavers go on to degree courses. French and German are offered to A-level; Spanish and Italian (as a supplement for keen linguists) to GCSE. There are regular exchanges with France and Germany.

School profile

Pupils Total age range 7–18; 520 pupils, 300 day (150 boys, 150 girls), 220 boarding (110 boys, 110 girls). Senior department 11–18, 440 pupils. Main entry ages, 7, 11, 13 and into sixth. Approx 5% are children of former pupils. *Transfer from maintained schools:* 60% intake at 11 and 13, plus 20% to sixth.

Entrance Common entrance and own entrance exam used. Oversubscribed for day pupils. Keen on musical entrants. Parents are expected to buy text books in the sixth form; no other extras. Assisted places available. 40 scholarships/bursaries available (including music and art), up to 75% of full fees.

Parents 10+ in professions; 15+% in industry or commerce. 10+% live overseas.

Staff Head Mr D S Harris, in post for 2 years. 41 full time staff, 2 part time, 20 music staff. Annual turnover 5%. Average age 40.

Academic work GCSE and A-levels. 17 subjects offered (including A-level general studies; GCSE geology and economics). In 1990, 75 pupils in upper fifth, 45 in upper sixth. *GCSE:* in 1990, 35 upper fifth gained at least grade C in 8+ subjects; 27 in 5–7; and 15 in 1–4 subjects. *A-levels:* 13 upper sixth passed in 4+ subjects; 19 in 3; 6 in 2; and 3 in 1 subject. 20 took science A-levels; 20 arts/humanities; 4 both. *Computing facilities:* 24 RM Nimbus computers. *Special provision:* Individual help (1 hour/week) available from specialist teachers for English as a foreign language.

European Community *Languages:* French offered: to age 14; GCSE; AS-level; A-level. German offered: to age 14; GCSE; A-level. Italian offered: to age 14; GCSE. Spanish offered: to GCSE. (Spanish and Italian taught to keen linguists as a supplement). 10–25% take GCSE in more than 1 EC language. *Exchanges:* Regular exchanges for pupils aged 14–16 to France and Germany. *Other:* 10 German 16-year-old pupils each year spend up to 1 year in school.

Senior pupils' non-academic activities *Music:* 140 learn a musical instrument, 35 up to Grade 6, several to Grade 8; 3 accepted for music courses, 50 in school orchestra, 70 in school choir, 12 in chamber choir, 12 in brass group, 2 in City of Sheffield Youth Orchestra. *Drama and dance:* 70 in school productions, 80 in junior plays, 50 in Drama Workshops, 9 in Recorder Group, 12 in Dancing Group. 1 accepted for Drama/Dance School. *Art:* 6 take art as non-examined subject; 20 take GCSE art; 6 A-level art; 1 accepted for Art School; 20 attend art workshops. *Sport:* Soccer, hockey, cricket, athletics, tennis, swimming, squash, netball, rounders available. 253 take non-compulsory sport. 75 take exams in eg gymnastics, swimming. 17 represent county/country (hockey, athletics, netball). *Other:* 75 take part in local community schemes. 30 have bronze Duke of Edinburgh's Award, 20 silver and 8 gold. 10% enter voluntary schemes after leaving school. Other activities include aero-modelling, natural history, gym, needlework, fabric printing, art workshop, cookery, badminton, electronics, weight training, canoeing, sailing, CDT workshops, pottery, drama, dancing, art studies, aerobics, jazz, computing, debating, printing, photography, Tae Kwan-do, Tai-Chi.

Careers In 1990, 75% leavers went on to degree courses; 10% to art/drama/music colleges; 10% to non-degree courses; 5% straight into careers (eg hairdressing, father's business). Of those going on to degree courses, 4% went to Oxbridge, 65% to other universities; 30% to poly/colleges. 5% those going on to higher education went to courses in practical art; 5% in music; 40% in humanities/social sciences; 10% in medicine; and 40% in science/engineering.

Uniform School uniform worn throughout.

Houses/prefects Competitive houses. No prefects, all sixth formers share duties. Head boy and girl, heads of houses, appointed by the Head and house staff after consultation with sixth formers. School Council.

Religion Religious worship is encouraged. All boarders attend Meeting for Worship in the manner of the Society of Friends but the school accepts and welcomes staff and pupils of other denominations and faiths and seeks to support their commitment.

Social Membership of Riding for Disabled Association, Mencap swimming and of local Music Society; involved in recycling and local crime prevention. Skiing and trips to cultural centres abroad. Travel scholarships are awarded to sixth formers. Pupils encouraged to bring bicycle to school; day pupils bring cars with special permission. Meals formal. School shop.

Discipline Each case looked at on its own merits. Alcohol and tobacco are not tolerated; anyone using drugs could expect to be expelled. The aim is to encourage self discipline.

Boarding Sixth formers in small bedrooms and also have single or double studies. Fifth formers have study cubicles. Pupils divided into different single-sex houses by age group. 30–60 in each house.

Resident qualified medical staff. Central dining rooms. Pupils can provide and cook own snacks. Weekend leave by arrangement with house staff. Visits to the local town allowed.

Alumni association is run by John Davies, 17 Ongar Road, Writtle, Chelmsford, Essex, CM1 3NA.

Former pupils Richard Denby (President, The Law Society); Prime Minister of Nepal; Basil Bunting (poet); numerous academics.

· *Adcote* ·

Adcote School	• Pupils 130	• Termly fees
Little Ness	• Boys None	£1275 (Day)
Near Shrewsbury	• Girls 7–18 (Day/	£2150
Shropshire	Board/Weekly)	(Board/Weekly)
SY4 2JY	• Upper sixth 6	• GSA
Tel 0939 260202		Enquiries/application to the Headmistress

What it's like

Founded in 1907, it occupies a neo-Tudor grade-one listed building (1879) in a glorious landscaped parkland with a view to the Briedden and south Shropshire hills; a comfortable and well-equipped establishment. A proportion of pupils' parents are on overseas contracts or serving abroad and full travel arrangements are made for such pupils. It also welcomes a few foreign girls. Being a small school a very friendly and 'family' atmosphere prevails. It gives a sound academic education and a wide range of extra curricular activities in a disciplined and caring community.

School profile

Pupils Total age range 7–18; 130 girls, 75 day, 55 boarding. Senior department 11–18, 100 pupils. Main entry ages 7–14 and into sixth. *Transfer from maintained schools:* 30% at 11.

Entrance Admission by school's own day of assessment. Not oversubscribed. No special skills or religious requirements although school is Anglican. Parents expected to buy text books for A-level pupils; other extras vary. Scholarships/bursaries available for sixth form (under review at other ages).

Staff Headmistress Mrs S B Cecchet, in post for 12 years. 11 full time staff, 10 part time. Low turnover.

Academic work GCSE and A-levels. 15 subjects offered (to GCSE; 13 to A-level, no general studies). In 1990, 25 pupils in upper fifth, 6 in upper sixth. *GCSE:* in 1990, 48% upper fifth gained at least grade C in 8+ subjects; 32% in 5–7; and 20% in 1–4 subjects. *A-levels:* All took science or Maths A-levels. *Computing facilities:* Curriculum subject and computer club. *Special provision:* Extra specialist teaching available for dyslexics and EFL.

European Community *Languages:* French offered: to age 14; GCSE; AS-level; A-level. German offered: to age 14; GCSE; AS-level; A-level. *Exchanges:* Regular exchanges for pupils aged 11–16 to France and Germany. *Other:* Several EC pupils enrolled in school, some for 1 year.

Senior pupils' non-academic activities *Music:* 50% learn a musical instrument; some up to Grade 6 or above. Many play in bands and orchestras and sing in choirs both in school and with local HMC schools. *Drama and dance:* Some pupils take part in school productions and to Grade 6 in ESB and in public speaking competitions; others take part in drama productions at neighbouring HMC schools. Some accepted for Drama School. *Art:* Popular as a non-examined subject, GCSE and A-level subject. Some are accepted for Art School. Some belong to photographic, ceramic and art clubs. *Sport:* Lacrosse, netball, gym, dance, tennis, rounders, swimming, riding and athletics available. Some represent county in various sports. Other activities include Duke of Edinburgh's Award, computer and book clubs and others. Driving lessons available.

Careers In 1990, 66% sixth form leavers went on to degree courses; 33% other. Of those going on to degree courses, 100% went to universities; 8% to courses in practical art; 8% in drama/acting; 8% in music; 35% in humanities/social sciences; 8% in medicine; and 35% in science/engineering.

Uniform School uniform worn except in the sixth form (second hand uniform exchange operates).

Houses/prefects Competitive houses. Prefects and head girl appointed by staff; head of house and house prefects elected by pupils.

Religion School assembly compulsory. Boarders attend local C of E or RC church.

Social Music, drama and lectures (careers and subject) with local HMC schools. Organised trips abroad (ski-ing and cultural); exchange systems with schools abroad. Pupils allowed to bring own car/bike to school. Some meals formal, others self service. School shop sells books, stationery, tuck.

Discipline No corporal punishment. Pupils failing to produce homework could expect to have to do it.

Boarding Sixth formers have single or twin study bedrooms, others in rooms of 3–6. School doctor attends daily. Central dining room. Weekly boarding available. Visits to the local town allowed for seniors unaccompanied. Sixth form centre.

· *Albyn* ·

Albyn School for Girls 17/23 Queens Road Aberdeen AB9 2PA Tel 0224 322408	● Pupils 470 ● Boys 3–5 only (Day) ● Girls 3–18 (Day/Board) ● Upper sixth 30	● Termly fees £900 (Day) £2150 (Board) Enquiries/application to the Headmistress

What it's like

Founded in 1867, it was privately owned until 1949 when it passed to the company which now controls it. It comprises four large, handsome, granite houses in the residential west end of Aberdeen which lie in pleasant grounds. It combines nursery and preparatory departments. There have been substantial additions to the main buildings in recent years and it is now a well-equipped establishment. Academic standards are high and results are good. Many sixth formers proceed to degree courses each year. There is plentiful musical activity; drama and arts are well supported. A standard range of sports and games is available and good standards are achieved (several representatives at county level). Clubs and societies are well catered for and the school participates in the Duke of Edinburgh's Award Scheme.

School profile

Pupils Total age range 3–18; 470 pupils, 448 day (7 boys, 441 girls), 22 boarding girls. Senior department 12–18, 274 girls. Main entry ages 5, 10, 12 and into fifth.

Entrance Own entrance exam used. Oversubscribed at certain stages. No special skills or religious requirements. Parents expected to buy text books; other extras variable. 22 assisted places.

Parents 60+% live within 30 miles; up to 10% live overseas.

Staff Head Mistress Miss Norma H Smith, in post for 9 years. 34 full time staff, 13 part time. Annual turnover 2–4%.

Academic work O-grade, S-grade, Highers, CSYS. Average size of O-grade year (SIV) 54; CSYS year (SVI) 35. *O-grade:* on average, 43 pupils in SIV pass 5–7 subjects; 10, 1–4 subjects; school policy to take 7 subjects at maximum. *Computing facilities:* Computers available in appropriate subjects.

European Community *Languages:* French offered: to age 14; S-grade; Highers; CSYS. German offered: to age 14; S-grade; Highers; CSYS. 10–25% take S-grade in more than 1 EC language. *Other:* Pupils frequently include EC girls whose parents are working in Aberdeen; Dutch, French, German in 1991.

Senior pupils' non-academic activities *Music:* 120 learn a musical instrument (all play recorder), 20 to Grade 6 or above; 50 pupils play in school orchestra, 140 in choir, 1 in National Youth Orchestra. *Art:* 4 take as a non-examined subject; 22 take O/S-grade; 17 Highers. 2 accepted for Art School. *Sport:* 77 take part in non-compulsory sport, 10 take exams in swimming. 9 pupils represent county (hockey, swimming, tennis, volleyball), 2 country (badminton). *Other:* 47 participate in bronze Duke of Edinburgh's Award, 8 silver, 2 gold. There is a debating society.

Careers In 1990, 81% leavers went on to degree courses; 3% to non-degree courses (eg agriculture, business and horse riding); 3% straight into careers (eg banking); 13% other (year out, Project Trust). Of those going on to degree courses, 65% went to universities; 35% to poly/colleges. 10% those going on to higher education went to courses in music; 55% in humanities/social sciences; 10% in medicine; and 25% in science/engineering.

Uniform School uniform worn throughout.

Houses/prefects Competitive houses. Prefects, head girl, head of house and house prefects – elected by the school. School Council.

Social Debates. Some organised trips abroad. Meals self service. No tobacco/alcohol allowed.

Discipline No corporal punishment.

Boarding One boarding house. Central dining room. Exeats permitted whenever required. Visits to local town allowed daily for pupils 10–18.

Alumni association is run by Mrs M Drummond, at the school.

· *Aldenham* ·

Aldenham School
Elstree
Hertfordshire
WD6 3AJ
Tel 0923 858122
Fax 0923 854410

- Pupils 375
- Boys 13–18
  (Day/Board)
- Girls 16–18
  (Day/Board)
- Upper sixth 75

- Termly fees
  £1927 (Day)
  £3034 (Board)
- HMC
  Enquiries/application to
  the Headmaster

What it's like

The school was founded in 1597 by Richard Platt, a brewer. It occupies its original site which has since been extended to 135 acres of grounds, playing fields and farm land, situated in the Hertfordshire Green Belt but only 15 miles from the centre of London. The school has firm ties with the Worshipful Company of Brewers and many brewing organisations are generous benefactors. The Elizabethan School was demolished in 1825 and the 19th century buildings that replaced it have been upgraded and added to constantly so as to maintain up to date fully equipped facilities in an historic framework. The School is a Christian foundation and Christian ideals are evident in its structure and life. Being a small school it enjoys a 'family' atmosphere and there are strong ties with the local community. Many sixth form leavers go on to degree courses. French, German and Spanish are offered to A-level and there are regular exchanges with France and Germany. The school seeks the all round development of its pupils within an environment setting high standards of achievement and mutual responsibility.

School profile

Pupils Age range 13–18; 375 pupils, 175 day (170 boys, 5 girls), 200 boarding (175 boys, 25 girls). Main entry ages: boys 13; boys and girls into sixth. Approx 5% are children of former pupils. *Transfer from maintained schools:* 10% main intake, plus 10% to sixth.

Entrance Common entrance and own entrance test used. Oversubscribed. Pupils skilled in sport, music and art welcomed. All religions welcome but attendance at C of E worship is compulsory. Typical extras £100 plus music tuition. 35 assisted places. Means tested scholarships/bursaries, £1250–£300 per term.

Parents 15+% are doctors, lawyers, etc; 35+% in industry or commerce. 80+% live within 30 miles; 10+% live overseas.

Staff Headmaster M Higginbottom, in post for 8 years. 35 full time staff, 8 part time. Annual turnover less than 5%.

Academic work GCSE and A-levels. 19 GCSE subjects offered; 18 at A-level (no general studies). In 1990, 75 pupils in upper fifth, 72 in upper sixth (now 75). *GCSE:* in 1990, 34 upper fifth gained at least grade C in 8+ subjects; 21 in 5–7; and 14 in 1–4 subjects. *A-levels:* 5 upper sixth passed in 4+ subjects; 31 in 3; 21 in 2; and 15 in 1 subject. 15% took science A-levels; 55% arts/humanities; 30% both. *Computing facilities:* new lab with desk top facilities. *Special provision:* extra help available, often one-to-one.

European Community *Languages:* French offered: to GCSE; A-level. German offered: to GCSE; A-level. Spanish offered: to GCSE; A-level. 10–25% take GCSE in more than 1 EC language. *Exchanges:* Regular exchanges for pupils aged 14–16 to France and Germany. *Other:* Lower sixth work experience arranged in France and Germany. Hertfordshire Training and Enterprise Council award for 'Partners in Education Scheme'.

Senior pupils' non-academic activi-

ties *Music:* 100 learn a musical instrument, 20 to Grade 6 or above, occasional pupil accepted for Major Music School; 25 in school orchestra, 30 in choir; 2 in county orchestra. *Drama:* 30+ in school productions; 40 in house productions. *Art:* 6–10 take A-level. 3–4 accepted for Art School. *Sport:* Soccer, hockey, cricket, athletics, tennis, fives, squash, fencing, sailing, judo, karate, badminton, netball, lacrosse, rounders available. Most major games have county representatives; soccer, hockey and cricket for country. Strong school tradition in team games. *Other:* 20 take part in local community schemes. 24 have bronze Duke of Edinburgh's Award, 12 have silver, 6 have gold. Other activities include a thriving Outward Bound style section, computer club, driving, electronics, chess, stamps, debating, public speaking.

Careers In 1990, 70% leavers went on to degree courses (some after Gap year); 3% to art/drama/music colleges; 7% to non-degree courses (eg HND); 15% straight into careers (eg commodity broking, hotel management, surveyor, RAF, small business); 5% other. Of those going on to degree courses, 55% went to universities; 45% to poly/colleges. 3% those going on to higher education went to courses in practical art; 77% in humanities/social sciences; 5% in medicine; and 15% in science/engineering.

Uniform School uniform (unobtrusive) worn throughout.

Houses/prefects Houses (4 boarding, 2 day) form pastoral and social structure. School prefects appointed by the Head; house prefects within the house.

Religion Compulsory framework of religious worship and teaching supplemented by a strong programme of voluntary worship. Non-Christians encouraged in their own religion outside the compulsory framework.

Social Involvement in local competitions, joint events etc with local schools. Organised trips abroad and exchange systems eg ski-ing, mountaineering, sailing, geography, language. Upper sixth day boys allowed to bring own car. Meals self service. School shop. No tobacco allowed; sixth form bar for over 17s.

Discipline No corporal punishment. Pupils failing to produce homework once might expect to be placed in detention and reported to tutor/housemaster; any involvement in drugs or stealing is likely to lead to expulsion.

Boarding Pupils in fifth and sixth have studies, a few have study bedrooms; most are in dormitories of 6+. Accommodation houses are mixed sex in the sixth. Resident qualified nurse. Central dining room. Pupils can provide and cook some food. Exeats every weekend (24 hours).

Alumni association Secretary B N Liddiard, c/o the School.

Former pupils Bishops of Winchester and Exeter; Lord Justice Kerr; Sir Richard Vincent; N Durden-Smith; Sir Denys Roberts.

· *Alice Ottley* ·

The Alice Ottley School
Britannia House
Upper Tything
Worcester
WR1 1HW
Tel 0905 27061

- Pupils 701
- Boys None
- Girls 4–18 (Day)
- Upper sixth 51

- Termly fees
  £1252 (Day)
- GSA
Enquiries/application to
Admissions Secretary

What it's like

Founded in 1883 as the Worcester High School for Girls; renamed after its first headmistress in 1914. It is a charitable educational trust, with a fine site right in the middle of the cathedral city. The main building is a splendid Georgian mansion, in delightful grounds, called Britannia House. New buildings have been added steadily over the last hundred years, and the school is now well equipped with two libraries, a modern science block, an impressive sports hall and new classrooms; plus, opposite the main building, a lecture theatre and a sixth-form centre. It adheres to Church of England traditions, but is ecumenical in spirit and practice. The junior school is nearby, in another fine Georgian house. Academically it is quite high-powered and results are good. The staff:pupil ratio is a favourable 1:10. Very many sixth formers go on to degree courses, many to Oxbridge. French, German and Spanish are offered to A-level. Many girls take GCSE in more than one European language and all non-linguists in the sixth form take a French course. Regular exchanges with France and Germany. Music and drama are strongly supported. Half the senior girls have individual tuition in instruments. There are two orchestras, smaller instrumental groups and three choirs. A wide range of drama is presented each year, often in conjunction with the neighbouring boys' school. Theatre visits to Stratford, Birmingham and London are a regular feature. There are good facilities for a standard range of sports and games on nearby playing fields. Levels of performance are high, especially in lacrosse (a lot of representatives at county and national level). There is a plentiful variety of extra-curricular activities (including archery and judo). Many girls take part successfully in the Duke of Edinburgh's Award Scheme. Much use is made of the cultural facilities of Worcester (particularly in connection with festivals and other events at the cathedral).

School profile

Pupils Total age range 4–18, 701 girls. Senior department 11–18, 588 girls. *Transfer from maintained schools:* 59% at 11, plus 50% to sixth.

Entrance Own entrance exam used. Assisted places and some scholarships available. Own junior school.

Staff Headmistress Miss C Sibbit, in post for 5 years.

Academic work GCSE and A-levels. 21 subjects offered (including A-level general studies). In 1990, 75 pupils in upper fifth, 51 in upper sixth. *GCSE:* in 1990, 55 upper fifth gained at least grade C in 8+ subjects; 18 in 5–7; and 2 in 1–4 subjects. *A-levels:* 32 upper sixth passed in 4+ subjects; 13 in 3; 4 in 2; and 1 in 1 subject. 18% took science A-levels; 58% arts/humanities; 24% both. *Computing facilities:* Archimedes and BBC Masters in computer room, technology suite, science laboratories, home economics area, sixth form centre, lecture theatre; Amstrad in careers room. *Special provision:* Extra coaching is available.

European Community *Languages:* French offered: to age 14; GCSE; AS-level; A-level. German offered: to age 14; GCSE; AS-level; A-level. Spanish offered: to age 14; GCSE; AS-level; A-level. 25–50% take GCSE in more than 1 EC language. French for all non-linguists in the sixth form, from 1991. *Exchanges:* Regular exchanges for pupils aged 11–16 to France and Germany.

Careers In 1990, 83% leavers went on to degree courses; 13% to non-degree courses (eg business studies, agriculture, biology); 4% straight into careers (eg banking). Of those going on to degree courses, 14% went to Oxbridge, 59% to other universities; 27% to poly/colleges. 2% those going on to higher education went to courses in drama/acting; 73% in humanities/social sciences; 7% in medicine; and 18% in science/engineering.

· Alleyn's ·

Alleyn's School
Townley Road
Dulwich
London SE22 8SU
Tel 081–693 3422

- Pupils 930
- Boys 11–18 (Day)
- Girls 11–18 (Day)
- Upper sixth 125

- Termly fees
  £1490 (Day)
- HMC
  Enquiries/application to
  the Headmaster

What it's like

Founded in 1619, endowed by Edward Alleyn the Elizabethan actor-manager, it occupies a single site in South London on 26 acres of fine grounds and playing fields. Very accessible on public transport. The main buildings date from 1887. Numerous additions (especially since 1961) provide excellent facilities of all kinds to a school which, academically and intellectually, is one of the foremost in southern England. A first-rate traditional education is provided, and it is strong in music, drama and art. Many pupils go on to degree courses, including Oxbridge. French and German are offered to A-level and not a few pupils take GCSE in both. Italian and Spanish are offered to A-level. There are regular exchanges with France, Germany and Spain. As a C of E foundation there is a certain emphasis on religious education, but of an ecumenical kind. Particular attention is given to pupils with individual needs, including those with slight physical handicaps. It is highly regarded in the locality where it enjoys vigorous support.

School profile

Pupils Age range 11–18; 930 day pupils, 482 boys, 448 girls. Main entry ages 11, 13 and into sixth. Approx 10% are children of former pupils. *Transfer from maintained schools:* 78% main intake, plus 20% to sixth.

Entrance Own entrance exam used. Oversubscribed. No special skills or religious requirements; any welcomed. Parents not expected to buy text books. 200 assisted places. 12 scholarships/bursaries available pa, half to one-third fees.

Staff Head D A Fenner, in post for 14 years. 81 full time staff, 6 part time. Annual turnover 5–6%. Average age 37.

Academic work GCSE and A-levels. 21 subjects offered at GCSE (including Russian in sixth form, with exchange in Yalta). 18 subjects offered at A-level. All sixth form students undertake an extension study in addition. In 1990 128 pupils in fifth, 125 in upper sixth. *GCSE:* in 1990, 75% upper fifth gained at least grade C in 8+ subjects; 16% in 5–7; 9% in 1–4 subjects. *A-level:* 4% upper sixth passed in 4+ subjects; 67% in 3; 25% in 2; and 3% in 1 subject. 30% took science A-levels; 50% arts/humanities; 20% both. *Computing facilities:* Apple Macintosh Network, BBC-B Network.

European Community *Languages:* French offered: to age 14; GCSE; AS-level; A-level. German offered: to age 14; GCSE; A-level. Italian: to AS-level. Spanish: AS-level. 10–25% take GCSE in more than 1 EC language. *Exchanges:* Regular exchanges for pupils aged 11–18 to France, Germany and Spain. *Other:* European Studies offered to pupils aged 16–18. Satellite TV for linguists.

Senior pupils' non-academic activities *Music:* 300 learn a musical instrument, 50 to Grade 6 or above, 2 accepted for Music School; 500+ pupils each in school orchestras and choir; 1 in National Youth Orchestra; 15 Chamber Music Groups. *Drama:* National Youth Theatre developed here. Strong performance drama. 5 productions annually, 3 for senior pupils; 2 entrants to Drama School and several to university drama departments. Some pupils members of National Youth Theatre and National Youth Music Theatre. *Art:* 34 take GCSE; 18 take A-level; emphasis on exhibition work throughout school; textiles, ceramics and photography options; 15 accepted for Art School. 10 belong to eg photographic club. *Sport:* Football, hockey, cricket, athletics, tennis, swimming, rugby-fives, badminton, water polo, basketball, fencing, judo, netball, gymnastics, cross-country, volleyball, weight training, riding, golf available. 100 take non-compulsory sport. 50 in London, county and international teams (gym, swimming, hockey, cricket, badminton, fencing, basketball, fives, judo, netball, football, athletics, cross-country). *Other:* 25 take part in local community schemes. 24 have bronze Duke of Edinburgh's Award and 24 have gold. 5 enter voluntary schemes after leaving school. Other activities include computer, bridge and chess clubs, table tennis, debating society and voluntary CCF.

Careers In 1990, 74% leavers went on to degree courses; 8% to art/drama/music colleges; 1% to non-degree courses (eg nursing); 10% straight into careers (eg city, industry, civil service, armed services); 7% other. Of those going on to degree courses, 14% went to Oxbridge, 64% to other universities; 23% to poly/colleges. 5% those going on to higher education went to courses in practical art; 3% in drama/acting; 2% in music; 64% in humanities/social sciences; 4% in medicine/dentistry/veterinary science; and 22% in science/engineering.

Uniform School uniform worn, except sixth form.

Houses/prefects Competitive houses. Prefects, head boy/girl (School Captain) and head of house (House Captain) appointed by the Headmaster in consultation with housemasters. School Council.

Religion Assemblies broad Anglican. Parents may withdraw pupils.

Social Occasional joint careers conferences, general election debates with other schools. Regular organised holiday visits to eg Russia; exchanges with French, German, Russian and Spanish schools. Pupils allowed to bring own car/bike/motorbike to school. Meals self service. School shop. No tobacco/alcohol allowed.

Discipline No corporal punishment. Detentions are given for bad work and bad behaviour; those caught in possession of illegal drugs on the premises can expect expulsion.

Alumni association is run by P J Reeve, 33 Carver Road, London SE24.

Former pupils Julian Glover; Simon Ward, John Stride (actors); Stuart Blanch, former Archbishop of York; C S Forester; Sir Victor Pritchett.

· *Alton Convent* ·

Convent of Our Lady of
Providence
Anstey Lane
Alton
Hampshire GU34 2NG
Tel 0420 82070

- Pupils 300
- Boys None
- Girls 11–18 (Day)
- Upper sixth 10

- Termly fees
  £720 (Day)

Enquiries/application to
the Headteacher

What it's like

The Congregation of 'Ste. Marie de la Providence' originated at Saintes, France in 1817. Since then convents have been established world wide. Alton Convent School was started in 1938 and transferred to Anstey Manor in 1946. It lies on the outskirts of the town, a beautiful manor house set in 18.5 acres of fine gardens and grounds. Extensive modern developments date from 1966 and it is now well equipped with, among other things, a large library, spacious laboratories, a computer studies centre, an impressive modern chapel and a new multi-purpose hall. It is a Roman Catholic foundation and its motto is Vita, dulcedo et spes nostra salve (Hail our life, our sweetness and our hope). Importance is given to prayer, the liturgy of the Church and religious instruction. The standard of teaching is high and results are impressive. Most sixth formers go on to degree courses. French, German and Spanish are offered to A-level and many girls take GCSE in more than one European language. Regular exchanges with France and Germany. The school prides itself on being a place where young people are happy and where they achieve success at all levels. There is considerable strength in music, drama and art. A standard range of sports and games is available and there are plentiful extra-curricular activities. Young Enterprise and the Duke of Edinburgh's Award Scheme are vigorously supported.

School profile

Pupils Age range 11–18; 300 day girls. Main entry ages 11 and into sixth. 25% are children of former pupils. Own junior school provides 20+% intake. *Transfer from maintained schools:* 40% main intake.

Entrance Own entrance exam used. Not oversubscribed at present. No special skills other than ability to cope with curriculum. No religious requirements but ethos of school is Roman Catholic. Parents occasionally expected to buy some text books. Scholarships/bursaries at sixth form stage.

Staff Headteacher Mr F A Martin, 2 years in post. 20 full time staff, 15 part time. Annual turnover very low. Average age 40–45.

Academic work GCSE and A-levels. 16 GCSE subjects offered; 10 at A-level (no A-level general studies). In 1990, 59 pupils in upper fifth, 10 in upper sixth. *GCSE:* in 1990, 51 upper fifth gained at least grade C in 8+ subjects; 6 in 5–7; and 2 in 1–4 subjects. *A-levels:* 8 upper sixth passed in 3 subjects; 2 in 2 subjects. 50% took science A-levels; 50% arts/humanities. *Computing facilities:* A specialist computer teaching room. *Special provision:* Dealt with individually in agreement with parents.

European Community *Languages:* French offered: to age 14; GCSE; AS-level; A-level. German offered: to age 14; GCSE; AS-level; A-level. Spanish offered: to age 14; GCSE; AS-level; A-level. 25–50% take GCSE in more than 1 EC language. *Exchanges:* Regular exchanges for pupils aged 14–16 to France, Germany and Spain. *Other:*

School takes EC pupils for 1 term–1 year.

Senior pupils' non-academic activities *Music:* Some learn a musical instrument (piano, cello), 1 to grade 6; some play in orchestra or sing in choir. Others take GCSE. *Sport:* hockey, netball, tennis, badminton, rounders available. *Other:* Some take part in Duke of Edinburgh's bronze, silver, gold Award. Other activities include a computer club, Spanish club, dramatic society, natural history club, careers talks, Latin society. Some pupils on British Schools Exploring Society expedition.

Careers In 1990, 90% sixth form leavers went on to degree courses; 10% to non-degree courses. Of those going on to degree courses, all went to universities; 90% to courses in humanities/social sciences, and 10% in science/engineering.

Uniform School uniform worn except in sixth.

Houses/prefects Competitive houses. Prefects, head girl, head of house and house prefects – selected by Headteacher and school.

Religion Catholic worship. Each Christian group is encouraged to be loyal to its own commitment.

Social Joint functions with other schools mostly at sixth form level (debates, conferences, dance and social outings, occasional dramatic or choral productions). Annual French and German exchanges, ski trip, day visit to France for 1st year pupils. Sixth form allowed to bring cars, others bike to school (not many do). Meals: most prefer a packed lunch. No tobacco/alcohol allowed.

Discipline No corporal punishment. Pupils failing to produce homework once might expect a verbal reminder. Any who might be caught smoking on the premises would be suspended – dialogue with offender and parents.

Former pupils Susan Osman (TV announcer); Anne Birrell (author and Chinese literature expert).

· *Ampleforth* ·

Ampleforth College
York
YO6 4ER
Tel 043 93 224
Fax 04393 770

- Pupils 687
- Boys 10–18
 (Day/Board)
- Girls None
- Upper sixth 130

- Termly fees
 £2342 (Day)
 £2940 (Board)
- HMC
Enquiries/application to the Headmaster

What it's like

Established at Ampleforth in 1802, the school adjoins the Benedictine monastery and abbey of St Laurence in a stretch of magnificent Yorkshire countryside a mile from the local village. The monastic community are the 'descendants' of the monks who, in 1608, founded a monastery at Dieulouard in Lorraine. The headmaster and some of the teaching staff are monks. The main purpose is to educate Catholics in their faith and in all branches of learning. The boarding houses are scattered over a big site and provide comfortable accommodation. Many first-rate modern facilities. A very good education is given and academic results are excellent. Very many boys go on to degree courses, many to Oxbridge. French, German, Spanish and, unusually, Portuguese are offered up to A-level. A large proportion of boys takes more than one European language at GCSE. There are regular exchanges with France, Germany and Spain. There are plans to establish pupil exchanges during termtime. An unusually strong music staff; musical activities play a major role in the life of the school. Games and outdoor pursuits are very popular; standards are high. As a Catholic school, discipline is somewhat tighter than elsewhere and the way of life is marginally more ascetic and rigorous. The preparatory department is at Gilling Castle, two miles from the College.

School profile

Pupils Total age range 10–18; 687 boys, 17 day, 670 boarding. Senior department 13–18, 592 boys. Main entry ages 10, 13 and into sixth. Own preparatory school (Gilling Castle), and Junior House each provides about 20% of intake. Approx 25+% are children of former pupils.

Entrance Common entrance and own entrance exam used. No special skills required but should be Roman Catholic. Extras vary. 12–14 scholarships, up to half fees; also a number of bursaries.

Parents 15+% are doctors, lawyers etc;

15+% in industry and commerce. Up to 10% live within 30 miles; up to 10% live overseas.

Staff Headmaster Reverend D L Milroy, in post for 11 years. 85 full time staff, 12 part time.

Academic work GCSE, AS- and A-levels. Portuguese is offered to GCSE and A-level. Average size of upper fifth 120; upper sixth 120 (now 130). *GCSE:* on average, 95 pupils in upper fifth pass 7–10 subjects; 25, 1–6 subjects (all took 1 to 4 the previous year). *A-levels:* on average, 10 pupils in the upper sixth pass 4 subjects; 75, 3 subjects; 25, 2 subjects and 10 pass 1 subject. On average, 20 take science/ engineering A-levels; 65 take arts and humanities; 35 a mixture. *Computing facilities:* An ECO-network of BBC micros plus several free-standing micros in use in maths, geography and science classrooms. *Special provision:* for eg mild handicap, learning difficulties and EFL.

European Community *Languages:* French offered: to age 14; GCSE; AS-level; A-level; non-examined. German offered: to GCSE; AS-level; A-level; non-examined. Italian: non-examined. Portuguese offered: to GCSE; A-level. Spanish offered: to GCSE; AS-level; A-level; non-examined. 50–75% take GCSE in more than 1 EC language. Extra tuition sometimes arranged in Italian and Portuguese. *Exchanges:* Regular exchanges for pupils aged 14–18 to France, Germany and Spain. Term-time exchanges being established. *Other:* Pupils from Belgium, Eire, France, Germany, Netherlands and Spain on temporary or permanent basis.

Senior pupils' non-academic activities *Music:* 178 learn a musical instrument, 26 to Grade 6 or above, 4 accepted to read music at university; 90 in school orchestra, 104 in choir. *Drama and dance:* 50 take part in school productions. 15 take GCSE Drama; 2 pa accepted for Drama/ Dance Schools; 2 pa go on to work in theatre; 2 into National Youth Theatre. *Art:* 35 take as non-examined subject; 22 take A-level. 11 accepted for Art School; 5 for Architectural School. 20 take art as a leisure activity; 45 belong to eg photographic club. *Sport:* Rugby, cricket, hockey, tennis, swimming, squash, badminton available. 400 take part in non-compulsory sport. 7 passed bronze medallion life saving. 6 represent county (cricket, rugby). *Other:* School has links with Cheshire Homes, Children's Home and other local needs. 12 pupils have bronze Duke of Edinburgh's Award, 6 have silver and 12 gold. 6 have Red Cross

Adult, 12 Youth certificates. Other activities include debating societies, historical bench, archaeological society, modern languages, bridge, chess and computer clubs.

Careers On average, 82% leavers go on to degree courses; 4% to art/drama/ music colleges; 6% to non-degree courses (eg HND business, agriculture, engineering); 5% straight into careers (eg banking, farming, film, retailing, armed forces); 5% other. Of those going on to degree courses, 13% go to Oxbridge, 67% to other universities; 20% to poly/colleges. 5% those going on to higher education went to courses in practical art; 2% in drama/acting; 1% in music; 65% in humanities/social sciences; 5% in medicine; and 22% in science/engineering.

Uniform None but dress regulations (jacket and tie, suit on Sundays).

Houses/prefects Competitive houses. Prefects and head boy, appointed by the Headmaster; head of house and house prefects, by housemasters.

Religion Compulsory religious worship.

Social Theatrical and choral productions and debates with other schools. Regular exchanges with 2 schools in France and Germany. Schola Tours; skiing, climbing etc abroad. Pupils allowed to bring own bike to school. Meals formal. School shop. No alcohol/tobacco allowed.

Discipline No corporal punishment. All punishments are dependent on circumstances.

Boarding 20% have own study bedroom, 20% share with 2–3; 60% are in dormitories of 6+. Houses of 60+. Local doctor and resident nursing staff. No central dining room – boys eat in own houses. Sixth form can provide and cook some own food. 2 weekend exeats each term and half-term in the autumn. Visits to local towns allowed.

Alumni association is run by The Secretary, The Ampleforth Society, Ampleforth Abbey, York YO6 4ER.

· *Ardingly* ·

Ardingly College	• Pupils 693	• Termly fees
Ardingly	• Boys 7–18	£2275 (Day)
Haywards Heath	(Day/Board)	£2890 (Board)
West Sussex	• Girls 7–18	• HMC, Woodard
RH17 6SQ	(Day/Board)	Enquiries/application to
Tel 0444 892 577	• Upper sixth 93	the Registrar

What it's like

Founded in 1858, it lies in one of the most beautiful parts of Sussex on a big estate. At the heart of its handsome buildings is the chapel. As a Woodard school it caters for and appeals to those seeking a C of E education. It has its own junior school, a mix of boarding/day co-ed and the aim is very much to be a 'family' school. One of its prides is the fine pastoral system based on individual tutors for each pupil. It offers a good all-round education, music, art and drama, the CCF and a very well-organised house system; plus a lot of emphasis on outdoor activities. Practical skills are much encouraged. It has a reputation for good teaching and a highly creditable academic record. Many pupils go on to degree courses. French, German, Italian and Spanish are offered up to A-level and a high proportion of pupils takes GCSE in more than one European language. Ardingly has its own rapidly expanding programme for Young Europeans which offers Europeans the opportunity to come to the school for one or more terms with the main objection of improving their English.

School profile

Pupils Total age range 7–18; 693 pupils, 265 day (129 boys, 136 girls), 428 boarding (234 boys, 194 girls). Senior department 13–18, 457 pupils (284 boys, 173 girls). Main entry ages 7, 11, 13 and into sixth. Approx 5% are children of former pupils. Approx 40% from own junior school. *Transfer from maintained schools:* 50% intake at 11, 10% at 13 and 25% intake to sixth.

Entrance Common entrance and own entrance exam used. No special skills except for scholarship candidates. Pupils expected to be in sympathy with aims and ethos of C of E. 5 pa assisted places at 11. Approx 25 scholarships/bursaries, full fees to instrumental tuition fees.

Parents 50+% live within 30 miles; 15+% live overseas.

Staff Head J W Flecker, in post for 11 years. 70 full time staff, 25 part time. Annual turnover 10%. Average age 35.

Academic work GCSE and A-levels. 23 subjects offered including theatre studies, archaeology, English language (no A-level general studies). In 1991, 94 pupils in upper fifth, 93 in upper sixth. *GCSE:* in 1990, 45 upper fifth gained at least grade C in 8+ subjects; 29 in 5–7; and 12 in 1–4 subjects. *A-level:* 6 upper sixth passed in 4+ subjects; 52 in 3; 22 in 2; and 10 in 1 subject. 20% took science A-levels; 40% arts/humanities; 40% both. *Computing facilities:* specialist room – UNIX system; several micros; two main computers, each with 8 terminals and 24 Nimbus. Pascal, 'C' and Prolog available. *Special provision:* limited specialist remedial teaching; some EFL from own qualified staff.

European Community *Languages:* French offered: to age 14; GCSE; AS-level; A-level. German offered: to age 14; GCSE; A-level. Italian offered: to age 14; GCSE; A-level. Spanish offered: to age 14; GCSE; A-level. 50–75% take GCSE in more than 1 EC language. *Exchanges:* Regular exchanges for pupils aged 11–18

74

to France, Germany and Spain. *Other:* EYE (English for Young Europeans) programme, for European pupils 11–18 – visits range from 3 weeks–1 year. Number of British pupils who are bi- or tri-lingual increasing.

Senior pupils' non-academic activities *Music:* 200 learn a musical instrument, 72 to Grade 6 or above, 2 accepted for Music colleges; 50 in school orchestra, 55 in choir, some in pop group. Chamber music, choral society and band available. *Drama and dance:* 150–200 participate in school productions. 2 accepted for Drama Schools; 2 go on to work in theatre. GCSE and A-level theatre studies available. *Art:* Many take as non-examined subject; 32 take GCSE; 24 A-level. 7 accepted for Art School. *Sport:* Soccer, hockey, tennis, cricket, netball, volleyball, squash, swimming, cross-country, athletics, sailing, lacrosse available. 300 take part in non-compulsory sport. 1 representation at Public Schools' soccer. *Other:* Numerous other activities including chess, learning to drive, computers.

Careers In 1990, 78% leavers went on to degree courses; 7% to art/drama/ music colleges; 8% to non-degree courses (eg nursing, secretarial, engineering apprenticeships); 7% straight into careers (eg armed forces, parents' business). Of those going on to degree courses, 4% went to Oxbridge, 56% to other universities; 40% to poly/colleges. 12% those going on to higher education went to courses in practical art; 1% in drama/ acting; 3% in music; 75% in humanities/ social sciences; 3% in medicine; and 6% in science/engineering.

Uniform School uniform worn except in sixth form.

Houses/prefects Competitive houses. Prefects, head boy/girl, head of house and house prefects – appointed after consultation.

Religion Compulsory religious studies and chapel attendance.

Social Continuous contact with local schools. Exchange with schools in Rhone valley (annual), Heidelberg and Pamplona (sporadic). Many other organised trips abroad. Day pupils allowed to bring own car/bike to school. Meals self service. School shop. No tobacco allowed; alcohol in supervised bar.

Discipline No corporal punishment. Pupils failing to produce homework once might expect to be asked why; those caught smoking cannabis on the premises could expect instant expulsion.

Boarding 40% have own study bedroom or share with 1 other; 60% in dormitories of 6+. Houses of 40+, single-sex, except for new Upper Sixth House. 2 resident qualified nurses. Central dining room. Pupils can provide and cook some own food. 2–5 24 hour exeats each term, plus half term (4–8 days). Visits to the local town allowed when free, to 6.30 (4.30 in winter).

Alumni association R C Munyard, FCA, c/o Touche Ross & Co, Hill House, 1 Little New Street, London EC4A 3TR.

Former pupils Terry Thomas; Dr Hayes (Director of National Portrait Gallery); Cdr Longhurst (potential astronaut); Ian Hislop (Private Eye); Stephen Oliver (composer); Andrew Bowden and T Gorst (MPs).

· *Arnold* ·

Arnold School
Lytham Road
Blackpool
Lancashire
FY4 1JG
Tel 0253 46391
Fax 0253 407245

- Pupils 1154
- Boys 4–18
  (Day/Board/
  Weekly)
- Girls 4–18
  (Day/Board/
  Weekly)
- Upper sixth 106

- Termly fees
  £882 (Day)
  £1780 (Board)
  £1652 (Weekly)
- HMC

Enquiries/application to
the Headmaster

What it's like

Founded in 1896, situated in Blackpool half a mile from the sea. It has adequate buildings and nearby playing fields. Considerable expansion in recent years has provided good up-to-date facilities. The aim is to inculcate 'lasting values of service, loyalty and self-discipline' in the belief that these are increasingly vital. Religious worship is encouraged and religious assemblies are compulsory. It is strong on music and in general has a reputation for sound traditional academic training, and its records are good. Very many sixth formers go on to degree courses, including many to Oxbridge. French and German are offered to A-level and a high proportion of pupils takes GCSE in both. Regular exchanges are offered with France and Germany. Throughout its life it has played a prominent part in the life of the Fylde and Blackpool. Strong back-up from old Arnoldians. A bonus is the outdoor pursuits centre at Glenridding, described as 'a classroom in the Lake District' and a new design centre.

School profile

Pupils Total age range 4–18; 1154 pupils, 1077 day (646 boys, 431 girls), 77 boarding (45 boys, 32 girls). Senior department 11–18, 801 pupils (482 boys, 319 girls). Main entry ages 5, 7, 11 and into sixth. Approx 5% are children of former pupils. 20+% senior intake from own junior school. *Transfer from maintained schools:* 60% main intake 11+, plus 20% to sixth.

Entrance Common entrance and own entrance exam used. Oversubscribed. No special skills or religious requirements. Parents not expected to buy text books; maximum extras, £65 including lunch for day pupils. 60 assisted places. 10 scholarships/bursaries, £500–£1400.

Parents 15% in hotel/tourism. 60+% live within 30 miles; up to 10% live overseas.

Staff Headmaster J A B Kelsall, in post for 4 years. 66 full time staff, 5 part time. Annual turnover 2%. Average age 41.

Academic work GCSE and A-levels. Subjects offered include A-level law and general studies. In 1990, 124 pupils in upper fifth, 101 in upper sixth (now 106). *GCSE:* in 1990, 64 upper fifth gained at least grade C in 8+ subjects; 47 in 5–7; and 11 in 1–4 subjects. *A-levels:* 56 upper sixth passed in 4+ subjects; 21 in 3; 10 in 2; and 12 in 1 subject. 60% took science A-levels; 35% arts/humanities; 5% both. *Computing facilities:* 2 laboratories. With 44 personal computers including 22 new IBM personals, one Weatherstat Satellite Dish. *Special provision:* Special teacher to help with learning difficulties – especially dyslexia.

European Community *Languages:* French offered: to age 14; GCSE; AS-level; A-level. German offered: to age 14; GCSE; AS-level; A-level. 50–75% take GCSE in more than 1 EC language. *Exchanges:* Regular exchanges for pupils aged 11–18 to France and Germany.

Other: Number of EC pupils in school for 1 year or more.

Senior pupils' non-academic activities *Music:* 130 learn a musical instrument, 10 to Grade 6 or above, 2 accepted for Music School; 40 in school orchestra, 6 in school pop group, 80+ in choir, 20 in wind band, 14 in dance band; others in Lancashire Schools Symphony Orchestra, wind band and dance band. 30 play in pop groups, 2 in hit parade. One manager of Sex Pistols/co-founder of Virgin Records. *Drama and dance:* 140 in school productions. 60 in outside productions. 1 accepted for drama/dance school; 2 go on to work in the theatre. *Art:* 4 take as non-examined subject; 16 GCSE; 6 A-level; 3 A-level photography. 3 accepted for Art School; 2 for architecture. 7 take ceramics allied to CDT. Ceramics option available. *Sport:* Rugby, hockey, netball, cricket, athletics, cross-country, squash, swimming, badminton, golf, tennis available. 150 take non-compulsory sport. 30 take exams in life saving. Many represent county (athletics, hockey, rugby, badminton). 1 Cambridge Blue, 1 England rugby international. *Other:* 35 take part in local community schemes (6th form games option). 67 have bronze Duke of Edinburgh's Award, 23 have silver and 20 gold. 3 enter voluntary schemes after leaving school. Other activities include a computer club, chess club, book-shop, CCF, CDT club.

Careers In 1990, 80% leavers went on to degree courses; 5% to art/drama/music colleges; 2% to non-degree courses; 10% straight into careers (eg banking, tourism); 3% other. Of those going on to degree courses, 14% went to Oxbridge, 62% to other universities; 24% to poly/colleges. 4% those going on to higher education went to courses in practical art; 2% in drama/acting; 5% in music; 33% in humanities/social sciences; 10% in medicine; and 46% in science/engineering.

Uniform School uniform worn throughout.

Houses/prefects Competitive houses. Prefects, head boy/girl, head of house and house prefects – appointed by the Head and school.

Religion Encouraged (religious assemblies are compulsory).

Social Debates, concerts, visits etc with local schools. Organised trips abroad for French, German, geology, geography; hockey tour of Holland, rugby tour of Canada. Pupils allowed to bring own car/motorbike/bike to school. Meals self service. School shop. No tobacco/alcohol allowed.

Discipline No corporal punishment. Pupils failing to produce homework once might expect a homework detention. Those caught smoking cannabis on the premises will be expelled.

Boarding 17% have own study bedroom, 73% share; 10% are in dormitories of 6+. Houses, of 15–36, are divided by age group, single sex. Resident qualified nurse. Central dining room. Pupils can provide and cook own food. 3 weekend exeats each term. Visits to the local town allowed.

Alumni association is run by P B Warhurst, 26 Edwinstowe Road, Ansdell FY8 4BG.

Former pupils David Ball (Soft Cell); Chris Lowe (Pet Shop Boys); J Armfield; G Eastham; Sir Walter Clegg MP; Peter Boydell QC; T Graveney; Stanley Matthews (junior tennis).

· *Arts Educational (London)* ·

The Arts Educational
School
Cone Ripman House
14 Bath Road
London W4 1LY
Tel 081-994 9366

- Pupils 140
- Boys 11–16+ (Day)
- Girls 11–16+ (Day)
- Upper sixth variable

- Termly fees £1603
  (Day)
- ISAI
Enquiries/application to
the Registrar

What it's like

Founded in 1919, it occupies a single site in a pleasant residential area of West
London. Well-designed buildings and good facilities. It is a school for the specific
training of boys and girls in the performing arts. There is a balanced curriculum in
academic and vocational disciplines in the performing arts for pupils aged 11–16. It
also offers post-16 courses; 3-year accredited courses in dance, musical theatre,
and adult drama; a 1-year postgraduate acting course for mature students.
Naturally, everyone is involved in dance, music and drama. There is a large staff of
42 for 140 pupils, plus 120 visiting teachers. Societies, extra-curricular activities
and frequent participation in national events concerned with the performing arts.
The Arts Educational Schools at both London and Tring are run by the same
Trust.

School profile

Pupils Age range 11–16+; 140 day
pupils (25 boys, 115 girls). Main entry
ages 11. Approx 10% are children of former pupils. *Transfer from maintained
schools:* 50% main intake.
Entrance Own entrance exam used
based on national tests. Not oversubscribed. Special skills in dance and drama
required; no religious requirements.
Maximum extras £100. Some assisted
places. 6 scholarships/bursaries, up to full
fees.
Staff Principal Peter Fowler, in post for 5
years. 42 full time staff, 120 part time.
Annual turnover (part time) 10%. Average
age 40.
Academic work GCSE. 7 GCSE subjects offered (including dance and drama
but no A-level general studies). In 1989,
26 pupils in upper fifth. *GCSE:* in 1989, 7
upper fifth gained at least grade C in 5–7
subjects; 19 in 1–4 subjects. *Computing
facilities:* A limited number of computers
in maths department. *Special provision:*
Dyslexic children are sent weekly to dyslexia centre.
European Community *Languages:*
French offered to age 14; GCSE.
Exchanges: Regular exchanges for pupils
11–16 to France.
**Senior pupils' non-academic activi-
ties** *Music:* 50% learn a musical instrument, 5 to Grade 6 or above; all sing in
school choirs; many in English National
Opera chorus and perform on radio and
TV. *Drama and dance:* Whole school participates in productions; many take up to
Grade 6 in ESB, RAD etc; 90% accepted
for Drama and Dance Schools. Many
dance with English National Ballet and
other major companies and on film and
television. *Art:* 19 take GCSE art. *Sport:*
Local sports centre used.
Careers In 1990, 50% pupils went on to
courses in dance, drama and musical
theatre; 40% to sixth form colleges; 2%
other.
Uniform School uniform worn 11–16.
Houses/prefects No competitive
houses. Prefects, head boy and girl,
selected by staff.
Religion No compulsory worship.
Social Organised local events occasionally. Pupils allowed to bring own bicycle to

78

school. Meals self service. No tobacco/alcohol allowed for pupils (ie 11–16).

Discipline No corporal punishment. Pupils failing to produce homework or committing other infringement might expect a detention.

Former pupils Huge number of well-known names including Julie Andrews; Claire Bloom; Leslie Crowther; Nigel Havers; Glynis Johns; Margaret Lockwood; Sarah Miles; Jane Seymour; Antoinette Sibley; Teresa Jarvis; Seth Gilber; Catherine Becqse; Finola Hughes; Sarah Brightman; Josephine Campbell.

· Arts Educational (Tring) ·

The Arts Educational
School
Tring Park
Tring
HP23 5LX

- Pupils 279
- Boys None
- Girls 10–18
  (Day/Board)
- Upper sixth 35

- Termly fees
  £1344 (Day)
  £2267 (Board)
  Enquiries/application to
  the Registrar

What it's like

The Arts Educational Schools had their origin in the Cone School of Dancing, founded in 1919, and the Ripman School, founded in 1922. These schools amalgamated in 1939 to form the Cone-Ripman Schools which in 1947 became the Arts Educational Schools. The two schools at Tring and London were pioneers in the field of combining a sound and general academic education with a vocational training in the Arts of the theatre. The heart of the school is Tring Park, a handsome 18th-century mansion which formerly belonged to the Rothschild family. It lies in 15 acres of beautiful grounds and gardens in the town of Tring. A large staff permits an unusually good staff:pupil ratio of about 2:15, which becomes even better because of the very large part-time staff. All pupils are prepared for GCSE. The vocational courses cater for the principal branches of the theatre: namely dance, drama and music. Older pupils may specialise in one branch; but, simultaneously, participation in the general application of the other two disciplines is required. The courses are based on the needs of those intending to follow a career in the professional theatre; they also provide the foundation for entry to dance, drama or music college. Highly professional and expert teaching is provided and results are very good. Naturally, standards of achievement in music, drama and dance are distinguished. There is a large number of vocational events each year. Of the upper sixth leavers, two-thirds go to drama/music courses in higher education, half to degree courses, half to non-degree courses at drama or music colleges. The school is closely involved with local churches and also with various charities for the elderly and disabled. Religious worship is compulsory. Some basic sports and games are provided and there is a fair range of extra-curricular activities.

School profile

Pupils Age range 10–18; 279 girls, 37 day, 242 boarding. Main entry ages 10–16. 5% are children of former pupils. *Transfer from maintained schools:* 35% main intake, plus 25% to sixth.

Entrance Audition and academic test. Special skills required in music, ballet and drama; no religious requirements. Parents not expected to buy text books. 50 assisted places. Local grants available.

79

Parents 15+% in theatre, media, music. Up to 10% live within 30 miles; up to 10% live overseas.

Staff Headmistress Mrs M A Sweet, in post for 2 years. 40 full time staff, 35 part time. Annual turnover 2%. Average age 35.

Academic work GCSE and A-levels. 15 GCSE subjects offered; 9 at A-level (including A-level theatre studies; GCSE but not A-level general studies). In 1990, 57 pupils in upper fifth, 24 in upper sixth (now 35). *GCSE:* in 1990, 60% upper fifth gained at least grade C in 5–7 subjects; and 40% in 1–4 subjects. *A-levels:* 25% upper sixth passed in 3 subjects; 29% in 2; and 38% in 1 subject. 92% took broad area of arts/humanities A-levels; 8% both arts and sciences. *Computing facilities:* 10 computers in computer room with individual study carrels. *Special provision:* One specialist member of staff gives help in English, individually or in small groups.

European Community *Languages:* French offered: to age 14; GCSE; AS-level; A-level. German offered: to GCSE. Spanish offered: to age 14; GCSE. Under 10% take GCSE in more than 1 EC language. *Other:* Occasional students from EC countries in school.

Senior pupils' non-academic activities *Music:* 86% learn a musical instrument, 47 to Grade 6 or above; 5 accepted for Music School, or music course at university; various ensembles, 45 in chamber choir. *Drama and dance:* All participate in school productions; festival ballet and NYMT. Most take elementary modern, 50% elementary RAD ballet. 75% accepted for Drama/Dance Schools. 25 go on to work in theatre or media. *Art:* 40 take GCSE; 4 A-level. 1 or 2 accepted for Art School. *Sport:* Swimming, tennis, horseriding available. 50% take part in non–compulsory sport. Other activities include a computer club.

Careers In 1990, 42% leavers went on to degree courses; 37% to art/drama/music colleges; 18% other. Of those going on to degree courses, 70% went to universities; 30% to poly/colleges. 61% those going on to higher education went to courses in drama/acting; 7% in music; and 30% in humanities/social sciences.

Uniform School uniform except in sixth.

Houses/prefects Competitive houses. Prefects, head girl, head of house and house prefects – appointed by the Head.

Religion Compulsory worship (inter-denominational).

Social Meals self service. No tobacco/alcohol allowed.

Discipline No corporal punishment. Pupils failing to produce homework once are given a second chance, then detention; those caught smoking cannabis on the premises could expect expulsion.

Boarding All share. 2 houses, divided by age group. Resident qualified nursing sister. Central dining room. Half terms (one week) and 2 weekend exeats per term. Visits to local town allowed for sixth formers.

Former pupils Jane Seymour; Stephanie Lawrence, Anna Carteret, Gillian Lynn, among others.

· Ashford ·

Ashford School	● Pupils 687	● Termly fees
East Hill	● Boys None	£1299 (Day)
Ashford	● Girls 3–18 (Day/	£2267 (Board)
Kent TN24 8PB	Board/Weekly)	£2237 (Weekly)
Tel 0233 625171	● Upper sixth 65	● GSA
		Enquiries/application to
		the Headmistress

What it's like

Founded in 1898, it occupies 23 acres of very pleasant grounds in the town, together with land bordering the Stour. The oldest building is the 16th-century Alfred House. Expansion has incorporated neighbouring houses and much accommodation is now purpose-built. There are many excellent modern facilities and results are good. It is strong on music and science and has a well-organised house system. Many sixth formers go on to degree courses, including Oxbridge. French and German are offered to A-level, Spanish to GCSE. Many girls take GCSE in more than one European language. There are regular exchanges with France and Germany. Being an urban school it has plentiful local ties and is well supported by the community. There is a pronounced sense of service to the town (helping the handicapped and elderly et al).

School profile

Pupils Total age range 3–18; 687 girls, 522 day, 165 boarding. Senior department 11–18, 500 girls. Main entry ages 5, 7, 11, 13 and into sixth. Approx 5% are children of former pupils. Own junior school provides approx 50% of senior intake. *Transfer from maintained schools:* 40% main intake at 11 and 13, plus a handful to the sixth.

Entrance Own entrance exam used. Oversubscribed in some areas. No special skills or religious requirements. Parents expected to buy sixth form text books; other extras vary. 41 assisted places. 4–6 scholarships/bursaries (including 1 music) £1299–£650 per term.

Parents 15+% are doctors, lawyers, farmers, etc; 15+% in industry or commerce. 30+% live within 30 miles; 10+% live overseas.

Staff Headmistress Mrs A T D Macaire, in post for 6 years. 53 full time staff, 6 part time (plus music). Annual turnover 4%. Average age 44.

Academic work GCSE and A-levels.

20 subjects offered (including ancient Greek and history of art; no A-level general studies). In 1990, 82 pupils in upper fifth, 71 in upper sixth (now 65). *GCSE:* in 1990, 56 upper fifth gained at least grade C in 8+ subjects; 21 in 5–7; and 4 in 1–4 subjects. *A-levels:* 6 upper sixth passed in 4+ subjects; 43 in 3; 9 in 2; and 8 in 1 subject. 20 took science A-levels; 28 arts/humanities; 23 both. *Computing facilities:* 12 BBC's, 12 Archimedes; computers in technology, science, geography, library; 1 computer in each boarding house. *Special provision:* Ad hoc extra help, with guidance from experts.

European Community *Languages:* French offered: to age 14; GCSE; AS-level; A-level. German offered: to age 14; GCSE; A-level. Spanish offered: to age 14; GCSE. 25–50% take GCSE in more than 1 EC language. *Exchanges:* Regular exchanges for pupils aged 11–16 to France and Germany. *Other:* 1–2 Spanish girls in school for 1–2 years; 3–4 German girls for up to a year in sixth. Work experience links being forged in Germany.

Senior pupils' non-academic activities *Music:* 131 learn a musical instrument, 11 to Grade 6 or above, 2 involved in music after leaving; 21 in school orchestra, 90 in choir, 13 in band, 10 in recorder groups; others in second orchestra, chamber choir, madrigal group. *Drama and dance:* 25–30 in school productions; 60 in sixth form panto; house drama competitions. 10 to Grade 6 in ESB; 2 accepted for Drama Schools, 1 each into alternative theatre and TV. Private lessons taken by 25–30, 50 in House drama competitions, 15 in eg Kent Festival. *Art:* 5 take as non-examined subject; 25 take GCSE; 8, A-level; 4 accepted for Art School, 1 for history of art at university. *Sport:* Hockey, netball, swimming, tennis, rounders, athletics, squash, badminton, fencing, trampolining, judo, ballet, dance, modern dance, gym available. 75+ take non-compulsory sport. (50 go horse-riding etc outside school). 40+ in school teams. 4 represent county (squash, tennis, hockey, swimming). *Other:* 60+ take part in local community schemes. 150 have bronze Duke of Edinburgh's Award, 7 have silver and 28, gold. 20 enter voluntary schemes after leaving. Other activities include a computer club, debating and public speaking (various competitions), bridge club (interschool matches), science club, outdoor pursuits, riding at weekends, visits etc. Challenge of Management, Young Enterprise.

Careers On average, 68% leavers go on to degree courses; 3% to art/drama/music colleges; 15% to non-degree courses (eg agricultural marketing, community health HND, P/A course, HND business studies); 10% straight into careers (eg banking, journalism, guide dog training); 4% other. Of those going on to degree courses, 10% go to Oxbridge, 85% to other universities; 5% to poly/colleges. 3% those going on to higher education go to courses in practical art; 1% in drama/acting; 2% in music; 57% in humanities/social sciences; 5% in medicine; and 32% in science/engineering.

Uniform School uniform worn except in sixth form.

Houses/prefects Competitive houses. Prefects, 2 head girls (one day, one boarding), head of house and house prefects elected by girls, staff and Head. Prefects represent forms at food and general meetings with Head, Deputy, Bursar and Catering Manager.

Religion Compulsory, non-denominational Christian-based assembly. Boarders attend Parish Church. Confirmation classes available. Chaplain/counsellor. Religious Studies in the curriculum is academically based, but with the major emphasis on Christianity.

Social Many joint events with local schools, eg productions and debates, local guitar orchestra, host discos, formal sixth form supper dance etc. Annual ski trip, Mediterranean cruise; many others eg Russia, Israel and Greece in 1990. Pupils with need allowed to bring own car/motorbike to school. Meals self service. No tobacco/alcohol allowed.

Discipline No corporal punishment. Pupils failing to produce homework once might expect a reprimand, thereafter detention; those caught smoking cannabis on the premises can expect to be expelled. Other infringements of school rules would bring progressive loss of privileges, communication with parents, suspension and, eventually, expulsion.

Boarding 16% have own study bedroom, 20% share, 38% are in dormitories of 6+. Houses, of 45–60, same as competitive houses. Resident qualified nurse (SRN). Weekly doctor's surgery. Central dining room. Sixth formers can provide and cook own food at weekends. Half term plus 2 weekend exeats and 3 single days (more for sixth). Visits to the local town allowed (accompanied and occasional to 13; unmonitored in sixth).

Alumni association is run by Mrs M Reader, c/o the school.

Former pupils Pamela Armstrong (ITV newscaster).

· *Ashville* ·

Ashville College
Harrogate
North Yorkshire
HG2 9JR
Tel 0423 566358

- Pupils 670
- Boys 7–18
  (Day/Board)
- Girls 7–18
  (Day/Board)
- Upper sixth 45

- Termly fees
  £1190 (Day)
  £2189 (Board)
- HMC
  Enquiries/application to
  the Headmaster

What it's like

Founded in 1877 by the United Methodist Free Church, it has incorporated two other non-Conformist schools: Emfield College and New College. It owns a fine estate of 45 acres 600 feet above sea level on the south side of the spa town. During the 1970s extensive additions were made and it now possesses many excellent facilities. It is kept fairly small deliberately to 'preserve the benefits of life in a family community'. Religious services are compulsory but the religious 'ethos' is ecumenical. Culturally, there is close rapport with the town; and there is a good deal of emphasis on outdoor activities (eg fishing, fell walking and rock climbing). Its academic record is very sound and many sixth formers go on to degree courses, including a small number to Oxbridge. French and German are offered to A-level and a large proportion of pupils take both at GCSE. It has a distinguished reputation in Harrogate.

School profile

Pupils Total age range 7–18; 670 pupils, 514 day (308 boys, 206 girls), 156 boarding (100 boys, 56 girls). Senior department 11–18, 495 pupils (318 boys, 177 girls). Main entry ages 7, 8, 11, 13 and into sixth. Approx 3% are children of former pupils.

Entrance Common entrance and own entrance exam used. Sometimes oversubscribed. No special skills or religious requirements but school is Methodist. Parents not expected to buy text books; music tuition and some incidentals extra. 106 scholarships/bursaries.

Parents 15+% in industry or commerce. 60+% live within 30 miles; up to 10% live overseas.

Staff Headmaster M H Crosby, in post for 4 years. 45 full time staff, 8 part time. Annual turnover 5%. Average age about 40.

Academic work GCSE and A-levels. Average size of upper fifth 66; upper sixth 45. *GCSE:* on average, 20 pupils in upper fifth pass 8+ subjects; 29, 5–7 subjects; 17 pass 1–4 subjects. *A-levels:* on average,

20 pupils in the upper sixth pass 4 subjects; 10, 3 subjects; 8, 2 subjects and 7 pass 1 subject. On average, 11 take science/engineering A-levels; 22 take arts and humanities; 12 a mixture. *Computing facilities:* Computer Room with 12 BBC computers and some in other departments. *Special provision:* links with the Dyslexia Institute in Harrogate; help for occasional foreign students with linguistic difficulties.

European Community *Languages:* French offered: to age 14; GCSE; A-level. German offered: to age 14; GCSE; A-level. 50–75% take GCSE in more than 1 EC language.

Senior pupils' non-academic activities *Music:* 230 learn a musical instrument, 4 to Grade 6 or above; 45 in school orchestra, 110 in choir. *Drama and dance:* 150 in school productions. 1 accepted for Drama School, 1 to work in theatre. 30 in workshop production, 2 take Guildhall acting exam. *Art:* 200 take as non-examined subject; 20 GCSE; 10 A-level; 5 accepted for Art School, 2 for architecture and degrees with art component. 20 take recreational art. *Sport:* Rugby, hockey, cricket, tennis, squash, badminton, swimming, karate, netball, basketball, sailing available. 80% take non-compulsory sport. 4 represent county (rugby, cricket, squash, sevens). 50 in university teams. *Other:* 20 take part in local community schemes. 60 are taking bronze Duke of Edinburgh's Award, 1 has silver. 2 work for Leprosy Centre and national charity after leaving. Other activities include a computer club, chess, horse-riding, art, archery, sub aqua, war-games, ski-ing.

Careers In 1990, 70% leavers went on to degree courses; 3% to art/drama/music colleges; 10% to non-degree courses; 10% straight into careers (eg banking, business). Of those going on to degree courses, 5% went to Oxbridge, 50% to other universities; 45% to poly/colleges.

Uniform School uniform worn throughout.

Houses/prefects Competitive houses.

Prefects, head boy and girl, head of houses appointed by the Head.

Religion Compulsory worship.

Social Joint Sixth Form Society with Harrogate Ladies' College. Organised trips abroad. Pupils allowed to bring own car with school approval. Meals self service. School shops for tuck and clothing. No tobacco/alcohol allowed.

Discipline No corporal punishment. Pupils failing to produce homework more than once might expect a prep detention; those caught smoking cannabis on the premises would be suspended, probably expelled.

Boarding Sixth form have own study bedroom or share with 2 or 3. Houses, of approximately 45 are single sex. Resident qualified nurses. Central dining room. 3 exeats each term (2 nights) plus half-term. Visits to the local town allowed on Saturday mornings.

Alumni association is run by Mr R Search, Cherry Tree Farm, Gill Lane, Kearby, Nr Wetherby.

Former pupils Sir Alastair Burnett.

· *Atherley* ·

The Atherley School	● Pupils 465	● Termly fees
Hill Lane	● Boys None	£1012 (Day)
Southampton	● Girls 4–18	● GSA, SHA, CSCL
Hampshire SO9 1GR	(Day)	Enquiries/application to
Tel 0703 772898	● Upper sixth 27	the Headmistress

What it's like

Opened in 1926 and governed by the Church Schools Company Ltd, it lies on a 5-acre site on the edge of Southampton Common. Since 1972 there has been considerable modernisation. Its facilities are more than adequate. French, German and Spanish are offered at A-level and many girls take GCSE in more than one European language. There are regular exchange arrangements with France, Germany and Spain. Many sixth formers go on to degree courses.

School profile

Pupils Total age range 4–18; 465 day girls. Senior department 11–18, 350 girls. Main entry ages 4, 11 and into sixth. Approx 1% are children of former pupils.

Transfer from maintained schools: 30% main intake at 11.

Entrance Own entrance exam used. Reasonable ability required; no religious allegiance necessary but school is C of E. Parents not expected to buy text books. 5–6 sixth form scholarships/bursaries, £550–£230.

Staff Headmistress Mrs M E Williams, in post for 3 years. 31 full time staff, 12 part time. Annual turnover 3%.

Academic work GCSE and A-levels. 16 subjects offered (no A-level general studies). In 1990, 52 pupils in upper fifth, 27 in upper sixth. *GCSE:* in 1990, 41 upper fifth gained at least grade C in 8+ subjects; 8 in 5–7; and 3 in 1–4 subjects. *A-levels:* 17 upper sixth passed in 3 subjects; 5 in 2; and 2 in 1 subject. 1 took science A-levels; 12 arts/humanities; 14 both. *Computing facilities:* 2 BBC's, 10 Archimedes (A3000) and 1 Archimedes A450.

European Community *Languages:* French offered: to age 14; GCSE; AS-level; A-level. German offered: to age 14; GCSE; AS-level; A-level. Spanish offered: to GCSE; AS-level; A-level. 25–50% take GCSE in more than 1 EC language. *Exchanges:* Regular exchanges for pupils aged 14–18 to France, Germany and Spain.

Senior pupils' non-academic activities *Sport:* Lacrosse, netball, tennis, rounders, athletics, badminton, table tennis, gymnastics available. *Other:* Pupils take part in the Duke of Edinburgh's Award Scheme (bronze). Other activities include drama, choir, orchestra, electronic club, recorders, debating club, Christian societies, individual instrumental tuition.

Careers In 1990, 60% leavers went on to degree courses; 4% to art/drama/music colleges; 8% to non-degree courses (eg army, nursing); 4% straight into careers (eg banking); 28% other. Of those going on to degree courses, 93% went to universities; 7% to poly/colleges. 4% those going on to higher education went to courses in practical art; and 4% in medicine.

Uniform School uniform worn except in sixth.

Houses/prefects Competitive houses. Prefects, head girl and head of house – elected by the staff and senior pupils.

Religion C of E but people of all faiths and none are welcomed.

Social Public speaking, games, BAYS with local schools. Organised trips abroad. Pupils allowed to bring own car/bike to school. Meals cafeteria-style. School shop selling uniform. No tobacco/alcohol allowed.

Discipline No corporal punishment. Those caught smoking on the premises or on the way to or from school could expect to be suspended, pending further action. Detentions are used and minus house points, according to seriousness of offence.

Alumni association is run by Mrs J Parrett.

· *Atlantic College* ·

United World College of the Atlantic
St Donats Castle
Llantwit Major
South Glamorgan
CF6 9WF
Tel 0446 792530

- Pupils 353
- Boys 16–19 (Day/Board))
- Girls 16–19 (Day/Board)
- Upper sixth 179

- Termly fees £2750 (Board)
- United World Colleges

Enquiries/application to the Principal

What it's like

Founded in 1962 (the co-founder was Kurt Hahn), it is one of six such colleges – the others being in British Columbia, Singapore, Mbabane (Swaziland), Trieste and Montezuma (New Mexico) – which belong to a group called United World Colleges. Atlantic College is a sixth-form college, under the patronage of the Queen and the presidency of HRH the Prince of Wales. It has an unusually fine single-campus site of 150 acres, rural and coastal. The heart of the college is the historic St Donat's Castle, a magnificent intact 13th-century stronghold whose curtain walls surround an Elizabethan courtyard. Next to it, in delightful gardens, are modern and very well-equipped buildings. It would probably be difficult to find a finer site or better facilities in Britain. By ethos and aim Atlantic College, like the sister colleges, is cosmopolitan and international. All the colleges offer students of all races and creeds the opportunity to develop international understanding through a programme which combines high quality academic studies with activities which encourage a sense of adventure and social responsibility. Atlantic College, like the others, has two main aims: to promote international understanding through education; to provide a pattern of education to meet the special needs of our time. In 1971 Atlantic College was the first school in the world to abandon national examinations in favour of an international diploma – the International Baccalaureate. There are two terms: early September to early December; mid-January to end of May. A well-qualified staff (who represent many different countries and cultures) provide an excellent all-round pre-university education and there is a very favourable staff:pupil ratio of 1:9. Standards are high and results consistently good. Almost all leavers proceed to degree courses, many to Oxbridge. Danish, Dutch, French, German, Italian and Spanish are offered from the I.B. Music and drama are very well supported. Sports and games are not stressed but there is a range of outdoor activities, including sailing, canoeing, swimming and orienteering. Clubs and societies (over 50) cater for a phenomenal number of enterprises and these play an important part in the life of the college. They are community activities. *All* students give college service: maintenance, simple building, cleaning, estate improvement. Estate service involves running the 50-acre college farm; students receive instruction in livestock management, crop-rotation, grassland management and market gardening. A marine science group is trained in sub-aqua diving and survey techniques. Cultural and aesthetic pursuits and training include pottery, sculpture, typography, silk-screen printing and film-making. *All* students are engaged in local community services of which there are a wide range. Equally important are the rescue services. In 1962 the college initiated the first co-ordinated cliff, beach and inshore rescue service in Britain which has already saved over 150 lives in the Bristol Channel. Extra-mural developments include a community arts centre (in the historic tithe barn) and the extra-mural centre which provides residential courses. College students are engaged in these undertakings and there is continual emphasis on international co-operation and understanding.

School profile

Pupils Age range 16–19; 353 pupils, 3 day (2 boys, 1 girl), 350 boarding (175 boys, 175 girls). Entry age, 16. 1% are children of former pupils. *Transfer from maintained schools:* 95%.

Entrance By competition for scholarships which are awarded on merit, by interview and school report. Oversubscribed. No special skills but must be academically suited to pre-university education; no religious requirements. Parents not expected to buy text books. Average extras £400 per annum. 160–170

pa scholarships/bursaries available, value up to £8250 (aim is to provide full scholarship, although these may be means tested).

Parents 60+% live overseas.

Staff Principal C D O Jenkins, first year in post. 40 full time staff, 2 part time. Annual turnover 2–3%. Average age 38.

Academic work International Baccalaureate. 35 subjects offered (including Russian, design technology, environmental systems, physical science, peace studies). In 1990, 179 pupils in upper sixth; 92% awarded IB Diploma. 30%

took science IB higher levels; 30% arts/ humanities; 40% both. *Computing facilities:* Nimbus network system in open access computing room; departmental machines throughout. *Special provision:* Pupils with visual, hearing, slight physical handicaps accepted although narrow spiral stone stairs can present insuperable problems to the severely physically handicapped.

European Community *Languages:* Danish, Dutch, French, German, Italian, Spanish offered to IB. *Exchanges:* Regular exchanges for pupils to France and Italy. *Other:* School has pupils from all European countries, east and west.

Senior pupils' non-academic activities *Music:* 120 learn a musical instrument, 60 up to Grade 6; 1 accepted for Music College. 30 in school orchestra, 40 in school choir, 6 in pop group. *Drama and dance:* 40 in school productions; 1 accepted for Drama/Dance school; 1 goes on to work in theatre. *Art:* 45 take IB art; 2 accepted for Art School. 100 belong to photographic club. *Sport:* Sport not stressed but rugby, soccer, tennis, badminton, squash, basketball, swimming available. 200 take part in non-compulsory sport; 100 take lifesaving exams. *Other:* 350 take part in local community schemes. 15 enter voluntary schemes after leaving school. Extensive range of over 50 varied activities . . . including beach rescue, pottery, India project, aerobics, Amnesty International, ecology, creative writing, weaving.

Careers In 1990, 95% leavers went on to degree courses; 3% to art/drama/ music colleges; 1% to non-degree courses; 1% straight into careers. Of those going on to degree courses, 12% went to Oxbridge; 81% to other universities; 2% to poly/colleges. 3% those going on to higher education went to courses in practical art; 1% in drama/acting; 1% in music; 45% in humanities/social sciences; 20% in medicine; and 30% in science/engineering.

Uniform No school uniform.

Houses/prefects No competitive houses, head of school or prefects. House representatives, elected by the house. School Council.

Religion Attendance at religious worship not compulsory.

Social School visits to enable the international students to provide an input to local schools. A number of language-orientated trips organised. Pupils not allowed to bring own transport. Meals self-service. School shop. Tobacco/ alcohol allowed (under certain constraints of place and time).

Discipline No corporal punishment. Pupils failing to produce homework once could expect a warning; those caught smoking cannabis on the premises could expect expulsion.

Boarding All share study bedrooms with 3 others. Pupils divided into different houses of approx 48. Resident qualified nurse. Pupils can provide and cook own food. 2 exeats per term and more informally. Visits to the local town allowed at any time convenient.

· Austin Friars ·

Austin Friars School	● Pupils 306	● Termly fees
Carlisle	● Boys 11–18	£1025 (Day)
Cumbria	(Day/Board)	£1800 (Board)
CA3 9PB	● Girls 11–18	● SHMIS
Tel 0228 28042	(Day)	Enquiries/application to
	● Upper sixth 40	the School Secretary

What it's like

Founded in 1951, it is situated on the outskirts of Carlisle, at its highest point, overlooking the River Eden. The grounds are spacious and the buildings are handsome. The sixth form residential area is in a comfortable house additional to the main site. A Catholic school, it is run by priests of the Order of St Augustine. The entire philosophy of the school is pervaded by ideals inspired by religious values and religious education is an integral part of the curriculum. Discipline is firm. Trustworthiness and self-discipline are deemed vital. A sound education is provided. Many sixth formers go on to degree courses, including Oxbridge. There is a good range of sports and activities. A fair commitment to local community schemes and the Duke of Edinburgh's Award Scheme.

School profile

Pupils Age range 11–18; 306 pupils, 233 day (144 boys, 89 girls), 73 boarding (all boys). Main entry ages 11 and into sixth. 20+% of intake from St Monica's School, Carlisle. Approx 3% are children of former pupils.

Entrance Common entrance and own entrance exam used. Sometimes oversubscribed. No special skills or religious requirements but is predominantly Catholic. Parents not expected to buy books; maximum extras, £41. Assisted places available. 13 scholarships available (8 boarders, 5 day), £942–£257.

Parents 15+% are doctors, lawyers, etc; 15+% in industry or commerce. 60+% live within 30 miles; up to 10% overseas.

Staff Head Master Reverend Thomas Lyons, in post 10 years. 27 full time staff, 3 part time. Annual turnover 6%. Average age 44.

Academic work GCSE and A-levels. Average size of upper fifth 50; upper sixth 40. *GCSE:* on average, 28 upper fifth gain at least grade C in 8+ subjects; 18 in 5–7 and 4 in 1 subject. *A-levels:* on average, 26 upper sixth pass in 4 subjects; 6 in 3; 5 in 2 and 3 in 1 subject. On average, 16 take science/engineering A-levels; 14 take arts and humanities A-levels; 10 a mixture of both. *Computing facilities:* SJ network; with hard disk serving 12 BBC micros in computer room and 3 for staff and administration. *Special provision:* English lessons for non native speakers.

European Community *Languages:* French offered: to age 14; GCSE; A-level. German (from 1991): to age 14; GCSE; A-level. None take GCSE in more than 1 EC language at present. *Other:* Pupils for short and long term from France, Spain and occasionally Italy.

Senior pupils' non-academic activities *Music:* 70 learn a musical instrument, 3 to Grade 6 or above; 10 in school orchestra, 10 in choir, 5 in school pop group. *Drama and dance:* 20 in school productions; 20 take LAMDA exams. *Art:* 20 take GCSE; 6 A-level; 4 accepted for Art School. 12 in photographic club. *Sport:* Rugby, cricket, athletics, basketball, netball, hockey, gymnastics, swimming, cross-country, tennis, badminton, rowing, sailing, canoeing available. 40 take noncompulsory sport. 10 take exams eg in gymnastics, swimming. 20 represent county (rugby, cricket, tennis). *Other:* 40 take part in local community schemes. 20 have bronze Duke of Edinburgh's Award, 20 silver. Other activities include a computer club, girls' keep-fit, judo, chess, debating society, public-speaking.

Careers In 1990, 85% leavers went on to degree courses; 5% to art/drama/ music colleges; 5% to non-degree courses; 5% straight into careers (eg banking, farming). Of those going on to degree courses, 10% went to Oxbridge, 50% to other universities; 30% to poly/ colleges. 3% those going on to higher education went to courses in drama/ acting; 50% in humanities/social sciences; 6% in medicine; and 30% in science/engineering.

Uniform School uniform worn, except in sixth form when suits are an alternative.

Houses/prefects 3 competitive houses. Prefects, head boy, head of house and house prefects appointed by the Head and housemasters.

Religion Assembly compulsory four days a week. All encouraged to attend Mass during the week; Sunday Mass compulsory for boarders.

Social Public speaking competitions, choral works, careers conventions with other local schools. Organised trips abroad to eg France, Russia. Pupils allowed to bring own car/bike/motorbike to school. Lunch self service; other meals formal. School tuck shop and clothing shop. No tobacco allowed; alcohol on supervised social occasions.

Discipline Pupils failing to produce homework once might expect to receive extra work; those caught smoking cannabis on the premises could expect expulsion.

Boarding 10% have own study bedroom, 30% share doubles; 60% are in dormitories of 6+, divided by age. Weekly visit by local GP, resident qualified nurse. Central dining room. Exeats each term: 1 week (autumn and summer) and 2 days (spring and autumn). Visits to the local town allowed on Saturday afternoons.

b

· *Badminton* ·

Badminton School	● Pupils 360	● Termly fees
Westbury on Trym	● Boys None	£1525 (Day)
Bristol	● Girls 7–18	£2775 (Board)
BS9 3BA	(Day/Board)	● GSA
Tel 0272 623141	● Upper sixth 46	Enquiries/application to the Headmaster

What it's like

Founded in 1858, agreeably sited on the outskirts of Bristol near the Downs and in spacious grounds. 'The style of the school is a combination of discipline and warmth.' Staff–pupil relationships are mature and friendly, based on 'principles of courtesy and mutual respect'. All pupils are encouraged to work hard and play hard. The all-rounder is encouraged. Good on science, music and the creative arts. There is an emphasis on 'thinking people' and 'exceptional talent'. The dull and mediocre do not particularly flourish. It has a reputation for good teaching and a distinguished academic record. Very many girls go on to degree courses, including Oxbridge. French, German and Spanish are offered to A-level and a high proportion of girls takes GCSE in more than one European language. There are regular exchanges with France, Germany and Spain, and a lot of emphasis on Europe and the wider world. Full advantage is taken of the facilities of the city and its university.

School profile

Pupils Total age range 7–18; 360 girls, 110 day, 250 boarding. Senior department 11–18, 310 girls. Main entry ages 7, 11, 12, 13 and into sixth. Approx 5% are children of former pupils. *Transfer from maintained schools:* 20% of senior intake.

Entrance Common entrance and own entrance exam used. Oversubscribed. Special skills in music, science, sport, languages, art looked for. No religious requirements. Parents expected to buy text books; average extras £30 per term. 20 scholarships/bursaries, £4000–£800.

Parents 45+% are doctors, lawyers, etc; 25+% in industry or commerce. 30+% live within 30 miles, 15+% English overseas, 5% foreign.

Staff Headmaster Mr C J T Gould, in post for 9 years. 36 full time staff, 16 part time. Annual turnover 5%. Average age 39.

Academic work GCSE and A-levels. 20 subjects offered (no A-level general studies). In 1990, 50 pupils in upper fifth, 46 in upper sixth. *GCSE:* in 1990, 98% upper fifth gained at least grade C in 8+ subjects; 2% in 5–7. *A-levels:* 22% upper sixth passed in 4+ subjects; 55% in 3; 18% in 2; and 5% in 1 subject. 40% took science A-levels; 50% arts/humanities;

10% both. *Computing facilities:* Separate rooms with 6 BBCs for juniors; 14 BBCs for middle school; 14 IBMs for seniors. *Special provision:* Very little.

European Community *Languages:* French offered: to age 14; GCSE; AS-level; A-level. German offered: to age 14; GCSE; AS-level; A-level. Italian: non-examined. Spanish offered: to age 14; GCSE; AS-level; A-level. 50–75% take GCSE in more than 1 EC language. Also offers Flaw (Foreign Languages at Work). *Exchanges:* Regular exchanges for pupils aged 11–18 to France, Germany and Spain. *Other:* Take part in European Youth Parliament; model United Nations. Bilinguals in school. Current affairs specialists on staff.

Senior pupils' non-academic activities *Music:* 300 learn a musical instrument, 40 to Grade 6 or above, 8 take GCSE, 4 take A-level, 2 accepted for Music School, 2 for music degrees; 100 in school orchestras, 4 in Avon Schools Orchestra, 100 in ensembles, 100 in main choir, 40 in middle choir, 18 in special choir; 3 in National Youth Orchestras. *Drama and dance:* 50 in school productions, 100 perform in house plays, 40 go on to Grade 6 in ESB, RAD etc, 20 take Guildhall exams. 1 accepted for Drama School. *Art:* 250 take as non-examined subject; 45 GCSE; 12 A-level. 4 accepted for Art School, 4 for degree courses, 6 for history of art; 30 belong to photographic club, 30 to Sunday art club. *Sport:* Hockey, netball, volleyball, badminton, tennis, squash, short-tennis, aerobics, rounders, golf, fencing, self-defence, judo, yoga, jazz dancing, skating, swimming, diving, ballet, gymnastics, athletics, riding, ski-ing available. 200 take non-compulsory sport. 120 take exams in eg gymnastics, swimming, life-saving, judo, self-defence. 15 represent county (hockey, riding, tennis, swimming, synchronised swimming, fencing). *Other:* 10 take part in local community schemes. 12 participate in survival weekends, 50 in activity weekends. 12 take first aid. 3 enter voluntary schemes after leaving school. Other activities include two computer clubs, driving, politics, science, art, photography, design, first aid, maths association, classical club,

historical society, drama, public speaking, debating society, bookshop, fundraising, social service.

Careers In 1990, 90% leavers went on to degree courses; 9% to art/drama/music colleges; 1% to non-degree courses. Of those going on to degree courses, 10% went to Oxbridge, 50% to other universities; 40% to poly/colleges. 10% those going on to higher education went to courses in practical art; 2% in drama/acting; 10% in music; 33% in humanities/social sciences; 5% in medicine; and 30% in science/engineering.

Uniform School uniform worn except in sixth form.

Houses/prefects Competitive houses; head girl and head of house elected. School Council.

Religion Worship not compulsory but encouraged.

Social Joint events including Bristol Schools Debating; choral/orchestral with Clifton and Queen Elizabeth Hospital; Science Society with Clifton; debates, socials, sports. Organised exchanges to France, Spain, Germany. Ski-ing trips abroad and expeditions to Italy, Jordan, Paris, Madrid, Russia. Day pupils allowed to bring own car/bike to school. Lunch formal with grace. Other meals self service. Second-hand uniform shop. No tobacco/alcohol allowed.

Discipline No corporal punishment. Firm approach to discipline. Pupils failing to produce homework once might expect report/detention; those caught with drugs would expect instant expulsion.

Boarding 20% have own study bedroom, 30% share; 10% in dormitories of 6+. Houses, of approx 35–50, divided by age. Qualified medical staff available. Central dining room. Sixth form can provide own breakfasts. 2 exeats (1 night) each term plus half-term. Weekend visits to the local town allowed but never alone nor after dark; reporting back in person.

Alumni association is run by Miss Leila Eveleigh, Yew Tree Farm, Winford, Bristol.

Former pupils Dame Iris Murdoch; Indira Gandhi; Polly Toynbee; Dame Margaret Miles among others.

· Bancroft's ·

Bancroft's School
Woodford Green
Essex
IG8 0RF
Tel 081-505 4821

- Pupils 873
- Boys 7–18 (Day)
- Girls 7–18 (Day)
- Upper sixth 98

- Termly fees
  £1328 (Day)
- HMC, SHA
  Enquiries/application to
  the Head Master

What it's like

Founded in 1737, it occupied its present premises in Woodford about 100 years ago. There are long-standing links with the Company of Drapers. The main buildings are handsome Victorian architecture and most of the later structures blend in sympathetically. The school is well equipped with excellent modern facilities. The playing fields are nearby. Some religious worship in the Anglican tradition. A well-run school with vigorous local support, it provides good teaching and the academic standards are high. Many leavers proceed to degree courses each year, including Oxbridge. French and German are offered to A-level, Italian and Spanish to GCSE. Many pupils take GCSE in more than one European language. There are regular exchanges with France and Germany. A wide range of sports and games is played with considerable success (a very large number of county representatives and some internationals). A certain amount of commitment to local community schemes and a most impressive record in the Duke of Edinburgh's Award Scheme.

School profile

Pupils Total age range 7–18, 873 day pupils. Senior department 11–18, 710 pupils (355 boys, 355 girls). Main entry ages 7, 11 and into sixth. Approx 5% are children of former pupils. *Transfer from maintained schools:* 50% main intakes at 11 and 80% to sixth.

Entrance Own entrance exam used. Oversubscribed. No special skills or religious requirements. Parents not expected to buy text books; maximum extras about £50. 80 assisted places. 90 scholarships, 35 bursaries (including music scholarship), £3984 pa.

Staff Head Master Dr P C D Southern, in post for 6 years. 58 full time staff in senior school, 4 part time. Annual turnover 5%. Average age 33.

Academic work GCSE and A-levels. 21 GCSE subjects offered; 20 at A-level (no A-level general studies). In 1991, 102 pupils in upper fifth, 98 in upper sixth. *GCSE:* in 1990, 66 upper fifth gained at least grade C in 8+ subjects; 35 in 5–7; and 4 in 1–4 subjects. *A-levels:* 5 upper sixth passed in 4+ subjects; 61 in 3; 21 in 2; and 9 in 1 subject. 40% took science A-levels; 45% arts/humanities; 15% both. *Computing facilities:* 2 specialised rooms and c15 machines in classrooms.

European Community *Languages:* French offered: to age 14; GCSE; AS-level; A-level. German offered: to age 14; GCSE; A-level. Italian offered: to GCSE. Spanish offered: to age 14; GCSE. 25–50% take GCSE in more than 1 EC language. *Exchanges:* Regular exchanges for pupils aged 11–16 to France and Germany. *Other:* European Studies offered to pupils aged 16–18. Biannual tour to EC centre.

Senior pupils' non-academic activities *Music:* 350 learn a musical instrument, 22 to Grade 6 or above, 2 accepted for Music School; 30 in school orchestra, 50 in school choir, 5 in school pop group. *Drama and dance:* 85 in school productions. 3 take Grade 6 in ESB, RAD etc. 1 accepted for Drama School. *Art:* 30 take as non-examined subject; 34 take

GCSE; 13 take A-level. 6 accepted for Art School. *Sport:* Rugby, hockey, athletics, netball, tennis, cricket, badminton, squash, gymnastics, trampolining, swimming and golf available. 150 take non-compulsory sport. 30 represent county, 4 represent country. *Other:* 15 take part in local community schemes. 35 have bronze Duke of Edinburgh's Award, 33 silver and 3 have gold. 3 enter voluntary schemes after leaving school. Other activities include clubs for a large variety of activities including chess and computers.

Careers In 1990, 70% leavers went on to degree courses; 8% to art/drama/ music colleges; 4% to non-degree courses (eg secretarial); 12% straight into careers; 6% other. Of those going on to degree courses, 12% went to Oxbridge, 75% to other universities; 13% to poly/colleges. 10% those going on to higher education went to courses in practical art; 2% in drama/acting; 3% in music; 40% in humanities/social sciences; 10% in medicine; and 35% in science/engineering.

Uniform School uniform worn throughout.

Houses/prefects Competitive houses. Prefects, head boy/girl, head of house – appointed by the Headmaster. School Council.

Religion Chapel/assemblies. Special Catholic and Jewish assemblies.

Social Lectures organised by departments. French and German exchanges plus other trips abroad. Pupils allowed to bring own car/bike to school. Meals self service. School shop. No tobacco/alcohol allowed.

Discipline No corporal punishment. Pupils failing to produce homework once might expect detention; those caught smoking cannabis on the premises might expect expulsion.

Alumni association run by The Secretary, P J Denhard Esq, Lower Flat, 20 Kendall Road, Beckenham, Kent BR3 4PZ.

Former pupils Denis Quilley; Sir Neil Macfarlane MP; Prof Sir Frederick Warner; Fred Emery.

· *Barnard Castle* ·

Barnard Castle School Barnard Castle Durham DL12 8UN Tel 0833 690222	● Pupils 610 ● Boys 8–18 (Day/Board) ● Girls 16–18 (Day/Board) ● Upper sixth 74	● Termly fees £1167 (Day) £1972 (Board) ● HMC Enquiries/application to the Headmaster

What it's like

The present foundation dates from 1883, derived, partially, from St John's Hospital (founded in the 13th century by John Baliol, whose widow founded the Oxford College). It is on a fine site in the Teesdale countryside on the outskirts of Barnard Castle. The grounds adjoin those of the Bowes Museum. The main Victorian building is used for admin and accommodation; all the teaching is done in purpose-built classrooms. In the last 25 years there has been much modernisation and development. Facilities are now excellent. The design technology centre is outstanding. Strong on music, drama and sport. Very good academic record. Very many pupils go on to degree courses, including Oxbridge. Chapel assembly on all weekdays; compulsory Sunday chapel for boarders. Vigorous local support and commitment to the community. Altogether a well run and flourishing establishment.

School profile

Pupils Total age range 8–18; 610 pupils, 340 day (322 boys, 18 girls), 270 boarding (250 boys, 20 girls). Senior department 11–18, 510 pupils (472 boys, 38 girls). Main entry ages 8, 11 and 13 (boys); into sixth (boys and girls). Approx 10% are children of former pupils. 20+% intake from own prep school. *Transfer from maintained schools:* 50% senior intake, plus 50% to sixth.

Entrance Common entrance and own entrance exam used. Not heavily oversubscribed. No special skills or religious requirements. Parents not expected to buy text books; no other compulsory extras. Assisted places. Scholarships/bursaries available, variable value.

Staff Headmaster F S McNamara. 48 full time staff, 4 part time, plus music staff. Small annual turnover.

Academic work GCSE and A-levels. 17 subjects offered (including A-level general studies). In 1990, 82 pupils in upper fifth, 74 in upper sixth. *GCSE:* in 1990, 47 upper fifth gained at least grade C in 8+ subjects; 25 in 5–7; and 10 in 1–4 subjects. *A-levels:* 28 upper sixth passed in 4+ subjects; 23 in 3; 8 in 2; and 10 in 1 subject. 30 took science A-levels; 34 arts/ humanities; 10 both. *Computing facilities:* Well-equipped computer room, plus computer club. *Special provision:* Specialist dyslexic teaching; EFL teaching.

European Community *Languages:* French offered: to age 14; GCSE; AS-level; A-level. German offered: to age 14; GCSE; AS-level; A-level. 10–25% take GCSE in more than 1 EC language. *Exchanges:* Regular exchanges for pupils aged 16–18 to France (inter-school student exchange).

Senior pupils' non-academic activities *Music:* 200 learn a musical instrument, 20 to Grade 6 or above; 40 in school orchestra, 60 in choir, 15 in jazz band, 5 in school pop group, 30 in wind band; 3 play in pop groups after leaving. *Drama and dance:* 120 in school productions. 1 goes on to work in theatre. *Art:* 20 take as non-examined subject in art club; 20 GCSE; 8 A-level; 3 accepted for Art School; 2 for architecture degree. 20 belong to photographic club. *Sport:* Rugby, cricket, squash, swimming, hockey, cross-country, athletics, tennis, basketball, badminton, soccer, judo, canoeing available. Sport is compulsory. 60–80 participate regularly in inter-school sport at 5th year or above. 19 represent county (rugby, cricket, hockey, squash, cross-country, athletics); 2 represent country (rugby). *Other:* 24 take part in local community schemes. 35 are taking gold Duke of Edinburgh's Award. Several enter voluntary scheme after leaving school. Other activities include a computer club, photography (good darkroom facilities), archery, public speaking, CCF, pottery, technology, various musical activities, car maintenance, drama, horse riding, model making, role playing, model railway.

Careers In 1990, 90% leavers went on to degree courses; 5% to art/drama/ music colleges; 2% to non-degree courses; 3% straight into careers. Of those going on to degree courses, 5% went to Oxbridge, 60% to other universities; 35% to poly/colleges. 4% those going on to higher education went to courses in practical art; 4% in drama/ acting; 2% in music; 46% in humanities/ social sciences; 2% in medicine; and 42% in science/engineering.

Uniform School uniform worn throughout.

Houses/prefects Competitive houses. Prefects, head boy/girl, head of house and house prefects appointed by the Head and housemasters.

Religion Compulsory Sunday chapel for boarders; chapel assembly each weekday.

Social Organised trips abroad. Pupils allowed to bring own bike to school; cars as privilege. Meals self service, few formal. School tuck and stationery shops. No tobacco allowed; alcohol allowed in Sixth Form Club.

Discipline No corporal punishment. Pupils failing to produce homework once would be dealt with according to circumstances; those caught smoking or possessing cannabis on the premises could expect to be expelled.

Boarding 10% have own study bedroom, 70% share; 15% in dormitories of 6+. Houses of 60–70. Resident qualified medical staff. Central dining room. Pupils can provide and cook some own food. 2 exeats a term (1.5 days), plus half-term. Visits to the local town allowed at housemaster's discretion.

Alumni association is run by Mrs D Cograve, O.B. Secretary, Barnard Castle School.

Former pupils Lord Mills (Minister of Power); Geoffrey Smith (TV gardening expert); Craig Raine (poet); Kevin Whately (actor); Bentley Beetham (climber – Everest Expedition 1924); Sir Edward Mellanby, FRS (MRC); Rory Underwood, Robert Andrew and Tom Danby (rugby internationals); Brian Patterson, Ian Nuttall, Peter Verow (squash internationals); Geoff Turner (international athlete); Kim Hamilton (international modern pentathlete); George Macaulay (test cricketer).

· Baston ·

Baston School	• Pupils 375	• Termly fees
Hayes	• Boys None	£1025 (Day)
Bromley	• Girls 3–18	£1930 (Board)
Kent	(Day/Board/	£1900 (Weekly)
BR2 7AB	Weekly)	• ISAI
Tel 081 462 1010	• Upper sixth 15	Enquiries/application to the Headmaster

What it's like

Founded in 1933, it has a very pleasant 14-acre site of playing fields, gardens and orchards, on the edge of broad common land in the green belt on the southern outskirts of Bromley. Many of its facilities are purpose built and of a high order (providing comfortable accommodation for the boarders). Well equipped for games and outdoor activities. It gives a sound traditional education and has a good academic record. Many sixth formers go on to degree courses. French and German are offered to A-level, Spanish to GCSE. Many girls take GCSE in more than one European language. There are regular exchanges with France. Strong in music, drama, arts and crafts. Plentiful use is made of the amenities of a capital city. A congenial school with a friendly informal atmosphere. The preparatory department is on the same site.

School profile

Pupils Total age range 3–18; 375 girls, 340 day, 35 boarding. Senior department 11–18, 198 girls. Main entry ages 3, 4, 5, 7, 11 and into sixth. Approx 8% are children of former pupils.

Entrance Own entrance exam used. Oversubscribed at most ages. No special skills or religious requirements. Parents expected to buy sixth form text books only; no other compulsory extras. Up to 3 scholarships/bursaries at 11, £300–£78 per term.

Parents 80+% live within 30 miles; up to 10% live overseas.

Staff Headmaster C R C Wimble. 29 full time staff, 13 part time. Annual turnover, 3%.

Academic work GCSE and A-levels. Business studies and accounting offered to GCSE/A-level. Average size of upper fifth 32; upper sixth 15. *GCSE:* on average, 12 pupils in upper fifth pass 8+ subjects; 7 pass 5–7 subjects; 13 pass 1–4 subjects. *A-levels:* on average, 1 upper sixth passed in 4 subjects; 8 in 3; 3 in 2; and 3 in 1 subject. On average, 6 take science/engineering A-levels; 5 take arts and humanities; 4 a mixture. *Computing facilities:* 5 BBC B/Master, 4 Amstrad 1640, 6 Acorn A3000, 1 Amstrad 2386. *Special provision:* for EFL.

European Community *Languages:* French offered: to age 14; GCSE; A-level. German offered: to age 14; GCSE; A-level. Spanish offered: to GCSE. 25–50% take GCSE in more than 1 EC language. *Exchanges:* Regular exchanges for pupils aged 11–14 to France.

Senior pupils' non-academic activities *Music:* 13 learn a musical instrument, 8 to Grade 6 or above, 1 accepted for Music School; 10 in school orchestra, 17 in choir. *Drama and dance:* 25 in school productions. *Art:* 2 take as non-examined subject; 15 GCSE; 4 A-level. 2 accepted for Art School. *Sport:* Lacrosse, netball, gymnastics, squash, tennis, athletics, swimming available. 35 take non-compulsory sport. 16 pupils represent county (lacrosse, tennis). *Other:* Activities include computer and art clubs, music, drama, sport.

Careers In 1990, 65% upper sixth leavers went on to degree courses; 30% to non-degree courses (eg business studies); 5% straight into careers (eg banking). Of those going on to degree courses, 20% went to universities; 80% to poly/colleges. 35% those going on to higher education went to courses in humanities/social sciences; 5% in medicine; and 60% in science/engineering.

Uniform School uniform worn, except in sixth form.

Houses/prefects Competitive houses. Prefects, head girl, head of house and house prefects – appointed by staff.

Religion Assemblies compulsory.

Social Organised trips abroad; ski trips, exchange visits to France and Germany, Russian trips, educational cruises, visit to Oberamergau for passion play. Trips to Orlando and (East) Germany. *Upper sixth* allowed to bring own car to school. Meals self service. No tobacco/alcohol allowed.

Discipline No corporal punishment. Pupils failing to produce homework once might expect admonishment; those caught smoking cannabis on the premises could expect expulsion.

Boarding 5% own study bedroom, 95% share with 2–5. No resident medical staff. Central dining room. Pupils can provide and cook own food. 3 weekend exeats each term. Weekend visits to local town allowed.

Alumni association is run by Mrs J C Wimble, c/o the School.

Former pupils Carol Thatcher.

· *Bath High* ·

Bath High School	● Pupils 615	● Termly fees
Hope House	● Boys None	£908
Lansdown	● Girls 4–18	● GSA,
Bath	(Day)	GPDST
Avon BA1 5ES	● Upper sixth 43	Enquiries/application
Tel 0225 422931		to the Headmistress

What it's like

Founded in 1872 and a member of the Girls' Public Day School Trust, it occupies beautiful Georgian buildings at Lansdown. There is a large terraced garden and fine views over the city. Games facilities are nearby. There have been extensive modern additions in the last 25 years and the facilities are good. A junior school and a senior school are combined. A large sixth form of about 90. A good general education is provided and academic standards are high. Many girls go on to degree courses, including a high proportion to Oxbridge. French and German are offered to A-level, Spanish to GCSE. Many girls take GCSE in more than one European language. There are regular exchanges with France and Germany. Music, drama and art are all strong. Full use is made of Bath's cultural amenities. Much time and care is devoted to careers advice. A good range of sports and games is provided and standards are very creditable. There is a wide variety of clubs and societies and considerable commitment to local community services.

School profile

Pupils Total age 4–18, 615 day girls. Senior department 11–18, 382 girls. Main entry age 11 and into sixth. *Transfer from maintained schools:* 33% at 11, plus 10% to sixth.

Entrance Own entrance exam used. Assisted places and scholarships available.

Staff Headmistress Miss Margaret Winfield, in post for 5 years.

Academic work GCSE, AS and A-levels. 20 subjects offered (including A-level general studies). In 1990, 65 pupils in upper fifth, 43 in upper sixth. *GCSE:* in 1990, 58 upper fifth gained at least grade C in 8+ subjects; 6 in 5–7 subjects. *A-levels:* 28 upper sixth passed in 4+ subjects; 9 in 3; 4 in 2+; and 3 in 1 subject at A- or AS-level. 18% took science A-levels; 34% arts/humanities; 48% both. *Computing facilities:* Computer room with 9 IBM compatible machines and 1 BBC computer; desk top publishing machine; 1 computer in each of science, CDT, home economics departments.

European Community *Languages:* French offered: to age 14; GCSE; AS-level; A-level. German offered: to age 14; GCSE; AS-level; A-level. Spanish offered: to GCSE. *Exchanges:* Regular exchanges for pupils aged 14–16 to France and Germany.

Careers In 1990, 77% leavers went on to degree courses; 2% to art/drama/music colleges; 5% to non-degree courses (eg HND computing, physiotherapy); 15% other (retaking A-levels, Gap year). Of those going on to degree courses, 18% went to Oxbridge, 59% to other universities; 23% to poly/colleges. 2% those going on to higher education went to courses in practical art; 2% in drama/acting; 2% in music; 67% in humanities/social sciences; 11% in medicine; and 13% in science/engineering.

· *Batley* ·

Batley Grammar School	● Pupils 617	● Termly fees
Carlinghow Hill	● Boys 11–19	£833 (Day)
Batley	(Day)	● HMC
West Yorkshire	● Girls 16–19	Enquiries/application to
WF17 0AD	(Day)	the Headmaster
Tel 0924 474980	● Upper sixth 84	

What it's like

Founded in 1612, it lies on the outskirts of Batley near the countryside. Playing fields adjoin it. The buildings are of Yorkshire stone and brick. They are well appointed and all the modern facilities are first class. Recent developments include spacious labs, a sixth form centre, sports hall and a new language laboratory and technology centre. It has remained very much a grammar school in the old tradition of such establishments and provides a sound education which produces consistently creditable results. Girls have been admitted to the sixth form since 1988. Many pupils go on to degree courses, including Oxbridge. French and German are offered to A-level and there are regular exchanges with France and Germany. A new language laboratory opened in 1991. Strong in music, sport and outdoor pursuits. Vigorous local support and commitment to the community.

School profile

Pupils Age range 11–19; 617 day pupils (600 boys, 17 girls). Main entry ages boys, 11, 12 and 13; boys and girls into sixth. Approx 5% are children of former pupils. *Transfer from maintained schools:* 90% main intake, plus 80% to sixth.

Entrance Own entrance exam used. Oversubscribed. No special skills or religious requirements. Parents not expected to buy text books; holiday trips etc extra. 251 assisted places. 5–10 scholarships/bursaries pa, full to 25% fees.

Staff Head C S Parker, in post for 5 years. 43 full time staff, 10 part time. Annual turnover less than 5%. Average age 40.

Academic work GCSE and A-levels. 18 GCSE subjects offered; 1 AS; 19 A-level (including A-level general studies, ancient history and literature, English language). In 1990, 110 pupils in upper fifth, 84 in upper sixth. *GCSE:* in 1990, 76% upper fifth gained at least grade C in 8+ subjects; 17% in 5–7; and 7% in 1–4 subjects. *A-levels:* On average 53% upper sixth passed in 4+ subjects; 22% in 3; 12% in 2; and 11% in 1 subject. 32% took science A-levels; 42% arts/humanities; 26% both. *Computing facilities:* 16 stations, 40 megabyte junior computing room with Tape Streamer back-up; 10 station senior computing room; 24 departmentally-based.

European Community *Languages:* French offered: to age 14; GCSE; AS-level; A-level. German offered: to age 14; GCSE; A-level. 10–25% take GCSE in more than 1 EC language. *Exchanges:* Regular exchanges for pupils aged 11–18 to France and Germany. *Other:* Satellite TV links. Trips to Britanny (second year), Paris (sixth form) and Rhineland.

Senior pupils' non-academic activities *Music:* 115 learn a musical instrument, 25 to Grade 6 or above, 45 in school orchestra/bands, 15 in percussion and recorder groups, 10 play in pop group, 14 members of local brass bands, 20 in local orchestra. *Drama and dance:* 30 in school productions. 1 accepted for Drama/Dance School, 1 to work in theatre. *Art:* 36 take GCSE; 10 A-level. 4 accepted for Art School. *Sport:* Soccer, cricket, cross-country, basketball, athletics, tennis, wind-surfing, sailing, squash, badminton available. 90 take non-compulsory sport. 12 represent county (cricket, cross-country, soccer, athletics, water polo); 1 England 15 group cricket. *Other:* 30 take part in local community schemes. 37 have silver Duke of Edinburgh's Award, 16 have gold. 220 in voluntary CCF. Other activities include a computer club, drama, chess clubs, choirs, orchestra, three brass bands, ski-ing, CARE group (care of environment), French film club, junior ornithology club, community service group, Christian fellowship.

Careers In 1990, 75% leavers went on to degree courses; 4% to art/drama/music colleges; 7% to non-degree courses (eg HND computer science, civil engineering, quantity surveying, agriculture, nursing); 14% straight into careers (eg banking, insurance). Of those going on to degree courses, 8% went to Oxbridge, 58% to other universities; 34% to poly/colleges. 3% those going on to higher education went to courses in practical art; 3% in music; 40% in humanities/social sciences; 6% in medicine; and 48% in science/engineering.

Uniform School uniform worn throughout.

Houses/prefects Competitive houses. Prefects, head boy appointed by Headmaster. Head of house and house prefects appointed by housemasters.

Religion Morning assembly unless parents request exclusion.

Social Local road safety quiz organised by seniors; British Association of Young Scientists meetings. Language trips to France and Germany; 2 organised ski

trips; 'Classical' trip to Greece/Italy and outward bound trips. Pupils allowed to bring own car/bike to school with Head's permission. Meals self service. No tobacco/alcohol allowed.
Discipline No corporal punishment. Pupils failing to produce homework once might initially expect extra work; Saturday detention for repeated offences.
Alumni association is run by Mr A Allen, 11 Monk-Ings, Birstall, Batley.
Former pupils Sir Willie Morris (Ambassador); Professor Norman Franklin (UKAE); Joseph Priestley (discovered oxygen in 1774).

· Battle Abbey ·

Battle Abbey School
Battle
East Sussex
TN33 0AD
Tel 04246 2385

- Pupils 240
- Boys 3–18 (Day/Board/Weekly)
- Girls 3–18 (Day/Board/Weekly)
- Upper sixth 8

- Termly fees
£1550 (Day)
£2520 (Board/Weekly)
- GSA
Enquiries/application to the Headmaster's Secretary

What it's like

Battle Abbey moved to its present site in 1922 and thus enjoys the privilege of being housed in one of the most remarkable buildings in Britain (set in 52 acres of fine parkland). As part of a valuable ancient monument it is maintained to the highest standards of English Heritage. Battle Abbey is a co-educational school for pupils aged 4–18, plus a kindergarten from $2\frac{1}{2}$. It is very comfortable and civilised and has excellent modern facilities. A new range of specialist classrooms and laboratories was opened in 1988. It offers a good all-round education in a family atmosphere and has all the advantages of a small school. Most pupils learn a musical instrument, all take art as a non-examined subject, take part in sport, and everyone, if at all possible, is involved in dramatic productions. Academic results are good. French and German are offered to A-level (Italian as an extra to juniors) and many pupils take GCSE in both languages. There are regular exchanges with France and Germany. Its major strength lies with pupils who lack self-confidence and who might sink without trace in a larger establishment. At Battle Abbey they can be 'big fish in a small pond'; there are no 'also-rans'. They produce confident young adults from sometimes the most unlikely of pupils. The house system is competitive in work, conduct, manners and sport. High standards of conduct and manners are expected and achieved.

School profile

Pupils Total age range $2\frac{1}{2}$–18; 240 pupils, 105 day (45 boys, 60 girls), 135 boarding (35 boys, 100 girls). Senior department 11–18, 150 pupils (26 boys, 124 girls). Main entry ages $2\frac{1}{2}$, 4, 5, 11, 13 and into sixth. Approx 5% are children of former pupils. *Transfer from maintained schools:* 80% main intake at 11 and 13, plus 10% to sixth.
Entrance Common entrance and own entrance exam used. Oversubscribed. No special skills or religious requirements, although school is Christian. Parents expected to buy A-level text books; no

other compulsory extras. 2 scholarships a year, half tuition fees.

Parents 15+% in armed services.

Staff Headmaster D J A Teall, in post for 9 years. 24 full time staff, 8 part time. Low annual turnover. Average age 45.

Academic work GCSE and A-levels. 14 GCSE subjects offered; 10 at A-level (no A-level general studies). On average, 25 pupils in upper fifth, 8 in upper sixth. *GCSE:* on average, 40% upper fifth gain at least grade C in 8+ subjects; 20% in 5–7; and 40% in 1–4 subjects. *A-levels:* 50% upper sixth passed in 3 subjects; 50% in 2 subjects. 40% took science A-levels; 40% arts/humanities; 20% both. *Computing facilities:* 2 computer rooms with BBC Master computers. *Special provision:* Special additional lessons can be arranged.

European Community *Languages:* French offered: to age 14; GCSE; A-level. German offered: to age 14; GCSE; A-level. Spanish offered: to age 14 (as an extra). 25–50% take GCSE in more than 1 EC language. *Exchanges:* Regular exchanges for pupils aged 11–14 to France and Germany. *Other:* 4–6 EC pupils for all or part of each summer term. Week-long trip to France or Germany annually.

Senior pupils' non-academic activities *Music:* Most learn a musical instrument, 6 to Grade 6 or above; 15 in school orchestra, 30 in choir, 12 in madrigal group. *Drama and dance:* All pupils participate in musical school productions; 30 in others. 2 up to Grade 6 ESB etc or above. 2 accepted for Drama/Dance Schools. *Art:* All take as non-examined subject; 12 GCSE; 5 A-level. 2 accepted for Art School. *Sport:* Football, cricket, hockey, netball, basketball, rounders, swimming, tennis, athletics, cross-country, badminton, volley ball, squash available. All take sport. 2 take exams in eg gymnastics, swimming. 2 represent county (cross-country, athletics). *Other:* 15 take part in local community schemes. Other activities include computer club, driving, judo, photography, dance (modern, ballroom and tap), bellringing, riding, scouts, guides and sailing.

Careers 2 part time careers advisers. Annual average accepted for *arts and humanities degree courses* at universities, 1; polytechnics/colleges, 1. *science and engineering degree courses* at universities, 1; polytechnics/colleges, 2. *other general training courses*, 10. Average number going straight into careers in armed services, 2; few into industry; music/drama, 2.

Uniform School uniform worn except in sixth form.

Houses/prefects Competitive houses. Prefects, head of house and house prefects appointed by the Head or housemaster/mistress. School Council.

Religion Christian morning assembly compulsory. Boarders attend Sunday Church (non-Christians excused).

Social Regular social functions with Eastbourne College and Tonbridge School. Organised trips to France and Germany, ski-ing. Meals formal. Sixth formers may smoke in designated room, and have wine for 18th birthdays.

Discipline No corporal punishment. Pupils failing to produce homework once might expect extra work and an 'order mark' (counting against their house); those caught smoking cannabis on the premises could expect to be expelled without hesitation.

Boarding Sixth have study bedrooms; others in dormitories of 5. Central dining room. Seniors can provide and cook own food. 3 or 4 weekend exeats per term, half-term and 4 Sundays. Visits to the local town allowed.

Alumni association is run by Mrs M Steward, c/o the School.

Bearwood

· Bearwood ·

Bearwood College
Bear Wood
Wokingham
Berkshire
RG11 5BG
Tel 0734 786915

- Pupils 330
- Boys 11–19 (Day/ Board/Weekly)
- Girls None
- Upper sixth 30

- Termly fees £1550 (Day) £2800 (Board/ Weekly)
- SHMIS Enquiries/application to the Headmaster

What it's like

Founded in 1827, as the Royal Merchant Navy School, it is now under the Queen's patronage and its president is the Duke of Edinburgh. The main building is a handsome neo-Renaissance mansion on a splendid estate of 500 acres with lakes, riding school and golf course. The more recent buildings are well appointed and comfortable. A new theatre and music school opened in 1991. The ethics and general tenor of the college encourage the growth of the individual. Organisation is directed towards self-discipline and leadership by example. Basically it is a C of E school but it takes all denominations. Academic education is sound and results very creditable. Many sixth formers go on to degree courses. A good deal of emphasis on leisure pursuits. Many extra-curricular activities available. Boarding accommodation is comfortable and there are good relationships between staff and pupils.

School profile

Pupils Age range 11–19; 330 boys, 70 day, 260 boarding. Main entry ages 11, 12, 13 and into sixth. *Transfer from maintained schools:* 20% main intake, plus 2% to sixth.

Entrance Common entrance and own entrance exam used. Well subscribed. No special skills. School is C of E but takes all denominations. Parents expected to pay £20 per term for books; maximum extras £70. 16–25 scholarships/bursaries; also for Merchant Navy children in need (education can be free – enquiries to Headmaster).

Parents 15+% are doctors, lawyers, etc, 15+% in industry or commerce. 30+% live within 30 miles, 10+% live overseas.

Staff Headmaster The Hon Martin C Penney, in post for 10 years. 30 full time staff, 5 part time. Annual turnover under 1%. Average age 39.

Academic work GCSE and A-level (including A-level general studies). In 1990, 75 pupils in upper fifth, 30 in upper sixth. *GCSE:* in 1990, 6 upper fifth gained at least grade C in 8+ subjects; 34 in 5–7; and 35 in 1–4 subjects. *A-levels:* 1 upper sixth passed in 4+ subjects; 14 in 3; 11 in 2; and 4 in 1 subject. 50% took science A-levels; 30% arts/humanities; 20% both. *Computing facilities:* 18 BBCs and Econet plus hard disc file. *Special provision:* Strong support for 1, 2 or 3 years for eg EFL/dyslexia.

European Community *Languages:* French offered: to age 14; GCSE; AS-level; A-level. German offered: to age 14; GCSE; AS-level; A-level. Spanish offered: to age 14; GCSE; AS-level; A-level. Under 10% take GCSE in more than 1 EC language.

Senior pupils' non-academic activities *Music:* Approx 100 learn a musical instrument, 16 to Grade 6 or above; 15 in school orchestra, 13 in choir, 12 in school pop group, 8 in school jazz group, 7 in brass ensemble, 3 in baroque group; 1 in Reading Youth Orchestra, 2 in Berkshire Youth Jazz Orchestra. *Drama and dance:* 30+ in school productions, 120+ in house plays. *Art:* 34 take GCSE; 4 A-level. 1 or 2 accepted for Art School.

Sport: Archery, squash, badminton, soccer, rugby, cricket, swimming, cross-country, athletics, tennis, croquet available. Many take non-compulsory sport. 7 represent county (cricket, rugby, athletics, including National Youth Champion at Hurdles). *Other:* Other activities include a computer club, sailing, golf, riding, chess, war games, angling, karate, dry ski-ing, fencing, team shooting, CCF, drama.

Careers In 1990, 60% sixth form leavers went on to degree courses; 40% to non-degree courses (eg HNDs). Of those going on to degree courses, 50% went to universities; 50% to poly/colleges. 30% those going on to higher education went to courses in humanities/social sciences; 10% in medicine; and 60% in science/engineering.

Uniform School uniform worn; variation allowed in sixth form.

Houses/prefects Competitive houses. Prefects, head boy, head of house and house prefects appointed by the Head or housemasters.

Religion Daily Chapel. Other denominations can attend own place of worship on Sundays.

Social Compete locally at all sports and chess. Annual local collection for King George VI Fund for Sailors. Activity Club travel extensively eg to Alaska. Pupils allowed to bring own bike to school. Meals self service. School tuck and uniform shops. No tobacco allowed. Limited alcohol (beer/lager) for 17+.

Discipline No corporal punishment. Pupils failing to produce homework once might expect a verbal warning; those caught smoking cannabis on the premises could expect dismissal.

Boarding 15% have own study bedroom, 70% share (2–5); 15% are in dormitories of 6+. Houses, of approximately 60, same as competitive houses. Resident medical staff; separate sanatorium. Central dining room. Sixth formers can cook snacks. 3 Sundays and 2 weekend exeats a term. Visits to the local town allowed with housemaster's permission.

Alumni association is run by J J Hann, c/o the College.

Former pupils Francis Scarfe (academic).

· *Bedales* ·

Bedales School
Petersfield
Hampshire
GU32 2DG
Tel 0730 63286

- Pupils 403
- Boys 13–18 (Day/Board)
- Girls 13–18 (Day/Board)
- Upper sixth 66

- Termly fees £2240 (Day) £3125 (Board)
- HMC, SHMIS Enquiries/application to the Registrar for Admissions

What it's like

Opened in 1893 (one of the very first co-ed schools in Britain), it has a splendid site of 120 acres in East Hampshire, 16 miles from the sea, on a hill overlooking the Rother valley. Civilised and comfortable buildings in beautiful grounds. The Memorial Library is one of the best school libraries in Britain. It was founded as a 'pioneer school' by J H Badley who developed it as a reformed version of the contemporary public schools. His reforms involved a serious commitment to the arts and crafts, rural skills and work out of doors as well as to academic study. Always progressive in the best sense, it is a product of its dissenting origins and idealistic drives; a school within a supporting community, believing strongly in itself and what it has to offer and resistant to orthodoxies and bureaucracies. It is a 'one-off' school with a unique character. Very strong on art, drama, dance and crafts – and music, which has a central position in the life of the school. A feature is the Outdoor Work Department where pupils maintain a large tree nursery, grow fruit, keep poultry, build their own barns and run it as a profit-making concern. Very much a 'family' atmosphere, relaxed, informal, friendly; informal personal relationships between pupils and staff. Very good academic results, and of the leavers who do go on to degree courses, a high proportion go to Oxbridge. There is a policy that every member of the lower sixth studies a European language (or Russian) besides A-level studies. French, German and Spanish are offered to A-level (Italian to GCSE), and a high proportion of pupils takes GCSE in more than one European language. There are regular exchanges with France, Germany and Spain.

School profile

Pupils Age range 13–18; 403 pupils, 64 day (29 boys, 35 girls), 339 boarding (159 boys, 180 girls). Main entry ages 13 and into sixth. Always less than 4% are children of former pupils. Own junior school provides 50% approx of intake. *Transfer from maintained schools:* 2$^1/_2$% intake at 13, plus 40% to sixth.

Entrance Own entrance exam used. Oversubscribed. School looks for pupils with a broad base – academic, art, music, design etc with potential for six or more GCSEs, 3 A-levels. Parents expected to buy a few text books; extras £38–£90 per subject per term. 5 assisted places in each year of sixth form only. Means tested scholarships/bursaries available.

Parents Up to 10% live within 30 miles; 15% live overseas.

Staff Headmaster E A M MacAlpine, in post for 10 years. 43 full time staff, 7 part time.

Academic work GCSE and A-levels. 15 subjects offered (no A-level general studies). In 1990, 86 pupils in upper fifth, 69 in upper sixth (now 66). *GCSE:* in 1990, 49 upper fifth gained at least grade C in 8+ subjects; 29 in 5–7; and 8 in 1–4 subjects. *A-levels:* 3 upper sixth passed in 4+ subjects; 53 in 3; 9 in 2; and 3 in 1 subject. 17 took science A-levels; 33 arts/humanities; 18 both. *Computing facilities:* 28 station Nimbus (PC 186 and PC 286) network (with, currently, a 300 megabyte server). *Special provision:* Extra English in year 3 (3 lessons/week) and years 4 & 5 (1 or 2 lessons/week) and remedial English lessons on a private basis.

European Community *Languages:* French offered: to age 14; GCSE; AS-level; A-level. German offered: to GCSE; AS-level; A-level. Italian offered: to GCSE. Spanish offered: to GCSE; AS-level; A-level. 50–75% take GCSE in more than 1 EC language. All lower sixth study a European language (or Russian) at a suitable level, in addition to A-level studies. *Exchanges:* Regular exchanges for pupils aged 11–16 to France, Germany and Spain. *Other:* Always has a few EC pupils in school. European Committee to promote more interchange.

Non-academic activities (whole school) *Music:* 200 learn a musical instrument; 60 in school orchestra; 80 in school choir; 20 in string chamber orchestra; 45 in concert band; 30 in chamber choir. 8 studying A-level music. 2 pupils accepted for higher education in music. Music is compulsory to age 15. *Drama and dance:* 80 in school productions; 80 in other productions. *Art:* 150 take as non-examined subject; 98 GCSE; 35 A-level. Art and design is compulsory in first year of senior school. *Sport:* Physical education compulsory part of core curriculum. Gymnastics, dance, swimming, life saving, water polo, canoeing, volleyball, basketball, athletics, badminton, tennis, judo, karate, squash, fencing, hockey, all forms of outdoor pursuits available, plus football and cricket (boys) and netball (girls). *Other:* 70–80 pupils take part in voluntary service in the village and beyond. Some 6 enter voluntary schemes after leaving school. Years 3 and 4 camp in Wales and Dartmoor. Participation in Schools Partnership Worldwide. Many pupils participate in Duke of Edinburgh's Award.

Careers In 1990, 43% leavers went on

to degree courses; 6% to art/drama/ music colleges; 6% to non-degree courses (eg foundation course); 45% other (Gap, retaking A-levels, etc). Of those going on to degree courses, 15% went to Oxbridge, 50% to other universities; 35% to poly/ colleges. 3% those going on to higher education went to courses in music; 15% in humanities/social sciences; 5% in medicine; and 10% in science/ engineering.

Uniform School uniform not worn.

Houses/prefects No competitive houses. Head boy/girl but no prefects. Sixth form committee. Boarding house committees and central committee.

Religion No compulsory worship.

Social Organised trips abroad include visits to CERN, Spain, ski trips etc. Meals self service. School shop.

Discipline No corporal punishment. Anyone caught buying, bringing in or consuming drugs will be expelled. Pupils punished for smoking and drinking.

Boarding Small dormitories; sixth formers can be in ones or twos. One large boys' house, one large girls' and two small out houses; all single sex. Resident medical staff. Central dining room. Pupils can provide and cook own food. Exeats allowed on all but 2–3 weekends a term.

Alumni association is run by T W Slack, c/o the School.

· *Bedford* ·

Bedford School	● Pupils 1125	● Termly fees
Burnaby Road	● Boys 7–18	£1835 (Day)
Bedford	(Day/Board)	£2890 (Board)
MK40 2TU	● Girls None	● HMC
Tel 0234 340444	● Upper sixth 150	Enquiries/application to the Registrar

---

What it's like

Founded in 1552, it lies in 50 acres of peaceful and extensive grounds in the centre of Bedford. All but two boarding houses are on site; two within 5 minutes' walk. The main school building was gutted by fire in 1979. All has been rebuilt and, over the last 30 years, there have been many modern additions. Its facilities are now excellent. It provides continuous education for boys from 7–18 with an unusual mix of local day and international boarders. Strong in all academic disciplines with first-rate exam results. Many leavers go on to degree courses, including a high proportion to Oxbridge. French, German and Spanish are offered to A-level, also Dutch to GCSE. A high proportion of boys takes GCSE in more than one European language. There are regular exchanges with France, Germany and Spain. Also very good at athletics, games and rowing. It has a fine range of extra-curricular activities, plus CCF, community service unit and outdoor pursuits. Vigorous local support, good back-up from alumni.

School profile

Pupils Total age range 7–18; 1125 boys, 840 day, 285 boarding. Senior department 11–18, 910 boys. Main entry ages 7, 8, 11, 13 and into sixth. Approx 10% are children of former pupils.

Entrance Common entrance and own entrance exam used. Oversubscribed. No special skills or religious requirements. Parents expected to buy some text books. 100 assisted places. 32 scholarships plus means tested bursaries for boys resident in Bedfordshire, full fee remission to £500.

Parents 15+% are doctors, lawyers, etc; 15+% in industry or commerce. 30+%

live within 30 miles; 10+% live overseas.
Staff Head Dr I P Evans, 1 year in post. 114 full time staff, 7 part time. Annual turnover 7%. Average age 35.
Academic work GCSE and A-levels. Average size of upper fifth 150; upper sixth 150. *GCSE:* on average, 107 pupils in upper fifth pass 8+ subjects; 9, 5–7 subjects; 8 pass 1–4 subjects. *A-levels:* on average, 12 pupils in the upper sixth pass 4 subjects; 89, 3 subjects; 17, 2 subjects and 7 pass 1 subject. On average, 60 take science/engineering A-levels; 60 take arts and humanities; 20 a mixture. *Computing facilities:* 50+ BBC/Archimedes computers netted into central hard disk facility.
European Community *Languages:* French offered: to age 14; GCSE; AS-level; A-level. German offered: to GCSE; AS-level; A-level. Spanish offered: to GCSE; A-level. 50–75% take GCSE in more than 1 EC language. *Exchanges:* Regular exchanges for pupils aged 14–18 to France, Germany and Spain. *Other:* German pupils, especially from Mülheim, regularly attend lower sixth for 1–3 terms. French pupils stay 1–3 weeks.
Senior pupils' non-academic activities *Music:* 80 learn a musical instrument, 30 to Grade 6 or above, 2 accepted for Music School, 5 play in pop groups; 80 in school orchestra, 70 in choir, 5 in school pop group, 30 in chamber groups; 30 in County Youth Orchestras; 2 in National Youth Orchestra; 20 in adult orchestras. *Drama and dance:* 100+ in school productions. *Art:* All take as non-examined subject; 20 take GCSE; 10 A-level. 4 accepted for Art School. 30 belong to eg photographic club. *Sport:* Cricket, hockey, rowing, rugby, athletics, badminton, basketball, boxing, canoeing, croquet, cross-country, fives, fencing, jujitsu, shooting, soccer, squash, swimming, table tennis, tennis, sub-aqua, water polo, weight training, golf, mountaineering available. 200+ take non-compulsory sport. 30+ represent county/country (rowing, rugby, hockey, athletics, shooting, cricket). *Other:* 150 take part in local community schemes. 30 have bronze Duke of Edinburgh's Award, 10 have silver and 3 gold. Boys' charities committee

raised £4500 last year. Other activities include computer club, driving lessons, strong bridge and chess clubs, printing, quiz club, CCF, stamp club, photography, wine and beer making, fish-keeping, debating.
Careers In 1990, 70% leavers went on to degree courses; 3% to art/drama/music colleges; 3% to non-degree courses (eg arts, HND technology); 15% straight into careers (eg city); 6% other (eg retaking A-levels). Of those going on to degree courses, 17% went to Oxbridge, 56% to other universities; 26% to poly/colleges. 2% those going on to higher education went to courses in practical art; 2% in drama/acting; 2% in music; 50% in humanities/social sciences; 2% in medicine; and 42% in science engineering.
Uniform School uniform worn throughout.
Houses/prefects Competitive houses. Prefects, head boy, head of house and house prefects appointed by the Head. Various advisory committees. Paid fagging in boarding houses.
Religion Compulsory assembly and chapel on Sunday for boarders (unless parents object on valid religious grounds).
Social Joint debates, choral productions, theatrical productions, dances with sister schools. Numerous organised trips abroad. Pupils allowed to bring own car/bike/motorbike to school with permission. Meals formal. School shop. No tobacco allowed. Limited beer for over 18s at weekends.
Discipline No corporal punishment. Punishments depend upon individual cases and personalities. Those caught smoking cannabis on the premises should expect severe punishment.
Boarding *Upper sixth* have own study bedroom. Senior pupils divided into 6 houses of 40–50, parallel to competitive houses. Resident qualified nurse. Central dining room. Pupils can provide and cook some own food. Flexible weekend leave, including 2 formal exeats per term plus half term (up to 2 weeks). Visits to local town allowed.
Alumni association is run by Fergus McKendrick, OB Club Office, 10 Glebe Road, Bedford MK40 2PL.

· *Bedford High* ·

The High School
Bromham Road
Bedford
Bedfordshire
MK40 2BS
Tel 0234 360221
Fax 0234 353552

- Pupils 1023
- Boys None
- Girls 7–18
  (Day/Board)
- Upper sixth 104

- Termly fees
  £1323 (Day)
  £2524 (Board)
  £2513 (Weekly)
- GSA
  Enquiries/application to
  the Headmistress

What it's like

Opened in 1882 as a sister school to Bedford School. It is sited in the centre of Bedford and has agreeable, well-appointed buildings in pleasant gardens. There are 21 acres of excellent playing fields. Academic standards are high and results very creditable; many girls go on to degree courses. French, German and Spanish are offered to A-level and there are regular exchanges with Belgium and Germany. Music, art and drama are all strong. Sports and games are well catered for and include golf and judo as well as the standard range. Levels of attainment are high. Numerous clubs and societies cater for most needs and there is keen participation in the Duke of Edinburgh's Award Scheme.

School profile

Pupils Total age range 7–18; 1023 girls (day, boarding from age 11). Senior department 11–18. Main entry ages 7, 8, 9, 11, 13 and into sixth. *Transfer from maintained schools:* 75% senior intake, plus 6% to sixth.

Entrance Own exam used. Assisted places. Means-tested bursaries.

Staff Headmistress Mrs D M Willis, in post for 4 years.

Academic work GCSE, AS and A-levels. 19 GCSE subjects offered; 10 at AS-level; 24 at A-level (including A-level general studies). In 1991, 123 pupils in upper fifth, 104 in upper sixth. *GCSE:* in 1990, 98 upper fifth gained at least grade C in 8+ subjects; 24 in 5–7; and 8 in 1–4 subjects. *A-levels:* 5 upper sixth passed in 4+ subjects; 67 in 3; 27 in 2; and 10 in 1 subject. 27 took science A-levels; 58 arts/humanities; 24 both. *Computing facilities:* Large computer room; many departmental computers; computer studies lessons.

European Community *Languages:* French offered: to age 14; GCSE; AS-level; A-level. German offered: to age 14; GCSE; AS-level; A-level. Spanish offered: to age 14; GCSE; AS-level; A-level. *Exchanges:* Regular exchanges for pupils aged 14–16 to Belgium, Germany and Spain.

Careers On average, 71% leavers go on to degree courses; 3% to art/drama/music colleges; 8% to non-degree courses (eg chiropody, hotel management, materials science, secretarial, cordon bleu); 5% straight into careers (eg secretarial, banking, nursing, retail management); 11% other. Of those going on to degree courses, 4% go to Oxbridge, 68% to other universities; 27% to poly/colleges. 3% those going on to higher education go to courses in practical art; 1% in music; 68% in humanities/social sciences; 9% in medicine; and 17% in science/engineering.

· *Bedford Modern* ·

Bedford Modern School
Manton Lane
Bedford
MK41 7NT
Tel 0234 364331

- Pupils 1202
- Boys 7–19
  (Day/Board)
- Girls None
- Upper sixth 133

- Termly fees
  £1020 (Day)
  £1885 (Board)
- HMC
  Enquiries to the
  Headteacher
  Application to the
  Admissions Secretary

What it's like

One of the Harpur Trust schools of Bedford, sharing in the endowment made to Bedford by Sir William Harpur in 1566. In 1974 the school moved to entirely new buildings on the northern outskirts of the town. It is a 45-acre wooded hill site with spacious playing fields. The new school is extremely well equipped in every respect and includes sophisticated facilities for sport and a new technology block. Teaching and academic standards are of a high order; many go on to degree courses each year, including many to Oxbridge. French and German are offered to A-level and there are regular exchanges with France and Germany. Not a few pupils go into agriculture and industry. Strong in music, it has a wide variety of clubs and societies. A very flourishing school with strong local support.

School profile

Pupils Total age range 7–19; 1202 boys, (1122 day, 80 boarding). Senior department 11–19, 950 boys. Main entry ages 7, 11, 13 and into sixth. *Transfer from maintained schools:* 80% intake 11+, plus small number to sixth.

Entrance Common entrance and own entrance exam used. Oversubscribed. No special skills or religious requirements. Parents not expected to buy text books; lunch for day boys and music tuition extra. 135 assisted places. Bursaries (some for inhabitants of Bedfordshire) full fee–£10 remission.

Parents 70+% live within 30 miles; up to 10% live overseas.

Staff Headmaster P J Squire, in post for 13 years. 81 full time staff, 2 part time. Annual turnover 5–10%. Average age 40.

Academic work GCSE and A-levels. 16 subjects offered (including A-level general studies). In 1990, 158 pupils in upper fifth, 133 in upper sixth. *GCSE:* in 1989, 53% upper fifth gained at least grade C in 8+ subjects; 42% in 5–7; and 5% in 1–4 subjects. *A-levels:* 15% upper

sixth passed in 4+ subjects; 65% in 3; 11% in 2; and 4% in 1 subject. 50% took science A-levels; 45% arts/humanities; 5% both. *Special provision:* Some provision for non-native English speakers.

European Community *Languages:* French offered: to age 14; GCSE; AS-level; A-level. German offered: to age 14; GCSE; A-level. 10–25% take GCSE in more than 1 EC language. *Exchanges:* Regular exchanges for pupils aged 11–16 to France and Germany. *Other:* Close link with school near Bonn; 3 sixth form boys in school for 1–2 years as boarders. Spanish pupil (age 11) for 1 year.

Senior pupils' non-academic activities *Music:* 94 learn a musical instrument; 40 in school orchestra, 10 in dance band, 15 in wind band, 16 in chamber group, 10 in school choir. *Drama and dance:* 60 in school productions. 1 in County Youth Theatre. *Art:* 32 take GCSE, 17 A-level. 3 accepted for Art School, 1 for Architecture School. 5 belong to eg photographic club. *Sport:* Rugby, football, cricket, rowing, athletics, cross-country, swimming, water polo, squash, badminton, table tennis, shooting, fencing, fives, tennis available. 250 take non-compulsory sport. 12 take GCSE theory and practice of physical education. 20 represent county (rugby, cricket, athletics, tennis, table tennis); 7 represent country (rowing, shooting, cricket). *Other:* 40 have bronze Duke of Edinburgh's Award, 6 have silver and 4 gold. Other activities include computer club, many other clubs and societies, music in particular.

Careers In 1990, 77% leavers went on to degree courses; 2% to art/drama/music colleges; 3% to non-degree courses; 13% straight into careers (eg banking, estate agency); 5% other. Of those going on to degree courses, 16% went to Oxbridge, 75% to other universities; 9% to poly/colleges. 1% those going on to higher education went to courses in drama/acting; 42% in humanities/social sciences; 10% in medicine; and 45% in science/engineering.

Uniform School uniform worn throughout.

Houses/prefects Competitive houses. Prefects, head boy – appointed by the Head after consultation with staff and sixth form. Sixth form Council.

Religion C of E assemblies (compulsory for those not specifically withdrawn). Optional communion services.

Social Debates, concerts, plays with other local schools. About 15 organised trips abroad each year, including French and German exchanges. Pupils allowed to bring own car/bike/motorbike to school. Meals cafeteria style. School shop. No tobacco/alcohol allowed.

Discipline No corporal punishment. Pupils failing to produce homework once might expect a warning or imposition; those caught smoking cannabis on the premises could expect to be suspended.

Boarding One house only. Central dining room. Exeats at half-term and weekends as necessary. Visits to the local town allowed, as requested.

Alumni association is run by A G Underwood, c/o the School.

Former pupils Keith Speed MP; R E G Jeeps; Vice Admiral Sir Ted Horlick; Major General Keith Burch; Richard Janko (Professor of Classics, University of Los Angeles); Sir Nicholas Lloyd (Editor Daily Express); Christopher Fry.

· *Bedgebury* ·

Bedgebury School	● Pupils 410	● Termly fees
Goudhurst	● Boys None	£1600 (Day)
Kent	● Girls 3–18	£2643 (Board/
TN17 2SH	(Day/Board)	Weekly)
Tel 0580 211954	● Upper sixth 45	● GSA
		Enquiries/application to the Headmistress or Registrar

What it's like

Founded in 1860, it lies in the Kentish Weald and consists of two establishments 6 miles apart. The Lower School at Hawkhurst is accommodated in the fine Victorian and Georgian houses of Lillesden and Collingwood which have delightful grounds. The Upper School occupies a fine 17th century country house in Bedgebury Park – a superb estate of 250 acres. Excellent modern accommodation and facilities are available, including a business school and new arts and technology centre. A pleasant friendly atmosphere prevails. Staff:pupil ratio of 1:7. The main aim is to achieve the all-round development of each girl and bring out her best. A sound general education is provided and results are creditable. Many go on to degree courses. French, German, Italian and Portuguese are offered to A-level. Also French, German and Italian conversation. There are regular exchanges with France and Spain. Very strong art, music and drama departments. An excellent range of sports and games. Activities are plentiful and include riding for many pupils. There are big stables and 45 horses and ponies are available. Some local community service work and an impressive record in the Duke of Edinburgh's Award Scheme.

School profile

Pupils Total age range 3–18; 410 girls, 120 day, 290 boarding. Senior department 13–18, 260 girls. Main entry ages 3–18. *Transfer from maintained schools:* 10% intake at 11–13, plus 10% to sixth.

Entrance Own entrance exam used. A variety of skills (music, riding, art, academic) looked for; demeanour and personality regarded as important. A C of E school but other religions accepted. Parents not expected to buy text books. 10–15 scholarships/bursaries pa, up to 60% day fees.

Parents 25+% live within 30 miles, 25+% live overseas.

Staff Headmistress Mrs M E A Kaye, in post for 4 years. 44 full time staff, 26 part time. Annual turnover 5–10%.

Academic work GCSE, AS and A-levels. 24 GCSE subjects offered; 9 at AS and 28 at A-level (including film and communication studies, A-level Greek and general studies). In 1990, 51 pupils in upper fifth, 45 in upper sixth. *GCSE:* in 1990, 32% fifth gained at least grade C in 8+ subjects; 39% in 5–7; and 29% in 1–4 subjects. *A-levels:* 5 upper sixth passed in 4+ subjects; 11 in 3; 8 in 2; and 3 in 1 subject. 25% took science A-levels; 50% arts/humanities; 25% both. *Computing facilities:* 25 computers in 2 computer rooms, plus 15 computers in business studies and others in science, art, history, modern languages, economics, fashion and other depts. *Special provision:* Dyslexic units with 6 trained staff; magnification of work, extra lights, individual help for visually handicapped. 5 trained EFL teachers.

European Community *Languages:* French offered: to age 14; GCSE; AS-level; A-level. German offered: to age 14; GCSE; AS-level; A-level. Italian offered:

to GCSE; A-level. Spanish offered: to age 14; GCSE; AS-level; A-level. 10–25% take GCSE in more than 1 EC language. *Exchanges:* Regular exchanges for pupils aged 11–14 to France and Spain. *Other:* French, German and Italian conversation. Regular visits to France and near continent.

Senior pupils' non-academic activities *Music:* 127 learn a musical instrument, 20 to Grade 6 or above, 2 accepted for Music College; 22 in school orchestra, 36 in school choir, 12 in chapel choir, 25 in wind band; 2 in local youth orchestra. *Drama and dance:* 100+ in school productions. 30+ take up to Gold Medal LAMDA examinations. 30 ballet pupils, 95% go to grade V examination, 50% to Elementary and Intermediate levels, Imperial Society of Teachers of Dancing in Ballet, and Modern Grades and Majors. 1 accepted for Ballet School. *Art:* 60 take as non-examined subject; 33 take GCSE including Jewellery and Ceramics; 23 A-level including jewellery and ceramics; 15 fashion and design, 25 take GCSE textiles; 60 take CDT introductory course, 20 take GCSE CDT creative arts; 5 accepted for Art School. *Sport:* tennis, lacrosse, netball, badminton, volleyball, basketball, table tennis, hockey, swimming, diving, rounders, athletics, gymnastics, trampolining, weight-training, cross-country, climbing, judo, fencing, self-defence, windsurfing, sailing, canoeing, orienteering; golf and squash off-site. All girls do sport. Some pupils represent county (lacrosse). *Other:* 6 take part in local community schemes. 11 taking bronze Duke of Edinburgh's Award and 11 on Police Service courses. Other activities include bridge, art, ceramics, drama, dance, CDT, textiles, photographic and science clubs, riding (45 horses and ponies), abseiling, driving and flying lessons.

Careers In 1990, 46% leavers went on to degree courses; 14% to art/drama/music colleges; 7% to non-degree courses (eg nursery nursing, secretarial); 11% straight into careers (eg nursing, stable work); 22% other (eg retaking A-levels). Of those going on to degree courses, 50% went to universities; 50% to poly/colleges. 19% those going on to higher education went to courses in practical art; 6% in music; 50% in humanities/social sciences; 6% in medicine; and 19% in science/engineering.

Uniform School uniform worn except in sixth.

Houses/prefects Competitive houses. Prefects, head girl and heads of houses – appointed after election. School Council.

Religion Compulsory daily assembly; Sunday church or school Chapel (Catholics go to own church; Muslims may have own instruction).

Social Joint musical and drama activities, debates and drama workshops, discos with other schools. Exchanges with France, Germany and Australia. Pupils allowed to bring own car/horse to school. Meals mostly self service. School shop. No tobacco/alcohol allowed.

Discipline No corporal punishment. Regular failure to produce work would lead to a week 'on reports' for lessons. Behaviour problems dealt with individually, according to need.

Boarding 25% have own study bedroom, 75% share with 1, 2 or more. Houses divided by age. 4 qualified nurses, 30 other resident staff. Central dining rooms on each site. Sixth formers can provide and cook own food. 2 weekend exeats autumn and summer term, more by special arrangement. Visits to local town allowed; sixth may go to London for weekends.

Alumni association c/o school.

Former pupils Virginia Leng (née Holgate (3 day eventer).

· *Belfast Academy* ·

Belfast Royal Academy	● Pupils 1574	● Annual fees
7 Cliftonville Road	● Boys 4–18	£50 (Day) plus £22
Belfast	(Day)	per term
BT14 6JL	● Girls 4–18	● HMC
Tel 0232 740423	(Day)	Enquiries/application to
	● Upper sixth 170	the Headmaster

What it's like

Founded in 1785 (the oldest school in the city), its new premises were opened in 1880 in north Belfast. The neo-Gothic buildings of that period have received extensive additions and modernisation now providing excellent facilities. It is non-denominational. The fees of 98% of pupils are paid by the local authority. A very high standard of teaching and consistently good results. Many go on to degree courses, including Oxbridge; many into medicine, dentistry and engineering. French, German and Spanish are offered to A-level, also Russian and Japanese in the sixth form. Spanish and German are offered in the sixth form for beginners. Very strong in music, drama and sport. Substantial commitment to local community schemes and Duke of Edinburgh's Award Scheme.

School profile

Pupils Total age range 4–18; 1574 day pupils (742 boys, 832 girls). Senior department 11–18, 1266 pupils (573 boys, 693 girls). Main entry ages 4, 11 and into sixth. Approx 10% are children of former pupils. Over 20% of senior intake from own prep.

Entrance Admission by test set by the Department of Education. Oversubscribed. Academic competence required; no religious requirements. Parents not expected to buy text books. No scholarships/bursaries available; 98% of pupils have fees paid by LEA.

Parents 6% engineering; 20% science and technology; 10% business and finance; 15+% doctors, lawyers.

Staff Headmaster W M Sillery, in post for 11 years. 77 full time staff, 12 part time. Annual turnover 5%. Average age 40.

Academic work GCSE and A-levels. 23 GCSE subjects offered; 24 at A-level (no A-level general studies); Russian and Japanese taught in sixth form. In 1990, 186 pupils in upper fifth, 170 in upper sixth. *GCSE:* in 1990, 118 upper fifth gained at least grade C in 8+ subjects; 51 in 5–7; and 20 in 1–4 subjects. *A-levels:* 27 upper sixth passed in 4+ subjects; 92 in 3; 32 in 2; and 13 in 1 subject. 34% took science A-levels; 37% arts/humanities; 29% both. *Computing facilities:* BBC and Nimbus networks.

European Community *Languages:* French offered: to age 14; GCSE; AS-level; A-level. German offered: to age 14; GCSE; A-level; non-examined (in sixth). Spanish offered: to age 14; GCSE; A-level; non-examined (in sixth). 10–25% take GCSE in more than 1 EC language. *Other:* Contacts with schools in France and Germany.

Senior pupils' non-academic activities *Music:* 45 learn a musical instrument, 10 to Grade 6 or above; 60 in school orchestra, 120 in choir; 15 in area youth orchestras; 12 go on to university orchestra/choir. *Drama and dance:* 75 act in school productions (120 backstage). 10 take GCSE drama; 12 in 'Studio' plays etc. 1 accepted for Drama School, 1 to work in theatre. *Art:* 3 take as non-examined subject; 36 take GCSE; 13 A-level. 3 accepted for Art School. *Sport:* Hockey, rugby, tennis, badminton, swimming, squash, netball, cross-country, cricket, athletics, sailing, basketball, volleyball, orienteering and Olympic gymnastics available. 235 take non-compulsory sport. 30 take life-saving exams. 23 represent Ulster (athletics, cricket, rugby, swimming, tennis, rifle shooting). *Other:* 80 take part in local community schemes. 57 have bronze Duke of Edinburgh's Award, 58 have silver and 85 gold. Other activities include computer club, chess, community service, Christian Union, ATC, rifle shooting, dramatic society, electronics society.

Careers In 1990, 75% leavers went on to degree courses; 5% to art/drama/music colleges; 5% to non-degree courses; 8% straight into careers (eg retail management); 7% other. Of those going on to degree courses, 8% went to Oxbridge, 84% to other universities; 8% to poly/colleges. 1% those going on to higher education went to courses in practical art; 1% in music; 31% in humanities/social sciences; 24% in medicine; and 43% in science/engineering.

Uniform School uniform worn throughout.

Houses/prefects Competitive houses. Prefects, head boy and girl, head of house and house prefects elected by pupils.

Religion Morning assembly compulsory, unless exclusion requested by a parent.

Social Youth club for handicapped children organised with community service group of neighbouring grammar school. Annual ski trip to France or Austria, visit to Paris and at least one other trip abroad. Pupils allowed to bring own car/bike/motorbike to school. Meals self service. School tuck shop. No tobacco/alcohol allowed.

Discipline No corporal punishment. Pupils failing to produce homework once might expect a scolding or extra work. Smoking cannabis would entail permanent exclusion.

Alumni association is run by Mr R P Tennant, 4 Donegall Park Avenue, Belfast BT15 4ET (boys) and Mrs Y Hollinger,

51 Collin Road, Ballyclare, Co Antrim (girls).
Former pupils Sir Francis Evans (soldier and diplomat); Archbishop John Armstrong; Archbishop Robin Eames; Major-General Eric Girdwood; Rear Admiral Dudley Gurd; John Cole, Douglas Gageby (journalists); Jack Kyle (sportsman).

· *Belmont House* ·

Belmont House School
Sandringham Avenue
Newton Mearns
Glasgow
G77 5DU
Tel 041 639 2922

- Pupils 385
- Boys 3–18 (Day)
- Girls None
- Higher year 41

- Termly fees £895 (Day)
  Enquiries/application to the Headmaster

What it's like

Founded in 1929, it is suburban single-site, 7 miles from the centre of Glasgow. The main building is a mansion on the Broom estate. Playing fields are nearby and the surroundings are pleasant. Good facilities are available. The school stresses the fact that it fosters an intimate caring attitude in the classroom with maximum individual attention so that a pupil can reach his academic potential in preparation for adult life. Academic standards are good and several pupils go on to degree courses each year. The school prides itself on its tutorial service: all members of staff stay on for an extra hour one day per week to give extra help for those who may need it. Adequate range of sports, games and activities. No community services, no Duke of Edinburgh's Award Scheme.

School profile

Pupils Total age range 3–18; 385 day boys. Senior department 12–18, 216 boys. Main entry ages 3, 5, 12 and into sixth. *Transfer from maintained schools:* 80% main intake, plus 100% to sixth.
Entrance Own entrance exam used. Oversubscribed. No special skills or religious requirements. Parents not expected to buy text books (book rental scheme); maximum extras, £40 plus £110 lunch. 18 assisted places pa. No bursaries/scholarships.
Parents 15+% are doctors, lawyers, etc; 15+% in industry or commerce.
Staff Headmaster J Mercer, in post for 19 years. 23 full time staff, 6 part time. Annual turnover 5%. Average age 40.
Academic work O-grades/S-grades/Highers/CSYS/Scotvec National Certificate. 15 subjects offered. In 1990/91, 31 pupils in O/S-grade year, 41 in Higher year. *O/S-Grade:* in 1990, 9 pupils gained 8+ subjects; 19, 5–7; and 13, 2–4 subjects. *Highers:* out of 36 pupils, 10 passed 5+ or more subjects; 4 passed 4, 5 passed 3, 6 passed 2, 11 passed 1 subject. *Computing facilities:* Network of 10 BBC Masters (maths) and 10 BBC Masters (computing); computers in all science rooms and geography department. *Special provision:* Specialist tuition 1 afternoon/week for dyslexic pupils.
European Community *Languages:* French offered: to age 14; S-grade; Higher. German offered: to age 14; S-grade; Higher. 10–25% take S-grade in more than 1 EC language.
Senior pupils' non-academic activities *Music:* 12 learn a musical instrument; school orchestra. *Drama and dance:* 12 in school productions. 1 takes Grade 6 in ESB, RAD etc. 1 accepted for Drama

School. *Art:* 28 take art as non-examined subject; 12 take S-grade; 7 take Higher. 2 accepted for Art School. *Sport:* Rugby, cricket, ski-ing, canoeing, swimming, orienteering, basketball, squash, tennis, curling, golf, athletics and shooting available. All take non-compulsory sport. Most take exams. 8 represent county/country (rugby). *Other:* Some enter voluntary schemes or work for national charities after leaving school. Other activities include a computer club, chess club, debating club, model making, hill walking, wind surfing.

Careers In 1990, 28% leavers went on to degree courses; 12% to art/drama/music colleges; 44% to non-degree courses; 8% straight into careers (eg army, electrician); 8% other (eg travel). Of those going on to degree courses, 100% went to universities. 20% those going on to higher education went to courses in practical art; 5% in humanities/social sciences; 15% in medicine; and 60% in science/engineering.

Uniform School uniform worn throughout.

Houses/prefects Competitive houses. Prefects, head boy – appointed by Head and staff; head of house and house prefects – elected by pupils.

Religion School prayers held each morning; Rabbi visits daily for Jewish pupils.

Social Debates with local girls' schools or in national competitions. Inter-school Trivial Pursuits competition hosted and organised by Belmont. 1 continental ski trip and 1 sightseeing trip annually. Pupils allowed to bring own car/bike/motorbike to school. Lunch formal (or packed lunch). No tobacco/alcohol allowed.

Discipline Punishment exercises, chores, after school detention. Pupils failing to produce homework once might expect to rewrite it with additional work. Those caught smoking cannabis on the premises might expect expulsion.

Former pupils Lord Goold (former Chairman of Scottish Conservative Party); Sandy Carmichael (most capped Scottish Rugby forward).

· *Belvedere* ·

The Belvedere School
17 Belvidere Road
Prince's Park
Liverpool
L8 3TF
Tel 051 727 1284

- Pupils 578
- Boys None
- Girls 4–18
  (Day)
- Upper sixth 51

- Termly fees
  £908 (Day)
- GSA, GPDST
Enquiries/application to
the Headmistress

What it's like

Opened in 1880 under the name of Liverpool High School, it has always been a part of Liverpool life and there are currently girls in the school representing at least two generations of their family to be educated there. It aims at a wide social spread. The senior school occupies four large Victorian houses (three of which are 'scheduled buildings') overlooking Prince's Park. It has agreeable gardens and lawns and some sports' facilities on site; others are nearby. Since 1964 there have been extensive additions in building: class-rooms, assembly hall/gymnasium, craftwork, art and music rooms, a science block. The junior school is in a separate building nearby. A pleasant friendly atmosphere prevails and the aim of the school is to educate the whole person. Religious practice is encouraged. A general education is provided and results are creditable. Each year many pupils proceed to degree courses, many of them to Oxbridge. French, German and Spanish are offered to A-level. An exceptionally high proportion of girls takes GCSE in more than one European language. There are regular exchange arrangements with France, Germany and Spain. Music, drama and art are well supported. A good variety of sports and games and a plentiful range of extra-curricular activities. The school also has a creditable record in the Duke of Edinburgh's Award Scheme. Fees are comparatively low.

School profile

Pupils Total age range 4–18; 578 day girls. Senior department 11–18, 437 girls. Main entry ages 4, 7, 11 and into sixth. Approx 10% are children of former pupils. *Transfer from maintained schools:* 75% senior intake.

Entrance Own entrance exam used. No special skills (other than academic potential) or religious requirements. Parents not expected to buy text books; no other extras. 25 assisted places pa plus 5 in sixth form. A number of bursaries and at least 1 entrance + 1 sixth form scholarship pa, value varies.

Parents 15+% in industry or commerce; 15+% are doctors, lawyers etc.

Staff Headmistress Miss S Downs, in post for 19 years. 35 full time staff, 8 part time. Annual turnover almost nil.

Academic work GCSE and A-levels. 22 subjects offered (including A-level general studies). In 1990, 63 pupils in upper fifth, 41 in upper sixth (now 51). *GCSE:* in 1990, 53 upper fifth gained at least grade C in 8+ subjects; 9 in 5–7; and 1 in 1–4 subjects. *A-levels:* 28 upper sixth passed in 4+ subjects; 9 in 3; 2 in 2; and 1 in 1 subject. 30% took science A-levels; 68% arts/humanities; 3% both. *Computing facilities:* 2 well equipped rooms. *Special provision:* Outside tuition for dyslexia/EFL.

European Community *Languages:* French offered: to age 14; GCSE; A-level. German offered: to age 14; GCSE; A-level. Spanish offered: to age 14; GCSE; A-level. Over 75% take GCSE in more than 1 EC language. *Exchanges:* Regular exchanges for pupils aged 14–18 to France, Germany and Spain. *Other:* Conference in Paris on 1992 attended by

sixth form. Travel scholarship to sixth former to visit and study European Parliament.

Senior pupils' non-academic activities *Music:* 60 learn a musical instrument, 12 to Grade 6 or above, 2 accepted for Music School; 80 in school orchestra, 140 in choirs; 30 in recorder group and wind ensemble; 8 in local orchestras or wind band. *Drama:* Many in school productions. 2 to Grade 6 Guildhall exam and 3 have LAMDA gold medals. 50 have regular drama lessons. 3 accepted for Drama Schools; 4 now work in theatre. *Art:* 5 take A-level; all lower sixth attend history of art talks. 1 accepted for Art School, 1 teacher training, 1 landscape architecture, 4 to foundation course. Art room open for interested pupils at lunchtime. *Sport:* Lacrosse, netball, rounders, tennis, volleyball, gymnastics, trampolining, swimming, aerobics, athletics, table tennis, basketball unihoc. 15 take noncompulsory sport. 5 represent county (lacrosse). *Other:* Many girls from lower fifth to sixth form participate in the 3 levels of the Duke of Edinburgh's Award. Other activities include computer club, chess club, debating society, Christian fellowship, Young Enterprise, choir, orchestra plus various subject groups.

Careers In 1990, 82% leavers went on to degree courses; 7% to art/drama/music colleges; 2% to non-degree courses (eg lab technician); 7% straight into careers (eg legal executive). Of those going on to degree courses, 16% went to Oxbridge, 64% to other universities; 20% to poly/colleges. 8% those going on to higher education went to courses in practical art; 8% in drama/acting; 5% in music; 48% in humanities/social sciences; 9% in medicine; and 22% in science/engineering.

Uniform School uniform worn except in sixth.

Houses/prefects No houses or prefects; head girl and deputies elected by school and staff.

Religion All attend assembly.

Social Debates and occasional musical events with local schools. Trips abroad arranged each year. Pupils allowed to bring own car/bike. Meals self service. No tobacco/alcohol allowed.

Discipline Punishment appropriate to offence. Detention is given for continuous unsatisfactory work.

Alumni association is run by Miss Eirlys Owen.

Former pupils Dame Rose Heilbron (High Court Judge); Alyson Bailes (Diplomatic Service); Muriel St Clare Byrne (writer).

· *Bembridge* ·

Bembridge School
Hillway
Bembridge
Isle of Wight
PO35 5PH
Tel 0983 872101

- Pupils 296
- Boys 7–18 (Day/Board/Weekly)
- Girls 7–18 (Day/Board/Weekly)
- Upper sixth 26

- Termly fees
  £1195 (Day)
  £2225 (Board)
  £2175 (Weekly)
- SHMIS
Enquiries/application to the Headmaster

What it's like

Founded in 1919 by J Howard Whitehouse, it has a beautiful site of 100 acres of fields and woodlands on the easternmost tip of the Isle of Wight, overlooking Whitecliffe Bay and Culver Cliff. Whitehouse was an educational pioneer and the first to establish the basic core of the modern curriculum now generally accepted. He also endowed the school with a priceless collection of original works by John Ruskin and his contemporaries. Special interests and ability in any non-academic field are strong qualifications for entry. It was one of the first British schools to introduce creative activities into the formal curriculum and much emphasis is put on the development of the individual by encouraging particular skills and enthusiasms. It is ideally suited to environmental studies, for geography, geology and natural history. It has its own golf course and a newly built sports hall. Outdoor pursuits are very popular (the school is one of the oldest members of the Duke of Edinburgh's Award Scheme). Also strong in music and art. Its academic record is highly creditable. In general its life is based on Christian values (daily prayers, chapel services, traditional Anglican teaching).

School profile

Pupils Total age range 7–18; 296 pupils, 111 day (86 boys, 25 girls), 185 boarding (141 boys, 44 girls). Senior department 13–18, 184 pupils (141 boys, 43 girls). Main entry ages 7–11, 13 and into sixth. Approx 2% are children of former pupils. *Transfer from maintained schools:* 30% main intake over 11, plus 60% to sixth.

Entrance Common entrance and own entrance exam used. No special skills or religious requirements. Parents expected to buy text books; maximum extras £100 per term. No assisted places. 6 scholarships (academic, art, music and day pupils) value up to half fees; bursaries for children of service personnel.

115

Parents 15+% in armed services. 20+% live within 30 miles; 10+% live overseas.

Staff Headmaster J High, in post for 5 years. 25 full time staff, 16 part time (including 12 music). Annual turnover 4%. Average age 38.

Academic work GCSE, AS and A-levels. 15 GCSE subjects offered; 14 at A-level (A/S level general studies). In 1990, 52 pupils in upper fifth, 26 in upper sixth. *GCSE:* in 1990, 23% upper fifth gained at least grade C in 8+ subjects; 30% in 5–7; and 46% in 1–4 subjects. *A-levels:* 12.5% upper sixth passed in 4+ subjects; 37.5% passed in 3; 37.5% passed in 2; and 12.5% in 1 subject. 43% took arts/humanities; 22% took science; 35% both. *Computing facilities:* Computer laboratory with 20 BBC computers and 2 Archimedes. Specialist teachers. GCSE and A-level courses. Computers in several subject classrooms. *Special provision:* Specific Learning Difficulty Unit gives specialist help for dyslexics. Specialist EFL teacher.

European Community *Languages:* French offered: to age 14; GCSE; AS-level; A-level. German offered: to age 14; GCSE; AS-level; A-level. Under 10% take GCSE in more than 1 EC language. *Exchanges:* Regular exchanges for pupils aged 14–18 to France (2 weeks in fourth form) and Germany (sixth form). *Other:* A number of EC pupils (Danish, French, German, Portuguese) staying in the school.

Senior pupils' non-academic activities *Music:* Most learn a musical instrument, 10 to Grade 6 or above; 30 in school orchestra, 40 in choir, 13 in pop group. *Drama and dance:* 150 in school productions. *Art:* 15 take as non-examined subject; 8 GCSE; 3 A-level. 1 accepted for Art School. 10 belong to photographic club. *Sport:* Rugby, football, netball, hockey, squash, rounders, basketball, tennis, volleyball, cricket, archery, swimming, sailing, windsurfing, shooting, riding, canoeing, golf, badminton and all indoor sports. Compulsory sport for all. 10 take life saving exams. 12 represent county (athletics, cricket). *Other:* 60 have bronze Duke of Edinburgh's Award, 6 have silver and 1 gold and 12 currently taking gold. Other activities include computer club. Two afternoons a week devoted to a wide range of activities.

Careers In 1990, 48% leavers went on to degree courses; 17% to art/drama/music colleges; 4% to non-degree courses; 40% straight into careers (eg banking, insurance). Of those going on to degree courses, 81% went to universities; 19% to poly/colleges. 50% those going on to higher education went to courses in humanities/social sciences; and 50% in science/engineering.

Uniform School uniform worn, modified in sixth.

Houses/prefects Competitive houses. Prefects, head boy/girl, head of house and house prefects appointed by the Headmaster or housemaster.

Religion Morning chapel compulsory unless parents request otherwise.

Social Joint Sixth Form Society and occasional social functions with local schools. Organised ski trip abroad. French exchange for 1 week fourth form, day-trip to Caen third form. Senior pupils allowed to bring own bike to school. Meals formal. School tuck and uniform shops. No tobacco allowed. Sixth formers allowed alcohol on supervised social occasions.

Discipline No corporal punishment. Pupils failing to produce homework once might expect a reprimand or detention. Gating for smoking or consumption of alcohol. Expulsion for possession or use of drugs.

Boarding 25% have own study bedroom, 40% share 3 to a room; 35% in dormitories of 6+. Single sex houses, of approx 50, same as competitive houses. Resident qualified nurse. Central dining room. 2 weekend exeats a term and half-term. Weekly visits to local town allowed.

Alumni association is run by Mr J Dearden, Bembridge School, Bembridge, Isle of Wight.

Former pupils Sir Robin Day; Dingle Foot; Frank Hilton QC HE; Sir Richard Parsons; Gen Sir Peter Whiteley; Richard Studt and Paul Gregory (musicians); John Heath-Stubbs (poet).

· *Benenden* ·

Benenden School
Cranbrook
Kent
TN17 4AA
Tel 0580 240592

- Pupils 407
- Boys None
- Girls 11–18
  (Board)
- Upper sixth 59

- Termly fees
  £3150 (Board)
- GSA
Enquiries/application to
the Admissions
Secretary/Registrar

What it's like

Founded in 1923 by three mistresses from Wycombe Abbey, the main building is a neo-Elizabethan mansion (built in 1862) in enormous gardens designed in the 19th century, set in 240 acres of parkland and woods in one of the loveliest regions of Kent. Numerous recent developments and excellent facilities. Exceptionally well equipped for sports, games and recreations. Predominantly middle/upper-class school, its academic standards are high and very many leavers go on to degree courses, including many to Oxbridge. French, German, Modern Greek and Spanish are offered to A-level and many girls take GCSE in more than one European language. It is strong in art, music and drama. The school follows Christian principles and its worship is based on Anglican practice (the Archbishop of Canterbury is the Visitor). It enjoys flourishing links with the local community. Senior girls help and visit the elderly in the neighbourhood and all girls are encouraged to make friends in the local community, particularly within the parish. Local voluntary organisations call on the school's support. There is liaison with local boys' schools for debates, dances and musical entertainment.

School profile

Pupils Age range 11–18; 407 boarding girls. Main entry ages 11, 12, 13 and into sixth. Approx 11% are children of former pupils.
Entrance Common entrance and own exam used. Oversubscribed. No special skills or religious requirements. Parents expected to buy text books; extras £140 per term for sailing, £80 for music. Academic, music and art scholarships, up to 100% of fees.
Parents 15+% in industry or commerce; 15+% are doctors, lawyers etc. 10+% live within 30 miles; 20+% live overseas.
Staff Head Mrs Gillian duCharme, in post for 6 years. 45 full time teaching staff, 45 part time. Annual turnover 8. Average age 40.
Academic work GCSE and A-levels. 19 GCSE subjects offered; 22 at A-level (no A-level general studies). In 1989, 68 pupils in upper fifth, 61 in upper sixth

(now 59). *GCSE:* in 1989, 85% upper fifth gained at least grade C in 8+ subjects; 15% in 5–7 subjects. *A-levels:* on average, 8% upper sixth pass in 4+ subjects; 68% in 3; 17% in 2; and 7% in 1 subject. On average, 15 take science A-levels; 19 arts/humanities; 26 both. *Computing facilities:* Computer centre equipped with Archimedes. Econet extends network through most of school. Information technology taught extensively. *Special provision:* Short-term assistance for learning difficulties and EFL.
European Community *Languages:* French offered: to age 14; GCSE; AS-level; A-level. German offered: to age 14; GCSE; A-level. Greek (modern): GCSE; A-level. Spanish offered: to age 14; GCSE; A-level. 25–50% take GCSE in more than 1 EC language. *Other:* Short stay students (1–3 terms) regularly from Germany and occasionally France.
Senior students' non-academic

117

activities *Music:* 200 learn a musical instrument, 20 to Grade 6 or above; 40 in area youth orchestra based at school, 100 in choirs, 75 in wind and string groups, 25 in junior orchestra. *Drama and dance:* 40–120 in school productions. 40–100 in workshops; 60 in house plays; 20–200 in competitions. 200 take LAMDA exams. 1–2 accepted for Drama Schools; 2–6 work in theatre; 12 involved in university drama; 30 in amateur groups. *Art:* 150 take as non-examined subject, 20 as a club activity; 9 GCSE; 3 A-level. 2–3 accepted for Art School. 15 belong to photographic club. *Sport:* Lacrosse, netball, basketball, badminton, fencing, judo, riding, rounders, squash, swimming, table tennis, tennis, ballet, golf, gymnastics, keep fit, modern dance, sailing, self-defence, tap dancing, trampolining, volleyball available. 99% take non-compulsory sport. 100 take exams eg BAGA (gymnastics), swimming – bronze medal and resuscitation. 20 represent county, region or country (junior) at lacrosse. *Other:* 46 take part in local community schemes. 20 have bronze Duke of Edinburgh's Award, 4 silver. Other activities include computer club, Young Enterprise (2 companies), literary society, bellringing, clay pigeon shooting, dressmaking and others.

Careers On average, 92% leavers go on to degree courses; 2% to art/drama/music colleges; 5% to non-degree courses (eg nursing, secretarial, acting, equestrian); 1% straight into careers. Of those going on to degree courses, 15% go to Oxbridge, 77% to other universities; 8% to poly/colleges. 2% those going on to higher education go to courses in practical art; 2% in drama/acting; 1% in music; 75% in humanities/social sciences; 5% in medicine; and 15% in science/engineering.

Uniform School uniform worn throughout.

Houses/prefects Competitive houses. Prefects, head girl (appointed by the Head). Head of house and house prefects elected by upper school and staff. Elected Student Union.

Religion Morning prayers, Sunday church service, weekday Communion.

Social Ad hoc joint functions with several local schools, eg drama and singing. Organised trips abroad eg ski-ing or to Italy or Greece. Senior students allowed to bring own bike to school. All meals self service. School shop. No tobacco allowed; sixth form allowed glass of wine in supervised weekly social club.

Discipline No corporal punishment. Students failing to produce homework once might expect work to be marked down or supervised to get it done; those caught smoking cannabis on the premises could expect expulsion.

Boarding 46 have own study bedroom, 28 share with 1 or 2; 200 are in dormitories of 4+ (many cubicled). Students in accommodation houses, of 50–64. Two resident qualified nurses, doctor on call. Central dining room. *Upper sixth* can provide and cook own food. 2 termly exeats of 1½ days and half term (4+ days). Visits to the local towns allowed in small groups.

Alumni association is run by the Seniors' Secretary, c/o the School.

Former students The Princess Royal; Baroness Ryder of Warsaw; Lady Medawar; Joanna Foster; Mrs Ellen Winser among others.

· *Beresford House* ·

Beresford House
School
Summerdown Road
Eastbourne
East Sussex
BN20 8BS
Tel 0323 31658

- Pupils 225
- Boys 4–7 only
- Girls 4–18
- (Day/Board)
- Upper sixth 15

- Termly fees
  £1525 (Day)
  £2825 (Board)
- GSA
  Enquiries/application to
  the Headmistress

What it's like

Founded in 1902, it has an agreeable site on the perimeter of the seaside town of Eastbourne at the foot of the Downs. The premises comprise attractive Edwardian buildings which overlook playing fields and tennis courts. There is a purpose-built classroom block, a modern food technology unit, a computer centre and well-equipped laboratories. A separate sixth-form house is next to the main school. A large and well-qualified staff allows a favourable staff:pupil ratio of 1:10. Academic standards and results are good; each year many sixth form girls go on to degree courses, including Oxbridge. French, German and Spanish are offered at GCSE and an exceptionally high proportion of girls takes GCSE in more than one European language. These languages, plus Italian, are offered at A-level. There are regular exchanges with France, Germany and Spain. The drama and music departments are particularly active and well-organised (almost everyone is involved). Pupils have achieved notable success in regional and national public speaking competitions. High standards are attained in art. There is considerable emphasis on careers education and the careers resource centre has a professional adviser. A variety of sports and games (field and court games, plus wind-surfing, sailing and golf) are well catered for. There have been a number of representatives at county and regional level, 1991 u16 hockey team county champions.

School profile

Pupils Total age range 4–18; 225 pupils (210 day, 15 boarding). Senior department 11–18, 165 girls. Main entry ages 4, 7, 11 and into sixth. *Transfer from maintained schools:* 33% senior intake, plus 8% to sixth.

Entrance Common entrance and own exam used. Special skills in music welcomed; no religious requirements. Parents not expected to buy text books. Scholarships/bursaries 50%–10% fees.

Parents 15+% are doctors, lawyers, etc. 90+% live within 30 miles; up to 6% live overseas.

Staff Headmistress Miss S B Jackson, 2 years in post. 19 full time staff, 16 part time. Annual turnover 5%. Average age 34.

Academic work GCSE and A-levels.

23 GCSE subjects offered; 21 at A-level (including politics). In 1991, 30 pupils in upper fifth, 15 in upper sixth. *GCSE:* on average, 62% upper fifth gained at least grade C in 8+ subjects; 15% in 5–7. *A-levels:* 80% upper sixth passed in 3 subjects. *Computing facilities:* Computer centre. *Special provision:* EFL.

European Community *Languages:* French offered: to age 14; GCSE; AS-level; A-level. German offered: to age 14; GCSE; AS-level; A-level. Italian offered: to A-level. Spanish offered: to GCSE; AS-level; A-level. Over 75% take GCSE in more than 1 EC language. *Exchanges:* Regular exchanges for pupils aged 11–18 to France, Germany and Spain. *Other:* Annual Europe Day, with visits from eg MEP. Group of EC pupils boarding each year. Europerson on staff to develop awareness of European opportunities.

Senior pupils' non-academic activities *Music:* 65% learn a musical instrument, 7 to Grade 6 or above. 2 accepted for Music School. 15 in school orchestra, 38 in school choirs, others play in recorder groups, sing in madrigal groups. Some in the National Youth Choir and the Royal Academy Junior Choir. *Drama and dance:* 100 in school productions. Some enter International Schools Public Speaking Competition (school has strong tradition of public speaking). *Art:* 20 take GCSE; 2 AS-level, 3 A-level. 2 pa accepted for Art School. 15 belong to photographic club; 30 to pottery club. *Sport:* Hockey, tennis, netball, rounders, athletics, badminton, squash, swimming, gymnastics available. Entire school take exams at appropriate level. 7 pupils represent county (athletics, hockey, swimming). *Other:* Whole school takes part in local community schemes. Other activities include 2 computer clubs, photography, chess, expeditionary, guides, French club, science club, first aid, pottery, sewing, 2 dance clubs (contemporary dance, classical ballet), performing arts.

Careers In 1990, 100% sixth form leavers went on to degree courses. Of those going on to degree courses, 10% went to Oxbridge, 80% to other universities; 10% to poly/colleges. 10% those going on to higher education went to courses in music; 80% in humanities/social sciences; and 10% in science/engineering.

Uniform School uniform worn except in sixth.

Houses/prefects Competitive houses. Prefects, head girl, heads of houses – appointed by the Head in conjunction with other members of staff.

Religion Morning prayers; confirmation encouraged; Christian discussion group.

Social Public speaking; Eastbourne Festival of Music & Arts with other local schools; joint dramatic productions with local boys' school. Exchange with schools in St Lo, France and Michigan, USA. Annual ski trip and visits to France and Germany. Pupils allowed to bring car/bike to school. Meals formal. School shop. No tobacco/alcohol allowed.

Boarding Sixth form only board. Pupils can provide and cook own food. Resident school doctor and dentist. Regular visits to the local town allowed.

Alumni association is run by Miss A M Barnett, 5 The Croft, St Anne's Road, Eastbourne.

Former pupils 1st Brain of Britain, Mrs Joan Taylor (née Long).

· *Berkhamsted (Boys)* ·

Berkhamsted School	● Pupils 800	● Termly fees
Castle Street	● Boys 7–18 (Day/	£1643 (Day)
Berkhamsted	Board/Weekly)	£2826 (Board)
Hertfordshire	● Girls None	● HMC
HP4 2BB	● Upper sixth 93	Enquiries/application to
Tel 0442 863236		the Headmaster's
Fax 0442 877657		Secretary

What it's like

Founded in 1541 by John Incent, Dean of St Paul's, it is in the historic centre of this busy and prosperous town surrounded by wooded Chiltern countryside. The original school building, the Old Hall, is still used; the rest comprises pleasant 19th-century buildings, and many modern additions. All-round facilities are excellent. Its outlook is in the English Grammar School tradition providing a strong all-round education; public exam results are good and very many go on to degree courses, including Oxbridge. French and German are offered to A-level, Spanish to GCSE and French for Business taught in the sixth form. There are regular exchanges with France. Strong in music, art, sports, CCF, community service and Duke of Edinburgh's Award Scheme. Use is made of the nearby Chiltern countryside for outdoor pursuits. With preparatory department, it provides continuity from 7–18 if desired. There are links with Berkhamsted School for Girls for some academic and social activities; also under the same board of governors. There is flexibility between day, boarding and weekly boarding. The boarding section has an international element (some being 'British Overseas', 25% foreign). The school is committed to the concept of all-roundness but encourages boys to develop their strengths. The aim is to turn out intelligent, considerate young people who can think for themselves.

School profile

Pupils Total age range 7–18; 800 boys, 655 day, 145 boarding. Senior department 13–18, 500 boys. Main entry ages 7, 10, 13 and into sixth. Approx 15% are children of former pupils. Berkhamsted Prep and Junior Schools provide 70+% senior intake. *Transfer from maintained schools:* 4% main senior intake, plus 4% to sixth.

Entrance Common entrance exam or own entrance assessment used. Oversubscribed. No religious requirements (although school itself is Anglican). Parents expected to buy text books; maximum extras £150 per term. 5 assisted places pa. 10–12 scholarships up to half fees (plus bursaries in case of need).

Parents 45+% in industry or commerce. 60+% live within 30 miles; up to 10% live overseas.

Staff Headmaster Keith Wilkinson, 2 years in post. 66 full time staff, 10 part time. Annual turnover 5%. Average age 39.

Academic work GCSE, AS- and A-levels. 24 subjects offered (no A-level general studies). In 1990, 95 pupils in upper fifth, 93 in upper sixth. *GCSE:* in 1990, 88 upper fifth gained at least grade C in 8+ subjects; 13 in 5–7; and 3 in 1–4 subjects. *A-levels:* 12 upper sixth passed in 4+ subjects; 66 in 3; 7 in 2; and 7 in 1 subject. 26% took science A-levels; 50% arts/humanities; 24% both. *Computing facilities:* new computer suite – 25 machines; CD Rom; BBC Masters in Junior School. *Special provision:* Extra tuition available.

European Community *Languages:* French offered: to age 14; GCSE; A-level; French for Business (in sixth). German offered: to age 14; GCSE; A-level. Spanish offered: to GCSE. 10–25% take GCSE in more than 1 EC language. *Exchanges:* Regular exchanges for pupils aged 11–18 to France. *Other:* Sixth form attending Paris conference on business and job opportunities in EC after 1992.

Senior pupils' non-academic activities *Music:* 94 learn a musical instrument in school, 21 to Grade 6 or above; 28 in school orchestra, 15 in chapel choir, 30 in choral society, 30 in wind groups, 8+ in brass group. Some of school in youth choral groups and orchestras (Watford, Dacorum and Berkhamsted Youth Theatre); 12+ in pop groups; Oxbridge Choral Scholar. *Drama and dance:* 60 in school productions; 15 in house plays. 1 now working in theatre; 10 in local dramatic society. *Art:* 25 take as non-examined subject; 41 GCSE; 10 A-level. 3 accepted for Art School. 20 involved in photographic activities; 20 in art and ceramic workshops; 25 take arts topics. *Sport:* Rugby, cricket, swimming, athletics, Eton fives, squash, tennis, volleyball, basketball, weight training, rowing, canoeing, cross-country, hockey, association football, judo, fencing available. Some sport or exercise compulsory for all. Some represent county (canoeing, rowing, swimming, shooting, rugby, cricket, athletics, squash, golf, tennis) and country (rugby, shooting). *Other:* 35 have silver Duke of Edinburgh's Award, 15 gold. 173 in CCF (140 Army, 33 Navy). Other activities include computer club, music, drama, chess, bridge, maths society, economics society, classics society, history society, biology society, debating and public speaking, ceramics, art, Young Enterprise, Industrial Society.

Careers In 1990, 81% leavers went on to degree courses; 3% to art/drama/music colleges; 1% to non-degree courses (eg HND minerals and technology); 3% straight into careers (eg armed services); 12% other (retake A-levels, reapplying). Of those going on to degree courses, 7% went to Oxbridge, 71% to other universities; 22% to poly/colleges. 3% those going on to higher education went to courses in practical art; 1% in drama/acting; 54% in humanities/social sciences; 1% in medicine; and 41% in science/engineering.

Uniform School uniform worn throughout.

Houses/prefects Competitive houses. Prefects, head boy, head of house and house prefects – appointed by Headmaster, after consulting housemasters, masters and prefects. No personal fagging, some collective responsibilities.

Religion Chapel attendance compulsory twice a week (and Sunday for boarders), but parents' 'conscience clause'.

Social Close co-operation with Berkhamsted (Girls), especially in music, drama, Chapel, social activities. Organised trips abroad for modern languages, skiing, classics, CCF, history. Day pupils allowed to bring own car/bike/motorbike to school. Meals self service (formal occasionally). School shops for sports clothes, second-hand clothing, stationery. No tobacco/alcohol allowed.

Discipline No corporal punishment. Pupils failing to produce homework once might expect a ticking-off; those caught smoking cannabis on or off the premises could expect expulsion. Bullying regarded as a very serious offence. The principal aim is to encourage self-discipline.

Boarding 15% have own study bedroom, 60% share 2–4; 25% are in dormitories of 6+. Houses of approximately 45–55. Resident SRN; visiting school medical officer. Central dining room. Pupils can sometimes provide and cook own food. Termly exeats: 2 weekends and half-term; plus optional exeats. Visits to local town allowed as requested.

Alumni association is run by Ian Player, The President, Old Berkhamstedian Association, c/o The Bursary, Berkhamsted School.

Former pupils Antony Hopkins (musician); Air Vice Marshal Sir David Parry Evans (airman); Mr Justice Michael Coombe (judge); Alexander Goehr (composer, 1987 Reith Lectures); Richard Mabey (writer and naturalist); Sir Kenneth Cork (accountant, former Lord Mayor of London); Tarn Hodder (chairman, Hockey Association); Alan Grimsdell (President RFU); Michael Meacher MP (Labour); Keith Mans MP (Conservative); John Bly (antique dealer and broadcaster); Michael van Straten (naturopath and broadcaster); Robin Knox-Johnston (explorer); Graham Greene (novelist).

· Bethany ·

Bethany School
Goudhurst
Cranbrook
Kent
TN17 1LB
Tel 0580 211273

- Pupils 275
- Boys 11–18
  (Day/Board)
- Girls 11–18
  (Day/Board)
- Upper sixth 25

- Termly fees
  £1636 (Day)
  £2556 (Board)
- SHMIS
Enquiries/application to
the Headmaster

What it's like

Founded on its present site in 1866 by the Rev J J Kendon, a Baptist minister. Thereafter it was run as a small 'family' school until 1948 by members of the minister's family. It remains a small school with a family atmosphere and the chapel is at the centre of its life. Services are in the evangelical tradition and every effort is made to relate religious teaching to daily modern life. The school has a delightful rural setting and its buildings comprise houses round the village green of Curtisden Green, near Goudhurst. A large staff allows a most favourable staff:pupil ratio of about 1:9. Academic results are good and several sixth formers go on to degree courses each year. There is considerable commitment to music, drama and art. A large variety of sports and games is provided and there are the usual extra-curricular activities.

School profile

Pupils Age range 11–18; 275 boys, 55 day, 220 boarding. Girls accepted from September 1991. Main entry ages 11, 13 and into sixth. Approx 3% are children of former pupils. *Transfer from maintained schools:* 50% main intake, plus most into sixth.

Entrance Common entrance and own entrance exam used. Sometimes oversubscribed. No special skills or religious requirements. Parents not expected to buy text books; maximum extras £200. 10 scholarships/bursaries, 50%–10% of fees.

Parents 30+% live within 30 miles; up to 10% live overseas.

Staff Headmaster W M Harvey, in post 2 years. 27 full time staff, 3 part time. Annual turnover 10%. Average age 39.

Academic work GCSE and A-levels. 15 subjects offered (no A-level general studies). In 1990, 50 pupils in upper fifth, 23 in upper sixth (now 25). *GCSE:* in 1990, 3 upper fifth gained at least grade C in 8+ subjects; 25 in 5–7; and 19 in 1–4 subjects. *A-levels:* 2 upper sixth passed in 4+ subjects; 14 in 3; 3 in 2; and 1 in 1

subject. 55% took science A-levels; 40% arts/humanities; 5% both. *Computing facilities:* Specialist computer room with BBC computers; computers in all departments. *Special provision:* Long-established dyslexic unit for able pupils.

European Community *Languages:* French offered: to age 14; GCSE; AS-level; A-level. German offered: to age 14; GCSE; AS-level; A-level. 10–25% take GCSE in more than 1 EC language. *Exchanges:* Regular exchanges for pupils aged 11–16 to France. *Other:* Some EC pupils study in school – 4 at a time.

Senior pupils' non-academic activities *Music:* 95 learn a musical instrument, 10 to Grade 6 or above; 20 in school orchestra, 40 in choir, 6 in school pop group. *Drama and dance:* 12–30 in school productions. 1 goes on to work in theatre. *Art:* 15 take as non-examined subject; 20 GCSE; 6 A-level. 3 accepted for Art School. 14 belong to eg photographic club. *Sport:* Rugby, cross-country, swimming, tennis, athletics, badminton, basketball, squash, rifle shooting, indoor cricket nets, soccer, hockey available. 70 take non-compulsory sport; 11 take GCSE PE. 5 represent county/country (rugby, cross-country). *Other:* 12 have bronze Duke of Edinburgh's Award. Other activities include a computer club, chess club, driving lessons etc.

Careers In 1990, 75% leavers went on to degree courses; 15% to art/drama/music colleges; 10% to non-degree courses (eg agriculture). Of those going on to degree courses, 50% went to universities; 50% to poly/colleges. 10% those going on to higher education went to courses in practical art; 5% in music; 30% in humanities/social sciences; 5% in medicine; and 50% in science/engineering.

Uniform School uniform worn except in the sixth.

Houses/prefects Competitive houses. Prefects, head boy, head of house and house prefects – appointed by Head and housemasters. School Council.

Religion Compulsory religious worship.

Social Discos, lectures, choral events with girls' schools. Rugby, ski-ing, cycling, natural history trips abroad. Pupils allowed to bring own bike to school. Meals self service. School tuck shop. No tobacco allowed, some alcohol in presence of staff.

Discipline Corporal punishment abolished in 1987. Pupils failing to produce homework once might expect to be detained to complete it. A pupil caught smoking cannabis on the premises would be expelled and the incident referred to the police.

Boarding 15 have own study bedroom, 35 share with 1 other, the rest are in dormitories mostly of 4. Houses, of 15–60, divided by age. Resident qualified nurses, doctor in village. Central dining room. 2 overnight exeats per term plus each Sunday, after chapel. Weekend visits to village allowed.

Alumni association run by P S Holmes Esq, Secretary, c/o the School.

Former pupils Lord Stamp.

· *Birkdale* ·

Birkdale School
Oakholme Road
Sheffield
S10 3DH
Tel 0742 668408

- Pupils 670
- Boys 4–18
  (Day)
- Girls None
- Upper sixth 60

- Termly fees
  £1080 (Day)
- SHA
Enquiries/applications
to the Headmaster

What it's like

Founded at the turn of the century, the school (then only preparatory) moved in 1915 to its present agreeable site in a Victorian residential suburb near the university and one and a half miles from the city centre. The pre-preparatory and preparatory schools are nearby. A senior school was established in 1978. Since the mid-sixties there has been steady development (in response to parental demand) which includes excellent laboratories, an art and design building, a sixth-form centre, a music school and a sports hall. There has been vigorous supporting response from the local community and wide interest outside the city. Birkdale is now the only independent secondary school for boys in Sheffield and South Yorkshire: the result of enterprise, energy and good organisation. It is a Christian school; there is some emphasis on religious instruction and all pupils are expected to attend morning prayers. It enjoys a favourable staff:pupil ratio of 1:12 and its academic standards and results are impressive. Very many leavers go on to degree courses, some to Oxbridge. French and German are offered to A-level, Spanish to

GCSE. A high proportion of boys taking GCSE in more than one European language. There are regular exchanges to France and Germany. Music is quite strong and is being further developed; a high proportion of boys learn an instrument. Some drama (joint productions with girls' school) and art. A standard range of sports and games, including soccer, is provided and there are good facilities for these on nine and a half acres of fields nearby. Outdoor activities (eg hill walking, climbing) are encouraged; there are expeditions to the Peak and Lake Districts. Some community service is undertaken and the Duke of Edinburgh's Award Scheme has been well supported.

School profile

Pupils Total age range 4–18; 670 day boys. Senior department 11–18, 380 boys. Main entry ages, 4, 7, 11, and into sixth. 10% are children of former pupils. *Transfer from maintained schools:* 30% main intake, plus 90% to sixth.

Entrance Common entrance and own exam used. Oversubscribed at most ages. No special skills or religious requirements. Parents not expected to buy text books. Average extras £10. 10 scholarships/bursaries pa, £600-£100 per term.

Parents 15+% are doctors, lawyers, etc; 15+% from industry/commerce. *Staff* Headmaster Revd Michael D A Hepworth, in post for 8 years. 55 full time staff, 9 part time. Annual turnover 4%. Average age 37.

Academic work GCSE and A-levels. 23 A-level subjects offered (including general studies). In 1990, 47 pupils in upper fifth, 25 in upper sixth (first year of upper sixth; planned to increase to 60 by 1995). *GCSE:* in 1990, 22 upper fifth gained at least grade C in 8+ subjects; 11 in 5–7; and 4 in 1–4 subjects. *A-levels:* 11 upper sixth passed in 4+ subjects; 5 in 3; 5 in 2; and 4 in 1 subject. 10 took science A-levels; 11 arts/humanities; 4 both. *Computing facilities:* New IT centre with Nimbus machines. 12 other machines in subject areas throughout senior school. CAD in Design Department. *Special provision:* Specialist teacher for dyslexic pupils.

European Community *Languages:* French offered: to age 14; GCSE; AS-level; A-level. German offered: to age 14; GCSE; AS-level; A-level. Spanish offered: to GCSE. 50–75% take GCSE in more than 1 EC language. *Exchanges:* Regular exchanges for pupils aged 14–18 to France and Germany. *Other:* Lectures from MEPs; French and German assistants; satellite TV. School won North Sea Ferries EC competition in 1989 and 3 Central Bureau membership (tenable in Germany) in 1991.

Senior pupils' non-academic activities *Music:* 15 learn a musical instrument, 4 up to Grade 8; 2 accepted for Music School. 15 in school orchestra, 2 in local orchestra, 25 in school choir, 3 in pop group. 3 play in pop group outside school. *Drama and dance:* 8 in school productions. *Art:* 20 take GCSE art; 7 A-level art; 2 accepted for Art School. 3 belong to photographic club. *Sport:* Rugby, soccer, cricket, athletics, cross country. 25 take non-compulsory sport. 3 represent county/country (decathlon, rugby, squash). *Other:* 10 take part in local community schemes. 30 have bronze Duke of Edinburgh's Award, 15 silver and 7 gold. Other activities include a computer club, chess (Northern U13 winners 1991), karate, drama, debating, history, geography (sixth form societies in conjunction with Sheffield High).

Careers In 1990, 92% leavers went on to degree courses; 8% straight into careers (eg banking, estate agency). Of those going on to degree courses, 4% went to Oxbridge; 56% to other universities; 40% to poly/colleges. 4% those going on to higher education went to courses in practical art; 4% in music; 37% in humanities/social sciences; 15% in medicine; and 40% in science/engineering.

Uniform School uniform worn throughout.

Houses/prefects Competitive houses. Head boy, prefects, head of house and house prefects, appointed by the head.

Religion Attendance at religious worship compulsory.

Social Trips to Germany/France; theatrical productions (eg Pirates of Penzance, Messiah, Merchant of Venice) – with Sheffield High. A-level German and French work placements as part of A-level coursework. Link schools with Albinus Realschule, Hamburg; annual study trip to France. Pupils allowed to bring own cars. Meals self-service. School shop. No tobacco/alcohol allowed.

Discipline Corporal punishment allowed in theory but never used. Pupils failing to produce homework once could expect, at most, supervision; detention if unsatisfactory. Those caught smoking cannabis on the premises (never arisen in last 10 years) likely to be suspended; expulsion for pushers.

Alumni association is run by P Todd Esq, Chairman OBA, 65 Tom Lane, Sheffield S10 3PA.

Former pupils Antony Favell MP, Mr Justice Paul Kennedy (High Court judge), Lord Riverdale, Colonel John Boddy (High Sheriff), Michael Palin, Rex Harrison.

· *Birkenhead* ·

Birkenhead School
58 Beresford Road
Birkenhead
Wirral
Merseyside L43 2JD
Tel 051 652 4014

- Pupils 1000
- Boys 4–18 (Day)
- Girls None
- Upper sixth 97

- Termly fees £865 (Day)
- HMC

Enquiries/application to the Head Master

What it's like

Founded in 1860 and soon established as the leading boys' school in the locality. It has pleasant late Victorian and modern buildings on an estate of some 50 acres on an open site in the village of Oxton, a suburb of Birkenhead. All the main buildings are on the same campus. The principal playing fields are central. Others lie two minutes' walk away. There have been many additions and improvements to facilities in the last 20 years. The school has embarked on a major development programme to provide an extension to the science block, a sports hall, a new music school and a new office block. The school is organised in 3 departments: the prep for pupils aged 4–11; the junior school, aged 11–13; and the senior school aged 13–19. There is a favourable staff:pupil ratio, especially in the sixth form. A good general education is given and academic results are highly creditable. Very many pupils go on to degree courses each year, including a number to Oxbridge. French, German and Spanish are offered to A-level. A high proportion of boys take GCSE in more than one European language. There are regular exchanges with France. The school has a strong Christian tradition and prayers are held each morning in the chapel. The Chapel Choir is well known to be outstanding and performs at the level of a cathedral choir. The music, drama and art departments are very active. A good range of sports and games in which high standards are attained. There is also a wide variety of extra-curricular activities and a flourishing CCF contingent. The Duke of Edinburgh's Award Scheme is well supported and pupils have had many successes.

School profile

Pupils Total age range 4–18; 1000 day boys. Senior department 11–18, 750 boys. Main entry ages 4, 11, 13 and into sixth. Approximately 15% are children of former pupils. *Transfer from maintained schools:* 55% main senior intake, plus 5% to sixth.

Entrance Common entrance and own

entrance exam used. Oversubscribed. Academic excellence and breadth of interests looked for; no religious requirements. 250 assisted places. 20 scholarships/bursaries per year dependent on parental need, £1,000–£100. Parents not expected to buy text books.

Parents 15+% doctors, lawyers etc; 15+% in industry and commerce; 15+% university staff.

Staff Head Master S J Haggett, in post for 3 years. 64 full time staff, 8 part time. Annual turnover 5%. Average age 42.

Academic work GCSE and A-levels. 18 subjects offered (including A-level general studies). In 1990, 112 pupils in fifth, 111 in upper sixth (now 97). *GCSE:* in 1990, 98 fifth gained at least grade C in 8+ subjects; 11 in 5–7; and 3 in 1–4 subjects. *A-levels:* 80 upper sixth passed in 4+ subjects; 19 in 3; 7 in 2; and 5 in 1 subject. 46 took science A-levels; 34 arts/humanities; 31 both. *Computing facilities:* Two fully equipped BBC laboratories.

European Community *Languages:* French offered: to age 14; GCSE; AS-level; A-level. German offered: to GCSE; AS-level; A-level. Spanish offered: to GCSE; A-level. 50–75% take GCSE in more than 1 EC language. *Exchanges:* Regular exchanges for pupils aged 11–14 to France.

Senior pupils' non-academic activities *Music:* 210 learn a musical instrument, 40 to Grade 6 or above; 2 accepted for Music School; 70 in school orchestra, 50 in choir. *Drama and dance:* 120 in school productions; 1 accepted for Drama school. 1 goes on to work in theatre. *Art:* 15 take GCSE; 5 A-level. 2 accepted for Art School. 30 belong to eg photographic club. *Sport:* Rugby, hockey, cricket, tennis, athletics, cross-country, rugby fives, swimming, sailing available. 150 take part in non-compulsory sport; 1 pupil represents country (rugby), 8 represent county (hockey). *Other:* 30 have Duke of Edinburgh's bronze award, 20 silver, 8

gold; 2 enter voluntary schemes after leaving school. Other activities include a computer club, scout and venture scout units, CCF (3 sections), community service.

Careers In 1990, 85% leavers went on to degree courses; 11% to art/drama/music colleges; 4% straight into careers (eg armed forces, banking). Of those going on to degree courses, 12% went to Oxbridge, 71% to other universities; 17% to poly/colleges. 2% those going on to higher education went to courses in practical art; 40% in humanities/social sciences; 9% in medicine; and 49% in science/engineering.

Uniform School uniform worn throughout; prefects and monitors wear gowns.

Houses/prefects Competitive houses. Prefects, head boy, head of house and house prefects – appointed by the Head in consultation with staff and outgoing prefects. No School Council, but Head Master has open-door policy.

Religion Daily service in the school chapel.

Social Joint debates, concerts, plays with Birkenhead High. 2 French exchange schemes, numerous other individual visits, ski trips, classical trips etc. Pupils allowed to bring own car/bike to school. Meals self service. School shop. No tobacco/alcohol allowed.

Discipline No corporal punishment. Pupils failing to produce homework once would be given extra work and expected to produce the original work; those caught smoking cannabis on the premises could expect automatic expulsion.

Alumni association is run by D Leaver Esq, 7 Eddisbury Road, West Kirby L48 5DR.

Former pupils Rt. Hon Lord Justice Nicholls, Alan Rouse, Earl of Birkenhead, Canon Graham Routledge, Sir Gordon Willmer, Professor Neville Willmer, Lord Evans of Claughton, Rt. Hon H Graham White.

· *Birkenhead High* ·

Birkenhead High
School
86 Devonshire Place
Birkenhead
Merseyside L43 1TY
Tel 051 652 5777

- Pupils 940
- Boys None
- Girls 4–18
  (Day)
- Upper sixth 109

- Termly fees
  £908 (Day)
- GPDST
Enquiries/application to
the Headmistress

What it's like

Founded in 1901, it is single-site in a quiet, pleasant, residential district. The junior school is nearby. There have been many modern developments and additions to its late Victorian buildings. A high standard of teaching to a traditional curriculum. Very many girls go on to degree courses, including Oxbridge. (Not a few go into medicine and the law). French, German and Spanish are offered to A-level and many girls take GCSE in more than one European language. There are regular exchanges with France and Germany. A distinguished school with vigorous local support, it is fundamentally Christian in ethos. A friendly, informal atmosphere in which plenty of freedom is given to sixth formers who play a considerable part in running the school. A wide range of sport and games, numerous societies and clubs. Very strong indeed in music and drama. Substantial commitment to local community schemes and to the Duke of Edinburgh's Award Scheme.

School profile

Pupils Total age range 4–18; 940 day girls. Senior department 11–18, 760 girls. Main entry ages 11 and into sixth. Approx 5% are children of former pupils. Over 20% of intake from own junior dept. *Transfer from maintained schools:* 50% intake at 11+, plus 75% to sixth.

Entrance Own entrance exam used. Oversubscribed. No special skills or religious requirements. Parents not expected to buy text books; no other extras. 40 assisted places pa. Some scholarships/ bursaries available.

Parents 15+% in industry or commerce; 15+% are doctors, lawyers etc.

Staff Headmistress Mrs Kathleen Irving, in post for 5 years. 57 full time staff, 19 part time.

Academic work GCSE and A-levels. 20 GCSE subjects offered; 22 at A-level (including A-level general studies and Russian). In 1990, 109 pupils in upper fifth, 109 in upper sixth. *GCSE:* in 1990, 95 upper fifth gained at least grade C in 8+ subjects; 11 in 5–7; and 3 in 1–4 subjects. *A-levels:* 61 upper sixth passed in

4+ subjects; 30 in 3; 12 in 2; and 6 in 1 subject. 40% took science A-levels; 40% arts/humanities; 20% both. *Computing facilities:* 2 Networks RML Nimbus; BBC's in junior department.

European Community *Languages:* French offered: to age 14; GCSE; AS-level; A-level. German offered: to age 14; GCSE; AS-level; A-level. Spanish offered: to age 14; GCSE; AS-level; A-level. 25–50% take GCSE in more than 1 EC language. *Exchanges:* Regular exchanges for pupils aged 11–16 to France and Germany.

Senior pupils' non-academic activities *Music:* 150 learn a musical instrument, 50 to Grade 6 or above; 1 now plays in a pop group; 3 accepted at universities and colleges for music degrees; 40 in school orchestra, 100 in choir, 20 in wind ensemble, 4 in string quartet. *Drama and dance:* 60–80 in school productions; 20 in drama clubs, 36 produce school drama festival; 1 takes Guildhall Grade 6, 20 GCSE drama. 2 accepted for Drama Schools; 4–10 outside auditions; 20 enter drama festivals; 1 entered playwriting competition. *Art:* 58 take GCSE; 9 A-level. 6 accepted for Art School; 2 for architecture. 18 in eg photographic club. *Sport:* Lacrosse, hockey, netball, tennis, rounders, badminton, trampolining, gymnastics, dance, athletics, volleyball, table tennis, swimming, squash, archery available. 100 take non-compulsory sport. 10 take exams eg judo; 40 GCSE; 20 trampolining. 25 represent county (lacrosse, netball, hockey, tennis, badminton, gymnastics, squash, swimming). *Other:* 100+ take part in local community schemes. 60 are participating in bronze Duke of Edinburgh's Award, 47 in silver and 3 gold. Other activities include computer, history, geography, modern languages, classical, biology, chemistry, political debating and St Vincent de Paul societies, Christian Union, orchestra, 2 choirs, wind ensemble, renaissance band, guitar club, gym, dance, badminton, volleyball, squash, table tennis clubs and trampolining group.

Careers In 1990, 83% leavers went on to degree courses; 1% to art/drama/music colleges; 5% to non-degree courses (eg HNDs in business and finance, estate management, hotel and catering, quantitative decision methods); 2% straight into careers (eg police); 9% other. Of those going on to degree courses, 8% went to Oxbridge, 63% to other universities; 29% to poly/colleges. 58% those going on to higher education went to courses in humanities/social sciences; 13% in medicine; and 29% in science/engineering.

Uniform School uniform worn except in sixth.

Houses/prefects Competitive houses. No prefects. Head girl and 3 deputies, head of house – elected by the school.

Religion Christian morning assembly.

Social Debates and joint theatrical productions with local boys' independent school. Organised trips abroad. Pupils allowed to bring own car/bike/motorbike to school. Meals self service. No tobacco/alcohol allowed.

Discipline No corporal punishment. Pupils failing to produce homework once might expect a reprimand.

Former pupils Patricia Routledge (actress and singer); Ann Bell (actress); Judith Collins (first Woman Curator of the Tate Gallery); Janet McNeill (novelist, especially of children's books); Doreen Sloane (actress); Dr Vivienne Nathanson (Scottish Secretary of British Medical Association (most senior woman in BMA hierarchy)).

· *Bishop Challoner* ·

Bishop Challoner School	● Pupils 382	● Termly fees
228 Bromley Road	● Boys 4–18 (Day)	£915 (Day)
Shortlands	● Girls 16–18 (Day)	● ISAI
Kent BR2 0BS	● Upper sixth 15	Enquiries/application to the Headmaster
Tel 081-460 3546		

What it's like

Founded in 1946 by two local parish priests, it is single-site and semi-rural on 4.5 acres and combines junior and senior schools. In 30 years there have been numerous extensions to the original house to provide good modern facilities. A sound education is given and academic attainments are creditable. The majority of pupils are Roman Catholic. Thus, assemblies are religious, Mass is said regularly and the curriculum incorporates religious instruction, including theology and philosophy. Latin compulsory for all boys in the first two years in the senior school. French and German are offered to A-level and there are regular exchanges with France and Germany.

School profile

Pupils Total age range 4–18; 382 day pupils (379 boys, 3 girls). Senior department 11–18, 242 pupils (239 boys, 3 girls). Main entry ages boys 4 and 11; boys and girls into sixth. Own junior school provides 50% of intake.

Entrance Own entrance exam used. Oversubscribed at junior level. No special skills or religious requirements but majority are Roman Catholic. Parents not expected to buy text books; maximum extras, £65 per term for lunches. Scholarships/bursaries available in Senior School.

Parents 15+% in industry or commerce; 15+% are doctors, lawyers etc.

Staff Head Terence Robinson, in post for 6 years. 27 full time staff, 9 part time. Annual turnover 1%. Average age 40.

Academic work GCSE and A-levels. Average size of fifth 40; upper sixth 15. *GCSE:* on average, 10% pupils in upper fifth pass 8+ subjects; 20%, 5–7 subjects; 30% pass 1–4 subjects. *A-levels:* on average, 9 pupils in the upper sixth passed 3 subjects; 2, 2 subjects; 1, 1 subject. On average, 8 take science/engineering A-levels; 5 take arts and humanities; 2 a mixture. *Computing facilities:* Computer room with 8 BBC micros. Facilities for GCSE and A-level computer studies.

European Community *Languages:* French offered: to age 14; GCSE; A-level. German offered: to age 14; GCSE; A-level. 10–25% take GCSE in more than 1 EC language. *Exchanges:* Regular exchanges for pupils aged 14–16 to France and Germany.

Senior pupils' non-academic activities *Music:* 80 learn a musical instrument. *Drama and dance:* 30 in school productions. *Art:* 12 take GCSE; 4 A-level. 1 accepted for Art School. 2 belong to eg photographic club. *Sport:* Soccer, rugby, athletics, basketball, tennis, cricket, fencing available. 50 take non-compulsory sport. *Other:* 10 take part in local community schemes. Other activities include computer, chess and fishing clubs and choir.

Careers In 1990, 70% sixth form leavers went on to degree courses; 10% straight into careers (eg aircraft engineering); 20% other. Of those going on to degree courses, 90% went to universities; 10% to poly/colleges. 30% those going on to higher education went to courses in humanities/social sciences; 20% in medicine; and 50% in science/engineering.

Uniform School uniform worn except in sixth.

Houses/prefects No competitive houses. Prefects and head boy appointed by the Head after consulting school. School Council.

Religion All attend religious assemblies. Regular Mass for Catholics.

Social Organised trips abroad for skiing, classics, adventure etc. Pupils allowed to bring own car/bike/motorbike to school. Meals formal. No tobacco/alcohol allowed.

Discipline No corporal punishment. Pupils failing to produce homework once might expect loss of free time to do the work; those caught smoking cannabis on the premises could expect expulsion.

· Bishop's Stortford ·

Bishop's Stortford
College
Maze Green Road
Bishop's Stortford
Hertfordshire
CM23 2QZ
Tel 0279 758575

- Pupils 364
- Boys 13–18
  (Day/Board)
- Girls 16–18
  (Day/Board)
- Upper sixth 70

- Termly fees
  £1960 (Day)
  £2710 (Board)
- HMC
  Enquiries/
  application to the
  Headmaster

What it's like

The college was founded in 1868, mainly by Nonconformists in East Anglia, and was then primarily intended for the education of Nonconformists. It was reconstituted in 1904 and now accepts members of all Christian denominations. It has a fine site on high ground on the edge of the pleasant town, next to open countryside, with gardens and grounds covering 100 acres. The buildings are agreeable and well equipped. At their centre stands an impressive Memorial Hall (erected in 1921). The school is divided into junior and senior sections and the organisation of each is largely separate. Religious instruction and worship are inter-denominational. Overall there is a favourable staff:pupil ratio of about 1:10. Academic standards are high and results are impressive. Very many sixth formers go on to degree courses. French and German are offered to A-level, Spanish to GCSE. Many pupils take GCSE in more than one European language. Italian is offered as a non-examined subject and there are regular exchanges with Germany. Music is very strong indeed throughout the school, and so is drama. There is a good deal of collaboration between the music and drama departments. There is a good range of sports and games and these are pursued to a high level. A plentiful variety of extra-curricular activities is available. A particular emphasis is placed upon personal tutoring and pastoral care.

School profile

Pupils Age range 13–18, 364 pupils, 182 day, 182 boarding. Main entry ages 13 (boys) and into sixth (boys and girls). Over 70% intake from own prep. *Transfer from maintained schools:* a small number at 13+ but over 50% at sixth form.

Entrance Common entrance or own entry testing as applicable. Scholarships and assisted places available, plus awards for sons of Free Church ministers and bursaries for those showing financial need.

Staff Headmaster S G G Benson, in post for 7 years.

Academic work GCSE and A-levels (no A-level general studies offered). In 1990, 69 pupils in upper fifth, 70 in upper sixth. *GCSE:* in 1990, 71% upper fifth gained at least grade C in 8+ subjects; 21% in 5–7; and 8% in 1–4 subjects.

A-levels: 4% upper sixth passed in 4+ subjects; 83% in 3; 9% in 2; and 4% in 1 subject. 31% took science A-levels; 51% arts/humanities; 18% both. *Computing facilities:* Apple Macintosh, BBC – classroom of 24. Many others in departments. No formal exam in computer studies or computer science but IT for all.

European Community *Languages:* French offered: to GCSE; A-level. German offered: to GCSE; A-level. Italian offered: non-examined subject. Spanish offered: to GCSE. 25–50% take GCSE in more than 1 EC language. *Exchanges:* Regular exchanges for pupils to Germany. *Other:* Regularly have lower sixth pupils from EC countries for 1–2 terms.

Careers In 1990, 80% leavers went on

to degree courses; 5% to art/drama/ music colleges; 6% to non-degree courses (eg sport, nursing, secretarial); 4% straight into careers (eg family business, navy, estate agency); 5% other. Of those going on to degree courses, 3% went to Oxbridge, 58% to other universities; 39% to poly/colleges. 2% those going on to higher education went to courses in practical art; 3% in music; 68% in humanities/social sciences; 4% in medicine; and 23% in science/engineering.

· *Blackheath High* ·

Blackheath High School
Wemyss Road
Blackheath
London SE3 0TF
Tel 081 852 1537

- Pupils 371
- Boys None
- Girls 11–18
  (Day)
- Upper sixth 35

- Termly fees
  £1024 (Day)
- GSA, GPDST
  Enquiries/application to
  the Headmistress

What it's like

Opened in 1880, it was the first purpose-built school in the Girls' Public Day School Trust. Its agreeable, well-appointed buildings lie in the centre of Blackheath Village and it draws its pupils from a wide catchment area including Eltham, Lewisham, Catford, Greenwich, Deptford, Bexleyheath and Dartford. Since the 1960s there have been many additions and improvements and facilities are now good. Close by are five acres of playing fields. The junior school, housed in a handsome 19th-century building in beautiful gardens, is nearby. The senior school has all the advantages of a small establishment and enjoys a favourable staff:pupil ratio of about 1:11. A broad general education (including some attention to classics) is provided and results are creditable. Music is strong and is part of the curriculum for the first three years. There are two orchestras, senior and junior choirs, a wind band and small chamber groups. Concerts are often given. Drama is also well supported, with school plays and drama competitions. A standard range of sports and games is available. There is a plentiful variety of clubs and societies.

School profile

Pupils Total age range 4–18. Senior department 11–18, 371 day girls. Main entry age 11. *Transfer from maintained schools:* 67% senior intake.

Entrance Own entrance exam. Assisted places. Scholarships and bursaries.

Staff Headmistress Miss R K Musgrave, in post 2 years.

Academic work GCSE and A-levels. 19 GCSE subjects offered (no A-level general studies). In 1989, 74 pupils in upper fifth, 35 in upper sixth. *GCSE:* in 1989, 28 upper fifth gained at least grade C in 8+ subjects; 33 in 5–7; and 13 in 1–4 subjects. *A-levels:* 3 upper sixth passed in 4+ subjects; 22 in 3; 6 in 2; and 4 in 1 subject. 7 took science A-levels; 22 arts/ humanities; 6 both. *Computing facilities:* Computing rooms in junior and senior schools. *Special provision:* Support offered; arrangements can be made with outside agencies.

· Bloxham ·

Bloxham School	• Pupils 360	• Termly fees
Bloxham	• Boys 13–18	£2070 (Day)
Near Banbury	(Day/Board)	£3000 (Board)
Oxfordshire	• Girls 16–18	• HMC, Woodard
OX15 4PE	(Day/Board)	Enquiries/application to
Tel 0295 720206	• Upper sixth 85	the Headmaster

What it's like

Founded in 1860 by the Rev. Philip Egerton on the site of a former grammar school and given to the Woodard Corporation in 1896. It has a very agreeable setting on the edge of the village of Bloxham, between Banbury and Oxford. Its handsome buildings of local stone lie in 60 acres of gardens and playing fields. There is comfortable modern accommodation and plentiful facilities. It is an Anglican foundation but its spirit and policy is ecumenical. Special arrangements are made for pupils to attend their own churches, but all are expected to attend school chapel services. A sound general education is provided and academic results are creditable. Very many pupils go on to degree courses, including Oxbridge. French, German and Spanish are offered to A-level. Many pupils take GCSE in more than one European language. There are regular exchanges with France, Germany and Spain. Drama, music and art are well catered for. A wide range of sports and games is available and there are numerous extra-curricular activities. Each pupil has the option of training with the CCF which is a strong contingent. Small groups of pupils are also involved in local public works, and there is a highly organised community service programme in the neighbourhood (over a hundred visits to the elderly, handicapped etc are made each week).

School profile

Pupils Age range, 13–18; 360 pupils, 70 day, 290 boarders (300 boys, 60 girls). Main entry ages 13 (boys) and into sixth (boys and girls). *Transfer from maintained schools:* 5–10% main intake, plus 15% to sixth.

Entrance 5 assisted places. Scholarships/bursaries available.

Staff Headmaster D K Exham, first year in post.

Academic work GCSE and A-levels. 20 subjects offered (including A-level general studies). On average, 60 pupils in upper fifth, 85 in upper sixth. *GCSE:* in 1990, 67% upper fifth gained at least grade C in 8+ subjects; 23% in 5–7; and 10% in 1–4 subjects. *A-levels:* 50% upper sixth passed in 4+ subjects; 21% in 3; 15% in 2; and 9% in 1 subject. 20% took science A-levels; 40% arts/humanities; 40% both. *Computing facilities:* Computer laboratory (network IBM system); terminal in science library. *Special provision:* Dyslexia Unit (5 pupils per year, IQ greater than 120); EFL.

European Community *Languages:* French offered: to GCSE; AS-level; A-level. German offered: to GCSE; AS-level; A-level. Spanish offered: to GCSE; AS-level; A-level. 25–50% take GCSE in more than 1 EC language. *Exchanges:* Regular exchanges for pupils to France, Germany and Spain. *Other:* Increasing number of EC pupils in school (Dutch, French, German, Italian); some from age 13–18, some for shorter periods.

Senior pupils' non-academic activities *Music:* Chapel choir, choral society, orchestra and wind band. Some play with County Youth Orchestra and go on to Music School. *Drama and dance:* 8 productions pa, 3 produced entirely by pupils.

Drama workshop. *Art:* A number take art as non-examined subject. Art and sculpture taught to A-level. Visits from practising artists arranged. *Sport:* Rugby, hockey, cross-country, athletics, cricket, swimming, archery, tennis, sailing, fives, squash, shooting, golf, soccer, rounders, badminton, netball, fencing available; some compulsory, some voluntary. Other activities include CCF, practical skills (map reading, raft building etc); local public works and community service.

Careers In 1990, 80% leavers went on to degree courses; 10% to art/drama/music colleges; 10% straight into careers. Of those going on to degree courses, 8% went to Oxbridge, 52% to other universities; 40% to poly/colleges. 5% those going on to higher education went to courses in practical art; 2% in drama/acting; 5% in music; 52% in humanities/social sciences; 5% in medicine; and 30% in science/engineering.

Houses/prefects Prefects, head of house and house prefects.

Religion Some services compulsory; school is Anglican foundation.

Social Orchestral and choral concerts with Tudor Hall. Ski-ing trip, sports tours etc. Wine and beer for 17+ in 'JCR' with parents' permission.

Discipline Pupils failing to produce homework once could expect counselling; those caught smoking cannabis on the premises could expect expulsion.

Boarding All sixth formers have own study bedroom. 6 boys' houses; girls in two separate houses. Central dining room. Pupils can provide and cook snacks.

· *Blundell's* ·

Blundell's School
Tiverton
Devon
EX16 4DN
Tel 0884 252543

- Pupils 485
- Boys 13–18
  (Day/Board)
- Girls 16–18
  (Day/Board)
- Upper sixth 100

- Termly fees
  £1800 (Day)
  £2900 (Board)
- HMC, BSA
  Enquiries/application to
  the Registrar

What it's like

Founded and endowed in 1604 at the sole charge of the estate of Peter Blundell, clothier of Tiverton, by Sir John Popham. In 1882 it moved to its present site on the outskirts of Tiverton. The site comprises a fine estate of 100 acres of beautiful gardens and playing fields and other grounds. Its pleasant and well-equipped buildings provide good facilities and comfortable accommodation. The school maintains a Christian tradition and Anglican practice; all pupils are expected to attend weekday morning chapel and the school service on Sundays. In the lower school the life and teaching of Christ is the main area of religious study. The curriculum includes exploration of other faiths, the Old Testament and moral issues. A large staff allows a staff:pupil ratio of about 1:8. Academic standards are high and results impressive. Many pupils go on to degree courses, including Oxbridge. French and German are offered to A-level and an exceptionally high proportion of pupils takes GCSE in both languages. There are regular exchanges with France and Germany. The school has always been strong in music (choir, 3 orchestras, wind and jazz bands, rock bands and brass ensemble). A good music centre provides excellent facilities. Music is studied by all pupils on entry to the school. Drama is also very strong (two theatres). There are house plays, inter-house drama competitions and at least two major school plays per year. Art, crafts and technology are also flourishing fields of work and study. A wide variety of sports and games is available and standards are high. Many clubs and societies cater for most conceivable needs. Every Tuesday afternoon is set aside for specifically non-sporting activities. There is a large CCF (Army and Navy sections). Everyone who enters the school in the lower and middle fifth forms does a year's service. Activities include climbing, canoeing, abseiling, flying, sailing and expeditions on Dartmoor and Exmoor. There is an unusually big commitment to local community service.

School profile

Pupils Age range 13–18; 485 pupils, 110 day (100 boys, 10 girls), 375 boarding (345 boys, 30 girls). Main entry ages: boys, 13; boys and girls into the sixth. 10–15% are children of former pupils. *Transfer from maintained schools:* 5–10% main intake, plus 20–25% to sixth.

Entrance Common entrance and own entrance exam used. Oversubscribed. All special skills are welcome; so is 'Joe Average'. No religious requirements. Over 50 scholarships/bursaries available up to 100% fees. Parents not expected to buy text books.

Parents 10+% live within 30 miles; 10+% live overseas.

Staff Head A J D Rees, in post for 11 years. 46 full time staff, 20 part time. Annual turnover 5%.

Academic work GCSE and A-levels. Wide range of general studies courses but no A-level. In 1990, 90 pupils in upper fifth, 100 in upper sixth. *GCSE:* in 1990, 50% upper fifth gained at least grade C in 8+ subjects; 45% in 5–7; and 5% in 1–4 subjects. *A-levels:* 5% upper sixth passed in 4+ subjects; 80% in 3; 10% in 2; and 5% in 1 subject. 30% took science A-levels; 45% arts/humanities; 25% both. *Computing facilities:* Computing room plus increasing number of computers in departments. *Special provision:* Specialist teacher for dyslexics and EFL.

European Community *Languages:* French offered: to GCSE; AS-level; A-level. German offered: to GCSE; AS-level; A-level. Over 75% take GCSE in more than 1 EC language. *Exchanges:* Regular exchanges for pupils aged 14–18 to France and Germany. *Other:* Links with schools in France and Germany. Travel bursaries available for development of international understanding. Regular EC students, from eg Germany, in sixth form.

Senior pupils' non-academic activities *Music:* 220 learn a musical instrument, over 40 to Grade 6 or above; 2–3 accepted for Music School, 140 pupils play in school orchestras, 70 in choir, 30 in school pop group; annual concert by Blundell's soloists in Purcell Room; many continue with music beyond school. *Drama and dance:* Approx 50 involved in school productions; 300–400 in house plays, house drama competition; new studio theatre of professional standard; GCSE drama. *Art:* 25% take as a non-examined subject, 60% take GCSE; 10–15% A-level, 15% history of art, 10% CDT (growing rapidly); 3–5 accepted for Art School, 2–3 for design courses. *Sport:* Rugby, cricket, athletics, golf, squash, fives, tennis, judo, karate, archery, basketball, swimming, badminton, hockey, soccer, fencing, sailing, canoeing. Some 25% take non-compulsory sport. 30–40 pupils represent county (judo, rugby, cricket, athletics, archery, squash, cross-country etc). *Other:* 60 pupils take part in local community schemes (music, CDT etc have community orientation). 20 pupils have bronze Duke of Edinburgh's Award, 10 silver, 2–3 gold. 5–10 enter voluntary schemes after leaving school. Over 35 other activities available, including aerobics, stage management, fly fishing, public speaking and a computer club.

Careers In 1990, 76% leavers went on to degree courses; 6% to non-degree courses; 6% straight into careers (eg army, retailing); 12% other. Of those going on to degree courses, 8% went to Oxbridge, 67% to other universities; 25% to poly/colleges. 3% those going on to higher education went to courses in practical art; 3% in music; 55% in humanities/social sciences; 6% in medicine; and 33% in science/engineering.

Uniform School uniform worn throughout, except in houses.

Houses/prefects Competitive houses (6 boarding, 2 day boy; 1 girl). Monitors, head boy/girl (1 girl as head of school so far), head of house and house monitors – appointed by Head after consultation with monitors, housemasters etc.

Religion Daily service for whole school; 6 Sunday services per term.

Social Debates, general knowledge competitions, musical events etc with local schools. French exchange, links with schools in Canada, Australia, West Berlin, South Africa, Czechoslovakia and USSR; plus trips to Germany, Russia etc. Pupils allowed to bring own bike to school. Meals self service (staff always present). School tuck and tailor's shop. Alcohol in '17' club; no tobacco.

Discipline No corporal punishment. Pupils failing to produce homework once might expect minor admonition, a little tease, whatever seems appropriate; those caught smoking cannabis on the premises could expect 'goodbye'!; repeated smoking and illegal drinking also lead to expulsion.

Boarding 30% have own study bedroom, 50% share (with 1–3); 20% are in dormitories of 6+. Houses, of approx 55, are single sex. 2 resident qualified nurses; doctor visits daily. Central dining room. Pupils can provide and cook own food. Exeats at half-term plus 2 weekends (Sat 4pm – Sun 9pm). Visits to local town allowed at all ages at housemaster's discretion.

Alumni association is run by E R Crowe, at Blundell's.

Former pupils Lord Stokes; Robert Fox; Michael Mates MP; John Gray (ex Ambassador to Lebanon); Richard Sharp; Clem Thomas; Vic Marks; Peter Hurford, Paul Levi.

· *Bolton (Boys)* ·

Bolton School Boys' Division
Chorley New Road
Bolton
Lancashire BL1 4PA
Tel 0204 40202

- Pupils 990
- Boys 8–18 (Day)
- Girls None
- Upper sixth 120

- Termly fees £998 (Day)
- HMC

Enquiries/application to the Headmaster

What it's like

Originally founded in 1524, endowed by Robert Lever in 1641 and re-endowed in 1913 by Sir W H Lever (later Viscount Leverhulme). It comprises impressive and very large buildings with a great hall, plus recent additions, which lie to the north west of Bolton in an urban residential area, a mile from the town centre on an estate of 32 acres. The prep and junior departments are nearby. The boys' and girls' divisions are in the same building and though the organisation of the two divisions provides basically single-sex schools there are many opportunities for boys and girls to meet and co-operate in the running of societies etc. A broad traditional education is given, academic standards are high and it has a high reputation far beyond Bolton. Very many pupils go on to degree courses, many to Oxbridge. French, German and Russian are offered to A-level; all boys take GCSE in two languages. There are regular exchanges with France and Germany. There are 300 assisted-place pupils. Though non-denominational, Christian beliefs are encouraged. A good deal of emphasis on health and fitness. Its outdoor activities centre in the Lake District is used a lot.

School profile

Pupils Total age range 8–18; 990 day boys. Senior department 11–18, 840 boys. Main entry ages 8, 11 and into sixth. Approx 5% are children of former pupils. 30% of senior intake from own junior school. *Transfer from maintained schools:* 58% intake at 11, plus 100% to sixth.

Entrance Own entrance exam used. Oversubscribed. No special skills or religious requirements. Parents not expected to buy text books; maximum extras, £200 lunch. 300 assisted places. 1 annual music bursary, £250 towards music tuition.

Staff Headmaster A W Wright, in post for 8 years. 66 full time staff, 4 part time. Annual turnover 3%. Average age 37.

Academic work GCSE, AS and A-levels. 19 subjects offered (including A-level general studies taken by all sixth formers). In 1991, 120 pupils in fifth, 120 in upper sixth. *GCSE:* in 1990, 110 upper fifth gained at least grade C in 8+ subjects; 8 in 5–7; and 2 in 1–4 subjects. *A-levels:* 101 upper sixth passed in 4+ subjects; 15 in 3; 3 in 2 subjects. 57 took science A-levels; 38 arts/humanities; 24 both. *Computing facilities:* Networked computer studies room with 30 workstations; plus facilities in 7 departments. *Special provision:* Lift, giving access to all floors, available for physically handicapped.

European Community *Languages:* French offered: to age 14; GCSE; AS-level; A-level. German offered: to age 14; GCSE; AS-level; A-level. Danish offered: non-examined (in sixth form). Dutch offered: non-examined (in sixth form). 50–75% take GCSE in more than 1 EC language; including Russian, all pupils take 2 languages at GCSE. *Exchanges:* Regular exchanges for pupils aged 14–16 to France and Germany. *Other:* Pupils from France and Netherlands in school (parents on short term contracts in NW England).

Senior pupils' non-academic activities *Music:* 250 learn a musical instrument, 50 to Grade 6 or above; 45 in school orchestra, 130 in choir, 20 in jazz group, 25 in concert brass band; 6 in Bolton or other local youth orchestras; 6 university organ scholars. *Drama and dance:* 100 participate in school productions. 3 now work in theatre. *Art:* 120 take as non-examined subject; 25 GCSE; 10 A-level. 3 accepted for Art School. 15 in eg photographic club. *Sport:* Soccer, rugby, cricket, cross-country, athletics, swimming, basketball, volleyball, hockey, badminton, tennis available. 300+ take non-compulsory sport. 12 represent county (soccer, rugby, athletics, cross-country). *Other:* 15 take part in local community schemes. 30 have bronze Duke of Edinburgh's Award, 10 have silver and 5 gold. 2 enter voluntary schemes after leaving school, 1 works for national charity. Other activities include computer club, camps, outdoor pursuits base near Ullswater, treks, large and flourishing scout group with new purpose built HQ.

Careers In 1990, 89% leavers went on to degree courses; 2% to art/drama/music colleges; 2% to non-degree courses; 8% straight into careers. Of those going on to degree courses, 14% went to Oxbridge, 77% to other universities; 10% to poly/colleges. 1% those going on to higher education went to courses in practical art; 2% in music; 45% in humanities/social sciences; 9% in medicine; and 44% in science/engineering.

Uniform School uniform worn except in sixth.

Houses/prefects Competitive houses. Prefects, head boy (appointed by Head), head of house and house captains of sports (elected by staff and school).

Religion Compulsory broadly Christian assembly.

Social Girls' division of same foundation adjacent; joint drama, music, opera, debating society, Christian Union, swimming team. Organised German and French exchanges each year; Russian visit every other year; school trips to Rhineland, classical sites in Europe; 4 weeks in central southern Europe or Asia each summer (trek camp); 3 ski trips each winter. Pupils allowed to bring own car/bike/motorbike to school. Meals formal. School shop. No tobacco/alcohol allowed.

Discipline No corporal punishment. Pupils failing to produce homework once might expect evening detention; those caught smoking cannabis on the premises could expect immediate and indefinite suspension.

Alumni association is run by N Slater, Hon Sec, Old Boltonians Association, c/o the School.

Former pupils Lord Haslam (former chairman of National Coal Board); Nigel Short (chess champion); the late Sir Geoffrey Jackson (British ambassador to Uruguay); Sir Ian McKellen (actor).

· *Bolton (Girls)* ·

Bolton School Girls'
Division
Chorley New Road
Bolton
Lancashire BL1 4PB
Tel 0204 40201

- Pupils 1150
- Boys 4–8 only (Day)
- Girls 4–18 (Day)
- Upper sixth 118

- Termly fees £998 (Day)
- GSA
Enquiries/application to the Headmistress

What it's like

Founded in 1877, it moved to other premises in 1891 and to its present site in 1928. The boys' and girls' divisions are a single foundation, provided for by Lord Leverhulme. It has an excellent site of 32 acres on the western side of Bolton and a mile from its centre. The handsome sandstone buildings are set among lawns, playing fields and woodland. They are extremely well equipped with a fine library and spacious hall and overall are dignified and comfortable. Many additions and improvements have been made in the last 25 years. Most of the facilities are shared by the boys' school. Recent improvements include an indoor sports complex. The school also has a field study centre in Cumbria, and a nearby 18 acre site for the Leverhulme centre. Academically it is a high powered and well-run school which has a notable reputation in the locality and further afield. Results are consistently good and each year very many go on to take degree courses, including many at Oxbridge. A very efficient careers advice service is provided for all pupils. Music, drama and art are extremely strong and involve a large number of pupils, who reach high levels of achievement. A wide range of sports and games is available and the school has had many representatives at county, regional and national level (especially in lacrosse). Numerous clubs and societies cater for extra-curricular needs. The school organises regular expeditions in Britain and abroad and pupils also have a big commitment to local community services and the Duke of Edinburgh's Award Scheme.

School profile

Pupils Total age range 4–18, 1150 day pupils (100 boys, 1050 girls). Senior department 11–18, 800 girls. Main entry ages 4 (boys and girls), 8, 11 and into sixth (girls). 5% are children of former pupils. Own junior department provides 25% senior intake. *Transfer from maintained schools:* 70% senior intake, plus 75% to sixth.

Entrance Own entrance exam used. No special skills or religious requirements. Oversubscribed. Parents not expected to buy text books. 38 assisted places (at 11), 5 (at 16). 1 music bursary, £250.

Staff Headmistress Mrs M A Spurr, in post for 12 years. 73 full time staff, 17 part time. Annual turnover 3%. Average age 36.

Academic work GCSE and A-levels. 21 subjects offered (including Greek and

A-level general studies). In 1989, 106 pupils in upper fifth, 118 in upper sixth. *GCSE:* in 1989, 98 upper fifth gained at least grade C in 8+ subjects; 6 in 5–7; and 2 in 1–4 subjects. *A-levels:* 92 upper sixth passed in 4+ subjects; 16 in 3; 7 in 2; and 3 in 1 subject. 25% took science A-levels; 45% arts/humanities; 30% both. *Computing facilities:* All pupils have computer studies lessons. Two fully equipped computer rooms; most departments have their own computers. *Special provision:* Lift for wheelchairs.

Senior pupils' non-academic activities *Music:* 300 learn a musical instrument, 50 to Grade 6 or above; 100 in school orchestra, 200 in choir, 2 in National Youth Orchestra; 3 accepted for music school. *Drama and dance:* 350 participate in school productions. *Art:* 110 take as non-examined subject; 33 GCSE; 8 A-level. 4 accepted for Art School. 10 in eg photographic club. *Sport:* Lacrosse, netball, tennis, rounders, athletics, swimming available. 100 take non-compulsory sport. 30 take exams. 5 represent county (tennis, lacrosse). *Other:* 100 take part in local community schemes. 35 have bronze Duke of Edinburgh's Award, 5 have silver. 5 enter voluntary schemes after leaving school. Clubs of all kinds flourish – chess, computers, drama, debating, language; field trips; visits abroad.

Careers 9 full time careers advisers.

Annual average accepted for *arts and humanities degree courses* at Oxbridge, 6; other universities, 35; polytechnics/colleges, 5. *science and engineering degree courses* at Oxbridge, 6; other universities, 30; medical schools, 8; polytechnics or colleges, 5. *BEd,* 5. *other training courses,* 1%. Average going straight into careers (eg Marks & Spencer trainee manager), 2%.

Uniform School uniform worn except in sixth.

Houses/prefects Competitive houses. Prefects, head girl elected by school.

Religion Attendance at religious worship compulsory but withdrawal by parents possible.

Social Joint activities with Boys' division eg drama productions, field trips, annual exchanges to France, Spain and Germany. Annual visits to Berlin, skiing holiday, debating society. Pupils allowed to bring own car/bike/motorbike to school. Meals self-service. School shop. No tobacco/alcohol allowed.

Discipline No corporal punishment. Pupils failing to produce homework once might expect verbal warning; those caught smoking cannabis on the premises could expect immediate suspension.

Alumni association is run by Mrs M Jones, c/o the school.

Former pupils Ann Taylor MP.

· Bootham ·

Bootham School	• Pupils 335	• Termly fees
York	• Boys 11–18	£1650 (Day)
YO3 7BU	(Day/Board)	£2560 (Board/
Tel 0904 623636	• Girls 11–18	Weekly)
	(Day/Board)	• HMC
	• Upper sixth 40	Enquiries/application to
		the Headmaster

What it's like

Founded in 1823, a Quaker Foundation (The Society of Friends), it has an agreeable site of 10 acres just outside York's medieval walls and a few minutes' walk from the City centre. Playing fields adjoin it. A number of Georgian houses constitute the core; there are numerous modern extensions and facilities. It has most of the advantages of being a comparatively small school. Full use is made of the city's amenities (several excellent museums, the theatre and art gallery). Quaker beliefs underlie the daily life of pupils and staff but those of other persuasions are welcome. Strong in music, art and the sciences. Many sixth form leavers go on to degree courses. French and German are offered to A-level and there are regular exchanges with Germany. In 1992 there will be a Pan-European Conference for the 17–24 age group. A European society started in 1991. Most seniors take part in a variety of local community schemes and there is vigorous local support.

School profile

Pupils Age range 11–18; 335 pupils, 230 day (125 boys, 105 girls), 105 boarders (boys and girls). Main entry ages, 11, 13 and into sixth. *Transfer from maintained schools:* 20–30% main intake, plus 90% to sixth.

Entrance Common entrance and own entrance exam used. Well subscribed (entry at 13 most accessible). No special skills or religious requirements. Parents not expected to buy text books; music tuition etc extra. Assisted places at 11. 12 scholarships, entrance awards and bursaries according to need as far as possible, value half fees to one-eighth fees; art and music scholarships to half fees. Bursary help adds 15 scholarships where there is need.

Parents 25+% in industry or commerce, 15+% are doctors and lawyers etc. 40+% live within 30 miles; up to 10% live overseas.

Staff Headmaster I M Small, in post for 3 years. 30 full time staff, 8 part time. Annual turnover 3%. Average age 40.

Academic work GCSE and A-levels. Subjects offered include A-level general studies. In 1990, 60 pupils in upper fifth, 38 in upper sixth (now 40). *GCSE:* in 1990, 44 upper fifth gained at least grade C in 8+ subjects; 12 in 5–7; and 4 in 1–4 subjects. *A-levels:* 18 upper sixth passed in 4+ subjects; 10 in 3; 7 in 2; and 3 in 1 subject. 16 took science A-levels; 16 arts/ humanities; 6 both. *Computing facilities:* Computer education room (18 work stations, BBC and Archimedes), classroom computers in 6 departments. *Special provision:* Dyslexic teaching in school or at local branch of Dyslexia Institute; EFL tuition.

European Community *Languages:* French offered: to age 14; GCSE; AS-level; A-level. German offered: to age 14; GCSE; AS-level; A-level. 10–25% take GCSE in more than 1 EC language. *Exchanges:* Regular exchanges for pupils aged 14–18 to Germany. *Other:* European Studies offered to pupils aged 11–14. Pan-European conference on Business Morality in 1992, with St Williams Foundation. European Society started 1991. German resident graduates on 1 year exchanges.

Senior pupils' non-academic activities *Music:* 60 learn a musical instrument, 25 to Grade 6 or above, 2 accepted for Music School; 32 in school orchestra, 18 in choir, 7 in pop group; 45 in other musical activities; 7 in local orchestras. *Drama and dance:* 140 in school productions. *Art:* 110 take as non-examined subject; 18 GCSE; 5 A-level. 3 accepted for Art School; 1 for architecture. 20 belong to eg photographic club. *Sport:* Football, hockey, cricket, tennis, swimming, squash, badminton, netball, volleyball, self defence, fencing, athletics, rowing available. All pupils take non-compulsory sport. 7 represent county (hockey, cross-country, athletics, swimming, netball). *Other:* Most seniors take part in local community schemes. Other activities include computer and chess clubs; eligible pupils can learn to drive. Leisure hour activities are structured and regarded as very important; wide range available.

Careers In 1990, 80% leavers went on to degree courses; 6% to art/drama/ music colleges; 6% to non-degree courses (eg retailing); 3% straight into careers (eg business); 5% other. Of those going on to degree courses, 4% went to Oxbridge, 60% to other universities; 36% to poly/ colleges. 7% those going on to higher education went to courses in practical art; 7% in music; 52% in humanities/social sciences; 11% in medicine; and 23% in science/engineering.

Uniform School uniform worn in first three years.

Houses/prefects Competitive houses for sport, music and speech-making. Prefects, head boy/girl, head of house and house prefects – elected by the school. There is a Communications Group.

Religion Quakerism (The Society of Friends).

Social Joint drama productions with sister school, The Mount. Organised exchanges abroad with school in West Germany; ski-ing trips and language trips abroad (including Russia). Pupils allowed to bring own car/bike/motorbike to school. Meals usually self service, few special meals formal. No tobacco/alcohol allowed.

Discipline No corporal punishment. Pupils failing to produce homework once might expect 'Columns' (writing out words from a dictionary) or 'Gating' (staying within the school campus); those caught smoking cannabis on the premises should expect expulsion.

Boarding 40% of sixth formers have own study bedroom, 60% share (with 1); very few pupils are in dormitories of 6+. Houses divided by age. Resident qualified nurse/doctor. Central dining room. Pupils can provide and cook own food. 2 weekend exeats each term. Visits to the local town allowed as required.

Alumni association is run by The Secretary, BOSA, c/o the School.

Former pupils A J P Taylor (historian); Philip Noel-Baker (Nobel Peace Prize).

· *Box Hill* ·

Box Hill School
Mickleham
Dorking
Surrey
RH5 6EA
Tel 0372 373382

- Pupils 288
- Boys 11–18 (Day/Board)
- Girls 11–18 (Day/Board)
- Upper sixth 26

- Termly fees
  £1454 (Day)
  £2596 (Board)
  £2420 (Weekly)
- SHMIS, Round Square, ISAI
  Enquiries/application to the Headmaster's Secretary

What it's like

Founded in 1959. The main building is a handsome Victorian mansion (plus purpose-built modern facilities) situated in 40 acres of delightful grounds, with big playing fields. It is in the village of Mickleham in whose life the school plays an active part. It belongs to The Round Square Conference and is run on the principles of Kurt Hahn, founder of Salem and Gordonstoun, setting academic work at the centre of a broad education. It thus has close international links with schools in Europe, USA, Canada, India and Australia. There is an annual conference at one of the sister schools. Sixth formers do project work in Indian and Kenyan villages in association with schools in India and Kenya. They have an efficient system of exchanges and post A-level attachments. A wide range of activities and expeditions is operated in the belief that all pupils may excel at something and will develop through challenging experiences. Drama, music and art are regarded as particularly important. The staff includes a dyslexia specialist and a specialist in teaching English as a second language. Expeditions to Hadrian's Wall, Canterbury and the Lake district part of junior curriculum. French, German and Spanish are offered to A-level; many sixth form leavers go on to polytechnics and some to university.

School profile

Pupils Age range 11–18; 288 pupils, 118 day (73 boys, 45 girls), 170 boarding (105 boys, 65 girls). Main entry ages 11, 12, 13 and into sixth. Very few are children of former pupils (because of age and initial size of school). *Transfer from maintained schools:* Approx 50% of intake.

Entrance Common entrance and own entrance exam used. Not oversubscribed. Good music or art and an ability to contribute to school life looked for. No religious requirements. Parents expected to buy some A-level text books; other extras vary. 2 scholarships up to half fees; 8–10 other scholarships for pupils entering sixth form, £450 per term; scholarships and bursaries lower down the school for 'all round' qualities.

Parents 15+% in industry or commerce. 45+% live within 30 miles; 20% live overseas.

Staff Headmaster Dr Rodney Atwood, in post for 4 years. 22 full time staff, 16 part time. Annual turnover 5%.

Academic work GCSE and A-levels. 18 GCSE subjects offered; 16 at A-level (including A-level general studies). In 1990, 49 pupils in upper fifth, 26 in upper sixth. *GCSE:* on average, 10 upper fifth gained at least grade C in 8+ subjects; 30 in 5–7; and 9 in 1–4 subjects. *A-levels:* on average 1 upper sixth pupil passed in 4+ subjects; 13 in 3; 6 in 2; and 5 in 1 subject. On average 9 took science A-levels; 12 arts/humanities; 5 both. *Computing facilities:* One room of Apple Macintosh computers; others, including Amstrads, held in departments. *Special provision:* qualified dyslexia specialist and a qualified teacher of English as a second language.

European Community *Languages:* French offered: to age 14; GCSE; A-level. German offered: to age 14; GCSE; A-level. Spanish offered: to age 14; GCSE; A-level. 10–25% take GCSE in more than 1 EC language. *Exchanges:* Regular exchanges for pupils aged 14–18 to Germany. Also exchanges with Cours Alphonse, Dandet, Montpelier in France, 3 schools in Germany, and Villamardin, Cadiz, Spain.

Senior pupils' non-academic activities *Music:* 90 pupils learn a musical instrument; whole school participates in annual internal music competition. *Drama and dance:* 95 in school plays. Whole school participates in annual internal drama competition scripted and directed by the pupils. *Art:* 6 take A-level. 15 belong to eg photographic club. *Sport:* Soccer, cricket, tennis, athletics, swimming, netball, hockey, volleyball, riding, squash, badminton, karate, judo, fencing, table tennis, climbing (expeditions and indoor climbing wall) available. Over 100 take non-compulsory sport. Over 100 take exams eg gymnastics, swimming. Others do karate, judo, life saving (St John Ambulance). Some represent county (athletics). *Other:* 22 have bronze Duke of Edinburgh's Award, 8 have silver and 6 have gold. All pupils raise money, help old people, the local primary school, the Talking Newspaper for the Blind, etc. Other activities include a computer club (part of the electronics club); St John Ambulance first aid, bee-keeping, conservation work, pony care.

Careers In 1990, 67% leavers went on to degree courses; 10% to art/drama/ music colleges; 10% to non-degree courses; 13% other. Of those going on to degree courses, 40% went to universities; 60% to poly/colleges.

Uniform School uniform worn throughout.

Houses/prefects Competitive houses. Prefects, head boy and girl, head of house and house prefects – elected by senior prefect body. School Council.

Religion Non-denominational service every Sunday from which parents may request exemption.

Social Sixth form conference and careers conference to which other schools are invited. Organised trips to Germany;

mountaineering trips to Alps; well developed exchanges. Sixth form and society/club dinners formal; self service at other times. School shop sells books. No tobacco/alcohol allowed.

Discipline No corporal punishment. Pupils failing to produce homework would be kept in on Saturday afternoon; those caught smoking cannabis on the premises could expect expulsion.

Boarding 2% have own study bedroom, 68% share (1–4); 30% are in dormitories of 6+. Single sex houses, of approximately 35–50, divided by age. Weekly boarding allowed. 1 SRN, 2 school doctors (non-resident). Central dining room. Pupils can provide and cook own food. 2 weekend exeats each term for full boarders plus half-term. Visits to the local town allowed.

Alumni association is run by Mr Jeremy Taylor, Box Hill School Association Secretary, c/o the School.

· *Bradfield* ·

Bradfield College
Reading
Berkshire
RG7 6AR
Tel 0734 744203

- Pupils 580
- Boys 13–18 (Day/Board)
- Girls 16–18 (Day/Board)
- Upper sixth 99

- Termly fees
  £2325 (Day)
  £3100 (Board)
- HMC
Enquiries/application to the Headmaster's Secretary

What it's like

Founded in 1850, it became well known by 1900 as one of the leading independent schools in southern England. In effect the school *is* the village of Bradfield and vice versa; a very attractive village of brick-and-half-timber and brick-and-flint houses in one of the prettiest regions of Berkshire. The total grounds cover about 200 acres. Its accommodation is excellent (comfortable small dormitories) and has outstandingly good facilities in general (including a modern design centre, an electronics centre, a TV studio and satellite tracking equipment). It is a C of E foundation and Christian values are embodied in the life of the school, but those of other denominations are very welcome. High academic standards and many go on to degree courses, including many to Oxbridge. French, German and Spanish are offered to A-level and many pupils take GCSE in more than one European language. All three, plus Italian, are offered as non-examined languages. There are regular exchanges with France and Spain. Strong in sport and games and very strong in music and drama. It is unusual in having an open-air Greek theatre where plays in Greek are performed every three years. Other strengths are the large CCF unit (much emphasis on adventure training and leadership skills), plentiful outdoor activities plus recreations such as fly-fishing on the Pang and sailing on the gravel pits at Theale. A point is made of keeping close contacts with industry, with 'attachments' for all lower sixth pupils.

School profile

Pupils Age range 13–18; 580 pupils, 30 day (25 boys, 5 girls), 550 boarding (475 boys, 75 girls). Main entry ages boys 13; boys and girls into sixth. Approx 15% are children of former pupils. *Transfer from maintained schools:* 3% main intake, plus 25% to sixth.

Entrance Common entrance exam plus own scholarship examination used. Oversubscribed. No special skills required, but

143

any are taken into account. No religious requirements. Parents expected to buy text books at sixth form level. 6 assisted places at sixth form level only. 18 scholarships/bursaries, 50–10% of fees.

Parents 15+% in industry or commerce, 15+% are doctors, lawyers etc. 10+% live within 30 miles; up to 10% live overseas.

Staff Head Master P B Smith, in post for 6 years. 56 full time staff, 21 part time. Annual turnover 4%. Average age 33.

Academic work GCSE and A-levels. 18 GCSE subjects offered; 25 at A-level (no A-level general studies). In 1990, 108 pupils in upper fifth, 99 in upper sixth. *GCSE:* in 1990, 88 upper fifth gained at least grade C in 8+ subjects; 13 in 5–7; and 7 in 1–4 subjects. *A-levels:* 5 upper sixth passed in 4+ subjects; 74 in 3; 16 in 2; and 3 in 1 subject. 33% took science A-levels; 33% arts/humanities; 33% both. *Computing facilities:* Central information technology room, plus computers in all departments and all houses.

European Community *Languages:* French offered: to age 14; GCSE; AS-level; A-level; non-examined. German offered: to age 14; GCSE; A-level; non-examined. Italian offered: non-examined. Spanish offered: to GCSE; A-level; non-examined. 25–50% take GCSE in more than 1 EC language. *Exchanges:* Regular exchanges for pupils aged 14–18 to France and Spain. *Other:* A number of European pupils (Dutch, German, Spanish) in school for 1 term–1 year.

Senior pupils' non-academic activities *Music:* 220 learn a musical instrument, 40 to Grade 6 or above. 5 take A-level music, 5 accepted for music degrees; 60 in orchestra, 80 in choir. *Drama and dance:* 200 in school productions. 4 accepted for Drama/Dance Schools. *Art:* 20 take as non-examined subject; 12 GCSE; 8 A-level. 4 accepted for Art School. 40 belong to eg photographic, architectural and art appreciation clubs. *Sport:* Football, hockey, cricket, tennis, athletics, shooting, swimming, sailing, golf, basketball, judo, karate, cross-country, fives, squash, water polo, fly-fishing, clay-pigeon shooting, fencing

available. Virtually all take non-compulsory sport. Pupils represent county at various sports. *Other:* 50 take part in local community schemes. 15 have bronze Duke of Edinburgh's Award, 15 have silver and 15 gold. Other activities include a computer club, chess club, 30 societies, electronics club, design centre, CCF.

Careers In 1990, 75% leavers went on to degree courses; 8% to art/drama/music colleges; 7% to non-degree courses (eg agriculture); 10% straight into careers (eg army). Of those going on to degree courses, 15% went to Oxbridge, 70% to other universities; 15% to poly/colleges. 5% those going on to higher education went to courses in practical art; 1% in drama/acting; 1% in music; 42% in humanities/social sciences; 5% in medicine; and 46% in science/engineering.

Uniform School uniform worn throughout.

Houses/prefects Prefects, head boy, head of house and house prefects appointed by the Head in consultation with staff and pupils.

Religion Attendance at school Chapel, once on Sunday, twice per week for morning prayers.

Social Many joint theatrical and choral productions with local girls' schools. Organised holiday expeditions, several per year. French school exchange. Pupils allowed to bring own bike to school. Meals self service. School shop. No tobacco allowed. School bar for 17 year olds.

Discipline No corporal punishment. Pupils failing to produce homework once would be asked to do it; those caught smoking cannabis on the premises could expect to be expelled.

Boarding 30% have own study bedroom, 30% share 1–3; 30% are in dormitories of 6+. Houses, of approximately 60–65. Resident qualified medical staff. Central dining room. Pupils can provide and cook own food. Up to 4 weekend exeats per term. Visits to the local town allowed for sixth form.

Alumni association is run by J B Johnson, c/o the College.

Former pupils Richard Adams (author); David Owen (politician).

· *Bradford (Boys)* ·

Bradford Grammar
School
Keighley Road
Bradford
West Yorkshire
BD9 4JP
Tel 0274 542492

- Pupils 1160
- Boys 8–18
  (Day)
- Girls 15–18
  (Day)
- Upper sixth 150

- Termly fees
  £1058 (Day)
- HMC
Enquiries/application to
the Headmaster

What it's like

It existed c1548 and was incorporated by royal charter in 1662. A mile from the centre of Bradford, it comprises five main buildings on a 20-acre site: the Clock House, a 17th-century manor house for the juniors; the handsome senior school (opened in 1949); the Kenneth Robinson Building (1974); the Edward Clarkson Library and Information Technology Centre (1988), the Chippendale Sports Hall and Hockney Theatre (1989). Its overall amenities are first-rate. The two principles of discipline laid down are: firstly, that pupils are expected to know what is and what is not good conduct and to do nothing likely to bring themselves and their school into disrepute; secondly, that study is a discipline in itself. It provides a sound, traditional education in many branches of learning, including not only classics and information technology but also economics and electronics systems and sets very high all-round standards. It enjoys strong local loyalties and support and in fact has long been one of the most distinguished schools in Britain with remarkable academic records. Many pupils go on to degree courses including a high proportion to Oxbridge. French and German are offered to A-level, Spanish to GCSE. Many pupils take GCSE in more than one European language. There are regular exchanges with France and Germany, and time-tabled French and German conversation classes.

School profile

Pupils Total age range 8–18; 1160 day pupils (1115 boys, 45 girls). Senior department 11–18, 1015 pupils (970 boys, 45 girls). Main entry ages: 8, 9, 10, 11, 13 (boys) and into sixth (boys and girls). Approx 10% are children of former pupils. *Transfer from maintained schools:* 82% intake 11+, plus 35% to sixth.

Entrance Own entrance exam used. Oversubscribed. No special skills or religious requirements. Parents not expected to buy text books. 35 assisted places. 5 scholarships/bursaries, up to £1000 pa.

Parents 15+% in industry or commerce; 15+% are doctors, lawyers etc.

Staff Headmaster D A G Smith, in post for 16 years. 77 full time staff, 7 part time. Annual turnover 4%. Average age 35.

Academic work GCSE, AS and A-levels. 21 GCSE subjects offered; 5 at AS, 21 at A-level (no A-level general studies). In 1990, 140 pupils in upper fifth, 150 in upper sixth. *GCSE:* in 1990, 78% upper fifth gained at least grade C in 8+ subjects; 21% in 5–7; and 1% in 1–4 subjects. *A-levels:* 12% upper sixth passed in 4+ subjects; 71% in 3; 13% in 2; and 1% in 1 subject. 42% took science A-levels; 40% arts/humanities; 18% both. *Computing facilities:* Purpose built information technology centre with 40+ PCs.

European Community *Languages:* French offered: to age 14; GCSE; AS-level; A-level. German offered: to age 14; GCSE; AS-level; A-level. Spanish offered: to GCSE. 25–50% take GCSE in more than 1 EC language. *Exchanges:* Regular exchanges for pupils aged 14–18 to France and Germany. *Other:* Native French and German speakers on staff give conversation lessons.

Senior pupils' non-academic activities *Music:* 250 learn a musical instrument, 30 to Grade 6 or above, 3 accepted for Music School; 120 in orchestras, 80 in choirs, 100 participate in brass, wind group, strings; 1 in National Youth Orchestra. *Drama and dance:* 100 in school productions. *Art:* 5 take GCSE, 5 A-level. 3 accepted for Art School. *Sport:* Athletics, badminton, basketball, cross-country, cricket, hockey, lawn tennis, rugby football, rowing, squash, swimming, water polo, aikido, golf, outdoor pursuits, table tennis available. 350 take non-compulsory sport. Pupils represent county (rugby, cricket, cross-country, athletics, squash, hockey). *Other:* activities include a computer club, venture scouts, CCF, archaeological society, chess, debating society, drama, ski club, voluntary action group, theatre club.

Careers In 1990, 86% leavers went on to degree courses; 1% to non-degree courses (eg agriculture, land management); 4% straight into careers (eg retailing, banking); 9% other. Of those going on to degree courses, 24% went to Oxbridge, 67% to other universities; 9% to poly/colleges. 1% those going on to higher education went to courses in drama/acting; 54% in humanities/social sciences; 7% in medicine; and 38% in science/engineering.

Uniform School uniform worn except in fifths and sixths.

Houses/prefects No competitive houses. Prefects and head boy/girl appointed by the Head.

Religion School prayers.

Social No organised local events; some trips abroad. Meals self service. School shop. No tobacco/alcohol allowed.

Discipline No corporal punishment. Pupils failing to produce homework once might expect a detention; those caught smoking cannabis on the premises could expect expulsion.

Alumni association is run by G Lodge, President: BGS Old Boys' Association, c/o the School.

Former pupils Dennis Healey; David Hockney; Sir Maurice Hodgson and others.

· *Bradford (Girls)* ·

Bradford Girls' Grammar School Squire Lane Bradford West Yorkshire BD9 6RB Tel 0274 545395	● Pupils 925 ● Boys 4–8 only (Day) ● Girls 4–18 (Day) ● Upper sixth 85	● Termly fees £1067 (Day) ● GSA Enquiries to the Headmistress Applications to the Registrations Secretary

What it's like

Founded in 1876, it comprises fine, solid, well-equipped buildings and excellent up-to-date facilities on 17 acres of pleasant grounds, playing fields and woodland, in an urban residential area near the city centre. It has its own sixth-form college on site. Its academic standards and reputation are high and its pupils very motivated. Many pupils go on to degree courses, including Oxbridge. French, German and Spanish are offered to A-level. Many girls take GCSE in more than one European language and there are regular exchanges with France, Germany and Spain. It is especially strong in music and drama and enjoys vigorous local community support as well as support from alumni.

146

School profile

Pupils Total age range 4–18; 925 day pupils (25 boys, 900 girls). Senior department 11–18, 690 girls. Main entry ages 4, 9, 11 and into sixth. Approx 10–15% are children of former pupils. *Transfer from maintained schools:* 50% main intake at 11, plus 5% to sixth.

Entrance Own entrance exam used. Oversubscribed. No special skills or religious requirements. Parents not expected to buy text books; music, dancing etc charged extra. 60 assisted places. Scholarships and bursaries available according to need.

Parents 15+% in industry or commerce; 15+% are doctors, lawyers etc.

Staff Headmistress Mrs L J Warrington, in post for 3 years. 45 full time staff, 16 part time. Annual turnover 5–10%. Average age 35–40.

Academic work GCSE and A-levels. 18 GCSE subjects offered (including Russian); 26 at A-level (including general studies). On average 110 pupils in upper fifth, 85 in upper sixth. *GCSE:* on average, 60% upper fifth gained at least grade C in 8+ subjects; 35% in 5–7; and 5% in 1–4 subjects. *A-levels:* 20% upper sixth passed in 4+ subjects; 70% in 3; 5% in 2; and 5% in 1 subject. 50% took science A-levels; 50% arts/humanities. *Computing facilities:* IT Centre with Nimbus network and stand-alone computers in various departments.

European Community *Languages:* French offered: to age 14; GCSE; AS-level; A-level; Institute of Linguists. German offered: to GCSE; AS-level; A-level; Institute of Linguists. Spanish offered: to GCSE; AS-level; A-level; Institute of Linguists. 25–50% take GCSE in more than 1 EC language. *Exchanges:* Regular exchanges for pupils aged 14–18 to France, Germany and Spain.

Senior pupils' non-academic activities *Music:* 200+ learn a musical instrument, 20–30 to Grade 6 or above; 60 in orchestra; 120 in choir, others in madrigals, string quartet, wind quintet etc; 3 in Leeds, Calderdale and Kirklees orchestras; 10 in other activities in musicals, church, choral groups etc. *Drama and dance:* 150 in school productions. 4 take GCSE drama in sixth form. *Art:* 10 take A-level art. 5 accepted for Art School. *Sport:* Hockey, netball, rounders, tennis, swimming, volleyball, athletics throughout, badminton, squash, self-defence, fencing available in sixth form. 200+ take non-compulsory sport. 27 represent county (hockey, netball). *Other:* 20+ take part in local community schemes. All forms organise annual event in aid of charity. Other activities include a computer club, drama societies, dance club, choir, orchestra, madrigal group, history society, horse riding club etc.

Careers In 1990, 79% leavers went on to degree courses; 3% to art/drama/music colleges; 10% to non-degree courses (eg HNDs, nursing, business); 7% straight into careers (eg accountancy, building societies, management); 1% other. Of those going on to degree courses, 8% went to Oxbridge, 68% to other universities; 24% to poly/colleges. $6\frac{1}{2}$% those going on to higher education went to courses in practical art; $1\frac{1}{2}$% in music; 62% in humanities/social sciences; 10% in medicine; and 20% in science/engineering.

Uniform School uniform worn except in sixth.

Houses/prefects No competitive houses. Prefects, President of Junior Common Room – elected by school and staff. School Council.

Religion Daily act of worship compulsory except in sixth form or unless withdrawn by parents.

Social Occasional careers conventions and debating society joint with other schools. Organised trips: 2nd year to France and exchanges with France, Germany and Spain. Pupils allowed to bring own car/bike/motorbike to school in sixth form only. Meals self service. School shop. No tobacco/alcohol allowed.

Discipline No corporal punishment. Pupils failing to produce homework once might expect a deadline if there was no good reason; those caught smoking cannabis on the premises could expect expulsion.

· *Brentwood* ·

Brentwood School
Ingrave Road
Brentwood
Essex
CM15 8AS
Tel 0277 214580

- Pupils 911
- Boys 11–18
  (Day/Board)
- Girls 11–18
  (Day)
- Upper sixth 122

- Termly fees
  £1384 (Day)
  £2423 (Board)
- HMC
  Enquiries/application to
  the Headmaster

What it's like

Founded in 1557, it occupies a single site in a relatively urban area with extensive gardens and nearly 70 acres of playing fields. It is architecturally pleasing (the old 'Big School' built in 1568 is still in use) and there have been many modern developments including a new building for the girls' school. Facilities are now first rate. The standard of teaching is high and a large number of leavers proceed to degree courses, including many to Oxbridge. French, German and Spanish are offered to A-level; also Italian for GCSE. Many pupils take GCSE in more than one European language. There are exchange arrangements with France, Germany and Spain. Some of its main strengths lie in music, drama and art, and there is a flourishing CCF. It enjoys good local support. Having been a boys' school with a mixed sixth, it is now becoming more mixed; girls were admitted from 11 in 1988 but are educated separately to GCSE. The sixth form remains fully co-ed.

School profile

Pupils Age range 11–18; 911 pupils, 811 day (659 boys, 152 girls), 100 boarding (all boys). Main entry ages, boys and girls, 11 and 16; 13 for boys. Approx 5% are children of former pupils. Own prep school (boys) provides c50% of intake. *Transfer from maintained schools:* 33% at 11, plus 60% to sixth.

Entrance Common entrance and own entrance exam used. Oversubscribed. No religious requirements but Protestant tradition. Parents not expected to buy text books; house account, fencing, music etc extra. Assisted places at 11 and for the 6th form. 12 scholarships pa, bursaries available.

Parents 15+% in industry or commerce; 15+% are doctors, lawyers etc. 60+% live within 30 miles.

Staff Headmaster J A E Evans, in post for 10 years. 84 full time staff, 8 part time. Annual turnover approx 10%. Average age 36.

Academic work GCSE and A-level. Electronic systems and ancient history are offered to GCSE/A-level. Average size of fifth 115; upper sixth 122. *GCSE:* on average, 64 pupils in fifth pass 8+ subjects; 46, 5–7 subjects; 15 pass 1–4 subjects. *A-levels:* on average, 16 pupils in upper sixth pass 4 subjects; 75, 3 subjects; 13, 2 subjects and 6 pass 1 subject. On average, 40 take science/engineering A-levels; 60 take arts and humanities; 20 a mixture. *Computing facilities:* Computer lab with 16 BBCs, 3 Amstrads, 2 Apples (Sinclair Spectrums in reserve), 16 Archimedes. *Special provision:* subsidiary EFL classes offered.

European Community *Languages:* French offered: to age 14; GCSE; AS-level; A-level. German offered: to age 14; GCSE; A-level. Italian offered: to GCSE. Spanish offered: to age 14; GCSE; A-level; Institute of Linguists. 25–50% take GCSE in more than 1 EC language. *Exchanges:* Regular exchanges for pupils aged 11–18 to France, Germany and Spain. *Other:* Close contacts, especially musical, with twin town in Bavaria. Visits to first world war battlefields, and classical sites. Courses in Spanish for sixth formers; developing links with Zaragoza.

Senior pupils' non-academic activities *Music:* 100 learn a musical instrument, 30 to Grade 6 or above. 1 accepted for Music School. 10 play in jazz group beyond school; 75 in orchestra, 75 in choir, 50 in jazz group. *Drama and dance:* 50 in school productions; 2 accepted for Drama/Dance Schools. *Art:* 50 take as non-examined subject; 32 take GCSE; 11, A-level; 16, Art History; 6, AS-level; 2 or 3 go on to study art including history of art degree courses. 24 belong to photographic club; 80 in general studies and short courses. *Sport:* Soccer, basketball, volleyball, cricket, squash, fencing, swimming, badminton, netball, athletics, cross-country, tennis available. 60 take part in school team practices each week. 15 take exams in gymnastics, swimming, 20 take fencing, life saving. 36 represent country/district/county (fencing, rugby, soccer, athletics, swimming, cross-country). *Other:* 30 take part in local community schemes. 300 in CCF. Other activities include a computer club, chess club, archery, athletics, life saving, art, brass ensemble, bridge, Chapel choir, choral choir, Christian Union, community service, rifle club.

Careers In 1990, 80% leavers went on to degree courses; 8% to art/drama/music colleges; 2% to non-degree courses; 10% straight into careers (eg banking). Of those going on to degree courses, 18% went to Oxbridge, 54% to other universities; 28% to poly/colleges. 5% those going on to higher education went to courses in practical art; 1% in drama/acting; 2% in music; 43% in humanities/social sciences; 11% in medi-

cine; and 38% in science/engineering.

Uniform School uniform worn throughout.

Houses/prefects Competitive houses. Prefects, head boy, head of house and house prefects – appointed by the Head.

Religion Regular chapel (C of E) services.

Social Debates, historical society, drama, foreign exchange visits, county sports of various kinds. Organised trips to Germany, France, USA and ESU scholars both ways. Pupils allowed to bring own car/cycle to school with permission. Self service meals. School shop. No tobacco/alcohol allowed.

Discipline No corporal punishment. Punishment by admonishment, detention and suspension.

Boarding 40% have own study bedroom, 40% share; 20% are in dormitories of 6+. Houses, of 25–50, divided mainly by age groups. Resident qualified medical staff. Central dining room. Visits to local town allowed with housemaster's permission.

Alumni association run by Mr I R West, Secretary, 11 Regent Square, London E3 3HQ.

Former pupils Sir Hardy Amies; Sir Robin Day; H Whittaker (Almanac); Jack Straw MP; Bishop Griggs of Ludlow; Bishop Adams late of Barking; Air Marshal Sir John Rogers; Douglas Adams (author); George Cansdale (TV); Griff Rhys-Jones (TV); Prof Roger Cowley (Prof of Experimental Philosophy, Oxford University), Dr Stephen Fleet (Registrar Cambridge Univ. & Vice Master of Downing College).

· *Brighton College* ·

Brighton College	● Pupils 498	● Termly fees
Eastern Road	● Boys 13–18 (Day/	£1905 (Day)
Brighton	Board/Weekly)	£2895 (Board)
East Sussex	● Girls 13–18 (Day/	£2600 (Weekly)
BN2 2AL	Board/Weekly)	● HMC
Tel 0273 697131	● Upper sixth 100	Enquiries/application to
		the Headmaster

What it's like

Founded in 1845, it stands on high ground in the Kemp Town district of Brighton and enjoys handsome buildings (the school chapel, which is in regular use, is especially striking) in attractive surroundings. Ample playing fields. Well over two million pounds have been spent in the last ten years on major developments. The teaching is of a high standard and academic results are impressive. Many go on to degree courses, including a high proportion to Oxbridge. French and German are offered to A-level; also modern Greek to GCSE. Many pupils take GCSE in both French and German and there are regular exchanges for 11–14 year olds with Germany. It is a good all-round school, with plenty of regard for the less talented. Strong in music, art and drama; also in sports and games. It possesses a wide range of clubs and societies and there is considerable involvement in local community schemes. Full use is made of the cultural amenities of Brighton.

School profile

Pupils Age range 13–18; 498 pupils, 352 day (337 boys, 15 girls), 146 boarding (116 boys, 30 girls). Main entry ages 13 and into sixth. Own prep school provides 20+% of intake. Approx 15% are children of former pupils.

Entrance Common entrance exam used. Oversubscribed. Pupils who have a positive contribution to make in any sphere are welcomed. No religious requirements but the College is a C of E foundation. Parents expected to buy text books. 20 assisted places. 14 scholarships/bursaries, full fees to 10% of fees.

Parents 15+% in industry or commerce; 15+% are doctors and lawyers etc. 60+% live within 30 miles; up to 10% live overseas.

Staff Headmaster J D Leach, in post for 4 years. 46 full time staff, 12 part time. Annual turnover 4% (very stable). Average age 39.

Academic work GCSE and A-levels. Average size of upper fifth 100; upper sixth 100. *GCSE:* on average, 67 pupils in upper fifth pass 8+ subjects; 10, 5–7 subjects; 16 pass 1–4 subjects. *A-levels:* on average, 55 pupils in upper sixth pass 3 subjects or more; 16, 2 subjects; 6 pass 1 subject. On average, over one-third take science/engineering A-levels; one-third take arts and humanities; well under one-third a mixture. Geology is offered to A-level. *Computing facilities:* 16 workstation RML Nimbus network. BBC 'B' stations in departments. Laser printer, computer graphics. Newly built computer laboratories.

European Community *Languages:* French offered: to age 14; GCSE; AS-level; A-level. German offered: to age 14; GCSE; AS-level; A-level. Greek (modern) offered: to A-level. 25–50% take GCSE in more than 1 EC language. *Exchanges:* Regular exchanges for pupils aged 13–14 to Germany.

Senior pupils' non-academic activities *Music:* 75 learn a musical instrument, 26 to Grade 6 or above. 1 accepted for Music School; 1 to university; 1–2 to polytechnic. 25 in school orchestra, 48 in school choir, 21 in band, 14 in ensembles; 7 play in Brighton Youth Orchestra, 2 in East Sussex Youth Orchestra. *Drama and dance:* All pupils are encouraged to take part in drama productions, musicals and concerts. *Art:* 50 take as non-examined subject; 18 take GCSE; 16, A-level. 5 accepted for Art School. *Sport:* Rugby, hockey, cricket, netball, tennis, sailing, volleyball, soccer, golf, squash, swimming, judo, fencing, badminton, basketball available. Some sport is compulsory (unless health reasons preclude); 12 take life saving. 23 represent county (hockey, cricket, rugby, athletics, swimming). *Other:* 70 take part in local community schemes. 2 have silver Duke of Edinburgh's Award, 5 have gold. Other activities include a computer club, alternative forum, auto club, Christian forum, computer science, debating, dialectic, economics/politics, history, industrial, law, literary/play reading, mathematical, medical, modern languages, music appreciation, philosophy, photography, physics, chemistry, biology, astronomy, sketch club, sports, travel, chess, electronics and radio, experimental science, junior debating, rock society, archives, weight training.

Careers In 1990, 70% leavers went on to degree courses; 10% to art/drama/music colleges; 5% straight into careers; 15% other. Of those going on to degree courses, 20% went to Oxbridge, 69% to other universities; 11% to poly/colleges. 3% of those going on to higher education went to courses in practical art; 15% in humanities/social sciences; 5% in medicine; and 20% in science/engineering.

Uniform School uniform worn including in the sixth.

Houses/prefects Competitive houses.

Prefects, head boy/girl, head of house and house prefects – appointed by the Headmaster and housemaster/mistress.

Religion Religious worship compulsory, in College Chapel or own place of worship for those of non C of E persuasion.

Social Public speaking competitions, concerts, participation in Brighton Festival, Challenge of Industry Conference. Organised trips abroad. Pupils allowed to bring own car/bike/motorbike to school (with permission from the Headmaster). Meals self service. School shop. No tobacco allowed; limited bar in sixth form club.

Discipline No corporal punishment. Pupils failing to produce homework once might expect a 'Yellow Paper' signed by the housemaster; those caught smoking cannabis on the premises could expect expulsion.

Boarding 20% have own study bedroom, 40% share; 40% are in dormitories of 6+. Houses, of 50–60. Resident matron, doctor visits daily. Central dining room. Pupils can provide and cook own snacks. Weekend exeats, by arrangement. Visits to the local town allowed.

Alumni association run by Mrs H Williamson, Brighton College, Eastern Road, Brighton.

Former pupils George Sanders (actor); Prof Noel Odell (mountaineer and Cambridge Professor); John Worsley (artist); Rt Rev T J Bavin (Bishop of Portsmouth); Rear Admiral P G V Dingemans (Falklands); Sir Michael Hordern (actor); Sir Vivien Fuchs (explorer); Sir Humphrey Edwardes-Jones (Air Commodore); Lord Alexander QC; Jonathan Palmer (doctor and Formula 1 racing driver).

· *Bristol Cathedral* ·

Bristol Cathedral
School
College Square
Bristol
BS1 5TS
Tel 0272 291872

- Pupils 460
- Boys 10–18 (Day)
- Girls 16–18 (Day)
- Upper sixth 59

- Termly fees £1100 (Day)
- HMC, CSA
Enquiries/application to the Headmaster

What it's like

The origins of the school are in the Grammar School of St Augustine's Abbey founded in 1140. It was refounded by Henry VIII in 1542 and is Bristol's only royal foundation. It stands in the cathedral precinct and the buildings span 800 years of architectural history. The main classrooms are on the original site of the old Abbey School. There have been many modern developments and facilities are very good. A first class liberal education is provided and results are most creditable. Many sixth formers go on to degree courses. French and German are offered to A-level and a high proportion of pupils takes GCSE in both. Italian and Spanish are offered as non-examined languages. There are regular exchanges with France and Germany. Because of the close links with the cathedral (which is the school's chapel) there is considerable emphasis on religious education in the Anglican tradition. The staff: pupil ratio is about 1:13. The art, drama and music departments are extremely strong and the school is quite famous for its range of musical activities. A standard range of sports and games is available and there is a fair variety of extra-curricular activities, clubs, societies etc. Work experience is undertaken by nearly all members of the fifth form and the school has close links with a wide range of commercial and industrial concerns in and about the city. Full use is made of the city's cultural amenities.

School profile

Pupils Age range 10–18, 460 day pupils (435 boys, 25 girls). Main entry ages 10 (boys) and into sixth (boys and girls).

Entrance Own entrance exam used. 25+ pa assisted places; music, academic and instrumental scholarships.

Staff Headmaster R A Collard, 1 year in post.

Academic work GCSE, AS and A-levels. 14 GCSE subjects offered, 17 A-levels (AS general studies taken by all sixth form). In 1991, 67 pupils in fifth, 59 in upper sixth. *GCSE:* in 1990, 50 pupils in upper fifth gained at least grade C in 8+ subjects; 15 in 5–7 subjects and 2 in 1–4 subjects. *A-levels:* 4 pupils in upper sixth passed in 4 subjects; 35 in 3; 14 in 2 and 6 passed in 1 subject. 27% took science A-levels; 37% arts/humanities; 36% both. *Computing facilities:* computer lab-

oratories plus departmental facilities.

European Community *Languages:* French offered: to age 14; GCSE; AS-level; A-level. German offered: to age 14; GCSE; AS-level; A-level. Italian offered: non-examined. Spanish offered: non-examined. 50–75% take GCSE in more than 1 EC language. *Exchanges:* Regular exchanges for pupils aged 11–18 to France and Germany. *Other:* Importance of European culture and heritage stressed across the curriculum, especially in history, geography, languages and literature. Europe and EC modules in current affairs and general studies.

Careers In 1990, 40% leavers went on to degree courses; 3% to art/drama/ music colleges; 27% to non-degree courses (eg business studies, computing, A-levels); 9% straight into careers (eg banking, Royal Marines, court work); 20% other. Of those going on to degree courses, 3% went to Oxbridge, 81% to other universities; 16% to poly/colleges. 3% those going on to higher education went to courses in drama/acting; 22% in humanities/social sciences; 6% in medicine; and 69% in science/engineering.

· *Bristol Grammar* ·

Bristol Grammar School
University Road
Bristol
BS8 1SR
Tel 0272 736006

- Pupils 1205
- Boys 7–18 (Day)
- Girls 7–18 (Day)
- Upper sixth 110

- Termly fees £1096 (Day)
- HMC

Enquiries/application to the Headmaster

What it's like

Founded in 1532, it lies in Tyndall's Park, to the north-west side of Bristol next door to the university. Its core consists of handsome Victorian buildings (especially the Great Hall) and there have been many developments in the last 15 years. It now has one of the best school libraries in England. It enjoys a high reputation academically. Very many pupils go on to degree courses, a high proportion to Oxbridge. French and German are offered to A-level (many pupils take GCSE in both) and there are regular exchanges with France and Germany. It has played a major part in the educational life of the city. Flourishing local ties and back-up from the community and from Old Bristolians. An exceptional number of activities (over 100) on offer each week. Though a big school it has a very friendly atmosphere and much is done to maintain high standards of pastoral care through the house system and year Head/Form tutor organisation.

School profile

Pupils Total age range 7–18; 1205 day pupils (873 boys, 332 girls). Senior department 11–18, 984 pupils (707 boys, 277 girls). Main entry ages 7, 11, 13 and into sixth. Approx 20% are children of former pupils. *Transfer from maintained schools:* 70% intake at 11 and 13, plus 50% to sixth.

Entrance 11+ entrance exam used. Oversubscribed. No special skills or religious requirements. Parents not expected to buy text books; no other extras. 350 assisted places (government and Governors). 7 scholarships/bursaries, 50% to 20% fees.

Parents 15+% in industry or commerce; 15+% are doctors, lawyers etc.

Staff Headmaster Charles Martin, in post for 5 years. 70 full time staff, 9 part time. Annual turnover 10%. Average age 38.

Academic work GCSE and A-levels. 18 subjects offered (including Greek, Russian; no A-level general studies). In 1990, 119 pupils in upper fifth, 110 in upper sixth. *GCSE:* in 1990, 80% upper fifth gained at least grade C in 8+ subjects; 13% in 5–7; and 7% in 1–4 subjects. *A-levels:* 47 upper sixth passed in 3 subjects; 51 in 2; and 17 in 1 subject. 35% took science A-levels; 52% arts/humanities; 13% both. *Computing facilities:* 25 IBM-compatible PC's.

European Community *Languages:* French offered: to age 14; GCSE; A-level. German offered: to GCSE; A-level. 25–50% take GCSE in more than 1 EC language. *Exchanges:* Regular exchanges for pupils aged 14–18 to France and Germany. *Other:* European Studies offered to pupils aged 11–14.

Senior pupils' non-academic activities *Music:* 150 learn a musical instrument, 20 to Grade 6 or above, 2 accepted for Music School, 10 play in pop group beyond school; 80 in school orchestra, 150 in school choir, 15 in pop group; 1 in National Youth Orchestra; 6 in County Orchestra. *Drama and dance:* 116 participate in school plays; 80 in house productions. *Art:* 337 take as non-examined subject; 13 take A-level. 4 accepted for Art School. 20 belong to photographic club. *Sport:* Cricket, rugby, soccer, hockey, netball, athletics, cross-country, bowls, golf, fives, volleyball, ski-ing, squash, badminton, swimming, weight-training, judo, gym club, fencing available. 70 take non-compulsory sport. 56 represent county/country (rugby, hockey, cricket, swimming, athletics, golf, tennis, ski-ing, fencing). *Other:* 60 take part in local community schemes. 10 enter voluntary schemes after leaving school. Other activities include a computer club. Weekly activities scheme offers 100 different options, from cookery, glass engraving to ice-skating and wind-surfing; compulsory to fifth, 70% of sixth continue voluntarily.

Careers In 1990, 90% leavers went on to degree courses; 5% to art/drama/music colleges; 1% to non-degree courses; 4% straight into careers (eg banking, insurance, services). Of those going on to degree courses, 20% went to Oxbridge, 65% to other universities; 15% to poly/colleges. 2% those going on to higher education went to courses in practical art; 2% in drama/acting; 1% in music; 55% in humanities/social sciences; 15% in medicine; and 25% in science/engineering.

Uniform School uniform worn throughout.

Houses/prefects 6 competitive houses. Prefects, head boy/girl, head of house and house prefects – appointed by the Head in consultation with staff. School Council.

Religion No compulsory religious worship.

Social Regular local, area and national debating competitions and joint competitions with neighbouring schools. Regular exchanges to USA, USSR, Bordeaux, Hanover. Trips to France, Russia, Italy and Greece. Pupils allowed to bring own bike/motorbikes to school. Meals self service. Second-hand uniform shop. No tobacco/alcohol allowed.

Discipline No corporal punishment. Punishment for pupils failing to produce homework would depend on circumstances; those caught smoking cannabis on the premises could expect expulsion.

Alumni association run by Michael L Booker MA, c/o Bristol Grammar School.

Former pupils Lord Franks (Ambassador to USA plus Oxford University), Tom Graveney (cricketer); Robert Lacey (author); Brian Barron (BBC); Clive Ponting (ex Civil Servant); Fred Wedlock (entertainer); General Tunku Osman (Malaysian Army); Geoffrey Cutter (hockey); Rt Rev Peter Nott (Bishop of Norwich); John Currie (rugby); Canon G A Ffrench-Beytagh (anti-apartheid); Basil Greenhill (Maritime Museum, Greenwich); G H Heath-Grace (organist); Dave Prowse (film star); Prof Keith Robbins (historian); Sir Richard Sheppard (architect); David Drew (ballet).

· Bromley High ·

Bromley High School
Blackbrook Lane
Bickley
Bromley
Kent BR1 2TW
Tel 081 468 7981

- Pupils 698
- Boys None
- Girls 4–18
- (Day)
- Upper sixth 53

- Termly fees
  £1024 (Day)
- GSA, GPDST
  Enquiries/application to
  the Headmistress

What it's like

Founded in 1883 by the Girls' Public Day School Trust and originally situated in the centre of Bromley. In 1981 it moved to Bickley to occupy new buildings, set in 24 acres of beautiful grounds which include seven laboratories and specialist rooms for art, technology, ceramics and drama and a music wing with a practice room and a recital room. Sports facilities include a gymnasium, athletics tracks and six-lane swimming pool. The junior department, on the same site, shares many facilities but also has its own gymnasium/hall and premises. Entrants come from well beyond the bounds of the Borough of Bromley. Academic studies are of paramount importance but girls are expected to prepare fully for adult life through an enthusiastic involvement in music, drama, art, sport and community activities. Academic standards are high: most of the upper sixth go on to degree courses, including Oxbridge. French, German and Spanish are offered to A-level. Very many girls take GCSE in more than one European language and there are regular exchanges with France, Germany and Spain. Also FLAW courses are offered. The school is strong in the performing arts. High standards in sports and games are maintained with members of regional and national squads: the school currently holds championship titles in tennis, swimming, netball, hockey and athletics. Extra-curricular activities flourish; the Duke of Edinburgh's Scheme, Young Enterprise, work experience/shadowing and voluntary service all enjoy enthusiastic support.

School profile

Pupils Total age range 4–18; 698 day girls. Senior department 11–18, 514 girls. Main entry ages 4, 11 and into sixth.

Entrance Own entrance exam used. Oversubscribed. No special skills or religious requirements. 150 assisted places; various scholarships/bursaries, including music scholarship. Parents not expected to buy text books.

Staff Headmistress Mrs E J Hancock, in post 3 years. 38 full time staff, 20 part time (plus 22 music and speech/drama). Variable turnover.

Academic work GCSE and A-levels. Average size of upper fifth 78; upper sixth 53. *GCSE:* on average, 53 pupils in upper fifth pass 8+ subjects; 18, 5–7 subjects; 7 1–4 subjects. *A-levels:* on average, 4 pupils in upper sixth pass 4 subjects; 33, 3 sub-

jects; 8, 2 subjects; and 4 pass 1 subject. On average, 19 take science/engineering A-levels; 19 take arts and humanities; 15 a mixture. *Computing facilities:* Nimbus network.

European Community *Languages:* French offered: to age 14; GCSE; AS-level; A-level. German offered: to age 14; GCSE; A-level. Spanish offered: to GCSE; AS-level; A-level. 50–75% take GCSE in more than 1 EC language. FLAW (Foreign Languages at Work) courses. *Exchanges:* Regular exchanges for pupils aged 14–18 to France, Germany and Spain. *Other:* Talks from MEPs.

Senior pupils' non-academic activities *Music:* 50% learn a musical instrument, many to Grade 6 or above; 2 school orchestras, 2 choirs, wind group, brass group, jazz group, recorder ensembles. *Other:* Some are working for Duke of Edinburgh's Award (bronze, silver and gold). Other activities include a computer, dance, drama, art, ceramics, chess, environment, pets' clubs, Christian Union. School dance production, school play annually.

Careers In 1990, 78% leavers went on to degree courses; 8% to art/drama/music colleges; 14% straight into careers (eg banking). Of those going on to degree courses, 7% went to Oxbridge, 55% to other universities; 38% to poly/colleges. 9% those going on to higher education went to courses in practical art; 63% in humanities/social sciences; 13% in medicine; and 16% in science/engineering.

Uniform School uniform worn except in sixth form.

Houses/prefects No competitive houses. Prefects, 2 head girls, elected by girls and staff. School Council.

Religion Christian tradition, non-denominational; assembly four days a week.

Social Many events with St Dunstan's (Catford) – plays, debates, concerts, discos, ski and other holidays. Regular exchanges to France, Germany and Spain; field courses to Alternative Energy Centre, North Wales; other occasional holidays (Italy, Russia, ski-ing). Pupils allowed to bring own car/bike to school. Meals self service. No tobacco/alcohol/personal stereos allowed.

Discipline Girls expected to behave with consideration for others and work to best of their abilities. Detention system but school values frequent consultation with parents. Serious offences, such as smoking or stealing would warrant suspension. School insists on punctuality and commitment to homework.

Former pupils Mrs Marion Roe, MP; Dr Janet Sondheimer; Professor Marilyn Strathern; Dame Dorothy Brock; Professor Joan Walsh; Dr Lucy Campion.

· *Bromsgrove* ·

Bromsgrove School
Bromsgrove
Worcestershire
B61 7DU
Tel 0527 579679

- Pupils 917
- Boys 8–18
  (Day/Board)
- Girls 8–18
  (Day/Board)
- Upper sixth 100

- Termly fees
  £1564 (Day)
  £2495 (Board)
- HMC
  Enquiries/application to
  the Headmaster

What it's like

Founded in 1548, a development of a medieval charity school and one of the original fourteen schools at the foundation of the HMC in 1869. Its site comprises 100 acres of unusually beautiful grounds and very civilised buildings, near the centre of Bromsgrove town and half an hour from both Birmingham and Stratford-on-Avon. It has strong links with Worcester College, Oxford, because it was re-founded by Sir Thomas Cooke in the same year (1693) as Worcester. All its modern facilities are excellent and it provides a first-rate academic education. A 'sense of family' (in the Christian tradition) is regarded as of prime importance. The chapel is in regular use. The school provides a wide range of opportunities for its pupils and its well-organised pastoral system encourages pupils to identify and develop their talents to the full. Each pupil has a tutor within the house organisation and there is a 'pupil-profiling' system by which each pupil's progress is monitored. It enjoys a high degree of academic success and sends many pupils on to degree courses each year, including Oxbridge. French, German and Spanish are offered to

A-level. Music, drama and art are all strong and well supported. There is considerable strength, too, in sports and games (a large number of representatives at county level). Thirty or more clubs and societies cater for most extra-curricular activities. There is great emphasis on outdoor pursuits linked with a vigorous CCF contingent. Local community services are an important feature of the school life and there is a substantial commitment to the Duke of Edinburgh's Award Scheme with an impressive record of success.

School profile

Pupils Total age range 8–18; 917 pupils, 572 day (352 boys, 220 girls), 345 boarding (200 boys, 145 girls). Senior department 13–18, 545 pupils (325 boys, 220 girls). Main entry ages 8, 11, 13 and into sixth. 60% of senior department from own junior department. *Transfer from maintained schools:* 15% main intake at 11 and 13, plus 50% to sixth.

Entrance Common entrance and own entrance exam used. Oversubscribed. School looks for a wide range of pupils; good all-rounders, talented pupils, good citizens. No religious requirements although school is an Anglican foundation. Parents not expected to buy text books; little in extras. 29 assisted places. Large number of scholarships, exhibitions, including music scholarships, all-rounder and forces bursaries, 80–10% fees.

Parents 15+% in industry or commerce. 60+% live within 30 miles; 10+% live overseas.

Staff Headmaster T M Taylor, in post for 4 years. 75 full time staff, 10 part time. Annual turnover 5%. Average age approx 38.

Academic work GCSE and A-levels. Subjects offered include A-level general studies. In 1990, 120 pupils in upper fifth, 87 in upper sixth (now 100). *GCSE:* in 1990, 58% upper fifth gained at least grade C in 8+ subjects; 26% in 5–7; and 15% in 1–4 subjects. *A-levels:* 53% upper sixth passed in 4+ subjects; 24% in 3; 15% in 2; and 7% in 1 subject. 18% took science A-levels; 49% arts/humanities; 33% both. *Computing facilities:* 20 Archimedes in the centre; 5 Archimedes and 20 BBCs in other places. *Special provision:* A small amount of extra tuition available, also back-up support from teachers and encouragement and understanding.

European Community *Languages:* French offered: to age 14; GCSE; AS-level; A-level. German offered: to GCSE; AS-level; A-level. Italian offered: to GCSE. Spanish offered: to age 14; GCSE; AS-level; A-level. 10–25% take GCSE in more than 1 EC language. *Other:* Usually 4–5 EC pupils in sixth form for 1 term–1 year.

Senior pupils' non-academic activities *Music:* Approximately 52 learn a musical instrument, over 20 to Grade 6 or above; 25 play in school orchestra, 50 in choir, 10 in school pop group, 40 perform in musicals, 60 in choral society. *Drama and dance:* 80 in school productions; 100 in house plays; 30 take GCSE drama; 5 on summer courses to NYT and NUMT; 3 accepted for Drama/Dance schools. *Art:* 140 take art as non-examined subject; 28 take GCSE; 16 A-level; 12 belong to other clubs. *Sport:* Rugby, cricket, hockey, soccer, netball, athletics, tennis, cross-country, badminton, squash, weight training plus others. All pupils take part in non-compulsory sport. 21 pupils represent county/country (hockey, rugby, cricket). *Other:* 30 have bronze Duke of Edinburgh's Award, 20 silver, 15 gold. 40 take part in local community schemes. About 30 other activities, including a computer club, pottery, cookery, croquet, aero modelling, folk club, debating society and outdoor pursuits.

Careers In 1990, 73% leavers went on to degree courses; 8% to art/drama/music colleges; 7% to non-degree courses (eg agriculture); 4% straight into careers; 8% other. Of those going on to degree courses, 5% went to Oxbridge, 60% to other universities; 35% to poly/colleges. 8% those going on to higher education went to courses in practical art; 5% in drama/acting; 2% in music; 55% in humanities/social sciences; 15% in medicine; and 15% in science/engineering.

Uniform School uniform worn except in sixth.

Houses/prefects Competitive houses. Prefects, head boy/girl, head of house and house prefects – appointed by the Head and homeparents.

Religion Compulsory worship.

Social Some trips abroad. Day pupils may drive to and from school. Meals self service. School shop. No tobacco/alcohol allowed.

Discipline No corporal punishment. Pupils failing to produce homework once might expect to repeat it, if necessary in detention; those caught smoking cannabis on the premises would be asked to leave.

Boarding 33% have own study bedroom, 33% share (with 1–4 others); 33% in dormitories of 6+. Houses, of approximately 50–70, same as competitive houses, single sex. Resident nurse, visiting doctor. Central dining room. Pupils can provide and cook snacks. 6–8 weekend exeats per term. Visits to local town up to 5 times a week allowed, depending on age.

Alumni association is run by the Registrar at Bromsgrove School.

· *Bruton (Sunny Hill)* ·

Bruton School for Girls
Sunny Hill
Bruton
Somerset
BA10 0NT
Tel 0749 812277

- Pupils 550
- Boys None
- Girls 8–18 (Day/ Board/Weekly)
- Upper sixth 48

- Termly fees
  £865 (Day)
  £1580 (Board/ Weekly)
- GSA, BSA
  Enquiries/application to the School Registrar

What it's like

Founded in 1900, it has a fine 40-acre rural site on the edge of the small town of Bruton in a beautiful part of Somerset with views of the Quantocks and the Mendips. Bath, Bristol and Salisbury are easily accessible and full use is made of their cultural facilities. The school is known locally as 'Sunny Hill'. Its buildings are pleasant and very well equipped and facilities are good. It serves the local community (which gives good support) and represents all sections of society. Boarders come from all over the British Isles and overseas. Its declared aims are to provide a full, well-balanced education, while at the same time developing musical, artistic and dramatic talents. Many sixth form leavers go on to degree courses. French, German and Spanish are offered to A-level and many girls take GCSE in more than one European language. There are regular exchanges with France, Germany and Spain. There is a strong commitment to local community schemes and to the Duke of Edinburgh's Award Scheme.

School profile

Pupils Total age range 8–18; 550 girls, 310 day, 240 boarding. Senior department 11–18, 500 girls. Main entry ages 8, 11, 13 and into sixth. *Transfer from maintained schools:* 50% intake at 11 and 13, plus 20% to sixth.

Entrance Own entrance exam used. Oversubscribed. No special skills or religious requirements. Parents not expected to buy text books; no other compulsory extras. 25 assisted places (20 at 11); 6 scholarships (including 1 for daughter of former pupil) 75–15% tuition.

Parents 15+% in the armed services. 60+% live within 30 miles; up to 10% live overseas.

Staff Headmistress Mrs J M Wade, in post 3 years. 42 full time staff, 10 part time. Annual turnover 5%. Average age 42.

Academic work GCSE and A-levels. 21 GCSE subjects offered; 22 at A-level (no A-level general studies). In 1990, 83 pupils in fifth, 48 in upper sixth. *GCSE:* in 1990, 50 fifth gained at least grade C in 8+ subjects; 27 in 5–7; and 6 in 1–4 subjects. *A-levels:* 3 upper sixth passed in 4+ subjects; 26 in 3; 10 in 2; and 5 in 1 subject. 27% took science A-levels; 29% arts/humanities; 44% both. *Computing facilities:* 2 computer rooms, plus computers in subject areas. *Special provision:* Specialist teaching available for ESL and dyslexia.

European Community *Languages:* French offered: to age 14; GCSE; A-level. German offered: to GCSE; A-level. Spanish offered: to GCSE; A-level. 25–50% take GCSE in more than 1 EC language. *Exchanges:* Regular exchanges for pupils aged 11–18 to France, Germany and Spain.

Senior pupils' non-academic activities *Music:* 150 learn a musical instrument, 38 to Grade 6 or above. 1 accepted for Music School; 2 for degree courses. 28 in school orchestra, 110 in school choirs, 3 in Somerset Youth Orchestra. *Drama and dance:* 50 in school productions; 150 in informal productions; 90 take LAMDA exams; 1 to degree course. *Art:* 10 take as non-examined subject; 20 take GCSE; 2, A-level; 2 accepted for Art School; 10 belong to photographic club. *Sport:* Hockey, netball, cross-country, athletics, tennis, rounders, swimming, gymnastics available. 200 take non-compulsory sport. 30 take exams eg gymnastics, swimming. 23 represent county/country (hockey, netball, athletics). *Other:* 20 take part in local community schemes. 90 in bronze Duke of Edinburgh's Award, 10 have silver, 4 gold. Other activities include a computer club, electronics club, conservation, music, art, drama, charity work and driving lessons. Modular sixth form general studies, including understanding industry course. Work experience week in fifth form.

Careers On average, 60% leavers went on to degree courses; 2% to art/drama/music colleges; 19% to non-degree courses; 2% straight into careers; 16% other. Of those going on to degree courses, 4% went to Oxbridge, 67% to other universities; 29% to poly/colleges. 2% those going on to higher education went to courses in practical art; 2% in drama/acting; 2% in music; 56% in humanities/social sciences; 4% in medicine; and 35% in science/engineering.

Uniform School uniform worn except in the sixth.

Houses/prefects Competitive houses. Head girl and prefects, appointed. Heads of house elected.

Religion Daily assembly. All boarders attend Church on Sundays, or school service conducted by school chaplain.

Social Many brothers attend King's School, Bruton; joint social events are arranged. Local schools are invited to sixth form functions. Organised trips abroad. Pupils allowed to bring own bikes to school. Meals self service. School shop. No tobacco/alcohol allowed.

Discipline Pupils failing to produce homework once might expect to do a repeat; those caught smoking cannabis on the premises would expect instant expulsion.

Boarding Single/double study bedrooms in upper sixth house; 3 senior houses of approx 50; lower sixth study cubicles, plus own sitting room; fifth cubicles; years 2–4 dormitories of 6+. Study rooms in each house. Junior house (8–11) dormitories of 6+. Resident qualified medical staff. Central dining room. Sixth formers can provide and cook own food. At least one 'fixed exeat' each half term, other exeats vary with age. Visits to the local town allowed.

Alumni association run by Mrs Joy Howard, c/o the School.

· *Bryanston* ·

Bryanston School
Blandford
Dorset
DT11 0PX
Tel 0258 452411

- Pupils 670
- Boys 13–18 (Board)
- Girls 13–18 (Board)
- Upper sixth 132

- Termly fees £3250 (Board)
- HMC

Enquiries/application to the Admissions Secretary

What it's like

Founded in 1928, it lies in a magnificent 400-acre estate just outside Blandford Forum, bordering a 2.5-mile stretch of the Stour in one of the most beautiful parts of England. For splendour of setting it probably has no equal among schools. The main building matches the surroundings: a huge palatial country house in red brick banded with Portland stone, designed by Shaw and completed in 1897. An example of monumental classicism, its main corridor is 100 yards long. This is the heart of the school. Some of the satellite buildings are, by comparison, somewhat plain and functional but they are well designed and exceptionally well equipped. There is also an open-air Greek theatre (built by the pupils), an observatory and the Coade Hall which contains a theatre with an auditorium seating 540 (better equipped than many professional theatres). The teaching is well known to be excellent and academic standards are high. Very many pupils go to degree courses each year, many to Oxbridge. French and German are offered to A-level and many pupils take GCSE in both. Spanish is offered for the Institute of Linguists and Italian as a non-examined subject. There are regular exchanges with France and Germany. There is much emphasis on creativity, on the development of individual talents; also on self-discipline, self-motivation, self-organisation and finding out how to find out on your own. It has long since been outstanding for its commitment to music; 450 pupils learn a musical instrument and there are many musical events. The drama and art departments are also very strong. At least 15 plays a year are produced, and the Arts Centre brings in some 20 professional musical and dramatic productions to Coade Hall each year (eg the RSC). Sport and games appear to be compulsory for virtually everyone but there is a gentlemanly, laid back attitude towards them; however, the old-fashioned 'amateur' approach in no way affects the high standards that are attained. There is strong back-up from the old boys' association and a substantial commitment to local community activities and the Duke of Edinburgh's Award Scheme.

School profile

Pupils Age range 13–18; 670 boarding pupils (430 boys, 240 girls). Main entry ages 13 and into sixth. Approx 15% are children of former pupils. *Transfer from maintained schools:* 3% main intake, plus 10% to sixth.

Entrance Common entrance and own entrance exam used. Oversubscribed. No special skills or religious requirements. Parents expected to buy text books. 20 scholarships/bursaries, 50% to 15% of fees.

Parents 15+% in industry or commerce; 15+% are doctors, lawyers etc; 15+% in the armed services; 15+% in theatre, media and music. Up to 10% live within 30 miles; 10+% live overseas.

Staff Headmaster T D Wheare, in post for 7 years. 67 full time staff, 36 part time. Annual turnover 6%. Average age 40.

Academic work GCSE and A-levels. 23 subjects offered (no A-level general studies). In 1990, 128 pupils in upper fifth, 132 in upper sixth. *GCSE:* in 1990, 95% upper fifth gained at least grade C in 8+ subjects; 5% in 5–7 subjects. *A-levels:* 5% upper sixth passed in 4+ subjects; 90% in 3; 5% in 2 subjects. 30% took science A-levels; 60% arts/humanities; 10% both. *Computing facilities:* BBC Bs, Archimedes, Apple Macintoshes. *Special provision:* Tutorial provision.

European Community *Languages:* French offered: to age 14; GCSE; AS-level; A-level. German offered: to age 14; GCSE; AS-level; A-level. Italian offered: non-examined. Spanish offered: Institute of Linguists. 25–50% take GCSE in more than 1 EC language. *Exchanges:* Regular exchanges for pupils aged 14–18 to France and Germany.

Senior pupils' non-academic activities *Music:* 450 learn a musical instrument, 100 to Grade 6 or above. 10 accepted for Music School. 60 in school orchestra, 60 in school choir, 5 in school pop group; 2 in National Youth Orchestra; 10 in county youth orchestra. *Drama and dance:* 120 in school productions; 80 in other; 50 take Grade 6 in ESB, RAD etc. 4 accepted for Drama/Dance Schools. *Art:* 300 take as non-examined subject; 40 take GCSE; 40 A-level. 15 accepted for Art School; 60 belong to photographic club. *Sport:* Rugby, hockey, cricket, tennis, rowing, athletics, netball, swimming, canoeing, lacrosse, cross-country, archery, squash, badminton, fencing available. 250 take non-compulsory sport. 20 represent county/country (rugby, athletics). *Other:* 100 take part in local community schemes. 50 have bronze Duke of Edinburgh's Award, 20 have silver and 1 gold. Other activities include a computer club, driving, chess, film, bell ringing, astronomy, clay pigeon shooting, soccer, reptiles, jazz.

Careers On average, 90% leavers go on to degree courses; 2% to art/drama/music colleges; 2% to non-degree courses; 2% straight into careers; 2% other. Of those going on to degree courses, 15% go to Oxbridge, 65% to other universities; 20% to poly/colleges. 2% those going on to higher education went to courses in practical art; 1% in drama/acting; 2% in music; 60% in humanities/social sciences; 8% in medicine; and 27% in science/engineering.

Uniform School uniform not worn.

Houses/prefects Prefects, head boy and girl, head of house and house prefects – elected by the school and appointed by the Head.

Religion Religious worship encouraged but not compulsory.

Social Very few organised local events. Regular exchanges with a German school, visits to France and Italy and ski-ing trips. Pupils allowed to bring own bike to school. Meals self service. School shop. Alcohol allowed for the upper sixth.

Discipline No corporal punishment. No punishment for failing to produce homework once; those caught smoking cannabis on the premises could expect expulsion.

Boarding 20% have own study bedroom, 20% share in 2s; less than 60% are in dormitories of up to 6. Single sex houses, of 55, divided by age group. Resident qualified nurse. Central dining room. Pupils can provide and cook some own food. 4 weekend exeats each term. Visits to local town allowed – any age, twice a week on average.

Alumni association run by W E Potter, c/o the School.

Former pupils Sir Terence Conran; Jasper Conran; Lucien Freud; Fred Sanger OM; John Eliot Gardner; Mark Elder.

· *Buckingham* ·

Buckingham College	● Pupils 198	● Termly fees
Hindes Road	● Boys 11–18	£1000 (Day)
Harrow	(Day)	● ISAI
Middlesex	● Girls 16–18	Enquiries/application to
HA1 1SH	(Day)	the Secretary
Tel 081 427 1220	● Upper sixth 15	

What it's like

Founded in 1936 it is single site in a pleasant residential area, conveniently placed for public transport. It has agreeable buildings which are well-equipped. The lower school is on a separate site at Northwick Park. The sixth form was re-opened in 1986. There is emphasis on the basic principles of Christian conduct, courtesy and a sense of duty to the community. A sound general education is provided and results are creditable. An adequate range of sports, games and extra-curricular activities. Some commitment to local community services and the Duke of Edinburgh's Award Scheme.

School profile

Pupils Age range 11–18; 198 day pupils, (197 boys, 1 girl). Main entry ages boys 11, 13; boys and girls into sixth. Buckingham College Lower School provides 20+% of intake. Approx 4% are children of former pupils.

Entrance Own entrance exam used. Oversubscribed. No special skills or religious requirements. Parents expected to buy sixth form text books; maximum extras, £120. 3 sixth form scholarships/bursaries, from one-third fees.

Parents 70% in industry or commerce. Up to 10% live overseas.

Staff Headmaster D F T Bell, in post for 4 years. 14 full time staff, 10 part time. Annual turnover 12.5%. Average age 38.

Academic work GCSE and A-levels. Average size of upper fifth 35; upper sixth 15. *GCSE:* on average, 7 upper fifth gain at least grade C in 8+ subjects; 12 in 5–7; 12 in 1–4 subjects. *A-levels:* on average, 4 upper sixth pass 3 subjects; 2, 2 subjects and 1, 1 subject. On average, 10 take arts and humanities A-levels, 5 science/engineering. *Computing facilities:* lab with BBC system. *Special provision:* for mild visual handicap, EFL and dyslexia.

European Community *Languages:* French offered: to age 14; GCSE.

German offered: to age 14; GCSE. Under 10% take GCSE in more than 1 EC language. *Exchanges:* Regular exchanges for pupils aged 11–16 to France. *Other:* European Studies offered to pupils aged 14–16.

Senior pupils' non-academic activities *Music:* 2 learn a musical instrument to Grade 6 or above, 2 accepted for Music School; 30 in school choir. *Drama and dance:* 6 in school productions. 1 accepted for Drama School. *Art:* 7 take GCSE. 1 accepted for Art School. *Sport:* Soccer, hockey, table tennis, swimming, athletics, badminton, cricket, tennis available. 12 take non-compulsory sport. 4 pupils represent county/country (judo, athletics, swimming). *Other:* Some take part in local community schemes. 24 have bronze Duke of Edinburgh's Award. Annual sixth form fund raising for national charities. Other activities include computer club, chess, electronics, crafts, debating.

Careers In 1990, 60% leavers went on to degree courses; 30% straight into careers (eg accountancy); 10% other. Of those going on to degree courses, 20% went to universities; 80% to poly/colleges, all to courses in humanities/social sciences.

Uniform School uniform worn except the sixth.

Houses/prefects Competitive houses. Prefects, head boy, head of house – appointed by Head.

Religion Worship encouraged.

Social Participation in E Ivor Hughes music festival and Rotary public speaking competition. Annual trips abroad. Pupils allowed to bring own bike/car. Meals self service. School shop. No tobacco/alcohol allowed.

Discipline Pupils failing to produce homework once might expect admonition; those caught smoking cannabis on the premises might expect suspension.

Alumni association run by J Musgrove.

Former pupils John Timpson; Tony Bastable.

· *Burgess Hill* ·

Burgess Hill School for Girls
Keymer Road
Burgess Hill
West Sussex
RH15 0AQ
Tel 0444 241050

- Pupils 578
- Boys 3–5 only (Day)
- Girls 3–18 (Day/Board)
- Upper sixth 35

- Termly fees £1259 (Day) £2186 (Board/ Weekly)
- GSA

Enquiries/application to the Registrar

What it's like

Founded in 1906, it combines junior and senior schools on a single 12.5 acre site on the highest point of Burgess Hill in well-kept gardens, plus ample playing fields. To the original Victorian houses have been added many modern facilities: assembly hall, labs, gym, music school, art complex and a business and computer studies centre. It is now very well equipped with a new block of 17 classrooms. Boarders are well cared for in comfortable family style accommodation. All religious assemblies are compulsory; the Anglican tradition prevails. The school is motivated by a strong belief in the merits of single-sex education, and the declared aim is to get the majority of leavers into higher education. Very many sixth formers go on to degree courses, a high proportion to Oxbridge. French, German and Spanish are offered to A-level, also Italian to GCSE. Many girls take GCSE in more than one European language. There are regular exchanges with France and Germany. Very strong in drama, music and sport. Extensive involvement in local community schemes. Vigorous local support.

School profile

Pupils Total age range 3–18; 578 pupils, 534 day (20 boys, 514 girls), 44 boarding (all girls). Senior department 11–18, 313 girls. Main entry ages 3–10, 11 and into sixth. Approx 5% are children of former pupils. 20+% of senior school from own junior department. *Transfer from maintained schools:* 10% main intake at 11, plus 2% to sixth.

Entrance Own entrance exam used. Oversubscribed in certain areas. No special skills or religious requirements. Parents expected to buy text books in sixth form only. Assisted places. 17 scholarships/bursaries, half fees to £150 pa.

Parents 15+% in industry or commerce; 15+% are doctors, lawyers etc. 60+% live within 30 miles; up to 10% live overseas.

Staff Headmistress Mrs B H Webb, in

post for 11 years. 33 full time staff, 29 part time. Annual turnover 1%. Average age 30.

Academic work GCSE and A-levels. 21 subjects offered (no A-level general studies). In 1989, 50 pupils in upper fifth, 35 in upper sixth. *GCSE:* in 1990, 97% upper fifth gained at least grade C in 8+ subjects. *A-levels:* 93% upper sixth passed in 3 subjects. 10 took science A-levels; 20 arts/humanities; 5 both. *Computing facilities:* Computing and business studies department with 16 computers. *Special provision:* EFL. Extra help for dyslexics.

European Community *Languages:* French offered: to age 14; GCSE; AS-level; A-level. German offered: to age 14; GCSE; A-level. Italian offered: to GCSE. Spanish offered: to age 14; GCSE; A-level. 25–50% take GCSE in more than 1 EC language. *Exchanges:* Regular exchanges for pupils aged 11–18 to France and Germany. *Other:* Variety of pupils from other EC countries attend the school.

Senior pupils' non-academic activities *Music:* 200 learn a musical instrument, 20 to Grade 6 or above. 13 take GCSE music. 2 accepted for Music College. 35 in school orchestra, 35 in school choir, 30 in chamber choir, 10 in chamber group; 2 in West Sussex CYO; 4 in jazz band and brass consort. *Drama and dance:* 100 in school productions; 14 NEA; 5 GCSE; 2 Guildhall; 40 ESB Grade 2. 3 accepted for Drama/Dance school; 2 go on to work in theatre. *Art:* 10 take GCSE art; 6 A-level; 16 take art history. 3 accepted for Art School. 20 belong to art club; 30 to pottery club. *Sport:* Tennis, hockey, netball, rounders, badminton, basketball, volleyball, athletics, jogging, cross-country, hill running, squash, swimming, short-tennis available. Matches and tournaments for each age group in major sports. County representatives (netball, volleyball), country representative (fenc-

ing). *Other:* 100 take part in local community schemes. Other activities include a computer club, stamp club, judo, gardening, calligraphy, aerobics, gym and dance clubs, art and craft clubs, fencing and sailing clubs, BAYS, social services, debating society.

Careers In 1990, 90% leavers went on to degree courses; 10% to art/drama/music colleges. Of those going on to degree courses, 20% went to Oxbridge, 70% to other universities; 10% to poly/colleges. 10% those going on to higher education went to courses in practical art; 60% in humanities/social sciences; 10% in medicine; and 20% in science/engineering.

Uniform School uniform worn except in the sixth.

Houses/prefects Competitive houses. Prefects, head girl, head of house and house prefects – appointed by the Head. School Council.

Religion Assembly is compulsory. Church attendance compulsory for Anglican boarders (but all faiths accepted).

Social Joint debates, matches, discos, with local boys' public schools. Organised ski trip, pony trekking, biennial Classics trip, history trip to Soviet Union, field trips, German/French and Soviet Union exchanges. Sixth form allowed to bring own car to school. Meals self service. School tuckshop. No tobacco/alcohol allowed.

Discipline No corporal punishment. Pupils caught smoking, drinking or any involvement with drugs would be asked to leave.

Boarding 3 houses, 9–18, divided by age group. Central dining room. 2 weekend exeats each term. Visits to the local town allowed.

Alumni association run by Miss J Anthony, Pine Court, Beacon Road West, Crowborough, East Sussex.

· *Bury Grammar (Boys)* ·

Bury Grammar School
for Boys
Tenterden Street
Bury
Lancashire BL9 0HN
Tel 061 797 2700

- Pupils 780
- Boys 8–18
  (Day)
- Girls None
- Upper sixth 75

- Termly fees
  £800 (Day)
- HMC
Enquiries/application to
the Headmaster

What it's like

Founded early 17th century, re-endowed in 1726. After World War II a new boys' school was erected near the original buildings in the town. It combines junior and senior schools and is purpose-built with every desirable amenity including swimming pool and spacious playing fields. The school has many active Christians among masters and boys, but is non-denominational and welcomes pupils of many faiths. It has a well-established tradition of good teaching and highly creditable results. Many pupils go on to degree courses, including Oxbridge. French and German are offered to A-level, also Spanish to GCSE. A high proportion of boys takes GCSE in more than one European language. There are regular exchanges with Germany. Very well equipped workshops and technology department (many pupils go on to become professional engineers). Flourishing ties with local community and good mutual support. Strong in sport and games; also outdoor pursuits in the Lake District.

School profile

Pupils Total age range 8–18; 780 day boys. Senior department 11–18, 660 boys. Main entry ages 10, 11 and into sixth. Own junior school provides 50+% of intake. *Transfer from maintained schools:* 50% intake at 11; plus 10% to sixth.

Entrance Own entrance exam used. Oversubscribed. No special skills or religious requirements. Parents not expected to buy text books; lunch (£45 per term) and school trips extra. 30 assisted places. 1 Kay Scholarship and one School Bursary per year.

Staff Headmaster K Richards, first year in post. 47 full time staff, 2 part time. Annual turnover 3%. Average age 42.

Academic work GCSE, AS and A-levels. 18 subjects offered (including A-level general studies). In 1990, 92 pupils in upper fifth, 79 in upper sixth (now 75). *GCSE:* in 1990, 67 upper fifth gained at least grade C in 8+ subjects; 19 in 5–7; and 6 in 1–4 subjects. *A-levels:* 58 upper sixth passed in 4+ subjects; 11 in 3; 5 in 2; and 3 in 1 subject. 22 took science

A-levels; 25 arts/humanities; 22 both. *Computing facilities:* Computer suite: computers for teaching and learning other subjects spreading through the school.

European Community *Languages:* French offered: to age 14; GCSE; A-level. German offered: to age 14; GCSE; A-level. Spanish offered: to GCSE. 50–75% take GCSE in more than 1 EC language. *Exchanges:* Regular exchanges for pupils aged 14–18 to Germany.

Senior pupils' non-academic activities *Music:* 40 learn a musical instrument, 12 to Grade 6 or above; 1 accepted for Music School; 23 in school orchestra; 60 in choral society. *Drama and dance:* 30 in school productions; 1–2 in Manchester Youth; occasional pupil accepted for Drama/Dance Schools. *Art:* 76 take as non-examined subject; 10–15 take GCSE; 5–8, A-level. 3–4 accepted for Art School. *Sport:* Soccer, rugby, cricket, tennis, hockey, basketball, badminton, swimming, cross-country, athletics available. Large numbers train for team membership. 23 pupils represent county/country (cricket, golf, table tennis, ski-ing, soccer, swimming, rugby, triathlon, gymnastics). *Other:* 20 take part in local community schemes. 14 have bronze Duke of Edinburgh's Award, 6 silver. Other activities include a computer club, chess club (frequent matches), Young Enterprise, bird-watching, hiking, CCF (strong contingent – army only).

Careers In 1990, 80% leavers went on to degree courses; 4% to non-degree courses (eg A-level resits, BTEC); 3% straight into careers (eg army, RAF, retailing); 14% other. Of those going on to degree courses, 7% went to Oxbridge, 75% to other universities; 18% to poly/colleges. 60% those going on to higher education went to courses in humanities/social sciences; 5% in medicine; and 35% in science/engineering.

Uniform School uniform worn to fifth year.

Houses/prefects Competitive houses. Prefects, head boy, head of house – appointed.

Religion Morning assembly compulsory.

Social Joint productions with Bury Grammar (Girls). French, German and ski trips, exchange with a school in Cologne. Pupils allowed to bring own bikes to school. Meals self service. School shop. No tobacco/alcohol allowed.

Discipline No corporal punishment. Great care is taken to suit the punishment of offenders to the character and age of each individual.

Alumni association run by Mr J T Grundy, 11 Hebburn Drive, Bury BL8 1ED.

Former pupils David Trippier MP; Alistair Burt MP.

· *Bury Grammar (Girls)* ·

Bury Grammar School
(Girls)
Bridge Road
Bury
Lancashire BL9 0HH
Tel 061 797 2808

- Pupils 1130
- Boys 4–8 only (Day)
- Girls 4–18 (Day)
- Upper sixth 94

- Termly fees £800 (Day)
- GSA

Enquiries/application to the Headmistress

What it's like

Founded in 1884, it lies a few minutes from the town centre and close to the rail and bus stations. The main school is housed in a handsome Edwardian building (to which there have been many fine modern additions), surrounded by ample playing fields. A Christian foundation, it has connections with Bury parish church but is ecumenical in spirit. All pupils follow a course of religious education and philosophy throughout the school. The standard of teaching is good and very many sixth formers move on to degree courses, including Oxbridge. French and German are taught to A-level and Spanish to GCSE. There are regular exchanges with France and Germany. (In 1992 the school will be the host of the European Youth Conference). There are good facilities for art, music and drama. There is a strong tradition of achievement in games and athletics; plus many clubs and societies. Vigorous local support. Extensive work is done on behalf of national charities.

School profile

Pupils Total age range 4–18; 1130 day pupils (96 boys, 1034 girls). Senior department 11–18, 815 girls. Main entry ages 4, 11 and into sixth. *Transfer from maintained schools:* 54% senior intake plus 90% to sixth.

Entrance Own entrance exam used. Oversubscribed. No special skills or religious requirements. Parents not expected to buy text books; dinners extra, 75p per day. 35 assisted places. 1 Kay Scholarship per year, full fees.

Parents 15+% in industry or commerce; 15+% are doctors, lawyers etc.

Staff Headmistress Miss J M Lawley, in post for 3 years. 85 full time staff, 19 part time.

Academic work GCSE, AS and A-levels. 22 subjects (including A-level general studies). In 1990, 120 pupils in upper fifth, 94 in upper sixth. *GCSE:* on average 100 upper fifth gained at least grade C in 8+ subjects; 20 in 5–7 subjects. *A-levels:* 45 upper sixth passed in 4+ subjects; 20 in 3; 10 in 2; and 9 in 1 subject. *Computing facilities:* Two computer rooms and computers within departments (BBC and Acorn Archimedes machines); computing used across the curriculum. *Special provision:* Good relations with local authority special sources.

European Community *Languages:* French offered: to age 14; GCSE; AS-level; A-level. German offered: to age 14; GCSE; AS-level; A-level. Italian offered: to GCSE. Spanish offered: to GCSE. 10–25% take GCSE in more than 1 EC language. *Exchanges:* Regular exchanges for pupils aged 11–18 to France and Germany. *Other:* Represented England in International Youth Conference in Belgium. 1992 host of European Youth Conference.

Senior pupils' non-academic activities *Music:* 220 learn a musical instrument, 65 to Grade 6 or above, 3 accepted for Music School; 75 in school orchestra, 120 in school choir; 22 in Bury Youth Orchestra, 75 in Bury Music Centre. School choirs take part in music festivals in England and abroad. *Drama and dance:*

75 in school productions; 18 in year plays. 1 accepted for Drama/Dance School; 3 to Manchester Youth Theatre. *Art:* 16 take as non-examined subject; 63 take GCSE; 7 A-level; 6 GCSE pottery. 6 accepted for Art School. *Sport:* Clubs: hockey (50), netball (70), badminton (80), swimming (30), tennis (60), rounders (100+), gymnastics (4). 248 take RLSS exams. 1 represents north-west at gymnastics; 4+ represent county (swimming, diving). Runners-up in under-16 National Championship Netball (1989). Other activities include a computer club, chess and many other clubs and activities.

Careers In 1990, 85% leavers went on to degree courses; 12% to art/drama/music colleges; 3% straight into careers (eg banking). Of those going on to degree courses, 12% went to Oxbridge, 53% to other universities; 35% to poly/colleges.

Uniform School uniform worn except in the sixth.

Houses/prefects No competitive houses or prefects. Head girl – elected. School Council.

Religion Compulsory religious study and philosophy throughout the school.

Social Many concerts, plays and societies are joint with Bury Grammar (Boys). Both schools share sixth form common room facilities. Pupils discouraged from bringing own car/bike/motorbike to school (limited parking). Meals self service. School tuckshop. No tobacco/alcohol allowed.

Discipline No corporal punishment. Pupils failing to produce homework would be expected to hand it in the next day; those involved in drugs or smoking could expect immediate suspension. Anyone with drugs on the premises could expect expulsion.

Former pupils Victoria Wood.

C

· Campbell College ·

Campbell College
Belfast
BT4 2ND
Tel 0232 763076

- Pupils 459
- Boys 11–18
  (Day/Board/Weekly)
- Girls None
- Upper sixth 72

- Termly fees
  £151 (Day)
  £1157 (Board/
  Weekly)
- HMC
  Enquiries/application to
  the Headmaster

What it's like

Founded in 1894 to give a liberal Protestant education similar to that in English and Scottish public schools. The college (and its prep department, Cabin Hill) lies on the north-east outskirts of Belfast, five miles from the city centre, on a splendid 100-acre estate with fine trees, an ornamental lake and superb playing fields; a tranquil and beautiful setting. An excellent all-round education is provided and results are very good. Many go on to degree courses, including Oxbridge. French and German are taught to A-level; Spanish to AS-level. A very high proportion of pupils takes GCSE in more than one European language. Strong in music and drama and outstanding in sport and games. A flourishing and large CCF with a pipe band. Social services are extensive. Though basically a Protestant foundation it is ecumenical.

School profile

Pupils Age range 11–18; 459 boys, 392 day, 67 boarding. Main entry ages 11, 13 and into sixth. Approx 20% are children of former pupils. Own prep school (Cabin Hill) provides 80+% of intake. *Transfer from maintained schools:* 40% main intake, plus 10% to sixth.

Entrance Common entrance exam used (unless entering via Cabin Hill). No special skills or religious requirements. Books supplied by LEA. 4 scholarships/ bursaries, £1000–£75; sons of Northern Ireland residents who qualify under 11+ selection procedure pay lower day fee. Maximum extras, £50.

Parents 15+% are doctors, lawyers, etc; 15+% in industry or commerce. 80+%

live within 30 miles; up to 10% live overseas.

Staff Headmaster Dr R J I Pollock, in post for 3 years. 42 full time staff, 14 part time. Annual turnover 1%. Average age 41.

Academic work GCSE and A-levels. 20 subjects offered (no A-level general studies). In 1989, 82 pupils in upper fifth, 72 in upper sixth. *GCSE:* in 1990, 47 upper fifth gained at least grade C in 8+ subjects; 23 in 5–7; and 11 in 1–4 subjects. *A-levels:* 7 upper sixth passed in 4+ subjects; 42 in 3; 17 in 2; and 6 in 1 subject. 45% took science A-levels; 35% arts/humanities; 20% both. *Computing facilities:* 20 BBC and 5 printers, 15 Apple

Macs and 2 Nimbus; 11 science lab BBC systems.

European Community *Languages:* French offered: to age 14; GCSE; AS-level; A-level. German offered: to age 14; GCSE; AS-level; A-level. Spanish offered: to age 14; GCSE; AS-level. 50–75% take GCSE in more than 1 EC language.

Senior pupils' non-academic activities *Music:* 63 learn a musical instrument, 16 to Grade 6 or above. 5 accepted for Music School; 45 in school orchestra, 100 in school choir, 20 in jazz orchestra, 2 in National Youth Orchestra, 5 in Studio Symphony, 1 Pro Corda (Senior). *Drama and dance:* 65 in school productions; 90 in house drama; 2 accepted for Drama/Dance schools; 3 go on to work in theatre. *Art:* 24 take GCSE art; 11, A-level. 2 accepted for Art School; 2 for graphic/furniture design; 1 for architecture; 33 belong to photographic club; 23 belong to pottery club. *Sport:* Rugby football, hockey, cricket, cross-country, athletics, lawn tennis, sailing, squash, swimming, shooting, golf available. 80 take non-compulsory sport (badminton, squash), 25 swimming. 15 represent county/country (rugby football, hockey, sailing, golf, squash, swimming, three-day eventing). *Other:* 6 enter voluntary schemes and 5 work for national charities after leaving school. Other activities include a computer club, archery club, badminton, basketball, bridge club, chess club, choir, orchestra, CCF, croquet club, dramatic society, debating society, geological society, historical society, mountaineering club, music society, natural history society, photographic society, pipe band, social services group.

Careers In 1990, 73% leavers went on to degree courses; 13% straight into careers (eg estate agency, business); 14% other. Of those going on to degree courses, 10% went to Oxbridge, 58% to other universities; 32% to poly/colleges. 39% those going on to higher education went to courses in humanities/social sciences; 10% in medicine; and 18% in science/engineering.

Uniform School uniform worn throughout.

Houses/prefects Competitive houses for sport, drama, music etc. Prefects, head prefect, head of house and house prefects – appointed by the Headmaster. Sixth Form Committee.

Religion Morning prayers. Family and parish services for boarders.

Social Dramatic productions, carol service, senior citizens' Christmas party run by social services group. Organised trips to France, Germany and ski-ing parties to Austria etc. Pupils allowed to bring own car/bike/motorbike to school. Meals self service. School shop. No tobacco/alcohol allowed.

Discipline No corporal punishment. Pupils failing to produce homework once might expect to have to copy out poetry; those caught smoking cannabis on the premises could expect expulsion.

Boarding All sixth form have own study bedroom. Others in dormitories of 6+. Houses, of approximately 37–38, same as competitive houses. Resident matron and assistant. Central dining room. Half-term and 2 weekend exeats each term. Visits to local town allowed in sixth form, usually once a week.

Alumni association is run by C F Gailey, c/o the College.

Former pupils Michael Gibson (rugby, captained Ireland, British Lions); Iain Johnstone (BBC interviewer and producer – interviewed President Reagan); Mark Lambert (Royal Shakespeare actor and film star); Air Marshal A H W Ball; Air Vice Marshal F D Hughes; Air Vice Marshal C J Thomson.

· *Carmel College* ·

Carmel College
Mongewell Park
Wallingford
Oxfordshire
Tel 0491 37505

- Pupils 263
- Boys 11–18
  (Day/Board)
- Girls 11–18
  (Day/Board)
- Upper sixth 44

- Termly fees
  £2250 (Day)
  £3650 (Board)
  £4212 (Overseas
  Board)
- SHMIS
  Enquiries/application to
  the Headmaster

What it's like

Founded in 1948 by Rabbi Kopul Rosen, it opened at Greenham Common, Newbury and in 1953 moved to Mongewell Park near Wallingford on the Thames. The mansion house is the focal point of a large and beautiful estate. Excellent modern facilities and accommodation. It is a Jewish public school committed to cultivating a love and appreciation of Jewish practice, learning and culture. It offers a 'total Jewish environment' within which Judaism is of prime importance. All pupils attend morning services and they are required to have Tefillin and Siddurim. Attendance at Shabbat service is compulsory for all. Everyone is encouraged to take part in the Synagogue ritual by taking service and reading from the weekly Parashah. A large staff allows a staff:pupil ratio of roughly 1:7. Academic standards are high and results are good. Many pupils go on to degree courses each year, including Oxbridge. Hebrew and Jewish studies are an important part of the curriculum. Strong music, art and drama (there is an amphitheatre as well as a synagogue). A good range of sport and games. Rowing is quite strong. A plentiful range of extra-curricular activities. Business and entrepreneurial training is included as an activity.

School profile

Pupils Age range 11–18; 263 pupils, 30 day (18 boys, 12 girls), 233 boarding (162 boys, 71 girls). Main entry ages 11 and into sixth. Approx 10% are children of former pupils. *Transfer from maintained schools:* 40% main intake, plus 5% to sixth.

Entrance Own entrance exam used. Oversubscribed. No special skills but required to be Jewish. Parents expected to buy text books; maximum extras, £90 per term. 91 assisted places. 120 scholarships/bursaries, £7000 to £500 pa.

Parents 15+% are doctors, lawyers, etc; 15+% in industry or commerce. Up to 10% live within 30 miles; 10+% live overseas.

Staff Headmaster P Skelker, in post for 7 years. 40 full time staff, 2 part time. Annual turnover 5%. Average age 40.

Academic work GCSE and A-levels. 17 subjects offered (including Hebrew but no A-level general studies). In 1990, 40 pupils in upper fifth, 41 in upper sixth (now 44). *GCSE:* in 1990, 11 upper fifth gained at least grade C in 8+ subjects; 12 in 5–7; and 17 in 1–4 subjects. *A-levels:* 24 upper sixth passed in 3 subjects; 17 in 2 subjects. 25% took science A-levels; 75% arts/humanities. *Computing facilities:* Two network systems (BBC B's and research machine Nimbus's). *Special provision:* Study skills and EFL departments.

European Community *Languages:* French offered: to age 14; GCSE; A-level. German offered: to GCSE; A-level. Spanish offered: to GCSE; A-level. 10–25% take GCSE in more than 1 EC language. *Other:* Discussing possible links with Jewish schools in Europe. Frequent visits to France; recently been visited by the Jewish community school in Denmark.

Senior pupils' non-academic activities *Music:* 60 learn a musical instrument, 19 to Grade 6 or above; 15 in school orchestra, 30 in school choir, 4 in school pop group. *Art:* 40 take GCSE; 30 take A-level. 4 accepted for Art School; 10 belong to photographic club, 25 in art club. *Sport:* Soccer, rowing, netball, hockey, tennis, athletics, judo, rounders, horse-riding, cricket, squash, swimming, basketball and dance available. 60 take non-compulsory sport. 80 take exams. 1 represents county/country (rowing). Other activities include a computer club, technology insight club, debating society, Young Enterprise Scheme, current affairs society, Israel Society.

Careers In 1990, 77% leavers went on to degree courses; 2% to art/drama/ music colleges; 15% to non-degree courses (eg agriculture, business studies, management); 12% straight into careers (eg army). Of those going on to degree courses, 10% went to Oxbridge, 49% to other universities, 39% to poly/colleges. $2^1/_2$% those going on to higher education went to courses in practical art; $7^1/_2$% in humanities/social sciences; and 5% in medicine.

Uniform School uniform worn except in the sixth.

Houses/prefects Competitive houses. Prefects, head boy and girl, head of house and house prefects – appointed by the Head after consultation with the staff. School Council.

Religion Compulsory attendance at religious service daily.

Social Many visits from local groups who wish to find out about Judaism. Organised trips abroad. Pupils allowed to bring own horse to school. Meals self service, formal on Sabbath. School shop. No tobacco/alcohol allowed (apart from wine on Sabbath).

Discipline No corporal punishment. Pupils failing to produce homework once might expect detention; those caught smoking cannabis on or off the premises will be expelled.

Boarding 5% have own study bedroom, 75% share with 1 other; 15% are in dormitories of 6+. Single sex houses, of 26–80, divided by age group. Resident qualified medical staff. Central dining room. 2 weekend exeats each term. Visits to local town allowed.

Alumni association is run by Mr A Barr-Taylor, Carmel College.

Former pupils Roland Joffe; Gary Davis; Prof Edward Lutwak; Professor Raymond Dwek; Rabbi Dr Abraham Levy; Stephen Frankel.

· Casterton ·

Casterton School
Kirkby Lonsdale
Carnforth
Cumbria
LA6 2SG
Tel 05242 71202

- Pupils 366
- Boys None
- Girls 8–18
  (Day/Board)
- Upper sixth 45

- Termly fees
  £1504 (Day)
  £2444 (Board)
  £2034 (Weekly)
- GSA
  Enquiries/application to
  the Headmaster

What it's like

Founded in 1823, established at Casterton in 1833, it stands in its own grounds of 50 acres on the outskirts of the village. The surroundings are very beautiful. Handsome solid buildings, excellent modern facilities, comfortable boarding accommodation. A sound traditional education is provided. Many sixth formers go on to degree courses, including Oxbridge. French, German and Spanish are offered to A-level and Italian as a non-examined subject. A very high proportion of girls takes GCSE in more than one European language. There are regular exchanges with France, Germany and Spain. Its religious life is based on Anglican practice and the village parish church is used regularly for worship. A happy, friendly place with a 'family' atmosphere, it is strong in music and drama and the Duke of Edinburgh's Award Scheme. Plentiful use is made of the superb Cumbrian countryside for outdoor pursuits (riding, fell walking, canoeing, camping, sailing, climbing). The junior school is adjacent (the Bronte sisters attended Casterton in 1824).

School profile

Pupils Total age range 8–18; 366 girls, 65 day, 301 boarding. Senior department 11–18, 328 girls. Main entry ages 11 and into sixth. Approx 3% are children of former pupils. *Transfer from maintained schools:* 50% intake at 11+ and into sixth.

Entrance Own entrance exam used. No special skills or religious requirements but school is Anglican. Parents not expected to buy text books. 43 assisted places. 48 scholarships/bursaries, £2000–£300.

Parents 15+% in industry or commerce. 10+% live within 30 miles; 10+% live overseas.

Staff Head A F Thomas, 1 year in post. 40 full time staff, 10 part time. Annual turnover 6%. Average age 40.

Academic work GCSE and A-levels. 25 subjects offered (including A-level general studies). In 1990, 57 pupils in upper fifth, 39 in upper sixth (now 45). *GCSE:* in 1990, 48 upper fifth gained at least grade C in 8+ subjects; 9 in 5–7 subjects. *A-levels:* 23 upper sixth passed in 4+ subjects; 11 in 3; 5 in 2 subjects. 8 took science A-levels; 30 arts/humanities. *Computing facilities:* 8 Archimedes and 4 BBC micros. Separate BBC micros in science dept. *Special provision:* Caters for mild dyslexia.

European Community *Languages:* French offered: to age 14; GCSE; A-level. German offered: to age 14; GCSE; A-level. Italian offered: non-examined. Spanish offered: to age 14; GCSE; A-level. 50–75% take GCSE in more than 1 EC language. *Exchanges:* Regular exchanges for pupils aged 14–18 to France, Germany and Spain.

Senior pupils' non-academic activities *Music:* 195 learn a musical instrument, 28 to Grade 6 or above, 34 in school orchestra, 44 in school choir, 28 in wind band; 7 in Cumbria Youth Orchestra. *Drama and dance* 35 in school productions. 32 take Associated Board, 5 theatre arts, ballet. 1 accepted for Drama/Dance School. *Art:* 16 take GCSE; 8 A-level. 2 pa accepted for Art School. 15 belong to photographic club. *Sport:* Netball, tennis, swimming, athletics, rounders, hockey, lacrosse, volleyball, badminton, trampolining, table tennis, gymnastics, sub-aqua diving, canoeing, cross-country, yoga available. Pupils represent county (hockey, netball, swimming, athletics, tennis). *Other:* 5 take part in local community schemes. 54 have bronze Duke of Edinburgh's Award, 22 have silver and 12 have gold. Other activities include a computer club, public speaking, choral society, video, cookery, Young Enterprise, electronics, driving lessons.

Careers In 1990, 63% leavers went on to degree courses; 12% to art/drama/music colleges; 10% to non-degree courses (eg radiography, nursing, physiotherapy); 15% other (Gap year). Of those going on to degree courses, 12% went to Oxbridge, 56% to other universities; 34% to poly/colleges. 17% those going on to higher education went to courses in practical art; 55% in humanities/social sciences; 7% in medicine; and 21% in science/engineering.

Uniform School uniform worn throughout. Home clothes at off-duty times.

Houses/prefects Competitive houses. Prefects, head girl, head of house and house prefects – appointed by the Head.

Religion Anglican, but girls of other denominations are accepted.

Social Theatre performances, Young Enterprise, debates and many social events with other schools. Organised trips to France, Nepal and ski-ing trips. Senior pupils allowed to bring own bike. Meals formal. School shop. No tobacco/alcohol allowed.

Discipline No corporal punishment. Pupils failing to produce homework once would be required to rewrite it. Involvement with drugs would lead to expulsion. The aim is to treat disciplinary offences sympathetically but firmly. Honesty is encouraged.

Boarding 10% have own study bedroom, 35% share (1–3). Houses of 20–45 (separate sixth form houses). Resident SRN. Central dining room. Sixth form can cook own food at weekends. 2 weekend exeats each term. Visits to the local town allowed at weekends.

Alumni association run by Mrs M Crisp, c/o the School.

· *Caterham* ·

Caterham School	● Pupils 740	● Termly fees
Harestone Valley	● Boys 8–18	£1340 (Day)
Caterham	(Day/Board)	£2460 (Board)
Surrey	● Girls 16–18	● HMC
CR3 6YA	(Day/Board)	Enquiries/application to
Tel 0883 343028	● Upper sixth 95	the Headmaster

What it's like

Founded in 1811 in Lewisham, it moved to Caterham in 1884. It stands in 80 acres of delightful grounds among the North Downs just inside the green belt. The prep school has its own buildings and staff. The senior school has very pleasant modern buildings and excellent facilities. It has strong links with the United Reformed Church. Christian worship and religious studies are an important part of its life. The aim is to provide a broad education based on Christian principles and practice. A broad general education is provided, academic standards are high and results good. Very many sixth formers go on to degree courses, including many to Oxbridge. French and German are offered to A-level and many pupils take GCSE in both. Spanish is being introduced gradually at all levels. There are regular exchanges with France and Germany. The drama, music and creative arts departments are strong. A wide variety of sports and games is available and standards are high in the major games, rugby, cricket and hockey (in rugby, the school won the 1990 National 7-a–side competition). There are numerous clubs and societies for extra-curricular activities.

School profile

Pupils Total age range 8–18; 740 pupils, 710 boys (520 day, 190 boarding) 30 day girls. Senior department 13–18; 450 pupils, 420 boys, 30 girls. Main entry ages 8–13 (boys) and into sixth (boys and girls). 10% are children of former pupils. *Transfer from maintained schools:* 30% intake, plus 10% to sixth.

Entrance Common entrance and own exam used. Oversubscribed. No special skills or religious requirements; school has URC affiliation but pupils of many faiths within school. Parents not expected to buy text books; maximum extras £50. 20 assisted places pa. 15 scholarships, 50–25% fees, plus bursaries for children of clergy, services and foreign office.

Parents Wide mix of professions.

173

60+% live within 30 miles.

Staff Headmaster S R Smith, in post for 15 years. 44 full time staff, 3 part time. Annual turnover approx 10%. Average age approx 38.

Academic work GCSE and A-levels. 18 subjects offered (no A-level general studies). In 1990, 90 pupils in fifth, 95 in upper sixth. *GCSE:* in 1990, 81% fifth gained at least grade C in 8+ subjects; 11% in 5–7; and 8% in 1–4 subjects. *A-levels:* 26% upper sixth passed in 4+ subjects; 62% in 3; 9% in 2; and 3% in 1 subject. 35% took science A-levels; 30% arts/humanities; 35% both. *Computing facilities:* Nimbus network. *Special provision:* Specialist dyslexic teacher available if required for small minority.

European Community *Languages:* French offered: to age 14; GCSE; A-level. German offered: to age 14; GCSE; A-level. Spanish offered: to age 14; GCSE (from 1992); A-level (from 1994). 25–50% take GCSE in more than 1 EC language. Some short language courses in General Studies in sixth form. *Exchanges:* Regular exchanges for pupils aged 14–18 to France and Germany. *Other:* Assistants from German and French universities.

Senior pupils' non-academic activities (Third form and above) *Music:* 70 learn a musical instrument, 12 to Grade 6 or above. 1 pa accepted to read music at university. 50 in school orchestra, 2 in orchestra outside school, 40 in school choir, 6 in jazz group, 5 play in pop group. *Drama and dance:* 40 actors/stage managers/technicians in school productions; 3 accepted for eg National Youth Music Theatre. *Art:* 60 take as non-examined subject; 20 take GCSE, 10 A-level. 6 accepted for Art School. 10 belong to photographic club, 30 to other art clubs. *Sport:* Rugby, hockey, cricket, athletics, cross-country, swimming, tennis, karate, shooting, orienteering, outdoor pursuits available. Sport compulsory up to fifth year; sixth can choose from options. 2 represent county (rugby, cricket, hockey). *Other:* 20 take part in local community schemes. 20 have bronze Duke of Edinburgh's Award, 11 silver, 3 gold. Other activities include a computer club, bridge club, debating, geography, history, English, science societies, Christian fellowship. COPEC (sixth form discussion group); a lot of musical activities in lunch hour.

Careers In 1990, 92% leavers went on to degree courses; 4% to non-degree courses; 4% other. Of those going on to degree courses, 10% went to Oxbridge, 9% to other universities or poly/colleges. 1% those going on to higher education went to courses in music; 54% in humanities/social sciences; 5% in medicine; and 40% in science/engineering.

Uniform School uniform worn, option of suits in sixth.

Houses/prefects Competitive houses. Prefects, head boy/girl, heads of house. Head of school elected by year group, ratified by Head. Regular prefects' meeting.

Religion Attendance at religious worship compulsory.

Social Regular debates, music courses with other local schools. Exchange with German and French schools. Pupils allowed to bring own car/bike/motorbike to school. Meals self-service and compulsory. School sports shop. No tobacco/alcohol allowed.

Discipline No corporal punishment. Pupils failing to produce homework once might expect to re-do with extra work, possibly academic detention. Pupils caught smoking cannabis on school premises could expect expulsion.

Boarding 25% have own study bedroom, 50% share (with 1 or 2); 10% in dormitories of 6+. Houses of approx 50. Resident qualified nurse. 1 exeat every 3 weeks; other days out at weekends, depending on seniority. Visits to the local village permitted, on request.

· *Cawston* ·

Cawston College
Cawston
Norwich
NR10 4JD
Tel 0603 871204

- Pupils 145
- Boys 11–19
  (Day/Board/Weekly)
- Girls 11–19
  (Day/Board/Weekly)
- Upper sixth New

- Termly fees
  £1160 (Day)
  £2085 (Board)
  £2045 (Weekly)
- Woodard
  Enquiries/application to
  the Headmaster

What it's like

Founded in 1964, it lies 12 miles north of Norwich in beautiful Norfolk countryside, near the coast and the Broads. It enjoys a handsome rural site of 126 acres and the main building is an old manor house. Modern extensions provide comfortable boarding accommodation and good teaching facilities. There is some emphasis on religious worship and instruction. It has recently become co-educational and a girls' boarding house has been built. A sixth form is also being developed. It has many of the advantages of being a small school and a large staff allows a most favourable staff:pupil ratio of 1:8. Very few schools can improve on that. GCSE results have been creditable. Music, drama and art are very strongly supported. There is a most impressive range of sports and games in which high standards are attained. Extra-curricular activities are well provided for and the school has shown considerable enterprise in recent years in mounting ambitious expeditions to, among other places, the Andes, the Sahara, the High Atlas and Malaysia. Pupils also participate very actively in the Duke of Edinburgh's Award Scheme.

School profile

Pupils Age range 11–19; 145 pupils, 40 day (30 boys, 10 girls), 105 boarding (94 boys, 11 girls). Main entry ages 11, 12, 13 and into sixth. *Transfer from maintained schools:* 20% main intake, none to sixth.

Entrance Common entrance and own entrance exam used. Not oversubscribed; school expanding. No special skills or religious requirements. Parents not expected to buy text books. 5 scholarships/bursaries per year, £1000–250.

Parents 30+% live within 30 miles; 10+% live overseas.

Staff Headmaster J Sutton, 1 year in post. 18 full time staff, 7 part time. Annual turnover 6%. Average age 40.

Academic work GCSE and A-levels. 16 subjects offered. In 1989, 30 pupils in upper fifth, sixth form only recently started. *GCSE:* in 1989, 3 upper fifth gained at least grade C in 8+ subjects; 15 in 5–7; and 6 in 1–4 subjects. *Computing facilities:* New Information Technology centre; IBM compatible machines and some BBCs. Art department recently had computer and printer with Camcorder installed. *Special provision:* Dyslexic and EFL departments.

European Community *Languages:* French offered: to age 14; GCSE; AS-level; A-level. *Other:* Occasional Spanish pupil in school for 1 term–1 year.

Senior pupils' non-academic activities *Music:* Approximately 20 learn a musical instrument, 2 to Grade 6 or above; 15 play in school orchestra, 10 in choir. *Drama and dance:* 50 in school productions. *Art:* 4 take as a non-examined subject, 20 take GCSE; 2 A-level. *Sport:* Rugger, hockey, athletics, cross-country, tennis, cricket, badminton, golf, swimming, sailing, riding, clay pigeon shooting, basketball, netball, volleyball, football, rounders. 12 have represented county (rugby, hockey, athletics). *Other:* 33 have bronze and silver Duke of Edinburgh's

Award. Other activities include a computer club and expeditions (local, Scotland and Wales, Andes, Malaysia etc), cadet force, radio modelling, pottery, conservation, model railway, electronics etc.

Careers In 1990, 10% leavers went on to art/drama/music colleges; 30% to non-degree courses; 30% straight into careers (eg family business, mostly farming, others building and catering). 25% those going on to higher education went to courses in practical art; and 15% in science/engineering.

Uniform School uniform worn throughout.

Houses/prefects Competitive houses. Prefects (appointed by Head and prefects), head boy/girl, head of house and house prefects (appointed by housemaster and prefects).

Religion Assembly compulsory (with hymn and prayers).

Social Joint plays and CCF exercises with other schools. Some organised trips abroad. Pupils allowed to bring own bike to school. Cafeteria system. School shop. No tobacco/alcohol allowed.

Discipline No corporal punishment. Pupils failing to produce homework once might expect detention or repeat signed by tutor; those caught smoking cannabis on the premises, or if supplying others, could expect certain expulsion.

Boarding Single sex houses of 20–64; junior boys, senior boys and girls. Resident qualified nurse. Central dining room. Pupils can provide and cook snacks. Half term plus 2 short break exeats each term. Visits to local town allowed with permission.

Alumni association is run by J Lilwall, c/o Cawston College.

· *Channing* ·

Channing School	● Pupils 450	● Termly fees
Highgate	● Boys None	£1340 (Day)
London	● Girls 5–18 (Day)	● GSA
N6 5HF	● Upper sixth 31	Enquiries/application to
Tel 081 340 2328		the Headmistress

What it's like

Founded in 1885 for 'the daughters of Unitarian ministers and others'. It occupies the large 18th century building now known as Channing, Highgate Hill. The present school is a combination of old and modern buildings which have been adapted and improved over the years. The senior school occupies a 3.5 acre site with fine views over London and Essex; the junior school has a nearby site of 2.5 acres. There are pleasant gardens and playing fields. A broad, general education is provided with a good spread of subjects up to GCSE and a wide range of A-level subjects. A large staff permits a favourable staff:pupil ratio. Academic results are good. Many go on to degree courses. French, German and Spanish are offered to A-level and there are regular exchanges with France, Germany and Spain. The music and drama depts are active. Sports and games are well catered for and there is a variety of extra-curricular activities. A substantial commitment to local community services.

School profile

Pupils Total age range 5–18; 450 day girls. Senior department 11–18, 304 girls. Main entry ages 5, 11 and into sixth. Approx 4% are children of former pupils. Over 20% from own junior school. *Transfer from maintained schools:* 10% intake at 11+, plus 5% to sixth.

Entrance Own entrance exam used. Oversubscribed. No special skills or religious requirements. Parents not expected to buy text books until GCSE and A-level. Scholarships for academic merit, bursaries for music and cases of financial need.

Parents 25+% are doctors, lawyers etc; 60+% in industry or commerce.

Staff Headmistress Mrs I R Raphael, in post for 6 years. 30 full time staff, 17 part time.

Academic work GCSE and A-levels. 14 GCSE subjects offered; 15 at A-level (no A-level general studies). In 1990, 43 pupils in upper fifth, 28 in upper sixth (now 31). *GCSE:* in 1990, 28 upper fifth gained at least grade C in 8+ subjects; 12 in 5–7; and 2 in 1–4 subjects. *A-levels:* 1 upper sixth passed in 4+ subjects; 18 in 3; 7 in 2; and 2 in 1 subject. 7 took science A-levels; 11 arts/humanities; 10 both. *Computing facilities:* 13 BBC Master terminals networked in computer laboratory and Apple Macintosh in art area.

European Community *Languages:* French offered: to age 14; GCSE; A-level. German offered: to age 14; GCSE; AS-level; A-level. Spanish offered: to age 14; GCSE; A-level. *Exchanges:* Regular exchanges for pupils aged 14–18 to France, Germany and Spain.

Senior pupils' non-academic activities *Music:* 75 learn a musical instrument, 50 in school orchestras, 35 in choir. *Drama and dance:* 30 in school productions. *Art:* 3 take A-level. 2 accepted for Art School. *Sport:* Hockey, netball, tennis, rounders, gymnastics, dance, trampolining, fencing, badminton available. 60 take non-compulsory sport. 150 BAGA acrobatic awards. Occasional pupils represent county (tennis). *Other:* 110 take part in local community schemes; Duke of Edinburgh's Award scheme; Young Enterprise.

Careers In 1990, 64% leavers went on to degree courses; 4% to art/drama/ music colleges; 4% to non-degree courses (eg secretarial); 29% other (eg retaking A-levels). Of those going on to degree courses, 89% went to universities; 11% to poly/colleges. 5% those going on to higher education went to courses in practical art; 40% in humanities/social sciences; 15% in medicine; and 40% in science/engineering.

Uniform School uniform worn except in the sixth.

Houses/prefects No competitive houses or prefects. Head girl. School Council.

Religion Compulsory school assembly and RE classes.

Social Some organised local events and trips abroad. Pupils allowed to bring own bike to school. Meals self service. No tobacco/alcohol allowed.

Discipline No corporal punishment.

Alumnae association run by Mrs M Banks, 57 Fordington Road, London N6 4TH.

· *Charterhouse* ·

Charterhouse	• Pupils 701	• Termly fees
Godalming	• Boys 13–18	£2700 (Day)
Surrey	(Day/Board)	£3265 (Board)
GU7 2DN	• Girls 16–18	• HMC
Tel 0483 426222	(Day/Board)	Enquiries/application to
	• Upper sixth 166	the Headmaster

What it's like

Founded in 1611, on the site of a Carthusian monastery established in London in 1371, it moved in 1872 to Godalming. It stands in a superb estate of 200 acres on a plateau above the River Wey with fine views south and south-west. With its towers and spires and its blend of neo-Gothic and neo-Tudor buildings in stone and brick, it presents an almost emblematic image of the traditional English public school. There is a number of modern buildings as well and the whole place is superbly equipped with virtually every facility that one might expect and hope for. The teaching is well known to be excellent and a first-rate education is provided. Very many Carthusians proceed to degree courses, including an exceptionally high proportion to Oxbridge. French, German and Spanish are offered to A-level; Italian to GCSE. A high proportion of pupils takes GCSE in more than one European language. There are regular exchanges with France, Germany and Spain. It also has the advantages of exceptionally good libraries, a museum, an art studio, a design and technology centre and the new Ben Travers Theatre which is better equipped than many professional theatres. Very strong in music, drama and art. Numerous productions and performances each year. Outdoor pursuits are various and popular. There is an impressive range of extra-curricular activities. There is even a school farm. The CCF, scouts and social services (locally and in London) are vigorously supported. There is a strong sporting tradition and wide range of sports and games; there are fixtures against the leading schools. A nine-hole golf course was recently opened.

School profile

Pupils Age range 13–18; 701 pupils, 24 day (17 boys, 7 girls), 677 boarding (588 boys, 89 girls). Main entry ages 13 (boys) and into sixth (boys and girls). Approx 13% are children of former pupils. *Transfer from maintained schools:* None at 13; 15% to sixth.

Entrance Common entrance and own scholarship exam. Oversubscribed. Academic ability and sound character looked for; no religious requirements. Parents not expected to buy text books in the Under School. 5 assisted places pa (sixth form only). Scholarships at 16 and 13 (21 academic, 7 music, 4 art) from full fees (in cases of financial hardship) to £500. Also awards for sons of lawyers, sons of IAPS teachers and for classics; awards may be supplemented by bursaries in case of financial need.

Parents 15+% in industry or commerce. 30+% live within 30 miles; 10+% live overseas.

Staff Headmaster P J Attenborough, in post for 9 years. 79 full time staff, 2 part time (plus music staff). Annual turnover 3%. Average age 41.

Academic work GCSE and A-levels. 19 GCSE subjects offered including logic and Russian; 20 at A-level (no A-level general studies). In 1990, 116 pupils in upper fifth, 166 in upper sixth. *A-levels:* 10 upper sixth passed in 4+ subjects; 140 in 3; 10 in 2; and 3 in 1 subject. 30 took science A-levels; 85 arts/humanities; 51 both. *Computing facilities:* Network of 27 BBC and Archimedes machines (18 in computer room), and about 30 other of various types in the school.

European Community *Languages:* French offered: to GCSE; AS-level; A-level. German offered: to GCSE; AS-level; A-level. Italian offered: to GCSE. Spanish offered: to GCSE; A-level. 25–50% take GCSE in more than 1 EC language. 1 year language courses in Italian and post-GCSE French. *Exchanges:* Regular exchanges for pupils aged 14–18 to France, Germany and Spain. *Other:* German pupils regularly stay in school for 1 year.

Senior pupils' non-academic activities *Music:* 300 learn a musical instrument, 100 to Grade 6 or above. 100 in school orchestra, 100 in choir, brass band and jazz band; 3 accepted for Music School; 3 go on to read music at university. *Drama and dance:* 100 in school productions, 150 in House plays, foreign language plays (French, German, Spanish) etc; 1 accepted for Drama/Dance School. *Art:* 250 take as non-examined subject; 24 take GCSE; 10 A-level; 6 A-level History of Art. 5 accepted for Art School; 1 for architecture; 2 take degrees in History of Art; 2 go into other art training; 50 belong to photographic club. *Sport:* Cricket, soccer, hockey, tennis, squash, fives, rackets, athletics, cross-country, swimming, shooting, rugby, water polo, fencing, lacrosse (girls), sailing, golf, canoeing, rowing, riding, climbing, windsurfing available. 400 take non-compulsory sport. 24 represent county/country (shooting, swimming, golf, soccer, hockey, tennis). *Other:* 40 take part in local community schemes. 13 have bronze Duke of Edinburgh's Award; 2 work for national charities after leaving school. Other activities include bridge, debating, farm, forestry, historical buildings, magical, motor, opera, railway, photography, ballroom dancing, antique film, astronomical, recording, art, politics, economics, natural history, play reading, science, stamps, stratagem, driving lessons etc.

Careers On average, 88% leavers go on to degree courses; 2% to art/drama/music colleges; 1% to non-degree courses (eg hotel and catering); 9% straight into careers (eg armed forces). Of those going on to degree courses, 20% went to Oxbridge, 70% to other universities; 10% to poly/colleges. 1% those going on to higher education went to courses in practical art; 4% in music; 60% in humanities/social sciences; 7% in medicine; and 28% in science/engineering.

Uniform School uniform worn throughout.

Houses/prefects Competitive houses. Prefects (monitors), head boy, head of house and house prefects (house monitors) – appointed.

Religion Charterhouse is a Christian foundation; religious worship compulsory.

Social Organised trips abroad annually. Pupils allowed to bring own bike to school. Meals formal. Four shops. Senior pupils allowed alcohol; no tobacco.

Discipline Corporal punishment not used (although not formally abolished). Pupils failing to produce homework once might expect a warning, or time extended and extra imposition; those caught smoking cannabis on the premises would expect expulsion.

Boarding 81% have own study bedroom, 11% share with 1 other. Houses, of approximately 65. Resident qualified nurses. Dining by houses. Pupils can provide and cook own food. Half-term exeats only. Visits to local town allowed.

Alumni association is run by The Recorder, c/o the School.

Former pupils Peter May; James Prior; John Wakeham; William Rees-Mogg; Max Hastings; Peter Gabriel; Jonathan King; Ian Wallace; Don Cupitt; Jonathan Dimbleby; David Dimbleby; Gerald Priestland; David Hicks; Simon Raven; Dick Taverne; Graham Seed; Nicholas Henson; Lord Donaldson; Mr Justice (Oliver) Popplewell; Bishop Whinney; C J Swallow; David Miller; Sir Ronald Millar; Frederick Raphael; Peter de Savary; Gerald Priestland; Hon. Mr Justice Alliott; Stephen Venables; Peter Oundjian; Lord Richardson; Sir Hugh Cunningham; Sir Brian Burnett.

· *Charters-Ancaster* ·

Charters-Ancaster
School
Penland Road
Bexhill-on-Sea
East Sussex
TN40 2JQ
Tel 0424 730499

- Pupils 324
- Boys 3–8 only
  (Day)
- Girls 3–18
  (Day/Board/
  Weekly)
- Upper sixth 18

- Termly fees
  £970 (Day)
  £1970 (Board/
  Weekly)
- GSA, GPDST
  Enquiries/application to
  the Headmistress

What it's like

The result of an amalgamation in 1986 of two long-established local schools (Ancaster House and Charters Towers) and joined the Girls Public Day Schools Trust in 1988. It comprises senior and junior schools in separate buildings close to each other on the outskirts of Bexhill-on-Sea. The school has undergone extensive modernisation and renovation, including a new swimming pool. Like all Trust schools, it is non-denominational. It has cosmopolitan links with Europe, USA and Australia. A sound traditional education is provided and it is strong in music, drama and extra-curricular activities. French and German are offered to A-level and many girls take GCSE in both. Flourishing local support and involvement with the Bexhill community.

School profile

Pupils Total age range 3–18; 324 pupils, 262 day, 62 boarding (boarding only from age 11). Senior department 11–18, 180 girls. Main entry ages, 3, 11 and into sixth. 1% are children of former pupils. *Transfer from maintained schools:* 25% intake at 11, plus 5% to sixth.

Entrance Own entrance exam used. Parents not expected to buy text books. Scholarships and bursaries available.

Parents Wide ranging – some local, some overseas.

Staff Headmistress Mrs K Lewis, first year in post. Staff:pupil ratio 1:10.

Academic work GCSE, A-levels, City & Guilds in certain subjects. 20 subjects offered (including A-level general studies). In 1990, 37 pupils in upper fifth, 12 in upper sixth (now 18). *GCSE:* in 1991, 50% upper fifth gained at least grade C in 8+ subjects; 30% in 5–7; and 20% in 1–4 subjects. *A-levels:* 50% upper sixth passed in 3 subjects; 20% in 2; and 25% in 1 subject. 16% took science A-levels; 58% arts/humanities; 25% both. *Computing facilities:* Networked (Acorn Econet) computer room and a number of free-standing computers throughout the school. *Special provision:* Assistance for dyslexic pupils able to cope with mainstream courses. EFL provision.

European Community *Languages:* French offered: to age 14; GCSE; AS-level; A-level. German offered: to age 14; GCSE; AS-level; A-level. 25–50% take GCSE in more than 1 EC language.

Senior pupils' non-academic activities 50% learn a musical instrument; school orchestra; chamber group; choirs; folk group. Concerts, plays and public speaking competitions held annually. *Sport:* Hockey, netball, swimming, athletics, tennis, rounders, squash, riding, badminton, self-defence, trampolining, lifesaving available. *Other:* Other activities include jazz dance, cookery, Faberge, typing, dress making, photography, drama, video.

Careers 85% sixth form leavers go on to higher education (33% arts courses, 33% science, 33% modern languages).

Uniform School uniform worn except in sixth.

Houses/prefects Competitive houses.

180

Prefects, head girl, head of house and house prefects.
Religion Non-denominational assembly. Some boarders attend nearby churches.
Social Debates, public speaking, outings, parties/discos with other schools etc.

Discipline The good behaviour of pupils expected at all times both during school hours and outside.
Boarding Seniors have single or double study bedrooms, most others in 3–4 bedrooms. 1 or 2 exeats each term.

· *Cheadle Hulme* ·

Cheadle Hulme School
Claremont Road
Cheadle Hulme
Cheadle
Cheshire SK8 6EF
Tel 061 485 4142

- Pupils 1128
- Boys 7–18 (Day/ Board)
- Girls 7–18 (Day/ Board)
- Upper sixth 116

- Termly fees £990 (Day) £2160 (Board)
- HMC
Enquiries/application to the Headmaster

What it's like
Founded in 1855, formerly the Manchester Warehousemen and Clerks' Orphan school. Urban, single-site, near Manchester in 80-acre grounds. The original Victorian building has been recently modernised. Extensive additions over the years. The boarding block is very spacious and comfortable. The junior school is nearby. An excellent academic education is given, many go on to higher education, including a number to Oxbridge. French and German offered to A-level, Modern Greek to GCSE. Many pupils take GCSE in more than one European language. There are regular exchanges with France and Germany. Altogether a well-run establishment, particularly strong in music, art and drama.

School profile
Pupils Total age range 7–18; 1128 pupils approx, 1053 day (525 boys, 528 girls), 75 boarding (33 boys, 42 girls). Senior department 11–18, 913 pupils approx (444 boys, 469 girls). Main entry ages 7, 8, 11 and into sixth.
Entrance Own entrance exam used. Oversubscribed. No special skills or religious requirements. Parents not expected to buy text books. 20 assisted places. 4 scholarships/bursaries for excellence in music or drama, 1 for boarding, full fees to £500.
Parents 15+% in industry or commerce; 15+% are doctors, lawyers etc. 60+% live within 30 miles; up to 10% live overseas.
Staff Headmaster Donald J Wilkinson, first year in post. 71 full time staff, 9 part time. Annual turnover 5%. Average age 45.

Academic work GCSE and A-levels. 19 subjects offered (including A-level general studies). In 1989, 123 pupils in upper fifth, 116 in upper sixth. *GCSE:* in 1989, 100 upper fifth gained at least grade C in 8+ subjects; 18 in 5–7; and 5 in 1–4 subjects. *A-levels:* 75 upper sixth passed in 4+ subjects; 24 in 3; 9 in 2; and 8 in 1 subject. 55 took science A-levels; 45 arts/humanities; 30 both. *Computing facilities:* Numerous 'hands on' facilities for pupils.
European Community *Languages:* French offered: to GCSE; A-level. German offered: to GCSE; A-level. Greek (modern): to GCSE; A-level. 25–50% take GCSE in more than 1 EC language. *Exchanges:* Regular exchanges for pupils aged 14–16 to France and Germany.
Senior pupils' non-academic activities *Music:* 200 learn a musical instru-

ment, 30 to Grade 6 or above. 3 or 4 per year accepted for Music School; 1 or 2 read music at university. 80 in school orchestra, 80 in choir, 2 in National Youth Orchestra. *Drama and dance:* 30 in school productions; 1 or 2 accepted for Drama/Dance Schools. *Art:* 20 take as non-examined subject; 30 take GCSE; 6 A-level. 2 or 3 accepted for Art School. 15 belong to photographic club. *Sport:* Rugby, hockey, lacrosse, cross-country, netball, swimming, tennis, cricket, athletics, badminton, fencing, archery available. Sport is compulsory. 12 represent county; 1 or 2 represent country. Other activities include a computer club, electronics, beekeeping, chess and many others.

Careers In 1990, 75% leavers went on to degree courses; 3% to art/drama/music colleges; 16% to non-degree courses (eg HND business decisions, secretarial, nursing, business studies, HND mechanical/electrical engineering); 6% other. Of those going on to degree courses, 14% went to Oxbridge, 61% to other universities; 25% to poly/colleges. 6% those going on to higher education went to courses in practical art; 2% in music; 38% in humanities/social sciences; 7% in medicine; and 47% in science/engineering.

Uniform School uniform worn throughout.

Houses/prefects No competitive houses. Prefects, head boy/girl, head of boarding house and house prefects – appointed by the Head on advice. School Council.

Religion No compulsory religious worship.

Social No organised events with other schools. Many organised trips to France, Germany, Italy/Greece, ski-ing each year. Pupils allowed to bring own car/bike/motorbike to school. Meals self service. No tobacco/alcohol allowed.

Discipline No corporal punishment. Pupils failing to produce homework once might expect a verbal reprimand; those caught smoking cannabis on the premises would be expelled.

Boarding 30% have own study bedroom, 30% share (with 1 other); 10% are in dormitories of 6+. Houses divided by age group, single sex. Resident medical staff. Central dining room. Many weekend exeats. Visits to local town allowed most weekends.

Alumni association run by Mr D H James, 32 Woodfield Road, Cheadle Hulme, Cheadle, Cheshire SK8 7JS.

· *Cheltenham (Boys)* ·

Cheltenham College
Bath Road
Cheltenham
Gloucestershire
GL53 7LD
Tel 0242 513540

- Pupils 560
- Boys 13–18
  (Day/Board)
- Girls 16–18
  (Day/Board)
- Upper sixth 145

- Termly fees
  £2370 (Day)
  £3150 (Board)
- HMC
  Enquiries/application to
  the Headmaster

What it's like

Founded in 1841, it has a fine site on the edge of the town. Handsome Victorian buildings in beautiful gardens and playing fields. In the period 1973–90 a great many developments and modernisations were achieved and the facilities are now excellent. It is a C of E foundation and chapel services and some Sunday services are compulsory. However, it is fully ecumenical. Academic standards are high and results good. Many leavers go on to degree courses each year, including Oxbridge.

Technology is strong; winner of Young Engineer of GB (1988) and Young Inventor (1989). Music is very strong and plays a large part in the lives of many pupils. There are joint musical activities with the Ladies' College. Drama is also strong and there are regular productions in the big classical theatre in Cheltenham's Everyman Theatre. The arts and crafts centre is a particularly active one. There are fine facilities for sports and games and the college achieves a high standard. A plentiful range of extra-curricular activities, clubs, societies and so on. A very energetic community scheme serves the town. Wherever possible all college facilities are made available to the town and other schools. One of the school's aims is to maintain a tradition of service to a modern industrial society. A feature is the thriving 'Industrial Link' organisation both in this country and in Japan.

School profile

Pupils Age range 13–18; 560 pupils, 181 day (163 boys, 18 girls), 379 boarding (343 boys, 36 girls). Main entry ages 13 (boys), and into sixth (boys and girls). Own junior school provides more than 20% of intake. Approx 15% are children of former pupils.

Entrance Common entrance and own sixth form scholarship or entry tests used. Oversubscribed. Motivation looked for; C of E foundation. Parents expected to buy seniors' text books; maximum extras £100. 20 scholarships/bursaries (for 16+, 13+), 80–10% of fees.

Parents 15+% in industry or commerce. 30+% live within 30 miles; up to 10% live overseas.

Staff Headmaster P D V Wilkes, 1 year in post. 56 full time staff, 4 part time. Annual turnover 5%. Average age 34.

Academic work GCSE and A-levels. 18 GCSE subjects offered; 19 at A-level (no A-level general studies). In 1989, 100 pupils in upper fifth, 145 in upper sixth. *GCSE:* in 1989, 63% upper fifth gained at least grade C in 8+ subjects; 30% in 5–7; and 6% in 1–4 subjects. *A-levels:* 6 upper sixth passed in 4+ subjects; 112 in 3; 15 in 2; and 4 in 1 subject. 40% took science A-levels; 40% arts/humanities; 20% both. *Computing facilities:* 3 IT centres with networked Macintosh computers; BBC computers in maths department computer centre. Moving to classrooms, each having their own computers for inter-active learning.

Senior pupils' non-academic activities *Music:* Tuition in many instruments to GCSE/A-level; choral society, chapel choir, orchestra, string orchestra, wind and big bands, small and close harmony ensembles, madrigal group. *Drama and dance:* 7–8 annual productions in fully equipped theatre. *Art:* Art school includes darkrooms, pottery, printmaking; open at all times. *Sport:* Rugby, hockey, tennis, squash, rackets, rowing, athletics, fives, swimming, shooting (small bore indoor range, use of 600 yd outdoor military range), badminton, basketball available; opportunities for golf, canoeing, sailing, orienteering, climbing and camping. School represented in cross-Channel relay race. *Other:* Fifth formers upwards take part in local community schemes. Duke of Edinburgh's Award Scheme. Wide range of societies and activities includes bridge, chess, computer club, debating, drama, Young Enterprise, mountaineering, music, opera, technology (micro-electronics and design), CCF.

Careers 12 full time careers advisers. 'Industrial Link' scheme. On average, 70+% pupils accepted for degree courses.

Uniform School uniform worn throughout.

Houses/prefects Competitive houses. Prefects, senior prefect (head boy), head of house and house prefects – appointed by Head.

Religion Compulsory daily chapel.

Social Musical links with Cheltenham Ladies' College. Industrial links with Boston and Tokyo. Pupils allowed to bring own bike to school. Meals self service. School shop. No tobacco; limited beer for upper sixth only in licensed club.

Discipline No corporal punishment. Pupils failing to produce homework once might expect 'sides'; taking or handling drugs leads to automatic expulsion.

Boarding Sixth form have own study bedroom; juniors in dormitories of 6+. Single sex houses, of approximately 70, same as competitive houses. Resident matron in each house. Central dining room. Pupils can provide and cook snacks in houses. 2 termly exeats. Visits to local town allowed.

Former pupils Nigel Davenport; Lindsay Anderson; Patrick White; Major General Sir Jeremy Moore.

· *Cheltenham Ladies* ·

The Cheltenham Ladies' College Cheltenham Gloucestershire GL50 3EP Tel 0242 520691	• Pupils 850 • Boys None • Girls 11–18 (Day/Board) • Upper sixth 132	• Termly fees £1920 (Day) £3025 (Board) • GSA Enquiries to the Principal. Application to the Registrar

What it's like

Founded in 1853 and a pioneer of the belief that the education of girls is every bit as important as that of boys, it opened in 1854 at Cambray House and in 1873 occupied fine new buildings at Bayshill. This is a very agreeable quarter of Cheltenham comprising Regency and early Victorian houses. There have been many additions since to provide a school which is well equipped by any standards and in which a civilised and friendly atmosphere prevails. The boarding houses are scattered around, within 10 minutes walk of the main teaching block. Recent additions include two sixth form boarding houses, a CDT centre and a large sports hall. There are seven junior boarding houses, each accommodating 60–70 girls, and four sixth form boarding houses. In addition there are three daygirl houses. Religious services of prayers (in the Anglican tradition) are held every morning and all girls are expected to attend. Girls also attend Sunday service at one of the local parish churches. The college has a strong academic tradition with a large, well-qualified staff of over 145 (the music department alone has over 30 members). This permits a staff pupil ratio of 1:8. Academic standards are high and results are consistently good. Very many girls go on to degree courses, including many to Oxbridge. French, German, Italian and Spanish are offered to A-level. Music, drama and art are strong and good standards are continuously achieved. Facilities for sports are first-rate and a wide variety of sports is available. Again, high standards are attained and the college has produced many representatives at county, regional and national level (especially in hockey, lacrosse, squash and gymnastics). The college is also closely associated with local community services and many girls participate successfully in the Duke of Edinburgh's Award Scheme.

School profile

Pupils Total age range 11–18; 850 girls (170 day, 680 boarding). Main entry ages, 11, 12, 13 and into sixth. Many are daughters of former pupils. *Transfer from maintained schools:* 10% main intake, plus 5% to sixth.

Entrance Common entrance, scholarships and sixth form exam used. Oversubscribed. No special skills or religious requirements although the school is run on Christian lines. Parents not expected to buy text books. Average charge for extras, £150 per term. 12 scholarships/bursaries available, 67–33%. 5 assisted places available for daygirls entering at 11+.

Parents 15+% doctors, lawyers. etc; 15% from industry/commerce. 10% live within 30 miles, 15% live overseas.

Staff Principal: Miss Enid Castle, in post for 4 years. 95 full time staff, 50 part time. Annual turnover 5%. Average age 40.

Academic work GCSE and A-levels, 24 subjects offered (Greek, Latin, Russian, Spanish and Italian available; no A-level general studies). In 1990, 130 pupils in upper fifth, 132 in upper sixth. *GCSE:* in 1990, 118 upper fifth gained at least grade C in 8+ subjects; 11 in 5–7; and 1 in 1–4 subjects. *A-levels:* 12 upper sixth passed in 4+ subjects; 107 in 3; 11 in 2; and 1 in 1 subject. 30% took science A-levels; 65% arts/humanities; 5 both. *Computing facilities:* 2 well-equipped computer rooms. *Special provision:* for those with mild dyslexia. Pupils should be fluent in English before being accepted.

European Community *Languages:* French offered: to age 14; GCSE; A-level. German offered: to age 14; GCSE; A-level. Italian offered: to GCSE; A-level. Spanish offered: to age 14; GCSE; A-level. 10–25% take GCSE in more than 1 EC language. European week held in 1991.

Senior pupils' non-academic activities *Music:* Over 200 girls are involved in school choirs and 100+ in school orchestras plus chamber music groups. *Drama and dance:* 25 in school productions; 40 up to grade 6. 3 accepted for Drama/Dance school. *Art:* 1 takes art as non-exam subject; 51 take GCSE art, 21 A-level art, 20 history of art; 6 accepted for Art School; 17 belong to photographic club including all those taking A-level Art. *Sport:* Hockey, lacrosse, volleyball, squash, badminton, tennis, swimming, ski-ing, golf, athletics, netball, riding, table-tennis, basketball, rounders, judo, aerobics, gymnastics, cricket, self-defence available. 80+ take non-compulsory sport. Most girls use sports centre for recreation. 18 represent county/country (hockey, lacrosse, tennis, netball, squash). *Other:* 300 take part in local community schemes. 130 have bronze Duke of Edinburgh's Award, 60 have silver and 30 gold. All work for national charities. A few enter voluntary schemes after leaving school. Other activities include clubs for art, Christian Union, classics, debating, drama, Green group, history, linguistics, photographic, sewing, all sports, choirs, orchestras, madrigal society, wind band, choral groups, P.E., Third World and computers.

Careers In 1990, 95% leavers went on to degree courses; 4% to art/drama/music colleges; 1% to non-degree courses (eg secretarial courses). Of those going on to degree courses, 15% went to Oxbridge; 80% to other universities; 5% to poly/colleges. 4% those going on to higher education went to courses in practical art; 4% in drama/acting; 2% in music; 50% in humanities/social sciences; 20% in medicine and 20% in science/engineering.

Uniform School uniform worn throughout.

Houses/prefects Senior prefect, prefects elected by the school; Head of house and house prefects, School Council.

Religion Attendance at religious worship compulsory.

Social Joint choral events, drama productions, debates, dances, etc. with other schools. French exchange to Annecy annually; other trips to Russia, Paris (art trip), hockey trips, cruises, cultural holidays. Meals formal; self-service in sixth-form houses. No tobacco/alcohol allowed.

Discipline No corporal punishment. Pupils failing to produce homework once could expect a mild reprimand; anyone caught smoking cannabis on the premises would expect to be dismissed.

Boarding All sixth formers have own study bedrooms; most fifth share with 1 other. 25% in dormitories of 6+. Pupils divided into different houses of approx 65. Resident qualified nurse. Pupils can provide and cook own food. Exeats at half-term, two weekends, plus Sundays after Church. Visits to the local town allowed by all year groups weekly, senior girls daily.

Alumni association is run by Mrs B. Morane-Griffiths, c/o the School.

Former pupils Bridget Riley (artist), Katherine Hamnett, Mary Archer, Penelope Walker (singer), Sue Lloyd-Roberts (broadcaster).

· Chetham's ·

Chetham's School of
Music
Long Millgate
Manchester
M3 1SB
Tel 061 834 9644

- Pupils 261
- Boys 8–18
  (Day/Board)
- Girls 8–18
  (Day/Board)
- Upper sixth 56

- Termly fees
  £3048 (Day)
  £3937 (Board)
- HMC
  Enquiries/application to
  the Headmaster or
  Headmaster's
  Secretary

What it's like

Founded in 1653, it lies in the centre of Manchester in its own grounds. The buildings are well designed and well equipped. The boarding accommodation is comfortable. It has been a specialist music school since 1969. It is possible to study any musical instrument, keyboard, guitar or voice. All entrants who have been resident in this country for at least two years prior to admission qualify automatically for the DES aided-pupil scheme. Pupils normally study one first-study instrument (or voice or composition) and one second study. They are also prepared for national public exams and results are good. Almost all leavers go on to study music, many to music college, most to a degree course and a very high proportion to Oxbridge. The range of facilities for sport and games and other recreations is limited by the city centre site, but includes swimming pool, squash court, gymnasium and multi-gym.

School profile

Pupils Total age range 8–18; 261 pupils, 47 day (31 boys, 16 girls), 214 boarding (65 boys, 149 girls). Senior department 11–18, 243 pupils (91 boys, 152 girls). Entry at any age (mainly 11 and 16). *Transfer from maintained schools:* 90% main entry at 11, plus 80% to sixth.
Entrance Admission only by audition. Oversubscribed. Musical potential looked for; no religious requirements. Parents not expected to buy text books. Government Aided Pupil Scheme for all entrants resident in UK for at least 2 years prior to entry, means tested, value up to £11,811 pa plus travel and uniform grants.
Parents 10+% live within 30 miles; up to 10% live overseas.
Staff Headmaster John Vallins, in post for 16 years. 38 full time staff, 80 part time. Annual turnover 8%. Average age 43.
Academic work GCSE and A-levels. 16 subjects offered (including A-level practical music and general studies). In 1991, 37 pupils in upper fifth, 56 in upper sixth. *GCSE:* in 1990, 23 upper fifth gained at least grade C in 5–7 subjects; and 14 in 1–4 subjects. *A-levels:* 11 upper sixth passed in 4+ subjects; 11 in 3; 18 in 2; and 11 in 1 subject. 43 arts/humanities; 8 both arts and sciences. *Computing facilities:* 12 computers (mixture of Amstrad/BBC; changing to Amstrad IBM compatible PCs). *Special provision:* Limited tuition for ESL/dyslexic pupils.
European Community *Languages:* French offered: to age 14; GCSE; AS-level; A-level. German offered: to age 14; GCSE; AS-level; A-level. Under 10% take GCSE in more than 1 EC language.
Senior pupils' non-academic activities *Music:* 140 learn a musical instrument, all to Grade 6 or above; 110 in school orchestras, 140 in choirs, 6 in school pop group; 10 in National Youth Orchestra; about 60% accepted for Music College; 5 play in pop group beyond school. *Drama and dance:* 40 in school productions. *Art:* 6 take GCSE; 3 A-level. *Sport:* Swimming, squash, badminton,

table-tennis, trampolining, netball, rounders, weight-training, running, aerobics, five-a-side football available. 50 take non-compulsory sport. *Other activities* include a computer club. Intensive musical studies predominate (orchestras, choirs, ensemble work, lunchtime concerts etc), including daily practice.

Careers In 1990, 66% leavers went on to degree courses; 34% to art/drama/music colleges. Of those going on to degree courses, 18% went to Oxbridge, 36% to other universities; 46% to poly/colleges. 86% those going on to higher education went to courses in music; 8% in humanities/social sciences; and 6% in science/engineering.

Uniform School uniform worn throughout.

Houses/prefects No competitive houses. Prefects, head boy/girl, head of house and house prefects – appointed by the Head/Heads of houses.

Religion Weekly (non-denominational) service in Manchester Cathedral except for those who specifically opt out. Sunday service is encouraged. RCs have own weekly instruction or service.

Social Regular weekend outings for boarders. Organised choral/orchestral tours (about 1 per year); ski-ing, individual or group competitions. Pupils allowed to bring own car/bike to school. Meals self service. School tuckshop. No tobacco/alcohol allowed.

Discipline No corporal punishment. Pupils failing to produce homework once might expect a reprimand, extra work; policy of involving families early in serious pastoral/moral/disciplinary matters. Head has power of suspension, Governors have power of expulsion.

Boarding 39% share (2 to a room); 18% (3); 9% (4); 29% (6). Single sex houses, of approximately 50. Resident and day-time nurses, 3 visiting doctors. Central dining room. Pupils can provide and cook own food in houses. Any number of weekend exeats. Visits to the local town allowed.

Alumni association is run by The Chairman, Chetham's Association, c/o the school.

Former pupils Peter Donohoe, Stephen Hough and Anna Markland (all pianists); Grant Llewellyn (conductor); Mike Lindup (pop group – Level 42); John Mundy (BBC TV announcer).

· *Chigwell* ·

Chigwell School	• Pupils 630	• Termly fees
Chigwell	• Boys 7–18 (Day/	£1527 (Day)
Essex	Board/Weekly)	£2322 (Board)
IG7 6QF	• Girls 16–18 (Day/	£2198 (Weekly)
Tel 081 500 1396/2570	Board/Weekly)	• HMC
Fax 081 500 6232	• Upper sixth 75	Enquiries/application to
		the Headmaster or
		Admissions Secretary

What it's like

Founded in 1629, it is well positioned since it lies in fine open countryside in Chigwell village on a delightful 70-acre estate, only 10 miles from central London. Architecturally it makes a most satisfying unit and the original 17th-century building is still in use. It has many excellent modern facilities. The junior school is combined. A sound general education is provided. Many leavers go on to degree courses, including Oxbridge. French and German are offered to A-level; also French for the Institute of Linguists. There are regular exchanges and placements with France and Germany. It is Christian in its ideals and inspiration. Considerable strengths are music, art and drama. A good range of extra-curricular activities and high standards in sport and games.

School profile

Pupils Total age range 7–18; 630 pupils, 565 day (535 boys, 30 girls), 65 boarding (60 boys, 5 girls). Senior department 13–18, 350 pupils (315 boys, 35 girls). Main entry ages 7, 11 (boys) and into sixth (boys and girls). Approx 10% are children of former pupils. *Transfer from maintained schools:* 40% intake at 11, plus 75% to sixth.

Entrance Own entrance exam used; few by common entrance. Oversubscribed. Pupils with skills in music and art given special consideration. No religious requirements. Parents expected to buy text books; maximum extras £50 pa. 60 assisted places. 6 scholarships/bursaries up to 100% of tuition fees.

Parents 15+% in industry or commerce. More than 60% live within 30 miles; up to 10% live overseas.

Staff Headmaster A R M Little, in post 1 year. 52 full time staff, 18 part time (music). Annual turnover under 10%. Average age 38.

Academic work GCSE and A-levels. 24 subjects offered (including GCSE CDT, ceramics, photography; no A-level general studies but GCSE taken by all sixth form). In 1989, 69 pupils in upper fifth, 75 in upper sixth. *GCSE:* in 1989, 75% upper fifth gained at least grade C in 8+ subjects; 15% in 5–7; and 10% in 1–4 subjects. *A-levels:* 55 upper sixth passed in 3 subjects; 17 in 2; and 3 in 1 subject; in addition 20 lower sixth pupils took 1 A-level. 22 took science A-levels; 36 arts/humanities; 17 both. *Computing facilities:* Computer teaching room (18 Archimedes) plus network with computers available in all senior classrooms. 38 computers around the school. *Special provision:* EFL specialist: assessment and teaching programme in place.

European Community *Languages:* French offered: to age 14; GCSE; A-level; Institute of Linguists. German offered: to age 14; GCSE; A-level. 10–25% take GCSE in more than 1 EC language. *Exchanges:* Regular exchanges for pupils aged 11–18 to France and Germany. *Other:* French and German pupils spend 1–2 terms in sixth form.

Senior pupils' non-academic activities *Music:* 150 learn a musical instrument, 15 to Grade 6 or above. 45 in school orchestra, 20 in school choir, 6 in pop group, 25 in ensemble; 1 in National Youth Orchestra; 2 in Essex Youth Orchestra; 15 in church choir; 1 accepted for Music School; 2 take up music as a career. *Drama and dance:* 50 in school productions. *Art:* 22 take GCSE art, 10 ceramics, 12 CDT; 8 A-level. 3 (average) accepted for Art School; 3 for BTEC. *Sport:* Soccer, athletics, cricket, badminton, swimming, squash, cross-country, rugger, hockey, basketball, tennis available. 100 take non-compulsory sport. 3 represent county/country (soccer, cricket). *Other:* 6 take part in local community schemes. 10 have bronze Duke of Edinburgh's Award. Other activities include a computer club, inter-house chess, Scouts, printing, debating, learning to drive.

Careers In 1990, 72% leavers went on to degree courses; 2% to art/drama/music colleges; 2% to non-degree courses (eg printing); 8% straight into careers (eg banking); 15% other. Of those going on to degree courses, 13% went to Oxbridge, 77% to other universities; 10% to poly/colleges. 2% those going on to higher education went to courses in practical art; 2% in music; 68% in humanities/social sciences; 3% in medicine; and 24% in science/engineering.

Uniform School uniform worn throughout.

Houses/prefects Competitive houses. Prefects, head boy, head of house and house prefects – appointed.

Religion All pupils attend Chapel but opting out possible on conscientious grounds.

Social Occasional joint musical functions with other schools. 8+ organised trips abroad/exchange systems each year.

Pupils allowed to bring own car/bike/ motorbike to school. Meals self service. School shop. No tobacco/alcohol allowed. **Discipline** No corporal punishment. Pupils failing to produce homework once might expect a warning or additional work; those caught smoking cannabis on the premises could expect expulsion. **Boarding** 40% share (2 or 3); 60% are in dormitories of 6–8. Houses, same as competitive houses. Resident qualified nurse. Central dining room. Pupils can provide and cook own food. Exeats every weekend. Visits to the local town allowed. **Former pupils** Professor Bernard Williams; Michael Thomas CMG, QC (Attorney General of Hong Kong); Ian Holm (actor).

· *Christ's (Blackheath)* ·

Christ's College
4 St Germans Place
Blackheath
London
SE3 0NJ
Tel 081 858 0692

- Pupils 246
- Boys 4–18 (Day/ Board/Weekly)
- Girls None
- Upper sixth 18

- Termly fees
  £930 (Day)
  £1680 (Board)
  £1525 (Weekly)
- ISAI
  Enquiries/application to the School Secretary

What it's like

Founded in 1823, there are two main school houses (one Georgian and one Victorian) on one of the finest sites in London, looking across 200 acres of Blackheath. It has five acres of private grounds. The Anglican tradition prevails but it is religiously tolerant. Music and drama taken to form three. The teaching is sound and there are EFL provisions throughout the school. Many sixth form leavers go on to degree courses, including Oxbridge. No great range of sport, games or extra-curricular activities.

School profile

Pupils Total age range 4–18; 246 boys, 108 day, 138 boarding. Senior department 11–18, 194 boys. Entry at any age. Approx 3% are children of former pupils. *Transfer from maintained schools:* 25% intake at 11, plus 10% to sixth.
Entrance Common entrance or interview plus school reports used. Not oversubscribed. No special skills or religious requirements. Parents expected to buy text books; other extras variable. 2 full fees scholarships, usually awarded to existing pupils in need.
Parents 15+% in industry or commerce; 15+% are doctors, lawyers etc. 60+% live within 30 miles; up to 40% live overseas.
Staff New Principal not appointed at time of going to press: Mr Engelheart-

Knight retired July 1991. 17 full time staff, 10 part time. Annual turnover 5%. Average age 30+.
Academic work GCSE and A-levels, JMB test in English, RSA English. 8 GCSE subjects offered; 7 at A-level (no A-level general studies). In 1990, 40 pupils in upper fifth, 18 in upper sixth. *GCSE:* in 1990, 1 upper fifth pupil gained at least grade C in 8+ subjects; 11 in 5–7; and 20 in 1–4 subjects. *A-levels:* 3 upper sixth passed in 4+ subjects; 7 in 3; 2 in 2; and 4 in 1 subject. 100% took science A-levels. *Computing facilities:* Nimbus PC186 network with 8 stations, mini BBC network. *Special provision:* Separate EFL classes at all levels.
European Community *Languages:* French offered: to age 14; GCSE; A-

level. German (by arrangement): to age 14; GCSE; A-level. Spanish offered: to age 14; GCSE; AS-level; A-level.

Senior pupils' non-academic activities *Music:* 4 learn a musical instrument, 1 to Grade 6 or above. 16 in school choir. *Art:* Taken as non-examined subject to form five; 5 take GCSE; 4 A-level. 10 belong to photographic club. *Sport:* Football, cricket, tennis, basketball, volleyball, athletics, judo, cross-country, swimming available. Sport compulsory. 2 represent county/country (athletics, judo). *Other:* 3 work for national charities after leaving school. Other activities include a computer club; driving lessons; chess, modelling and Roamers' clubs, horse-riding, karate.

Careers In 1990, 85% leavers went on to degree courses; 15% straight into careers (eg hotel management). Of those going on to degree courses, 14% went to Oxbridge, 86% to other universities. 3% those going on to higher education went to courses in practical art; 14% in medicine; and 83% in science/engineering.

Uniform School uniform worn throughout.

Houses/prefects Competitive houses. Prefects, head boy, appointed by the Head.

Religion Religious worship encouraged. There are many religious denominations in the school; all respect one another's point of view.

Social Discos with local girls' school. Infrequent trips abroad (many pupils are from overseas). Pupils not allowed to bring own car/bike/motorbike to school. Meals formal. School tuckshop. No tobacco/alcohol allowed.

Discipline Corporal punishment allowed. Pupils failing to produce homework once might expect detention; those caught smoking cannabis on the premises would be removed from school.

Boarding 25 share with 1 or 2 others, 25 share (3–5 to a room); 10 dormitories of 6+. Houses, of approximately 75, divided by age group. Resident qualified nurse. Central dining room. Sixth formers can provide and cook own food. 4 weekend exeats each term. Visits to local town allowed, but not alone.

Alumni association (Friends of the College) run by Mr R Belle-Fortune, 40 The Orchard, Winchmore Hill, London N21.

· *Christ (Brecon)* ·

Christ College	● Pupils 348	● Termly fees
Brecon	● Boys 11–18	£1579 (Day)
Powys	(Day/Board)	£2083 (Board)
LD3 8AG	● Girls 16–18	● HMC
Tel 0874 3359	(Day/Board)	Enquiries to the
	● Upper sixth 54	Headmaster's
		Secretary
		Applications to the
		Headmaster

What it's like

Founded by Henry VIII in 1541, it has long been one of the most distinguished schools in Britain. It has a magnificent site on the River Usk just to the north of the Brecon Beacons and a couple of minutes' walk from the pleasant market town of Brecon. The foundations of the College chapel are those of the original Dominican friary church. The dining halls are reputedly on the sites of the former rectory and chapter house. It enjoys handsome and well-equipped modern buildings in beautiful grounds and all are within a designated national park. During the last ten years there have been major developments and extensions. There is a new CDT centre and a new science block. Each sixth form boarder has a private study/bedroom. Pupils of all faiths are accepted: the Anglican liturgy is used in services. Importance is attached to spiritual education. Academically it is a high-powered school with a reputation for good teaching. A small school with a large staff, it has a very favourable staff:pupil ratio of 2:19. Academic results are excellent. Almost all leavers go on to degree courses, some to Oxbridge. French, German, Italian, Spanish and (unusually) Welsh are offered at GCSE and many pupils take GCSE in more than one European language. Music, drama and art are very strong; music especially so. The choir recently represented the UK in a UNICEF CBS recording made in Poland. Numerous societies and clubs cater for most needs. They include a young farmers' club, a mountain rescue group and an angling club. Sports and games are very well organised and the College has a distinguished record in many. Many members of the College have been selected for county and national representation. There is a large and vigorous CCF contingent and much emphasis is put on outdoor pursuits and self-reliance. A number of pupils take part in local community schemes and the College has had an impressive record in the Duke of Edinburgh's Award Scheme.

School profile

Pupils Age range 11–18; 348 pupils, 50 day (44 boys, 6 girls), 298 boarders (268 boys, 30 girls). Main entry ages, 11, 13 (boys); and into sixth (boys and girls). Some 1–2% are children of former pupils. *Transfer from maintained schools:* Most of intake at 11, 10% at 13, plus 75% to sixth.

Entrance Common entrance and own entrance exam used. Marginally oversubscribed. Skill in sport, music, academic, drama, chess, general knowledge an advantage. No religious requirements, but school is Anglican. 70 assisted places. 18 scholarships/bursaries pa (academic, music, forces), £4686–£300. Parents not expected to buy text books.

Parents 15+% in industry or commerce; 15+% doctors, lawyers etc. Up to 15% live within 30 miles; up to 15% live overseas.

Staff Headmaster S W Hockey, in post for 9 years. 38 full time staff, 8 part time. Annual turnover 7%. Average age 40.

Academic work GCSE and A-levels. 22 subjects offered (including Italian, CDT, business studies, archaeology, sports studies and AS-level general studies). In 1989, 56 pupils in fifth, 54 in upper sixth. *GCSE:* in 1990, 71% upper fifth gained at least grade C in 8+ subjects; 21% in 5–7; and 9% in 1–4 subjects. *A-levels:* 8% upper sixth passed in 4+ subjects; 70% in 3; 17% in 2; and 5% in 1 subject. 20% took science A-levels; 36% arts/humanities; 44% both. *Computing facilities:* Computer room (10 computers); WPs in library, English and other depts; CAD and CAM in CDT. *Special provision:* EFL available; specialist tutor for mild dyslexia.

European Community *Languages:* French offered: to age 14; GCSE; AS-level; A-level. German offered: to age 14; GCSE; AS-level; A-level. Italian offered: to age 14; GCSE. Spanish offered: to age 14; GCSE; AS-level; A-level. Welsh offered: to age 14; GCSE. 10–25% take GCSE in more than 1 EC language. *Exchanges:* Regular exchanges for pupils aged 14–16 to France. *Other:* Number of European pupils (French, German, Italian) in school.

Senior pupils' non-academic activities *Music:* 129 pupils learn a musical instrument, 23 have taken Grade 6 or above, 6 have distinction at Grade 8. 44 pupils play in school orchestra; 45 sing in choir; 130 in choral society; all junior forms produce annual musicals; 550 in house music competitions; 42 in jazz/brass bands; 25 concerts arranged each year in concert hall. *Drama and dance:* 45 in school productions; 10 in drama club; 40 in House play competition; 18 in debating/public speaking; 2 go on to work in TV/films. *Art:* 12 take GCSE; 14 A-level. 2 accepted for Art School. 18 belong to eg photographic club. *Sport:* Rugby football, soccer, hockey, cricket, athletics, tennis, netball, basketball, judo, swimming, rounders, keep fit, squash, shooting, clay pigeon shooting, climbing, canoeing, sailing, sailboarding available. 85 pupils take part in non-compulsory sport; 12 take GCSE PE; 25 pupils represent county (cross-country, rugby, cricket, athletics, swimming, netball, basketball, hockey). *Other:* 140 have bronze Duke of Edinburgh's Award, 8 silver, 3 gold. 24 in community service group; 1 or 2 enter voluntary schemes after leaving school. Other activities include a computer club; chess (lively), general knowledge competitions, aero modelling, railway modelling, photography, drama, school magazine and newspaper, ornithology, electronics, CCF, Italian, Scrabble, bands, choirs, Welsh, printing.

Careers In 1990, 95% leavers went on to degree courses (8% after a Gap year); 3% to art/drama/music colleges; 2% straight into careers (eg retail management). Of those going on to degree courses, 8% went to Oxbridge, 55% to other universities; 37% to poly/colleges. $1^1/_2$% those going on to higher education went to courses in practical art; $1^1/_2$% in drama/acting; $1^1/_2$% in music; 55% in humanities/social sciences; 5% in medicine; and 36% in science/engineering.

Uniform School uniform worn; some variations allowed in sixth.

Houses/prefects Competitive houses. Prefects, head boy/girl, head of house and house prefects – appointed by Head.

Religion Compulsory worship.

Social Joint music society with town; choral society with local convent school. CCF linked with local Army. Organised ski trips and exchange systems. Pupils allowed to bring own bike to school. Meals self service. School shop and tuck shop. Sixth form bar, no private drink or tobacco allowed.

Discipline No corporal punishment. Pupils failing to produce homework once would be expected to get it done by a deadline with extra work; any caught smoking cannabis on the premises would be expelled.

Boarding 20–25% have own study bedroom, 20–25% share (with 1 other); 45–50% are in dormitories of 6+. Houses, of approximately 60, are same as for competitive purposes plus one junior house (11–12 years) and one girls' house. Resident medical staff. Central dining room; and new tuck shop gives cafe type service. Pupils can provide and cook snacks. 2 termly exeats plus half-term. Limited visits to local town allowed (number increasing with age).

Alumni association is run by J J M Arter, Secretary, 61 Heol Urban, DanesMcourt, Llandaff, Cardiff.

Former pupils Major General W G Fryer CB CBE; E P Silk; P R Watkins (film producer 'The War Game', 'Privilege'); Sqdn Ldr R M Thomas (former leader of the Red Arrows); Rev D Thomas (former warden of St Stephens House, Oxford); Rev Professor D P Davies (Dean of Theology, Lampeter); Canon D E R Isitt (former Dean of King's College, Cambridge); Professor B R Rees (Classics Faculty, Lampeter); Professor D G Owen (Offshore Engineering, Heriot Watt); Sir A J Smith (Court of Appeal, Bahamas and Belize); Judges W L N Davies, R D G David; Simon Hughes MP; Robert Ackerman (rugby footballer); Rev C I Dyter (MC, Falklands); His Honour Judge D A Thomas MBE.

· *Christ's Hospital* ·

Christ's Hospital Horsham West Sussex RH13 7YP Tel 0403 52547	● Pupils 850 ● Boys 11–18 (Board) ● Girls 11–18 (Board) ● Upper sixth 110	● Termly fees Means tested ● HMC Enquiries/application to the Admissions Officer Tel 0403 211297

What it's like

Founded in 1552 by King Edward VI for children in need. In September 1985 the boys' school at Horsham and the girls' at Hertford joined to form one co-educational boarding school. Originally the boys' school had moved out of London in 1902 and a complete new school was built on an estate of 1200 acres. The buildings and campus are splendid and facilities are first-rate. Among other things there is a very good careers centre, a fine library and a purpose-built theatre which seats 500. It has been described as 'an extraordinary school for the children of ordinary people' and it is an apt description. Worship in the Anglican tradition is compulsory (within the 1944 Act) and the Chapel is central to the school life. The school is an extremely well run establishment with high standards of teaching and distinguished academic results. The staff:pupil ratio is 1:9. Many pupils go on to degree courses each year, including Oxbridge. There is great strength in the music and drama departments. The school is famous for its bands. Numerous dramatic entertainments are staged each year. Also very strong in games and sport. A wide variety of activities is available. The CCF has a big contingent and scout group is very active. The school's record in the Duke of Edinburgh's Award Scheme is phenomenal and is almost certainly the best in the country (48 bronze, 45 silver, 72 gold).

School profile

Pupils Age range 11–18; 850 boarding pupils (approx 530 boys, 320 girls). Main entry ages 10. 10–12 only. Approx 5% are children of former pupils.

Entrance Own entrance exam used. Oversubscribed. Music and drama skills looked for. No special religious requirements. Parents not expected to buy text books, uniform etc; extras means tested if not free. 80% of all costs are funded from the Hospital's endowments according to parental income which, in most cases, must not exceed £20000 gross at date of entry. Many families pay nothing at all; only one in 16 pays full fee. The original charitable intention is still very strongly maintained. Children are assessed on grounds of need as well as ability.

Parents 30+% live within 30 miles; less than 1% live overseas.

Staff Head R C Poulton, in post for 4 years. 86 full time staff, 40 part time. Annual turnover 6%. Average age 41.

Academic work GCSE and A-levels. Average size of upper fifth 120; upper sixth 110. *GCSE:* on average, 77 pupils in upper fifth pass 8+ subjects; 31, 5–7 subjects; 12 pass 1–4 subjects. *A-levels:* on average, 8 pupils in upper sixth pass 4 subjects; 80, 3 subjects; 16, 2 subjects; 6 pass 1 subject. On average, 35 take science/engineering A-levels; 52 take arts and humanities; 23 take a mixture. GCSE drama and A-level Archaeology, Latin, Greek, Russian offered.

Computing facilities: Computer centre with admin machine and micros. All laboratories and most departments have their own micros. *Special provision:* for mild dyslexia.

Senior pupils' non-academic activities *Music:* 145 learn a musical instrument, 70 to Grade 6 standard or above, 9 take A-level, 5 accepted for Music School, 2 gain choral scholarships, 2 now play in pop groups; 46 in school orchestra, 85 in school choir, 40 in school pop and jazz groups, 53 in concert band, 19 in show band; 18 in holiday music courses, 24 in holiday choir tours. *Drama and dance:* 100 in school productions, 100 in house plays, 30 in departmental plays. 2 accepted for Drama Schools, 2 go on to work in theatre; 11 take GCSE drama, 40 take drama classes and 20 take dance classes. *Art:* 90 take as non-examined subject; 15 take GCSE; 12 take A-level. 10 accepted for Art School. *Sport:* Association football, rugby football, hockey, cricket, swimming, shooting, netball, athletics, tennis, squash, rackets available. 260 take non-compulsory sport. 2 take exams. 4 represent county/country (rugby, cricket, hockey). *Other:* 40 take part in local community schemes. 48 have bronze Duke of Edinburgh's Award, 45 have silver and 72 have gold. 5 enter voluntary schemes after leaving school. Other activities include a computer club, chess, debating, drama, music (military band, orchestra, many chorus), CCF, cycling.

Careers 6 part time advisers. Average number of pupils accepted for *arts and humanities degree courses* at Oxbridge, 12; other universities, 26; polytechnics or CHE, 14. *science and engineering degree courses* at Oxbridge, 6; other universities, 18; medical schools, 4; polytechnics or CHE, 6. *BEd,* 1. *other general training courses,* 2. Average number of pupils going straight into careers in the armed services, 4; industry, 1; the City, 2.

Uniform Distinctive school uniform worn throughout, provided by the school.

Houses/prefects Competitive houses. Prefects, head boy/girl, head of house and house prefects – appointed by Headmaster and/or housemaster/mistress.

Religion Chapel (C of E) compulsory.

Social No organised local events. Organised trips abroad and exchange systems. Pupils allowed to bring own bike to school. Meals formal. School shop. No tobacco allowed, pupils over 17 may join sixth form club and buy beer and wine.

Discipline No corporal punishment. Pupils failing to produce homework once might expect a warning.

Boarding 2% have own study bedroom, 20% share with others; 78% are in large dormitories. Houses, of approx 50–60, same as competitive houses and single sex. Resident qualified nurses and doctor. Central dining room. Pupils can provide and cook own food. No overnight exeats. Visits to local town allowed for over 14s.

Alumni association run by Dr J R A Kennedy, CH Club, c/o Hospital.

Former pupils John Snow; Stuart Holland; Lord Stewart; Keith Douglas; Air Cmdr E M Donaldson; Bryan Magee; Bernard Levin; Colin Davis.

· *Christian Brothers'* ·

Christian Brothers'
Grammar School
Glen Road
Belfast BT11 8NR
Tel 0232 615321

- Pupils 1200
- Boys 11–18
  (Day)
- Girls None
- Upper sixth 165

- Termly fees
  None

Enquiries/application to
the Headmaster

What it's like

Founded in 1866, it has two sites: one in the centre of Belfast, the other in the suburbs. It is a Roman Catholic foundation but pupils of all faiths are admitted. Religious worship is encouraged. There is strong emphasis on hard work and academic excellence. Many go on to degree courses. Five European languages are offered up to A-level – French, German, Italian, Spanish and (unusually) Irish. An exceptionally high proportion of boys takes GCSE in more than one European language. Very strong in all sciences and humanities; art, music and drama flourish. Vigorous participation in local community schemes.

School profile

Pupils Age range 11–18; 1200 day boys. Main entry ages, 11 and into the sixth. 40% are children of former pupils. *Transfer from maintained schools:* 3% main intake, plus 10% to sixth.

Entrance Own selection procedure used. Oversubscribed. No special skills or religious requirements but school is a Catholic foundation. Parents not expected to buy text books.

Staff Headmaster Rev Br D R Gleeson, appointed 1988. 71 full time staff, 2 part time. Annual turnover 4%. Average age 36.

Academic work GCSE and A-levels. 25 subjects offered. In 1990, 176 pupils in upper fifth, 165 in upper sixth. *GCSE:* in 1989, the vast majority of upper fifth pupils gained at least grade C in 8+ subjects. *A-levels:* 7% upper sixth passed in 4+ subjects; 60% in 3; 20% in 2; and 13% in 1 subject. 65 took science A-levels; 62 arts/humanities; 38 both. *Computing facilities:* 1 480–Z network, 2 RM Nimbus networks, 1 Apple Macintosh network, 4 stand alone Apple Macintosh, 9 stand alone BBC micros.

European Community *Languages:* French offered: to age 14; GCSE; AS-level; A-level. German offered: to age 14; GCSE; AS-level; A-level. Irish offered: to age 14; GCSE; AS-level; A-level. Italian offered: to age 14; GCSE; AS-level; A-level. Spanish offered: to age 14; GCSE; AS-level; A-level. Over 75% take GCSE in more than 1 EC language. *Other:* Language assistants in French, German, Italian and Spanish.

Senior pupils' non-academic activities *Music:* 80 learn a musical instrument, 30 to Grade 6 or above; 40 in school orchestra, 40 in choir; 10 play in pop group beyond school. *Drama and dance:* 120 participate in school productions. 6 accepted for Drama/Dance schools. *Art:* 500 take art as non-examined subject; 45 take GCSE; 12 A-level. 4 accepted for Art School. 60 belong to photographic club.

Sport: Football, hurling, basketball, swimming, water-polo, weight-training, badminton, handball, ski-ing, athletics, cross-country available. 300 take non-compulsory sport. 40 pupils represent county/country (athletics, football, hurling, water polo, ski-ing, chess). *Other:* 50 take part in local community schemes. 30 enter voluntary schemes after leaving school. Other activities include a computer club, chess club (championship standard), Napoleonic society, driving lessons, golf club and triathlon.

Careers In 1990, 63% leavers went on to degree courses; 4% to art/drama/music colleges; 16% to non-degree courses (eg FE courses); 6% straight into careers; 11% other. Of those going on to degree courses, 95% went to universities; 5% to poly/colleges. 4% those going on to higher education went to courses in practical art; 61% in humanities/social sciences; 5% in medicine; and 30% in science/engineering.

Uniform School uniform worn except in the sixth.

Houses/prefects Prefects, head boy – elected. School Council.

Religion Religious worship encouraged.

Social Peace and Reconciliation Inter Schools Movement (PRISM). Strong debating society – All-Ireland Champions many times. Organised trips to Europe, Eastern bloc, USA and Canada. Pupils allowed to bring own car/bike/motorbike to school. Meals self service. Senior pupils allowed tobacco, no alcohol.

Alumni association run by Mr P Cochrane, President, 287 Antrim Road, Belfast.

Former pupils The late Cardinal Conway; The Most Rev Dr P Walsh (Bishop of Down and Connor); Bernard Davey (BBC TV); Professor Vincent McBriarty (Trinity College Dublin), Professor John Larkin (Trinity College Dublin); Patrick Carville (Permanent Sec. NI Department of Education).

· *Churcher's* ·

Churcher's College
Petersfield
Hampshire
GU31 4AS
Tel 0730 63033

- Pupils 480
- Boys 11–18 (Day/ Board/Weekly)
- Girls 11–18 (Day/ Board/Weekly)
- Upper sixth 50

- Termly fees
  £1220 (Day)
  £2260 (Board)
  £2210 (Weekly)
- HMC
  Enquiries/application to the Headmaster

What it's like

Founded in 1722 by Richard Churcher, an East India Company merchant, it opened in 1730 in Petersfield, Hampshire. In 1881 it moved to new buildings on the present site on the edge of the very pleasant market town. To the agreeable Victorian buildings have been added a number of modern extensions, and facilities and accommodation are good. The school overlooks spacious grounds and gardens. There is some emphasis on Christian worship and religious studies is a compulsory part of the curriculum. A large and well-qualified staff allows a staff:pupil ratio of about 1:12. A traditional sound academic education is provided and results are impressive. Many leavers go on to degree courses. French, German and Spanish are offered up to A-level and a very high proportion of pupils takes GCSE in more than one European language. Business language courses are offered to sixth formers. There are regular exchanges with France, Germany and Spain. Music and drama are very strongly supported. A wide variety of sports and games is available and facilities for these are excellent. High standards are achieved and there have been many representatives at county level. Extra-curricular activities are well catered for and there is much emphasis on outdoor pursuits, including adventure training, canoeing, sailing and shooting. The school has a large CCF unit which began as an OTC in 1905. A number of pupils take part in local community schemes.

School profile

Pupils Age range 11–18; 480 pupils, 420 day (335 boys, 85 girls), 60 boarders (49 boys, 11 girls). Main entry ages 11, 12, 13 and into sixth. *Transfer from maintained schools:* 50% main intake, plus 5% to sixth.

Entrance Common entrance and own entrance exam used. Oversubscribed. No special skills or religious requirements. Parents not expected to buy text books; other extras, maximum £80. 19 assisted places pa. Variable number of scholarships/bursaries up to half fees.

Parents 15+% in industry. 60+% live within 30 miles.

Staff Headmaster G W Buttle, 3 years in post. 43 full time staff, 12 part time. Annual turnover 5%. Average age 40.

Academic work GCSE and A-levels (no A-level general studies). In 1990, 80 pupils in upper fifth, 50 in upper sixth. *GCSE:* in 1990, 55 upper fifth gained at least grade C in 8+ subjects; 16 in 5–7; and 6 in 1–4 subjects. *A-levels:* 8 upper sixth passed in 4+ subjects; 22 in 3; 8 in 2; and 8 in 1 subject. On average, 15 take science/engineering A-levels; 15 take arts and humanities; 20 both. *Computing facilities:* BBC Econet System, Apple's, Amstrad PCs.

European Community *Languages:* French offered: to age 14; GCSE; AS-level; A-level; business language course (sixth). German offered: to age 14; GCSE; AS-level; A-level; business languages course (sixth). Spanish offered: to age 14; GCSE; AS-level; A-level; business languages course (sixth). 50–75% take GCSE in more than 1 EC language. *Exchanges:* Regular exchanges for pupils aged 11–18 to France, Germany and Spain. *Other:* Italian and German nationals as pupils in sixth form. Foreign nationals often take part in lessons as guests of pupils or staff.

Senior pupils' non-academic activities *Music:* 120 learn a musical instrument, 10 to Grade 6 or above; 2 accepted for Music School, 6 in pop group beyond school. 12 pupils play in school orchestra, 2 in County Youth Orchestra, 12 in school choir, 12 in school pop group. *Drama and dance:* 120 in school productions; 20 in other. *Art:* 10 take art as non-examined subject; 15 take GCSE; 4 A-level. 2 accepted for Art School. 15 belong to photographic club. *Sport:* Rugby, hockey, cricket, netball, tennis, swimming, athletics, cross-country, golf available. Most take part in non-compulsory sport. 50 take exams. 28 pupils represent county (hockey, cricket, rugby, golf). *Other:* 40 take part in local community schemes. Other activities include a computer club, chess, bridge, clay pigeon shooting, CCF, drama, Christian, grum, archery.

Careers In 1990, 70% leavers went on to degree courses; 2% to non-degree courses (eg secretarial); 14% straight into careers (eg retail management, banking); 14% other (year off). Of those going on to degree courses, 2% went to Oxbridge, 65% to other universities; 33% to poly/colleges. 4% those going on to higher education went to courses in practical art; 4% in drama/acting; 4% in music; 36% in humanities/social sciences; 4% in medicine; and 48% in science/engineering.

Uniform School uniform worn, modified in sixth.

Houses/prefects Competitive houses. Prefects, head boy/girl, head of house and house prefects – appointed by the Head.

Religion Religious worship encouraged.

Social Exchanges and visits to France, Germany, Spain and Austria, plus ski trips and cultural tours. Sixth form pupils allowed to bring own car/bike to school. Meals self service. School shop. No tobacco/alcohol allowed.

Discipline No corporal punishment. Pupils failing to produce homework once might expect a detention; those caught smoking cannabis on the premises would be expelled.

Boarding 50% have own study bedroom, 50% share (with up to 5 others). Single sex houses, of approx 25, divided by age group. Resident medical staff. Central dining room. Pupils can provide and cook snacks. 4 weekend exeats each term. Visits to local town allowed, restricted according to age.

Alumni association is run by Old Churcherians Club President, Mr D Hale, c/o Churcher's College.

· *City of London (Boys)* ·

City of London School
Queen Victoria Street
London
EC4V 3AL
Tel 071 489 0291

- Pupils 850
- Boys 10–18
- (Day)
- Girls None
- Upper sixth 125

- Termly fees £1578
- (Day)
- HMC

Application to the
Admissions Secretary

What it's like

The original foundation dates from 1442. The first school building opened in 1837 and the school moved to its present brand-new and very fine buildings in 1986. These occupy a superb riverside site, near Blackfriars with St Paul's vista as the eastern boundary. Its various terraces and open spaces command fine views of St Paul's and of the river from Tower Bridge to Westminster. The new buildings are outstandingly well equipped and comfortable in every respect. The playing fields are at Grove Park. A high standard of academic excellence is aimed at and achieved. Many leavers go on to degree courses, including a high proportion to Oxbridge. (Also to medical schools: the study of medicine is a vigorous tradition.) French and German are offered to A-level; a high proportion of pupils take both at GCSE. There is also a strong tradition of musical excellence (the choristers of the Temple Church and the Chapel Royal, St James's, are all pupils). Drama and art also flourish. Sport and games are compulsory and standards are high. A substantial commitment to local community schemes.

School profile

Pupils Age range 10–18; 850 day boys. Main entry ages 10, 11, 13 and into sixth. *Transfer from maintained schools:* 70% main intake, plus 80% to sixth.

Entrance Own entrance exam used. Oversubscribed. No special skills or religious requirements. Parents not expected to buy text books. 25 assisted places. 25 scholarships (academic, music) full fees to one-third fees. Choral bursaries, two-thirds fees.

Staff Headmaster B G Bass, 1 year in post. 76 full time staff, 3 part time. Annual turnover 3%.

Academic work GCSE and A-levels. 20 subjects offered (no A-level general studies). In 1989, 130 pupils in upper fifth, 125 in upper sixth. *A-levels:* on average, 95% pass 3 subjects. *Computing facilities:* Some 45 machines either in computer centre or spread around the departments.

European Community *Languages:* French offered: to age 14; GCSE; A-level. German offered: to age 14; GCSE; A-level. 50–75% take GCSE in more than 1 EC language. *Exchanges:* Regular exchanges for pupils to Germany.

Pupils' non-academic activities *Music:* 200 learn a musical instrument, 35 to Grade 6 or above; 145 in school orchestras, 150 in choir. *Drama:* 80+ in school productions. *Sport:* Cricket, football, rugby, athletics, tennis, rowing, fencing, squash, judo, karate, table-tennis, swimming, water-polo, shooting, sailing, cross-country, volleyball, basketball, badminton, indoor hockey available. Sport compulsory up to sixth form; most sixth-formers participate. County and national representatives in several sports. *Other:* 75 take part in local community schemes. Duke of Edinburgh's Award.

Careers In 1990, 65% leavers went on to degree courses; 3% to art/drama/ music colleges; 31% other (Gap year; retaking A-levels). Of those going on to degree courses, 22% went to Oxbridge, 67% to other universities; 10% to poly/ colleges. 4% those going on to higher education went to courses in practical art; 1% in drama/acting; 2% in music; 57% in humanities/social sciences; 10% in medicine; and 26% in science/ engineering.

Uniform School uniform worn except in the sixth.

Houses/prefects Competitive houses. Prefects, head boy, head of house and house prefects – elected. School Council.

Religion No compulsory worship.

Social There are several joint functions with City of London School for Girls. Several organised trips and an exchange with a school in Hamburg. Pupils allowed to bring own bike to school. Meals self service. No tobacco/alcohol allowed.

Discipline No corporal punishment. Inclining to the traditional; pupils failing to produce homework might expect detention; use of drugs could lead to expulsion.

Alumni association is run by G A Coulson, 11 Mapleton Close, Bromley, Kent.

Former pupils H H Asquith; Kingsley Amis; Denis Norden; Mike Brearley.

· City of London (Girls) ·

City of London School
for Girls
Barbican
London EC2Y 8BB
Tel 071 628 0841
Fax 071 638 3212

- Pupils 653
- Boys None
- Girls 7–18
  (Day)
- Upper sixth 77

- Termly fees
  £1362 (Day)
- GSA
Enquiries/application to
the Admissions
Secretary

What it's like

Founded in the City in 1894, it is on a single-site with some open spaces. A very well equipped establishment in the attractive and stimulating Barbican environment. A sound education is given and many leavers go on to degree courses, including many to Oxbridge. French and German are offered to A-level; Spanish to GCSE. Many girls take GCSE in more than one European language. There are regular exchanges with France and Germany. The music and art departments are especially strong (the majority of the school is involved in musical activities) and there is a good range of clubs and societies. Being in the Barbican there are numerous opportunities for trips to the theatre, art galleries and museums. The Corporation of London provides further opportunities for girls to participate in a variety of civic functions.

School profile

Pupils Total age range 7–18; 653 day girls. Senior department 11–18, 550 girls. Main entry ages 7, 11 and into sixth. Less than 1% are children of former pupils. *Transfer from maintained schools:* 40% main intake at 11, 10% to sixth.

Entrance Own entrance exam used. Oversubscribed. No special skills or religious requirements. Parents not expected to buy text books. 104 assisted places. Scholarships up to full fees, 4 at 11+ and 2 at 16+ pa; 1 scholarship joint with Guildhall School of Music and Drama; one leaving scholarship; bursaries available to older pupils in financial need.

Staff Head Lady France, in post for 5 years. 55 full time staff, 9 part time.

Academic work GCSE and A-levels. 22 subjects offered (including Russian and history of art; no A-level general studies). In 1990, 78 pupils in upper fifth, 77 in upper sixth. *GCSE:* in 1990, 75 upper fifth gained at least grade C in 8+ subjects; 3 in 5–7 subjects. *A-levels:* 5 upper sixth passed in 4+ subjects; 58 in 3; 10 in 2; and 4 in 1 subject. 14 took science A-levels; 25 arts/humanities; 38 both.

Computing facilities: Computer room with Archimedes network computers available in many departments. *Special provision:* No special teaching but cooperation with extra-mural specialists.

European Community *Languages:* French offered: to age 14; GCSE; AS-level; A-level. German offered: to age 14; GCSE; AS-level; A-level. Spanish: to GCSE. 25–50% take GCSE in more than 1 EC language. *Exchanges:* Regular exchanges for pupils to France and Germany.

Senior pupils' non-academic activities *Music:* 334 learn a musical instrument, 75 to Grade 6 or above. 2 accepted for Music School; 6–8 junior exhibitioners at various Saturday music colleges; 94 in school orchestra, 150 in choirs, 4 chamber groups, 16 in senior madrigal group, 4 in Finchley Children's Choir, 10 in other local orchestras, 2 in ENO children's chorus. *Drama and dance:* 50 in school productions; 25 in recreational activity (sixth option); 160 in speech and drama lessons; drama lessons also form part of the curriculum; 30 LAMDA medals; 1–2 go to drama courses at university or college. *Art:* 250 take as non-examined subject; 30 take GCSE; 10, A-level. 40 in recreational activity art clubs; 4 accepted for Art School; 3 for history of art; 2 for architecture. *Sport:* Netball, volleyball, basketball, gymnastics, swimming, hockey, fencing, badminton, multi-gym, tennis, rounders, athletics available. 60 take non-compulsory sport; 200 take awards eg gymnastics, swimming; BAGA Gym Awards, ASA Survival and Bronze Medallion Awards, Fencing. 10 represent county/country (tennis, tumbling, gymnastics); PE at college/university (1), Oxford Blue (1). *Other:* 60 take part in local community schemes. School takes part in Duke of Edinburgh's Award Scheme. Whole school supports national charities. Other activities include a computer club, pre-driver training and word–processing/typing courses, political society, debating clubs, theatre club, bridge club, board game club.

Careers In 1990, 67% leavers went on to degree courses; 7% to art/drama/music colleges; 1% to non-degree courses (eg catering); 4% straight into careers (eg modelling); 21% other (deferred degree application). Of those going on to degree courses, 10% went to Oxbridge, 82% to other universities; 8% to poly/colleges. 16% those going on to higher education went to courses in practical art; 61% in humanities/social sciences; 7% in medicine; and 16% in science/engineering.

Uniform School uniform worn except in the sixth.

Houses/prefects No competitive houses or prefects. Head girl – nominated and elected by staff and sixth form. School Council.

Religion Daily act of worship for all.

Social Joint concerts, theatrical productions, fund raising and social activities with City of London (Boys). Organised exchanges to France/Germany, trips to USSR, Italy, Greece and Austria. Friends of CLSG Association and OGA organise social functions. Meals self service. No tobacco/alcohol allowed.

Discipline No corporal punishment. Pupils failing to produce homework once might expect a warning and firm deadline; those caught smoking cannabis on the premises could expect expulsion.

Alumni association run by Mrs G Dyson, c/o School.

Former pupils Anne Farrell (actress); Claire Rayner; Katharine Dyson (D'Oyly Carte); Elizabeth Emmanuel (dress designer).

· *City of London Freemen's* ·

City of London Freemen's School Ashtead Park Ashtead Surrey KT21 1ET Tel 0372 277933	● Pupils 665 ● Boys 8–18 (Day/ Board/Weekly) ● Girls 8–18 (Day/ Board/Weekly) ● Upper sixth 62	● Termly fees £1593 (Day) £2481 (Board) £2400 (Weekly) ● HMC Enquiries/application to the Headmaster

What it's like

Founded in 1854, it moved to Ashtead Park in 1926 where it stands in 57 acres of splendid parkland, playing fields and woodlands, between Epsom and Leatherhead. The main building is a magnificent 18th century house (formerly home of the Howard family). Conversion and modernisation have provided good facilities. A steady expansion programme has gone on for the last 30 years. The house system operates and there are two boarding houses (one for girls, one for boys) which provide comfortable accommodation. About 25% of parents have taken out Freedom of the City and about 40% of the present pupils have a brother or sister currently at the school. Thus, with its Foundation, Corporation patronage and City connections the school has a flourishing family and community element. The declared aims are to promote the spiritual, academic and social development of all to the fullest extent in an atmosphere of hard work, self-criticism, loyalty and enthusiasm. A sound general education is provided and academic standards and results are highly creditable. Each year many leavers go on to degree courses, including Oxbridge. French and German are offered to A-level; Spanish to GCSE. About 50% of the pupils take GCSE in more than one European language. There are regular exchanges with France and Germany. The school is particularly strong in music and drama. The art department is also a flourishing organisation. A good range of sports and games is available for boys and girls and high standards are achieved. There are many clubs and societies for extra-curricular activities, of which one of the most popular is the Duke of Edinburgh's Award Scheme in which the school has a remarkable record of successes. There is also active commitment to local community services in the parish among the senior pupils.

School profile

Pupils Total age range 8–18; 665 pupils, 605 day (288 boys, 317 girls), 60 boarders (30 boys, 30 girls). Senior department, age range 13–18, 369 pupils (195 boys, 174 girls). Main entry ages 8, 13 and into sixth. 1–2% are children of former pupils. *Transfer from maintained schools:* 10% main intake at 13, plus 10% to sixth.

Entrance Common entrance and own entrance exam used. Oversubscribed. Any and all special skills looked for at entry. No religious requirements; school is inter/non-denominational with C of E affiliation. 5 assisted places pa (at 13+). 20+ scholarships pa (funded by Corporation of London) up to two-thirds fees. Approx 25 bursaries, £2000–£200 pa.

Parents 60+% live within 10 miles; up to 10% live overseas.

Staff Headmaster D C Haywood, in post for 3 years. 60 full time staff, 25 part time (incl music). Annual turnover 4–5% (usually promotion!). Average age 37.

Academic work GCSE, AS and A-levels. 21 GCSE subjects offered; 6 at AS; 16 at A-level (including A-level general studies). In 1991, 92 pupils in upper fifth, 62 in upper sixth. *GCSE:* in 1990, 60 upper fifth gained at least grade C in 8+ subjects; 20 in 5–7; and 5 in 1–4 subjects. *A-levels:* 32 upper sixth passed in 4+ subjects; 10 in 3; 4 in 2; and 2 in 1 subject. 45% took science A-levels; 24% arts/humanities; 31% both. *Computing facili-*

ties: Junior and senior computing laboratories plus computers in various departments, boarding houses etc. *Special provision:* Some individual help for dyslexic pupils; mildly visually handicapped supported.

European Community *Languages:* French offered: to age 14; GCSE; AS-level; A-level. German offered: age 13–14; GCSE; AS-level; A-level. Spanish offered: age 13–14; GCSE. Some 50% take GCSE in more than 1 EC language. *Exchanges:* Regular exchanges for pupils aged 11–18 to France and Germany. *Other:* EC pupils often spend 1 term, occasionally 1 year, as boarders in lower sixth.

Senior pupils' non-academic activities *Music* 100 learn a musical instrument, 40 to Grade 6 or above; 2 accepted for Music School, 65 play in school orchestra, 110 in choir, 50 in various ensembles; 23 in eg County Youth Orchestra; 2 play in pop group. *Drama and dance:* 50 in school productions; 40 in house drama; 1 accepted for Drama/Dance school; 1 goes on to work in theatre. *Art:* 10 take art as non-examined subject; 26 take GCSE; 11 A-level. 1 accepted for Art School; 15 belong to eg photographic club; 10 on scenery making. *Sport:* Hockey, rugby, cricket, athletics, tennis, squash, badminton, swimming, cross-country, fencing, karate available. 180 pupils take part in non-compulsory sport. 26 pupils represent county (rugby, hockey, swimming, judo, cricket). 40 take life-saving. *Other:* 42 working for bronze Duke of Edinburgh's Award, 30 for silver, 20 for gold. 20 in local community schemes; approx 10 work for national charities after leaving school. Other activities include a computer club, pottery, karate, chess, modern dancing, debating society, etc.

Careers On average, 75% sixth form leavers to on to degree courses; 10% to art/drama/music colleges; 2% to non-degree courses; 13% straight into careers (eg banking, insurance, farming, catering). Of those going on to degree courses, 12% go to Oxbridge, 48% to other universities; 40% to poly/colleges. 5% those going on to higher education go to courses in practical art; occasional pupil in drama/acting; 2% in music; 50% in humanities/social sciences; 15% in medicine; and 25% in science/engineering.

Uniform School uniform worn throughout.

House/prefects Competitive houses.

Prefects, head boy/girl, head of house and house prefects – appointed by Head after consultation with staff and pupils. School Council.

Religion Morning assembly daily.

Social Organised trips abroad and exchange systems. Pupils allowed to bring own car/bike/motorbike to school. Meals self service. No tobacco/alcohol allowed.

Discipline No corporal punishment. Pupils failing to produce homework once might expect a detention; those caught smoking cannabis on the premises could expect expulsion.

Boarding 15% have own study bedroom, 10% in dormitories of 6+. Houses, of approximately 35 cover whole age range 8–18, single sex. Resident qualified nurse, GP local. Central dining room. Flexible weekend exeats. Visits to local town allowed, mainly in sixth.

Alumni association is run by Mr Steven Jenkins, Chairman (O.F.A.), 10 Downlands Close, Tattenham Corner, Surrey KT18 5NQ.

· *Clayesmore* ·

Clayesmore School	● Pupils 310	● Termly fees
Iwerne Minster	● Boys 13–18	£1960 (Day)
Blandford Forum	(Day/Board)	£2780 (Board)
Dorset	● Girls 13–18	● SHMIS
DT11 8LL	(Day/Board)	Enquiries/application to
Tel 0747 811217	● Upper sixth 45	the Headmaster

What it's like

Founded in 1896, Clayesmore was formerly in London, Pangbourne and Northwood Park. In 1933 it moved to its present site, the former seat of Lord Wolverton on the edge of the pretty village of Iwerne Minster. The impressive house has large gardens and a 62-acre estate, surrounded by beautiful Dorset countryside. Extensive modern additions provide first-rate facilities. The playing fields are on the estate. There is some compulsory worship in the Anglican tradition. A staff:pupil ratio of 1:9. Academic standards are high and results good. Many sixth form leavers go on to degree courses, including Oxbridge. Very active music, art and drama depts. A good reputation for sports and games (a large number of representatives at county level). A lively CCF and considerable emphasis on outdoor pursuits for which the environment is ideal. Some commitment to local community services and an impressive record in the Duke of Edinburgh's Award Scheme.

School profile

Pupils Age range 13–18; 310 pupils, 80 day (45 boys, 35 girls), 230 boarding (135 boys, 95 girls). Main entry ages 13 and into sixth. Approx 3% are children of former pupils. About 40% of intake from own prep. *Transfer from maintained schools:* 10% main intake, plus 10% to sixth.

Entrance Common entrance and own tests used. No special skills or religious requirements. Services are C of E but all denominations and faiths are welcome. Text books supplied; maximum extras £200. Up to 20 scholarships/bursaries pa, 100%–5% fees.

Parents 15+% in the armed services. 30+% live within 30 miles; 10+% live overseas.

Staff Headmaster D J Beeby, in post for 4 years. 30 full time staff, 6 part time. Annual turnover 8%. Average age 40.

Academic work GCSE and A-levels. 20 subjects offered (including ceramics, food and nutrition). In 1990, 72 pupils in upper fifth, 56 in upper sixth (now 45). *GCSE:* in 1989, 28 upper fifth gained at least grade C in 8+ subjects; 24 in 5–7; and 25 in 1–4 subjects. *A-levels:* 6 upper sixth passed in 4+ subjects; 9 in 3; 11 in 2; and 4 in 1 subject. 12 took science A-levels; 15 arts/humanities; 5 both. *Computing facilities:* 11 BBCs and 7 IBM compatible PCs in computer teaching room. Computers in most departments. *Special provision:* Language Development Unit catering for EFL and those with learning difficulties.

European Community *Languages:* French offered: to age 14; GCSE; AS-level; A-level. German offered: to age 14; GCSE; AS-level; A-level. Spanish: GCSE. 10–25% take GCSE in more than 1 EC language. *Exchanges:* Regular exchanges for pupils aged 14–18 to France, Germany and Spain. *Other:* Some 10 pupils from other EC countries in school.

Senior pupils' non-academic activities *Music:* 110 learn a musical instrument, 11 to Grade 6 or above, 1 accepted for Music College; 20 in school orchestra, 47 in school choir, 8 in Barber Shop group, four major concerts per year. *Drama and dance:* 35% of pupils involved in school drama productions. *Art:* 20 take as non-examined subject; 20 take GCSE; 3 take A-level, 3 take A-level History of Art. 2 or 3 each year accepted for Art School; a few go onto BTEC courses at 16+. *Sport:* Rugby football, hockey, netball, soccer, squash, swimming, cross-country, badminton, judo, lacrosse, athletics, cricket, tennis, golf and sailing available. 120 take non-compulsory sport. 20 represent county (hockey, rugby, cricket, athletics). *Other:* 25 take part in local community schemes. 43 have bronze Duke of Edinburgh's Award, and 18 have silver. Other activities include debating and public speaking.

Careers In 1990, 60% leavers went on to degree courses; 20% to art/drama/music colleges; 15% to non-degree courses (eg secretarial with languages); 5% straight into careers (eg airline pilot). Of those going on to degree courses, 7% went to Oxbridge, 63% to other universities; 30% to poly/colleges. 3% those going on to higher education went to courses in practical art; 3% in music; 43% in humanities/social sciences; and 50% in science/engineering.

Uniform School uniform worn except the sixth.

Houses/prefects Competitive houses. Prefects, head boy and girl, head of house and house prefects – appointed by the Head.

Religion Church of England. Compulsory daily assembly service in chapel; longer service on Sunday, not compulsory for other faiths.

Social Community Service Group, regularly and successfully in debating, public speaking and general knowledge competitions. Regular exchanges organised by Modern Languages department; visits abroad by games teams, choirs etc. Pupils allowed to bring own bike to school. Meals self service. School shop. No tobacco allowed. Sixth form bar twice a week.

Discipline No corporal punishment. Pupils failing to produce homework once might expect to repeat it or do additional work; those caught smoking cannabis on the premises will be expelled.

Boarding Most Upper Sixth formers have own study bedroom, Lower Sixth share. Houses, of approx 55, same as competitive houses, single sex. Resident SRN. Central dining room. Pupils can provide and cook own food. Two weekend exeats each term. Visits to local town allowed once a week.

Alumni association Mr Ronald Spinney, Chairman of Old Clayesmorian Society, Leconfield House, Curzon Street, London W1Y 8AS.

· *Clifton* ·

Clifton College
32 College Road
Clifton
Bristol BS8 3JH
Tel 0272 735945
Fax 0272 466826

- Pupils 680
- Boys 13–18
  (Day/Board)
- Girls 13–18
  (Day/Board)
- Upper sixth 139

- Termly fees
  £2170 (Day)
  £3100 (Board)
- HMC
  Enquiries/application to
  the Registrar

What it's like

Founded in 1862, it became a prominent public school very quickly and was the first of the great Victorian foundations to adopt co-education at all levels. It is fortunate in its situation above the city, on the edge of Clifton Downs and near open country. Its handsome buildings are neo-Tudor and neo-Gothic and stand in beautiful grounds. Much money has been spent and its facilities are exceptionally good; there is now a large new leisure development with three artificial pitches. It has a modern theatre and two superb libraries (as well as house libraries). A girls day house opened in 1991. An unusual feature is that one of the boarding houses is reserved for boys of Jewish faith. Religious worship is compulsory for Jews at their synagogue. Some Christian services are compulsory for others. It provides a thoroughly good and liberal education and academic standards are high. Of the leavers who go on to degree courses, a high proportion go to Oxbridge. French, German, Italian and Spanish are offered to A-level and a high proportion of pupils takes GCSE in more than one European language. There are regular exchanges with France, Germany and Spain. Very strong indeed in music and the arts. A very high standard in games and sports. Unique in having a research scientist in residence. Numerous extra-curricular activities and a strong CCF. A big commitment to local community schemes and the Duke of Edinburgh's Award Scheme. Much use is made of Bristol's cultural amenities.

School profile

Pupils Age range 13–18; 680 pupils, 261 day (238 boys, 23 girls), 419 boarding (307 boys, 112 girls). Main entry ages 13 and into sixth. Approx 20% are children of former pupils. Clifton College Prep provides about 20% of intake. *Transfer from maintained schools:* 1% main intake plus 2% to sixth.

Entrance Common entrance and own entrance exam used. Oversubscribed. No special skills or religious requirements.

Parents expected to buy text books; maximum extras £500. 24 scholarships/bursaries, for academic, artistic and musical excellent, to £8316 pa.

Parents 15+% are doctors, lawyers, etc; 15+% in industry or commerce. 30+% live within 30 miles; 10+% live overseas.

Staff Headmaster A H Monro, in post for 1 year. 70 full time staff, 8 part time. Annual turnover 4%. Average age 37.

Academic work GCSE and A-levels.

23 subjects offered (including A-level general studies; Italian, Chinese and other exotic languages by request). In 1990, 140 pupils in fifths, 116 in upper sixth (now 139). *GCSE:* in 1990, 67% fifth gained at least grade C in 8+ subjects; 18% in 5–7; and 14% in 1–4 subjects. *A-levels:* 10% upper sixth passed in 4+ subjects; 59% in 3; 22% in 2; and 6% in 1 subject. 21% took science A-levels; 54% arts/humanities; 25% both. *Computing facilities:* Room of 16 BBCs plus many departmental computers, and one in most boarding houses.

European Community *Languages:* French offered: to age 14; GCSE; AS-level; A-level. German offered: to age 14; GCSE; AS-level; A-level. Italian offered: to GCSE; A-level. Spanish: GCSE; A-level. 25–50% take GCSE in more than 1 EC language. Extra language tuition on request. *Exchanges:* Regular exchanges for pupils aged 11–14 and 16–18 to France, Germany and Spain. *Other:* Some EC students for 1 year in sixth.

Senior pupils' non-academic activities *Music:* 200 learn a musical instrument, 65 to Grade 6 or above, 2 accepted for Music School; 45 in school orchestra, 45 in wind band, 100 in school choir, 15 in 3 school pop groups, 15 in jazz band, 20 in barber shop/a capella; 2 in National Youth Orchestra, 6 in county orchestra, 1 in National Youth choir. *Drama and dance:* 60 in school productions. 1 or 2 per year accepted for Drama/Dance Schools. 300 in house drama festival. *Art:* 25 take as non-examined subject; 45–50 take GCSE; 17 take A-level art, 12 history of art, 10 take AS history of art. 6 accepted for Art School, 1 for architectural college, 1 to Courtauld Institute. 30–40 in extra art, 40+ in extra pottery groups, 20 belong to photographic club. *Sport:* Rugby football, association football, hockey, cricket, rowing, athletics, cross-country, netball, tennis, sailing, badminton, volleyball, basketball, fives, squash, rackets, fencing, karate, tetrathlon, weight training, riding, shooting, aerobics, swimming, water polo and gymnastics available. 280 take non-compulsory sport. 4 or 5 represent county (rugby, hocket, cricket, athletics). 2 1987 and 2 1989 Young England cricketers.

Public schools rackets champion 1990. *Other:* 60 take part in local community scheme. 20 have bronze Duke of Edinburgh's Award and 20 have silver. Other activities include a computer club, rock climbing, chess, debating, country dancing, choral singing, arctic expeditions and CCF.

Careers In 1990, 35% leavers went on to degree courses; $^1/_2$% to art/drama/music colleges; 15% to non-degree courses (eg hotel, tourism, land management, sports management, sales, marketing); $^1/_2$% straight into careers (eg services, police, family business, banking, computing); 41% other (eg Gap, tutorial college, return to home country). Of those going on to degree courses, 16% went to Oxbridge, 53% to other universities; 31% to poly/colleges. 2% those going on to higher education went to courses in practical art; $^1/_2$% in drama/acting; 1% in music; 70% in humanities/social sciences; 1% in medicine; and 25% in science/engineering.

Uniform School uniform worn throughout.

Houses/prefects Competitive houses. Prefects, head boy/girl, head of house and house prefects – appointed by the headmaster, after consultation.

Religion For Jewish pupils attendance at Synagogue is compulsory. For Christians some Chapel services are compulsory, others voluntary.

Social School debates, co-productions of plays, including modern language play, subject conferences in the school theatre with other local schools. Strong connection with an earthquake damaged school in Mexico City; organised trips there. Exchanges with France and Germany. Meals self service. School shop selling stationery. No tobacco allowed; bar for over-17s.

Discipline No corporal punishment. Pupils failing to produce homework once might expect detention. Those caught smoking cannabis on the premises would have specific circumstances considered before disciplinary action taken, but might expect expulsion.

Boarding 25% have own study bedroom, 45% share with others; 30% are in dormitories of 6+. Houses, of approximately 60, are the same as competitive houses and are single sex. School doctor visits daily, two qualified nurses in sanatorium. Central dining room. Pupils can provide and cook own snacks. 1 Saturday night exeat plus half term each term. Visits to the local town allowed with permission. **Alumni association** is run by H G Edwards, OBE, Old Clifton Society, c/o the College.

Former pupils Lord (Clyde) Hewlett and Lord (Patrick) Jenkin (politicians); Sir Michael Redgrave, Trevor Howard, John Cleese, John Houseman and Simon Russell Beale (the stage); Sir David Willcocks and Joseph Cooper (music); Mark Tully, David Bonavia and Stephen Pile (the media).

· *Clifton High* ·

Clifton High School for Girls
College Road
Clifton
Bristol
BS8 3JD
Tel 0272 730201

- Pupils 785
- Boys 3–7 only (Day)
- Girls 3–18 (Day/Board/ Weekly)
- Upper sixth 58

- Termly fees £1025 (Day) £2000 (Board) £1900 (Weekly)
- GSA Enquiries/application to the Headmistress

What it's like

Founded in 1877, it occupies a splendid site in the middle of the Georgian village of Clifton, near the Downs and the Suspension Bridge. There are some fine buildings and the surroundings are most agreeable. The facilities and accommodation are first-class. Religious worship is non-denominational, and religious studies are taught throughout the school. The school has a long standing reputation for providing an excellent education. Results are very good. Each year very many sixth formers go on to degree courses, including Oxbridge. French, German and Spanish are offered to A-level. Very many pupils take GCSE in more than one European language and there are regular exchanges with France, Germany and Spain. There are extremely strong music, drama and art depts involving a large number of pupils. There is also a good choice of games and sports (many representatives at county level). There is a great commitment to social services and the school has a good record in the Duke of Edinburgh's Award Scheme. Full use is made of Bristol's cultural amenities.

School profile

Pupils Total age range 3–18; 785 pupils, 725 day (54 boys, 671 girls), 60 boarding (girls). Senior department 11–18, 478 girls. Main entry ages 3, 7, 10, 11 and into sixth. Approx 10% are children of former pupils. *Transfer from maintained schools:* 30% intake at 11, plus 5% to sixth.
Entrance Own entrance exam used. Oversubscribed. Skills in sport, music and art welcomed. No religious requirements. Parents not expected to buy text books. 13 assisted places; 11 scholarships available at entry, up to full fees.
Parents 15+% are doctors, lawyers, etc; 15+% in industry or commerce. 60+% live within 30 miles; up to 10% live overseas.
Staff Headmistress Mrs J D Walters, in

post for 6 years. 58 full time staff, 18 part time. Annual turnover 5%. Average age 35.

Academic work GCSE and A-levels. 21 subjects offered (including Greek; no A-level general studies). In 1990, 75 pupils in upper fifth, 58 in upper sixth. *GCSE:* in 1989, 52 upper fifth gained at least grade C in 8+ subjects; 15 in 5–7; and 6 in 1–4 subjects. *A-levels:* 2 upper sixth passed in 4+ subjects; 30 in 3; 9 in 2; and 7 in 1 subject. 45% took science A-levels; 53% arts/humanities. *Computing facilities:* 2 computer rooms, one for the Lower School and one for the Senior School. *Special provision:* Special coaching in English.

European Community *Languages:* French offered: to age 14; GCSE; AS-level; A-level. German offered: to GCSE; AS-level; A-level. Italian: Institute of Linguists. Spanish offered: to GCSE; AS-level; A-level. 50–75% take GCSE in more than 1 EC language. *Exchanges:* Regular exchanges for pupils aged 14–18 to France, Germany and Spain.

Senior pupils' non-academic activities *Music:* 210 learn a musical instrument, 15 to Grade 6 or above, 6 take GCSE, 2 A-level; 30 in school orchestra, 130 in school choir, 30 in wind band. *Drama and dance:* 50+ in school productions, 100+ in house plays, clubs etc; 4 or 5 take Guildhall, LAMDA exams, 4 or 5 take AO course in theatre arts in sixth form. 2 accepted for Drama Schools, 2 or 3 accepted for university or FE courses in drama. Some go on to work in theatre. *Art:* 19 take as non-examined subject; 25 GCSE; 6 A-level. 5 applying for Art School. *Sport:* Hockey, netball, tennis, swimming, rounders and athletics are available. Sport compulsory. 60 teams and extra–curricular sport, 18 take fencing, 40 take self defence, outdoor pursuits and riding. A number take exams in gymnastics; some have skating certificates and life saving. 10 represent county (swimming,

hockey, netball, tennis, athletics). *Other:* 20 take part in bronze Duke of Edinburgh's Award, 9 have silver and 13 gold. Other activities include a computer club, woodwork, technology club, Christian Union, art club, pottery.

Careers In 1990, 80% leavers went on to degree courses; 4% to art/drama/music colleges; 2% to non-degree courses; 2% straight into careers (eg retail management); 12% other. Of those going on to degree courses, 12% went to Oxbridge, 60% to other universities; 28% to poly/colleges. 75% those going on to higher education went to courses in humanities/social sciences; and 25% in science/engineering.

Uniform School uniform worn except in sixth.

Houses/prefects Competitive houses. Prefects, head girl, head of house and house prefects – appointed by staff and school. School Council.

Religion Non-denominational religious worship.

Social Debates, plays, choral performances with Clifton College. Organised trips to France, Ireland, Mediterranean, Iceland, Switzerland, Germany. Language exchanges with France, Spain, Germany. Pupils allowed to bring own bike to school. Meals self service. Second-hand clothes shop. No tobacco/alcohol allowed.

Discipline No corporal punishment. Pupils failing to produce homework twice might expect detention; those caught smoking cannabis on the premises would be expelled.

Boarding Sixth form share bedrooms or have individual studies. Central dining room. Senior pupils can provide and cook own food. Exeats most weekends. Visits to village allowed daily; Bristol Centre at weekends.

Alumni association is run by Mrs J Liddiatt, Little Stretton, 4 Mariners Drive, Stoke Bishop, Bristol BS9 1QJ.

Former pupils Jo Durie; Mary Renault.

· Cobham Hall ·

Cobham Hall
Cobham
Nr Gravesend
Kent
DA12 3BL
Tel 0474 82 3376
Fax 0474 82 2995

- Pupils 250
- Boys None
- Girls 11–18
  (Day/Board/
  Weekly)
- Upper sixth 36

- Termly fees
  £2140 (Day)
  £3190 (Board/
  Weekly)
- GSA, Round
  Square
  Enquiries/application to
  the School Secretary

What it's like

It opened as an independent public school for girls in 1962 and is a member of the Round Square Conference. Thus its aims are based on the pioneering ideals of Kurt Hahn. The main building was once the home of the Earls of Darnley, a very fine example of an Elizabethan country mansion which contains some work by Inigo Jones. Some 18th century developments include designs by James Wyatt. It lies in a superb site of 140 acres of landscaped gardens and parkland in the countryside. There are modern extensions including a purpose-built activities centre. Overall, the facilities are first class. Accommodation for boarders is comfortable, some in the main building and others in two modern houses set apart from the main part of the school. The house system operates and there is an efficient tutorial system. The school is international and interdenominational. The standards of teaching are high and the staff:student ratio is a very favourable 1:6. Many sixth formers go on to degree courses. French, German, Italian and Spanish are offered to A-level; Portuguese to GCSE. Very many girls take GCSE in more than one European language. There are regular exchanges with Denmark, France, Germany, the Netherlands and Spain. Music, drama, dance and art play an important part in the life of the school. Sport and games are well catered for and standards are high. There is a plentiful range of extra-curricular activities. Many of the senior girls are involved in voluntary community services locally and help local organisations in their spare time; some participate in the Duke of Edinburgh's Award Scheme.

School profile

Pupils Age range 11–18; 250 girls, 25 day, 225 boarding. Main entry ages 11, 12, 13 and into sixth. Approx 1% are children of former pupils (school too young to have any). *Transfer from maintained schools:* Less than 1% intake.

Entrance Own entrance exam used. Oversubscribed. All-rounders looked for; no religious requirements. Parents not expected to buy text books; maximum extras £100. 7 sixth form scholarships, full day fees – one-third boarding fees.

Parents 15+% in industry or commerce. 10+% live within 30 miles; 10+% live overseas.

Staff Headmistress Mrs Rosalind McCarthy, in post 1 year. 36 full time staff, 19 part time. Annual turnover 9%. Average age 40.

Academic work GCSE and A-levels (including Russian; no A-level general studies). In 1989, 59 pupils in upper fifth, 36 in upper sixth. *GCSE:* in 1989, 43% upper fifth gained at least grade C in 8+ subjects; 37% in 5–7; and 18% in 1–4 subjects. *A-levels:* 42% upper sixth passed in 3 subjects; 31% in 2; and 25% in 1 subject. 28% took science A-levels; 72% arts/humanities. *Computing facilities:* Nimbus. *Special provision:* Dyslexic unit; EFL.

European Community *Languages:*

French offered: to age 14; GCSE; A-level. German offered: to age 14; GCSE; A-level. Italian offered: to age 14; GCSE; A-level. Portuguese: GCSE. Spanish offered: to age 14; GCSE; A-level. 50–75% take GCSE in more than 1 EC language. *Exchanges:* Regular exchanges for pupils aged 11–18 to Denmark, France, Germany, Netherlands and Spain. *Other:* Language week. 1992 conference in 1989. 34 pupils from Europe (close to Dover and airports).

Senior pupils' non-academic activities *Music:* 124 learn a musical instrument, 14 to Grade 6 or above, 2 accepted for Music School; 18 in school orchestra, 65 in choir; wind band; regular concerts and inter-house music festivals. *Drama and dance:* 50 in school productions; 45 take GCSE theatre studies. 6 take GCSE dance; 25 Associated Board Grade 6 upwards. 2 go on to work in theatre. *Art:* 10 take as non–examined subject; 79 GCSE; 17 A-level. 3 accepted for Art School. Pre-foundation art course. 10 belong to photographic club; 25 to art clubs; 24 make jewellery. *Sport:* Swimming, tennis, netball, hockey, volley ball, table tennis, cross-country, rounders, athletics, squash, trampolining, gymnastics, yoga, aerobics, self-defence, badminton, life saving, riding, weight training, ski-ing, judo available. Some compulsory sport, 50% take non-compulsory; 35–40% take awards. *Other:* 120 take part in local community schemes. 22 have bronze Duke of Edinburgh's Award, 23 have silver and 10 gold. Many enter voluntary schemes on leaving; at least 4 work for national charities. Other activities include computer, driving, cookery, pottery, toy making, dress, French, Spanish and psychology clubs.

Careers In 1990, 60% sixth form leavers went on to degree courses; 20% to art/drama/music colleges; 18% to non-degree courses; 2% straight into careers (eg banking, retail management). Of those going on to degree courses, 3% went to Oxbridge, 60% to other universities; 37% to poly/colleges. 23% those going on to higher education went to courses in practical art; 5% in drama/acting; 2% in music; 57% in humanities/social sciences; 5% in medicine; and 9% in science/engineering.

Uniform School uniform worn except in sixth.

Houses/prefects Competitive houses. Head girl and deputy elected by school; head of house and house prefects. School Council.

Religion All religions welcomed.

Social General knowledge quizzes, debates, joint musical productions, sixth form dances and discos with other schools. Trips to Russia, America, France, Spain, Italy, Egypt; exchanges with America, Switzerland, Germany, France, Spain, India. Senior pupils allowed to bring own bike to school. Meals self service. School shop. No tobacco/alcohol allowed.

Discipline No corporal punishment; firm discipline but not repressive. Pupils failing to produce prep might expect detention and work re-done at weekend under supervision (at discretion of staff concerned).

Boarding Sixth form have own study bedroom. Houses, of approximately 60, mixed ages. Resident qualified nurse. Central dining room (seniors can provide and cook own food). 2 termly exeats. Visits to local town allowed at weekends.

Alumni association Cobham Hall Elders – Chairman: Miss C Cawston, 73 Warner Road, London SE5 9NE.

Former pupils Jane How; Taryn Power; Ramina Power; Princess Mutawakkilah of Brunei.

· *Coleraine* ·

Coleraine Academical
Institution
Castlerock Road
Coleraine
Londonderry BT51 3LA
Tel 0265 44331
Fax 0265 52632

- Pupils 850
- Boys 11–19
  (Day/Board)
- Girls None
- Upper sixth 125

- Termly fees
  £660 (Day)
  £1480 (Board/
  Weekly)
- HMC
  Enquiries/application to
  the Headmaster

What it's like

Founded in 1859, it is semi-rural and single-site in 70 acres of playing fields and grounds on the outskirts of Coleraine with a view over beautiful landscapes and the lower reaches of the River Bann. There has been much expansion since 1955. A well-run school with high academic standards, it aims to provide a full and thorough instruction in all branches of a liberal education. Many leavers go on to degree courses. French, German and Spanish are offered up to A-level. European studies are offered to the sixth form, and there are regular exchanges with France and Germany. Music and drama are strong departments and there is a good range of sports, games, clubs, societies etc. A fair commitment to local community schemes and the Duke of Edinburgh's Award Scheme.

School profile

Pupils Total age range 11–19; 850 boys, 720 day, 130 boarding. Main entry ages 11 and into sixth. Approx 25% are children of former pupils. *Transfer from maintained schools:* 95% main intake, plus 75% to sixth.

Entrance Very few admitted by common entrance. Not oversubscribed. Above average IQ expected. No religious requirements. Parents not expected to buy text books; other extras, maximum £25. Sons of clergymen given 10% reduction of fees.

Parents Up to 10% of boarders' parents live within 30 miles; 40+% live overseas.

Staff Headmaster R S Forsythe, in post for 7 years. 58 full time staff, 6 part time. Annual turnover 5%. Average age 45.

Academic work GCSE and A-levels. 23 subjects offered (no A-level general studies). In 1990, 134 pupils in upper fifth, 116 in upper sixth (now 125). *GCSE:* in 1990, 71 upper fifth gained at least grade C in 8+ subjects; 37 in 5–7; and 26 in 1–4 subjects. *A-levels:* 23 upper sixth passed in 4+ subjects; 60 in 3; 10 in 2; and 16 in 1 subject. 44 took science A-

levels; 28 arts/humanities; 44 both. *Computing facilities:* Three networks. *Special provision:* EFL assistance.

European Community *Languages:* French offered: to age 14; GCSE; A-level; non-examined. German offered: to age 14; GCSE; A-level. Spanish offered: to age 14; GCSE; A-level. 10–25% take GCSE in more than 1 EC language. *Exchanges:* Regular exchanges for pupils aged 14–18 to France and Germany. *Other:* European Studies offered to pupils aged 16–18. Participation in EC affairs when talks/lectures presented in Northern Ireland.

Senior pupils' non-academic activities *Music:* 60 learn a musical instrument, 5 to Grade 6 or above. 40 in school orchestra, 80 in school choir. *Drama and dance:* 100 in school productions; 1 accepted for Drama School. *Art:* 50 take GCSE art, 20 A-level; 10 accepted for Art School. 30 belong to photographic club. *Sport:* Rugby, cricket, athletics, swimming, cross-country, tennis, squash, badminton, rowing, sailing, angling, canoeing available. 300 take non-compulsory sport, 10 take exams. 17 represent county/country (rugby football, badminton, athletics, table tennis, cross-country). *Other:* 40 take part in local community schemes. 30 have bronze Duke of Edinburgh's Award, 12 have silver and 10 gold. Other activities include a computer club, chess club, bridge club, debating society, dramatics, stamp club, school bank, community services, scouts, scripture union.

Careers In 1990, 69% leavers went on to degree courses; 1% to art/drama/music colleges; 18% to non-degree courses (eg HNDs in science, engineering, business); 4% straight into careers (eg army, business); 8% other. Of those going on to degree courses, 2% went to Oxbridge, 75% to other universities; 23% to poly/colleges. 2% those going on to higher education went to courses in practical art; 33% in humanities/social sciences; 9% in medicine; and 56% in science/engineering.

Uniform School uniform worn throughout.

Houses/prefects Competitive houses. Prefects, head boy, head of house and house prefects – elected by staff and sixth form.

Religion Religious worship is encouraged.

Social Joint schools' community service group, debating society meet together, girls assist in drama. Ski trip, modern language trip and rugby tour each year. Pupils allowed to bring own car to school. Meals self service. School shop. No tobacco/alcohol allowed.

Discipline No corporal punishment. Pupils failing to produce homework once might expect to do it by the following day; those caught smoking cannabis could expect expulsion.

Boarding 30% have own study bedroom, 60% are in dormitories of 6+. Houses, of approximately 30/40, divided by age group. Resident qualified nurse. Central dining room. Pupils can provide and cook own food. 2 day exeats 3–5 times a term depending on term length. Visits to local town allowed.

Former pupils Air Marshal Sir George Beamish.

· *Colfe's* ·

Colfe's School
Horn Park Lane
London
SE12 8AW
Tel 081 852 2283/4

- Pupils 866
- Boys 7–18 (Day)
- Girls 16–18 (Day)
- Upper sixth 88

- Termly fees
  £1125 (Day)
- HMC
Enquiries/application to
the Registrar

What it's like

Founded in 1652 and original site below Blackheath. In 1964 it moved to Lee, in south east London, to new purpose-built premises on a single urban site with 18 acres of pleasant grounds and playing fields. It retains strong links with the Leathersellers' Company and its official visitor is Prince Michael of Kent who takes a close interest in the school. Worship and religious instruction are encouraged (C of E foundation). A very good general and academic education is provided and results are impressive. Many sixth formers go on to degree courses, including Oxbridge. There is a tremendously strong music dept involving a great many people, also much strength in drama and art. An excellent range of sports and games is available and high standards are attained. A good range of extra-curricular activities.

211

School profile

Pupils Total age range 7–18; 866 day pupils (819 boys, 47 girls). Senior department 11–18, 688 pupils (641 boys, 47 girls). Main entry ages 7–13 (boys) and into sixth (boys and girls). Approx 1% are children of former pupils. *Transfer from maintained schools:* 63% main intake at 11, plus 10% to sixth.

Entrance Common entrance and own entrance exam used. Oversubscribed. Candidates who are strong academically and in sports and music looked for. No religious requirements. Parents not expected to buy text books; maximum extras £125. 222 assisted places. 30 scholarships/bursaries pa, from two-thirds fees to £500.

Staff Headmaster D J Richardson, 1 year in post. 60 full time staff, 12 part time. Annual turnover minimal. Average age 36.

Academic work GCSE, AS and A-levels. 18 subjects offered plus 6 AS-level. In 1990, 98 pupils in upper fifth, 88 in upper sixth. *GCSE:* in 1990, 61 upper fifth gained at least grade C in 8+ subjects; 25 in 5–7; and 12 in 1–4 subjects. *A-levels:* 21 upper sixth passed in 4+ subjects; 36 in 3; 15 in 2; and 15 in 1 subject. Pupils taking 2 or 3 A-levels also take AS-levels or extra GCSEs. 25% took science A-levels; 25% arts/humanities; 50% both. *Computing facilities:* A network of 15 micro computers. *Special provision:* for mild dyslexia.

European Community *Languages:* French offered: to age 14; GCSE; AS-level; A-level. German offered: to age 14; GCSE; AS-level; A-level. Spanish: GCSE. *Exchanges:* Regular exchanges for pupils aged 14–18 to Germany. *Other:* Regular trips to France, include a stay with a French family.

Senior pupils' non-academic activities *Music:* 200 learn a musical instrument, 20 take orchestra and 15 organ and piano to Grade 6 or above, 3 accepted for Music School; 70 in school orchestra, 160 in school choir, 10 in 2 school pop groups, 40 in senior band, 20 in wind ensemble; 30 in local youth orchestras; 15 go into university choirs/orchestras; 1 to pop group. *Drama and dance:* 120 in school productions, 20 take GCSE drama, 10/12 take A-level. 2/3 go on to work in the theatre. *Art:* 120 take as non-examined subject; 40 take GCSE; 20 A-level. 2 accepted for Art School. *Sport:* Cricket, tennis, golf, swimming, football, rugby, squash, athletics, judo, sailing, hockey, netball, basketball, badminton, table tennis, windsurfing, cross-country, outdoor pursuits, climbing, abseiling, canoeing, orienteering and fell–walking available. 7 represent county/country (rugby). *Other:* 3 take part in local community schemes. 2 have gold Duke of Edinburgh's Award, 20 have Barnardo's award. Other activities include a computer club and clubs for technology, chess, ATC, crafts, badminton, comics, photography, art, Christian Union, modelling, war games and ski-training.

Careers In 1990, 50% leavers went on to degree courses; 1% to art/drama/music colleges; 18% to non-degree courses; 21% straight into careers; 10% other. Of those going on to degree courses, 9% went to Oxbridge, 68% to other universities; 23% to poly/colleges. 2% those going on to higher education went to courses in practical art; 62% in humanities/social sciences; 2% in medicine; and 34% in science/engineering.

Uniform School uniform worn throughout.

Houses/prefects Competitive houses. Prefects and head boy/girl – appointed by the Head and staff.

Religion Worship encouraged.

Social From time to time large scale choral productions with other schools. Organised trips to France, Germany, USA, Russia, Egypt, Romania, Switzerland. Some meals formal, some self service. School shop. No tobacco/alcohol allowed.

Discipline No corporal punishment. Pupils failing to produce homework once might expect rebuke; those caught smoking cannabis on the premises might expect expulsion.

Former pupils Eric Ambler; Henry Williamson; sundry ambassadors.

· *Colston's (Boys)* ·

Colston's School
Stapleton
Bristol
BS16 1BJ
Tel 0272 655207

- Pupils 320
- Boys 13–18 (Day/ Board/Weekly)
- Girls 16–18 (Day/ Board/Weekly)
- Upper sixth 60

- Termly fees
  £1325 (Day)
  £2195 (Board/ Weekly)
- HMC, SHMIS
  Enquiries/application to the Headmaster

What it's like

Founded in 1710, it is single-site at Stapleton in the northern outskirts of Bristol, it is merging with Colston's Girls' School in 1991. The present school has 30 acres of good grounds and playing fields and the main building is the former palace of the Bishop of Bristol. There have been numerous modern developments and facilities are of a high standard. The preparatory department is nearby. A sound education is provided and many sixth formers go on to degree courses, including Oxbridge. French and German are offered to A-level and an exceptionally high proportion of boys takes both at GCSE. Being a C of E school, chapel is quite an important part of school life; all denominations are welcome. There are flourishing music, art and drama departments. There is a substantial commitment (nearly 50% of pupils) to their own local community schemes. Full use is made of the cultural and other amenities of Bristol.

School profile

Pupils Age range 13–18; 320 pupils, 248 day (241 boys, 7 girls), 72 boarding (65 boys, 8 girls). Main entry ages 13 (boys) and into sixth (boys and girls). Approx 5% are children of former pupils. Own prep school provides more than 20% of intake. *Transfer from maintained schools:* 50% main intake, plus 50% to sixth.

Entrance Common entrance and own exam used. Oversubscribed. Any special ability is taken into account; no religious requirements. Parents not expected to buy text books; extras vary £3–£100. 90 assisted places. 8 scholarships/bursaries, full fees to £300 per term.

Parents 15+% in industry or commerce; 15+% are doctors, lawyers, etc. 30+% live within 30 miles; 11–30% live overseas.

Staff Headmaster S B Howarth, 2 years in post. 28 full time staff, 5 part time. Annual turnover 5%. Average age 40.

Academic work GCSE and A-levels. 14 subjects offered (including AS level general studies, not A-level). On average,

76 pupils in upper fifth, 45 in upper sixth. *GCSE:* on average, 28 upper fifth gain at least grade C in 8+ subjects; 22 in 5–7; and 23 in 1–4 subjects. *A-levels:* on average, 3 upper sixth pass in 4+ subjects; 26 in 3; 9 in 2; and 4 in 1 subject. 16% take science A-levels; 52% arts/humanities; 32% both. *Computing facilities:* 10 Amstrad (IBM compatible), 2 Apple, 6 BBC model B. *Special provision:* Dyslexia Unit for limited numbers.

European Community *Languages:* French offered: to age 14; GCSE; A-level. German offered: to age 14; GCSE; A-level. Over 75% take GCSE in more than 1 EC language. *Exchanges:* Regular exchanges for pupils aged 14–16 to France.

Senior pupils' non-academic activities *Music:* 34 learn a musical instrument, 10 to Grade 6 or above; 1 accepted for Music School; 23 in school orchestra, 20 in choir, 6 in pop group. *Drama and dance:* 40–50 participate in school productions. 10 in local productions; 1 goes on to work in theatre. *Art:* 50 take GCSE; 6–8 A-level. 2 accepted for Art School. 10 belong to photographic club. *Sport:* Rugby, hockey, cross-country, rugby fives, cricket, tennis, swimming, squash, volleyball, badminton and indoor bowls available plus netball for girls. Sport compulsory; 80% also take part in non-compulsory sport. About 30–40 represent county/country (rugby, hockey, cricket, cross-country, tennis, squash, badminton). *Other:* 130 take part in our own local community schemes. Other activities include a computer club, chess, walking, climbing, CCF (RAF and Army) and driving lessons.

Careers In 1990, 59% leavers went on to degree courses; 3% to art/drama/music colleges; 21% to non-degree courses (eg HND estate management, transport management); 14% straight into careers; 3% other. Of those going on to degree courses, 3% went to Oxbridge, 72% to other universities; 25% to poly/colleges. 5% those going on to higher education went to courses in practical art; 3% in music; 58% in humanities/social sciences; and 36% in science/engineering.

Uniform School uniform worn throughout.

Houses/prefects Competitive houses. Prefects, head boy, head of house and house prefects – appointed by the Head.

Religion Religious worship compulsory.

Social Choir, choral society and plays often with other schools. Organised French and German exchanges. Pupils allowed to bring own bike to school; cars – day pupils only. Meals self service. School shop. No tobacco/alcohol allowed.

Discipline No corporal punishment. Pupils failing to produce homework once might expect to do it by the following day; those caught smoking cannabis on the premises could expect expulsion.

Boarding 15% have own study bedroom, 20% share (with 1 other); 50% are in dormitories of 6+. Houses, of 45–50, same as competitive houses. Resident qualified nurse. Central dining room. Kitchens are provided; pupils can prepare hot drinks and snacks. 2 termly exeats to 16; 4 for 16–18 year olds. Visits to the local town allowed by arrangement with housemaster.

Alumni association run by J Cook, Dean Lodge, Iron Acton, Bristol.

Former pupils Professor Peter Mathias (Master of Downing College, Cambridge); Chris Broad (England cricketer); Alan Morley and Austin Sheppard (England rugby players); John Mason (Daily Telegraph rugby correspondent); Simon Mugglestone (international athlete).

· *Colston's (Girls)* ·

Colston's Girls' School	● Pupils 640	● Termly fees
Cheltenham Road	● Boys None	£978 (Day)
Bristol	● Girls 10–18	● GSA
BS6 5RD	(Day)	Enquiries/application to
Tel 0272 424328	● Upper sixth 65	the Registrar

What it's like

Founded in 1891, urban, inner city and single-site, it is merging with Colston's, the boys' school, in 1991. The original buildings form the nucleus of the modern school and have been extensively augmented to provide very good facilities. Every girl is treated as an individual and encouraged to discover her own strengths and gifts so that she can further them. The teaching is good and so are the results. Many sixth formers go on to degree courses, including Oxbridge. French and German are offered to A-level; also modern Greek, Italian and Spanish to GCSE. An exceptionally high proportion of girls takes GCSE in more than one European language. There are regular exchanges with France and Germany. Religious education is Christian but non-denominational. A fair range of standard sports, games and activities. There is a big commitment to music, with a fine string ensemble, and to drama.

School profile

Pupils Age range 10–18; 640 day girls. Main entry age 11 and into sixth. Approx 5% are children of former pupils. *Transfer from maintained schools:* 90% main intake, plus 1% to sixth.

Entrance Own entrance exam used. Fully subscribed. No special skills required. C of E foundation, but all denominations welcome. Parents not expected to buy text books; lunch is optional extra. 150 assisted places. 60 scholarships (music and sixth form) and school assisted places, variable value.

Parents 15+% in industry or commerce; 25+% are doctors, academics, lawyers, etc; 15+% in the church.

Staff Headmistress Mrs J P Franklin, in post 2 years. 40 full time staff, 20 part time. Annual turnover 4%. Average age 30–40.

Academic work GCSE and A-levels. 23 subjects offered (no A-level general studies). In 1989, 100 pupils in upper fifth, 65 in upper sixth. *GCSE:* in 1989, 44 upper fifth gained at least grade C in 8+ subjects; 32 in 5–7; and 22 in 1–4 subjects. *A-levels:* 3 upper sixth passed in 4+ subjects; 34 in 3; 8 in 2; and 10 in 1 subject. 20% took science A-levels; 66% arts/humanities; 14% both. *Computing facilities:* Apple Macintosh network. IT is taught throughout the school; computing facilities in most departments.

European Community *Languages:* French offered: to age 14; GCSE; A-level. German offered: to age 14; GCSE; A-level. Greek (modern): GCSE. Italian: GCSE. Spanish: GCSE. Over 75% take GCSE in more than 1 EC language. *Exchanges:* Regular exchanges for pupils aged 11–16 to France and Germany.

Senior pupils' non-academic activities *Music:* 140 learn a musical instrument, 60 to Grade 6 or above, 3 accepted for Music School; 70 in school orchestra, 100 in choir, 40 in chamber group; 1 in National Youth Orchestra, 6 in county orchestra, 25 in senior schools orchestras, 1 in youth choir. *Drama and dance:* Between 50–100 in school productions. *Art:* 30 take GCSE; 12 A-level. 6 accepted for Art School. *Sport:* Dance, gymnastics, hockey, squash, badminton, aerobics, athletics, weight training, swimming available. All sport compulsory. 200 take exams eg gymnastics, swimming. 6 represent county/country (athletics, hockey, netball, swimming). *Other:* 40 have bronze Duke of Edinburgh's Award, 10 have silver and 2 have gold. Other activities include a computer club, drama clubs, electronics, music groups, dance club.

Careers In 1990, 80% leavers went on to degree courses; 1% to art/drama/music colleges; 6% to non-degree courses (eg occupational therapy); 13% straight into careers (eg nursing, management). Of those going on to degree courses, 4% went to Oxbridge, 40% to other universities; 50% to poly/colleges. 4% those going on to higher education went to courses in practical art; 4% in music; 73% in humanities/social sciences; 4% in medicine; and 15% in science/engineering.

Uniform School uniform worn except in the sixth.

Houses/prefects Competitive houses. Prefects, head girl, house captains – elected by the school.

Religion Religious worship encouraged. Voluntary attendance at religious services in church once a term.

Social Debates, choir, drama productions, dance with other schools. Organised trips to Russia, Germany, Austria, France, Spain, Italy, Greece. A few pupils allowed to bring own car/bike/

motorbike to school. Meals self service. Small tuckshop. No tobacco/alcohol allowed.

Discipline No corporal punishment.

Pupils failing to produce homework once might expect a discussion with staff member; those caught smoking cannabis on the premises could expect expulsion.

· *Combe Bank* ·

Combe Bank School	• Pupils 445	• Termly fees
Educational Trust Ltd	• Boys None	£1300 (Day)
Sundridge	• Girls 3–18	• GSA
Sevenoaks	(Day)	
Kent TN14 6AE	• Upper sixth 30	Enquiries/application to
Tel 0959 63720		the Secretary

What it's like

Founded in 1868, it passed to the Educational Trust in 1972. Housed in a superb Palladian country mansion (an historic building) built in 1720 and set in 27 acres of beautiful parkland, the prep school is nearby. It is Roman Catholic but accepts all denominations. Christian doctrine is central to the curriculum; the syllabus is ecumenical. It caters for a wide range of abilities and talents; recently very strong in music and quite strong in drama. French, German and Spanish are offered to A-level. Many girls take GCSE in more than one European language and there are regular exchanges with France and Germany. (Second years are offered a tour to France: French cuisine and culture.) There is an adequate range of sports, games and activities and the standard in games is high. Vigorous participation in local community schemes. All pupils day.

School profile

Pupils Total age range 3–18; 445 girls. Senior department 11–18, 245 girls. Main entry ages 3, 11, 12, 13 and into sixth. *Transfer from maintained schools:* 25% intakes 11–13, plus 33% to sixth.

Entrance Common entrance and own exam used. Well subscribed. No special skills or religious requirements; any special skills (eg music) an advantage. School is Roman Catholic foundation although only 30% pupils are RC. Parents expected to buy some text books. No assisted places yet. Some scholarships/bursaries are available.

Staff Head Mrs A J K Austin, in post for 8 years. 18 full time staff, 14 part time. Annual turnover under 10%. Average age about 40.

Academic work GCSE and A-levels. (No A-level general studies offered.) In 1989, 40 pupils in upper fifth, 30 in upper sixth. *GCSE:* in 1989, 26 upper fifth gained at least grade C in 8+ subjects; 12 in 5–7; and 10 in 1–4 subjects. *A-levels:* 1 pupil in upper sixth passed in 3+ subjects; 5 in 3; 2 in 2; and 5 in 1 subject. 1 took science A-levels; 3 arts/humanities; 4 both. *Computing facilities:* BBC B Master, Archimedes network. *Special provision:* Extra teaching for mild dyslexia.

European Community *Languages:* French offered: to age 14; GCSE; AS-level; A-level. German offered: to age 14; GCSE; AS-level; A-level. Spanish offered: to age 14; GCSE; A-level. 25–50% take GCSE in more than 1 EC language. *Exchanges:* Regular exchanges for pupils aged 14–16 to France and Germany. *Other:* European Studies offered to pupils aged 16–18. Second year tour to France, French cuisine and culture.

Senior pupils' non-academic activities *Music:* 180 learn a musical instrument, 15 to Grade 6 or above. 30 in school orchestra, 100 in school choir, 20 in wind, 20 in recorder, 10 in string groups. *Drama and dance:* Large number in school productions; many take Guildhall exams. *Art:* 3 or 4 take as a non-examined subject, 10 take GCSE; 2–6 A-level. 30 belong to pottery and sculpture clubs. *Sport:* Hockey, netball, rounders, athletics, cross-country running, swimming, badminton, volleyball are available. 100 take non-compulsory sport. *Other:* 40 take part in local community schemes. 30 have bronze Duke of Edinburgh's Award, 15 have silver and 5 gold. Other activities include a computer club, pottery and craft, music and survival swimming.

Careers In 1990, 25% leavers went on to degree courses; 25% to art/drama/music colleges; 50% to non-degree courses. Of those going on to degree courses, 50% went to universities; 50% to poly/colleges.

Uniform School uniform worn except in the sixth.

Houses/prefects Competitive houses (for sport). Prefects, head girl, head of house and house prefects – head girl appointed after discussion by staff. School Council.

Religion Religious worship encouraged; occasional services compulsory.

Social Young Enterprise, voluntary service (with all Sevenoaks schools), choir with schools and local choirs, Ernest Reed concerts. Ski trip, French exchange, German exchange, Russian trip, hockey tour to Zimbabwe. Pupils allowed to bring own car/bike to school. Meals self service. School shop sells second-hand uniform. No tobacco/alcohol allowed.

Discipline No corporal punishment. Pupils failing to produce homework once might expect to have to repeat it; detention. Those caught smoking cannabis on the premises could expect immediate suspension, almost certain expulsion.

Alumni association run by Mrs K Lagarde, c/o the School.

· *Commonweal Lodge* ·

Commonweal Lodge
Woodcote Lane
Purley
Surrey CR8 3HB
Tel 081 660 3179

- Pupils 250
- Boys None
- Girls 4–18
  (Day)
- Upper sixth 3

- Termly fees
  £1045 (Day)
- GSA
Enquiries/application to
the Headmistress

What it's like

Founded in 1916, it lies on the west side of Purley in an agreeable residential area with four acres of private grounds. The buildings are purpose-designed and have good facilities. The lower junior school is nearby. Its general aim is to educate girls to use their individual abilities – mentally, physically, spiritually. Sound standards and values based on Christian principles are fostered. French and German are offered to A-level and a high proportion of pupils take GCSE in both. Assembly and religious education are an integral part of the life. Sport, games and extra–curricular activities are adequate.

School profile

Pupils Total age range 4–18; 250 day girls. Senior department 11–18, 135 girls. Main entry ages 4, 5, 8, 11. Approx 1% are children of former pupils. *Transfer from maintained schools:* 25% intake at 11+.

Entrance Own entrance exam used. No

special skills or religious requirements. Parents not expected to buy text books; maximum extras £65 plus music tuition. No assisted places. 3 scholarships/bursaries.

Staff Headmistress Miss J M Brown, in post for 9 years. 17 full time staff, 14 part time. Annual turnover 6–10%. Average age 40.

Academic work GCSE and A-levels (no A-level general studies). In 1990, 26 pupils in upper fifth. *GCSE:* in 1990, 9 upper fifth gained at least grade C in 8+ subjects; 9 in 5–7; and 8 in 1–4 subjects. *Computing facilities:* 9 BBC Masters, 2 Acorns, 1 IBM. *Special provision:* EFL specialist teacher. Visiting teacher for the dyslexic.

European Community *Languages:* French offered: to age 14; GCSE; AS-level; A-level. German offered: to age 14; GCSE; AS-level; A-level. 50–75% take GCSE in more than 1 EC language. *Exchanges:* Regular exchanges for pupils aged 11–16 to France. *Other:* Short stay tuition for 4 weeks in summer for girls from EC.

Senior pupils' non-academic activities *Music:* 50 learn a musical instrument, 4 to Grade 6 or above, 2 in school groups, 36 in school choir. *Art:* 3 take as non-examined subject, 15 take GCSE. *Sport:* Tennis, swimming, rounders, net-ball, lacrosse, badminton, volleyball and gymnastics available. 15 take non-compulsory sport. *Other:* Activities include music, drama and art clubs and choirs.

Uniform School uniform worn except in the sixth.

Houses/prefects Competitive houses. Prefects, head girl, head of house and house prefects – appointed by the Head and the school.

Religion Religious worship is encouraged. Daily assemblies.

Social No regular events with local schools. Trips to France and Germany, ski parties and Mediterranean cruises. Pupils allowed to bring own car/bike/motorbike to school. Meals self service. No tobacco/alcohol allowed.

Discipline No corporal punishment. Pupils failing to produce homework once might expect a warning; those caught smoking cannabis on the premises could expect immediate suspension – probably expulsion.

Alumni association run by The Old Knots Secretary, Miss E Bland, 317 Fir Tree Road, Epsom Downs, Surrey KT17 3LG.

Former pupils Jacqueline du Pre (cellist); Alex Hildred (archaeologist); Angharad Rees (actress); Yvonne Sintes (first woman airline pilot).

· *Craigholme* ·

Craigholme School
72 St Andrew's Drive
Glasgow
G41 4HS
Tel 041 427 0375

- Pupils 562
- Boys None
- Girls 4–18 (Day)
- Higher year 51

- Termly fees £860 (Day)
- SHA, HAS

Enquiries/application to the Secretary or Headmistress

What it's like

Founded in 1894, it has handsome well-equipped premises in a pleasant residential suburb of Glasgow. The playing fields are on the Pollok estate a few minutes away. Primary and secondary departments are combined. The infant department is on a separate site. Excellent facilities are provided. Religious worship is compulsory. Academic standards are high and results good. Many pupils proceed to degree courses each year. There is a tremendously strong music dept (300 pupils learn an instrument), and also much strength in drama (a third of the school being engaged in productions each year). Sports and games are also of a high standard and quite a lot of pupils represent the school at county level. A plentiful range of extra-curricular activities. Many enterprising trips and expeditions at home and abroad are organised. The school's record in the Duke of Edinburgh's Award Scheme is outstanding.

School profile

Pupils Total age range 4–18; 562 day girls. Senior department 12–18, 321 girls. Main entry age 5 and 12. Approx 30% are children of former pupils. *Transfer from maintained schools:* 10% main intake at 11.

Entrance Own entrance exam used. Senior school oversubscribed. No special skills or religious requirements. Parents expected to buy text books/music lessons/lunch. 20 assisted places. 2–4 Packer Bursaries – partial assistance with fees, means tested.

Staff Headmistress Mrs Gillian R Burt, first year in post. 42 full time staff, 7 part time. Annual turnover 2 or 3. Average age 40.

Academic work GCSE O-grades, S-grades, Highers, CSYS. 18 subjects offered. In 1990, 59 pupils in O/S-grade year, 51 in Higher, 27 in CSYS year. *O/S-grade:* in 1990, 26 pupils passed in 8+ subjects; 25 in 5–7; and 8 in 1–4 subjects. *Highers:* 16 passed in 5+ subjects; 9 in 4; 9 in 3; 10 in 2; and 19 in 1 subject. *CSYS:* 1 passed in 3 subjects; 6 in 2; 10 in 1. 50% took science; 20% arts/humanities; 30% both. *Computing facilities:* Well stocked computer room with 10–12 computers (BBCs and Amstrads) plus computers in many departments primary and secondary. *Special provision:* Remedial help by staff but no specialist teaching.

European Community *Languages:* French offered: to age 14; GCSE; AS-level; A-level. German offered: to age 14; GCSE; AS-level; A-level. Spanish offered: to GCSE; AS-level; A-level. *Exchanges:* Regular exchanges for pupils aged 16–18 to Germany.

Senior pupils' non-academic activities *Music:* 250 learn a musical instrument, Grade 3 to Grade 6 or above; 80 in school orchestras; 3 in Independent Schools Orchestra; 20 in brass ensemble; 100 in carol singing choir. *Drama and dance:* Approximately 200 participate in school productions and musicals. *Art:* 15 take O-grade; 15 Higher; 2 CSYS. 2 accepted for Art School; 1 for architecture; 3 for design (various); personal sketchbooks are encouraged. Visits arranged to art galleries and current exhibitions. *Sport:* Hockey (9 teams), tennis, athletics, netball, volleyball, badminton, gymnastics, dance/keep-fit/yoga, recreational swimming, and curling (as requested) available. 84 take non-compulsory sport. 5 pupils represent county/country (tennis, hockey, golf, equestrian). *Other:* Some work for national charities and 5 at Oxfam shops. 39 have bronze Duke of Edinburgh's Award, 19 have silver and 15 have gold. 14 take first aid course with St Andrew's Ambulance Association. Other activities include a stamp club, debating society, public speaking, German and French clubs.

Careers In 1990, 76% leavers went on to degree courses; 14% to non-degree courses (eg secretarial, hotel management); 10% straight into careers (eg nursing, secretarial, estate agency). Of those going on to degree courses, 53% went to universities; 47% to poly/colleges. 12% those going on to higher education went to courses in practical art; 3% in music; 56% in humanities/social sciences; 12% in medicine; and 16 in science/engineering.

Uniform School uniform worn throughout.

Houses/prefects Competitive houses. Head girl (appointed by staff), head of house and house prefects (elected). School Council.

Religion Assembly compulsory three mornings a week; separate Jewish assembly weekly.

Social Joint disco for charity with local schools. Frequent organised trips abroad (at least one annually) including ski-ing, France, Germany, Russia and Pompeii. Pupils allowed to bring own bike to school. Meals self service. No tobacco/alcohol allowed.

Discipline No corporal punishment. After-school detentions – S1 to S6. Pupils failing to produce homework once might expect extra homework; those caught smoking cannabis on the premises could expect suspension or expulsion.

Alumni association run by Mrs Joan Henderson, 14 Darnley Road, Glasgow G41.

Former pupils Jane Will (nurse) Scotswoman of the Year 1981; Susan Wighton (nurse) Scotswoman of the Year 1987.

· *Cranleigh* ·

Cranleigh School	• Pupils 560	• Termly fees
Cranleigh	• Boys 13–18	£2400 (Day)
Surrey	(Day/Board)	£3195 (Board)
GU6 8QQ	• Girls 16–18	• HMC
Tel 0483 273997	(Day/Board)	Enquiries/application to
	• Upper sixth 134	the Head

What it's like

Founded in 1865 as a boys' boarding school it became partly co-educational in 1971 with the admission of girls to the sixth form. It has a splendid site in 200 acres of Surrey farmland near the small town of Cranleigh. The buildings are striking and well appointed. During the last 15 years there has been considerable expansion and the school is now extremely well equipped by any standards and a new studio theatre has just been built. The prep school adjoins the main campus. The chapel was built as the central point of the school and the policy is to maintain Christian values as a way of life. There is quite a lot of emphasis on worship and instruction in the Anglican tradition. It is an extremely well run, energetic and purposeful school which displays considerable enterprise in many fields. A large staff allows a staff:pupil ratio of about 1:9. Academic standards are high and results consistently good. Many pupils go on to degree courses each year, including Oxbridge. French, German and Spanish are offered to A-level; many pupils take GCSE in more than one European language. There are regular exchanges with France, Germany and Spain. There are particularly good facilities for science, computer studies, electronics and technology. For many years Cranleigh has maintained a high reputation for music. There are as many as 25 visiting music teachers. There are several choirs and orchestras and at least a quarter of the school learns an instrument. It is no less strong in drama. There are as many as 10 productions each year, including house plays and plays in French, Spanish and German. Some plays are presented in the open-air theatre. First-rate facilities are available for art, pottery and printing. The school also has a long-standing reputation for its achievements in games and sports, of which there is a wide range available including sailing and golf (there is a 9-hole course on the estate). It has both indoor and outdoor swimming pools. Numerous clubs and societies cater for most needs. A large and active voluntary CCF provides adventure training and trips abroad to military units. There is also a fire brigade section. Field trips and expeditions overseas are frequent and there are regular scientific expeditions to Iceland. Travel grants are available to allow pupils to carry out their own projects. The school has a substantial commitment to local community services; especially through the physically handicapped/able bodied course, a residential event at the school. There has been considerable success in the Duke of Edinburgh's Award Scheme.

School profile

Pupils Age range 13–18, 560 pupils (480 boys, 80 girls). Main entry age 13 (boys) and into the sixth (boys and girls). 20% intake from own prep.

Entrance Common entrance exam used. Assisted places, music and academic scholarships available.

Staff Head Anthony Hart, in post for 7 years.

Academic work GCSE and A-levels. 20 subjects offered (no A-level general studies). In 1990, 98 pupils in upper fifth, 134 in upper sixth. *GCSE:* in 1990, 62 upper fifth gained at least grade C in 8+ subjects; 32 in 5–7; and 4 in 1–4 subjects. *A-levels:* 6 upper sixth passed in 4+ subjects; 106 in 3; 12 in 2; and 7 in 1 subject. 17% took science A-levels; 53% arts/ humanities; 30% both. *Computing facilities:* 2 computing laboratories with BBCs, Masters, Archimedes and IBM. *Special provision:* Occasional EFL lessons.

European Community *Languages:* French offered: to age 14; GCSE; AS- level; A-level. German offered: to age 14; GCSE; AS-level; A-level. Spanish offered: to age 14; GCSE; AS-level; A- level. 25–50% take GCSE in more than 1 EC language. *Exchanges:* Regular exchanges for pupils aged 16–18 to France, Germany and Spain. *Other:* Parental involvement in exchange/training schemes and conferences on European issues. European Week in 1992, involving all aspects of school life.

Careers In 1990, 68% leavers went on to degree courses; 22% to art/drama/ music colleges; 3% to non-degree courses; 3% straight into careers; 4% other. Of those going on to degree courses, 12% went to Oxbridge, 78% to other universities; 10% to poly/colleges. 1% those going on to higher education went to courses in practical art; 1% in drama/acting; 1% in music; 69% in humanities/social sciences; 3% in medicine; and 25% in science/engineering.

· *Croft House* ·

Croft House School	● Pupils 200	● Termly fees
Shillingstone	● Boys None	£1635 (Day)
Blandford	● Girls 11–18	£2350 (Board/
Dorset	(Day/Board/	Weekly)
DT11 0QS	Weekly)	● GSA
Tel 0258 860295	● Upper sixth 14	Enquiries/application to the Headmistress

What it's like

Started in 1941 by Colonel and Mrs Torkington in their own house (in the village of Shillingstone) to provide education for their daughter and the daughters of friends. Thus began the tradition of a small family school which has been preserved. It has a very pleasant environment and there have been considerable extensions. It is C of E by foundation but other persuasions are welcomed. A sound education is provided. French and German are offered to A-level; also Spanish and Italian as extras. Many girls take GCSE in more than one European language. There are regular exchanges with France and Germany. The music, art and drama departments are very active and there is a good range of sports, games and other activities, including a flourishing riding school.

School profile

Pupils Age range 11–18; 200 girls, 20 day, 180 boarding. Main entry ages 11, 12, 13 and into sixth. Approx 7% are children of former pupils. *Transfer from maintained schools:* 10% main intake, plus 5–10% to sixth.

Entrance Own entrance exam used. Early application advised. Parents expected to buy sixth form text books; maximum extras £150 per term. 5 major scholarships and some bursaries (riding, academic, art, music, sixth form), up to 40% of fees.

Parents 12% in the armed services. 30% live within 30 miles; 14% live overseas.

Staff Headmistress Mrs S Rawlinson, in post for 6 years. 19 full time staff, 18 part time. Annual turnover 6%. Average age 30–35.

Academic work GCSE and A-levels. 20 subjects offered (including drama and keyboard applications; GCSE but not A-level general studies). In 1990, 42 pupils in upper fifth, 14 in upper sixth. *GCSE:* in 1990, 6 upper fifth gained at least grade C in 8+ subjects; 10 in 5–7; and 28 in 1–4 subjects. *A-levels:* 4 upper sixth passed in 3 subjects; 3 in 2; and 3 in 1 subject. 15% took science A-levels; 45% arts/humanities; 30% both. *Computing facilities:* 2 computer rooms, mainly BBC. *Special provision:* Some EFL tuition; pupils with mild dyslexia and minor physical handicaps accepted.

European Community *Languages:* French offered: to age 14; GCSE; AS-level; A-level; non-examined. German offered: to age 14; GCSE; AS-level; A-level. Italian offered: to GCSE; A-level; non-examined (as extra). Spanish offered: to GCSE; A-level; non-examined (as extra). 25–50% take GCSE in more than 1 EC language. *Exchanges:* Regular exchanges for pupils aged 14–18 to France and Germany. *Other:* Girls from EC countries frequently stay in school, 6 weeks to 1 year.

Senior pupils' non-academic activities *Music:* Music is important; many girls play or sing. *Drama and dance:* Drama GCSE and A-level popular. Many drama competitions and major school productions. Some girls go on to careers in the theatre. *Art:* Many take as non-examined subject. Pottery, screen-printing, batik etc also available. A few accepted for Art School. *Sport:* Hockey, netball, tennis, swimming, athletics, basketball, gymnastics, riding, volleyball, badminton, rounders available. Everyone takes sport. *Other:* Pupils take part in local community schemes, Duke of Edinburgh's bronze, silver and gold Awards. Other activities include a computer club, riding, judo, dance (modern), ballet, bellringing (church).

Careers 1 full time adviser. Annual average accepted for *arts and humanities degree courses* at universities, 2; polytechnics or colleges, 2. *science and engineering degree courses* at universities, 2. *BEd*, 3. *Other general training courses*, 4. Average number of pupils going straight into careers in industry, 2.

Uniform School uniform worn except in the sixth.

Houses/prefects Competitive houses (halls). Prefects, head girl, head of house and house prefects – appointed by staff discussion.

Religion Anglican religious worship encouraged.

Social Choral society; Christian Union; Gilbert & Sullivan; dances, etc with local schools. Organised trips abroad. Pupils allowed to bring own bike to school. Meals semi-formal. School tuck shop and stationery shop. No tobacco/alcohol allowed.

Discipline A high standard of behaviour is expected and encouraged.

Boarding Most sixth form have own study bedroom, others share with one other; 20% are in dormitories of 6+. Houses, 100–20 pupils. Resident qualified medical staff. Central dining room. 3 exeats each term; unlimited in sixth form. Unaccompanied visits to the local town rarely allowed except for seniors.

· Croham Hurst ·

Croham Hurst School
79 Croham Road
Croydon
Surrey
CR2 7YN
Tel 081 680 3064

- Pupils 580
- Boys None
- Girls 4–18
  (Day)
- Upper sixth 32

- Termly fees
  £1030 (Day)
- GSA
Enquiries to the
Headmistress's
Secretary
Application to the Head

What it's like

Founded in 1897, it is single-site and semi-rural and stands on a slope facing Croham Hurst, on the verge of woodlands, parkland and the green belt. Altogether it is a pleasant environment with gardens and playing fields. The buildings are comfortable and well appointed and there are plentiful modern facilities. Many sixth form leavers go on to degree courses, including Oxbridge. The junior school is nearby. Basically a Christian foundation, it provides a sound academic training and is particularly strong in music.

School profile

Pupils Total age range 4–18; 580 day girls. Senior department 11–18, 340 girls. Main entry ages 4, 7, 11 and into sixth. Approx 5–10% are children of former pupils. *Transfer from maintained schools:* Up to 40% intake at 11, and into sixth.
Entrance Own entrance exam used. No special skills or religious requirements. Parents not expected to buy text books; music, drama etc extra, £60 each per term. 5 scholarships/bursaries at 11+ and 16+, 100–25% fees; assisted places scheme.
Staff Headmistress Miss J M Shelmerdine, in post for 4 years. 35 full time staff, 15 part time. Annual turnover less than 10%. Average age 35.
Academic work GCSE and A-levels; a few RSA/Pitmans. 19 GCSE subjects offered; 17 at A-level (no A-level general studies). Average of 60 pupils in upper fifth, 32 in upper sixth. *GCSE:* in 1990, 70% upper fifth gained at least grade C in 8+ subjects; 28% in 5–7; and 2% in 1–4 subjects. *A-levels:* 6% upper sixth passed in 4+ subjects; 70% in 3; 28% in 2; and 2% in 1 subject. 25% took science A-levels; 52% arts/humanities; 23% both. *Computing facilities:* Computer room in senior school and several departmental computers. *Special provision:* Outside tui-

tion (linked with school) recommended for learning difficulties.
European Community *Languages:* French offered: to age 14; GCSE; A-level. German offered: to age 14; GCSE; A-level. Italian: non-examined. Spanish offered: to age 14; GCSE. Under 10% take GCSE in more than 1 EC language. *Exchanges:* Regular exchanges for pupils aged 11–18 to France.
Senior pupils' non-academic activities *Music:* 200 learn a musical instrument, 25–30 in school orchestras, wind bands, etc, 50–60 in school choir. *Art:* 10–20 take GCSE; 6 A-level; 6 A-level textiles. 3 accepted for Art School. *Sport:* Lacrosse, netball, tennis, rounders, athletics, basketball available. *Other:* Activities include a computer club, drama.
Careers In 1990, 73% leavers went on to degree courses; 9% to art/drama/ music colleges; 9% to non-degree courses (eg nursing, occupational therapy); 9% straight into careers (eg secretarial, underwriting). Of those going on to degree courses, 13% went to Oxbridge, 37% to other universities; 50% to poly/colleges. 12% those going on to higher education went to courses in practical art; 6% in music; 56% in humanities/social sci-

ences; 16% in medicine; and 10% in science/engineering.

Uniform School uniform worn except in the sixth.

Houses/prefects Competitive houses. No prefects. Head girl and head of house – elected by the school. School Council.

Religion Christian assembly compulsory.

Social Debates. Joint theatre productions with Whitgift Boys' School.

Exchange trips to Germany and France; ski trips. Pupils allowed to bring own car/bike/motorbike to school. Meals self service.

Discipline No corporal punishment. Pupils failing to produce homework once would have no punishment.

Alumni association run by Secretary, Mrs A Stewart, 67 Greenacres Ring, Angmering Village, West Sussex BN16 4BY.

· *Croydon High* ·

Croydon High School
for Girls
Old Farleigh Road
Selsdon
South Croydon
Surrey CR2 8YB
Tel 081 651 5020

- Pupils 1050
- Boys None
- Girls 4–18 (Day)
- Upper sixth 90

- Termly fees £1024 (Day)
- GSA, GPDST

Enquiries/application to the Headmistress

What it's like

Founded in 1874, it moved to its present site on the outskirts of Croydon in 1966. This comprises a purpose-built and extremely well-equipped and comfortable establishment in beautiful landscaped grounds. The teaching is well known to be very good and standards are high (a large number of degree course entrants per year, including Oxbridge). French and German are offered to A-level, Spanish to GCSE. An exceptionally high proportion of girls take GCSE in more than one European language. There are regular exchanges with France, Germany and Spain. It is particularly strong in music, games (especially netball and hockey) and in drama. Big commitment to local community schemes and the Duke of Edinburgh's Award Scheme.

School profile

Pupils Total age range 4–18; 1050 day girls. Senior department 11–18, 750 girls. Main entry ages 4, 5, 7, 11 and into sixth. Approx 10% are children of former pupils. *Transfer from maintained schools:* 50% intake at 11. (National Curriculum implemented in junior school, so girls from maintained sector can merge easily.)

Entrance Own entrance exam used. Oversubscribed. Good academic ability required; no religious requirements. Parents not expected to buy text books. 24 assisted places pa. 4 scholarships pa (11+ and sixth form), 33–50% fees.

Staff Headmistress Mrs P E Davies, 1 year in post. 61 full time staff, 23 part time. Annual turnover less than 10%.

Academic work GCSE, AS and A-levels. 21 A-level subjects offered (4, including general studies, at AS-level). In 1990, 105 pupils in upper fifth, 90 in upper sixth. *GCSE:* in 1990, 86% upper fifth gained at least grade C in 8+ subjects; 12% in 5–7; and 2% in 1–4 subjects. *A-levels:* 12% upper sixth passed in 4+ subjects; 55% in 3; 27% in 2; and 5% in 1 subject. 33% took science A-levels; 27% arts/humanities; 40% both.

Computing facilities: 2 Nimbus Networks, 1 stand alone BBC.

European Community *Languages:* French offered: to age 14; GCSE; AS-level; A-level; Institute of Linguists. German offered: to age 14; GCSE; A-level; Institute of Linguists. Spanish offered: to GCSE; A-level; Institute of Linguists. Over 75% take GCSE in more than 1 EC language. *Exchanges:* Regular exchanges for pupils aged 11–16 to France, Germany and Spain.

Senior pupils' non-academic activities (Pupils of 15+.) *Music:* 150 learn a musical instrument, 80 to Grade 6 or above. 1 accepted for Music School, 2 for university. 50 in school orchestra, 80 in school choir, 30 in wind band; 20 in Croydon Youth Philharmonic Orchestra, 20 in Croydon Wind Bands. *Drama and dance:* 150 in school productions and 300 in Drama Festivals. 10 take drama GCSE; 100 take Associated Board Exams. 2 accepted for Drama/Dance Schools; 2 take drama as a university subject. *Art:* 30 take GCSE art; 9 A-level. 2 accepted for Art School. 40 take non-examination course in sixth form. *Sport:* Hockey, netball, tennis, swimming, synchro-swimming, rounders, cricket, athletics, cross-country, badminton, squash, table tennis, volleyball, gymnastics, sports acrobatics available. 50 take awards, eg gymnastics, athletics, swimming. 18 national netball and hockey players in last 25 years. Many play at club and county level and for university in many sports. *Other:* 85+ take part in local community schemes. 40 have bronze Duke of Edinburgh's Award, 25 have silver and 1 gold. All participate in School's annual Guild of Charity fund-raising effort. Two weeks Work Experience undertaken by fifth years, preceded by Understanding Industry course. Other activities include a computer club, Young Enterprise, a wide range of music and drama, sporting clubs and other subject based clubs, chess and bridge clubs.

Careers 2 part time advisers. Annual average accepted for *arts and humanities degree courses* at Oxbridge, 8; other universities, 22; polytechnics/colleges, 8. *Science and engineering degree courses* at Oxbridge, 5; other universities, 24; medical schools, 3; polytechnics/colleges, 5. *BEd*, 5. *Other general training courses*, 8. Average number of pupils going straight into careers in banking, insurance, etc, 4.

Uniform School uniform worn except in the sixth.

Houses/prefects No competitive houses. Prefects, 4 senior prefects and 2 head girls – elected by school. School Council.

Religion Compulsory regular school assemblies.

Social Joint sixth form society with Trinity Boys' School. Exchange trips, educational courses, study trips, and ski trips abroad. Meals self service. Second-hand uniform shop. No tobacco/alcohol allowed.

Discipline In any disciplinary actions parents are always closely involved. For example, pupils failing to produce homework would expect a letter home at the third instance.

Alumni association run by Mrs M Knight, c/o the School.

Former pupils Baroness Seear; Marion Roe; Jill Tweedie; Jane Drew; Wendy Savage; Jacqueline du Pré.

· Culford ·

Culford School
Bury St Edmunds
Suffolk
IP28 6TX
Tel 0284 728615
Fax 0284 728631

- Pupils 670
- Boys 8–18
  (Day/Board)
- Girls 8–18
  (Day/Board)
- Upper sixth 75

- Termly fees
  £1531 (Day)
  £2355 (Board)
- HMC
  Enquiries/application to
  the Headmaster

What it's like

Founded in 1881, it has a splendid site 4 miles north of Bury St Edmunds. The main building is Culford Hall, a fine and palatial 18th-century mansion (formerly the seat of Earl Cadogan) in 400 acres of beautiful gardens and parkland. Numerous modern extensions, including several new and comfortable boarding houses. It is a Methodist foundation but all denominations are welcome. The school has a deep-rooted respect for tradition in teaching methods, manners and behaviour and sees education as something that goes on outside as well as in the classroom. It seeks to establish a partnership with parents and expects pupils to work hard and make the most of their abilities whether they are outstanding academically or not. Many sixth form leavers go on to degree courses, including Oxbridge. French, German and Spanish are offered to A-levels. Many pupils take GCSE in more than one European language. There are regular exchanges with France and Germany. Strong emphasis on sense of community. The music and drama departments are very vigorous and there are many outdoor pursuits (including angling and clay-pigeon shooting). There are close social service ties with Bury. The junior school is also in the park.

School profile

Pupils Total age range 8–18; 670 pupils, 356 day (176 boys, 180 girls), 314 boarding (184 boys, 130 girls). Senior department 13–18, 427 pupils (223 boys, 204 girls). Main entry ages 8, 11, 13 and into sixth. Approx 20% are children of former pupils.

Entrance Common entrance and own entrance exam used. Oversubscribed. No special skills or religious requirements. Parents not expected to buy text books; few extras. 8 pa assisted places. 4 scholarships/bursaries up to 50% fees.

Parents 15+% in industry or commerce; 15+% in the armed services. 30+% live within 30 miles; 10+% live overseas.

Staff Headmaster D Robson, in post for 20 years. 67 full time staff, 6 part time. Annual turnover 5%. Average age 41.

Academic work GCSE and A-levels. Average size of upper fifth 90; upper sixth 75. *Computing facilities:* Econet terminal in each classroom of main teaching block. Computer room with 12 terminals. Computers in other departments. *Special provision:* for dyslexia, EFL etc.

European Community *Languages:* French offered: to age 14; GCSE; A-level. German offered: to GCSE; A-level. Spanish offered: to GCSE; A-level. 25–50% take GCSE in more than 1 EC language. *Exchanges:* Regular exchanges for pupils aged 14–18 to France and Germany.

Senior pupils' non-academic activities Music, drama, art and sport.

Careers In 1990, 67% leavers went on to degree courses; 3% to art/drama/music colleges; 3% to non-degree courses; 12% straight into careers (eg pilot, surveyor, matron); 15% other (eg retaking A-levels). Of those going on to degree courses, 7% went to Oxbridge,

75% to other universities; 18% to poly/colleges. 7% those going on to higher education went to courses in practical art; 23% in humanities/social sciences; 5% in medicine; 23% in science/engineering; and 40% in law/finance.

Uniform School uniform worn throughout.

Houses/prefects Competitive houses. Prefects, head boy and girl, head of house and house prefects – nominated by pupils, appointed by the Head.

Religion Religious worship compulsory; a Methodist foundation.

Social Some organised local events and trips abroad. Upper sixth allowed to bring own car/bike/motorbike to school. Meals self service. School shop. No tobacco/alcohol allowed.

Discipline No corporal punishment.

Boarding Most share study bedrooms; none in large dormitories. Houses of varying size, divided by age group, single sex. Resident qualified medical staff. Central dining room. Pupils can provide and cook own food. 2 exeats each term. Visits to the local town allowed.

Alumni association run by Roland Beaney, Fieldgate, Church Road, Beyton, Bury St Edmunds, Suffolk.

Former pupils Sir David Plastow (Chief Executive, Vickers); Admiral Sir Derek Reffell; John Motson (sports commentator).

d

· *Dame Alice Harpur* ·

The Dame Alice Harpur
School
Cardington Road
Bedford MK42 0BX
Tel 0234 340871

- Pupils 1006
- Boys None
- Girls 7–18
  (Day)
- Upper sixth 109

- Termly fees
  £1086 (Day)
- GSA

What it's like

Opened in May 1882, it is one of the four schools of the Bedford Charity, the Harpur Trust, which share equally in the benefaction of Sir William Harpur and Dame Alice, his wife, who originally endowed the foundation with land in Holborn (London) and Bedford. It has a Christian ethos but, while upholding traditional values and standards, is fundamentally ecumenical. The main school has modern buildings with good facilities, plus agreeable gardens and playing fields, on a riverside site. Two listed Georgian houses on site have been adapted to provide a sixth-form centre and music centre. A third building houses English and drama rooms. New library facilities offer excellent study opportunities. Opposite the main school is Howard House, the preparatory department. The school offers a broad general education. Academic standards are high and results are good. Many sixth form leavers go on to degree courses, including Oxbridge. French, German, Modern Greek and Spanish are offered at GCSE. Many girls take GCSE in more than one European language. French and German are also offered at A-level and there are regular exchanges with France and Germany. Drama is strong and the music department is especially flourishing (with four choirs, four orchestras, string quartets, a string orchestra and other ensembles, including brass). A standard range of sports and games is provided; teams compete at county and regional level, plus some at national level. Extra-curricular activities include exchange visits with German and French schools, public speaking, archaeology, field-work and a range of open-air activities leading to participation in the Duke of Edinburgh's Award Scheme in which the school has had considerable success.

School profile

Pupils Total age range 7–18; 1006 day girls. Senior department 11–18, 791 girls. Main entry ages 11, 13 and into the sixth. *Transfer from maintained schools:* 90% of secondary intake plus 50% to sixth form.
Entrance Own entrance exam used. Bursaries and assisted places.

Staff Headmistress Mrs R Randle, 1 year in post.
Academic work GCSE and A-levels. 21 subjects offered. In 1990, 126 pupils in upper fifth, 109 in upper sixth. *GCSE:* in 1990, 126 upper fifth gained at least grade C in 8+ subjects; 22 in 5–7; and 6 in 1–4

228

subjects. *A-levels:* 8 upper sixth passed in 4+ subjects; 42 in 3; 25 in 2; and 14 in 1 subject. On average 20% take science A-levels; 50% arts/humanities; 30% both. *Computing facilities:* Computer room with 11 workstations; computer workstation for private study in the AV Resources room; computers in some departmental areas.

European Community *Languages:* French offered: to age 14; GCSE; AS-level; A-level. German offered: to age 14; GCSE; A-level. Greek (modern): to GCSE. Spanish offered: to GCSE. 25–50% take GCSE in more than 1 EC language. *Exchanges:* Regular exchanges for pupils aged 11–16 to France and Germany.

Careers On average, 75% leavers go on to degree courses; 15% to art/drama/music colleges; 5% to non-degree courses; 5% straight into careers (eg retail management, banking, accountancy, nursing). Of those going on to degree courses, 10% went to Oxbridge, 75% to other universities; 15% to poly/colleges. 10% those going on to higher education went to courses in practical art; 2% in drama/acting; 10% in music; 33% in humanities/social sciences; 5% in medicine; and 40% in science/engineering.

· *Dame Allan's (Boys)* ·

Dame Allan's Boys'
School
Fowberry Crescent
Fenham
Newcastle upon Tyne
NE4 9YJ
Tel 091 2750 608

- Pupils 443
- Boys 9–18 (Day)
- Girls None but joint sixth with girls' school
- Upper sixth 50

- Termly fees £850 (Day)
- HMC

Enquiries/application to the Principal

What it's like

Founded in 1705, established at Fenham in 1926 and occupied new buildings on an urban site (with playing fields attached) in 1935. It is an Anglican foundation with a fair amount of emphasis on worship and very close links with the cathedral church of St Nicholas. The sixth form is now merged with that of the sister school, on the same site. It aims to provide a sound general education and results are good. Many sixth form leavers go on to degree courses. French and German are offered to A-level, Spanish to GCSE. Many boys take GCSE in more than one European language. There are regular exchanges with France and Germany. Music is an important part of the school life. There are plentiful societies and a challenging range of games, sports and activities. Full involvement in local community schemes, charities (fund-raising) and in the Duke of Edinburgh's Award Scheme.

School profile

Pupils Total age range 9–18; 443 day boys. Senior department 11–18, 430 boys; joint sixth with sister school. Main entry ages 9, 10, 11 and into sixth. Approx 5% are children of former pupils. *Transfer from maintained schools:* 50% intake at 11, plus 95–100% to sixth.

Entrance Own entrance exam used. Oversubscribed. Academic ability and broad interests looked for; no exclusive religious requirements. Parents not expected to buy text books; other extras, lunch £1/day, theatre visits etc. 23 assisted places pa. 8 scholarships pa of half fees; bursaries according to need.

Parents 15+% in industry or commerce. 60+% live within 30 miles.

Staff Principal T A Willcocks, 3 years in

post. 30 full time staff, 1 part time. Annual turnover 3–7%. Average age 38.

Academic work GCSE, AS and A-levels. 15 subjects offered (including A-level general studies). In 1990, 68 pupils in fifth, 50 in upper sixth. *GCSE:* in 1989, 43 upper fifth gained at least grade C in 8+ subjects; 16 in 5–7; and 3 in 1–4 subjects. *A-levels:* 39 upper sixth passed in 4+ subjects; 6 in 3; 4 in 2; and 1 in 1 subject. 33% took science A-levels; 33% arts/humanities; 34% both. *Computing facilities:* Computing laboratory; computing for all 1st formers. GCSE IT and computer studies AS-level offered. *Special provision:* few pupils involved; concern and guidance; referral to the specialists. (1 profoundly deaf, several dyslexics).

European Community *Languages:* French offered: to age 14; GCSE; AS-level; A-level. German offered: to age 14; GCSE; AS-level; A-level. Spanish offered: to GCSE. 25–50% take GCSE in more than 1 EC language. *Exchanges:* Regular exchanges for pupils aged 14–18 to France and Germany.

Senior pupils' non-academic activities Flourishing choir and orchestra, both shared with Girls' School. Full range of sporting provision, including orienteering (winners of Small Schools category in British Schools' Championships). Community Service. Duke of Edinburgh's Award. Other activities include a computer club, chess, philately, Christian Fellowship, debating, science society (BAYS), mountain walking, ski-ing, Action Aid (sponsoring schools in the Gambia).

Careers In 1990, 89% leavers went on to degree courses; 5% to art/drama/music colleges; 2% to non-degree courses; 4% straight into careers (eg banking, army, modelling). Of those going on to degree courses, 3% went to Oxbridge, 62% to other universities; 35% to poly/colleges. 3% those going on to higher education went to courses in drama/acting; 70% in humanities/social sciences; 11% in medicine; and 16% in science/engineering.

Uniform School uniform worn throughout.

Houses/prefects Competitive houses. Prefects, head boy – appointed by the Head in consultation with staff and sixth form. School Council.

Religion Morning assembly compulsory unless parents request otherwise.

Social Joint events with neighbouring Girls' School on same foundation – choir and orchestra, drama productions. Christian Fellowship. Sponsored walks. Exchanges and organised trips to France and Germany. Pupils allowed to bring own car/bike/motorbike to school. Meals self service. No tobacco/alcohol allowed.

Discipline Corporal punishment not needed; no discipline problem. Pupils failing to produce homework once might expect to produce it in spare time; suspension/expulsion for serious offences (rarely used).

Alumni association run by W F Armstrong, Hon Sec Dame Allan's Old Boys' Assoc, c/o the School.

Former pupils Ian La Frenais (TV); Sir David Lumsden (Royal Academy of Music); Sir Michael Scott (Royal Commonwealth Society); Prof A E Bell (Kew Gardens); Dr R Laws (British Antarctic Survey); Graham Rose (journalism/gardening); Fenwick Allison and Colin White (England Rugby XV); Captain Ridley (Commodore Cunard Line).

· Dame Allan's (Girls) ·

Dame Allan's Girls'
School
Fowberry Crescent
Fenham
Newcastle upon Tyne
NE4 9YJ
Tel 091 275 0708

- Pupils 463
- Boys None but joint sixth with boys' school
- Girls 9–18 (Day)
- Upper sixth 59

- Termly fees £850 (Day)
- GSA

Enquiries/application to the Principal

What it's like

Founded in 1705 by Eleanor Allan, daughter of a Newcastle goldsmith, a successful businesswoman and widow of a tobacco merchant. Originally it was a charity school for 40 poor boys and 20 poor girls who were taught to 'read, write and cast accompts' and receive instruction according to the doctrines of the Church of England. Gradually it burgeoned to include 440 girls and was twinned with a brother school on the same site. In 1935 the schools moved to a 13-acre site in Fenham where they occupied new buildings with nearby playing fields. In 1989 the sixth form merged with the boys' school for joint teaching (but there are no plans for co-education below sixth-form level). Recent facilities include a classroom block and an auditorium for drama lessons, rehearsals and studio performances. The school has a wide catchment area covering some 18 neighbouring townships. Academic standards are high and very many girls go on to degree courses, including Oxbridge. French and German are offered to A-level; also Spanish at GCSE. Many girls take GCSE in more than one European language. There are regular exchanges with France and Germany. Drama is well supported and the school has a strong musical tradition, with a joint schools orchestra and choir, plus other orchestras and choirs. A standard range of sports and games is provided. Girls have been successful at city and county level competitions. Extra-curricular activities are well catered for with a plentiful variety of clubs and societies (some run in conjunction with the boys' school). Some participation in the Duke of Edinburgh's Award Scheme.

School profile

Pupils Total age range 9–18, 463 day girls. Senior department 11–18. Main entry ages 9, 10, 11 and into sixth. *Transfer from maintained schools:* 50% intake over 11, plus 95–100% to sixth.
Entrance Own entrance exam used. 8 scholarships and 20 assisted places. Over-subscribed.
Staff Principal T A Willcocks, 3 years in post.
Academic work GCSE, AS and A-levels. 14 subjects offered (including A-level general studies). In 1990, 65 pupils in upper fifth, 45 in upper sixth (now 59). *GCSE:* in 1990, 49 upper fifth gained at least grade C in 8+ subjects; 11 in 5–7; and 5 in 1–4 subjects. *A-levels:* 29 upper

sixth passed in 3+ subjects; 6 in 2; and 8 in 1 subject. 31% took science A-levels; 67% arts/humanities; 2% both. *Computing facilities:* Computing lab; GCSE and AS-level computing studies. *Special provision:* Observation and liaison with professionals.
European Community *Languages:* French offered: to age 14; GCSE; AS-level; A-level. German offered: to age 14; GCSE; AS-level; A-level. Spanish offered: to GCSE. 25–50% take GCSE in more than 1 EC language. *Exchanges:* Regular exchanges for pupils aged 14–18 to France and Germany.
Careers In 1990, 80% leavers went on to degree courses; 2% to art/drama/

231

music colleges; 17% other. Of those going on to degree courses, 13% went to Oxbridge, 57% to other universities; 30% to poly/colleges. 5% those going on to higher education went to courses in drama/acting; 60% in humanities/social sciences; 14% in medicine; and 21% in science/engineering.

· *Daniel Stewart's* ·

Daniel Stewart's and Melville College Queensferry Road Edinburgh EH4 3EZ Tel 031 332 7925	• Pupils 780 • Boys 12–18 (Day/Board) • Girls None • Higher year 135	• Termly fees £1012 (Day) £1956 (Board) • HMC Enquiries/application to the Principal

What it's like

Daniel Stewart's 'Hospital' was founded in 1855 and transformed into a day school in 1870. Melville College (formerly Edinburgh Institution) was founded in 1832. In 1972 the two schools amalgamated. There is a particularly close association with the Mary Erskine girls' school and a joint junior school. Joint activities are intended to ensure that the boys of Stewart's Melville and the girls of Mary Erskine receive the advantages of both single sex and combined education. The college has a fine site near the centre of Edinburgh. The main building (the original college) is a remarkable piece of architecture, a kind of Victorian extravaganza resembling a mixture of private mansion/palace and *hotel de ville*, with towers, turrets and pinnacles, plus neo-classical and pseudo-Tudor features. It stands in superb gardens and grounds and its rooms are very fine. This building is mostly occupied by the senior school, while the junior school is housed in a building nearby. Overall it is well equipped. Recent additions include a games hall, technical workshops, an art school and music school, plus computer rooms and a lecture theatre. Morning assemblies take the form of non-denominational religious services. Pupils are prepared for the Scottish Certificate of Education. Academic standards are high and results consistently creditable. Many pupils go on to degree courses, including Oxbridge. Music is very strong indeed; there are 25 visiting music teachers and the majority learn an instrument. Most of the orchestral activity is combined with the Mary Erskine School, including a junior orchestra of 100, two other orchestras of 50 each, plus two concert bands, a jazz band, and several chamber groups. There are several choirs and choral societies. Many concerts are given throughout the year. Drama is also strong and there are frequent performances in the Little Lyceum and the Churchill Theatre as well as at the school. There is much strength and depth in sports and games especially rugby, cricket, hockey, squash and rowing. Many pupils have won individual national honours. The large voluntary CCF contingent has Army, Navy and Air Force sections (which also involve girls from the Mary Erskine School) and its Pipe Band is famous. There is much emphasis on 'outdoor education' (an integral part of the curriculum), with numerous activities in the Highlands. Pupils are strongly encouraged to take part in the Duke of Edinburgh's Award Scheme and have had many successes. A wide variety of clubs and societies provides for most conceivable needs. The college enjoys vigorous local support.

School profile

Pupils Age range 12–18, 780 boys (day and boarding). Main entry age 12. Own junior school with Mary Erskine's. *Transfer from maintained schools:* 20% main intake.

Entrance Own entrance exam used. Assisted places. 7 scholarships pa.

Staff Principal P F J Tobin in post 2 years.

Academic work S-grade, Highers and CSYS. 18 subjects offered. In 1990–91, 146 pupils in main S-grade year, 135 in Highers, 105 in CSYS year. *S-grade:* in 1990, 84 pupils gained passes in 8+ subjects; 40 in 5–7; and 13 in 1–4 subjects. *Highers:* 42 of the main Higher year pupils passed in 5+ subjects; 23 in 4; 20 in 3; 21 in 2; 17 in 1. *CSYS:* In 1990 5 pupils passed in 4+ subjects; 9 in 3; 13 in 2; 16 in 1. 40% took science CSYS; 45% arts/humanities; 15% both. *Computing facilities:* 2 computer rooms, networked and many other computers.

European Community *Languages:* French offered: to age 14; S-grade; Higher; CSYS. German offered: to age 14; S-grade; Higher; CSYS. 10–25% take GCSE in more than 1 EC language. *Exchanges:* Regular exchanges for pupils aged 11–16 to France and Germany. *Other:* Visits to EC countries, including to European Parliament and ski-ing; cultural tours eg pipe band.

Careers In 1990, 62% leavers went on to degree courses; 10% to art/drama/music colleges; 2% to non-degree courses; 11% straight into careers; 15% other. Of those going on to degree courses, 2% went to Oxbridge, 70% to other universities; 28% to poly/colleges. 6% those going on to higher education went to courses in practical art; 5% in drama/acting; 54% in humanities/social sciences; 5% in medicine; and 30% in science/engineering.

· *Dauntsey's* ·

Dauntsey's School
West Lavington
Devizes
Wiltshire
SN10 4HE
Tel 0380 812446

- Pupils 600
- Boys 11–18
 (Day/Board)
- Girls 11–18
 (Day/Board)
- Upper sixth 100

- Termly fees
 £1610 (Day)
 £2600 (Board)
- HMC
 Enquiries/application to
 the Head Master or
 Academic Registrar

What it's like

Founded in 1542, it lies on 100 acres of fine estate in West Lavington, a pleasant village in the Vale of Pewsey, five miles south of Devizes. The junior school is in an attractive manor house nearby, with its own estate. It is a Christian foundation, ecumenical in spirit and practice, and aims to provide a sound education avoiding undue specialisation. Standards of teaching are high and academic results are impressive. Very many sixth form leavers go on to degree courses, including Oxbridge. Very strong tradition in music; pretty strong in drama and art. It enjoys a good reputation for sport and games and there are many activities (including outdoor pursuits and ocean sailing).

School profile

Pupils Age range 11–18; 600 pupils, 330 day, (185 boys, 145 girls), 270 boarding (150 boys, 120 girls). Main entry ages 11, 13 and into the sixth. 3–5% are children of former pupils. *Transfer from maintained schools:* 50% intake at 11 and 13, plus 30% to sixth.

Entrance Common entrance and own entrance exam used. Oversubscribed. No special skills or religious requirements. Parents not expected to buy text books; maximum extras £30 plus music lessons. 55 assisted places. Flexible number of scholarships/bursaries, £1300–£150 per term.

Parents 15+% in industry or commerce; 15+% in the armed services; 15+% are doctors, lawyers, etc. 50+% live within 30 miles; up to 10% live overseas.

Staff Head Master C R Evans, in post for 6 years. 62 full time staff, 18 part time. Annual turnover 5%. Average age 38.

Academic work GCSE, AS- and A-levels. 22 subjects offered. In 1990, 85 pupils in fifth, 100 in upper sixth. *GCSE:* in 1990, 12% fifth gained at least grade C in 8+ subjects; 83% in 5–7; and 5% in 1–4 subjects. *A-levels:* 68% upper sixth passed in 4+ subjects; 20% in 3; 10% in 2; and 2% in 1 subject. 45% took science A-levels; 30% arts/humanities; 25% both. *Computing facilities:* 25 Archimedes machines. *Special provision:* Some help with those pupils found to have special learning difficulties (dyslexia), mild cases only. Some classes for foreign pupils. JMB university entrance exam in English.

European Community *Languages:* French offered: to age 14; GCSE; AS-level; A-level. German offered: to age 14; GCSE; AS-level; A-level. 10–25% take GCSE in more than 1 EC language. *Exchanges:* Regular exchanges for pupils aged 11–14 to France. Exchange/work experience organised by Wiltshire County Council with Niort in France.

Senior pupils' non-academic activities *Music:* 270 learn a musical instrument, 80 to Grade 6 or above. 4 accepted for Music scholarships. A few play in pop groups and many play in college/amateur orchestras or sing in choirs after leaving; 120 in school orchestras, 150 in school choirs, 6 in school pop group, 20 in brass groups, 40 in wind group; 5 in Wiltshire Youth Concert Orchestra. *Drama and dance:* 100 in school productions. 1 accepted for Drama/Dance School. *Art:* 40 take GCSE; 26 A-level. 6 accepted for Art School. 30 study art-design and photography in sessions after school. *Sport:* Rugby, cricket, hockey, tennis, athletics, swimming, netball, badminton, cross-country, golf, gymnastics, sailing, canoeing available. 100 take non–compulsory sport. 10 take exams, eg gymnastics, swimming. 30 represent county/country (rugby, hockey, netball, athletics, tennis, swimming). *Other:* 10 take part in local community schemes. 8 have bronze Duke of Edinburgh's Award, 8 have silver and 2 gold. 4 enter voluntary schemes after leaving school. Other activities include a computer club, Moonrakers (outward bound organisation), sailing club with 56ft gaff cutter for ocean cruising, adventure club (mountaineering, canoeing, expeditions, etc).

Careers In 1990, 92% sixth form leavers went on to degree courses; 2% to art/drama/music colleges; 2% to non-degree courses (eg secretarial); 2% straight into careers (eg banking); 2% other. Of those going on to degree courses, 7% went to Oxbridge, 77% to other universities; 23% to poly/colleges. 3% those going on to higher education went to courses in practical art; 3% in drama/acting; 51% in humanities/social sciences; 1% in medicine; and 42% in science/engineering.

Uniform School uniform worn except in the sixth.

Houses/prefects Competitive houses. Prefects, head boy and girl, head of house and house prefects – appointed by the Head Master and house staff.

Religion Christian non-denominational assembly compulsory.

Social Regular visits abroad, ski trips, climbing/adventure club expeditions, ocean sailing, French and German exchange. Day pupils allowed to bring own car/bike/motorbike to school. Meals self service. School shop. No tobacco

allowed; alcohol only in sixth form club.
Discipline No corporal punishment. Pupils failing to produce homework once might expect to have to do it; those caught smoking cannabis on the premises could expect expulsion.

Boarding 30% have own study bed-room, 70% share with one other. 4 junior, 6 senior houses, of approx 64, single sex. Resident qualified sister. Central dining room. Pupils can provide and cook own food. Exeats on request. Visits to local town allowed.

Alumni association run by H J Hodges, c/o the School.

Former pupils Desmond Morris; Rev W Awdry (Thomas the Tank Engine); Simon May; Jeremy James Taylor; Andrew Gardner.

· *Denstone* ·

Denstone College
Uttoxeter
Staffordshire
ST14 5HN
Tel 0889 590484

- Pupils 337
- Boys 11–18 (Day/Board/Weekly)
- Girls 11–18 (Day/Board/Weekly)
- Upper sixth 66

- Termly fees
  £1916 (Day)
  £2690 (Board)
- HMC, Woodard
Enquiries to the Headmaster's Secretary
Application to the Headmaster

What it's like

Founded in 1868, a Woodard school, it stands five miles north of Uttoxeter, in open hilly countryside on 70 acres of very pleasant grounds. The main building is Victorian. Numerous modern extensions provide excellent up-to-date facilities of all kinds, including new IT and CDT centres, as well as an all-weather hockey and tennis surface. The standard of teaching is high and the results are good. For a comparatively small school it sends a large number of pupils to degree courses, including to Oxbridge. It is particularly strong in music and drama and has a very impressive range of clubs and societies. Vigorous participation in the Duke of Edinburgh's Award Scheme (20 Gold Awards last year). The declared aim is to encourage pupils to develop their individual talents – to the extent of awarding scholarships to any outstanding talent which contributes to the life of the school. Its pupils speak enthusiastically of it and parents comment on the relaxed courteous relationships between pupils and staff. A friendly hard-working school where high standards of manners are maintained without any rigid formality or oppression.

School profile

Pupils Age range 11–18; 337 pupils, 97 day (54 boys, 43 girls), 240 boarding (164 boys, 76 girls). Main entry ages 11, 13 and into sixth. *Transfer from maintained schools:* 20% main intake, plus 60% to sixth.

Entrance Common entrance and own entrance exam used. Special skills required for scholarships only. No religious requirements but pupils expected to attend C of E services. Parents expected to buy sixth form text books but buy-back scheme operates. Assisted places. Scholarships (academic, instrumental, choral, sporting, art and any other useful talent, eg drama) – up to 90% fee, and bursaries (for children of clergy, service-men) – up to two-thirds fees.

Parents 15+% in industry or com-

235

merce; 15+% in farming. 30+% live within 30 miles; up to 10% live overseas.
Staff Headmaster H C K Carson, in post for 1 year. 35 full time staff, 4 part time. Annual turnover 8%. Average age 39.
Academic work GCSE and A-levels. 18 subjects offered (including A-level general studies introduced this year). In 1990, 68 pupils in upper fifth, 66 in upper sixth. *GCSE:* in 1990, 26 upper fifth gained at least grade C in 8+ subjects; 12 in 5–7; and 16 in 1–4 subjects. *A-levels:* 2 upper sixth passed in 4+ subjects; 42 in 3; 21 in 2; and 5 in 1 subject. 25% took science and tech. A-levels; 50% arts/humanities; 25% both. *Computing facilities:* New IT Centre. *Special provision:* Specialist teaching for dyslexics.
European Community *Languages:* French offered: to age 14; GCSE; AS-level; A-level; AO French for business studies. German offered: to age 14; GCSE; A-level. Spanish: GCSE; A-level (for native speakers). Under 10% take GCSE in more than 1 EC language. *Exchanges:* Regular exchanges for pupils aged 14–18 to Germany. *Other:* German pupils regularly attend sixth form. EFL courses in summer for German pupils.
Senior pupils' non-academic activities *Music:* 100 learn a musical instrument, 32 to Grade 6 or above. 2 accepted for Music School. 70 in school orchestra, 80 in school choir; 1 in National Youth Orchestra; 35 in Schola Cantorum (chapel choir: visits cathedrals, makes TV, radio and private recordings; foreign tours). *Drama and dance:* 3 in school productions, drama training in first two years. 2 accepted for Drama/Dance Schools, including 1 to RADA. *Art:* 20 take as non-examined subject; 26 take GCSE art; 21 A-level art/ceramics. 15 belong to photographic club, etc. *Sport:* Rugby, cricket, hockey, athletics, fives, squash, cross-country, soccer, orienteering, shooting, fencing, riding, netball, rounders, swimming, table tennis, trampolining, badminton available. 13 represent county/country (rugby, hockey, athletics, squash, cricket and shooting). *Other:* 30 have bronze Duke of Edinburgh's Award, 30 silver and 20 gold. 2 members of British Schools' Exploring Society Expeditions. 2 ESU

scholarships to US high schools. Other activities include a computer club, cycling club, chess, bridge, scenery construction and whatever is a current staff enthusiasm. The CCF is popular (voluntary – alternatives are D of E or outward bound training).
Careers In 1990, 80% leavers went on to degree courses; 19% to art/drama/music colleges; 1% to non-degree courses (eg secretarial, agriculture). Of those going on to degree courses, 13% went to Oxbridge, 51% to other universities; 36% to poly/colleges. 15% those going on to higher education went to courses in practical art; 3% in drama/acting; 7% in music; 41% in humanities/social sciences; 2% in medicine; and 32% in science/engineering.
Uniform School uniform worn throughout. (Sensible home clothes after school day.)
Houses/prefects Competitive houses. Prefects, head boy/girl, head of house and house prefects – appointed by Head in consultation with staff.
Religion Attendance at Chapel compulsory (simple service Tue-Fri; full scale communion service weekly; Sunday worship for full boarders).
Social Foreign tours by Schola Cantorum; expeditions abroad for climbing/hill–walking; annual ski-ing holiday; school exchanges; CCF camp abroad. Rugby tours. Pupils allowed to bring own bike to school. Meals self service. School tuck, general equipment and uniform shops. No tobacco allowed; alcohol allowed only in sixth form bar.
Discipline No corporal punishment. Withdrawal of privileges and community help used.
Boarding 10% have own study bedroom, 55% share; 35% in dormitories of 6+. Single sex houses, of approx 60, same as competitive houses (boys), divided by age (girls). Resident qualified nurse. Central dining room. Pupils can provide and cook own food. Half-term and 2 28-hour exeats termly. Visits to local town allowed. Weekly boarding available. Girls – members of main school houses for social/tutorial/competitive purposes.
Former pupils T A Kemp (physician/

rugby international/President RFU); Geoffrey Smith (political columnist); Alistair Hignell (sportsman); John Makepeace (furniture designer); Ian Platt (operatic singer); Sir Christopher French (High Court Judge); Rear Admiral P G Hammersley; P D Kelly (Walker Cup captain); Professor A K Mant (pathologist); Professor M L H Green (chemist); W P C Davies (Rugby international); T Marlow, M Liggins (broadcasters).

· Dollar Academy ·

Dollar Academy
Dollar
Clackmannanshire
FK14 7DU
Tel 02594 2511

- Pupils 1000
- Boys 5–18 (Day/ Board/Weekly)
- Girls 5–18 (Day/ Board/Weekly)
- Higher year 130

- Termly fees
  £945 (Day)
  £2095 (Board)
  £1998 (Weekly)
  Enquiries/application to the Rector

What it's like

Founded in 1818, as a result of the munificence of one John McNabb, who left half a fortune made in merchant shipping 'for the benefit of the parish of Dollar'. It is a purpose-built school designed by William Playfair. Its austere but handsome neo-classical buildings are set in 40 acres of superb grounds in the magnificent rural environment of the Ochil Hills about thirty miles from Edinburgh. At the same time it is an integral part of the neighbouring township of Dollar. Junior and senior school are combined; the preparatory school has its own premises nearby in the grounds. The Academy has been co-educational since its foundation. Originally a Church of Scotland foundation, it is now interdenominational and ecumenical. The values of Christian ethics form the basis of the spiritual life of the school. A religious assembly is held each week-day. Academic standards are high and results extremely good. Music, drama and art are very strong. Music is part of the core curriculum throughout the school. Drama is an integral part of work in and outside the classroom. Art is very popular. There are excellent facilities for sports and games on site and high standards are attained in these; in fact, few British schools could surpass them. Over twenty clubs and societies provide for most needs. The CCF contingent (Army and Air Force) is voluntary but strongly supported by girls and boys. There is also a very active scout group. Much emphasis on open-air pursuits of all kinds for which the environment is ideal.

School profile

Pupils Total age range 5–18, 1000 pupils. Senior department 12–18, 730 pupils. Main entry ages 5, 12. *Transfer from maintained schools:* 20% main intake at 12, plus 20% to sixth.
Entrance Own entrance exam used.
Staff Rector L Harrison, in post for 7 years.
Academic work O-grades, S-grades, Highers, A-levels, CSYS. 25 Highers offered (including anatomy, physiology and health). In 1989, 138 pupils in O/S-grade year, 131 in Higher, 99 in CSYS. *O/S-grade:* in 1989, 83 pupils passed in 8+ subjects; 45 in 5–7; and 10 in 1–4 subjects. *Highers:* 58 pupils passed in 5+ subjects; 24 in 4; 18 in 3; 15 in 2; 16 in 1. *CSYS:* 4 pupils in Form 6 passed in 4+ subjects; 4 in 3; 11 in 2; 25 in 1. 16% took science CSYS; 29% arts/humanities; 5% both. *Computing facilities:* 17 BBC B, 12 BBC masters. *Special provision:* Internal and external tuition for non-native English speakers.

· Douai ·

Douai School
Upper Woolhampton
Reading
Berkshire
RG7 5TH
Tel 0734 713114

- Pupils 280
- Boys 10–18 (Day/
  Board/Weekly)
- Girls None
- Upper sixth 42

- Termly fees
  £1640 (Day)
  £2600 (Board)
  £2325 (Weekly)
- HMC
  Enquiries/application to
  the Headmaster

What it's like

Founded in 1615 in Paris, the school and the Benedictine community moved to the present site in 1903. Its handsome buildings lie in a setting of considerable beauty and comprise 200 acres, bordered by fields and woodlands on the southern edge of the Berkshire Downs, overlooking the Kennet valley. The school adjoins the Benedictine monastery and its abbey church. It is run by monks (the Head is a monk) as well as lay staff and the pupils are brought up in the Benedictine tradition of learning and service to God and the community in which they live. It is a popular school because it is comparatively small and well located and there is a strong atmosphere of community. It is very well equipped with every modern facility (including comfortable boarding accommodation) and has particularly fine playing fields. The teaching is of a high standard and results are very creditable. About half the leavers go on to degree courses, a very high proportion to Oxbridge. There is much emphasis on physical fitness and games and sports are important. Music, drama and art are flourishing. Very good facilities for such activities as light engineering, electronics and woodwork. There is a strong tradition of participation in community service and an impressive record in the Duke of Edinburgh's Award Scheme.

School profile

Pupils Age range 10–18; 280 boys, 40 day, 240 boarding. Main entry ages 10, 11, 13 and into sixth. Approx 6% are children of former pupils. *Transfer from maintained schools:* 5% main intake, plus 5% to sixth.

Entrance Common entrance and own entrance exam used. No special skills required; most pupils are Roman Catholics, other Christians welcome. Parents not expected to buy text books; maximum extras £200. 5 pa assisted places. 10 scholarships/bursaries, £2600–£900.

Parents 15+% in the armed services; 10+% are doctors, lawyers, etc. 25% live within 30 miles; 25% live overseas.

Staff Headmaster Rev Geoffrey Scott, in post since 1987. 35 full time staff, 13 part time. Annual turnover 5%. Average age 43.

Academic work GCSE and A-levels. 15 subjects offered (including photography GCSE and A-level; theology; and A-level general studies). In 1990, 42 pupils in upper fifth, 42 in upper sixth. *GCSE:* in 1990, 24 upper fifth gained at least grade C in 8+ subjects; 12 in 5–7; and 11 in 1–4 subjects. *A-levels:* 14 upper sixth passed in 4+ subjects; 16 in 3; 3 in 2; and 4 in 1 subject. 24% took science A-levels; 48% arts/humanities; 28% both. *Computing facilities:* Word processing room, 25 Amstrads; main computer room with 9–station Nimbus Network, 1 in CDT department; 4 BBC machines in science departments. *Special provision:* Dyslexic and EFL teachers attend each week.

European Community *Languages:* French offered: to age 14; GCSE; A-level. Spanish offered: to GCSE; A-level. Under 10% take GCSE in more than 1 EC language. *Exchanges:* Regular exchanges for pupils aged 11–16 to France. *Other:* Increasing number of EC students join the school for a year or more, especially German, Italian, Spanish.

Senior pupils' non-academic activities *Music:* 80 learn a musical instrument, 6 to Grade 6 or above. 15 in school orchestra, 48 in school choir, 12 in school pop group. *Drama and dance:* 30 in school productions, 10 in informal productions. *Art:* 3 take as non-examined subject; 27 take GCSE art, 19 A-level; 8 A-level photography. 5 accepted for Art School; 1 for architecture; 50 belong to photographic club. *Sport:* Rugby, soccer, cricket, fencing, swimming, badminton, squash, hockey, sailing, canoeing, tennis, judo, athletics, cross-country, kung-fu, karate, multi-gym, squash available. Many represent county/country (especially soccer, rugby, athletics). *Other:* 8 take part in local community schemes. 20 have bronze Duke of Edinburgh's Award, 9 silver and 5 gold. 12 help with handicapped children's pilgrimage to Lourdes. Other activities include a computer club, driving lessons, chess club, debating, amateur politics, bookbinding, bridge.

Careers In 1990, 54% leavers went on to degree courses; 9% to art/drama/music colleges; 4% to non-degree courses; 16% straight into careers; 6% other. Of those going on to degree courses, 23% went to Oxbridge, 55% to other universities; 23% to poly/colleges. 5% those going on to higher education went to courses in practical art; 2% in drama/acting; 14% in humanities/social sciences; 2% in medicine; and 19% in science/engineering.

Uniform School uniform worn, relaxed for sixth form.

Houses/prefects Competitive houses. Prefects, head boy, head of house and house prefects – appointed after consultation with staff and boys.

Religion Compulsory Sunday mass; other religious events available during week.

Social Debates with other schools, dances and other social functions. Regular ski trips, art trips, sporting tours. Exchanges with Germany and France. Meals self service. School shop. No tobacco/alcohol allowed.

Discipline No corporal punishment.

Boarding *Upper sixth* have own study bedroom, fifth and lower sixth in cubicles; others are in dormitories of 6+. Houses are administrative (65 in each), not residential. 4 SRNs in rotation; doctor visits daily. Central dining room. 2 weekend exeats each term and half-term. Visits to local town allowed for fifth form and above.

Alumni association run by Godfrey Linnett, 26 Den Road, Shortlands, Bromley, Kent.

· *Dover College* ·

Dover College
Dover
Kent
CT17 9RH
Tel 0304 215079

- Pupils 313
- Boys 11–18 (Day/ Board/Weekly)
- Girls 11–18 (Day/ Board/Weekly)
- Upper sixth 60

- Termly fees
  £1890 (Day)
  £2860 (Board)
  £2750 (Weekly)
- HMC
Enquiries to the
Headmaster's
Secretary
Application to the
Headmaster

What it's like

Founded in 1871 and granted a royal charter by George V in 1923, it has a fine site in Dover on the grounds formerly occupied by the medieval Priory of St Martin, some of whose monastic buildings survive and are occupied by the school. The refectory (c 1130) is the school dining hall, the Guest house is the chapel and the Gatehouse contains the headmaster's study and offices. The college Close is surrounded by the ancient buildings. There have been numerous improvements and extensions in recent years and the school is now very well equipped. Accommodation for boarders is comfortable. The preparatory school is a separate establishment at Westbrook House, Folkestone. The college tries to order its life according to Christian principles and also to provide ample opportunity for Christian worship and study of the Christian faith. Quite a large staff permits a staff:pupil ratio of about 1:10. A sound general education is provided and results are consistently creditable. French, German, Italian and Spanish are offered to A-level and languages are particularly strong; many pupils are bi- or tri-lingual. Many leavers go on to degree courses. Music plays an important part in the school's life. There is an orchestra, a choir and various ensembles and bands. Drama is also strong and there are several productions each year, plus a house drama festival. Art and information technology are well provided for. A wide range of sports and games is available.

School profile

Pupils Age range 11–18; 313 pupils, 49 day (40 boys, 9 girls), 264 boarders (166 boys, 98 girls); all boarders over 13. Main entry ages 11, 13 and into sixth. 5% are children of former pupils. Own junior provides 20% pupils. *Transfer from maintained schools:* 5% main intake, plus 5% to sixth.

Entrance Common entrance and some own tests used. General range of skills looked for; no religious requirements. 5 assisted places pa. 12 scholarships/ bursaries pa, full fees – £200.

Parents 15+% in industry. Up to 10% live within 30 miles; 60+% live overseas.

Staff Headmaster M P G Wright, first year in post. 33 full time staff, 10 part time. Annual turnover 5%. Average age 38.

Academic work GCSE and A-levels. 17 GCSE subjects offered; 16 at A-level (no A-level general studies). In 1990, 55 pupils in fifth, 51 in upper sixth (now 60). *GCSE:* in 1990, 18% fifth gained at least grade C in 8+ subjects; 44% in 5–7; and 33% in 1–4 subjects. *A-levels:* 8 upper sixth passed in 4+ subjects; 21 in 3; 10 in 2; and 6 in 1 subject. 20% took science A-levels; 48% arts/humanities; 32% both. *Computing facilities:* BBC computers in many departments. Computer lab equipped with RM Nimbus/network. *Special provision:* Good EFL provision. Special needs provision limited.

European Community *Languages:* French offered: to age 14; GCSE; AS-level; A-level. German offered: to age 14; GCSE; AS-level; A-level. Italian offered: to age 11; GCSE; A-level. Spanish offered: to age 14; GCSE; AS-level; A-level. 10–25% take GCSE in more than 1 EC language. *Exchanges:* Regular exchanges for pupils aged 14–16 to France, Germany and Spain. Number of individual visits and exchanges, as distinct from group visits. *Other:* Number of European pupils for 1 term–1 year, particularly from Germany.

Senior pupils' non-academic activities *Music:* 100 learn a musical instrument, 5 to Grade 6 or above; 30 pupils play in school orchestra, 1 in National Youth Orchestra; 30 in choir, 10 in school pop group. *Drama and dance:* 100 in school productions. *Art:* 20 take art as non-examined subject; 20 GCSE; 12 A-level; 3 accepted for Art School. 15 belong to eg photographic club. *Sport:* Rugby, hockey, cricket, tennis, athletics, netball, swimming, basketball, volleyball, badminton, cross-country running, sailing etc available. Approx 100 take part in non–compulsory sport. 5 pupils represent county (hockey, rugby, athletics). *Other:* 15 have bronze Duke of Edinburgh's Award, 10 silver, 2 gold. 60 in local community schemes. Other activities include a computer club, debating, film society, discussion groups, academic clubs, sixth form lectures, chess club, learning to drive.

Careers In 1990, 70% leavers went on to degree courses; 8% to art/drama/music colleges; 3% to non-degree courses (eg BTEC social studies, business studies); 6% straight into careers (eg RAF, sports centre); 13% other (eg repeating A-levels). Of those going on to degree courses, 3% went to Oxbridge, 66% to other universities; 31% to poly/colleges. 3% those going on to higher education went to courses in practical art; 73% in humanities/social sciences; 3% in medicine; and 21% in science/engineering.

Uniform School uniform worn, modified in sixth form.

Houses/prefects Competitive houses. Prefects, head boy/girl, head of house and house prefects – appointed by the Head or house staff.

Religion Compulsory worship, with specific exceptions.

Social Occasional joint functions with other local schools. Some organised trips abroad. Pupils allowed to bring own bike to school, cars only with specific permission. Meals self service. No tobacco; sixth form Common Room is licensed.

Discipline No corporal punishment. Pupils failing to produce homework once might expect some rudeness and a new deadline; those caught smoking cannabis on the premises would be dismissed instantly.

Boarding 70% have own study bedroom, 30% share (with 2 or 3). Single sex houses, of 30–70, same as for competitive purposes. Resident qualified nurse. Central dining room. Pupils can provide and cook snacks to a limited extent. Unlimited termly exeats subject to Sunday Chapel attendance. Visits to local town allowed daily for an hour or so.

Alumni association is run by Mrs J Glyn Thomas, Endfield, 6 Lookers Lane, Saltwood, Hythe, Kent.

Former pupils Sir Frederic Ashton.

· Downe House ·

Downe House
Cold Ash
Newbury
Berkshire RG16 9JJ
Tel 0635 200286

- Pupils 470
- Boys None
- Girls 11–18
- (Day/Board)
- Upper sixth 65

- Termly fees
  £2115 (Day)
  £2920 (Board)
- GSA, BSA

What it's like

Founded by Miss Olive Willis in 1907 in Darwin's home, Downe House, in Kent. It moved to its present site in 1921. This is a very beautiful site indeed of 110 acres in the village of Cold Ash, on a wooded ridge 5 miles north of Newbury. Extensive modernisation and building has taken place over the years (a new science building is the latest addition) and facilities are now first-rate. There are about 470 pupils, of whom 34 are day girls. The senior school takes girls from 12–18; the 11-year-olds live in two separate boarding houses. There are 4 houses of a mixed age range. When girls reach their second year in the sixth form they move to the York Houses where they live in single study bedrooms. The accommodation is very civilised. Life in the sixth form is planned to provide a transition between school and higher education. Girls are given a greater degree of independence. The school has its own chapel which is central to school life. A full range of academic subjects is taught, the teaching is very good and so are the results. A high proportion of the sixth form go on to degree courses, including Oxbridge. French, German and Spanish are offered up to A-level and a high proportion of girls takes GCSE in more than one European language. Italian is offered as a non-examined language. The school is very strong indeed in music; the art and drama departments are very active. There are excellent sports facilities and a wide range of extra-curricular activities.

School profile

Pupils Age range 11–18, 470 girls. Main entry age 11. *Transfer from maintained schools:* 4% main intake.

Entrance Common entrance exam used. Scholarships available (academic and music).

Staff Headmistress Miss S Cameron, 2 years in post.

Academic work GCSE and A-levels. 20 subjects offered (including A-level general studies). In 1990, 74 pupils in upper fifth, 65 in upper sixth. *GCSE:* in 1990, 65 upper fifth gained a grade C or above in 8+ subjects; 9 in 5–7 subjects. *A-levels:* 44 upper sixth passed in 4+ subjects; 11 in 3; 10 in 2; and 1 in 1 subject. 26% took science A-levels; 32% arts/ humanities; 42% both.

European Community *Languages:* French offered: to age 14; GCSE; AS-level; A-level. German offered: to age 14; GCSE; AS-level; A-level. Italian offered: to age 14; non-examined. Spanish offered: to age 14; GCSE; A-level. 25–50% take GCSE in more than 1 EC language. *Exchanges:* Regular exchanges for pupils aged 14–16 to France.

Careers In 1990, 21% leavers went on to degree courses; 3% to art/drama/ music colleges; 6% to non-degree courses (eg agriculture, secretarial); 70% other (Gap year). Of those going on to degree courses, 14% went to Oxbridge, 48% to other universities; 18% to poly/colleges. 5% those going on to higher education went to courses in practical art; 5% in music; 33% in humanities/social sciences; 9% in medicine; and 28% in science/engineering.

· Downside ·

Downside School
Stratton-on-the-Fosse
Bath
Avon
BA3 4RJ
Tel 0761 232206

- Pupils 485
- Boys 11–18
  (Day/Board)
- Girls 16–18
  (Day)
- Upper sixth 100

- Termly fees
  £1766 (Day)
  £2760 (Board)
- HMC
  Enquiries/application to
  the Head Master

What it's like

Founded in 1606 at Douai for English Catholics in exile because of the penal laws. At the time of the French Revolution the monks of the community were obliged to flee to England and were accommodated at Acton Burnell near Shrewsbury. In 1814 the school was removed to Downside where the English Benedictine community of St Gregory became established. It lies at the foot of the Mendip Hills in splendid Somerset countryside, 12 miles from Bath. Handsome buildings and excellent modern facilities (including a new sports hall) make a compact campus. The monastery and its Abbey Church are a part of it. Superb playing fields, gardens and grounds surround it. The aim of the school is to help each boy to become fully Catholic and adult. The monastic influence is strong. The headmaster and the housemasters are monks. There are 15–20 monks on the teaching staff. The staff:pupil ratio is 1:7. A good general education is provided and results are very creditable. Many pupils go on to degree courses, including Oxbridge. French, German, Italian, Portuguese and Spanish are offered up to A-level. An exceptionally large proportion of pupils takes GCSE in more than one European language. There are regular exchanges with France, Germany and Spain. The music and art departments are active and much use is made of the purpose-built theatre for a wide range of dramatic productions. The school is strong in sports and games (about 20 are available). A very large number of societies and clubs (about 40) cater for extra-curricular activities.

School profile

Pupils Total age range 11–18; 485 pupils, 9 day (7 boys, 2 girls), 476 boarding (all boys). Senior department 13–18, 432 pupils (431 boys, 1 girl). Main entry ages 11, 13 (boys) and into sixth (boys and girls). Approx 24% are children of former pupils.

Entrance Common entrance and own entrance exam used. Not oversubscribed. No special skills required. Roman Catholicism required. Parents not expected to buy text books but hiring fee. 10 scholarships pa for art, music, maths, and for sixth form entrants, up to half fees. Bursaries available at discretion of headmaster.

Parents Up to 10% live within 30 miles; 10+% live overseas.

Staff Head Master Dom Aidan Bellenger, first year in post. 76 full time staff, 16 part time. Annual turnover 4%.

Academic work GCSE and A-levels. Portuguese, Russian, Italian and Theology are offered to GCSE/A-level. Average size of upper fifth 90; upper sixth 100. GCSE and A-level results are available on request. On average, 20 take science/engineering A-levels; 45 take arts and humanities; 25 take a mixture. *Special provision:* for EFL, dyslexia, mild visual, aural or physical handicap and special dietary needs.

European Community *Languages:* French offered: to GCSE; AS-level; A-level. German offered: to GCSE; A-level. Italian offered: to GCSE; A-level.

Portuguese offered: to GCSE; A-level. Spanish offered: to age 14; GCSE; AS-level; A-level. Over 75% take GCSE in more than 1 EC language. *Exchanges:* Regular exchanges for pupils aged 14–18 to France, Germany and Spain. *Other:* European library. Special committee fosters European links. Several members of staff (beside linguists) have family links and/or studies at universities in EC.

Senior pupils' non-academic activities *Sport:* Rugby, soccer, hockey, cricket, tennis, athletics, squash, fencing, golf, judo, basketball, swimming, archery and cross-country available. Other activities include a computer club, driving, horse riding, chess, cookery and local history.

Careers In 1990, 50% leavers went on to degree courses; 6% to art/drama/music colleges; 3% to non-degree courses (eg land management, agriculture); 30% straight into careers (eg army, engineering, family business); 11% other. Of those going on to degree courses, 10% went to Oxbridge, 80% to other universities; 10% to poly/colleges. 3% those going on to higher education went to courses in practical art; 1% in drama/acting; 75% in humanities/social sciences; 3% in medicine; and 18% in science/engineering.

Uniform School uniform worn throughout.

Houses/prefects Houses. Prefects, head boy, head of house and house prefects – appointed by the Head.

Religion Mass on Sunday; house service once a week; morning and evening prayers, all compulsory.

Social Choral society production with St Antony's-Leweston. Occasional theatrical productions and debates with local comprehensive schools. Organised trips abroad for ski-ing, various sports tours, exchange with Austrian, Spanish and French schools. Pupils allowed to bring own bike to school. Meals self service. School shop. No pupils allowed tobacco.

Discipline No corporal punishment. Pupils failing to produce homework once might expect to be kept from the Sunday film; those caught smoking cannabis on the premises will be expelled; rustication for bringing alcohol into the school; 3 weeks gating for being found in a pub.

Boarding All sixth formers have own study bedroom. Others in dormitories. Houses of approximately 60. Resident qualified nursing staff on site 24 hrs a day, local doctor visits frequently. Central dining room. 1 weekend exeat each term. Weekend visits to the local town allowed for sixth form unsupervised.

Alumni association (St Gregory's Society) is run by Dom Martin Salmon, c/o the School.

Former pupils Richard Stokes (Privy Seal); Lord Rawlinson (former Attorney General); Simon Halliday (rugby international); Maurice Couve-de-Murville (Archbishop of Birmingham).

· *Duchy Grammar* ·

The Duchy Grammar School	● Pupils 190	● Termly fees
Tregye	● Boys 7–18 (Day/ Board/Weekly)	£980 (Day) £1985 (Board)
Truro	● Girls 7–18 (Day/ Board/Weekly)	£1825 (Weekly)
Cornwall		● ISAI
TR3 6JH	● Upper sixth 10	Enquiries/application to
Tel 0872 862289		the Headmaster

What it's like

Founded in 1982, it lies on a single site of eight acres in pleasant countryside 4 miles from Truro. The central building is Tregye, a small 19th-century country house. A sound general education is provided and its ethos is intended to reflect the values of the former Cathedral School from which it derives. French and German are offered throughout the school to A-level; both, plus Spanish, are offered for the Institute of Linguists. There are regular exchanges with France and Germany. There are good modern facilities and comfortable boarding accommodation. A more than adequate range of sport, games and extra–curricular activities is provided.

School profile

Pupils Total age range 7–18; 190 pupils, 146 day (83 boys, 63 girls), 44 boarding (31 boys, 13 girls). Senior department 11–18, 120 pupils (80 boys, 40 girls). Main entry ages 11 and into sixth. *Transfer from maintained schools:* 75% intake at 11, plus 20% to sixth.

Entrance No special skills or religious requirements. Parents not expected to buy text books; extras approx £20 per term (music, extra-curricular activities etc). 6 scholarships/bursaries, 33–75% tuition fees.

Parents 60+% live within 30 miles; up to 10% live overseas.

Staff Headmaster Michael Fuller, in post for 4 years. 18 full time staff, 4 part time. Annual turnover 5%. Average age 32.

Academic work GCSE and A-levels. 20 subjects offered (including GCSE nautical studies; no A-level general studies). In 1990, 26 pupils in upper fifth, 10 in upper sixth. *GCSE:* in 1990, 4 upper fifth gained at least grade C in 8+ subjects; 5 in 5–7; and 17 in 1–4 subjects. *A-levels:* 50% upper sixth passed in 4+ subjects; 50% in 3 subjects. 70% took science A-levels; 30% took both science and arts/humanities. *Computing facilities:* 6 micros in a computing base, two in graphics dept. *Special provision:* Individual tuition with dyslexic specialist. EFL course.

European Community *Languages:* French offered: to age 14; GCSE; AS-level; A-level; Institute of Linguists. German offered: to age 14; GCSE; AS-level; A-level; Institute of Linguists. Spanish: Institute of Linguists. 10–25% take GCSE in more than 1 EC language. *Exchanges:* Regular exchanges for pupils aged 11–16 to France and Germany. *Other:* Pupils from Denmark and Germany. Vacation language courses for pupils from France and Germany.

Senior pupils' non-academic activities *Music:* 20 learn a musical instrument, 6 to Grade 6 or above. 8 in school orchestra, 34 in school choir. *Drama and dance:* 25 in school productions. *Art:* 12 take GCSE art. *Sport:* Soccer, rugby, netball, basketball, volleyball, hockey, squash, tennis, athletics, swimming, cricket, sailing, canoeing, snorkelling available. All pupils take part in an outdoor education programme from 11 to 16. *Other:* 4 take part in local community schemes. 10 have bronze Duke of Edinburgh's Award and 2 have silver. Other activities include a computer club, chess club, electronics club, horse riding, recorder consort, hiking (10 Tors expedition), drama (annual Shakespeare production).

Careers In 1990, 12% leavers went on to degree courses; 3% to art/drama/music colleges; 70% to non-degree courses (eg agriculture, RE college); 15% straight into careers (eg armed forces, marine construction). Of those going on to degree courses, 75% went to universities; 25% to poly/colleges. 25% those going on to higher education went to courses in humanities/social sciences; and 75% in science/engineering.

Uniform School uniform worn throughout.

Houses/prefects Competitive houses. Prefects, head boy/girl, head of house and house prefects – appointed by the Head. School Council.

Religion Daily assembly.

Social Debates with other local sixth forms. Joint visit to France each autumn with local state school. 5-day French visit. 7-day ski-ing trip. Exchange visits with pupils in Germany. Pupils allowed to bring own car/bike/motorbike to school. Meals formal. School shop. No tobacco/alcohol allowed.

Discipline Pupils failing to produce

homework once might expect immediate after-school detention; those caught smoking cigarettes on the premises could expect talk in presence of parents and suspension; expulsion for subsequent offences.
Boarding 20% have own study bed-room, 60% share (3); 20% are in dormitories of 6+. Central dining room. Pupils allowed to provide and cook food and drink. 2 weekend exeats each term. Visits to local town allowed at weekends.
Alumni association Just being launched.

· *Duke of York's* ·

Duke of York's Royal
Military School
Dover
Kent CT15 5EQ
Tel 0303 49541 ext
5024

- Pupils 475
- Boys 11–18 (Board)
- Girls None
- Upper sixth 45

- Termly fees £266 (Board)
- GBA

Enquiries/application to the Headmaster

What it's like

Founded in 1803, the modern establishment is purpose-built, rural, in about 150 acres of pleasant parkland 2 miles from Dover. Its president is the Duke of Kent and the governing body consists of 15 commissioners some of whom are appointed by the monarch. Though largely financed by the Ministry of Defence it is a school not a military unit. About 15% of leavers enter the services and those who wish to do so are given every help and encouragement. However the school aim is to offer a broad, traditional grammar boarding school education. Standards are high and academic results are good. In religious terms it is in the 'main stream' of Anglican practice. Sports and games are well supported; high standards are expected and attained. There is an impressive range of extra-curricular activities. The military ethos survives in a large and active CCF; membership of which is compulsory from the third form.

School profile

Pupils Age range 11–18; 475 boarding boys. Main entry ages 11 and 13; exceptionally into sixth.
Entrance Own entrance exam used. Ability to benefit from a grammar boarding education looked for. Only sons of army personnel of at least 4 years' service (serving or retired) admitted; must accept the Christian ethos of the school. Parents not expected to buy text books; maximum extras approx £75. School is largely financed by MoD, hence low fees; free places may be offered in cases classed as 'compassionate'.
Parents Up to 10% live within 30 miles; 30+% live overseas.
Staff Headmaster Lieutenant Colonel C F P Horsfall, in post for 3 years. 48 full time staff; part time music and modern language conversationalists. Annual turnover 5%.
Academic work GCSE, A-levels and BTEC National Diplomas. Average size of upper fifth 75; upper sixth 45. *GCSE:* on average, 35 pupils in upper fifth pass 8+ subjects; 30, 5–7 subjects; 10 pass 1–4 subjects. *A-levels:* on average, 15 pupils in upper sixth pass 4 subjects; 15, 3 subjects; 3, 2 subjects and 2 pass 1 subject. On average, 22 take science/engineering A-levels; 3 take arts and humanities; 10 a mixture. On average, 10 students per year take BTEC National Diplomas in Engineering and in Business and Finance.

Computing facilities: Very extensive, include computer science, IT and technology blocks.

Senior pupils' non-academic activities *Music:* 3 learn a musical instrument; 3 in school orchestra, 3 in school choir, 5 in school jazz group; occasional A-level students. *Drama and dance:* 10 in school productions. *Art:* 11 take GCSE art/ceramics, 1 takes A-level art. 5 belong to photographic club. *Sport:* Major school (representative) sports are rugby, hockey, cricket, athletics and swimming. 60 take non-compulsory sport; swimming and life saving awards. On average 4–8 per year (more with rugby and hockey team group) represent county (swimming, water polo, rugby, hockey). *Other:* 300 take part in CCF (compulsory from third until upper sixth). All pupils must take part in activities (1 or 2) twice a week: art, astronomy, ballroom dancing, badminton, bridge, business club, canoeing, chess, choir, choral society, Christian Union, classical music, climbing, computers, dance band, debating society, drama, indoor football, fishing, gymnastics and trampoline, gardening, horse riding, judo, languages, library, life saving, meteorology, modelling, plastic and metal work, model railway, orchestra, photography, pottery, philately, quizzes, science, shooting (.22 and .303), amateur radio and electronics, table tennis, war gaming, water polo, weight training, woodwork.

Careers 1 part time adviser. More than 70% go on to degree courses. On average 15% go into the armed services.

Uniform School uniform worn throughout.

Houses/prefects Competitive houses. Prefects, head boy, head of house and house prefects – appointed by the Head.

Religion Compulsory Sunday services.

Social Drama, musical, debates, industrial conferences with local girls' grammar school. Skiing and language trips abroad. Meals – some formal, some self service. School shop. No tobacco/alcohol allowed.

Discipline No corporal punishment. Pupils failing to produce homework once might expect extra work; firm disciplinary policy in respect of any habits that endanger health.

Boarding Fifth and sixth form have own study bedroom, forms 1–4 share (with 1 other). 8 houses of between 70 and 55, divided by age group. Resident qualified nurse; doctor non-resident. Central dining room. 1 exeat each term (autumn term, 1 week; others: long weekend). Visits to local town allowed on request.

Alumni association run by A Sadler, President and Secretary of the Old Boys Association, 'Birnham', 1 Bush Road, Fetcham, Leatherhead, Surrey KT22 9SX.

· *Dulwich* ·

Dulwich College	• Pupils 1400	• Termly fees
Dulwich	• Boys 8–18	£1625 (Day)
London	(Day/Board)	£3250 (Board)
SE21 7LD	• Girls None	£3125 (Weekly)
Tel 081 693 3601	• Upper sixth 200	• HMC, BSA, SHA
		Enquiries to the Master
		Application to the
		Admissions Secretary

What it's like

Founded by Edward Alleyn, the Elizabethan actor-manager; in 1619 a licence was granted for his 'College of God's Gift' at Dulwich. In 1857 Alleyn's College was reconstituted by Parliament – the upper part was known as Dulwich College and moved (1870) to its present site. It has very handsome, patrician buildings (designed by Charles Barry the younger) on a big expanse of playing fields and extensive building programmes have enormously improved the facilities: the college is now one of the best equipped in the country. Notable features include the Picture Gallery (designed by Sir John Soane) which contains a priceless collection of paintings and the Wodehouse Library which houses some 30,000 books, plus 40,000 books and documents published before 1800. The college is divided into 3 sections: lower, middle and upper. There are 4 comfortable boarding houses for 120 full and weekly boarders. There is some emphasis on religious worship and practice in the Anglican tradition. This includes daily assemblies. A special school service once a term where Muslims, Jews and Roman Catholics meet separately. Religious instruction is part of the curriculum for all pupils up to and including the fifth form. Thereafter sixth formers do further work in the philosophy of religion. Academically, the college is very high powered indeed. Academic studies are extremely well run by a large and well qualified staff (staff:pupil ratio is about 1:11) who consistently produce outstanding results. Each year very many leavers go on to degree courses (including very many to Oxbridge). French, German and Spanish are offered up to A-level. Many boys take GCSE in more than one European language, and Italian is offered as a non-examined language. There are regular exchanges with France, Germany and Spain. Music plays an important part in the life of the school. A 250 strong choir undertakes major works in regular concerts at the Festival Hall and the Fairfield Hall. There are several orchestras and smaller instrumental groups. Drama involves a very large number of pupils throughout the school. There are numerous productions each year. Art is no less strong. A very well-equipped art school produces work of a high order. The design and technology centre has sophisticated workshops for engineering, boatbuilding and cabinet making. There is a first-class computer centre. A wide variety of sports and games is available. Games are compulsory on certain afternoons. The huge multi-purpose sports hall is in constant use by (on average) about 500 boys daily. Standards in sports and games are very high and the college has produced many representatives at county, regional and national level. There are 3 scout troops, a venture scout unit, a large, enterprising and active CCF contingent and a voluntary service unit. About 50 clubs and societies form the College Union.

School profile

Pupils Total age range 8–18; 1400 boys (1280 day, 120 boarding). Senior department 11–18, 1275 boys. Main entry ages 8, 9, 11, 13 and into the sixth. Approx 10% are children of former pupils. *Transfer from maintained schools:* 70% intake at 11 and 13, plus 60% to sixth.

Entrance Common entrance and own exam used. Oversubscribed in some areas. No special skills required other than the potential to gain from what the school offers; no religious requirements (wide religious and ethnic mix). Parents not expected to buy text books; extras vary widely – often zero. 50 assisted places pa. 30 scholarships/bursaries pa (including music and art), half school fees (more if genuine financial need) to £450.

Parents 65+% in industry or commerce. 85+% live within 30 miles; up to 10% live overseas.

Staff Head Master A C F Verity, in post for 4 years. 120 full time staff, 6 part time. Annual turnover approx 5%. Average age approx 40.

Academic work GCSE and A-levels. 17 GCSE subjects offered; 18 at A-level (no A-level general studies – extensive non-examined minority time programme). In 1990, 200 pupils in upper fifth, 200 in upper sixth. *GCSE:* in 1990, 176 upper fifth gained at least grade C in 8+ subjects; 28 in 5–7; and 5 in 1–4 subjects. *A-levels:* 33 upper sixth passed in 4+ subjects; 125 in 3; 32 in 2; and 10 in 1 subject. 31% took science A-levels; 31%

arts/humanities; 38% both. *Computing facilities:* Networks of Archimedes and Apple Macintosh, each for class-size groups. Other machines are available in smaller numbers.

European Community *Languages:* French offered: to age 14; GCSE; A-level. German offered: to GCSE; A-level. Italian: non-examined. Spanish offered: to GCSE; A-level. 25–50% take GCSE in more than 1 EC language. *Exchanges:* Regular exchanges for pupils aged 14–16 to France, Germany and Spain. *Other:* Talks from politicians (and political candidates), business managers, leaders of industry and are open to all pupils.

Senior pupils' non-academic activities *Music:* 160 learn a musical instrument, 50 to Grade 6 or above. 40 in school orchestra, 1 in National Youth Orchestra, 100 in school choir, 20 in wind band; 10 play in pop group after leaving. *Drama and dance:* 70 in school productions; 3 accepted for Drama/Dance Schools. *Art:* 20 take as non-examined subject (6th form minority time); art as out of school club activity, 10. 19 A-level. 6 accepted for Art School. 15 belong to photographic club. *Sport:* Sport compulsory. Rugby, hockey, cricket, soccer, athletics, badminton, tennis, squash, swimming, water polo, shooting, basketball, fencing, baseball available. 7 represent county (rugby, swimming, athletics, squash, tennis). 20 take life-saving exams. *Other:* 50 take part in local community schemes. 20 have bronze Duke of Edinburgh's Award, 10 silver. 15 enter voluntary schemes in GAP year. Other activities include a computer club, electronics, debating, chess, drama, charitable fund raising, riding, sailing, ski-club, climbing, adventurous experience, conservation, community service.

Careers In 1990, 85% leavers went on to degree courses; 4% to art/drama/music colleges; 6% straight into careers (eg armed services, city, family business); 5% other (Gap, temporary work, repeat A-levels, pop groups). Of those going on to degree courses, 12% went to Oxbridge, 75% to other universities; 13% to poly/colleges. 3% those going on to higher education went to courses in practical art; 50% in humanities/social sciences; 8% in medicine; and 39% in science/engineering.

Uniform School uniform worn throughout.

Houses/prefects Competitive houses. Prefects, school captain, heads of house – appointed by the Head with advice from pupils and staff.

Religion Parents may opt pupils out of attendance at religious worship.

Social Drama, music, joint society meetings, shared classes in certain minority subjects with sister school (JAGS). Regular holiday visits abroad (educational and recreational) and language exchanges; rugby, hockey, cricket tours. Pupils allowed to bring own car/bike/motorbike to school. Meals self-service. School shop. No tobacco/alcohol allowed.

Discipline No corporal punishment. Pupils failing to produce homework once might expect a gentle reprimand. Pupils caught smoking cannabis on school premises or offering illegal drugs for sale would be invited to leave forthwith.

Boarding All boarders over 15 have own study bedroom. All boarders under 15 are in dormitories of 6+. 25–36 pupils in 4 houses, divided by age. 2 resident nurses, local GP on call. Limited cooking facilities for senior pupils for supplementary foods (take away delivery service does some trade with senior boys!). Half-term (3 days–1 week) plus 2 weekend exeats each term; weekly boarding is popular. Visits to the local shops and to London allowed, with permission and at the discretion of house master.

Alumni association is run by T J Walsh, Secretary of the Alleyn Club, c/o Dulwich College.

Former pupils P G Wodehouse, A E W Mason, Trevor Bailey, Raymond Chandler, Sir Ernest Shackleton, Sir Harold Hartley, Gordon Jacob, 5 First World War VC's, 3 Second World War VC's.

· *Dundee High* ·

High School of Dundee
Euclid Crescent
Dundee
DD1 1HU
Tel 0382 202921

- Pupils 1145
- Boys 5–18 (Day)
- Girls 5–18 (Day)
- Higher year 128

- Termly fees
  £962 (Day)
- HMC, SCIS
  Enquiries/application to
  the Rector

What it's like

Founded in 1239 by the Abbot of Lindores. The main buildings are very striking: neo-classical/Georgian erected in 1832–34. Excellent modern facilities are provided. The playing fields are about a mile away. The school enjoys a very strong corporate life and spirit and has a high reputation, with vigorous local support. Academically high-powered, it produces consistently excellent results. Very many pupils go on to degree courses each year and, in the Scottish tradition, few head for Oxbridge. French, German and Spanish are offered up to Highers and there are regular exchanges with France, Germany and Spain. Notably strong in music, drama and art. There is a very large number of extra-curricular activities and many of these are carried to high levels of achievement. Sports and games are also of a high standard and the school produces many representatives at county level. The record in the Duke of Edinburgh's Award Scheme is impressive.

School profile

Pupils Total age range 5–18; 1145 day pupils (557 boys, 588 girls). Senior department 12–18, 779 pupils (384 boys, 395 girls). Main entry ages 5, 9, 10, 11, 12 and a few into sixth. Approx 30–40% are children of former pupils.

Entrance Own entrance exam used. Oversubscribed in some forms. Good average ability looked for; no religious requirements. Parents expected to buy text books; other extras mostly optional. 150 assisted places. 30 scholarships/bursaries, half fees – £200.

Staff Rector R Nimmo, in post for 14 years. 85 full time staff, 7 part time. Annual turnover 5%. Average age 40.

Academic work O-grade/S-grade, Highers and CSYS. 30 subjects offered. In 1990, 120 pupils in O/S-grade year, 128 in Higher year, 105 in CSYS year. *O/S grade:* in 1989, 110 pupils gained at least grade C in 8+ subjects; 8 in 5–7; and 2 in 1–4 subjects. *Highers:* 65 passed in 5+ subjects; 27 in 4; 21 in 3; 12 in 2; and 3 in 1 subject. Most take a combination of arts and science Highers. *Computing facilities:* 2 computer laboratories; computers in most departments. *Special provision:* Learning Skills Centre.

European Community *Languages:* French offered: to age 14; S-grade; Highers; CSYS. German offered: to S-grade; Highers; CSYS. Spanish offered: to age 14; S-grade; Highers; CSYS. 10–25% take S-grade in more than 1 EC language. *Exchanges:* Regular exchanges for pupils aged 11–18 to France, Germany and Spain.

Senior pupils' non-academic activities *Music:* 115 learn a musical instrument, 40 to Grade 6 or above, 4 accepted for Music School; 23 in school orchestra, 115 in choir, 6 in pop group, 24 in folk group; 6 in National Youth Orchestra. *Drama and dance:* 60 in school productions. 30 take Grade 6 in ESB, RAD etc. 2 accepted for Drama/Dance Schools; 1 goes on to work in theatre. *Art:* 30 take as non-examined subject; 30 take O-grade; 15 Higher. Approx 2 or 3 accepted for Art School. *Sport:* Rugby, hockey, cricket, tennis, athletics, netball, golf, swimming, squash available. 320 take non-compulsory sport. 12 take exams eg gymnastics, swimming. 18 pupils represent county (hockey, rugby, cricket). *Other:* 12 take part in local community schemes. 25 have silver Duke of Edinburgh's Award, 12 have gold. 5 enter voluntary schemes after leaving school. Other activities: a wide variety of extra-curricular activities in terms of clubs (several computer clubs), hobbies and leisure interests (41 at the last count).

Careers In 1990, 83% leavers went on to degree courses; 15% to art/drama/music colleges or other non-degree courses; 2% other. Of those going on to degree courses, 3% went to Oxbridge, 79% to other universities; 18% to poly/colleges. 2% those going on to higher education went to courses in practical art/drama/acting/music; 60% in humanities/social sciences; 38% in medicine/science/engineering/technology.

Uniform School uniform worn throughout.

Houses/prefects Competitive houses. Prefects, head boy and girl – elected by staff and pupils. School Council.

Religion Weekly school assembly and end-of-term services.

Social Debates, ESU, United Nations, Press and Journal with other local schools. Organised exchanges with France, Spain and Germany; trips to Italy, Belgium; ski trips; rugby/hockey tours to Canada. Meals self service. School tuck and thrift shops. No tobacco/alcohol allowed.

Discipline No corporal punishment. Pupils failing to produce homework once might expect to write it out twice for next day; those caught smoking cannabis on the premises could expect expulsion.

Alumni association run by Harvey Findlay, 8 Abercrombie Street, Barnhill, Dundee.

Former pupils Sir Robert Lickley (designer of the Harrier jet); Lord Perry (former Principal of the Open University); Sir David Anderson (designer of Forth Road Bridge); Sir Alan Peacock (former Principal of Independent University); Lord Fulton (former Principal of Sussex University); Lord Ross (Lord Justice Clerk); Chris Rae (sports commentator); Bill Hamilton (BBC newscaster).

· *Dunottar* ·

Dunottar School	● Pupils 450	● Termly fees
High Trees Road	● Boys None	£1150 (Day)
Reigate	● Girls 5–18	● GSA, SHA
Surrey RH2 7EL	(Day)	Enquiries/application to
Tel 0737 761945	● Upper sixth 16	the Headmistress

What it's like

Founded in 1926, it lies high on the North Downs on the south side of Reigate and Redhill and has handsome buildings in very pleasant surroundings with beautiful gardens and playing fields. Modern facilities for teaching are very good and the accommodation is comfortable. A non-denominational but specifically Christian school, religious studies are included in the curriculum and there are daily assemblies. A happy and efficient working atmosphere is maintained by the encouragement of common sense, an insistence on self-discipline and good manners. A large staff allows a staff:pupil ratio of 1:10. Academic standards and results are good and most girls go on to degree courses. French, German and Spanish are offered to A-level. There are regular exchanges with France, Germany and Spain. There is a strong sport and games tradition and good standards are achieved. A great number of extra-curricular activities is provided and the school participates successfully in the Duke of Edinburgh's Award Scheme, at bronze, silver and gold levels.

School profile

Pupils Total age range 5–18, 450 day girls. Senior department 11–18. Main entry ages 5, 8, 11 and into sixth. *Transfer from maintained schools:* 50% intake at 11, plus 50% to sixth.

Entrance Common entrance used. No special skills or religious requirements. 4 scholarships at age 11 and a number for the sixth form.

Staff Headmistress Miss J Burnell, in post for 5 years.

Academic work GCSE and A-levels. 17 subjects offered to GCSE, 18 to A-level. Also RSA word processing. In 1990, 56 pupils in upper fifth, 16 in upper sixth. *GCSE:* in 1990, 79% upper fifth gained at least grade C in 8+ subjects. *A-levels:* 9 upper sixth passed in 3 subjects; 7 in 2 subjects. 5 took science A-levels; 11 arts/humanities. *Computing facilities:* A fully equipped computer room containing BBC Master machines.

European Community *Languages:* French offered: to age 14; GCSE; A-level. German offered: to age 14; GCSE; A-level. Spanish offered: to age 14; GCSE; A-level. 10–25% take GCSE in more than 1 EC language. *Exchanges:* Regular exchanges for pupils aged 11–16 to France, Germany and Spain.

Non-academic activities Some pupils take exams of Associated Board of Royal Schools of Music, LAMDA, Imperial School of Dancing. School orchestra; 3 choirs. *Sport:* Tennis, badminton, rounders, lacrosse, netball, volleyball, fencing, gymnastics, athletics and swimming available. Senior girls also use local leisure centre.

· *Durham* ·

Durham School	● Pupils 379	● Termly fees
Durham City	● Boys 11–18	£1933 (Day)
DH1 4SZ	(Day/Board)	£2900 (Board)
Tel 091 38 47977	● Girls 16–18	● HMC
Fax 091 38 31025	(Day/Board)	Enquiries/application to
	● Upper sixth 79	the Headmaster's
		Secretary

What it's like

One of the oldest schools in England, it has been closely associated with the Dean and Chapter of Durham Cathedral for 450 years. As the Bishop's School it was reorganised and re-endowed by Cardinal Langley in 1414 and refounded in 1541 by Henry VIII. It has occupied its present site since 1842 and enjoys a magnificent position below the west towers of the cathedral. During the last 15 years over one million has been spent in providing first-class facilities for a wide range of activities, including most recently, a centre for art, craft, design and technology, and an extension to the girls' boarding house. It is physically compact with playing fields nearby and makes full use of the advantages of an ancient cathedral and university city. A strong Anglican tradition prevails and religious worship is compulsory with a daily service in the School Chapel. A high standard of education is provided (staff ratio of 1:10) and many sixth form leavers proceed to degree courses; an unusually high proportion of the others go straight into careers. Strong in music, drama and art and local community services. Very strong in sport, with players at county and international level.

School profile

Pupils Age range 11–18; 379 pupils, 171 day (162 boys, 9 girls), 208 boarding (174 boys, 34 girls). Main entry ages 11 and 13 (boys) and into sixth (boys and girls). Approx 20% are children of former pupils. *Transfer from maintained schools:* 4% main intake, plus 24% to sixth.

Entrance Common entrance and own entrance exam used. No special skills or religious requirements but school is C of E foundation. Scholarships/bursaries available. Maximum extras, £100.

Parents 60+% live within 30 miles; up to 10% live overseas.

Staff Headmaster M A Lang, in post for 8 years. 38 full time staff, 10 part time. Annual turnover 10%.

Academic work GCSE and A-levels. Subjects offered include Chinese and A-level general studies. In 1990, 60 pupils in upper fifth, 75 in upper sixth (now 79). *GCSE:* in 1990, 33 upper fifth gained at least grade C in 8+ subjects; 16 in 5–7; and 11 in 1–4 subjects. *A-levels:* 36 upper sixth passed in 4+ subjects; 22 in 3; 12 in 2; and 5 in 1 subject. 17 took science A-levels; 35 arts/humanities; 23 both. *Computing facilities:* 30 BBC Masters and 2 Archimedes. *Special provision:* Dyslexia teaching available.

European Community *Languages:* French offered: to age 14; GCSE; AS-level; A-level. German offered: to GCSE; AS-level; A-level. 10–25% take GCSE in more than 1 EC language. *Other:* Talks to sixth form by MEPs. Pupils from France and Spain in school on occasions. Regular visits annually to France by 12 and 16 year olds.

Senior pupils' non-academic activities *Music:* 30% of school learn a musical instrument, 20 to Grade 6 or above. 50 in school orchestra, 50 in school choir, 7 in school pop group. *Drama and dance:* 50 in school productions. *Art:* All pupils take as non-examined subject, 37 take GCSE, 9 A-level. 2 accepted for Art School. 20 belong to photographic club. *Sport:* Athletics, rugby, rowing, swimming, cross-country, squash, fives, shooting, basketball, badminton, tennis, hockey, netball available. All pupils take non-compulsory sport. 8 represent England (rugby, cricket), 18 senior county rugby players. *Other:* Some pupils take part in local community schemes. Duke of Edinburgh's Bronze and Silver Awards. Other activities include a computer club, highland cattle society, chess club, bridge club, archaeology, model building, railway society, rambling society, music society, debating society.

Careers In 1990, 73% leavers went on to degree courses; 1% to art/drama/music colleges; 24% straight into careers (eg marketing, estate agency, racing driver); 2% other. Of those going on to degree courses, 7% went to Oxbridge; 48% to other universities; 45% to poly/colleges. 3% those going on to higher education went to courses in practical art; 5% in music; 52% in humanities/social sciences; and 40% in science/engineering.

Uniform School uniform worn throughout.

Houses/prefects Competitive houses. Prefects, head boy/girl, head of house and school prefects – appointed by the Headmaster.

Religion Religious worship compulsory.

Social Many organised trips abroad. Meals self service. School shop. No tobacco/alcohol allowed.

Discipline No corporal punishment. Pupils failing to produce homework once might expect repeat work; those caught smoking cannabis could expect expulsion.

Boarding Some share study bedroom with one other; most are in dormitories of 6+. Single sex houses, of approx 70, same as competitive houses. Resident qualified nurse. Central dining room. Pupils can provide and cook own food. 2 weekends and 3 Sunday exeats each term. Visits to local town allowed.

Alumni association run by N G E Gedye, c/o the School.

· *Durham High* ·

Durham High School
Farewell Hall
Durham
DH1 3TB
Tel 0385 43226

- Pupils 450
- Boys 4–7 only (Day)
- Girls 4–18 (Day)
- Upper sixth 24

- Termly fees £860 (Day)
- GSA
Enquiries/application to the Head

What it's like

Founded in 1884, its aim is to give a sound general education within a Christian framework (it is a Church school), but all faiths are accepted. In 1968 it moved to a new purpose-built school at Farewell Hall on the southern edge of Durham – a semi-rural site. The junior school is combined. Academic results are promising. Many sixth form leavers go on to degree courses, including Oxbridge. French and German are offered throughout the school to A-level; also as non-examined languages. Many pupils take GCSE in both. The school enjoys a good local reputation. A fair range of sports, games and extra-curricular activities is available.

School profile

Pupils Total age range 4–18; 450 day pupils (23 boys, 427 girls). Senior department 11–18, 269 girls. Main entry ages 4, 7, 10, 11 and into sixth. 65% intake at 11 from own junior. *Transfer from maintained schools:* 35% intake at 11, plus 4% to sixth.

Entrance Own entrance exam used. Often oversubscribed. No special skills or religious requirements. Parents expected to buy some text books; maximum extras approx £100 per term. Bursaries up to 75% of fees.

Staff Head Miss B E Stephenson, in post for 13 years. 30 full time staff, 11 part time. Annual turnover 5%. Average age 40.

Academic work GCSE and A-levels. Subjects offered include A-level general studies. In 1990, 45 pupils in upper fifth, 24 in upper sixth. *GCSE:* in 1990, 36 upper fifth gained at least grade C in 8+ subjects; 4 in 5–7; and 5 in 1–4 subjects. *A-levels:* 4% upper sixth passed in 4+ subjects; 83% in 3; 8% in 2; and 3% in 1 subject. 3 took science A-levels; 15 arts/humanities; 5 both. *Computing facilities:* Computer room with 8 BBCs and Master. Computers in music, home economics, science areas. *Special provision:* No regular provision but individual needs considered and provided for where possible.

European Community *Languages:* French offered: to age 14; GCSE; AS-level; A-level; non-examined. German offered: to age 14; GCSE; AS-level; A-level; non-examined. 25–50% take GCSE in more than 1 EC language. *Exchanges:* Regular exchanges for pupils aged 14–16 to France.

Senior pupils' non-academic antivities *Music:* 100+ pupils learning a musical instrument, 6 gained Grade 6 or above; 2 in National Youth Orchestra; 1 in National Youth Choir. *Drama and dance:* Regular school productions; 25 to Grade 6 (LAMDA, Guildhall) elocution and acting; 1 accepted for degree in performing arts. *Art:* 16 take GCSE art. 1 accepted for Art School; art appreciation is sixth form general studies. *Sport:* Hockey, netball, tennis, rounders, swimming, badminton, squash, golf, rowing available. *Other:* 21 have silver Duke of Edinburgh's Award and 12 have gold. Other activities include a drama club, music, karate; camera and clothing clubs.

Careers In 1990, 95% leavers went on to degree courses; 5% to art/drama/music colleges. Of those going on to degree courses, 9% went to Oxbridge, 59% to other universities; 32% to poly/colleges. 4% those going on to higher education went to courses in practical art; 4% in drama/acting; 61% in humanities/social sciences; $8^1/_2$% in medicine; and 22% in science/engineering.

Uniform School uniform worn except in the sixth.

Houses/prefects Competitive houses. Head girl, appointed by the Head with consultation; head of house and house prefects – elected.

Religion Daily Christian worship.

Social Organised trips abroad. Pupils allowed to bring own car to school. Meals self service. No tobacco/alcohol allowed.

Discipline No corporal punishment.

Alumni association run by Headmistress (Chairman) and Mrs K Hankey (Secretary) c/o the School.

e

· Ealing College ·

Ealing College Upper
School
83 The Avenue
London
W13 8JS
Tel 081 997 4346

- Pupils 280
- Boys 11–18
  (Day)
- Girls 16–18
  (Day)
- Upper sixth 30

- Termly fees
  £965 (Day)
- ISAI
  Enquiries/application to
  the Headmaster or
  Secretary

What it's like

Founded in 1820, it is single-site in a residential urban area with good public transport facilities. It comprises pleasant and well–equipped buildings with recent extensions. It provides a sound general education and its declared philosophy is to maximise the potential of each individual whatever their innate ability. A reasonable range of sport and games for which local grounds are used.

School profile

Pupils Age range 11–18; 280 day pupils (274 boys, 6 girls). Main entry ages 11, 12 and 13 (boys) and into sixth (boys and girls). Approx 1% are children of former pupils.

Entrance Own informal tests set in English and maths. Sometimes oversubscribed. No special skills or religious requirements. Parents expected to buy text books beyond form 3, maximum approx £40. Annual scholarships/bursaries for sixth form entrants.

Staff Head B Webb, in post for 6 years. 23 full time staff, 2 part time. Annual turnover 4%. Average age 35–40.

Academic work GCSE and A-levels (law offered to A-level). On average, 60 pupils in upper fifth, 30 in upper sixth. *GCSE:* on average, 7 upper fifth gain at least grade C in 8+ subjects; 15 in 5–7; and 28 in 1–4 subjects. *A-levels:* on average, 1 upper sixth passes in 4+ subjects; 9 in 3; 7 in 2; and 8 in 1 subject. On average, 10 take science A-levels; 7 arts/

humanities; 13 both. *Computing facilities:* Comprehensive system of Amstrad PCs in computer room; computers used by other departments. *Special provision:* extra English language tuition available for overseas students.

European Community *Languages:* French offered: to GCSE; AS-level.

Senior pupils' non-academic activities *Music:* 10 learn a musical instrument, 5 to Grade 6 or above. *Drama and dance:* Small number in school productions. Occasional pupil accepted for Drama School. *Art:* 15 take GCSE; 3, A-level. Occasional pupil accepted for Art School. *Sport:* Football, rugby, cricket, athletics, swimming, cross-country, badminton, tennis, squash, basketball, table tennis, karate available. 30 take non-compulsory sport (mainly football, cricket, tennis, squash, table tennis, badminton, karate). 2 represent county/country (karate and swimming). *Other:* Small number take part in local community schemes.

Other activities include a computer club, chess and debating.

Careers In 1990, 67% leavers went on to degree courses; 17% to non-degree courses (eg hotel/catering, engineering foundation); 16% other. Of those going on to degree courses, 5% went to Oxbridge, 70% to other universities; 25% to poly/colleges. 48% those going on to higher education went to courses in humanities/social sciences; 4% in medicine; and 48% in science/engineering.

Uniform School uniform worn except in the sixth.

Houses/prefects Competitive houses. Prefects, head boy/girl – appointed by the Head.

Religion No compulsory worship; religious studies is part of the curriculum.

Social Occasional debates with local schools. Annual ski trip, outward bound activities and trips to France. Meals self service. School canteen. No tobacco/alcohol allowed.

Discipline No corporal punishment.

· *Eastbourne* ·

Eastbourne College
Old Wish Road
Eastbourne
East Sussex
BN21 4JX
Tel 0323 37655

- Pupils 541
- Boys 13–18 (Day/Board)
- Girls 16–18 (Day/Board)
- Upper sixth 117

- Termly fees £2158 (Day) £2919 (Board)
- HMC
Enquiries/application to the Headmaster

What it's like

Founded in 1867 by the 8th Duke of Devonshire, it has an excellent site in the residential area of Eastbourne with elegant buildings and fine grounds and gardens. It is a few minutes' walk from the station, a modern shopping centre and two theatres. The sea front is 400 yards away and the South Downs are within easy reach. The school is divided into 5 boarding houses, 3 day-boy houses and two sixth form houses for girls. Accommodation is comfortable. The college sets out to be a Christian school and its pupils are expected to attend instruction in Christian beliefs and chapel services. There are also voluntary services. The choir plays an important part in the worship of the school. The emphasis on Christianity extends to a more than usual amount of local community services through an organisation called Action Care. Large numbers of pupils (the Social Commandos) assist old and elderly residents and also entertain them with plays, concerts and other social events. A large staff allows a staff:pupil ratio of about 1:9. There is a very large sixth form. The teaching is good and academic standards and results are consistently high. A number of leavers go on to degree courses, including Oxbridge. The music, drama and art departments are all strong and work closely together, forming an integral part of the academic and social life of the school. There is a strong liaison with the Eastbourne symphony orchestra which gives public performances with professional musicians. Many plays of quality are put on each year in the purpose-built theatre; and in the very well-equipped art school work of a high standard is produced. The technology, electronics and computer departments are also very active. The college has long had a high reputation for excellence in sports and games and there is a wide range of these including golf and sailing. There have been many representatives at county, regional and national levels. A large CCF shows great enterprise and there is considerable emphasis on adventure training and expedition. Numerous clubs and societies cater for most needs.

School profile

Pupils Age range, 13–18; 541 pupils, 186 day (162 boys, 24 girls), 355 boarders (320 boys, 35 girls). Main entry ages 13 (boys) and into sixth (boys and girls). 20% are children of former pupils. 20% of pupils from St Andrew's School, Eastbourne. *Transfer from maintained schools:* 2–3% main intake, plus 6% to sixth.

Entrance Common entrance exam used. Oversubscribed. Skills in sport, music and drama an asset. No religious requirements. Parents not expected to buy text books; extras £10–100, eg exam fees, outings, insurance premium (voluntary), etc. 10 academic and up to 6 music and art scholarships per year, 75–10% fees.

Parents 15+% in industry; 15+% doctors, lawyers etc. 30+% live within 30 miles; up to 10% live overseas.

Staff Headmaster C J Saunders, in post for 10 years. 55 full time staff, 1 part time. Annual turnover 10%. Average age 35.

Academic work GCSE and A-levels. 21 GCSE subjects offered; 19 at A-level (no A-level general studies). In 1990, 108 pupils in upper fifth, 117 in upper sixth. *GCSE:* in 1990, 74% upper fifth gained at least grade C in 8+ subjects; 17% in 5–7; and 9% in 1–4 subjects. *A-levels:* 75% upper sixth passed in 3 subjects; 16% in 2; and 6% in 1 subject. 27 took science A-levels; 65 arts/humanities; 25 both. *Computing facilities:* Extensive facilities: purpose-built computer centre.

European Community *Languages:* French offered: to age 14; GCSE; A-level. German offered: to age 14; GCSE; A-level. Spanish offered: to age 14; GCSE. Under 10% take GCSE in more than 1 EC language. *Exchanges:* Regular exchanges for pupils aged 16–18 to France and Germany.

Senior pupils' non-academic activities *Music:* 62 learn a musical instrument, 12 to Grade 6 or above; 3 A-level, 3 accepted for Music School, 6 to university music courses, 6 in pop group. 30 pupils play in school orchestra, 80 in school choir, 7 in small singing group; 55 in musicals; congregational practices for the whole school; *Drama and dance:* 70 in school productions; 120 in house plays; 2 take exams; 1 accepted for Drama School; 1 goes on to work in theatre. *Art:* 115 take art as non-examined subject; 50 take GCSE; 15 A-level. 14 accepted for Art School. 10 belong to eg photographic club; *Sport:* 50% of school take exams in eg gymnastics, swimming; 21 represent county (rugby, cricket, athletics, hockey, swimming, netball). *Other:* 16 have bronze Duke of Edinburgh's Award. Other activities include a computer club, learning to drive (private outside tuition), bridge, chess, Christian Fellowship, debating, music.

Careers In 1990, 80% leavers went on to degree courses; 6% to art/drama/ music colleges; 4% to non-degree courses; 5% straight into careers; 5% other (Gap year). Of those going on to degree courses, 6% went to Oxbridge, 55% to other universities; 39% to poly/ colleges. 12% those going on to higher education went to courses in practical art; 5% in drama/acting; 2% in music; 58% in humanities/social sciences; 3% in medicine; and 20% in science/ engineering.

Uniform School uniform worn throughout.

Houses/prefects Competitive houses. Prefects, head boy/girl, head of house and house prefects – appointed by the Head.

Religion Compulsory worship.

Social Debates with other local schools. Organised trips abroad and exchange systems. Day pupils allowed to bring own car to school (with permission). Meals self service. School shop. No tobacco/alcohol allowed.

Discipline No corporal punishment. Pupils failing to produce homework once would have their Housemaster informed and made to do it at some time inconvenient to the pupil (eg when he should have had some free time); those caught smoking cannabis on the premises would be expelled.

Boarding Majority of sixth form have own study bedroom, forms 3–5, about 4 to a room; very few are in dormitories of 6+. Houses, of approximately 60, same as for competitive purposes, single sex. Resident qualified medical staff. Central dining room. Pupils can provide and cook snacks. 1 exeat in Lent term; 2 in other terms, Sat noon to Sun pm. Visits to local town allowed: $1^1/_2$ hours Tuesday afternoon for the sixth form; Saturday, the bottom two forms are allowed town leave for 1 hour, fifth form $1^1/_2$ hours.

Alumni association is run by Robin Harrison, The Bursary, Old Wish Road, Eastbourne, E Sussex.

Former pupils Sir Hugh Casson; Sir Woodrow Wyatt; Professor Soddy; John Wells; Sir Christopher Leaver; Sir Derek Empson; Michael Fish; Michael Praed.

· *Edgbaston High* ·

Edgbaston High School for Girls
Westbourne Road
Edgbaston
Birmingham B15 3TS
Tel 021 454 5831

- Pupils 900
- Boys None
- Girls 3–18 (Day)
- Upper sixth 67

- Termly fees £1040 (Day)
- GSA

What it's like
Founded in 1876 it is the oldest girls' independent school in Birmingham. It comprises a pre-prep and prep departments and a senior school (11–18) on an attractive 4-acre site (plus 8 acres of playing fields) next to the Botanical Gardens and 2 miles from the city centre. The school moved to its present site in 1962 and is very well equipped with purpose built facilities including a sixth form area, music, art and design blocks and an indoor swimming pool. Teaching is good and academic standards are high. Many sixth formers go on to degree courses, including Oxbridge. French, German and Spanish are offered to A-level and Russian to GCSE (Italian is taught as a non-examined subject). There are regular exchanges with France, Germany and Spain. There is a wide range of cultural and sporting activities such as drama, debating, dance, choir, orchestra, wind band, ceramics, aikido, life-saving and Duke of Edinburgh's Award. Girls have opportunities for community service, work experience and an excellent careers programme which aims to help each girl develop as an individual.

School profile
Pupils Total age range 3–18, 900 day girls. Senior department 11–18. Main entry ages 11 and into sixth. *Transfer from maintained schools:* 8% to sixth.

Entrance Own entrance exam and interview. Entrance scholarships and a music scholarship at 11+ and 6 free places at 16+ including one for music.

Staff Headmistress Mrs S J Horsman, in post for 4 years.

Academic work GCSE, AS and A-levels. Subjects offered include Latin, Greek and Russian (school exchange with Leningrad). In 1989, 79 pupils in upper fifth, 63 in upper sixth (now 67). *GCSE:* in 1989, 97.5% upper fifth gained at least grade C in 8+ subjects; 2.5% in 5–7 subjects. *A-levels:* 29% upper sixth passed in 4+ subjects; 49% in 3; 16% in 2; and 6% in 1 subject. 27% took science A-levels; 71% arts/humanities; 2% both. *Computing facilities:* 15 networked BBCs, 2 Archimedes.

European Community *Languages:*

French offered: to age 14; GCSE; AS-level; A-level. German: GCSE; A-level. Italian: non-examined. Spanish offered: to age 14; GCSE; A-level. *Exchanges:* Regular exchanges for pupils aged 11–18 to France, Germany and Spain.

Careers In 1990, 88% leavers went on to degree courses; 8% to art/drama/music colleges; 2% to non-degree courses (eg secretarial, optician); 2% straight into careers (eg nursing, banking). Of those going on to degree courses, 8% went to Oxbridge, 62% to other universities; 30% to poly/colleges. 10% those going on to higher education went to courses in practical art; 5% in music; 49% in humanities/social sciences; 10% in medicine; and 14% in science/engineering.

· *Edgehill* ·

Edgehill College
Bideford
Devon
EX39 3LY
Tel 0237 471701

- Pupils 511
- Boys 3–8 only
  (Day/Board/Weekly)
- Girls 3–18
  (Day/Board/Weekly)
- Upper sixth 42

- Termly fees
  £1235 (Day)
  £2260 (Board)
  £2040 (Weekly)
- GSA
  Enquiries/application to the Admissions Secretary

What it's like

Founded in 1884, this Methodist foundation is single-site in the splendid countryside of North Devon, overlooking Bideford and the Torridge estuary. Its five elegant houses and other buildings form part of an estate of 50 acres in a peaceful and delightful situation. Comfortable accommodation and excellent modern facilities. The junior and kindergarten departments are attached. A Christian school, it worships in Bideford Methodist church. A sound education is provided and a fair number of leavers go on to degree courses, including Oxbridge. The music and drama departments are flourishing and there is a good range of extra-curricular activities.

School profile

Pupils Total age range 3–18; 511 pupils, 341 day (39 boys, 302 girls), 170 boarding (3 boys, 167 girls). Senior department 11–18, 360 girls. Main entry ages 3–5 (boys and girls), 11, 13 and into sixth (girls). Approx 10% are children of former pupils. *Transfer from maintained schools:* 50% main entry at 11 and 13, plus 10% to sixth.

Entrance Common entrance and own entrance exam used. Oversubscribed. No special skills or religious requirements. Parents not expected to buy text books. 20 assisted places pa at 11; 2 at 16. Scholarships/bursaries, up to full fees.

Parents 30+% live within 30 miles; up to 10% live overseas.

Staff Headmistress Mrs E M Burton, in post for 4 years. 27 full time staff, 8 part time. Annual turnover 8%.

Academic work GCSE and A-levels. 19 GCSE subjects offered; 16 at A-level (no A-level general studies). In 1991, 55 pupils in upper fifth, 42 in upper sixth. *GCSE:* in 1990, 27 upper fifth gained at least grade C in 8+ subjects; 12 in 5–7; and 16 in 1–4 subjects. *A-levels:* 1 upper sixth pupil passed in 4+ subjects; 18 in 3; 15 in 2; and 6 in 1 subject; plus 2 sat 1 A-level early. 8 took science A-levels; 20

arts/humanities; 13 both. *Computing facilities:* 2 computer studies rooms; computers in many departments. *Special provision:* Specialist teachers for dyslexic children and for EFL.

European Community *Languages:* French offered: to age 14; GCSE; AS-level; A-level. German offered: to age 14; GCSE; AS-level; A-level. Italian offered: to GCSE. 10–25% take GCSE in more than 1 EC language. *Exchanges:* Regular exchanges for pupils aged 11–18 to France and Germany. *Other:* European Studies offered to pupils aged 14–16. French and German pupils for 1 term.

Senior pupils' non-academic activities *Music:* 172 learn a musical instrument, 24 to Grade 6 or above. 1 accepted for university music degree. 22 in school orchestra (string group), 90 in school choir, 16 in wind band, 10 in brass group; 6 in Bideford Youth Orchestra; 3 in Devon County Youth Choir; 2 in Cornwall County Youth Orchestra; several play in local town bands, sing in church choirs or play organ in church. *Drama and dance:* 60 in school productions; some take GCSE drama and A-level theatre studies. Several have gone on to drama courses, some in county youth theatre. *Art:* 38 take GCSE; 18 A-level; 2 art history. 6 belong to photographic club; usually approx 20 involved in societies; 10 in ceramic society. *Sport:* Hockey, netball, volleyball, trampolining, badminton, squash, tennis, archery, swimming, cross-country, athletics, gymnastics available. 40 take non-compulsory sport; 20 take exams. 11 represent county (hockey). *Other:* 25 take part in Young Enterprise Scheme. 40 have bronze Duke of Edinburgh's Award, 14 silver and 2 gold. Each form/house supports a charity. Other activities include a computer club, driving lessons and horse riding, CREST Science Awards (gold, silver and bronze levels), Young Farmers' club.

Careers In 1990, 60% leavers went on to degree courses; 10% to art/drama/music colleges; 10% to non-degree courses; 5% straight into careers (eg pilot, retailing); 15% other. Of those going on to degree courses, 10% went to Oxbridge, 50% to other universities; 40% to poly/colleges. 8% those going on to higher education went to courses in practical art; 2% in drama/acting; 2% in music; 68% in humanities/social sciences; and 20% in science/engineering.

Uniform School uniform worn except in the sixth.

Houses/prefects Competitive houses. Prefects, head girl, head of house and house prefects – elected by the school. School Council.

Religion Sunday morning worship. Morning assembly. Christian Union.

Social Dancing lessons, dances/socials, joint choir, theatrical productions and film society with nearby boys' schools. Organised trips abroad. Meals self service. School shop. No tobacco/alcohol allowed.

Boarding Houses, of 50–60, same as competitive houses, plus separate sixth form house. Resident qualified nurse. Central dining room. Pupils can provide and cook own food. Two weekend exeats each term. Visits to local town allowed.

Former pupils Debbie Thrower.

· Edinburgh Academy ·

The Edinburgh
Academy
42 Henderson Row
Edinburgh
EH3 5BL
Tel 031 556 4603

- Pupils 959
- Boys 3–18
  (Day/Board/Weekly)
- Girls 16–18
  (Day/Board/Weekly)
- Higher year 95

- Termly fees
  £1265 (Day)
  £2590 (Board)
  £2545 (Weekly)
- HMC
  Enquiries/application to
  the Registrar or Rector

What it's like

Founded in 1824 (Sir Walter Scott was one of the founding spirits and presided at the opening ceremony). The upper school buildings include the handsome original hall. All the modern facilities are spacious and first–rate and the playing fields are a short walk from the school. The Academy is well known as one of the outstanding British schools, a civilised establishment which provides an extremely thorough, broad education. It is non-denominational within the Christian tradition. There are monthly school services and, for boarders, compulsory local church attendance. The Academy has a tradition of academic excellence – it enjoys a staff:pupil ratio of 1:11 and achieves high standards of scholarship and excellent results. It caters best for boys and girls with university ambitions, and facilities are particularly good for experimental science and art. No subject is weak. Several pupils study Greek and Latin and each year very many leavers go on to degree courses, including Oxbridge. The drama, art and music departments are all very strong. High standards are also attained in sport and games of which there is a wide range including hailes, curling and riding. There is also a wide variety of extra-curricular activities and considerable emphasis on outdoor pursuits (the Academy has its own field centre in the Highlands). The CCF contingent is unusually strong (compulsory at 14.5 and six terms' service are required). The Academy also has a good record in the Duke of Edinburgh's Award Scheme. Much use is made of Edinburgh's cultural amenities.

School profile

Pupils Total age range 3–18; 959 pupils, 878 day (843 boys, 35 girls), 81 boarding (75 boys, 6 girls). Upper school 10–18, 563 pupils (531 boys, 32 girls). Main entry ages 10 and 12 (boys) and into sixth (boys and girls). Approx 10% are children of former pupils. *Transfer from maintained schools:* 80% main senior intake, plus 20% to sixth.

Entrance Own entrance exam or common entrance used. Oversubscribed at certain levels. No special religious requirements; pupils should immediately be able to receive all teaching in English. Parents billed for text books; maximum extras usually £150 per term. 7 assisted places pa. 5 scholarships/bursaries (academic, art or music), half of day fees plus a quarter of boarding fees if required.

Parents 15+% are doctors, lawyers etc; 15+% in industry or commerce. 60+% live within 30 miles; up to 10% live overseas.

Staff Rector L E Ellis, in post for 13 years. 56 full time staff, 5 part time plus 11 part time music staff. Annual turnover 2%. Average age 43.

Academic work GCSE/O-grades, Highers, A-levels. 21 subjects offered (including classical civilisation, business studies, Russian, Greek; no A-level general studies). In 1990, 97 pupils in O/S-grade/GCSE year, 100 in Higher (now 95), 59 in A-level year. *GCSE/O grade:* in 1990, 63 upper fifth gained at least grade C in 8+ subjects; 14 in 5–7; and 20 in 1–4

262

subjects. *Highers:* 22 passed in 5+ or more subjects; 25 in 4; 21 in 3; 21 in 2; 11 in 1. *A-levels:* 2 passed in 4+ subjects; 35 in 3; 18 in 2; and 6 in 1 subject. 29 took science A-levels; 29 arts/humanities; 3 both. *Computing facilities:* Computer room: 32, including 14 IBM equivalent. *Special provision:* Specialist help of learning support services for dyslexic pupils who are otherwise able to cope with the curriculum.

European Community *Languages:* French offered: to age 14; GCSE; Highers; A-level. German offered: to age 14; GCSE; Highers; A-level. 25% take GCSE in more than 1 EC language. *Exchanges:* Regular exchanges for pupils aged 11–16 to France and Germany. Regular exchanges with a school in Paris. Some pupils exchange for up to 1 year. Usually 3–5 French boys in the school at any time.

Senior pupils' non-academic activities *Music:* 54 learn a musical instrument, 28 to Grade 6 or above; 27 in school orchestra, 24 in school choir, 11 in dance band; 6 in Edinburgh Youth Orchestra; 4 sing in cathedral and church choirs. *Drama and dance:* 60 in school productions. 2 accepted for Drama/Dance Schools; 2 go on to work in theatre. *Art:* 20 take as non-examined subject; 27 take GCSE; 19 A-level; 21 Higher. 5 accepted for Art School; 3 to study architecture; 1 for art history; 2 joint art course. 20 belong to photographic club; 35 to art society. *Sport:* Rugby, soccer, cross-country, cricket, athletics, tennis, sailing, canoeing, shooting, badminton, squash, curling, fencing, fives, golf, hockey, ski-ing, hailes, judo, horse-riding available. 200 take non–compulsory sport. 15 represent county/country (athletics, fencing, cricket, squash). *Other:* 35 have bronze Duke of Edinburgh's Award, 18 have silver and 15 gold. Other activities include a computer club, pipe band, chess, reel club, art, photography, bridge, expeditions during holidays, canal cruising.

Careers In 1990, 83% leavers went on to degree courses; 1% to art/drama/music colleges; 10% to non-degree courses (eg nursing, business studies, secretarial); 5% straight into careers (eg insurance, sound engineering, army, property management); 2% other. Of those going on to degree courses, 7% went to Oxbridge, 79% to other universities; 14% to poly/colleges. 2% those going on to higher education went to courses in practical art; 60% in humanities/social sciences; 6% in medicine; and 32% in science/engineering.

Uniform School uniform worn throughout.

Houses/prefects Competitive houses. Prefects (called Ephors), head boy and girl, head of house and house prefects – elected by school and appointed by Rector.

Religion Non-denominational morning prayers for whole school; school services once a month; compulsory local church attendance for boarders; weekly RE teaching period for all.

Social Regular joint productions, debates, Speakers' Dinner, Burns suppers, reel club with St George's School for Girls. Organised trips and exchange systems with school abroad. Pupils allowed to bring own bike to school (car may be parked nearby with permission). Meals formal. School shop (books and stationery). No tobacco/alcohol allowed.

Discipline No corporal punishment. Pupils failing to produce homework once might expect a request via parents; those caught smoking cannabis on the premises may expect automatic expulsion.

Boarding 18 have own study bedroom, 5 share, 2 dormitories of 6+. Houses, of up to 35, two for boys over 13, one for boys under 13 and one for girls. 2 resident qualified nurses plus 4 matrons. Central dining room. Pupils can provide and cook own food. 2 weekend exeats and half term each term. Visits to city allowed.

Alumni association run by Mr J J Burnet, Secretary, Edinburgh Academical Club, c/o the Academy.

Former pupils Magnus Magnusson; Gordon Honeycombe; Paul Jones; Lord Cameron of Lochbroom; Giles Gordon; David Caute; Vice Admiral Jock Slater; Ian Vallance; Ian Glen; Nick Campbell.

· *Elizabeth College* ·

Elizabeth College	• Pupils 700	• Termly fees
Guernsey	• Boys 7–18	£645 (Day)
Channel Islands	(Day/Board)	£1565 (Board)
Tel 0481 726544	• Girls None	• HMC
	• Upper sixth 56	Enquiries to the
		Principal's Secretary
		Application to the
		Bursar

What it's like

Founded in 1563 by royal charter of Queen Elizabeth, it is one of the original HMC schools. It comprises an upper school and a lower school. The former lies on a hill overlooking the town and harbour of St Peter Port. The playing fields are on 2 sites of about 20 acres. A well-equipped establishment with plentiful modern resources. Religious worship is compulsory. A sound basic education is given and results are good. Many sixth formers go on to degree courses, including Oxbridge. French, German and Spanish are offered at GCSE and a very high proportion of boys takes GCSE in more than one European language. Only French and German are offered at A-level but they, together with Italian and Spanish, are also taught as non-examined languages. There are regular exchange arrangements with France, Germany and Spain. A good range of games, sports and activities provided. Strong in music and drama. It has an active community service unit, a voluntary CCF and takes part in the Duke of Edinburgh's Award Scheme.

School profile

Pupils Total age range 7–18; 700 boys, 640 day, 60 boarding. Senior department 11–18, 550 boys. Main entry ages 7, 11, 13 and into sixth. Approx 25% are children of former pupils. *Transfer from maintained schools:* 55% senior intakes.

Entrance Common entrance and own exam used. No special skills or religious requirements. Parents not expected to buy text books; maximum extras £100 although most charged none. Gibson Fleming scholarships.

Parents 50+% in industry or commerce. 90% live within 10 miles; up to 10% live overseas.

Staff Principal J H F Doulton, in post 2 years. 48 full time staff. 2 part time. Annual turnover less than 4%. Average age 40.

Academic work GCSE and A-levels. 14 subjects offered (no A-level general studies). In 1990, 85 pupils in upper fifth, 56 in upper sixth. *GCSE:* in 1990, 46 upper fifth gained at least grade C in 8+ subjects; 13 in 5–7; and 19 in 1–4 subjects. *A-levels:* 6 upper sixth passed in 4+ subjects; 44 in 3; 10 in 2; and 1 in 1 subject. 16 took science A-levels; 23 arts/humanities; 22 both. *Computing facilities:* Computing centre equipped with 30 BBC Archimedes linked by Econet.

European Community *Languages:* French offered: to age 14; GCSE; A-level; non-examined. German offered: to age 14; GCSE; A-level; non-examined. Italian: non-examined. Spanish offered: to age 14; GCSE; non-examined. 50–75% take GCSE in more than 1 EC language. *Exchanges:* Regular exchanges for pupils aged 11–14 to France, Germany and Spain.

Senior pupils' non-academic activities *Music:* 40% learn a musical instrument, 3% to Grade 6 or above. 20% in school orchestra, wind band, brass band etc, 10% in school choir; 4% in Guernsey

Youth Orchestra; 2% in rock groups. *Drama and dance:* 4% in school productions. *Art:* 10% take as non-examined subject. 4% belong to photographic club. *Sport:* Cricket, football, hockey, tennis, squash, basketball, athletics, cross-country, swimming, shooting, sailing, badminton, volleyball, fencing and golf available. Sport is compulsory. 10% take exams in life saving, AAA five star awards and fencing. 10% represent county at sport. *Other:* 10% take part in local community schemes. 30% have bronze Duke of Edinburgh's Award, 20% silver and 5% gold. 35% take part in CCF. Other activities include a computer club, sixth form society, theatre, debating, chess, art club, outdoor pursuits.

Careers In 1990, 81% leavers went on to degree courses; 3% to art/drama/music colleges; 14% straight into careers (eg civil service, building inspector, pilot); 2% other. Of those going on to degree courses, 8% went to Oxbridge, 70% to other universities; 22% to poly/colleges. 2% those going on to higher education went to courses in practical art; 4% in music; 64% in humanities/social sciences; 5% in medicine; and 25% in science/engineering.

Uniform School uniform worn throughout.

Houses/prefects Competitive houses. Prefects, head boy, head of house and house prefects – appointed by Principal.

Religion Christian worship compulsory.

Social Debates, joint theatre, ski trips, music occasions with local schools. Trips to France, Germany, Spain. Exchanges with Germany and Spain. Pupils allowed to bring own car/bike/motorbike to school. School tuck and book shops. No tobacco/alcohol allowed.

Boarding 15% share with 1 or 2 others; 85% in dormitories of 6+. Resident qualified nurse. Central dining room. Pupils can provide and cook own food. 2 overnight exeats per term plus half-term; other leave as required. Visits to local town allowed at housemaster's discretion.

Alumni association run by R C N Roussel, Coles Farm, Castel, Guernsey.

Former pupils Air Chief Marshal Sir Peter Le Cheminant (Lt Governor of the Bailiwick of Guernsey) 4 Victoria Crosses.

· Ellerslie ·

Ellerslie
Abbey Road
Malvern
Worcestershire
WR14 3HF
Tel 0684 575701

- Pupils 250
- Boys None at present
- Girls 11–18 (Day/Board)
- Upper sixth 40

- Termly fees
  £1735 (Day)
  £2670 (Board)
- GSA, BSA
  Enquiries/application to the Registrar

What it's like

Founded in 1922, it expects to merge with Malvern College in 1992. Ellerslie is urban and semi-rural on the east side of the Malvern Hills in a superb position with splendid views across the Severn Valley and out to the Cotswolds. Its handsome and well-equipped buildings are set in beautiful gardens and a homely and congenial atmosphere prevails. It is a Christian foundation in the Anglican tradition but girls of all denominations are welcome. A sound general education is provided up to GCSE, followed by a joint sixth form with the neighbouring Malvern College. There is a good staff:pupil ratio and academic results are most creditable. Each year 10 to 15 girls go on to university. French, German and Spanish are offered up to A-level; Italian for the Institute of Linguists. Many girls take GCSE in more than one European language. Music and drama are well supported. A wide variety of sports and games is available and there are plentiful extra-curricular activities, including a very extensive programme of evening and weekend enterprises. The Duke of Edinburgh's Award Scheme is very vigorously supported and the school has a remarkable record of success.

School profile

Pupils Age range 11–18; 250 girls (30 day, 220 boarders). Main entry ages 11, 12, 13 and into sixth. 8% are children of former pupils.

Entrance Common entrance and own entrance exam used. No special skills or religious requirements. Parents are expected to buy some text books. 5 assisted places pa. 3 scholarships/ bursaries per year, up to full fees.

Parents 15+% in the armed services; 15+% doctors, lawyers etc; 15+% in industry. 30+% live within 30 miles; 10+% live overseas.

Staff Head Mrs E M Baker, in post for 3 years. 21 full time staff, 9 part time. Annual turnover 6%. Average age 38.

Academic work GCSE and A-levels. 27 subjects offered. In 1991, 39 pupils in upper fifth, 40 in upper sixth (taught jointly with Malvern College). *GCSE:* in 1990, 84% gained at least grade C in 8+ subjects. *A-levels:* 25 upper sixth passed in 3 subjects; 12 in 2; and 3 in 1 subject. 3 took science A-levels; 23 arts/humanities; 13 both. *Computing facilities:* Network 6 Apple Macintosh computers and 3 BBCs. *Special provision:* SLD individual tuition.

European Community *Languages:* French offered: to age 14; GCSE; A-level. German offered: to age 14; GCSE; A-level. Italian offered: to age 14; Institute of Linguists. Spanish offered: to age 14; GCSE; A-level. 25–50% take GCSE in more than 1 EC language. *Exchanges:* Regular exchanges for pupils aged 11–14 to France and Germany. *Other:* One or two Spanish girls in school.

Senior pupils' non-academic activities *Music:* 100 in the school learn musical instruments, 23 to Grade 6 or above; 16 pupils play in school orchestra, 32 in choir, 6 in school pop group, 38 in other musical productions; 8 in electronic workshop; 5 play in pop group and 7 take courses outside school. *Drama and dance:* 40 in school productions; 80 take exams eg LAMDA; 32 take part in Cheltenham Festival; 1 accepted for Drama School; 1 in National Youth Theatre. 2 National Youth Choir. *Art:* 18 take GCSE; 5 A-level. 3 accepted for Art School. 6 belong to eg photographic club, 5 to others. *Sport:* Lacrosse, netball, tennis, squash, athletics, volleyball, cross-country, basketball, badminton, golf, tabletennis, judo, swimming available. 60% take part in non-compulsory sport. *Other:* 45 have bronze Duke of Edinburgh's Award, 25 silver, 23 gold. 40 in local community schemes.

Careers 2 part time careers advisers. Annual average accepted for *arts and humanities degree courses* at Oxbridge, 1; other universities, 11; polytechnics/ colleges, 7. *science and engineering degree courses* at Oxbridge, 1; other universities, 3; medical schools, 2. Some on GAP year. *other general training courses*, 14. Average number going straight into careers, 4.

Uniform School uniform worn. New uniform in sixth.

Houses/prefects Competitive houses. Prefects, head girl, head of house and house prefects – appointed by Headmistress after recommendation by staff and pupils.

Religion Compulsory worship.

Social Numerous activities, academic/ social/cultural with all local schools, both independent and state. Organised trips abroad and exchange systems. Meals cafeteria. No tobacco/alcohol allowed.

Discipline No corporal punishment.

Boarding 14% have own study bedroom, less than 5% are in dormitories of 6+. Houses, of 40–50, divided by age group. Resident qualified nurses. Central dining room. Pupils can provide and cook snacks. Termly exeats, 2 weekends and half-term. Visits to local town allowed for all ages at least weekly.

Alumni association is run by Mrs Ann Style, 66 Tuddenham Road, Ipswich.

· *Elmhurst* ·

Elmhurst Ballet School
Heathcote Road
Camberley
Surrey
GU15 2EU
Tel 0276 65301

- Pupils 271
- Boys 9–19
  (Day/Board)
- Girls 9–19
  (Day/Board)
- Upper sixth 35

- Termly fees
  £1730 (Day)
  £2360 (Board)
- GSA
  Enquiries/application to
  the Principal

What it's like

Founded early in the 20th century, Elmhurst gradually evolved to its present position as a leading centre for training in dance and drama and has an international reputation. It has very pleasant premises and gardens in Camberley and excellent modern facilities, including a purpose-built 230 seat theatre. Religious education is an important part of the school's life. The school is basically C of E but other denominations are welcome. Services are held in the chapel. A full academic programme for GCSE and A-levels, as well as business studies, is provided and results are good. The main vocational emphasis, of course, is on dance and drama. A highly qualified staff give instruction on all aspects of dance. The school has a number of large modern studios. Classical ballet (including Cecchetti), modern and contemporary dance, jazz, tap as well as Spanish and national dance are taught. Naturally, music and singing are a very strong part of the school life.

School profile

Staff Principal Jeffrey Skitch, in post for 11 years.

Entry by dancing audition. Selected A-levels offered.

· *Eltham College* ·

Eltham College
Grove Park Road
London SE9 4QF
Tel 081 857 1455

- Pupils 720
- Boys 7–18 (Day/
  Board/Weekly)
- Girls 16–18 (Day)
- Upper sixth 76

- Termly fees
  £1290 (Day)
  £2724 (Board)
  £2594 (Weekly)
- HMC
  Enquiries/application to
  the Headmaster

What it's like

Founded in 1842, originally for the sons of missionaries, it occupies a single suburban site of 25 acres, in handsome buildings (formerly those of the Royal Navy School). Its sister school, Walthamstow Hall, is in Sevenoaks. It remains loyal to its Christian foundation. The junior school is attached and 95% of junior pupils stay on to spend 11 years at the school. In terms of its size it has a most impressive careers record: very many pupils go on to degree courses and an exceptionally high proportion goes to Oxbridge. French and German are offered to A-level; Italian to GCSE. There are regular exchanges with France, Germany and Italy. Very strong indeed in musical activities, travel and in drama (new performing arts centre just completed). Excellent all-round facilities are provided. Standards in sports and games are high and there is a substantial commitment to local community service.

School profile

Pupils Total age range 7–18; 720 pupils, 695 day (680 boys, 40 girls), 25 boarding (all boys). Senior department 11–18, 530 pupils (490 boys, 40 girls). Main entry ages 7, 8 and 11 (boys) and into sixth (boys and girls). Approx 8% are children of former pupils. *Transfer from maintained schools:* 50% main intake at 11, plus 20% to sixth.

Entrance Own entrance exam used. Oversubscribed. Special skills welcome. No religious requirements but Christian (non-denominational) foundation emphasised. Parents not expected to buy text books; maximum extras, £140. 15 assisted places pa. 19 scholarships/bursaries, 66–33% fees.

Parents 15+% in industry or commerce; 15+% in theatre, media, music, etc; 15+% are doctors, dentists, lawyers, etc. 90+% live within 30 miles; up to 10% live overseas.

Staff Headmaster Mr D M Green, in post for 1 year. 51 full time staff, 9 part time. Annual turnover 5%. Average age 34.

Academic work GCSE and A-levels. 20 subjects offered (including A-level geology; not A-level general studies). In 1990, 68 pupils in upper fifth, 76 in upper sixth. *GCSE:* in 1990, 58 upper fifth gained at least grade C in 8+ subjects; 6 in 5–7; and 4 in 1–4 subjects. *A-levels:* 14 upper sixth passed in 4+ subjects; 52 in 3; 9 in 2; and 1 in 1 subject. 30 took science A-levels; 30 arts/humanities; 40 both. *Computing facilities:* 2 networks of 12 + 4 users. Stand alone PC-AT machines; various departmental BBC machines.

European Community *Languages:* French offered: to age 14; GCSE; AS-level; A-level. German offered: to age 14; GCSE; AS-level; A-level. Italian offered: to GCSE. 50–75% take GCSE in more than 1 EC language. *Exchanges:* Regular exchanges for pupils aged 11–18 to France, Germany and Italy.

Senior pupils' non-academic activities *Music:* 185 learn a musical instrument, 25 to Grade 6 or above. 6 accepted for Music scholarship. 45 in school orchestra, 160 in school choir, 12 in school pop group, 30 in senior concert band; 46 in local orchestras; 8 play in pop group after leaving. Annual tour of cathedrals (eg Salisbury, Gloucester, Winchester). *Drama and dance:* 50–150 in school productions; 1 or 2 accepted for Drama Schools. *Art:* 19 take as non-examined subject, 16 take GCSE; 16 A-level. 2 or 3 accepted for Art School. 25 belong to photographic club. *Sport:* Rugby, cricket, tennis, swimming, some hockey and soccer, badminton, squash, golf, table tennis, cross-country, athletics available. All pupils take non-compulsory sport. 17 represent county (rugby, cricket, swimming); 2 represent country (rugby, swimming). *Other:* 78 take part in local community schemes. D of E award scheme recently relaunched. 20 work for national charities. Other activities include a computer club, biology club, CDT, chess, International Society, College Society (distinguished speakers are invited), debating, public speaking, film, astronomical (observatory on site), printing, Christian Union.

Careers In 1990, 78% leavers went on to degree courses; 3% to art/drama/music colleges; 6% to non-degree courses (eg computing, environmental recreation, business studies); 1% straight into careers; 2% other. Of those going on to degree courses, 19% went to Oxbridge, 61% to other universities; 13% to poly/colleges. 1% those going on to higher education went to courses in practical art; 1% in music; 58% in humanities/social sciences; 5% in medicine; and 23% in science/engineering.

Uniform School uniform worn throughout.

Houses/prefects Competitive houses. Prefects, head boy/girl, head of house and house prefects – elected by the school, appointed by the Head. School Council.

Religion Daily chapel compulsory.

Social Debates, conferences, dances, discos regularly shared with other local schools. 6 partner schools in France and Germany. Approximately 100 exchanges annually. Pupils allowed to bring own car/bike/motorbike to school. Meals formal. No tobacco/alcohol allowed.

Discipline No corporal punishment. Pupils failing to produce homework once might expect either a 40-minute detention or a double homework; those engaged in any drug-connected activities could expect expulsion. Constant contact between school and home actively encouraged and practised.

Boarding 25% have own study bedroom, 75% share with maximum of 3. Two houses of 18 and 7, divided by age group, single sex. Central dining room. Senior pupils can provide and cook own food. Exeats, very flexible (families in difficulties or emergencies often helped out). Visits to the local town allowed.

· *Emanuel* ·

Emanuel School
Battersea Rise
Wandsworth
London SW11 1SH
Tel 081 870 4171

- Pupils 760
- Boys 10–19 (Day)
- Girls None
- Upper sixth 82

- Termly fees £1165 (Day)
- HMC

Enquiries/application to the Headmaster

What it's like

Founded in Westminster in 1594 by Lady Dacre (two of whose descendants are members of the governing body) it moved to Wandsworth in 1883 where it occupies a 10-acre site next to Wandsworth Common, just off the south circular and a few minutes' walk from Clapham Junction. There are many fine trees, lawns and big playing fields (there are other playing fields at Raynes Park) and, considering the site is less than 5 miles from the West End, it is surprisingly rich in fauna (including foxes). The main building is a handsome example of mid-Victorian architecture. Recent developments include excellent labs and two new classroom blocks. Facilities are good. The school is interdenominational and ecumenical; worship in the Anglican tradition is encouraged. There is a staff:pupil ratio of 1:13. Academic standards are high and results are good (especially in maths and the sciences). Many pupils go on to degree courses, a high proportion of them to Oxbridge. French, German and Spanish are offered to A-level; also modern Greek to GCSE. An exceptionally high proportion of boys takes GCSE in more than one European language and there are regular exchanges with France and Germany; regular visits include these two countries, and Denmark and further afield. The music department is particularly strong (the choir is well known) and there is considerable strength in drama and art. The CDT centre is a very active and successful part of school life. A wide range of sports and games is available and standards are high, especially in rowing. Emanuel is one of the best rowing schools in Britain (its boat house is at Barnes Bridge) and has produced 5 Olympic oarsmen and over 50 international 'vests'. A flourishing CCF is RAF-based. A fair range of extra-curricular activities is provided and much use is made of London's cultural amenities.

School profile

Pupils Total age range 10–19; 760 day boys. Senior department 11–19, 740 boys. Main entry ages 10, 11, 13 and into sixth. Approx 1% are children of former pupils.

Transfer from maintained schools: 95% main intake, plus 50% to sixth.

Entrance Common entrance and own entrance exam used. Oversubscribed. Music and sport skills looked for; no religious requirements. Parents not expected to buy text books; maximum extras, £110. 322 assisted places. 82 scholarships/bursaries, full fees to £100.

Staff Headmaster P F Thomson, in post for 7 years. 60 full time staff, 5 part time. Annual turnover 8%. Average age 35–40.

Academic work GCSE and A-levels. 26 GCSE subjects offered; 23 at A-level (general studies offered but not at A-level). In 1990, 122 pupils in upper fifth, 82 in upper sixth. *GCSE:* in 1990, 65 upper fifth gained at least grade C in 8+ subjects; 46 in 5–7; and 20 in 1–4 subjects. *A-levels:* 8 upper sixth passed in 4+ subjects; 45 in 3; 13 in 2; and 16 in 1 subject. 43 took science A-levels; 30 arts/humanities; 10 both. *Computing facilities:* New computing laboratory plus facilities with each major department. *Special provision:* Some small group extra help but not extra specialist staffing.

European Community *Languages:* French offered: to age 14; GCSE; AS-level; A-level. German offered: to age 14; GCSE; A-level. Greek (modern): to age 14; GCSE. Spanish offered: to GCSE; A-level. Over 75% take GCSE in more than 1 EC language. *Exchanges:* Regular exchanges for pupils aged 11–18 to France and Germany. *Other:* European Studies offered to pupils aged 16–18. Regular visits to and from Denmark, France and Germany.

Senior pupils' non-academic activities *Music:* 75 learn a musical instrument, 10 to Grade 6 or above, 2 accepted for Music School; 27 in school orchestra, 52 in choir, 200 in house groups and inter-school pop groups. *Drama and dance:* 30–40 in school productions; 71 Junior play; 50–60 in other productions. 3 accepted for Drama School. 1 enters competitions, 2–3 go on to work in theatre. *Art:* 310 take as non-examined subject; 30 take GCSE; 10 A-level. 2 accepted for Art School. *Sport:* Rowing, rugby, cricket, soccer, tennis, badminton, golf, squash, table tennis, athletics, soft-ball, .22 rifle range, gymnastics available. Sport compulsory for all. Large number represent county/country eg in cricket, rugby, and rowing (50 internationals). 1st XI won final of London Cup (under 19, 13 and 12) and Surrey Cup. Under 13 and 14 County Champions 7-a-side rugby. *Other:* 10 take part in local community schemes. Other activities include active computer, chess and French clubs; debating, war games, dramatic societies, CCF.

Careers In 1990, 50% leavers went on to degree courses; 5% to art/drama/music colleges; 5% to non-degree courses (eg hotel and catering, surveying, computing HNDs); 10% straight into careers (eg banking, diamond trade, armed services, boatman, zookeeping); 30% other (Gap year). Of those going on to degree courses, 20% went to Oxbridge, 60% to other universities; 20% to poly/colleges. 5% those going on to higher education went to courses in practical art; 5% in drama/acting; 5% in music; 25% in humanities/social sciences; 10% in medicine; and 50% in science/engineering.

Uniform School uniform worn throughout.

Houses/prefects Competitive houses. Prefects, head boy, head of house and house prefects – appointed by Head after consultation with staff.

Religion Compulsory assembly/chapel (Muslims exempt if parents wish); communion services.

Social Joint cultural events with local girls' schools. 3–4 trips abroad pa; exchange with French schools. Pupils allowed to bring own car/bike/motorbike to school. Meals self service. No tobacco/alcohol allowed.

Discipline No corporal punishment. Pupils failing to produce homework once might expect reprimand or detention; other offences might involve supervised hard labour, detention on Saturday morning, suspension or expulsion.

Former pupils Stuart Surridge (cricketer); Michael Aspel (TV presenter); Leslie Henson (actor); Sir Denis Noble FRS; N F Simpson (dramatist).

· Embley Park ·

Embley Park School
Romsey
Hampshire
SO51 6ZE
Tel 0794 512206

- Pupils 220
- Boys 11–18
  (Day/Board/Weekly)
- Girls 16–18
  (Day/Board/Weekly)
- Upper sixth 30

- Termly fees
  £1540 (Day)
  £2355 (Board/
  Weekly)
- SHA, BSA, ISAI
  Enquiries/application to
  the Headmaster's
  Secretary

What it's like

Founded in 1946, it is housed in a neo-Tudor mansion (formerly the family home of Florence Nightingale). It is in 80 acres of private park, including wild gardens, woodland and a lake, surrounded by splendid countryside bordering the New Forest. Altogether a delightful and healthy environment. It has all the advantages of a small school and takes boys of a wide ability range, but without remedial provision. The ethos and regime is basically that of a boarding school but there is an increasing number of day pupils. The sixth form is expanding and many sixth formers go on to degree courses. French and German are offered to A-level and many pupils take GCSE in more than one European language. There are regular exchanges with France and Germany. Very good, modernised facilities. Drama and art are quite strong, and there is strong emphasis on games and activities – which form part of every afternoon's curriculum. For a small school it has a phenomenal record of success in the Duke of Edinburgh's Award Scheme.

School profile

Pupils Age range 11–18; 220 pupils, 110 day (102 boys, 8 girls), 110 boarding (108 boys, 2 girls). Main entry ages 11 and 13 (boys) and into sixth (boys and girls). Approx 5% are children of former pupils. *Transfer from maintained schools:* 20% main intake, plus 20% to sixth.

Entrance Common entrance and own entrance exam used. Oversubscribed. No special skills or religious requirements. Average extras, £20. Academic/sporting scholarships and bursaries, up to half termly fee; bursaries for the children of services, clergy and teachers.

Parents 60% in industry or commerce; 15+% in the armed services. 30+% live within 30 miles; 10+% live overseas.

Staff Headmaster D F Chapman, 4 years in post. 20 full time staff, 5 part time. Annual turnover 5%. Average age 39.

Academic work GCSE, AS and A-levels. 17 subjects offered (including government & politics and A-level general

studies). In 1990, 45 pupils in upper fifth, 30 in upper sixth. *GCSE:* in 1990, 5 upper fifth gained at least grade C in 8+ subjects; 20 in 5–7; and 20 in 1–4 subjects. *A-levels:* 1 upper sixth pupil passed in 4+ subjects; 8 in 3; 8 in 2; and 3 in 1 subject. 25% took science A-levels; 50% arts/humanities; 25% both. *Computing facilities:* Computer centre – 12 BBC/2 IBM 'clone'/1 Archimedes; 1 computer each in maths and economics departments. *Special provision:* for EFL and dyslexia.

European Community *Languages:* French offered: to age 14; GCSE; AS-level; A-level. German offered: to age 14; GCSE; AS-level; A-level. 25–50% take GCSE in more than 1 EC language. *Exchanges:* Regular exchanges for pupils aged 11–18 to France and Germany. *Other:* Small proportion of sixth form from EC. Small numbers of EC pupils, particularly from France, visit for 3–4 weeks. MEP visits school regularly. Extra language tuition available. EFL expert on staff.

Senior pupils' non-academic activities *Music:* 50 learn a musical instrument; 20 in school choir; 1 plays in pop group. *Drama and dance:* 70 in school productions, 60 in other drama/dance–related activities. *Art:* 6 take as non-examined subject; 25 take GCSE; 7, A-level. 2 accepted for Art School. 10 belong to photographic club. *Sport:* Cricket, tennis, golf, swimming, football, rugby, squash, athletics, basketball, table tennis, shooting available. 70 take non-compulsory sport. 20 take exams. 4 represent county/country (cricket, rugby, squash). *Other:* 18 take part in local community schemes. 70 have bronze Duke of Edinburgh's Award, 25 silver and 7 gold. Other activities include a computer club, riding, shooting, fishing, drama, chess, debating, philately, canoeing (own canoe lake), golf (miniature practice golf course), driving lessons etc. All pupils participate in activities programme on non-games afternoon.

Careers In 1990, 80% leavers went on to degree courses; 5% to art/drama/music colleges; 10% to non-degree courses (eg HND); 5% straight into careers (eg banking, insurance, retailing, construction). Of those going on to degree courses, 30% went to universities; 70% to polys. 5% those going on to higher education went to courses in practical art; 60% in humanities/social sciences; 5% in medicine; and 30% in science/engineering.

Uniform School uniform worn throughout.

Houses/prefects Competitive houses. Prefects, head boy, head of house and house prefects – appointed by housemaster and Headmaster.

Religion Some compulsory religious worship; more encouraged.

Social Ski-ing trips (France/Switzerland), cultural exchanges (France and Germany), canoeing (France), geography field trip (S. France). Pupils allowed to bring own car/bike/motorbike to school. Meals formal. School shop. No tobacco/alcohol allowed.

Discipline No corporal punishment. Pupils failing to produce homework once might expect to re-do work, be detained, gated or put on housemaster's report; those caught smoking cannabis on the premises could expect expulsion.

Boarding 4% have own study bedroom (but all sixth have studies), 50% are in dormitories of 6+. Houses, of approx 30, same as competitive houses, single sex. Resident matron + assistant (RGN). Central dining room. Pupils can provide and cook own food. 5 weekend exeats each term. Visits to local town allowed occasionally and where necessary (15+).

Alumni association (Old Embleian's) run by R Bell, Hon Secretary, 3 Windbrook Meadow, Stratton St Margaret, Swindon, Wiltshire.

· *Eothen* ·

Eothen School
3 Harestone Hill
Caterham
Surrey CR3 6SG
Tel 0883 43386
Fax 0883 341837

- Pupils 340
- Boys None
- Girls 3–18
  (Day)
- Upper sixth 9

- Termly fees
  £1122 (Day)
- GSA, CSCL
  Enquiries/application to
  the Headmistress

What it's like

Founded in 1892, it belongs to the Church Schools' Company and occupies a pleasant wooded site of six and a half acres near the middle of Caterham, 2 minutes from the station. The junior school adjoins the main school in its own grounds. It has a good range of modern facilities including a new arts and science centre opened in 1989 and provides good teaching and a sound general education. There is a fair amount of musical and dramatic activity. Sport and games are well provided for.

School profile

Pupils Total age range 3–18; 340 day girls. Senior department 11–18, 200 girls. Main entry ages 3, 7, 11 and into sixth. Approx 10% are children of former pupils. Over 50% of senior department from own junior. *Transfer from maintained schools:* 20% intake at 11, plus occasionally to sixth.

Entrance Common entrance and own entrance exam used. Not oversubscribed. No special skills or religious requirements although the school belongs to the Church Schools Company (an Anglican body). Parents not expected to buy text books; extras are lunch (£1.30/day), music (£60/instrument/term) and outings. Scholarships/bursaries 50%–33$\frac{1}{3}$% of fees.

Staff Headmistress Miss D C Raine, in post for 18 years. 23 full time staff, 13 part time. Annual turnover 5%. Average age 45.

Academic work GCSE and A-levels. 16 subjects offered (no A-level general studies). In 1990, 35 pupils in upper fifth, 7 in upper sixth (now 9). *GCSE:* in 1990, 12 upper fifth gained at least grade C in 8+ subjects; 9 in 5–7; and 12 in 1–4 subjects. *A-levels:* 3 upper sixth passed in 3 subjects; 3 in 2; and 1 in 1 subject; 4 gained AS-level. 3 took science A-levels; 5 arts/humanities. *Computing facilities:* 12 computers in Information Technology centre plus 5 in specialist rooms. *Special provision:* Extra lessons may be arranged for mild dyslexia problems and for preparation for EFL certificates.

European Community *Languages:* French offered: to age 14; GCSE; AS-level; A-level. German offered: to age 14; GCSE; AS-level; A-level. 10–25% take GCSE in more than 1 EC language. *Other:* European Studies offered to pupils aged 11–14. Occasional visits to France for girls to stay with families and see Paris. Interested parents are helped to arrange exchanges.

Senior pupils' non-academic activities *Music:* 60 learn a musical instrument, 6 to Grade 6 or above, occasional pupil accepted for Music College. 5 in school orchestra, 20 in school choir; 1 in Croydon Wind Band, 1 in Sutton Schools Orchestra. *Drama and dance:* Numbers in school productions vary; occasional pupil accepted for Drama School or goes on to work in theatre. *Art:* 20 take GCSE; 3 A-level. Senior pupils can take life drawing classes. Occasional pupils accepted for Art School. Others have gone on to window dressing or theatrical costume design. *Sport:* Netball, lacrosse, tennis, rounders, short tennis, pop lacrosse, badminton, volleyball, basketball, gymnastics, athletics, judo, horse riding, golf, fitness gym, squash, swimming available. 50 take non-compulsory sport. Occasionally pupils have represented county (judo, swimming, hurdles, golf). *Other:* 15 are working for bronze Duke of Edinburgh's Award. Some pupils enter voluntary schemes after leaving school. Other activities include a computer club, sixth form pre-driving course and electronics club.

Careers On average, 50% leavers go on to degree courses; 15% to art/drama/music colleges; 25% to non-degree courses (eg executive secretarial, foundation accountancy); 10% straight into careers (eg banking, financial services, nursing). Of those going on to degree courses, 65% go to universities; 35% to poly/colleges. 15% those going on to higher education go to courses in practical art; 35% in humanities/social sciences; and 45% in science/engineering.

Uniform School uniform worn except in sixth.

Houses/prefects Competitive houses. All sixth formers act as prefects. Head girl appointed by the Head after consultation with staff and sixth form; house captains elected by school.

Religion Daily general assembly.

Social Trips to Austria, France and

Amsterdam and ski-ing. Pupils allowed to bring own car/bike to school. Meals self service. School shop selling second-hand uniform, run by parents. No tobacco/alcohol allowed.

Discipline No corporal punishment. Pupils failing to produce homework more than once might expect warning; those caught smoking on the premises could expect parents to be asked to see Head.

Alumni association is run by Mrs M Gabain, c/o the School.

Former pupils Imogen Holst; Dame Albertine Winner (co-founder of St Christopher's Hospice); Beroe Bicknell KC, Cicely Berry (voice coach – RSC).

· *Epsom College* ·

Epsom College
Epsom
Surrey
KT17 4JQ
Tel 0372 723621

- Pupils 660
- Boys 13–18
  (Day/Board/Weekly)
- Girls 16–18
  (Day/Board/Weekly)
- Upper sixth 144

- Termly fees
  £2000 (Day)
  £2850 (Board)
  £2800 (Weekly)
- HMC
  Enquiries/application to
  the Headmaster

What it's like

Founded in 1853, it has a fine site of 80 acres close to open countryside on Epsom Downs, 15 miles south of central London. The main buildings are handsome Victorian architecture; the modern ones fit in well. Considerable modernisation and extension in recent years. Now very well equipped with every facility. It is a school which expects pupils to aim for high academic standards and at the same time to be fully involved in the general life of an active community. The teaching is well known to be good and the standards are high. Very many leavers go on to degree courses, including many to Oxbridge. French and German are offered throughout the school to A-level; also as non-examined subjects. Many pupils take GCSE in both. There are regular exchanges with France and Germany. A wide range of sport and games (again standards are high), plus many clubs and societies. Very strong in art, music and drama. A substantial commitment to local community schemes. As a C of E school, religious worship is encouraged.

School profile

Pupils Age range 13–18; 660 pupils, 279 day (264 boys, 15 girls), 381 boarding (333 boys, 48 girls). Main entry ages 13 (boys) and into sixth (boys and girls). Approx 10% are children of former pupils. *Transfer from maintained schools:* 7% main intake plus 15% to sixth.

Entrance Common entrance and own entrance exam used. Oversubscribed. No special skills or religious requirements. Parents not expected to buy text books; music tuition only major extra. 10 assisted places. 30 scholarships/bursaries for aca-demic, all-rounder, music and art, 50% to 5% of fees.

Parents 20+% in industry or commerce; 20+% are doctors, lawyers, etc. 70+% live within 30 miles; up to 10% live overseas.

Staff Headmaster Dr J B Cook, in post for 9 years. 63 full time staff, 20 part time (mostly music). Annual turnover 5%. Average age 38.

Academic work GCSE and A-levels. 17 subjects offered (no A-level general studies). In 1990, 120 pupils in fifth, 144

274

in upper sixth. *GCSE:* in 1989, 116 upper fifth gained at least grade C in 8+ subjects; 3 in 5–7; and 1 in 1–4 subjects. *A-levels:* 10 upper sixth passed in 4+ subjects; 118 in 3; 16 in 2; and 5 in 1 subject. 45% took science A-levels; 35% arts/humanities; 20% both. *Computing facilities:* Well-equipped computer studies department; most other departments have own computers. *Special provision:* Very little.

European Community *Languages:* French offered: to age 14; GCSE; A-level; non-examined. German offered: to age 14; GCSE; A-level; non-examined. 25–50% take GCSE in more than 1 EC language. *Exchanges:* Regular exchanges for pupils aged 16–18 to France and Germany.

Senior pupils' non-academic activities *Music:* 270 learn a musical instrument, 50 to Grade 6 or above, 3 accepted for Music College; 100 in school orchestra/band, 85 in school choir; 2 in National youth orchestra or band. *Drama and dance:* 250 participate in school or house productions. Exams in drama and dance not offered. *Art:* 30 take as non-examined subject; 30 take GCSE, 25 take A-level. 5 accepted for Art College. 60 belong to photographic club. *Sport:* Rugby, cricket, hockey, soccer, athletics, tennis, squash, badminton, cross-country, golf, shooting, chess, bridge, netball, lacrosse, sailing, riding, swimming, sailboarding, fencing, gymnastics, volleyball, basketball, archery and rounders available. 500 take non-compulsory sport. Exams in sport not offered. 30 represent county/country (rugby, cricket, hockey, shooting, athletics, swimming, squash, tennis, golf). *Other:* 50 take part in local community schemes. 100 have bronze Duke of Edinburgh's Award, 50 have silver and 2 gold. Other activities include a computer club and 25 non–sporting clubs and societies.

Careers In 1990, 90% leavers went on to degree courses; 3% to art/drama/music colleges; 5% to non-degree courses; 2% straight into careers. Of those going on to degree courses, 12% went to Oxbridge, 68% to other universities; 20% to poly/colleges. 2% those going on to higher education went to courses in practical art; 2% in drama/acting; 2% in music; 34% in humanities/social sciences; 15% in medicine; and 45% in science/engineering.

Uniform School uniform worn throughout.

Houses/prefects Competitive houses. Prefects, head boy/girl and head of house appointed by the Head or housemaster.

Religion Worship compulsory except for practising members of non-Christian religions.

Social Debates, intellectual and sporting competitions. Average of 5 trips abroad a year. Pupils allowed to bring own car/bike/motorbike to school. Meals self service. School shop. *Upper sixth* allowed beer on supervised occasions. No tobacco allowed.

Discipline No corporal punishment. All breaches of discipline dealt with according to the circumstances.

Boarding 10% have own study bedroom, 50% share; 30% are in dormitories of 6+. Single sex houses, of approximately 60. Two resident qualified nurses. Central dining room. Pupils can provide and cook own food. Exeats each weekend or each 3 weeks. Visits to the local town allowed.

Alumni association is run by Mrs B A Thorne, c/o the College.

Former pupils Graham Sutherland; John Piper.

· *Eton* ·

Eton College	• Pupils 1270	• Termly fees
Eton	• Boys 13–18	£3600
Windsor	(Board)	• HMC
Berkshire SL4 6DB	• Girls None	Enquiries/application to
Tel 0753 869991	• Upper sixth 255	the Registrar

What it's like

Founded in 1440 by Henry VI for the worship of God, and for the training of young men to the service of Church and State. His aim was to have 70 so trained, first at Eton, then at King's College, Cambridge. These were his Scholars. He also provided for other boys to come from any part of the realm to be taught at Eton, paying for their own maintenance. In Henry's time, or shortly afterwards, most of the school's ancient buildings were completed. These include the chapel, the cloisters, the lower school, College Hall and part of College. Building and rebuilding have gone on ever since. The whole architectural complex constitutes an urbane and civilised enclave. The numerous premises are scattered in the town of Windsor and thus there is a close 'town and gown' relationship. There are beautiful gardens and playing fields and the school is one of the best-equipped in existence. There are several excellent libraries: both College and School libraries have remarkable collections of rare books and manuscripts. There is considerable emphasis on religious instruction. Worship during a boy's time in the school is designed to meet his spiritual needs at each stage of his development. Academically Eton is very high-powered indeed. A large and very well-qualified staff permits a staff:pupil ratio of 1:9. Academic results are outstanding. Each year 205–210 pupils (more than any other school in Britain) go on to university; this figure includes 65–70 to Oxbridge. Under its general studies arrangements senior boys are offered an exceptional range of linguistic options – Arabic, African, Oriental and European. Russian and the main European Community languages are offered as main subjects to A-level and all boys take French in their first batch of GCSE's. Subsequently they may choose Oral French, German and Spanish or take additional French at AO-level; seniors may be offered Italian and Portuguese. There are regular exchange arrangements with France, Germany and Spain and all boys are encouraged to visit the countries of the languages they study. It is immensely strong in music (600 boys learn an instrument) and also in drama. The purpose-built Farrer theatre is in constant use and the English department has a drama studio in the Caccia Schools. In the course of a year there may be 20 main productions and house plays. The art department is also extremely strong. There is a very wide range of sports and games (including the Eton Wall Game and the Eton Field Game, both peculiar to the college) in which very high standards are achieved (a very large number of representatives at county and national level). At any one time 50 or more clubs and societies are active and these cater for every conceivable need. The school has its own newspaper (The Eton College Chronicle) which has been published regularly each half since 1863. There is a substantial commitment to local community services, plus the Eton–Dorney project for conferences, discussion and social work involving disadvantaged children from elsewhere, and the Eton Action fund-raising organisation. The CCF is very well supported.

School profile

Pupils Age range 13–18; 1270 boarding boys. Main entry ages 13 and exceptionally into sixth. Approx 40% are children of former pupils. *Transfer from maintained schools:* 1% main intake, plus 35% to sixth.

Entrance Common entrance used following preliminary entrance exam at age 10. Oversubscribed. No special skills or religious requirements, although school is C of E. Parents expected to buy a few senior text books; private tuition (eg music) extra. 155 scholarships (academic, music, junior and sixth form for boys from maintained schools), full fees to £250 per term. 120 bursaries.

Parents 15+% are doctors, lawyers etc; 15+% in industry or commerce. 30+% live within 30 miles; up to 10% live overseas.

Staff Head Master W E K Anderson, in post for 11 years. 136 full time staff, 6 part time. Annual turnover 6%. Average age mid thirties.

Academic work GCSE and A-levels. 29 subjects offered (including Arabic and A-level general studies). In 1989, 258 pupils in upper fifth, 255 in upper sixth. *GCSE:* in 1989, 250 upper fifth gained at least grade C in 8+ subjects; 8 in 5–7 subjects. *A-levels:* 72 upper sixth passed in 4+ subjects; 168 in 3; 10 in 2; and 5 in 1 subject. 18% took science A-levels; 53% arts/humanities; 29% both. *Computing facilities:* Two computer rooms and one or more computers in most departments.

European Community *Languages:* French offered: to age 14; GCSE; AO-level; A-level; oral French. German offered: to age 14; GCSE; A-level. Spanish offered: to age 14; GCSE; A-level. Italian and Portuguese offered to seniors. *Exchanges:* Regular exchanges for pupils to France, Germany and Spain.

Senior pupils' non-academic activities *Music:* Occasional pupil accepted for Music School; 2/3 organ/choral awards to Oxbridge. *Drama and dance:* 360 in 20 school productions pa; 100 house drama competition. 6 take A-level Drama; 1 accepted for Drama School. *Art:* 350 take as non-examined subject; 40 take GCSE; 25, A-level. 6 accepted for Art School. *Sport:* Soccer, rugby, cricket, rowing, squash, rackets, fives, swimming, judo, aikido, basketball, fencing, athletics, shooting, tennis, golf, badminton, Eton Field Game, Eton Wall Game available. 1100 take non-compulsory sport, 400 take exams (sub-aqua, gymnastics, life-saving, survival swimming). 36 pupils represent county; 17, country (rowing, swimming, water polo, rugby, cricket, athletics, golf, fencing, fives, shooting). *Other:* 130 take part in local community schemes. Other activities include computer club, social service, political, Keynes, art, history societies, CCF, beagles.

Careers 4 part time advisers. Annual average accepted for *arts and humanities degree courses* at Oxbridge, 43; other universities, 105; polytechnics/colleges, 10. *science and engineering degree courses* at Oxbridge, 22; other universities, 35; medical schools, 3; polytechnics/colleges, 5. Average going straight into careers in armed services, 8%; 2–3% in industry, the City, music/drama, other.

Uniform School uniform worn throughout.

Houses/prefects Competitive houses. Prefects, head boy, head of house and house prefects.

Religion Compulsory religious assembly unless parents request otherwise.

Social 4-day exchanges with certain comprehensive schools. French, Spanish and German exchanges; 1- or 2-person exchanges with USA, Japan; occasional trips to Russia, Malawi, Australia etc. Meals formal in some houses, self service in the remainder. Some alcohol allowed for senior boys; no tobacco.

Discipline No corporal punishment. Pupils failing to produce homework once might expect extra work; those caught smoking cannabis on the premises might expect rustication or expulsion.

Boarding All have own study bedroom. Houses, of approximately 50, same as competitive houses. Resident qualified nurse and doctor. Central dining room (for half houses). Pupils can provide and cook own food within limits. 1 exeat per

term (week in autumn term, weekend in other 2 terms). Visits to local town allowed.
Alumni association run by N J T Jaques Esq, c/o the College.

Former pupils Alec Douglas-Home; Harold Macmillan; Douglas Hurd; Lord Hailsham; Sir Robert Armstrong; Anthony Powell; Lord Carrington; Robin Leigh-Pemberton; Archbishop of York.

· *Ewell Castle* ·

Ewell Castle
Church Street
Ewell
Surrey
Tel 081 393 1413

- Pupils 545
- Boys 3–18 (Day)
- Girls 3–11 only (Day)
- Upper sixth 30

- Termly fees £1090 (Day)
- SHMIS
Enquiries/application to the Headmaster

What it's like

Founded in 1926, the main building is a castellated mansion in 15 acres of gardens and playing fields which were once part of Nonsuch Park (the grounds of Henry VIII's Nonsuch Palace). Altogether a pleasant environment in the Surrey green belt. There have been extensive modern additions and facilities are good. The co-educational junior school has a separate site close by. An interdenominational school, it is not narrowly academic, but many sixth form leavers go on to degree courses. French, German and Spanish are offered to A-level and many pupils take GCSE in more than one European language. Its sporting record is good and it has a well-organised pastoral system. High standards of discipline are expected.

School profile

Pupils Total age range 3–18; 545 day pupils (495 boys, 50 girls). Senior department 11–18, 370 boys. Main entry ages 3 (boys and girls); 11, 13 and into sixth (boys). Approx 5% are children of former pupils. *Transfer from maintained schools:* 50% intake at 11 and 13.

Entrance Common entrance and own entrance exam used. Moderately oversubscribed. No special skills or religious requirements. Parents not expected to buy text books. Some scholarships/bursaries available, up to 100% of fees.

Staff Headmaster R A Fewtrell, in post for 8 years. 41 full time staff. Annual turnover 5%. Most staff under 40.

Academic work GCSE, AS and A-levels. 16 GCSE subjects offered; 15 at AS/A-level (including A-level general studies). In 1990, 65 pupils in upper fifth, 30 in upper sixth. *GCSE:* in 1990, 30% pass 7+ subjects. *A-levels:* on average, 2

pupils in upper sixth pass 4 subjects; 15, 3 subjects; 4, 2 subjects and 3 pass 1 subject. On average, 12 take science/engineering A-levels; 6 take arts and humanities; 6 both. *Computing facilities:* 14 BBC Bs on a network. *Special provision:* Setting in English and individual help for dyslexic pupils.

European Community *Languages:* French offered: to age 14; GCSE; AS-level; A-level. German offered: to age 14; GCSE; A-level. Spanish offered: to GCSE; A-level. 25–50% take GCSE in more than 1 EC language. *Exchanges:* Regular exchanges for pupils aged 11–16 to France.

Senior pupils' non-academic activities *Music:* 30 learn a musical instrument, 2 to Grade 6 or above. About 6 play in orchestras. Some 6 continue their interest in music beyond school. *Drama and dance:* School productions; exams not offered. *Art:* 20 take GCSE; 10 take A-level; 1–2 pa accepted for Art School. 50 belong to eg photographic club. *Sport:* Rugby, soccer, cricket, tennis, fencing, squash, cross country, athletics, swimming, badminton, basketball available. Sport compulsory to 5th year; most sixth form take part in non-compulsory sport. 6 represent county/country (squash, cricket, rugby). *Other:* Some take part in local community schemes. Other activities include a computer club, bridge, rifle club, Army Cadet Force, railway club.

Careers In 1990, 84% leavers went on to degree courses; 7% to art/drama/music colleges; 3% to non-degree courses; 6% straight into careers (eg banking). Of those going on to degree courses, 50% went to universities; 50% to poly/colleges. 6% those going on to higher education went to courses in practical art; 40+% in humanities/social sciences; 6% in medicine; and 40% in science/engineering.

Uniform School uniform worn throughout.

Houses/prefects Competitive houses. Prefects and head boy appointed by head.

Religion Religious worship is compulsory unless exempted by parental request.

Social Joint theatrical ventures with local girls' school. Rugby, ski-ing trips abroad. French exchange with Avignon. Pupils allowed to bring own car/bike/motorbike to school. Meals self service. School tuck shop. No tobacco/alcohol allowed.

· *Exeter* ·

Exeter School
Exeter
Devon
EX2 4NS
Tel 0392 73679

- Pupils 715
- Boys 11–18 (Day/Board/Weekly)
- Girls 16–18 (Day)
- Upper sixth 128

- Termly fees £995 (Day) £1855 (Board/Weekly)
- HMC

Enquiries to the Headmaster
Application to the Headmaster's Secretary

What it's like

Founded in 1633, it stands in 27 acres of pleasant grounds within a mile of the city centre. It has occupied its present site since 1880 and most of its well-designed buildings date from that time. There have been many recent additions and it now enjoys first-rate facilities. A C of E school, its moral and spiritual life depends on a general acceptance of Christian values. There is emphasis on encouragement to the individual, on self-discipline and self-motivation. A well-run school with high all-round standards and impressive academic results. Many go on to degree courses, including a high proportion to Oxbridge. French and German are offered at GCSE and many pupils take both; in addition, Spanish is taught at A-level. There are regular exchanges with France and Germany. There is a massive involvement in music and drama. A very good range of games and sports (high standards attained) and outdoor activities (eg adventure training on Dartmoor). The school has always been closely involved with the life of the city and its university and it has a substantial commitment to local community schemes.

School profile

Pupils Age range 11–18; 715 pupils, 660 day (612 boys, 48 girls), 55 boarding (all boys). Main entry ages 11, 12 and 13 (boys); and into sixth (boys and girls). Approx 20% are children of former pupils. 25% of intake from Exeter Prep School. *Transfer from maintained schools:* 50% main intake, plus 50% to sixth.

Entrance Common entrance and own entrance exam used. Oversubscribed. No special skills required but sport and the arts help. No particular religious persuasion required, but Christians fit most easily. Parents not expected to buy text books; extras unlikely to exceed £10 (CCF, sixth form common room sub etc). 30 assisted places pa. 4+ scholarships/bursaries, 10–100% fees pa.

Parents 10+% are doctors. 60+% live within 30 miles; up to 10% live overseas.

Staff Headmaster G T Goodall, in post for 12 years. 55 full time staff, 11 part time. Average age 39.

Academic work GCSE and A-levels. 20 GCSE subjects offered; 28 at A-level (including Russian and Electronics; no A-level general studies but non-examined sixth form general studies course). In 1990, 105 pupils in upper fifth, 110 in upper sixth (now 128). *GCSE:* in 1990, 86 upper fifth gained at least grade C in 8+ subjects; 15 in 5–7; and 4 in 1–4 subjects. *A-levels:* 9 upper sixth passed in 4+ subjects; 79 in 3; 8 in 2; and 9 in 1 subject. 55% took science A-levels; 40% arts/humanities; 5% both. *Computing facilities:* 27 computers in total: 15, plus robot, in computer lab plus one in each main department. *Special provision:* Mild handicaps accepted.

European Community *Languages:* French offered: to age 14; GCSE; AS-level; A-level; non-examined. German offered: to GCSE; AS-level; A-level; non-examined. Spanish offered: to AS-level; A-level. 25–50% take GCSE in more than 1 EC language. *Exchanges:* Regular exchanges for pupils aged 11–18 to France and Germany. *Other:* Talks from MEPs. European students stay for 1 year, in boarding house. Some pupils go on to become language assistants in France.

Senior pupils' non-academic activities *Music:* 300+ learn a musical instrument, 30 up to Grade 6 or above, 3 accepted for Music Colleges/University; 7 orchestras with a total of 200 pupils, 100 in school choir, 30 in school pop groups (joint with St Margaret's School); 15 in county orchestra. *Drama and dance:* 200 in school productions; 3 in NYMT. 3 accepted for Drama Schools and degree courses. *Art:* 20 take as non-examined subject; 50 take GCSE, 24 take A-level. 2 accepted for Art School. 20 belong to eg photographic club. *Sport:* Rugby, hockey, cross-country, cricket, athletics, tennis, swimming, squash, badminton, basketball, golf, canoeing, volleyball available. 150–200 take non-compulsory sport. Over 60 pupils represent county (cricket, squash, golf, tennis, rugby, badminton, athletics, hockey, basketball, running) 3 internationals. *Other:* 100 take part in local community schemes. 360 in CCF (voluntary). 12 have bronze Duke of Edinburgh's Award, 6 have silver and 3 are going for gold. Other activities include a computer club, 20 or more clubs from debating to classics or chess.

Careers In 1990, 83% leavers went on to degree courses; 3% to art/drama/music colleges; 3% to non-degree courses (eg HND courses); 3% straight into careers (eg banking); 8% other. Of those going on to degree courses, 16% went to Oxbridge; 75% to other universities; 9% to poly/colleges. 1% those going on to higher education went to courses in practical art; 2% in drama/acting; 3% in music; 18% in humanities/social sciences; 8% in medicine; 18% in science/engineering; and 50% in other subjects.

Uniform School uniform worn except in the sixth form.

Houses/prefects Competitive houses. Prefects, head boy, head of house and house prefects – appointed by the Head, staff and upper sixth.

Religion Morning assemblies in chapel, 11–16 year olds.

Social Joint sixth form lessons and theatrical productions with local girls' schools. Annual trips abroad. Exchanges to Rennes and Hildesheim, Soviet Union and USA.

Pupils allowed to bring own car/bike/ motorbike to school. Meals self service. School shop. No tobacco/alcohol allowed. **Discipline** No corporal punishment. Pupils failing to produce homework once might expect detention; if caught smoking cannabis on the premises punishment would depend on whether it was repeated. **Boarding** Sixth formers have own study bedroom, others share, 2–3. One boarding house of 55 pupils. Qualified resident matron; school doctor visits. Central dining room. Pupils can provide and cook own food. Exeats at weekends and half-term. Visits to the local town allowed. **Alumni association** is run by D Mullins, c/o the School. **Former pupils** MPs, bishops, TV commentators, actors, conductors, generals, explorers, scientists and so on. Former CinC NATO NW Europe and Commandant of the Parachute Regiment.

f

· *Farlington* ·

Farlington School
Strood Park
Horsham
West Sussex
RH12 3PN
Tel 0403 54967

- Pupils 275
- Boys None
- Girls 9–18
  (Day/Weekly Board)
- Upper sixth 15

- Termly fees
  £1325 (Day)
  £2150 (Weekly)
- GSA, BSA
  Enquiries/application to
  the Headmistress

What it's like

Founded in 1896, it lies in delightful grounds and gardens in a large park. The main building, formerly a country house, is part Jacobean and part Georgian. Other handsome buildings are nearby. New facilities were added in 1980 and further classrooms and sixth form facilities in 1988/89. A sound general education is provided and results are creditable. The sixth form has recently expanded significantly; most upper sixth leavers go to degree courses each year. French, German and Spanish are offered at GCSE and many girls take GCSE in more than one European language. The music, games and art depts are very active. A good range of sport, games and activities. Excellent record in the Duke of Edinburgh's Award Scheme.

School profile

Pupils Total age range 9–18; 275 girls, 205 day, 70 boarding. Senior department 11–18, 248 girls. Main entry ages 11, 12, 13 and into sixth. Approx 1% are children of former pupils. *Transfer from maintained schools:* 40% intake over 11, plus 2% to sixth.

Entrance Own entrance exam used. Oversubscribed. No special religious requirements; favours girls with active extra-curricular interests (music, sport). Parents not expected to buy text books; extras £60 each per term. 6 scholarships/bursaries pa, half to one-third fees.

Staff Headmistress Mrs P Metham, in post for 3 years. 27 full time staff, 27 part time. Annual turnover 5%. Average age 45.

Academic work GCSE, AS and A-levels. 19 GCSE subjects offered; 15 at A-level (no A-level general studies). In 1990, 40 pupils in upper fifth, 15 in upper sixth. *GCSE:* in 1990, 50% upper fifth gained at least grade C in 8+ subjects; 35% in 5–7; and 15% in 1–4 subjects. *A-levels:* 52% upper sixth passed in 3 subjects; 37% in 2; and 11% in 1 subject. 90% took arts/humanities; 10% took mixture of science/engineering and arts/humanities. *Computing facilities:* Word processors and 16 BBC computers plus graphic design facilities in an Information Technology room. *Special provision:* Some individual help can be arranged.

European Community *Languages:* French offered: to age 14; GCSE; AS-level; A-level. German offered: to age 14; GCSE; AS-level; A-level. Spanish offered: to age 14; GCSE. 25–50% take GCSE in more than 1 EC language. *Exchanges:* Regular exchanges for pupils aged 14–16 to France and Germany. *Other:* Regularly host 4 European girls from France and Germany for half a term; also Spanish girls spending 1 year; likely to be continuing pattern.

Senior pupils' non-academic activities *Music:* 50 learn a musical instrument, 20 to Grade 6 or above. 5 accepted for Music School; 20 in school orchestra, 50 in school choir, 15 in wind band, 8 in jazz group. *Drama and dance:* 15 in school productions, 20 take LAMDA exams. 1 accepted for Drama/Dance School; 25 take extra speech and drama. *Art:* 20 take as non-examined subject; 20 take GCSE; 4, A-level; 2 accepted for Art School. 15 belong to photographic club. *Sport:* Hockey, netball, volleyball, rounders, tennis, athletics, swimming, dance, gym, running, ice skating, riding, ballet, judo, skiing available. 15 take non-compulsory sport. 20 take sailing, windsurfing, riding etc. 10 take exams. 6 represent county (hockey, volleyball, tennis). *Other:* 5 take part in local community schemes. 22 have bronze Duke of Edinburgh's Award, 16 have silver and 5 gold. 2 work for national charities. Other activities include computer, art and typing clubs.

Careers In 1990, 65% sixth form leavers went on to degree courses; 10% to art/drama/music colleges; 25% to non-degree courses (eg secretarial, equestrian, HND hotel management, nursing). Of those going on to degree courses, 50% went to universities; 50% to poly/colleges. 5% those going on to higher education went to courses in practical art; 10% in drama/acting; 5% in music; 75% in humanities/social sciences; and 5% in medicine.

Uniform School uniform worn except in the sixth.

Houses/prefects Competitive houses. Prefects, head girl, head of house and house prefects, elected by staff and pupils. School Council.

Religion Short religious assembly each day, juniors 1 period of RS per week; seniors 1 period of ethics.

Social Joint concerts, mainly choral, with neighbouring schools eg Cranleigh, Hurstpierpoint. Annual ball and discos. Organised trips to France, art trips to Italy, ski holidays in Alps, individual exchanges. Pupils allowed to bring own car/bike/motorbike to school. Some meals self service. No school shop but frequent sales of goods for charity. No tobacco/alcohol allowed.

Discipline No corporal punishment. Pupils failing to produce homework once might expect discussion with the subject teacher; those caught smoking on the premises should expect suspension, parental involvement and likely expulsion; drug abuse would incur immediate expulsion.

Boarding Weekly boarding only (from 1992). 5% have own study bedroom, 12% share with others; 70% in dormitories of 6+. Houses are divided as for competitive purposes. Resident qualified nurse. Central dining room. Visits to the local town allowed for 14+.

Alumni association is run by Mrs M Ladenburg, Farlington School.

· *Farnborough Hill* ·

Farnborough Hill
Farnborough
Hampshire
GU14 8AT
Tel 0252 545197
	• Pupils 500
	• Boys None
	• Girls 11–18
	  (Day)
	• Upper sixth 40
		• Termly fees
		  £1063 (Day)
		• GSA, SHA
		Enquiries to the
		Headmistress

What it's like

Founded in 1889 by the Religious of Christian Education, the school was favoured by the ex-Empress Eugenie. After her death and that of Prince Victor Napoleon the trustees of the college bought her estate of Farnborough Hill (in 1927). The whole school is established in the Empress's former home. This lies in the highest part of Hampshire on an estate of parklands and gardens covering 65 acres. Four school blocks and a chapel have been added, to make a very agreeable campus. It is Roman Catholic but girls of other Christian denominations and religious faiths are welcomed provided that they participate in the religious activities of the school and respect its Christian ideals. The school is committed to the education of the whole person within an environment based on gospel values. Each pupil is valued for herself and helped to develop her gifts in a friendly and stable atmosphere. As well as traditional emphasis on academic excellence, achievements are prized in a wider context, for example in creative arts and sports.

School profile

Pupils Age range 11–18; 500 day girls. Main entry ages 11 and into sixth. *Transfer from maintained schools:* 46% main intake, plus 25% to sixth.

Entrance Common entrance, APS, own tests used and interview. Usually oversubscribed. No special skills required. Preference given to Roman Catholics, but girls from all Christian denominations are welcomed. Parents not expected to buy text books. Assisted places (179) and bursaries (21) available.

Staff Headmistress Sister Elizabeth McCormack, in post for 3 years. 35 full time staff, 18 part time. Annual turnover 8–10%.

Academic work GCSE, AS- and A-levels. 19 GCSE subjects offered; 3 at AS-level and 22 at A-level (including Greek; no A-level general studies). In 1990, 84 pupils in upper fifth, 43 in upper sixth (now 40). *GCSE:* in 1990, 71 upper fifth gained at least grade C in 8+ subjects; 9 in 5–7; and 4 in 1–4 subjects. *A-levels:* 1 upper sixth passed in 4+ subjects; 32 in 3; 4 in 2; and 5 in 1 subject. 6 took science A-levels; 23 arts/humanities; 14 both. *Computing facilities:* 18 networked BBC Masters, 1 Nimbus. Wordprocessing and computing lessons for all; RSA exams in fifth or sixth. *Special provision:* Extra help in English – remedial help.

European Community *Languages:* French offered: to age 14; GCSE; A-level. German offered: to age 14; GCSE; A-level. Spanish offered: to age 14; GCSE; A-level. 10–25% take GCSE in more than 1 EC language. *Exchanges:* Regular exchanges for pupils aged 11–18 to France, Germany and Spain.

Senior pupils' non-academic activities Many pupils involved in music and drama. *Sport:* Hockey, netball, basketball, volleyball, badminton, tennis, cross-country, athletics, gymnastics, swimming, lacrosse, archery available (also squash, windsurfing, riding, popmobility, keep-fit, ballroom dancing, outside school for sixth form). Other activities include a computer club, fund-raising through house system, drama, sports, art workshops, strong choral tradition.

Careers In 1990, 86% leavers went on to degree courses; 9% to non-degree courses (eg nursing, secretarial); 2% straight into careers (eg legal executive); 3% other. Of those going on to degree courses, 84% went to universities; 15% to poly/colleges. 3% those going on to higher education went to courses in music; 83% in humanities/social sciences; 10% in medicine; and 3% in science/engineering.

Uniform School uniform worn except in the sixth form.

Houses/prefects Houses competitive for sports and interhouse challenges. Prefects, head girl, head of house (house captain) appointed by the Head after consultation with staff and senior pupils.

Religion School Mass compulsory on holy days of obligation and pupils attend assembly. The school aims to build a Christian community of faith. There are regular opportunities to attend Mass and receive the Sacrament of Reconciliation. The whole school attends Mass on holy days of obligation and assembly is compulsory for all.

Social Debates with other schools; oratoria with other schools and parents; dances for sixth form. Regular visits abroad; exchanges with France, Spain, Germany. Pupils allowed to bring own car/bike to school. School meals or sandwiches. School shop. No tobacco/alcohol allowed.

Discipline Various sanctions imposed according to misdemeanour. Detentions may be given outside school hours. Suspension reserved for serious offences.

Alumni association is run by Miss Kim Hasty (Secretary), FHOGA.

· *Farringtons* ·

Farringtons Girls' School Chislehurst Kent BR7 6LR Tel 081 467 0256	• Pupils 500 • Boys None • Girls 3–18 (Day/Board/Weekly) • Upper sixth 30	• Termly fees £1193 (Day) £2180 (Board) £2095 (Weekly) • GSA Enquiries to the Headmistress

What it's like

Founded in 1911, it lies in 22 acres of fine wooded parkland in the green belt on the borders of Kent and 12 miles south-east of central London. The buildings are well designed, comfortable and pleasant to look at. A full size sports hall has recently been completed. Every modern facility is provided and the boarding accommodation is comfortable. The junior and senior schools are combined so education can be continuous from 5–18. A Christian atmosphere is fostered; the chapel is central both physically and spiritually. A sound all-round education is given and exam results are good; many sixth formers go on degree courses. French, German and Spanish are offered throughout the school and an exceptionally high proportion of girls takes GCSE in more than one European language. The music and drama departments are flourishing. A good range of sports and games and a fair commitment to the Duke of Edinburgh Award Scheme, a flourishing British Association of Young Scientists and Young Enterprise Scheme.

School profile

Pupils Total age range 3–18; 500 girls, 298 day, 202 boarding. Senior department 11–18, 300 girls. Main entry ages 3, 5 and into sixth. Approx 30% are children of former pupils. *Transfer from maintained schools:* 5% main secondary intake, plus 3% to sixth.

Entrance Own entrance exam used; rarely common entrance. Sometimes oversubscribed. No special skills or religious requirements. Parents expected to buy text books after year 3; approx extras £80. Organ scholarship; 4 bursaries, from full fees to fractional fees.

Parents 15+% in industry or commerce. 10+% live within 30 miles; 30+% live overseas.

Staff Headmistress Mrs B J Stock, in post for 4 years. 30 full time staff, 12 part time. Annual turnover 2%. Average age 35.

Academic work GCSE and A-levels. 21 GCSE subjects offered; 17 at A-level (no A-level general studies). On average, 50 pupils in upper fifth, 30 in upper sixth. *GCSE:* in 1990, 17 upper fifth gained at least grade C in 8+ subjects; 15 in 5–7; and 17 in 1–4 subjects. *A-levels:* 1 upper sixth pupil passed in 4+ subjects; 9 in 3; 4 in 2; and 6 in 1 subject. 9 took science A-levels; 14 arts/humanities; 6 both. *Computing facilities:* Computer studies in curriculum up to GCSE, AS and A-level. Computers in departmental use also. *Special provision:* Extra coaching, extra English lessons, EFL.

European Community *Languages:* French offered: to age 14; GCSE; AS-level; A-level. German offered: to age 14; GCSE; AS-level; A-level. Spanish offered: to age 14; GCSE; AS-level; A-level. Over 75% take GCSE in more than 1 EC language. *Exchanges:* Regular exchanges for pupils aged 14–18 to France. *Other:* Pupils from France, Germany and Spain boarding in school; $1/2$ term or 1–2 year courses.

Senior pupils' non-academic activities *Music:* 24 learn a musical instrument, 8 to Grade 6 or above, 1 accepted for Music School; 5 in school orchestra, 44 in school choir. *Drama and dance:* 23 take ballet or modern/tap dancing; 3 take ballet exams. *Art:* 25 take GCSE; 11 take A-level, 6 take history of art; 3 accepted for Art School, 1 for university course. *Sport:* Lacrosse, tennis, basketball, badminton, netball, squash, judo, trampolining, dry ski-ing, gymnastics and athletics available. Most take non-compulsory sport. 30–40 take exams in gymnastics, swimming, trampolining, and 30 in ski-ing. 8 represent county (lacrosse). *Other:* 36 have bronze Duke of Edinburgh's Award, 9 silver. Other activities include computer, debating and philately clubs and science society, BAYS.

Careers In 1990, 70% leavers went on to degree courses; 25% to art/drama/music colleges; 5% to non-degree courses. Of those going on to degree courses, 97% went to universities; 3% to poly/colleges.

Uniform School uniform worn except in the sixth form.

Houses/prefects Competitive houses. Prefects, head girl and head of house elected by the upper sixth and appointed by the Head. School Council.

Religion Religious attendance compulsory.

Social Joint musical productions with Eltham College. Organised trips abroad. Pupils allowed to bring own car/bike to school. Meals self service. School shop. No tobacco/alcohol allowed.

Discipline No corporal punishment. Pupils failing to produce homework once might expect to repeat it twice; those caught smoking/drinking on the premises could expect expulsion.

Boarding Houses divided by age group. Qualified nurse. Central dining room. 2-day exeats twice a term. Visits to the local town allowed for years 4 upwards, Saturday afternoons; sixth form have greater weekend freedom.

Alumni association is run by Mrs Melanie O'Neill, c/o the School.

· *Felixstowe* ·

Felixstowe College
Maybush Lane
Felixstowe
Suffolk
IP11 7NQ
Tel 0394 284269

- Pupils 300
- Boys None
- Girls 11–18
- (Day/Board)
- Upper sixth 49

- Termly fees
  £1650 (Day)
  £2695 (Board)
- GSA, ESHA
Enquiries/application to
Mrs P Dangerfield
(Registrar)

What it's like

Founded in 1929, on a single site by the sea, within range of London, Ipswich, Cambridge and Norwich. Many of the school buildings were originally family homes. A continuous programme of modernisation and extension has created a compact, well-equipped campus with spacious playing fields, large sports hall and agreeable gardens. A friendly, happy family atmosphere prevails. The education is sound and broad-based. Exam results are good and many pupils go on to degree courses. Strong emphasis on Europe. The school is a member of the ESHA (European Secondary Heads Association). Six European languages are offered at GCSE – Dutch, French, German, Modern Greek, Italian and Spanish. Many pupils take GCSE in more than one European language, and there are regular exchanges with Belgium, France, Germany and Spain. Very strong indeed in music and dance (almost everyone is involved); pretty strong in drama. A fair and standard range of sport, games and extra-curricular activities. Substantial commitment to local community services, and a remarkable record in the Duke of Edinburgh's Award Scheme.

School profile

Pupils Age range 11–18; 300 girls, 35 day, 265 boarding. Main entry ages 11, 12 and into sixth. Approx 5% are children of former pupils. Own junior school. *Transfer from maintained schools:* 23% main intake, plus 15% to sixth.

Entrance Common entrance exam used. Sometimes oversubscribed. No special skills required. Church of England foundation; other religions accepted. Parents not expected to buy text books; maximum extras, £400. Assisted places. Some scholarships/bursaries up to half fees.

Parents 20+% professional (accountants, lawyers, doctors, etc); 15+% commerce; 15+% armed forces. 30+% live within 30 miles; 10+% live overseas.

Staff Headmistress Mrs A F Woodings. 44 full time staff, 12 part time. Annual turnover 10%. Average age 38.

Academic work GCSE and A-levels. 30 subjects offered. In 1990, 56 pupils in upper fifth, 51 in upper sixth (now 49). *GCSE:* in 1990, 36 upper fifth gained at least grade C in 8+ subjects; 15 in 5–7; and 5 in 1–4 subjects. *A-levels:* 6 upper sixth passed in 4+ subjects; 32 in 3; 7 in 2; and 4 in 1 subject. 7 took science A-levels; 30 arts/humanities; 11 both. *Computing facilities:* Fully equipped computer room; computers and printers in all major departments. *Special provision:* EFL for foreign students.

European Community *Languages:* Dutch offered: to GCSE. French offered: to age 14; GCSE; AS-level; A-level. German offered: to age 14; GCSE; AS-level; A-level. Greek (modern): GCSE. Italian: GCSE. Spanish offered: to age 14; GCSE; AS-level; A-level. 25–50% take GCSE in more than 1 EC language. *Exchanges:* Regular exchanges for pupils aged 11–18 to Belgium, France, Germany and Spain. *Other:* Member of ESHA

(European Secondary Heads Association). Pupils from Belgium, France, Germany, Greece and Netherlands. EFL and extra English available. Flexible academic courses (1–3 years) for European girls. Duke of Edinburgh Award expeditions in Europe. Sports fixtures against European schools.

Senior pupils' non-academic activities *Music:* 189 learn a musical instrument, 57 to Grade 6 or above, 9 take GCSE, 3 A-level, 1 accepted for Music School, 1 accepted for teacher training (music), 36 in school orchestra, 40 in school choir, 6 in school pop group, 7 in jazz band, 13 in wind ensemble, 16 in string ensemble, 12 in Gilbert and Sullivan group, 1 in Suffolk Schools Orchestra. *Drama and dance:* 95 in school productions; 90 in speech and drama lessons, 46 public speaking course, 152 take dance, 73 STD syllabi (ballet, modern and tap); 88 take LAMDA exams, 29 ISTD Dance Exam; 1 accepted for Drama School, 1 for Dance School. *Art:* Varying numbers take as non-examined subject, 40 take GCSE, 10 A-level, 12 history of art. 2–3 go on to history of art degrees; 2–3 accepted for Art School. *Sport:* Hockey, tennis, rounders, swimming, netball, trampolining, golf, badminton, squash, fencing, orienteering, cricket, volleyball available. 120 take non-compulsory sport. 4–6 pupils represent county (junior) at hockey. *Other:* 42 take part in local community schemes. 50 have bronze Duke of Edinburgh's Award, 20 have silver and 15 gold. Other activities include computer club, chess club, debating society, gym club, Christian Union, bridge club, country dancing, Young Enterprise, mathematics club, ballroom dancing, photography, mini-enterprise, Felixstowe Leadership and Enterprise Awards Scheme.

Careers In 1990, 90% leavers went on to degree courses; 4% to art/drama/music colleges; 4% to non-degree courses (eg pre-nursing courses, HND computer studies). Of those going on to degree courses, 2% went to Oxbridge; 82% to other universities; 16% to poly/colleges. 4% those going on to higher education went to courses in practical art; 2% in drama/acting; 66% in humanities/social sciences; and 28% in science/engineering.

Uniform School uniform worn, with some flexibility in sixth form.

Houses/prefects Competitive houses. Prefects, head girl, head of house and house prefects – appointed by the Headmistress, staff and pupils.

Religion Religious worship compulsory.

Social Combined choir performances, community service, lectures, sixth form dances with local schools. Organised trips abroad. Sixth formers allowed to bring own bike. Meals self service. School bookshop. School bank. No tobacco/alcohol allowed.

Discipline No corporal punishment. Smoking results in gating or suspension.

Boarding Upper fifth have own study bedroom, lower sixth own study bedroom or share with 1/2; 16% are in dormitories of 6+. 7 houses, of 14–58, divided by age group. Resident qualified nurse. Central dining room. Sixth form cook own food at weekends. Termly exeats: half-term plus 2 weekends (juniors); flexible weekends (sixth form). Visits to the local town allowed.

Alumni association is run by Mrs J Copland, Boundary House, North Waltham, Basingstoke, Hants RG25 2BG.

· *Felsted* ·

Felsted School	● Pupils 479	● Termly fees
Dunmow	● Boys 13–18	£2390 (Day)
Essex	(Day/Board)	£3030 (Board)
CM6 3LL	● Girls 16–18 (Board)	● HMC
Tel 0371 820258	● Upper sixth 111	Enquiries/application to
		the Headmaster

What it's like

Founded in 1564, it lies in the village of Felsted in beautiful countryside. A number of the original 16th-century buildings are still in use. Many modern developments. Architecturally the whole school is extremely pleasing and it has splendid grounds covering some 70 acres. Virtually every conceivable modern facility is provided, including comfortable boarding accommodation. It is a C of E school and all pupils attend the various services in chapel. An excellent all-round education is given and a large number of leavers proceed to degree courses, including many to Oxbridge. French, German and Spanish are offered up to A-level and four languages – Italian, Portuguese, Spanish and German – are offered not only for RDAs but as non-examined languages. There are regular exchanges with France, Germany and Spain. The music, drama and art departments are strong and there is a very good range of sports and games (in which high standards are achieved, especially in hockey). Many extra-curricular activities. Substantial commitment to local community services and participation in the Duke of Edinburgh Award Scheme.

School profile

Pupils Age range 13–18; 479 pupils, 20 day (all boys), 459 boarding (400 boys, 59 girls). Main entry ages 13 (boys) and into sixth (boys and girls). Approx 12% are children of former pupils. More than 20% from Felsted Prep School. *Transfer from maintained schools:* 5% main intake, plus 15% to sixth.

Entrance Common entrance and own entrance exam used. No special skills or religious requirements. Parents expected to buy text books in sixth form only; average extras £150. 38 assisted places. 16 scholarships/bursaries, 50%–10% of fees with extra bursary funding available in cases of proven need.

Parents 10+% live within 30 miles; up to 10% live overseas.

Staff Headmaster E J H Gould, in post for 8 years. 50 full time staff, 2 part time. Annual turnover 6%. Average age 40.

Academic work GCSE and A-levels. 25 subjects offered (no A-level general studies). In 1990, 88 pupils in upper fifth, 111 in upper sixth. *GCSE:* Over last 2 years upper fifth pupils gained an average of 7.7 subjects at grade C or above. *A-levels:* Over last 3 years 88% pupils passed 2 or more subjects. Slightly more took humanities than science. *Computing facilities:* Extensive network around both residential and teaching areas. *Special provision:* Certificate of competence in English taken.

European Community *Languages:* French offered: to GCSE; A-level. German offered: to GCSE; A-level; RSA; non-examined. Italian offered: RSA; non-examined. Portuguese offered: RSA; non-examined. Spanish offered: to GCSE; A-level; RSA; non-examined. Under 10% take GCSE in more than 1 EC language. Occasionally modern Greek and Italian provided for GCSE and A-level. *Exchanges:* Regular exchanges on demand for pupils aged 14–18 to France, Germany and Spain. *Other:* Pupils from France, Germany and Italy attended the school recently.

Senior pupils' non-academic activities *Music:* Significant number learn a musical instrument. Associated Board exams, Grade 8 taken in a range of instruments. Orchestras, chamber groups, choir, choral society; some pupils reach National Youth Orchestra and win choral scholarships. Each year pupils are in Essex Youth Orchestras. Music is compulsory part of curriculum in 1st year. *Drama:* Drama on the curriculum (compulsory in 1st year) but no A-level. Regular school, house and year group productions. *Art:* Art and history of art to A-level. Well-supported as examined and extra-curricular subject. Compulsory part of the curriculum in 1st year. *Sport:* Rugby, football, cricket, hockey, squash, swimming, cross-country running, tennis, athletics, shooting, fencing, badminton, netball and others. Sports Hall related activities available. All pupils take athletic exercise, from health related fitness programmes to specialised coaching in a range of sports. Regular county representation; higher/national selection gained by some. *Other:* Duke of Edinburgh's Award Scheme available. Contributions are made to local community activities. Other activities include computer club and wide range of (40) society/club activity based on the Bury, a special house for societies and spare time activities.

Careers In 1990, 80% leavers went on to degree courses; 3% to art/drama/music colleges; 5% to non-degree courses (eg accountancy, secretarial, agriculture); 10% straight into careers (eg army, navy, insurance, advertising); 2% other. Of those going on to degree courses, 10% went to Oxbridge; 61% to other universities; 29% to poly/colleges. 6% those going on to higher education went to courses in practical art; 1% in drama/acting; 1% in music; 63% in humanities/social sciences; 4% in medicine; and 25% in science/engineering.

Uniform School uniform worn except girls in sixth.

Houses/prefects Prefects. No fagging but community duties for juniors.

Religion Chapel (C of E) 4 times per week (pupils of other religions may be exempted at parents' request). Voluntary Holy Communion services weekly.

Social Meals self service; weekday lunch family service. School shop sells clothing, sports equipment and tuck. No tobacco allowed; sixth form bar at weekends (wine and beer).

Discipline No corporal punishment.

Boarding 66% in studies of 1 or 2. Single sex houses, same as competitive houses, up to 60 pupils (girls houses up to 30). Resident SRNs; daily doctor's surgery. Central dining room. Half-term plus 2 weekend exeats (one in spring term).

· *Fernhill* ·

Fernhill School	● Pupils 165	● Termly fees
Fernbrae Avenue	● Boys None	£695
Fernhill, Rutherglen	● Girls 12–18	Enquiries/application to
Glasgow G73 4SG	(Day)	the Headmistress
Tel 041 634 2674	● Higher year 32	

What it's like

Founded in 1972, it is a single site of 9 acres in the southern outskirts of Rutherglen, high above Glasgow and overlooking the Cathkin Braes and a golf course; an altogether pleasant and healthy environment. It has good accommodation. A Roman Catholic school but other denominations are welcome. Attendance at religious services in school is compulsory. Its declared priorities are the training of the intellect and will according to Christian principles, the development of habits of hard work, the fostering of good social relationships and success in study. A sound education is given and results are good. A high proportion (for a small school) go on to degree courses. Strong in music, art, drama and chess. A decent range of games, sports and activities.

School profile

Pupils Age range 12–18; 165 day girls. Main entry age, 12. Own primary department provides over 50%. *Transfer from maintained schools:* 45% main intake, plus 8% to sixth.

Entrance Own entrance exam used. Oversubscribed. No special skills; school is Roman Catholic but other denominations accepted. Parents not expected to buy text books. 38 assisted places.

Parents 15+% are doctors, lawyers etc; 15+% in industry or commerce.

Staff Headmistress Mrs E M Fitzpatrick, in post for 14 years. 7 full time staff, 9 part time. Annual turnover low. Average age 43.

Academic work O/S-grades/Highers and A-levels. 15 subjects offered (no A-level general studies). On average, 28 pupils in O/S-grade year, 32 in Highers, 4 in A-level year. *O/S-grade:* on average, 22 pupils passed in 8+ subjects; 5 in 5–7; and 1 in 1–4 subjects. *Highers:* 16 pupils passed in 5+ subjects; 8 in 4; 5 in 3; 2 in 2; and 1 in 1 subject. *A-levels:* On average 1 pupil passed in 3 subjects; 2 in 2; 1 in 1. On average 15% took science Highers; 15% arts/humanities; 70% both. *Computing facilities:* One computer room and facilities in the science lab.

European Community *Languages:* French offered: to age 14; S-grade; Higher. German offered: to age 14; S-grade; Higher. Italian offered: to Higher. 10–25% take S-grade in more than 1 EC language.

Senior pupils' non-academic activities *Music:* 30 learn a musical instrument, 4 to Grade 6 or above; 30 in school choir, 15 in ensembles. *Drama and dance:* 40 in school productions; 16 in Scottish country dance display teams. 2 take up to Grade 6 in ESB, RAD etc. 1 goes on to work in theatre. *Art:* 60 take as non-examined subject; 16, O-grade; 5, Higher. 2 accepted for Art School. *Sport:* Hockey, netball, tennis, badminton, volleyball, swimming available. 60 take non-compulsory sport. 3 pupils represent county/country (athletics, golf, hockey). Other activities include chess – regional and national competitions; public speaking – regional and national competitions.

Careers In 1990, 65% leavers went on to degree courses; 13% to non-degree courses (eg HND business studies, computing, secretarial); 22% straight into careers (eg modelling, nursing, banking). Of those going on to degree courses, 73% went to universities; 27% to poly/colleges. 6% those going on to higher education went to courses in practical art; 54% in humanities/social sciences; 12% in medicine; and 24% in science/engineering.

Uniform School uniform worn, modified in sixth.

Houses/prefects Competitive houses. Prefects, head girl, head of house and house prefects elected by staff and school.

Religion Attendance at services compulsory; participation not.

Social Chess, debates, hockey, swimming competitions with local schools; regular ski trips in Scotland and abroad, occasional educational trips abroad. Pupils allowed to bring own car/bike/motorbike to school. Meals self service. No tobacco/alcohol allowed.

Discipline No corporal punishment. Pupils failing to produce homework once might expect a warning; any pupils caught smoking cannabis on the premises would be expelled.

Alumni association run by Mrs L McLay, Deputy Headmistress.

· Fettes ·

Fettes College
Carrington Road
Edinburgh
EH4 1QX
Tel 031 332 2281

- Pupils 450
- Boys 10–18
  (Day/Board)
- Girls 10–18
  (Day/Board)
- Higher year 100

- Termly fees
  £2095 (Day)
  £3120 (Board)
- HMC
  Enquiries/application to
  the Headmaster

What it's like

Founded in 1870 under the will of Sir William Fettes, twice Lord Provost of Edinburgh. It occupies a splendid estate of 100 acres a mere $1\frac{1}{2}$ miles from the centre of the city. The main building is Victorian Gothic; since 1945 there have been extensive additions. Boarding accommodation and facilities are good. The junior school is in the college grounds. The college has a Christian approach but is non-denominational. There are Anglican and Presbyterian chaplains and there is emphasis on religious instruction and worship. A distinguished and well-run school with a friendly atmosphere, in which great attention is given to individual needs. Its declared aim is to provide a balanced and challenging education. Pupils are encouraged to aim at and to achieve the very highest standard of which they are capable. A large staff permits a staff:pupil ratio of 1:8. Academic standards are high and results are excellent. Very many pupils go on to degree courses, including many to Oxbridge. Very strong indeed in music, art and drama. Excellent range of sports and games (high standards); equally good range of extra-curricular activities. The CCF (founded 1908) is a large and particularly active contingent. Much emphasis on specialist skills and adventure training. The college has a big commitment to community service and a strong record in the Duke of Edinburgh's Award Scheme. Copious use is made of Edinburgh's cultural amenities.

School profile

Pupils Age range 10–18; 450 pupils, 70 day (47 boys, 23 girls), 380 boarding (210 boys, 170 girls). Main entry ages, 10, 13 and into the sixth. 17% are children of former pupils. Own junior school provides over 20% of intake. *Transfer from maintained schools:* 20% main intake, plus 30% to sixth.

Entrance Common entrance and own entrance exam used. Special skills taken into account; no religious requirements. Parents buy text books on a sale or return basis; branch of university bookshop on campus. 30 assisted places. Scholarships (academic and music) up to 50% fees; foundation awards and assisted places up to the full value of the fees; bursaries for forces, clergy and Old Fettesians.

Parents 15+% are doctors, lawyers etc; 15+% in industry or commerce. 50% live in Scotland; 20% elsewhere in the UK; 30% overseas.

Staff Headmaster M T Thyne, 3 years in post. 50 full time staff, 9 part time. Annual turnover 5%. Average age 40.

Academic work GCSE, Highers, A-levels. 18 subjects offered (no A-level general studies). In 1990, 69 pupils in main GCSE/O-grade year, 99 in A-level/Higher year. *GCSE/O/S-grade:* in 1990, 48 pupils passed in 8+ subjects; 12 in 5–7; and 9 in 1–4 subjects. *Highers:* 11 passed in 5+ or more subjects; 17 in 4; 7 in 3; 5 in 2; 8 in 1. *A-levels:* 3 passed in 4+ subjects; 43 in 3; 4 in 2; and 1 in 1 subject. Usually an equal number of pupils study science/engineering and the arts/humanities. *Computing facilities:* Compaq system; network links 3 teaching rooms. *Special provision:* Extra tuition in English.

European Community *Languages:* French offered: to age 14; GCSE; AS-level. German offered: to GCSE; AS-level. Spanish offered: to GCSE; AS-level. 25–50% take GCSE in more than 1 EC language. Extra tuition available in minority languages, eg Italian, Gaelic. *Exchanges:* Regular exchanges for pupils aged 11–14 to France. *Other:* Eruopean Society arranges lectures from international lawyers, civil servants, academics, MEPs. Some 5% pupils are domiciled in other EC countries and are native speakers.

Senior pupils' non-academic activities *Music:* 40% learn a musical instrument, 40 in school orchestra, 130 in concert choir; some in Scottish National Youth Orchestra and in Edinburgh Youth Orchestra. *Drama and dance:* many productions annually. *Art:* Art, photographic and ceramics clubs. *Sport:* Rugby, hockey, lacrosse, swimming, shooting, fencing, squash, fives, badminton, basketball, netball, cross-country running and ski-ing, athletics, cricket, tennis, soccer, sailing, canoeing, climbing available. *Other:* community service, Duke of Edinburgh's Award, computer club, bell-ringing, chess, CCF, sub-aqua, climbing, ski mountaineering, driving lessons, pipe band, country dancing, political society and many others.

Careers In 1990, 90% leavers went on to degree courses; 10% to art/drama/music colleges. Of those going on to degree courses, 8% went to Oxbridge; 55% to other universities; 37% to poly/colleges. 30% those going on to higher education went to courses in practical art;

1% in music; 38% in humanities/social sciences; 5% in medicine; and 27% in science/engineering.

Uniform School uniform worn including the sixth.

Houses/prefects Competitive houses. Prefects, head boy/girl, head of house and house prefects.

Religion Daily interdenominational chapel services.

Social Joint careers talks and society meetings with other local schools. Organised expeditions to eg Norway, Greenland, Kashmir, Ecuador, Kenya; exchanges with Canadian, American, German and Australian schools. Meals self service. School shop. No tobacco allowed; alcohol on specified occasions for sixth formers.

Discipline No corporal punishment. Strong emphasis on discipline and good manners. Anyone involved in drugs may expect expulsion.

Boarding Nearly all sixth form in study bedrooms; most others in dormitories of 4–6. Single sex houses, of approx 60. Resident qualified medical staff. Central dining room. Pupils can provide and cook own food to a limited extent. 4 Sunday exeats or 2 weekends each term. Visits to the local town allowed at specified times.

Alumni association is run by G D C Preston, c/o the College.

Former pupils Iain Macleod; Selwyn Lloyd; Lord Fraser of Kilmorack; Lord Drumalbyn; Tilda Swinton; Lt General Sir John Learmont; Tony Blair MP; Lord Justice Woolf.

· *Forest School* ·

Forest School	• Pupils 1149	• Termly fees
College Place	• Boys 7–18	£1348 (Day)
Near Snaresbrook	(Day/Board/Weekly)	£2033 (Board/
London	• Girls 7–18	Weekly)
E17 3PY	(Day)	• HMC
Tel 081 520 1744	• Upper sixth 118	Enquiries/application to
		the Warden

What it's like

Founded in 1834 as 'The Forest Proprietary School', it became Forest School in 1847, and in 1947 attained charitable status and became a public school. It has a big campus in an open part of Epping Forest. In effect, three schools share this campus: the boys' school, divided into senior and junior departments and the girls' school. The latter has its own block for teaching girls up to age 16. The sixth form is co-educational. The original Georgian building is used for dormitories, libraries, recreation rooms and offices. There have been many additions since 1950, including a theatre, a sports hall and a large computer centre. Excellent playing fields cover the 27 acres. Religious worship is in accordance with Anglican faith and practice. All pupils are required to attend services in chapel. A broad general education is provided for GCSE and A-level. Academic standards and results are high. French and German are offered to A-level and there are regular exchanges with France and Germany. The music, drama and art departments are strong. A good range of sports and games is available. All pupils are expected to take part in these. Standards in hockey, cricket, soccer and rowing are high. Extra-curricular activities are numerous. There is a big commitment to local community services. Full use is made of the cultural amenities of London.

School profile

Pupils Total age range 7–18; 1149 pupils (795 boys, 354 girls). Senior department 11–18, 977 pupils (639 boys, 338 girls). Main entry ages 7, 11 and into sixth. *Transfer from maintained schools:* 47% senior intake, plus 70% to sixth.

Entrance Common entrance and own exam used. Assisted places. Substantial number of scholarships, including music.

Staff Warden J C Gough, in post for 8 years.

Academic work GCSE, AS and A-levels. 19 GCSE subjects offered; 11 at AS-level; 18 at A-level (including computer studies at AS/A-level and general studies at A-level). In 1989, 153 pupils in fifth, 111 in upper sixth (now 118). *GCSE:* in 1989, 66% fifth gained at least grade C in 8+ subjects; 19% in 5–7; and 15% in 1–4 subjects. *A-levels:* 56% upper sixth passed in 4+ subjects; 20% in 3; 16% in 2; and 8% in 1 subject. 28% took science A-levels; 59% arts/humanities; 13% both. *Computing facilities:* Excellent; 3 fully equipped labs with Archimedes and 6km of networking to every dept of school.

European Community *Languages:* French offered: to GCSE; AS-level; A-level. German offered: to GCSE; A-level. 25–50% take GCSE in more than 1 EC language. *Exchanges:* Regular exchanges for pupils aged 11–18 to France and Germany.

· Fort Augustus ·

Fort Augustus Abbey
School
Fort Augustus
Inverness-shire
PH32 4DB
Tel 0320 6232
Fax 0320 6218

- Pupils 70
- Boys 12–18
- (Board/Weekly)
- Girls None
- Higher year 16

- Termly fees
  £1372 (Day)
  £2100 (Board)
  £2000 (Weekly)
- SCIS
  Enquiries/application to
  the Headmaster

What it's like

Founded in 1878. The Benedictine Abbey was founded in 1876 as a successor to two much older monasteries: the Abbey of St James of the Scots in Ratisbon on the Danube (founded c1100), and the English Abbey of SS Adrian and Denys at Lamspring near Hanover (founded 1645). The monastery, abbey and school have a magnificent site, on the position of the old redcoat fort, at the southern end of Loch Ness. The buildings are fine examples of late Victorian architecture and the whole complex constitutes a grade 1 listed building. The present school accommodation (which can take up to 150 boys) comprises the original main school block of 1878, a new wing opened in 1960 and a completely refurbished block for studies and administration taken over from the monastery in 1988. It has all the advantages of a very small school and there are 11 teaching staff for 70 boys. Some 80% of the pupils are Roman Catholics. Doctrine according to the Church is taught throughout the school and some religious services are compulsory. Some of the school's declared aims are: to give an all-round education, mental and physical, spiritual and academic; to produce a young adult who is a Christian and a responsible citizen who is alive to the challenges facing him in the world and the Church. Academic standards are high and a number of leavers go on to degree courses each year. There is considerable strength in music, drama and art. Most pupils are involved in sport and games. There is a good range of activities, with quite a lot of emphasis on outdoor pursuits for which the highland environment is ideal. The CCF contingent is particularly strong.

School profile

Pupils Age range 12–18; 70 boarding boys. Main entry ages 12, 14 and into sixth. Approx 5% are children of former pupils. *Transfer from maintained schools:* 80% main intake, plus 90% to sixth.

Entrance By interview and school report. Not oversubscribed. No special skills or religious requirements, but 80% of pupils are Roman Catholic. Extras: music tuition £60; otherwise rarely above £25. 35 assisted places; discounts for service families and sons of old boys.

Parents 20+% in industry or commerce; 20% farmers, etc.; 15+% are doctors, lawyers etc. Up to 10% live within 30 miles; 10+% live overseas.

Staff Headmaster T E Delepine, in post 2 years. 11 full time staff, 6 part time. Annual turnover 5%. Average age 45.

Academic work O/S-grades, Highers, A-levels, CSYS. In 1990, 17 pupils in O/S-grade year, 16 in Higher, 2 in A-level/CSYS. *O/S-grade:* in 1990 5 pupils passed in 8+ subjects; 7 in 5–7; and 5 in 1–4 subjects. *Highers:* 2 pupils passed in 5+ or more subjects; 10 in 4; 4 in 3 subjects. *Computing facilities:* 3 BBC, 3 Apple Macs. *Special provision:* Special personal tuition.

European Community *Languages:* French offered: to age 14; GCSE; AS-level; A-level. Italian offered: to age 14;

GCSE; AS-level; A-level. Spanish offered: to age 14; GCSE; AS-level; A-level. *Other:* EC pupils occasionally visit the school or attend for 1 or more terms. **Senior pupils' non-academic activities** *Music:* 7 learn a musical instrument. *Drama:* 25 participate in school productions. *Art:* 10 take S-grade; 5 Higher. *Sport:* Rugby, hockey, cricket, athletics, golf available. 50% take non-compulsory sport. *Other:* Other activities include a computer club, sailing, chess, bridge, photography, piping, archery, ski-ing.

Careers On average, 90% leavers went on to degree courses; 8% to non-degree courses (eg agriculture, hotel training); 2% straight into careers (eg armed services, engineering, catering). Of those going on to degree courses, 50% went to universities; 50% to poly/colleges. 1% those going on to higher education went to courses in practical art; 1% in humanities/social sciences; and 98% in science/engineering.

Uniform School uniform worn throughout.

Houses/prefects Competitive houses. Prefects, head boy, head of house and house prefects – appointed by the Head.

Religion Compulsory Mass and evening service every Sunday. Weekday worship encouraged.

Social Meals self service. School shop. Senior boys allowed some tobacco on the premises; no alcohol.

Discipline No corporal punishment. Pupils failing to produce homework once might expect to have to produce it in free time; those caught smoking cannabis (or other drugs) on the premises could expect to be expelled. Other offences: given manual tasks for several days; parents would be informed; a further offence would bring expulsion.

Boarding 20% have own study bedroom, 80% share (3). Houses, of approximately 40, same as competitive houses. Central dining room. Visits to local village allowed.

Alumni association run by Rev M B Seed, c/o the school.

· *Fosse Bank* ·

Fosse Bank School	● Pupils 191	● Termly fees
Tonbridge	● Boys None	£965 (Day)
Kent TN9 2NT	● Girls 2$^1/_2$–18	£1935 (Board)
Tel 0732 353820	(Day/Board/Weekly)	£1905 (Weekly)
	● Upper sixth Few	Enquiries/application to
		the Headmistress

What it's like

Founded in 1892, it moved to Quarry Hill in 1938. In 1947 Bidborough Court was opened for boarders. It has an urban site in pleasant surroundings and its facilities are good. A sound general education is given and results are creditable. Classes are small. Most girls leave at the end of the fifth year to go on to sixth form elsewhere; a sixth form for less academic pupils is being developed to provide for study at A-levels in art, business studies etc. Dutch, French and German are offered at GCSE and a large proportion of pupils takes GCSE in more than one European language. Art, music and drama. Adequate sports and games. A fair range of activities.

School profile

Pupils Total age range $2\frac{1}{2}$–18; 191 girls, 115 day, 76 boarding. Senior department, 12–16 or 18; 151 girls. Main entry ages 5 and 12. 1% are children of former pupils. *Transfer from maintained schools:* 20% main senior intake.

Entrance No entrance exams. Not over-subscribed. No special skills or religious requirements, but most are C of E. Parents expected to pay a stationery charge. 4 bi-annual scholarships/ bursaries, 75% of fees – £100 a term.

Parents 15+% in the armed services; 15+% in industry. 60+% live within 30 miles; 10+% live overseas.

Staff Headmistress Mrs J A Mills, in post for 3 years. 11 full time staff, 22 part time. Annual turnover 5%. Average age 40.

Academic work GCSE and A-levels. 18 subjects offered (including Dutch and A-level general studies). In 1990, 37 pupils in upper fifth. *GCSE:* in 1990, 5 upper fifth gained at least grade C in 8+ subjects; 11 in 5–7; and 14 in 1–4 subjects. *Computing facilities:* BBC and Commodore computers. *Special provision:* English as a foreign language and special teaching for mild learning problems.

European Community *Languages:* Dutch offered: to GCSE. French offered: to GCSE. German offered: to GCSE. 50–75% take GCSE in more than 1 EC language.

Senior pupils' non-academic activities *Music:* 60 learn a musical instrument, 19 play in school orchestra, 30 in choir, 14 take singing lessons. *Sport:* Hockey, netball, swimming, volleyball, badminton, athletics, tennis, gymnastics available. 11 take part in non-compulsory sport; 60% take exams eg gymnastics, swimming. Other activities include a computer club, country dancing, choir and orchestra.

Careers 1 part time careers adviser. Most fifth year leavers go on to sixth form schools or colleges of further education; some opt for A-level and/or business study courses within the school.

Uniform School uniform worn except in sixth.

Houses/prefects Competitive houses. Prefects, head girl, head of house and house prefects – appointed by the Headmistress in conjunction with staff and fifth years.

Religion Sunday church service.

Social Joint junior and senior events, eg country dancing, drama, speech and music festivals. Ski-ing holidays and language trips annually. Lunch self service, formal in boarding house. No tobacco/alcohol allowed.

Discipline No corporal punishment. Pupils failing to produce homework once might expect a verbal warning; any pupil caught smoking cannabis on the premises could expect immediate suspension and investigation (has never occurred).

Boarding Sixth have own study bedroom; large study rooms provided. Resident qualified nurse. Central dining room. Termly exeats, 2 weekends and half-term. Visits to local town allowed on Saturday mornings, third year and up.

· *Framlingham* ·

Framlingham College
Framlingham
Woodbridge
Suffolk IP13 9EY
Tel 0728 723 789
Fax 0728 724546

- Pupils 425
- Boys 13–18
  (Day/Board)
- Girls 13–18
  (Day/Board)
- Upper sixth 73

- Termly fees
  £1523 (Day)
  £2373 (Board)
- HMC
Enquiries/application to
the Headmaster's
Secretary

What it's like

Founded in 1864, it has a splendid rural site on a hill overlooking the ruins of Framlingham Castle and the town below. There are 50 acres of gardens and playing fields. The well-designed buildings are excellently equipped and provide comfortable boarding accommodation. It has a particularly fine technology and activities centre. The two latest developments have been the installation of a language laboratory and a top-class, floodlit artificial grass hockey/tennis surface. An extra girls' boarding house opened in 1991. Religious worship in the Anglican tradition is encouraged. Very strong indeed in music, drama and art. The academic standards are high and exam results are consistently good. Many sixth formers go on to degree courses. French, German and Spanish are offered at GCSE, also as non-examined languages, and French and German at A-level. All three European languages are also offered as non-examined languages. Many pupils take GCSE in more than one European language. Excellent range of sports and games in which high standards are achieved.

School profile

Pupils Age range 13–18; 425 pupils, 130 day (65 boys, 65 girls), 295 boarding (225 boys, 70 girls). Main entry ages 13 and into sixth. Approx 20% are children of former pupils. Own junior school, Brandesten Hall, provides 30+% of intake. *Transfer from maintained schools:* 4% main intake, plus 4% to sixth.

Entrance Common entrance and own entrance exam used. No special skills or religious requirements but school is C of E. Parents not expected to buy text books; other extras minimal. Assisted places. Many scholarships/bursaries, 100–10% tuition fees.

Parents 50+% live within 50 miles; 10+% live overseas.

Staff Headmaster J Miller, 2 years in post. 50 full time staff, 3 part time, plus music staff. Annual turnover 10–12%. Average age 30–35.

Academic work GCSE, AS, A-levels, City & Guilds, RSA. 19 GCSE subjects offered; 18 at A-level (including AS general studies, not A-level). In 1990, 93 pupils in upper fifth, 73 in upper sixth. *GCSE:* in 1990, 39% upper fifth gained at least grade C in 8+ subjects; 43% in 5–7; and 18% in 1–4 subjects. *A-levels:* 6% upper sixth passed in 4+ subjects; 42% in 3; 26% in 2; and 21% in 1 subject. 11% took science A-levels; 54% arts/humanities; 35% both. *Computing facilities:* Fully equipped computer centre and computers in main teaching areas and word processors in all houses and desk top publishing facilities. *Special provision:* Some special provision for EFL, dyslexia etc (contact Headmaster).

European Community *Languages:* French offered: to age 14; GCSE; AS-level; A-level; non-examined. German offered: to GCSE; AS-level; A-level; non-examined. Spanish offered: to GCSE; non-examined. 25–50% take GCSE in more than 1 EC language.

Other: Some EC pupils in school, particularly from Denmark, Germany and Spain; further links being developed. European affairs taught as part of general studies.

Senior pupils' non-academic activities *Music:* 130 learn a musical instrument, 30 to Grade 6 or above, 1 accepted for Music School; 40 in school orchestra, 70 in chapel choir, 100 in school choir. *Drama and dance:* 200 in school productions; 20 in other; 20 do GCSE drama each year; 10 A-level theatre studies; 2 accepted for Drama School, 1 now works in theatre. *Art:* 52 take GCSE, 30 take A-level. 6–10 accepted for Art School. 25 belong to eg photographic club. *Sport:* Hockey, rugby, netball, cricket, cross-country, athletics, sailing, shooting (.303, .22, clay pigeon), squash, badminton, football, archery, gymnastics, multiple indoor games, swimming, tennis, canoeing, golf, rounders available. 150 take non-compulsory sport. 10 take exams in eg gymnastics or swimming. 30 represent county (rugby, hockey, cricket, tennis). *Other:* Some pupils take part in local community schemes. 12 have silver Duke of Edinburgh's Award and 2 have gold. 4 enter voluntary schemes after leaving school. Other activities include electronics club, driving, chess, bridge, cookery, pottery, printing, wood and metal work, ballroom dancing, modelling, debating, etc.

Careers In 1990, 65% leavers went on to degree courses; 10% to art/drama/music colleges; 4% to non-degree courses (eg HND tourism, HND agriculture); 20% straight into careers (eg armed forces, nursing, estate agency); 1% other. Of those going on to degree courses, 3% went to Oxbridge; 59% to other universities; 38% to poly/colleges. 7% those going on to higher education went to courses in practical art; 5% in drama/acting; 2% in music; 60% in humanities/social sciences; 4% in medicine; and 24% in science/engineering.

Uniform School uniform, modified in the sixth, worn throughout formal part of the day.

Houses/prefects Competitive houses. Prefects, head boy/girl, head of house and house prefects – appointed by Head and housemasters/housemistress.

Religion Religious worship (C of E) encouraged.

Social Debates, choral productions, dances. Organised trips abroad. Day pupils allowed to travel to and from school in own car. Meals self service. School shop. No tobacco allowed; limited alcohol allowed for upper sixth.

Discipline Corporal punishment not allowed. Pupils failing to produce homework once would have to do it as soon as possible and may be put into detention. A pupil caught smoking cannabis on the premises must expect to be expelled (hasn't happened!).

Boarding 20–25% have own study bedroom, 55–60% share with 1–3, 15–20% in dormitories of 6+. Single sex houses, of 50–55, same as competitive houses. Resident qualified nurse. Central dining room. Pupils can provide and cook own food. Sunday exeats except when there are other commitments – occasionally overnight. Visits to the local town allowed.

Alumni association is run by V Bromage, 51 Park Road, Aldeburgh, Suffolk.

Former pupils Gen Sir Patrick Howard Dobson; N F Borrett; J F Larter; A Hancock; Gp Captain P Pickard DSO; J Paice MP; A de Cadanet.

· *Francis Holland (Regent's Park)* ·

Francis Holland School
Clarence Gate
London NW1 6XR
Tel 071-723 0176
Fax 071-706 1522

- Pupils 360
- Boys None
- Girls 11–18
- (Day)
- Upper sixth 42

- Termly fees
  £1212 (Day)
- GSA
  Enquiries/application to
  the Headmistress

What it's like

The Francis Holland (C of E) schools were founded by Canon Francis Holland. The first was opened in 1878 in Baker Street, London, and transferred in 1915 to its present building at Clarence Gate, near Regent's Park. There has been a continuous programme of modernisation and the facilities in its fine buildings are excellent. There are about 360 day girls (11–18). A sophisticated school with high academic standards, it produces first-rate results. Many go on to degree courses each year. French, German and Italian are offered to A-level, Spanish to GCSE. Many girls take GCSE in more than one European language. Religious teaching is based on the principles of the Church of England. There is much emphasis on music throughout the school. The drama and art departments are very strong and active. Regent's Park provides good facilities for sports and games, in which standards are also high. There is a good range of extra-curricular activities. Full use is made of the cultural amenities of the capital.

School profile

Pupils Age range 11–18; 360 day girls. Main entry ages 11, and into sixth. 5–10% are children of former pupils. *Transfer from maintained schools:* 25% main intake, plus 5–10% to sixth.

Entrance Own entrance exam used. Oversubscribed. No special skills or religious requirements. Parents expected to buy text books. 5 assisted places pa (age 11). 1 music, 2 sixth-form scholarships pa, £1,650-£300.

Parents 15+% are doctors, lawyers etc; 15+% from theatre, media, music; 15+% from industry/commerce.

Staff Headmistress Mrs Pamela Parsonson, in post for 3 years. 28 full time staff, 17 part time.

Academic work GCSE, AS- and A-levels. 20 subjects offered (not A-level general studies). On average, 54 pupils in upper fifth, 42 in upper sixth. *GCSE:* in 1990, 40 upper fifth gained at least grade C in 8+ subjects; 13 in 5–7 subjects. *A-levels:* In 1990 2 upper sixth passed in 4+ subjects; 24 in 3; 7 in 2; and 3 in 1 subject. 8 took science A-levels; 18 arts/ humanities; 10 both. *Computing facilities:* Network of 15 Apple Macs, 7 BBC machines.

European Community *Languages:* French offered: from age 11; GCSE; AS-level; A-level. German offered: from age 13; GCSE; AS-level; A-level. Italian offered: from age 13; GCSE; A-level. Spanish offered: to GCSE. 25–50% take GCSE in more than 1 EC language. *Exchanges:* Regular exchanges arranged individually to France.

Senior pupils' non-academic activities *Music:* 48 learn a musical instrument in school, 16 up to Grade 6; occasional pupil accepted for Music School, 16 in school orchestra, 50 in school choir, 20 in chamber choir. *Drama and dance:* 33 in school productions; 15 LAMDA Grades 7,8, Bronze, Silver. 23 participate in script-writing course (writing and performing). 4 accepted for Drama/Dance Schools over past 5 years. *Art:* 20 take GCSE art; 15 A-level art; 2–4 accepted for Art School. 20 belong to art club. *Sport:* Hockey, netball, rounders, tennis, volleyball, badminton available. 20 sixth-formers take non-compulsory sport. 2 represent county/country (tennis, gym). *Other:* 10 take part in local community schemes. 2 have bronze Duke of Edinburgh's Award and 2 silver; 2–4 enter voluntary schemes after leaving school. Other activities include debating, Young Enterprise, charity fund raising, conservation weekends with the National Trust. No formal computer club but computer room always full when open during lunchtime and breaks.

Careers In 1990, 80% leavers went on to degree courses; 5–10% to art/drama/music colleges; 5–10% to non-degree courses (eg physiotherapy, journalism) or straight into careers (eg actuarial work, advertising). Of those going on to degree courses, 6% went to Oxbridge; 72% to other universities; 22% to poly/colleges. 4% those going on to higher education went to courses in practical art; 60% in humanities/social sciences; 18% in medicine and 18% in science/engineering.

Uniform School uniform worn except in sixth.

Houses/prefects No competitive houses or prefects. Head girl, elected by the school and staff. School Council.

Religion Attendance at religious worship compulsory.

Social Occasional debates with other schools. Trips abroad by sixth-form historians (Paris); history of art group (Italy); school trip (eg Russia, Italy); individual exchanges encouraged. Pupils allowed to bring own bike. Meals self-service. No tobacco/alcohol allowed.

Discipline No corporal punishment. Pupils failing to produce homework once would be spoken to; if consistently failing then parents would be contacted (a rare problem). Those caught smoking cannabis on the premises would be suspended, probably expelled.

Alumni association is run by Mrs Carol Michaelson, 66 Marlborough Place, St John's Wood, London NW8.

· *Francis Holland (Sloane Square)* ·

Francis Holland School
39 Graham Terrace
Westminster
London SW1W 8JF
Tel 071 730 2971

- Pupils 350
- Boys None
- Girls 4–18
  (Day)
- Upper sixth 24

- Termly fees
  £1296
- GSA
  Enquiries/application to
  the Headmistress

What it's like

The Francis Holland (Church of England) Schools Trust was founded in 1878. This school opened in 1881 in Eaton Terrace and transferred to its present site in 1884. This is very near Sloane Square in central London. It has close links with its sister school in Clarence Gate, Regent's Park. The junior school shares the main site. It has handsome buildings which have been well adapted to modern needs. A strong local and family tradition prevails. Its position makes possible a wide use of London's amenities for outings of all kinds. The teaching is good and academic results are creditable. A high proportion of leavers for a small school go on to degree courses, including Oxbridge. French, German and Spanish are offered at GCSE and many girls take GCSE in more than one European language. Italian is offered as a non-examined language. There is a strong music dept and drama is popular. Some sport and games take place on the school site, otherwise local sports centres and Battersea Park are used.

School profile

Pupils Total age range 4–18; 350 day girls. Senior department 11–18, 180 girls. Main entry ages 4, 5, 11 and into the sixth. Own junior school provides over 50%. *Transfer from maintained schools:* Minimal.

Entrance Own entrance exam used. Oversubscribed. No special skills; C of E school but all denominations accepted. Parents expected to buy text books. Bursaries available; 5 scholarships, half to one-twelfth fees.

Parents Drawn from a wide range of professions: medicine, law, banking, the Church, the academic world, the theatre etc.

Staff Headmistress Mrs J A Anderson, in post for 9 years. 26 full time staff, 11 part time.

Academic work GCSE and A-levels. 26 subjects offered (including politics, theatre studies, history of art; AS general studies, not A-level). In 1990, 26 pupils in upper fifth, 24 in upper sixth. *GCSE:* in 1990, 99% upper fifth gained at least grade C in 8+ subjects. *A-levels:* 77% upper sixth passed in 3 subjects; 17% in 2 subjects. *Computing facilities:* Apple Mackintoshes in special room and some elsewhere in the school. *Special provision:* Time concessions requested for dyslexic girls in public exams.

European Community *Languages:* French offered: to age 14; GCSE; A-level. German offered: at age 14; GCSE. Italian: non-examined. Spanish offered: to GCSE; A-level. 25–50% take GCSE in more than 1 EC language. *Other:* Pupils arrange personal exchanges and go on language courses.

Senior pupils' non-academic activities *Music:* Many learn musical instruments. School orchestra, choir, woodwind ensemble, string group; some girls help with junior musical events. *Drama:* at least one school play a year is produced. *Sport:* Tennis, hockey, netball, gymnastics, swimming available. Other activities include a computer club, clubs for drama, debating, pottery and aerobics, inter-form play competitions, ballet, Scottish dancing, fencing.

Careers In 1990, 60% leavers went on to degree courses; 10% to art/drama/music colleges; 10% to non-degree courses (eg photography, French at Grenoble); 20% straight into careers (eg retailing) or retaking A-levels. Of those going on to degree courses, 10% went to Oxbridge; 80% to other universities; 10% to poly/colleges. 5% those going on to higher education went to courses in practical art; 5% in drama/acting; and 90% in humanities/social sciences.

Uniform School uniform worn except in sixth.

Houses/prefects Competitive houses. Head girl, head of house and house prefects – elected by school and staff. School Council.

Social Organised trips abroad, ski-ing, history of art to Italy, France and Spain, also Greece. Meals self service. No tobacco/alcohol allowed.

Discipline No corporal punishment. Conduct marks for minor offences, detention for more serious ones. Suspension or expulsion in extreme cases.

· *Frensham Heights* ·

Frensham Heights
School
Rowledge
Farnham
Surrey GU10 4EA
Tel 025 125 2134

- Pupils 275
- Boys 11–18
  (Day/Board/Weekly)
- Girls 11–18
  (Day/Board/Weekly)
- Upper sixth 31

- Termly fees
  £1881 (Day)
  £2992 (Board/
  Weekly)
- HMC

What it's like

Founded in 1925 as part of a progressive movement to promote co-education and less formal relationships between teachers and pupils. It has always been a genuinely co-educational school, not a boys' school with girls in it, nor is it dominated by male perception. It has no religious affiliation but sees the pursuit of enlightenment as a fundamental aim and discipline. It eschews the dogmatic and admires the open mind. It recognises that children are not enlightened simply by being at Frensham Heights; they are constantly told that enlightenment is hard work. The site comprises 150 acres of beautiful woodland and parkland. Boarding accommodation is comfortable and the school is spacious, well-equipped and deliberately small enough for everyone to be known as a person. The staff:pupil ratio is 1:8. There is a broad curriculum. The school is well known in the creative and performing arts. It has recently opened a new art and design centre and a sports hall.

School profile

Pupils Age range 11–18; 275 pupils, 113 day (51 boys, 62 girls), 162 boarding (66 boys, 96 girls). Main entry age 11 and into sixth. *Transfer from maintained schools:* 40% main intake, plus 15% to sixth.

Entrance Own exam used. Scholarships (academic and music).

Staff Headmaster Alan L Pattinson, in post for 18 years.

Academic work GCSE and A-levels. 21 GCSE subjects offered; 16 at A-level (no A-level general studies). *Computing facilities:* Computer centre with 8 Archimedes; BBC Bs and Masters in many departments. *Special provision:* Dyslexic, if able to follow curriculum without remedial help.

European Community *Languages:* French offered: to age 14; GCSE; A-level. German offered: to age 14; GCSE; A-level. Spanish offered: to age 14. *Other:* Annual visits for pupils 14–16 to France. Pupils whose native tongue is other than English, French and German are encouraged to take GCSE and A-level in their language and are supported by staff.

Careers In 1990, 3.5% leavers went on to degree courses; 0.5% to art/drama/music colleges. Of those going on to degree courses, 64% went to universities; 36% to poly/colleges. Some went on to courses in practical art, some in drama/acting, some in dance.

· Friends' (Great Ayton) ·

Friends School	● Pupils 211	● Termly fees
High Green	● Boys 7–18 (Day/	£1058 (Day)
Great Ayton	Board/Weekly)	£2281 (Board)
Middlesbrough	● Girls 7–18 (Day/	£2009 (Weekly)
TS9 6BN	Board/Weekly)	● Quaker
Tel 0642 722141	● Upper sixth 14	Enquiries/application to
		the Headmaster

What it's like

Founded in 1841, it has a fine site of 60 acres of beautiful grounds in the shadow of the North Yorkshire moors, 9 miles south of Middlesbrough. The attractive buildings are very well equipped with modern facilities. A Quaker school (though 90% of the pupils are not Quakers) it lays stress on the need for self-discipline and the creation of a calm, well-ordered community. A lively and purposeful establishment it is interested in academic success and gets good results. Strong in music, drama and art. There is an excellent range of sports and games and these are pursued with enthusiasm and in a spirit of vigorous competition. A wide variety of extra-curricular activities is provided. Considerable commitment to local community schemes and national charities.

School profile

Pupils Total age range 7–18; 211 pupils, 185 day (93 boys, 92 girls), 26 boarding (20 boys, 6 girls). Senior department 11–18, 156 pupils (81 boys, 75 girls). Main entry ages 7, 11, 13 and into sixth. Approx 12% are children of former pupils. *Transfer from maintained schools:* 70% main senior intake, plus 100% to sixth.

Entrance Common entrance and own exam used. No special skills or religious requirements; 10% come from Quaker backgrounds. Parents expected to buy only very few specialist sixth form text books; other extras vary. Various scholarships/bursaries.

Parents 15+% in industry or commerce; 15+% are doctors, lawyers, etc. 60+% live within 30 miles; up to 10% live overseas.

Staff Headmaster D G Cook, in post for 5 years. 20 full time staff, 8 part time. Annual turnover 10%. Average age 40.

Academic work GCSE and A-levels. 20 subjects offered (including A-level general studies). All exam statistics are available to serious enquirers at the school. *Computing facilities:* Lab of BBC Bs; several BBC Bs in other departments. *Special provision:* Qualified teacher of EFL and for dyslexic pupils.

European Community *Languages:* French offered: to age 14; GCSE; AS-level; A-level. German offered: to age 14; GCSE; AS-level; A-level. Spanish offered: to GCSE; AS-level; A-level. 10–25% take GCSE in more than 1 EC language. *Other:* Small number of EC pupils in school.

Senior pupils' non-academic activities *Music:* 10 learn a musical instrument, 8 to Grade 6 or above, 2 accepted for Music School, 2 play in pop group; 10 in school orchestra, 10 in school choir; 1 in National Youth Orchestra, 3 in county orchestra. *Drama and dance:* 30 in school productions. Occasional pupil works in theatre. *Art:* 10 take as non-examined subject; 20 take GCSE, 3 take A-level. 5 belong to eg photographic club. 2–3 accepted for Art School. *Sport:* Football, hockey, netball, tennis, cricket, athletics, swimming, cross-country, rounders, badminton, gymnastics/trampolining available. Sport is compulsory. 10 take exams in sport. 5 represent county (basketball, tennis). *Other:* 20 take part in local community schemes. 5 have bronze Duke of Edinburgh's Award. Many work for national charities. Other activities include computer club, hiking/outward-bound, drama (own theatre), music and art/pottery/textiles.

Careers In 1990, 100% upper sixth leavers went on to degree courses; 100% upper fifth leavers to non-degree courses (eg f.e. colleges). Of those going on to degree courses, 66% went to universities; 33% to poly/colleges. 33% those going on to higher education went to courses in practical art; and 66% in humanities/social sciences.

Uniform School uniform worn except in sixth.

Houses/prefects 3 competitive houses. No prefects; all sixth form shares responsibilities. Head boy/girl appointed by the Head after consultation; heads of houses appointed by houses.

Religion Daily assemblies compulsory.

Social Support village events, local (and distant) charities and take part in competitions eg public speaking. 2 organised trips abroad annually. Pupils allowed to bring own car/bike/motorbike to school. Meals formal. School shops (food and second-hand uniform). No tobacco/alcohol allowed.

Discipline No corporal punishment. Pupils failing to produce homework once will produce it next morning.

Boarding 66% have own study bedroom, 33% share with 1 other; not in houses. Central dining room. Pupils can provide and cook some food. Termly exeats; half term, 2 set weekends and according to individual circumstances. Visits to local town allowed for pupils of 14 and above.

Former pupils Allan Gilmour (actor); David Holden (murdered reporter).

· *Friends' (Lisburn)* ·

The Friends' School	● Pupils 1065	● Termly fees
Lisburn	● Boys 4–19	£636 (Day)
Antrim	(Day/Board/Weekly)	£1464 (Board)
Northern Ireland	● Girls 4–19	£1431 (Weekly)
BT28 3BH	(Day/Board/Weekly)	Enquiries/application to
Tel 0846 662156	● Upper sixth 112	the Headmaster

What it's like

Founded in 1774, a Quaker school, its site is on Prospect Hill near the centre of the town. The grounds are spacious and provide ample playing areas for 1000 pupils. Since 1960 there has been extensive development and modernisation. A new sixth form centre, library, art and technology suites and lecture theatre have just opened. Excellent boarding accommodation and good up-to-date facilities of all kinds. Pupils are taken from a wide range of religious backgrounds and a general form of Christian worship is practised. Academic attainments are high and many go on to degree courses. Very strong musically. A good range of games and sports. A remarkable record in the Duke of Edinburgh's Award Scheme.

School profile

Pupils Total age range 4–19; 1065 pupils, 1015 day (498 boys, 517 girls), 50 boarding (26 boys, 24 girls). Senior department 11–19, 863 pupils (412 boys, 451 girls). Main entry ages 4, 11 and into sixth. Approx 28% are children of former

305

pupils. *Transfer from maintained schools:* 82% main senior intake, plus 50% to sixth.

Entrance Sometimes oversubscribed. Good academic ability required; no religious requirements. Parents of fee-paying pupils expected to buy text books; maximum extras £100 pa. Tuition fees paid by Education Department for all pupils admitted who are resident in Northern Ireland.

Parents 60+% live within 30 miles; up to 10% live overseas.

Staff Headmaster J T Green, 1 year in post. 62 full time staff, 5 part time. Annual turnover 3–4%. Average age 40.

Academic work GCSE, AS and A-levels. 22 GCSE subjects offered; 4 at AS; 20 at A-level (no A-level general studies). In 1990, 127 pupils in fifth, 112 in upper sixth. *GCSE:* in 1990, 64 upper fifth gained at least grade C in 8+ subjects; 46 in 5–7; and 15 in 1–4 subjects. *A-levels:* 10 upper sixth passed in 4+ subjects; 59 in 3; 27 in 2; and 7 in 1 subject. 50% took science A-levels; 28% arts/humanities; 22% both. *Computing facilities:* 2 × 15 station networks of Nimbus; 10 other computers in departments. IT courses forms 1–4 and lower sixth. *Special provision:* Extra tuition is available (but not included in fees).

European Community *Languages:* French offered: to age 14; GCSE; A-level. German offered: to age 14; GCSE; A-level. Spanish offered: to GCSE. Under 10% take GCSE in more than 1 EC language. *Exchanges:* Regular exchanges for pupils aged 16–18 to Germany.

Senior pupils' non-academic activities *Music:* 125 learn a musical instrument, 40 to Grade 6 or above. 80 in school orchestra, 200 in choir. *Drama and dance:* 30 in school productions, 25 in other. *Art:* 59 take GCSE; 25 take A-level; 2 accepted for Art School. 15 belong to photographic club. *Sport:* Rugby, hockey, cricket, tennis, athletics, badminton, squash, netball, swimming, soccer available. 150 take non-compulsory sport. 25 take exams, eg swimming, gymnastics. 7 pupils represent county (rugby, hockey, soccer, ski-ing). *Other:* 18 take part in local community schemes. 46 have bronze Duke of Edinburgh's Award, 21 have silver and 34 have gold. Other activities include computer club, chess club, debating society, scripture union, swimming and life-saving (own pool), ski-ing (on artificial slope and tours). School bank run by sixth form.

Careers In 1990, 56% leavers went on to degree courses; 6% to art/drama/music colleges; 15% to non-degree courses (eg teacher training – primary); 2% straight into careers (eg nursing, banking); 19% other. Of those going on to degree courses, 2% went to Oxbridge; 50% to other universities; 38% to poly/colleges. 2% those going on to higher education went to courses in practical art; 4% in music; 35% in humanities/social sciences; 20% in medicine; and 40% in science/engineering.

Uniform School uniform worn throughout.

Houses/prefects Competitive houses for sport. Prefects (volunteer), head boy/girl (appointed) and heads of house (elected). School Council.

Religion General Christian worship with Bible teaching, prayer and praise.

Social Link with a school in the Republic of Ireland (Co-operation North), joint lectures with a local grammar school. Frequent ski trips and cultural visits to Europe. Pupils allowed to bring own bike to school. Lunch self service; meals for boarders formal. School milk bar. No tobacco/alcohol allowed.

Discipline No corporal punishment. Pupils failing to produce homework once might expect to do it after school; those caught smoking cannabis on the premises could expect expulsion.

Boarding 10% share a study bedroom with 1 other. 2 houses, single sex. Resident qualified nurse; doctor on call. Central dining room. Pupils can provide and cook own food at weekends. Saturday and Sunday afternoon exeats. Visits to local town allowed.

Alumni association is run by Mrs F MacLeod, Friends' School OS Association, c/o the School.

· *Friends' (Saffron Walden)* ·

Friends' School
Mount Pleasant Road
Saffron Walden
Essex
CB11 3EB
Tel 0799 25351

- Pupils 272
- Boys 11–18
  (Day/Board)
- Girls 11–18
  (Day/Board)
- Upper sixth 25

- Termly fees
  £1598 (Day)
  £2550 (Board)
- SHMIS
  Enquiries/application to
  the Head

What it's like

Founded in 1702, it is single-site and on the edge of the countryside. It has handsome well-equipped buildings in delightful grounds. Saffron Walden itself is a most attractive country town in a beautiful part of Essex. Christian worship in the Quaker tradition is compulsory. A good all-round education is provided and the facilities are first-rate. For a small school, a large proportion of sixth form leavers go on to degree courses. Strong in art and drama. A good range of games, sports and activities. It has the bonus of a Young Farmers' Club with a 35-acre estate.

School profile

Pupils Total age range 11–18; 272 pupils, 122 day (57 boys, 65 girls), 150 boarding (74 boys, 76 girls). Main entry age 11, also 12, 13, 14 and into sixth. Approx 2% are children of former pupils. *Transfer from maintained schools:* 40% main senior intake, plus 5% to sixth.
Entrance Own entrance exam used. No special skills or religious requirements. Parents not expected to buy text books; extras voluntary, average £50. 80 assisted places. Sixth form awards and Quaker bursaries, means tested.
Parents 50% live within 30 miles; up to 10% live overseas.
Staff Head S H Evans, 2 years in post. 28 full time staff, 4 part time. Annual turnover 5%. Average age 40.
Academic work GCSE, AS and A-levels. 15 subjects offered (including A-level general studies). On average, 60 pupils in upper fifth, 25 in upper sixth. *GCSE:* on average, 15 pupils in upper fifth pass 8+ subjects; 40, 5–7 subjects; 15 pass 1–4 subjects. *A-levels:* on average, 3 pupils in upper sixth pass 4 subjects; 12, 3 subjects; 8, 2 subjects and 2 pass 1 subject. 40% took science A-levels; 40% arts/humanities; 20% both. *Computing facilities:* Adequate.
European Community *Languages:* French offered: to age 14; GCSE; AS-level; A-level. German offered: to age 14; GCSE; AS-level; A-level. 25–50% take GCSE in more than 1 EC language. *Exchanges:* Regular exchanges for pupils aged 14–16 to Germany.
Senior pupils' non-academic activities *Music:* 120 learn a musical instrument, 30 in school orchestra, 30 in school choir. *Drama and dance:* 50 in school productions. *Art:* 25 take GCSE, 8 take A-level. 3 accepted for Art School. *Sport:* Soccer, rugby, hockey, cricket, athletics, tennis, swimming, badminton (and others) available. 200 take non-compulsory sport. 6 pupils represent county (cricket, hockey, athletics). *Other:* 10 take part in local community schemes. 5 enter voluntary schemes after leaving school. Other activities include a computer club, scouts, young farmers, chess, silk screen printing, Duke of Edinburgh Award Scheme and Young Enterprise.
Careers On average, 75% leavers went on to degree courses; 19% to art/drama/music colleges; 5% to non-degree courses; 1% straight into careers. Of those going on to degree courses, 60% went to universities; 40% to poly/colleges. 15% those going on to higher education went to courses in practical art; 5% in

307

drama/acting; 5% in music; 35% in humanities/social sciences; 15% in medicine; and 25% in science/engineering.

Uniform School uniform worn except in sixth.

Houses/prefects Competitive houses. No prefects. Head boy/girl – elected by the school and staff. School Council.

Religion Religious worship compulsory.

Social Organised local events and trips abroad. Pupils allowed to bring own bike to school. Meals self service. School shop. No tobacco/alcohol allowed.

Discipline No corporal punishment.

Pupils failing to produce homework once might expect detention. Detentions, gating, work around the school all used. Attempts made to ensure 'the punishment fits the crime'. Suspension and expulsion for serious offences.

Boarding Accommodation divided by age; sixth form in separate co-educational house. Qualified nurse (non-resident). Central dining room. Exeats, any weekend. Visits to local town allowed daily.

Former pupils Tom Robinson; Ralph Erskine; Eric Beale; Deborah Norton; Matthew Evans.

· *Fulneck (Boys)* ·

Fulneck Boys' School
Pudsey
West Yorkshire
LS28 8DT
Tel 0532 571864

- Pupils 325
- Boys 7–18 (Day/ Board/Weekly)
- Girls None
- Upper sixth 30

- Termly fees
  £1082 (Day)
  £2097 (Board)
  £1852 (Weekly)
- SHMIS
  Enquiries/application to the Headmaster

What it's like

Founded in 1753, established by the Moravian Church (Unitas Fratrum) for the education of its own ministers and missionaries. The Moravian Church claims to be the oldest Protestant church and Comenius himself presided over the original school of Fulneck, in Moravia. Essentially a Christian establishment its aim is to provide an education which will enable a pupil to lead a full life, of varied interest and abundant in opportunity for service. Religious education is quite an important part of the curriculum. It has well-designed buildings which stand in a semi-rural site on the side of a valley in the green belt near Leeds and Bradford. It has good modern facilities and extensive grounds and playing fields. A sound traditional education is given and results are good. Many sixth formers go on to degree courses. Quite strong in music, drama and art. A fair range of sports, games and activities. Very creditable results in the Duke of Edinburgh Award Scheme.

School profile

Pupils Total age range 7–18; 325 boys, 290 day, 35 boarding. Senior department 11–18, 260 boys. Main entry ages 7–11, 13 and into sixth. Approx 10% are children of former pupils. *Transfer from maintained schools:* 80+% senior intake, plus 5% to sixth.

Entrance Common entrance and own exam used. Not oversubscribed. No special skills or religious requirements. Parents not expected to buy text books; maximum extras, £75.

Parents 15+% in industry or commerce; 15+% in armed services. 60+% live within 30 miles; up to 10% live overseas.

Staff Headmaster I D Cleland, in post for 11 years. 25 full time staff, 7 part time.

Annual turnover 7%. Average age 41.

Academic work GCSE and A-levels. 17 subjects offered (including A-level general studies). On average, 48 in upper fifth, 30 in upper sixth. *GCSE:* on average, 10 upper fifth gain at least grade C in 8+ subjects; 30 in 5–7; and 8 in 1–4 subjects. *A-levels:* on average, 10 upper sixth pass in 4+ subjects; 12 in 3; 5 in 2; and 3 in 1 subject. 50% take science A-levels; 40% arts/humanities; 10% both. *Computing facilities:* Specialised IT room. *Special provision:* Small classes, some limited individual help for dyslexics.

European Community *Languages:* French offered: to age 14; GCSE; A-level. German offered: to age 14; GCSE; AS-level; A-level. 10–25% take GCSE in more than 1 EC language. *Exchanges:* Regular exchanges for pupils aged 14–16 to France and Germany.

Senior pupils' non-academic activities *Music:* 55 learn a musical instrument, 5 to Grade 6 or above; 25 in school orchestra, 20 in choir, 3 in school pop group; 5 in other pop group. *Drama and dance:* 20 in school productions. *Art:* 10 take as non-examined subject; 25 take GCSE; 3 A-level. 2 accepted for Art School. 20 belong to eg photographic club. *Sport:* Rugby, tennis, cricket, golf, badminton, sailing, athletics, cross-country available. 70 take non-compulsory sport. 5 represent county (rugby, athletics, tennis, sailing). *Other:* 20 take part in local community schemes. 20 have bronze Duke of Edinburgh's Award, 15 silver and 10 gold. Most enter voluntary schemes after school; a few work for national chari-ties. Other activities include a computer club, chess, theatre workshop, outward-bound type holidays.

Careers In 1990, 78% leavers went on to degree courses; 12% straight into careers; 10% other. Of those going on to degree courses, 46% went to universities; 54% to poly/colleges. 43% those going on to higher education went to courses in humanities/social sciences; 7% in medicine; and 50% in science/engineering.

Uniform School uniform worn except in sixth.

Houses/prefects Competitive houses. Prefects, head boy – appointed by the Head, staff and pupils.

Religion Compulsory Chapel once a week, prayers on other 4 days.

Social Close links, at sixth form, with Fulneck (Girls') for music and drama. Usually 1–3 foreign trips. Exchanges with France and Germany. Pupils allowed to bring own car/bike to school. Meals self service. No tobacco/alcohol allowed.

Discipline No corporal punishment. Pupils failing to produce homework once might expect a reprimand.

Boarding 10% have own study bedroom; 90% are in dormitories of 6+. No resident qualified medical staff. Central dining room. Sixth form can provide and cook own food. Weekend exeats as required. Saturday visits to local town allowed.

Former pupils include one prime minister; one Nobel prize winner; Sir Frank Cooper (Permanent Secretary, MOD).

g

· Gateways ·

Gateways School
Harewood
Leeds
Yorkshire LS17 9LE
Tel 0532 886345

- Pupils 380
- Boys None
- Girls 4–18
  (Day)
- Upper sixth 10

- Termly fees £860
- GSA
Enquiries to the
Headmistress
Application to Secretary

What it's like

Founded in 1941, it is sited in the delightful village of Harewood, 4 miles from Leeds and Harrogate. It incorporates the quondam dower house of the Harewood estate which lies in beautiful surroundings and is a conservation area. Very good modern facilities and accommodation. The prep department is in separate buildings within the school grounds. It has the advantage of being a fairly small school where pupils get individual encouragement and reach a high level of personal achievement. Emphasis is placed on initiative, and education for leadership. Girls are given the opportunity to take serious responsibility for their courses and the development of the school. The sixth form is expected to expand rapidly over the next few years; some girls go on to degree courses. French, German and Spanish are offered right through the school at A-level and many girls take GCSE in more than one European language. There are regular exchange arrangements with France and Germany. An adequate range of sport, games and activities. A good record in the Duke of Edinburgh's Award Scheme and the Young Enterprise Scheme.

School profile

Pupils Total age range 4–18; 380 day girls. Senior department 12–18, 220 girls. Main entry ages 4, 8, 11, 13 and into sixth. Approx 20% are children of former pupils. *Transfer from maintained schools:* 50% main senior intake, plus 10% to sixth.

Entrance Own entrance exam used. Sometimes oversubscribed. No special skills or religious requirements. Parents not expected to buy text books; maximum other extras, £70. 8 scholarships/bursaries, £100 per term.

Parents 20+% are doctors, lawyers etc; 20+% in industry or commerce.

Staff Head Miss L M Brown, in post for 6 years. 28 full time staff, 3 part time. Annual turnover 2%. Average age 32.

Academic work GCSE and A-levels. 19 subjects offered (including A-level general studies). In 1990, 37 pupils in upper fifth, 10 in upper sixth. *GCSE:* in 1990, 15 upper fifth gained at least grade C in 8+ subjects; 18 in 5–7; and 4 in 1–4 subjects. *A-levels:* 3 upper sixth passed in 4+ subjects; 3 in 3; 3 in 2 and 1 in 1 subject; all in broad area of arts and humanities. *Computing facilities:* Computer room. Computers in subject areas. *Special provision:* Work with outside agencies; individual programme; support and advice.

European Community *Languages:*

310

French offered: to age 14; GCSE; A-level; non-examined. German offered: to age 14; GCSE; A-level; non-examined. Spanish offered: to age 14; GCSE; A-level; non-examined. 25–50% take GCSE in more than 1 EC language. *Exchanges:* Regular exchanges for pupils aged 14–18 to France.

Senior pupils' non-academic activities *Music:* 20 learn a musical instrument, 2 choirs. 1 orchestral group. Biennial music festival. *Drama and dance:* 30 in school productions; 30, other. *Art:* 25 take as non-examined subject; 20 take GCSE; 6, A-level; 3 accepted for Art School. *Sport:* Lacrosse, netball, gymnastics, trampolining, athletics, table tennis, volleyball, outdoor pursuits, badminton, tennis, dance, gymnastics, rounders available. 100 take non-compulsory sport. *Other:* 38 enter bronze Duke of Edinburgh's Award; some enter voluntary schemes after leaving school. Other activities include computer, card, walking, two drama, art, cookery, debating, science and technology, music, chess, history and languages clubs.

Careers In 1990, 80% leavers went on to degree courses; 10% to art/drama/music colleges; 8% to non-degree courses; 2% straight into careers. Of those going on to degree courses, 60% went to universities; 40% to poly/colleges. 9% those going on to higher education went to courses in practical art; 1% in drama/acting; and 80% in humanities/social sciences.

Uniform School uniform worn except in the sixth.

Houses/prefects Competitive houses. Prefects and head girl appointed by headmistress. School Council.

Religion Religious worship encouraged.

Social Local school debating and public speaking competitions. Choir concerts. Adventure weekends. Organised trips abroad. Work experience, community work. Pupils allowed to bring own car to school. Meals self service. No tobacco/alcohol allowed.

Discipline No corporal punishment. Pupils failing to produce homework once might expect a reprimand; those caught smoking cannabis on the premises might expect expulsion. In any problem with discipline the circumstances are always taken into account. Pupils are told clearly what is expected of them and any pupil unable to conform would be expected to leave.

Alumni association run by Mrs Swift, c/o the School.

· George Heriot's ·

George Heriot's School
Lauriston Place
Edinburgh EH3 9EQ
Tel 031 229 7263
Fax 031 229 6363

- Pupils 1448
- Boys 5–18 (Day)
- Girls 5–18 (Day)
- Higher year 145

- Termly fees £950
- HMC
Enquiries/application to the Headmaster

What it's like

Founded in 1628 by George Heriot, an Edinburgh jeweller and banker and goldsmith to James VI and I, for the fatherless sons of burgesses. It has very elegant buildings and fine grounds in the centre of Edinburgh. The original building has been preserved and comprises the chapel, council room, common room, class rooms and school offices. In the last 100 years a succession of developments has produced excellent facilities. A Junior School building was completed in 1983 and a new library and music suite were opened in 1988. Non-denominational, Heriot's is deeply rooted in the Scottish tradition and its pupils come from far afield and from a wide variety of social backgrounds. The playing fields are at Goldenacre. Academically high-powered, it produces consistently good results. Many pupils go on to degree courses each year and, in the Scottish tradition, tend not to head for Oxbridge. Music and drama flourish. Virtually all sports and games are available and high standards are achieved. There is a CCF contingent, plus a scout troop and guides. Some 50 clubs and societies cater for an unusually wide range of extra-curricular activities. There is much emphasis on outdoor pursuits and a fine record in the Duke of Edinburgh's Award Scheme.

School profile

Pupils Total age range 5–18; 1448 day pupils (841 boys, 607 girls). Senior department 12–18, 967 pupils (555 boys, 412 girls). Main entry ages 5, 12 and into sixth. Approx 15% are children of former pupils. *Transfer from maintained schools:* 95% main senior intake, plus 50% to sixth.

Entrance Own entrance exam used. Oversubscribed. No special skills or religious requirements. Parents expected to buy senior school text books. 234 assisted places. 29 scholarships and 60 foundationers.

Parents 15+% in education; 15+% are doctors, lawyers etc; 15+% in industry or commerce.

Staff Headmaster Mr K P Pearson, in post for 8 years. 95 full time staff, 6 part time. Annual turnover 4%. Average age 40.

Academic work O/S-grade and Highers. c25 subjects offered (including Gaelic). In 1989, 170 pupils in O/S-grade year; 170 in Higher; 130 in CSYS year. *Highers:* on average, 104 pupils pass 5+ subjects; 20, 4 subjects; 12, 3 subjects; 16, 2 subjects; 10, 1 subject. On average, 60% take science/engineering Highers; 30% take arts and humanities; 10% both. *Computing facilities:* a network of 32 BBC micros with a 40 megabyte file server and 2 printers; facilities also in most other departments, eg Computing 10 Apple Macs with an Image writer and laser printer; Business Studies 10 Apple Macs with Intjet printer. *Special provision:* for dyslexia and EFL.

European Community *Languages:* French offered: to age 14; S-grade; Higher; CSYS. German offered: to S-grade; Higher; CSYS. Italian offered: to S-grade. Spanish offered: to S-grade; Higher; CSYS. 10–25% take S-grade in more than 1 EC language. *Exchanges:* Regular exchanges for pupils aged 14–18 to France and Germany. *Other:* School attracts families of foreign diplomats, encourages exchanges etc; one French pupil in school applying for British universities. Strong European Club invites speakers, including MEP. Orchestra tours abroad. Pupils encouraged to undertake work experience abroad.

Senior pupils' non-academic activities *Music:* 3 school orchestras, 3 choirs, a pipe band and many smaller groups; regular public concerts. *Drama and dance:* 40–60 in school productions. 1 or 2 accepted for Drama/Dance Schools. *Art:* 8 take as non-examined subject; 43 O-grade; 12 Higher. 1 accepted for Art School, 4 for architecture courses, 3 to foundation courses. 8 belong to photographic club, 16 to craft workshop. *Sport:* Virtually all sports available. 500 take non-compulsory sport. 31 pupils represent county/country (rugby, hockey, rowing, shooting, fencing, swimming). *Other:* 8 take part in local community schemes. 100 take part in bronze Duke of Edinburgh's Award, 53 in silver and 45 in gold. 41 work for national charities. Other activities include a computer club and 50 other clubs and activities.

Careers In 1990, 70% leavers went on to degree courses; 2% to art/drama/music colleges; 14% to non-degree courses; 14% straight into careers. Of those going on to degree courses, 4% went to Oxbridge; 74% to other universities; 22% to poly/colleges. 1% those going on to higher education went to courses in practical art; $1/2$% in drama/acting; $1/2$% in music; 55% in humanities/social sciences; 4% in medicine; and 39% in science/engineering.

Uniform School uniform worn throughout.

Houses/prefects Competitive houses. Prefects, head boy and girl and house captains elected by upper school.

Religion Compulsory morning assembly with broad Christian element.

Social Music, inter-school and ESU debating with other schools; own school theatrical production. Many organised trips abroad including Canada, Greece, Majorca, Zimbabwe; music trips abroad; and school French exchange. Pupils allowed to bring own bike to school. Meals self service; tuck shop. No tobacco/alcohol allowed.

Discipline No corporal punishment. Pupils failing to produce homework once might expect a written exercise or detention.

Former pupils Lord Mackay (Lord Chancellor); several ex-Lord Provosts of Edinburgh; former Chief Constable of Lothian and Borders Police; Robert Urquhart and Paul Young (actors); Sir William Ryrie (World Bank); Professor Norman Dott; many well-known sporting figures including Kenneth Scotland, Andrew Irvine, Iain and Kenneth Milne and George Goddard.

· George Watson's ·

George Watson's College Colinton Road Edinburgh EH10 5EG Tel 031 447 7931	• Pupils 2107 • Boys 3–18 (Day/Board) • Girls 3–18 (Day/Board) • Higher year 212	• Termly fees £1012 (Day) £1956 (Board) • HMC Enquiries/application to the Principal

What it's like

Founded in 1741, it moved to its present site in 1932. The George Watson's Ladies' College and the Boys' College were amalgamated in 1974. The site is on the outskirts of the city and playing fields on the campus. The impressive buildings are very well equipped with modern facilities. It is a school with a distinguished record of achievement where excellent teaching is provided and academic standards are high. The bulk of the pupils are local. Its declared objectives are to enable pupils to live their lives to the full, to understand the world they live in, to be active in serving other people and to commit themselves to causes with open-eyed and critical awareness. It caters for individualists. The majority of its pupils go on to degree courses each year (many of them to Scottish universities and, in the Scottish tradition, do not tend to head for Oxbridge). Five European languages are offered from GCSE to CSYS – French, German, Modern Greek, Italian and Spanish. There are regular exchange arrangements with France, Germany, Italy and Spain for all age groups. Immensely strong music, drama, art and technology depts involving a very large number of pupils. A wide variety of sports and games are available (including curling) and high standards are achieved. (A very large number of county and international representatives.) About 50 clubs and societies cater for most extra-curricular activities. There is a big commitment to local community schemes, an active scout group and considerable emphasis on outdoor pursuits. (There is a fine outdoor centre at Glen Isla.) The college's record in the Duke of Edinburgh's Scheme is outstanding.

School profile

Pupils Total age range 3–18; 2107 pupils, 2037 day (1139 boys, 898 girls), 70 boarding (44 boys, 26 girls). Senior department 12–18, 1249 pupils (691 boys, 558 girls). Main entry ages 3, 5, 10, 11, 12 and into sixth.

Entrance Own entrance exam used. Oversubscribed. No special skills or religious requirements. Parents expected to buy text books. 237 assisted places. 11 scholarships/bursaries, £450 to £1000.

Parents 15+% are doctors, lawyers, etc, 15+% in industry or commerce. 85+% live within 30 miles; up to 10% live overseas.

Staff Principal F E Gerstenberg, in post for 5 years. 128 full time staff, 12 part time. Annual turnover 5%. Average age 44.

Academic work S-grade, Highers and CSYS. Russian and Italian offered to Highers. Average size of S-grade year, 212; Higher year, 212; CSYS year, 180. *Highers:* in 1990, 96 passed in 5+ subjects; 36 in 4 subjects; 62 in 3; 71 in 2; and 67 in 1 subject. *CSYS:* In 1990, 14 passed in 4+ subjects; 17 in 3 subjects; 34 in 2; and 43 in 1 subject. 36% took science CSYS, 42% arts/humanities; 22% both. *Computing facilities:* 2 computer labs and numerous computers in departments. *Special provision:* Highly specialised learning support department for dyslexic pupils; EFL teaching.

European Community *Languages:* French offered: to age 14; S-grade; Higher; CSYS. German offered: to age 14; S-grade; Higher; CSYS. Greek (modern): S-grade; Higher; CSYS. Italian offered: S-grade. Portuguese offered: Higher; CSYS. Spanish offered: to age 14; S-grade; Higher; CSYS. 10–25% take S-grade in more than 1 EC language. *Exchanges:* Regular exchanges for pupils aged 11–18 to France, Germany, Italy and Spain. *Other:* Attendance at Youth Parliament in Strasbourg.

Senior pupils' non-academic activities *Music:* 450 learn a musical instrument, 14 to Grade 6 or above; 2 accepted for Music School, 160 in school orchestras, 120 in school choir, 10 in jazz band, 40 in other various music groups, 30 in Barbershop choir, 45 in ensemble choir, 15 in local youth orchestra, 1 in National Youth Orchestra for Scotland. *Drama and dance:* 250–300 in school productions, 80 in house productions, 9 accepted for Drama/Dance Schools, 2 go on to work in theatre. *Art:* Most take as non-examined subject, 49 take O-grade, 20 take Higher, 2 accepted for Art School, 4 go on to architecture, 1 to textiles, 30 belong to photographic club, 50 in sketch club. *Sport:* Angling, athletics, badminton, basketball, cricket, cross-country, curling, fencing, golf, gymnastics, hockey, orienteering, rowing, rugby, sailing, ski-ing, squash, table tennis, tennis and volleyball available. 700 take non-compulsory sport. 38 pupils represent county/country in variety of sports. *Other:* 56 take part in local community schemes. 65 have bronze Duke of Edinburgh's Award, 47 have silver and 30 have gold. Variety of other activities including a computer club.

Careers In 1990, 72% leavers went on to degree courses; 2% to art/drama/music colleges; 6% to non-degree courses (eg secretarial, sciences); 6% straight into careers (eg secretarial, printing, hotels); 14% other. Of those going on to degree courses, 4% went to Oxbridge; 75% to other universities; 21% to poly/colleges. 2% those going on to higher education went to courses in practical art; 1% in drama/acting; 59% in humanities/social sciences; 6% in medicine; and 32% in science/engineering.

Uniform School uniform worn throughout.

Houses/prefects Competitive houses. Prefects, head boy and girl, head of house and house prefects – elected by pupils, confirmed by Head. School Council.

Religion Morning assembly compulsory.

Social Some co-operation with other Merchant Company schools (Daniel Stewarts, Mary Erskine) otherwise large enough to be self-sufficient. Exchanges with France, Germany, Spain, Italy, United States, USSR and many other organised trips abroad. Day pupils allowed to bring own car/bike/motorbike to school. Meals self service. School shop sells second-hand clothing. No tobacco/alcohol allowed.

Discipline No corporal punishment. Pupils failing to produce homework once expected to do it within 24 hours. Parents of those caught smoking cannabis on the premises would be asked to withdraw the pupil; if parents refused, pupil would be expelled.

Boarding Half share with 1 or 2 others; others in dormitories of 6+. Resident qualified nurse. Central dining room.

Pupils can provide and cook some own food. Exeats any weekend. Visits to local town allowed.

Alumni association run by Alastair Milliken, Myreside Pavilion, Myreside Road, Edinburgh.

Former pupils Malcolm Rifkind; David Steele; Gavin Hastings (rugby); Scott Hastings (rugby); Alison Kinnaird (clarsach); David Johnstone (rugby); Eric Anderson (Head of Eton); Martin Bell (ski); Magda Sweetland (novelist); Sir Ian MacGregor.

· *Giggleswick* ·

Giggleswick School	● Pupils 304	● Termly fees
Giggleswick	● Boys 13–18	£1890 (Day)
Settle	(Day/Board)	£2850 (Board)
North Yorkshire	● Girls 13–18	● HMC
BD24 0DE	(Day/Board)	Enquiries/application to
Tel 0729 823545	● Upper sixth 54	the Headmaster

What it's like

Founded in 1512, it moved to its present site in 1869 on the edge of the village. This is a superb position overlooking the Ribble valley in North Yorkshire within an hour of Manchester, Leeds and the Lakes. It has handsome buildings and most of the boys' accommodation is being refurbished. The junior school, Catteral Hall, is on an adjacent site and continuous education is available from 8–18. 90% of the pupils are boarders. The school prides itself on its happy atmosphere and offers an excellent all round education. High importance is attached to personal courtesy and the school aims to develop 'the whole person' whilst having proper regard for the importance of helping all pupils to achieve their best personal academic potential. Prayers, morning assemblies and one service each Sunday, in the Anglican tradition, are compulsory. Many upper sixth leavers go on to degree courses, including many to Oxbridge. Music, drama and art are strong departments and there is considerable strength in a wide variety of sports. An extensive range of outdoor education is provided including fell walking, orienteering, rock-climbing, canoeing, mountaineering and pot-holing. There are numerous successes in the Duke of Edinburgh's Award Scheme and flourishing community service projects.

School profile

Pupils Age range 13–18; 304 pupils, 33 day (15 boys, 18 girls), 271 boarding (179 boys, 92 girls). Main entry ages 13 and into sixth. Approx 10% are children of Old Giggleswickians. *Transfer from main-tained schools:* 12% main intake, plus 20% to sixth.

Entrance Common entrance, interviews and other methods used. Oversubscribed for girls. Anglican foundation but other faiths and convictions welcomed. Fees include text books, stationery, most art, CDT and home economics materials, compulsory GCSE visits etc. Assisted places. Scholarships/exhibitions available (academic, music, art, general distinction and continuation), up to full fees; also forces bursaries.

Parents 15+% in industry or commerce. Some 1% live within 30 miles; up to 18% live overseas.

Staff Headmaster Peter Hobson. 36 full time staff, 12 part time. Annual turnover 5%. Average age 40.

Academic work GCSE and A-levels. 17 subjects offered (including A-level general studies). In 1990, 60 pupils in upper fifth, 54 in upper sixth. *GCSE:* in 1990, 48% upper fifth gained at least grade C in 8+ subjects; 27% in 5–7; and 21% in 1–4 subjects. *A-levels:* 28 upper sixth passed in 4+ subjects; 9 in 3; 7 in 2; and 8 in 1 subject. 13% took science A-levels; 38% arts/humanities; 44% both. *Computing facilities:* Computing department with 20 BBC/Archimedes computers; other departments have computers linked by an Econet system. *Special provision:* Some special coaching for dyslexics.

European Community *Languages:* French offered: to age 14; GCSE; AS-level; A-level. German offered: to age 14; GCSE; AS-level; A-level. 10–25% take GCSE in more than 1 EC language. *Exchanges:* Regular exchanges for pupils aged 13–18 to France and Germany. *Other:* EC pupils spend some time in the school. Sixth form pupils go to linked German school.

Senior pupils' non-academic activities *Music:* 100+ learn a musical instrument, 40 to Grade 6 or above; 28 in school orchestra, 48 in concert band, 36 in choir; 1 accepted for Music School. *Drama and dance:* 100+ in school productions. *Art:* 25 take GCSE, 11 take A-level (art, graphics, sculpture). 5 accepted for Art School, 2 foundation course, 1 fine arts, 2 design graphics. *Sport:* Rugby, soccer, cricket, athletics, tennis, hockey, swimming, squash, fives, athletics, cross-country, gym, rounders, netball, basketball, badminton, fencing and golf available. 12 represent county (rugby union, athletics,

hockey). Girls hockey XI North Yorkshire Schools Champions 1990. *Other:* 50 undertake bronze Duke of Edinburgh's Award, 6 have silver and 12 gold. Other activities include a computer club, debating, fishing, outward-bound, motor club, driving lessons, etc. CCF contingent (affiliated to Duke of Wellington's regiment), Christian Union, mountain rescue unit, clay pigeon gun club, photographic club.

Careers In 1990, 80% leavers went on to degree courses; 7% to art/drama/music colleges; 2% to non-degree courses; 7% straight into careers; 4% other. Of those going on to degree courses, 11% went to Oxbridge; 62% to other universities; 27% to poly/colleges. 5% those going on to higher education went to courses in practical art; 2% in music; 55% in humanities/social sciences; 15% in medicine; and 21% in science/engineering.

Uniform School uniform worn except in sixth.

Houses/prefects Competitive/pastoral houses. Praeposters and head boy/girl appointed by Head; head of house and house prefects, appointed by house staff.

Religion House prayers and morning services are compulsory.

Social Rugby, hockey, music, drama and ski trips abroad, foreign language visits to stay with families; 1991 rugby trip to Canada, concert band trip to Australia. Sixth form centre has facilities for debates, balls, discos, reading rooms and a bar where strictly limited amounts of beer and wine are served with parents' permission and under staff supervision. No tobacco allowed.

Discipline No corporal punishment. Pupils failing to produce prep once might expect extra work; anyone found in possession of drugs would be expelled (this has not arisen).

Boarding 30% have own study bedroom, 50% in doubles; rest in dormitories of 4–6. Single sex houses, of 50–60. Resident SRN Matron with a qualified assistant; doctor visits 4–5 times a week. Central dining room. Pupils can provide and cook own snacks. 2 weekend exeats each term and half-term. Visits to local town allowed at set times.

Alumni association is run by D E W Morgan, Secretary OG Club, c/o the school.
Former pupils Judges Christopher Oddie and Roger Hunt; Sir Douglas Glover; Sir Anthony Wilson; Richard Whiteley; Keith Duckworth.

· Glasgow Academy ·

The Glasgow Academy
Colebrooke Street
Glasgow G12 8HE
Tel 041 334 8558

- Pupils 1050
- Boys 4–18 (Day)
- Girls 4–18 (Day)
- Higher year 125

- Termly fees £1025
- HMC

Enquiries/application to the Rector

What it's like

Founded in 1846, it is single-site (with its own junior department) in the west end of the city. A compact campus with handsome buildings in the classical Victorian manner. Very good modern facilities. The academy has a high reputation academically and produces consistently good results. Between 65–70 leavers go on to university each year. Music, drama and art are quite strong. A wide range of sports and games in which high standards are attained. A good variety of extra-curricular activities, and a promising record in the Duke of Edinburgh's Award Scheme. Now merging with the nearby girls' school, Westbourne School for Girls (see separate description).

School profile

Pupils Total age range 4–18; 1050 day pupils, boys and girls. Senior department 11–18, 550 pupils, boys and girls. Main entry ages 4, 8, 11 and into sixth. Approx 20% are children of former pupils. *Transfer from maintained schools:* 15% main senior intake, plus 2% to sixth.
Entrance Own entrance exam used. Oversubscribed. No special skills or religious requirements. Maximum extras, £200. 70 assisted places. Various scholarships/bursaries, up to £350.
Parents 15+% are doctors, lawyers etc; 15+% in industry or commerce. 60+% live within 30 miles.
Staff Rector C W Turner, in post for 8 years. 85 full time staff, 7 part time. Annual turnover 2%. Average age 40.
Academic work O-grade/S-grade/Highers/A-levels. In 1990, 90 pupils in O/S-grade year, 60 in Higher, 90 in A-level year. *Highers:* in 1990, 26 pupils passed in 5+ subjects; 15 in 4; 14 in 3; 21 in 2; 13 in 1 subject (many Highers taking as an extra, with A-levels). *A-levels:* 15 pupils passed in 3 subjects; 16 in 2 subjects. 50% took science A-levels; 40% arts/humanities; 10% both. *Computing facilities:* Computer laboratory. *Special provision:* General support but no specialist teaching.
European Community *Languages:* French offered: to age 14; S-grade; Higher; A-level. German offered: to age 14; S-grade; Higher; A-level. Spanish: non-examined subject. 25–50% take S-grade in more than 1 EC language. *Exchanges:* Regular exchanges for pupils aged 11–14 to France.
Senior pupils' non-academic activities *Music:* 75 learn a musical instrument, 8 to Grade 6 or above; 4 in school orchestra, 19 in choir, 6 in pop group. *Drama and dance:* 50 in school plays; 60 in pantomime; 50 in musicals. *Art:* 30 take O-grade; 26 Higher; 5 A-level. 3 accepted for Art School. 4 belong to photographic club, 6 to printing. *Sport:* Rugby, cricket, athletics, tennis, indoor rackets, shooting, swimming, sports hall games, ski-ing, sail-

ing, canoeing available. 200 take non-compulsory sport including sub-aqua, soccer, basketball, curling, squash, climbing, badminton. 20 take RLSS exams; 8 sub-aqua; 10 sailing; 20 ski-ing. 9 represent county/district (rugby, windsurfing); 1 represents country (ski-ing). *Other:* 5 take part in local community schemes. 30 have bronze Duke of Edinburgh's Award, 20 have silver and 10 gold. Other activities include a very active computer club, public speaking, debating, chess, SU, bridge, mountaineering, rock climbing.

Careers 4 part time careers advisers. Annual average accepted for *arts and humanities degree courses* at Oxbridge, 4; other universities, 30; polytechnics/colleges, 10. *science and engineering degree courses* at Oxbridge, 4; other universities, 30; medical schools, 15; polytechnics/colleges, 10. *other general training courses*, very few. Average number going straight into careers in armed services, 2; industry, 5; the City, 2; civil service, 2; music/drama, 1; other, 5. Traditional school careers are accountancy, law, medicine.

Uniform School uniform worn throughout.

Houses/prefects Competitive houses. Prefects, head boy, head of house and house prefects – appointed by the Rector.

Religion Compulsory morning assembly for all.

Social Debates, Young Enterprise Scheme, drama, some games (eg hockey), dances with other local schools. Organised trips to France, Greece, Crete; ski-ing at Christmas and Easter. Pupils allowed to bring own car/bike to school. Meals self service but formal seating. School shops (tuck, sports equipment and stationery). No tobacco/alcohol allowed.

Discipline No corporal punishment. Pupils failing to produce homework once might expect to do it or detention; those caught taking drugs on the premises can expect expulsion.

Alumni association run by The President, Glasgow Academical Club, New Anniesland, Helensburgh Drive, Glasgow.

Former pupils Lord Reith (BBC Governor General); Jeremy Isaacs (Channel 4 TV); Iain Vallance (Chairman, British Telecom); Robert McLennan, MP; Lord Goold; Donald Dewar, MP; John Beattie (Scotland, British Lions).

· *Glasgow High* ·

The High School of Glasgow
637 Crow Road
Glasgow G13 1PL
Tel 041 954 9628

- Pupils 950
- Boys 3–18 (Day)
- Girls 3–18 (Day)
- Higher year 84

- Termly fees £1010
- HMC

Enquiries/application to the Rector

What it's like

Founded in 1124 as the Grammar School of Glasgow and closely associated with the cathedral. It was closed in 1976. The new independent co-educational High School came into being the same year as a result of a merger involving the Former Pupil Club of the old High School and Drewsteignton School in Bearsden. The senior school has modern purpose-built premises at Anniesland on the western outskirts of the city next to 23 acres of playing fields. The junior school is in the former Drewsteignton School buildings about 3 miles away which have been modernised and extended. The school is non-denominational. Its academic standards are high, results are very good and relationship between teachers and pupils excellent. Very many pupils go on to degree courses, almost all to university although, in the Scottish tradition, they do not necessarily head towards Oxbridge.

French, German and Spanish are offered and many pupils take more than one S-grade in a European language. Music and drama are strong. The educational experience provided is of commendable breadth and of high quality. It has a good record in games and sports (many representatives at county level) and an excellent range of activities. An impressive list of awards in the Duke of Edinburgh's Award Scheme. Full use is made of the city's cultural amenities.

School profile

Pupils Total age range 3–18; 950 day pupils (488 boys, 462 girls). Senior department 11–18, 582 pupils (316 boys, 266 girls). Main entry ages 4, 10, 11 and into sixth. Approx 5–10% are children of former pupils. *Transfer from maintained schools:* 95% main intake, plus 50% to sixth.

Entrance Own entrance exam used. Oversubscribed. Academic potential is looked for and ability to contribute to life of school; no religious requirements but school has a Christian background. Parents not expected to buy text books; maximum extras, £20. 38 assisted places. 2 scholarships pa, 5 bursaries pa, full fees to £300.

Parents 15+% in industry or commerce, 15+% are doctors, lawyers etc.

Staff Rector R G Easton, in post for 8 years. 39 full time staff in senior school, 11 part time. Annual turnover 5%. Average age 39.

Academic work O-grades/S-grade/Highers/CSYS. 17 subjects offered. In 1990, 87 pupils in O/S-grade year. 84 in Higher. *O/S-grade:* in 1990, 84 pupils passed in 5–8 subjects; and 3 in 1–4 subjects. *Highers:* 46 pupils passed in 5+ subjects; 15 in 4; 12 in 3; 6 in 2; 4 in 1 subject. *Computing facilities:* 1 computer laboratory with BBC B Econet network (14 BBC micros), 14 Apple Macs, 6 Amstrads (IBM compatible).

European Community *Languages:* French offered: to age 14; S-grade; Higher; CSYS. German offered: to age 14; S-grade; Higher; CSYS. Spanish offered: to S-grade; Higher. 25–50% take S-grade in more than 1 EC language.

Senior pupils' non-academic activities *Music:* 102 learn a musical instrument, 40 to Grade 6 or above; 70 in school orchestra, 110 in choirs, 67 in instrumental groups; 12 play in pop group beyond school. *Drama and dance:* 80 in school productions; 1 goes on to work in theatre. *Art:* 21 take O-grade; 18 Higher. 1 accepted for Art School. 6 belong to photographic club. *Sport:* Rugby, hockey, athletics, cricket, tennis, badminton, basketball, netball, volleyball, swimming, cross-country running, golf, gymnastics, orienteering, canoeing, sailing and ski-ing available. 150 take non-compulsory sport. 12 represent county (rugby, hockey, swimming, athletics, cross-country, orienteering). Some 5 internationalists (athletics, cross-country, swimming, fencing). *Other:* 6 take part in local community schemes. 25 have bronze Duke of Edinburgh's Award, 15 have silver and 8 gold. 4 work for national charities beyond school. Other activities include a computer club, literary and debating, historical and zoological societies, satellite-tracking, chess, bridge, stamp club, Scripture Union, explorers' club (hill walking and sailing).

Careers In 1990, 88% leavers went on to degree courses; 2% to art/drama/music colleges; 7% to non-degree courses (eg business studies, HNDs in technology, management, computer studies); 2% straight into careers (eg insurance, electrical distribution); 1% other. Of those going on to degree courses, 4% went to Oxbridge; 91% to other universities; 5% to poly/colleges. 3% those going on to higher education went to courses in practical art; 1% in drama/acting; 60% in humanities/social sciences; 18% in medicine; and 18% in science/engineering.

Uniform School uniform worn throughout.

Houses/prefects Competitive houses. Prefects, head boy and girl (school captains), head of house and house prefects – voting by senior pupils and staff used by Head in making appointments.

Religion Morning assembly (non-denominational).

Social Debating and public-speaking

competitions. Joint Scripture Union meetings. Usually two organised trips abroad per annum. Pupils allowed to bring own car/bike/motorbike to school. Meals self service. No school shop but some items of uniform are sold. No tobacco/alcohol allowed.

Discipline No corporal punishment. Pupils failing to produce homework once might expect additional work.

Alumni association run by N M Alexander, Secretary, Messrs Bird, Semple, Fyfe, Ireland, 249 West George Street, Glasgow G2 4RB.

Former pupils Sir Henry Campbell-Bannerman, Andrew Bonar Law (prime ministers); Viscount James Bryce (diplomat); Sir Norman Macfarlane.

· *Glenalmond* ·

Glenalmond College
Perthshire
PH1 3RY
Tel 073 888 205

- Pupils 322
- Boys 12–18 (Board)
- Girls 16–18 (Board)
- Upper sixth 70

- Termly fees
  £3100 (Board)
- HMC
Enquiries/application to
the Warden

What it's like

Founded in 1841 as Trinity College by Mr W E Gladstone and others, it stands in magnificent countryside, 10 miles west of Perth, beside the River Almond on the edge of the Highlands. It has an estate of about 250 acres, with beautiful gardens and playing fields. A very healthy environment. The main buildings are grouped round two quadrangles and belong to the Victorian collegiate style, with neo-Gothic features, towers and turrets. There have been many modern developments, including a superb sports complex, a purpose-built theatre, concert hall, art school, design and technology centre, new girls' house and an all-weather pitch for hockey and tennis. The chapel, built by the Episcopalian founders, is one of the finest in the country. Religious education forms part of the curriculum and all denominations attend chapel. A succession of gifted headmasters has ensured a very active, energetic school with an enthusiastic commitment to all enterprises. Academic standards are high and results consistently good. Very many pupils go on to degree courses each year, including Oxbridge. Music is very strong and plays a central part in school life. The theatre, which seats 400, is in regular use. Art is also strong. There is a wide range of sports and games and the college has long had a reputation for excellence in these (a large number of representatives at county and national level). A very wide range of clubs and societies cater for most needs. Golf, ski-ing, salmon fishing, rock-climbing, sailing and canoeing are also available. There is a large CCF with its own pipe band. A substantial commitment to local community services and a promising record in the Duke of Edinburgh's Award Scheme.

School profile

Pupils Age range 12–18; 322 boarding pupils, 300 boys, 22 girls (admitted to sixth form since 1990). Main entry ages 12, 13 (boys) and into sixth (boys and girls). 20–25% are children of former pupils. *Transfer from maintained schools:* 20% main intakes, plus occasional pupil in sixth.

Entrance Common entrance and own entrance tests used. No special skills or religious requirements. Parents expected to buy some text books; maximum extras £100. 36 assisted places. 63 scholarships (for academic and musical excellence) and bursaries (in cases of genuine need), 80%–10% of fees.

Parents 10+% in the armed services; 25+% are doctors, lawyers etc; 30+% in industry or commerce. 10+% live within 30 miles; up to 10% live overseas.

Staff Warden S R D Hall, in post for 4 years. 40 full time staff, 7 part time. Annual turnover up to 5%. Average age 30–35.

Academic work GCSE, Highers, A-levels. 18 subjects offered (no A-level general studies). In 1990, 55 pupils in fifth, 70 in upper sixth. *GCSE:* in 1990, 45 fifth gained at least grade C in 8+ subjects; 10 in 5–7 subjects. *A-levels:* 4 upper sixth passed in 4+ subjects; 40 in 3; 15 in 2; and 11 in 1 subject. A significant proportion take Highers in addition to A-levels. 13 took science A-levels; 32 arts/humanities; 25 both. *Computing facilities:* Large computing laboratory in new CDT centre.

European Community *Languages:* French offered: to age 14; GCSE; A-level. German offered: to GCSE; A-level. Spanish offered: to GCSE; A-level. *Other:* Frequent holiday trips arranged to EC countries. EC pupils study in college on an occasional basis.

Senior pupils' non-academic activities *Music:* 101 learn a musical instrument, 19 to Grade 6 or above, 35 in school orchestra, 20 in string orchestra, 65 in choir, 45 in choral society, 10 in brass group. *Drama and dance:* 50 in school and 90 in house productions; 25 take part in drama evening; 20 in revue. *Art:* Many take as non-examined subject. Some take GCSE, Highers and A-level. *Sport:* Rugby, hockey, cricket, tennis, squash, athletics, swimming, golf (own course), fly-fishing (own river), basketball, badminton, shooting, rock/snow/ice climbing, sailing, curling, sub-aqua available. 25 take life-saving exams. 11 represent county (cricket, rugby); 5 represent country (cricket, rugby, eventing, tetrathlon). *Other:* 15 take part in local community schemes. Other activities include a computer club, debating, design, electronics, technology, pipe band, taxidermy, ornithology, fly-tying, bridge, photography.

Careers On average, 75% leavers go on to degree courses; 4% to art/drama/music colleges; 9% to non-degree courses (eg agriculture, HND business studies, estate management); 6% straight into careers (eg retailing, agriculture, army); 6% other. Of those going on to degree courses, 90% go to Oxbridge; 70% to other universities; 21% to poly/colleges. 2% those going on to higher education went to courses in practical art; 2% in drama/acting; 2% in music; 10% in humanities/social sciences; 6% in medicine; and 28% in science/engineering.

Uniform School uniform worn throughout.

Houses/prefects Competitive houses. Prefects, head boy, heads of houses and house prefects appointed by the Warden and housemasters.

Religion Compulsory attendance at chapel services.

Social Public speaking competitions, theatrical productions, and some dances with local schools. Ski-ing trips abroad; 1987 Kashmir expedition (some boys climbed to over 20,000 ft). Pupils allowed to bring own bike to school. Meals formal. School shops (tuck and sports equipment). No tobacco allowed. *Upper sixth* bar opens once each week.

Discipline Firm but not oppressive. All pupils issued with pocket-size rule book. No corporal punishment. Pupils failing to produce homework once might expect extra work or detention; any involvement with drugs results in immediate expulsion.

Boarding 20% have own study bedroom, 20% share with 1 or 2; 10% are in dormitories of 6+; remainder in cubicles. 7 houses of 50–55, same as for competitive purposes. 2 resident qualified nurses. Central dining room for 5 houses: 2 others eat separately. Pupils can provide and cook own food. 2 weekend exeats each term plus half-term. Visits to local town allowed.

Alumni association run by A R Muir, Springkell, Callum's Hill, Crieff, Perthshire P47 3LS.

Former pupils Sandy Gall (TV newscaster); Sir David Wilson (Governor, Hong Kong); David Leslie and David Sole (Captains of Scottish Rugby XV); Lord Sanderson of Bowden and Alick Buchanan-Smith (politicians); Alan Massie (novelist).

· *Godolphin* ·

Godolphin School
Milford Hill
Salisbury
Wiltshire SP1 2RA
Tel 0722 333059

- Pupils 335
- Boys None
- Girls 11–18
  (Day/Board)
- Upper sixth 41

- Termly fees
  £1570 (Day)
  £2640 (Board)
- GSA, BSA
Enquiries/application to
the Headmistress

What it's like

The original foundation is based on the will of Elizabeth Godolphin made in 1726. The school was started on a small scale late in the 18th century and in 1891 moved to its present site in the outskirts of Salisbury. The premises comprise agreeable modern buildings, including a new science and technology building and a new arts centre, in gardens with playing fields nearby. There are four boarding houses and the accommodation is comfortable. The day girls are divided into two houses. It is a C of E foundation and some religious services and prayers are compulsory. On Sundays pupils worship in school or in one of various churches in the city or in the cathedral. A broad general education is provided and results are good. A large staff allows a favourable staff:pupil ratio of about 1:10. There are very active music, drama and art departments. About 50% of the girls learn one or more instruments. There are regular dramatic productions. The school is well equipped with sporting facilities, including a modern sports hall. There is a fair range of extra-curricular and weekend activities.

School profile

Pupils Age range 11–18; 335 girls, 125 day, 210 boarding. Main entry ages 11, 12, 13 and into sixth. *Transfer from maintained schools:* 30% main intakes, none to sixth.
Entrance Common entrance used. 5 assisted places pa. Scholarships and bursaries.
Staff Headmistress Mrs H A Fender, in post 2 years.
Academic work GCSE and A-levels. 16–20 subjects offered (including GCSE/A-level theatre studies and A-level general studies). In 1990, 54 pupils in upper fifth, 41 in upper sixth. *GCSE:* in 1990, 89% upper fifth gained at least grade C in 8+ subjects; 4% in 5–7 subjects. *A-levels:* 5% upper sixth passed in

4+ subjects; 93% in 3; 3% in 2 subjects. 30% took science A-levels; most others took both science and arts/humanities. *Computing facilities:* RM Nimbus network (15 stations). Most departments and the library have computers. *Special provision:* For dyslexic pupils, some support lessons.
European Community *Languages:* French offered: to age 14; GCSE; A-level. German offered: to age 14; GCSE; AS-level; A-level. Spanish offered: to GCSE. 10–25% take GCSE in more than 1 EC language. All sixth form have to continue with a modern language, regardless of A-level subjects. Flaw (Foreign Languages At Work) offered. *Exchanges:* Regular exchanges for pupils aged 11–14 to France. *Other:* Visits by MEP.

Careers In 1990, 85% leavers went on to degree courses; 8% to art/drama/music colleges; 7% other. Of those going on to degree courses, 71% went to universities; 29% to poly/colleges. 9% those going on to higher education went to courses in practical art; 57% in humanities/social sciences; and 34% in science/engineering.

· *Godolphin and Latymer* ·

Godolphin and Latymer
Iffley Road
Hammersmith
London W6 0PG
Tel 081 741 1936

- Pupils 700
- Boys None
- Girls 11–18
  (Day)
- Upper sixth 95

- Termly fees
  £1400 (Day)
- GSA
  Enquiries/application to
  the Headmistress

What it's like

Founded in 1905 (formerly the Godolphin school for boys, built in 1861). It is single-site and urban on 4 acres of grounds with playing fields attached. Extensive additions, including a new art, science and technology building, have been made to the original Victorian buildings and facilities are first rate. A well-run and academically high-powered school which gets very good results. Very many pupils go on to degree courses each year, including many to Oxbridge. French, German, Italian and Spanish are offered at GCSE and many girls take GCSE in more than one European language. There are regular exchanges with France, Germany and Italy. Very strong indeed in music, drama and art. There is a massive commitment among the pupils. An excellent record in games and sports (a wide variety offered) and an impressive number of clubs and societies.

School profile

Pupils Age range 11–18; 700 day girls. Main entry ages 11 and into sixth. Approx 4% are children of former pupils. *Transfer from maintained schools:* 40% main intake, plus 7% to sixth.

Entrance Own entrance exam used. Oversubscribed. No special skills or religious requirements. Fees include text books, stationery and public examination fees. 25 assisted places available at 11, 3 at 16. Music scholarship worth half fees available. School bursaries awarded in cases of need.

Parents 15+% are doctors, lawyers, etc; 15+% in industry or commerce; 15+% in theatre, media, music, etc.

Staff Headmistress Miss Margaret Rudland, in post for 5 years. 45 full time staff, 28 part time.

Academic work GCSE and A-levels. 20 GCSE subjects offered; 25 at A-level (no A-level general studies). In 1990, 101 pupils in upper fifth, 95 in upper sixth. *GCSE:* in 1990, 93 upper fifth gained at least grade C in 8+ subjects; 6 in 5–7 subjects. *A-levels:* 12 upper sixth passed in 4+ subjects; 70 in 3; 10 in 2; and 2 in 1 subject. 21% took science A-levels; 45% arts/humanities; 29% both. *Computing facilities:* A specialist computer room with network of BBC computers. *Special provision:* Some pupils for whom English is not native tongue, but no special provision is made.

European Community *Languages:* French offered: to age 14; GCSE; A-level. German offered: to age 14; GCSE; A-level. Italian offered: to GCSE. Spanish offered: to GCSE; A-level. 50–75% take GCSE in more than 1 EC language. *Exchanges:* Regular exchanges for pupils to France, Germany and Italy.

Senior pupils' non-academic activities *Music:* 200+ learn a musical instrument, 50 to Grade 6 or above, 1 accepted for Music School; 100 in school orchestra, 160 in school choir. *Drama and dance:* 200+ in school productions. 2 accepted for Drama School, 1 gone on to work in theatre. *Art:* 300 take art as non-examined subject; 45 take GCSE; 14 take A-level art; 20 take A-level history of art. 3 accepted for Art School or fine art degrees, 4 taking art history degrees. *Sport:* Tennis, hockey, athletics, gymnastics, dance, basketball, badminton, fencing and squash available. 75 take non-compulsory sport. 6 pupils represent county (hockey) and 1 country (fencing). *Other:* 3 enter voluntary schemes after leaving school, 1 works for a national charity. Other activities include a computer club, and many other clubs and societies.

Careers In 1990, 91% leavers went on to degree courses; 2% to art/drama/music colleges; 1% to non-degree courses (eg BTEC business and finance); 3% straight into careers (eg film, fashion); 3% other. Of those going on to degree courses, 10% went to Oxbridge; 76% to other universities; 14% to poly/colleges. 2% those going on to higher education went to courses in practical art; 1% in drama/acting; 72% in humanities/social sciences; 12% in medicine; and 12% in science/engineering.

Uniform School uniform worn except the sixth.

Houses/prefects No competitive houses or prefects. Head girl and team of Deputies – elected by the school. School Forum.

Religion Morning assembly for whole school.

Social Joint orchestra with Latymer Upper School. Language exchange visits to France, Germany, Italy and Soviet Union. Senior pupils allowed to bring own bike to school. Meals self service. School shop. No tobacco/alcohol allowed.

Discipline Discipline matters are looked after on an individual basis. High standards of honesty and courtesy are expected. Pupils failing to produce homework are followed up and extra help given when required.

· *Gordonstoun* ·

Gordonstoun School
Elgin
Morayshire
IV30 2RF
Tel 0343 830445

- Pupils 475
- Boys 13–18 (Day/Board)
- Girls 13–18 (Day/Board)
- Upper sixth 92

- Termly fees £1860 (Day) £2900 (Board)
- HMC, SHA, Round Square
  Enquiries/application to the Headmaster

What it's like

Founded in 1934 by Kurt Hahn from Salem. It began in two historic houses: Gordonstoun House and the famous 17th century 'Round Square'. In 1951 part of the school moved to Altyre. In 1960 an intensive building programme enabled the school to re-unite. There was further expansion and development in the 1970s and thereafter and it is now one of the best-equipped schools in the country. The complex lies on a 150-acre estate in magnificent countryside which includes a mile of the Moray Firth foreshore. The prep school is at Aberlour House, 20 miles away on the banks of the River Spey. There are beautiful gardens and playing fields at both. The school's motto is, appropriately, 'Plus est en vous' (There is more in you than you think). Hahn's celebrated Platonic view of education has been made a

324

basis for a philosophy of education which is exemplified in Gordonstoun life. It aims to produce balanced men and women who know the value of working hard but 'who have tried their hands at boats as well as books'. It strives for all-round development and lays emphasis on skill, enterprise, a sense of adventure and compassion. There is much emphasis, too, on self-reliance and responsibility to oneself as well as to others. Hahn's vision of a school as a place where international understanding should be fostered has also become part of the Gordonstoun way of life. About 15% of the school come from overseas and exchanges are made regularly with schools in Australia, New Zealand, Canada, France and Germany. All are expected to attend the non-denominational Chapel services. A large staff allows a staff:pupil ratio of 1:7. The teaching is very good and academic standards are high. Results are consistently impressive and many pupils go on to degree courses, including Oxbridge. Music and drama are very strong indeed and high standards are achieved in performance. There is a wide range of sports and team games with a high level of attainment and plenty of fixtures. Outdoor pursuits, including ski-ing, wind-surfing, gliding, game shooting, fishing, canoeing and rock-climbing and all pupils do a course in seamanship and some expeditions. Not surprisingly the school has a remarkable record in the Duke of Edinburgh's Award Scheme. Many pupils are also involved in a fire service, a coastguard unit, plus mountain rescue and inshore rescue units. There is an Air Training Corps and a large community service unit.

School profile

Pupils Age range 13–18; 475 pupils, 28 day (16 boys, 12 girls), 447 boarding (249 boys, 198 girls). Main entry ages 13 and into sixth. Approx 10% are children of former pupils. Aberlour House provides approx 30% of intake. *Transfer from maintained schools:* 15% main intake, plus 40% to sixth.

Entrance Common entrance and own scholarship exams used. No special skills or religious requirements but abilities in different areas will always be helpful. Parents not expected to buy text books. 24 assisted places. 25 scholarships/bursaries pa, full fees to £850 pa; music scholarships; art bursary; bursaries for sons of armed forces personnel.

Parents 5% live within 100 miles; 15% live overseas.

Staff Headmaster M C S-R Pyper, 1 year in post. 58 full time staff, 21 part time. Annual turnover 2–3%. Average age 38.

Academic work GCSE and A-levels. 15 GCSE subjects offered; 18 at A-level (no A-level general studies). In 1990, 74 pupils in upper fifth, 92 in upper sixth. *GCSE:* in 1990, 38 upper fifth gained at least grade C in 8+ subjects; 26 in 5–7; and 10 in 1–4 subjects. *A-levels:* 8 upper sixth passed in 4+ subjects; 50 in 3; 21 in 2; and 10 in 1 subject. 40 took science

A-levels; 32 arts/humanities; 20 both. *Computing facilities:* Network of 20 RM Nimbus micro computers; 300 MB storage laser printers. *Special provision:* Tuition is available for those with specific learning difficulties in English.

European Community *Languages:* French offered: to GCSE; AS-level; A-level. German offered: to GCSE; AS-level; A-level. 10–25% take GCSE in more than 1 EC language. *Exchanges:* Regular exchanges for pupils aged 14–18 to France and Germany. *Other:* School runs an international summer school – 240 students 11–16 from 25 countries.

Senior pupils' non-academic activities *Music:* 200 learn a musical instrument, 80 to Grade 6 or above, 2 accepted for Music School; 64 in school orchestra, 40 in school choir, 20 in various ensembles; 2 in National Youth Orchestra, Scotland, 6 in Grampian Symphony Orchestra. *Drama and dance:* 150 pa in school productions (opera/light musical/serious drama/revue). Occasional acceptances for Drama/Dance Schools, 2–3 for drama at university. 2 pa for National Youth Theatre. *Art:* 45 take as non-examined subject; 18 GCSE; 10 A-level. 4 accepted for Art School; 2 for other art courses. 40 belong to art project, 20 to art society. *Sport:* All usual games plus ski-ing, windsurfing, gliding, game shooting, fishing, canoeing, orienteering and rock climbing. All pupils do a course in seamanship and go on expeditions. More than 250 take non-compulsory sport. More than 50 take exams. 3 represent county/country in rugby; also cross-country and downhill ski-ing, athletics. *Other:* 64 take part in local community schemes. 69 have bronze Duke of Edinburgh's Award, 16 have silver and 25 gold. Participation also in fire service (24); community service (55); coastguards (20); mountain rescue (45); inshore rescue (39). Other activities include a computer club, a wide variety of clubs, projects and societies.

Careers On average, 75% leavers go on to degree courses; 17% to art/drama/music colleges; 8% to non-degree courses; 7% straight into careers (eg business, commerce, banking). Of those going on to degree courses, 10% go to Oxbridge; 70% to other universities; 20% to poly/colleges.

Uniform School uniform worn throughout the formal day.

Houses/prefects Prefects (Colour Bearers), head boy/girl, head of house and house prefects. School Council.

Religion Services are non-denominational and pupils are expected to attend.

Social Many games fixtures and debates with other schools. Exchanges with schools in Germany, USA, Australia, France; trips abroad for ski-ing and with rugby, squash teams and orchestra. Pupils allowed to bring own bike to school. Meals self service. School shop. No tobacco allowed; beer and wine allowed on specified occasions.

Discipline No corporal punishment.

Boarding Single sex houses, of 55–60. Resident qualified medical staff. Central dining room. Pupils can on occasion provide and cook their own food. Weekend exeats and visits to local town allowed.

Alumni association run by G Neil (Chairman), The Gordonstoun Association, 45 Berkeley Square, London W1X 5DB.

· *Grange* ·

The Grange School	● Pupils 928	● Termly fees
Bradburns Lane	● Boys 4–18	£870 (Day)
Hartford	(Day)	● ISAI
Northwich, Cheshire	● Girls 4–18	Enquiries/application to
CW8 1LR	(Day)	the Admissions
Tel 0606 74007	● Upper sixth 50	Secretary

What it's like

Founded in 1933 as a kindergarten/prep school. In 1978, as a result of parental concern about comprehensivisation, a grammar school was built and this venture has been a resounding success. The school has pleasant modern buildings with 13 acres of sports grounds. In the last 11 years well over a million pounds have been spent on building programmes and facilities are now first-rate. A busy, purposeful school with an expanding sixth form where academic results are good. A high percentage of the sixth form and, consistently over 90%, go on to university or polytechnic. French, German and Spanish are offered up to A-level and an exceptionally high proportion of pupils takes GCSE in more than one European language. There are active music, drama and art depts. A good range of games and sports, plus extra-curricular activities. A promising record in the Duke of Edinburgh's Award Scheme.

School profile

Pupils Total age range 4–18; 928 day pupils (458 boys, 470 girls). Senior department 11–18, 486 pupils (228 boys, 258 girls). Main entry ages 4, 11 and into sixth. *Transfer from maintained schools:* 35% main senior intake, plus 15% to sixth.

Entrance Own entrance exam used. Oversubscribed. No special skills or religious requirements.

Parents 75+% in industry or commerce. 90+% live within 30 miles.

Staff Head E Scott Marshall, in post for 14 years. 55 full time staff, 9 part time.

Academic work GCSE and A-levels. 22 subjects offered (including A-level general studies). In 1990, 72 pupils in fifth, 43 in upper sixth (now 50). *GCSE:* in 1990, 95% upper fifth gained at least grade C in 8+ subjects; *A-levels:* 65% upper sixth passed in 4+ subjects; 26% in 3; 7% in 2; and 2% in 1 subject. 45% took science A-levels; 45% arts/humanities; 10% both. *Computing facilities:* 14 BBC, 14 Amstrad 2000 plus computers in a specialist room and some in classrooms.

European Community *Languages:* French offered: to age 14; GCSE; A-level. German offered: to age 14; GCSE; A-level. Spanish offered: to age 14; GCSE; A-level. Over 75% take GCSE in more than 1 EC language. *Exchanges:* Regular exchanges for pupils aged 11–18 to France (linked school). *Other:* Talks from MEPs. Sixth formers attend Spanish university for 2 week course.

Senior pupils' non-academic activities *Music:* 60 learn a musical instrument, 20 to Grade 6 or above; 40 in school orchestra, 16 in chamber orchestra, 40 in school choir, string quartet, 6 in brass group; 2 in National Children's Orchestra, 5 in local youth orchestra, 2 in 'Bessies' Brass Band. *Drama and dance:* 18 in school productions, 30 in house plays. 10 Grade 6 in ESB, RAD etc. 2 accepted for Drama Schools. *Sport:* Football, rugby, hockey, netball, athletics, tennis, rounders and cricket available. All take part in non-compulsory sport. *Other:* 12 have silver Duke of Edinburgh's Award, 16 have gold. Other activities include a computer club, art, bookshop, chess, bridge, debating, drama, electronics, mathematics clubs.

Careers In 1990, 91% leavers went on to degree courses; 7% to art/drama/music colleges; 2% to non-degree courses. Of those going on to degree courses, 10% went to Oxbridge; 75% to other universities; 15% to poly/colleges. 10% those going on to higher education went to courses in practical art; 52% in humanities/social sciences; 5% in medicine; and 33% in science/engineering.

Uniform School uniform worn except in sixth.

Houses/prefects Competitive houses. Prefects, head boy/girl, head of house and house prefects – appointed by Headmaster and staff.

Religion Regular religious worship.

Social Organised trips abroad, regular exchange with French school. Sixth form students allowed to bring own car/motorbike to school. Meals self service. Clothing shop. No tobacco/alcohol allowed.

· *Greenacre* ·

Greenacre School for
Girls
Sutton Lane
Banstead
Surrey
SM7 3RA
Tel 0737 352114

- Pupils 420
- Boys None
- Girls 4–18
  (Day/Board/Weekly)
- Upper sixth 35

- Termly fees
  £1277 (Day)
  £2428 (Board)
  £2319 (Weekly)
  Enquiries/application to
  the Headmistress

What it's like

Founded in 1933, it is single-site on the edge of the green belt in pleasant surroundings. The buildings include converted houses but are mainly purpose-built accommodation. Facilities are good. A sound general education is provided and results are creditable. A high proportion of the girls are involved in music, drama and art. French, German and Spanish are offered throughout the school and there are regular exchanges with France for all age groups. An adequate range of games and sports and other activities. No local community services and no Duke of Edinburgh's Award Scheme.

School profile

Pupils Total age range 4–18, 420 girls (400 day, 20 boarding). Main entry ages, 4, 5, 10, 11 and into sixth. 5% are children of former pupils. *Transfer from maintained schools:* 20% main intake at 11.

Entrance Own entrance exam used. Oversubscribed. No special skills or religious requirements. Parents not expected to buy text books. 1 Founder scholarship pa at 11+ for half day fees; several sixth form scholarships and bursaries; 10% reduction for service children.

Parents 15+% are doctors, lawyers, etc; 15+% in industry or commerce. 60+% live within 30 miles; up to 5% live overseas.

Staff Headmistress Mrs P M Wood, 1 year in post. Annual turnover 5%.

Academic work GCSE and A-levels. 17–20 subjects offered (including photography and A-level general studies). In 1990, 50 pupils in upper fifth, 35 in upper sixth. *A-levels:* 11 upper sixth passed in 4+ subjects; 7 in 3; 6 in 2; and 7 in 1 subject. 20% took science A-levels; 60% arts/humanities; 20% both. *Computing facilities:* 20 computers and printers. *Special provision:* EFL lessons. Remedial teaching can be arranged for slight cases.

Teacher responsible for dyslexic girls' exam entries.

European Community *Languages:* French offered: to age 14; GCSE; AS-level; A-level; Institute of Linguists. German offered: to age 14; GCSE; AS-level; A-level; Institute of Linguists. Spanish offered: to age 14; GCSE; AS-level; A-level; Institute of Linguists. 10–25% take GCSE in more than 1 EC language. *Exchanges:* Regular exchanges for pupils aged 11–18 to France. *Other:* Often have EC pupils in school, particularly French pupils in small groups or individually for 1 year.

Senior pupils' non-academic activities *Music:* 103 learn a musical instrument, 20% in school orchestra, 30% in school choir; 1 Choral Award to Cambridge. *Drama:* 60% in school productions. 30% do speech and drama exams. *Art:* 60% take as non-examined subject; 5% take GCSE; 20% of sixth form take A-level and accepted for Art School. 5% belong to photographic club. *Sport:* Lacrosse, netball, tennis, rounders, swimming, golf, squash and badminton are available. 20% take non-compulsory sport. Some represent county/country (lacrosse, squash, netball). Some pupils work for national charities, other activities include a computer club, drama technology and music societies.

Careers In 1990, 50% leavers went on to degree courses; 30% to art/drama/music colleges; 10% to non-degree courses or straight into careers (eg management training in retail or banking, legal work); 5% other (eg travel). Of those going on to degree courses, 60% went to universities; 40% to poly/colleges. 20% those going on to higher education went to courses in practical art; 40% in humanities/social sciences; 12% in medicine; and 28% in science/engineering.

Uniform School uniform worn except in sixth.

Houses/prefects Competitive houses. Prefects, head girl, head of house and house prefects – elected by the school. School Council.

Religion Worship compulsory.

Social No organised local events. Many organised trips abroad. Pupils allowed to bring own car/bike/motorbike to school. Some meals formal, some self service. No tobacco/alcohol allowed.

Discipline No corporal punishment. Pupils failing to produce homework once might expect a sharp word; those caught smoking cannabis on the premises might expect parental involvement and expulsion (has never happened).

Boarding One House. Central dining room. Sixth form pupils can provide and cook their own food. 2–3 exeats each term. Visits to the local towns allowed on Saturdays.

· *Gresham's* ·

Gresham's School
Holt
Norfolk
NR25 6EA
Tel 0263 713271

- Pupils 477
- Boys 13–19
  (Day/Board)
- Girls 13–19
  (Day/Board)
- Upper sixth 101

- Termly fees
  £2075 (Day)
  £2965 (Board)
- HMC
  Enquiries/application to
  the Registrar

What it's like

Founded in 1555 by Sir John Gresham. The endowments were placed under the management of the Fishmongers' Company with which the school retains close associations. It enjoys a fine position in one of the most beautiful parts of England, a few miles from the sea near Sheringham. There are delightful grounds of about 50 acres and some 90 acres of woodland as well. All the buildings except the Old School House (1870) are 20th century. Since 1964 there have been extensive developments and accommodation and facilities are now excellent. There are five boys' boarding houses and two girls' houses. It is a C of E foundation and a good deal of attention is given to religious instruction. However, all denominations are accepted. Academic standards are high and results good. Very many leavers go on to university each year, especially to Cambridge. French and German are offered to A-level, Italian to GCSE standard and offered to the sixth form. There are regular exchanges to France and Germany. A wide variety of sports and games are available and the facilities for these are first-rate. Music and drama are an important part of the school's life and there is considerable strength in these fields. A very good range of extra-curricular activities. The CCF contingent is strong and there is a good deal of emphasis on outdoor pursuits. The prep school and pre-prep school are affiliated.

School profile

Pupils Age range 13–19; 477 pupils, 137 day (93 boys, 44 girls), 340 boarding (220 boys, 120 girls). Main entry ages, 13 and into sixth. 10% are children of former pupils. Gresham's prep school provides more than 20% of intake. *Transfer from maintained schools*: 5% main intake, plus 10+% to sixth.

Entrance Common entrance and own scholarship exam used. Oversubscribed. All special skills are encouraged; no special religious requirements. Parents not expected to buy text books. Average charge for extras £200 per term. 5 assisted places pa. 9 scholarships (including music) pa, 50% fees–£600.

Parents 15+% farmers. 10+% live within 30 miles, up to 10% live overseas.

Staff Head J Arkell, first year in post. 52 full time staff, 20 part time. Annual turnover low. Average age 35.

Academic work GCSE and A-levels. 19 subjects offered (including A-level general studies). In 1990, 81 pupils in fifth, 99 in upper sixth. *GCSE:* in 1990, 65 upper fifth gained at least grade C in 8+ subjects; 11 in 5–7; and 5 in 1–4 subjects. *A-levels:* 3 upper sixth passed in 4+ subjects; 72 in 3; 15 in 2; and 5 in 1 subject. 35% took science A-levels; 49% arts/ humanities; 16% both. *Computing facilities:* Computing room with network of machines; CDT department with CDT/ CAD machines. *Special provision:* Help available from specialist member of staff.

European Community *Languages:* French offered: to age 14; GCSE; A-level. German offered: to age 14; GCSE; A-level. Italian offered: to GCSE in sixth. 20% take GCSE in more than 1 EC language. *Exchanges:* Regular exchanges for pupils aged 14–16 to France and Germany. *Other:* Up to 12 German pupils each year.

Senior pupils' non-academic activities *Music:* 100 learn a musical instrument, 35 up to Grade 6; 3 accepted for Music School per year. 30 in school orchestra, 35 in school choir, 10 in school pop group, 15 in chamber groups. 4 play in pop group outside school. 15 pa in amateur orchestras, choirs and chamber groups outside school. *Drama:* 100 in school productions. 9 entered competitions. *Sport:* Rugby, hockey, cricket; also tennis, squash, swimming, athletics, shooting. Main three sports compulsory for all; some 50% take part in voluntary sports. Large number represent country (hockey, rugby, squash, shooting; 20 pupils have shot for Britain in past 10 years). *Other:* 50 take part in local community schemes. 80 have bronze Duke of Edinburgh's Award, 50 silver and 60 gold. Over 30 other activities including computer club, chess club, learn to drive, tae kwon do, CCF, astronomy, beekeeping, yachtmaster.

Careers In 1990, 78% leavers went on to degree courses; 5 to art/drama/music colleges; 3 to non-degree courses; 2% straight into careers (eg armed forces); 12% other. Of those going on to degree courses, 5% went to Oxbridge; 89% to other universities; 6% to poly/colleges. 58% those going on to higher education went to courses in humanities/social sciences, 7% in medicine and 35% in science/engineering.

Uniform School uniform except in sixth.

Houses/prefects Competitive houses. Head boy/girl, prefects, head of house and house prefects, appointed by the head. No formal School Council but regular meetings with prefects and deputy head.

Religion Attendance at religious worship compulsory.

Social Many joint events with other schools, mostly sport. Sri Lankan badminton tour. Pupils allowed to bring own car/bike/motorbike. Meals self-service. School shop. Tobacco/alcohol allowed in sixth form club.

Discipline No corporal punishment. Pupils failing to produce homework once could expect extra work period; those caught smoking cannabis on the premises could expect expulsion.

Boarding 45% have own study bedrooms; 22% share with 1–3 others. 33% in dormitories of 6+. Single sex houses 38–69, same as competitive houses. Resident qualified nurse and sanatorium.

2 exeats per term (1–2 nights). Visits to the local town allowed for all (2 hours Mon–Sat and on Sunday afternoons).
Alumni association is run by Bursar's Secretary, c/o The School.

Former pupils Stephen Spender, W H Auden, Leonard Berkeley, John Reith, Benjamin Britten.

· Grosvenor High ·

Grosvenor High School
Grosvenor Place
London Road
Bath
Avon BA1 6AX
Tel 0225 314458

- Pupils 140
- Boys 11–16 (Day)
- Girls 11–16 (Day)
- Upper sixth No

- Termly fees £775 (Day)
- ISAI
Enquiries/application to the Headmaster

What it's like

Founded in 1912, moved to its present site in 1954. Own prep school takes pupils of 8–11. Main school teaches up to GCSE and many pupils transfer to other schools for A-levels. Classes are small (average of 13) and pupils given much personal attention. Separate unit within the school caters for children with specific learning difficulties, liaising with external consultant psychologists and tailoring the timetable to suit the individual child. Parents of children using the unit are charged an extra fee. The school operates a branch of the Midland Bank (staffed by pupils). There is a strong tradition of outdoor activities: youth hostelling trips; weekend camps in summer including sailing camps; caving, climbing and abseiling. The Duke of Edinburgh's Award Scheme is popular.

School profile

Pupils Age range 11–16; 140 day pupils (70 boys, 70 girls). Main entry age 11. Own junior school and Roundstone School (Trowbridge) provide 20+% of intake. Small proportion are children of former pupils. *Transfer from maintained sector:* 50% main intake.
Entrance Not oversubscribed. No special skills or religious requirements. Parents not expected to buy text books; maximum extras, £320 (for dyslexia unit). 1 scholarship pa, £100 per term.
Parents 40% in industry or commerce.
Staff Headmaster R H Side, in post for 6 years. 5 full time staff, 7 part time, plus 5 music staff. Annual turnover 1. Average age 35–40.
Academic work GCSE and occasional A-level. 12 subjects offered including sociology. In 1990, 28 pupils in upper fifth. *GCSE:* in 1989, 3 pupils in upper fifth gained at least grade C in 8+ sub-jects; 4 in 5–7 subjects and 9 in 1–4 sub-jects. *Computing facilities:* IBM com-patibles throughout school (1 computer to every 4 pupils) with links with local industry. Dual certification of GCSE with RSA. *Special provision:* special unit for dyslexic pupils (high success rate); specia-list EFL teaching, overseas students in school for year, term or few weeks.
European Community *Languages:* French offered: to age 14; GCSE. Spanish offered: to GCSE. Under 10% take GCSE in more than 1 EC language. *Exchanges:* Regular exchanges for pupils aged 11–14 to France and Spain. *Other:* French, Italian and Spanish pupils visit the school for up to 4 weeks – groups given special EFL course, single pupils absorbed in normal programme.
Senior pupils' non-academic activi-ties *Music:* 28 learn a musical instru-ment; 12 take GCSE. 34 in choir. *Drama*

and dance: 40 in school productions; 1 accepted for Drama School, 1 for Dance School; 20 enter competitions (Mid Somerset and Trowbridge Festivals). *Art:* All take GCSE fine arts or graphics. *Sport:* Wide range of sports and activities all played and coached at Bath University. 6 represent county (swimming, athletics). *Other:* 16 have bronze Duke of Edinburgh's Award. Other activities include computer, robotics and science clubs. Gymnastics, sailing, judo, craft. YHA trips, activity days out and weekend camps. School Council runs many activities and own bank account.

Careers In 1990, 56% leavers went on to FE colleges; 30% to other schools/sixth form colleges; 1% to art/drama/music colleges; 10% to non-degree courses; 3% straight into careers.

Uniform School uniform worn throughout.

Houses/prefects Competitive houses. Prefects, head boy and girl – appointed after written application and interview. School Council.

Religion Compulsory morning assembly.

Social Organised French trips in summer. Annual ski trip abroad or Scotland. Pupils allowed to bring own bike to school. All pupils bring own lunch. School shop. No tobacco/alcohol allowed.

Discipline No corporal punishment. Pupils failing to produce homework once might expect a detention. Conduct report for minor offences. Work report in conjunction with parental co-operation. Any serious matter would be dealt with through parental consultation and counselling. Relationships in school given high priority and disciplinary problems are rare.

<u>h</u>

· *Haberdashers' Aske's (Boys)* ·

The Haberdashers' Aske's School Butterfly Lane Elstree Borehamwood Hertfordshire WD6 3AF Tel 081 207 4323	● Pupils 1300 ● Boys 7–18 (Day) ● Girls None ● Upper sixth 155	● Termly fees £1381 (Day) ● HMC Enquiries to the School Secretary Applications to the Admissions Secretary

What it's like

Founded in 1690 by the Worshipful Company of Haberdashers; the original buildings were opened at Hoxton in 1692. In 1898 it moved to new buildings in Hampstead and in 1947 a prep school was opened at Mill Hill. The whole school moved to Elstree in 1961. Thirteen years later the Haberdashers' Aske's School for Girls moved to the adjoining site. The two now occupy fine grounds and playing fields in green belt country covering about 104 acres. With the exception of the original building (Aldenham House) all were purpose-built. The result is a fine modern school with splendid facilities. Standards of teaching are high. Very many pupils go on to degree courses, including an exceptionally high proportion to Oxbridge. French, German and Spanish are offered throughout the school. A high proportion of pupils takes GCSE in more than one European language and there are regular exchanges, for all age groups, with France, Germany and Spain. Very strong in music, drama and art. Also has much strength in sports and games. There are no fewer than 48 clubs and societies providing as many different activities. Extra-curricular activities are shared with the Girls' School. Excellent results in the Duke of Edinburgh's Award Scheme.

School profile

Pupils Total age range 7–18; 1300 day boys. Senior department 11–18, 1100 boys. Main entry ages 7, 11 and into sixth. Approx 5% are children of former pupils. *Transfer from maintained schools:* 70% intake at 11, plus 80% to sixth.

Entrance Common entrance sometimes used; usually own entrance exam. Oversubscribed. No special skills or religious requirements. Parents not expected to buy text books; maximum extras £360 (music, lunches, coaches etc). 35 assisted places pa. 12 bursaries (including at least one for music), £1500–£900. Small number of scholarships.

Parents 15+% in industry or commerce; 15+% are doctors, lawyers, etc.

Staff Head K Dawson, in post for 4 years. 96 full time staff, 23 part time. Annual turnover 8%. Average age 39.

Academic work GCSE and A-levels. 25 GCSE subjects offered; 20 at A-level (no A-level general studies). In 1990, 155 pupils in upper fifth, 155 in upper sixth.

GCSE: in 1990, 146 upper fifth gained at least grade C in 8+ subjects; 8 in 5–7; and 1 in 1–4 subjects. *A-levels:* 10 upper sixth passed in 4+ subjects; 127 in 3; 13 in 2; and 5 in 1 subject. 34% took science A-levels; 54% arts/humanities; 12% both. *Computing facilities:* 2 Nimbus networks (18 and 30 stations); Apple Macintosh network (6 stations) and various BBCs, Archimedes, Amstrads around school, library and departments.

European Community *Languages:* French offered: to age 14; GCSE; AS-level; A-level. German offered: to age 14; GCSE; AS-level; A-level. Italian: non-examined subject. Spanish offered: to age 14; GCSE; A-level. 50–75% take GCSE in more than 1 EC language. *Exchanges:* Regular exchanges for pupils aged 11–18 to France, Germany and Spain. *Other:* European Studies offered to pupils aged 16–18. European Fellow to foster EC links. Work experience scheme for sixth formers in France and Germany.

Senior pupils' non-academic activities *Music:* 500+ learn a musical instrument, 180 to Grade 6 or above; 1 accepted for Music School; 4 orchestras, 80 in senior orchestra, 250 in choir. *Drama and dance:* 70 in school productions; 1 accepted for Drama School, 1 to work in theatre. *Art:* 60 take as non-examined subject; 45 take GCSE, 10 take A-level, 5 take AS-level. 4 accepted for Art School. 10 belong to photographic club, 20 to life drawing and art club after school, 5 to typography group, 10 to stage group. *Sport:* Archery, athletics, badminton, basketball, cricket, cross-country, fencing, football, golf, hockey, rugby, sailing and sail-boarding, shooting, squash, swimming, table tennis, tennis, and water-polo available. 450–500 take non-compulsory sport. 8 take lifesaving exams. 9 pupils represent county (rugby, hockey, cricket). *Other:* 6 have bronze Duke of Edinburgh's Award, 60 have silver and 5 gold. Other activities include a computer club and 48 others – wide variety.

Careers In 1990, 87% leavers went on to degree courses; 3% to art/drama/music colleges; 2% to non-degree courses (eg HNDs in mineral technology, electrical engineering, computing); 2% straight into careers; 6% other. Of those going on to degree courses, 30% went to Oxbridge, 60% to other universities; 10% to poly/colleges. 1% those going on to higher education went to courses in practical art; 1% in drama/acting; 1% in music; 60% in humanities/social sciences/arts/languages; 10% in medicine; and 27% in science/engineering.

Uniform School uniform worn except in sixth.

Houses/prefects Competitive houses. Prefects, head boy, head of house and house prefects – appointed after consultation. Sixth Form Committee.

Religion Daily assemblies.

Social Extra-curricular activities shared with Haberdashers' Aske's (Girls). Organised trips to Europe and USA. Pupils allowed to bring own bike/motorbike to school. Meals self service. School shop. No tobacco/alcohol allowed.

Discipline No corporal punishment. Pupils failing to produce homework once might expect extra work; those caught smoking cannabis on the premises could expect exclusion from school pending enquiry and consultation with parents.

Alumni association is run by Jeremy Gibb, Secretary, Old Haberdashers' Association, c/o the School.

Former pupils Rt Hon Leon Brittan PC, QC; Martin Sorrell (WPP); Peter Oppenheimer (economist); Simon Schana (Professor of History, Harvard University); Michael Green (Carlton Communications Group – Thames Television, LWT etc); Nicholas A Serota (Director: Tate Gallery).

· *Haberdashers' Aske's (Girls)* ·

Haberdashers' Aske's
School for Girls
Aldenham Road
Elstree
Hertfordshire WD6 3BT
Tel 081 953 4261

- Pupils 1115
- Boys None
- Girls 5–18
  (Day)
- Upper sixth 108

- Termly fees
  £900 (Day)
- GSA
  Enquiries/application to
  the Admissions
  Secretary

What it's like

Founded in 1690, in 1974 it moved to Aldenham estate which is semi-rural and comprises 43 acres of fine park and woodland. A single-site school with first-rate modern facilities. Religious worship is compulsory. Academic standards are very high and results first-class. Very many leavers go on to degree courses each year, including many to Oxbridge. French, German and Spanish are offered throughout the school. Many girls take GCSE in more than one European language, and there are regular exchanges with France, Germany and Spain and links with schools in all three countries. Immensely strong in music, drama and art. A very good range of games and sports in which high standards are achieved (several representatives at county and national level). A wide variety of activities are available. The school has an outstanding record in the Duke of Edinburgh's Award Scheme.

School profile

Pupils Total age range 5–18; 1115 day girls. Senior department 11–18, 831 girls. Main entry ages 5, 11 and into sixth. Approx 2% are children of former pupils. *Transfer from maintained schools:* 70% main senior intake, plus 50% to sixth.

Entrance Own entrance exam used. Oversubscribed. All special skills welcomed. Parents not expected to buy text books; maximum extras, £100 per term. 180 assisted places. 6–10 scholarships/bursaries pa (academic), £1000 to £300.

Parents 15+% are doctors, lawyers, etc; 15+% in industry or commerce.

Staff Head Mrs P Penney, first year in post. 67 full time staff, 18 part time. Annual turnover 10%. Average age 39.

Academic work GCSE, AS and A-levels. 19 GCSE subjects offered; 21 at A-level. In 1990, 119 pupils in upper fifth, 108 in upper sixth. *GCSE:* in 1990, 94% upper fifth gained at least grade C in 8+ subjects; 6% in 5–7 subjects. *A-levels:* 14% upper sixth passed in 4+ subjects; 80% in 3; 5% in 2 subjects. 35% took science A-levels; 35% arts/humanities; 30% both. *Computing facilities:* Computer room equipped with 30 computers and computers in most departments.

European Community *Languages:* French offered: to age 14; GCSE; AS-level; A-level. German offered: to age 14; GCSE; AS-level; A-level. Spanish offered: to age 14; GCSE; AS-level; A-level. 25–50% take GCSE in more than 1 EC language. *Exchanges:* Regular exchanges for pupils aged 11–14 to France, Germany and Spain. *Other:* Most classes are paired with classes in France and correspond. Links with 5 schools in France and others in Germany and Spain.

Senior pupils' non-academic activities *Music:* 296 learn a musical instrument, 162 to Grade 6 or above, 23 take GCSE, 13 take A-level, 2 accepted for London Music Colleges; 4 take university degree, 140 in school orchestra, 215 in school choirs, 30 in chamber ensembles; 24 in outside choirs, 30 in LEA choir/orchestra, 4 in County Youth Orchestra, 5 in Jewish Youth Club. *Drama and dance:* 30–50 in school productions, 10 in other. *Art:* 33 take GCSE, 5 take A-level. 4 accepted for Art School. *Sport:* Lacrosse, netball, rounders, tennis, trampolining, badminton, swimming, fencing, table tennis, keep fit, golf, gymnastics, dance, synchronized swimming, self defence, judo, cross country, squash, basketball, volleyball and riding available. 125 take non-compulsory sport. 20 represent county or higher teams (lacrosse, swimming, tennis, athletics). 75 take ski-ing trip. *Other:* 94 have bronze Duke of Edinburgh's Award, 38 have silver and 6 gold. Other activities include a computer club, bridge, chess, community service, science, electronics, debating and public speaking, cultural society, modern languages, Christian Union, school magazine and Young Enterprise.

Careers In 1990, 92% leavers went on to degree courses; $1/2$% to art/drama/music colleges; $1/2$% straight into careers; 7% other. Of those going on to degree courses, 14% went to Oxbridge, 81% to other universities; 5% to poly/colleges.

2% those going on to higher education went to courses in practical art; 2% in music; 60% in humanities/social sciences; 14% in medicine; and 22% in science/engineering.

Uniform School uniform worn except the sixth.

Houses/prefects No competitive houses. Prefects and head girl elected by school. School Council.

Religion Compulsory worship.

Social Debates, quizzes and many extra-curricular activities with Haberdashers' Aske's (Boys). Organised trips abroad. Pupils allowed to bring own car/bike to school. Meals self service. School shop. No tobacco/alcohol allowed.

Discipline No corporal punishment. Pupils failing to produce homework once might expect a warning; those caught smoking cannabis on the premises might expect expulsion.

· *Haileybury* ·

Haileybury and Imperial Service College Hertford SG13 7NU Tel 0992 463353/ 462352	● Pupils 640 ● Boys 11–18 (Day/Board) ● Girls 16–18 (Day/Board) ● Upper sixth 162	● Termly fees £2150 (Day) £3195 (Board) ● HMC Enquiries/application to the Registrar

What it's like

Founded in 1862, it lies in a beautiful estate of 500 acres of countryside and playing fields. By any school standards the buildings are magnificent. The main buildings, quadrangle and terrace front were designed by William Wilkins in 1806 for the East India College where, for 50 years, students of the East India Company were educated. In 1874 one of the Haileybury housemasters became head of the United Services College at Westward Ho! This later moved to Windsor and became the Imperial Service College. In 1942 Haileybury and the ISC combined. The school maintained the tradition of 'imperial service' well into the 1950s. The original main quadrangle forms the centre of the school and round it are the domed Romanesque chapel, the library, council chamber and six houses. There have been many additions since the beginning of this century and the overall facilities are first-class. The religious education aims to prepare pupils for adult membership of the C of E and some chapel services are compulsory. A large staff allows a staff:pupil ratio of about 1:10. The teaching is very good, academic standards are high and results are excellent. Many go on to degree courses, including Oxbridge, each year. French, German and Spanish are offered throughout the school and a high proportion of pupils takes GCSE in more than one European language. The music department is one of the strongest in the country (about 260 pupils learn an instrument, there are several orchestras and choirs, a concert band and a pop group). Drama is also extremely strong and there are many productions each year. The art and design centre is very active and work of high quality is achieved. A wide variety of sports and games is provided and the school is well-known for its successes (numerous representatives at county and national levels). A good deal of emphasis on outdoor pursuits. A large and flourishing CCF and an impressive record in the Duke of Edinburgh's Award Scheme.

School profile

Pupils Age range 11–18; 640 pupils, 154 day (143 boys, 11 girls), 486 boarding (405 boys, 81 girls). Main entry ages 13 (boys) and into sixth (boys and girls). Approx 12% are children of former pupils. Haileybury Junior School, Windsor provides proportion of intake. *Transfer from maintained schools:* 15 boys at 11, plus 6 into sixth.

Entrance Common entrance and own entrance exam used. Oversubscribed. No special skills required; C of E school but others accepted. Parents expected to buy text books; music tuition, expeditions etc also extra. Assisted places available for day entry from state schools at 11+. 15 scholarships (academic, music and art) and bursaries (by arrangement), half fees to £600.

Parents 30+% live within 30 miles; up to 12% live overseas.

Staff Master D J Jewell, in post for 4 years, 70 full time staff, 10 part time.

Academic work GCSE and A-levels. 17 GCSE subjects offered; 20 at A-level (no A-level general studies). In 1990, 109 pupils in fifth, 149 in upper sixth (now 162). *GCSE:* in 1990, 94 fifth gained at least grade C in 8+ subjects; 10 in 5–7; and 5 in 1–4 subjects. *A-levels:* 9 upper sixth passed in 4+ subjects; 112 in 3; 18 in 2; and 8 in 1 subject. 40% took science A-levels; 45% arts/humanities; 15% both. *Computing facilities:* CDT block has a fully equipped computer room: all pupils do a CDT course in their first year; thereafter GCSE option or hobby. *Special provision:* Extra coaching in early stages for those mildly dyslexic and overseas pupils whose written English is not strong.

European Community *Languages:* French offered: to age 14; GCSE; AS-level; A-level. German offered: to age 14; GCSE; AS-level; A-level. Spanish offered: to age 14; GCSE; AS-level; A-level. 25–50% take GCSE in more than 1 EC language. *Other:* 1–2 German boys annually in lower sixth for 1 year, occasionally other European boys. Access to EC TV satellite broadcasts. Professionally organised school visits to EC countries – France, Germany and Spain annually.

Senior pupils' non-academic activities *Music:* 250 learn a musical instrument, 4 accepted for Music School; 4 accepted to read music at university; 60 in school orchestra, 120 in choir, 8 in pop group, 20 in brass ensemble. *Drama and dance:* One-third in school productions, remainder in small group productions. About 20 former pupils now professional actors. *Art:* 50 take as non-examined subject; 40 GCSE; 18 A-level; 8 History of Art. 6 accepted for Art School; 50 belong to Art Society. 30 belong to photographic club. *Sport:* Rackets, tennis, squash, fives, basketball, badminton, hockey, football, rugby, cricket, archery, windsurfing, sailing, canoeing, lacrosse, netball, trampolining, weight training, athletics, cross-country, golf, swimming, scuba diving, judo, fencing available. All take non-compulsory sport as well as compulsory. Many pupils have represented county/country in all sports. *Other:* 55 take part in local community schemes. 30 are involved in bronze Duke of Edinburgh's Award, 21 in silver and 10 in gold. 3 enter voluntary schemes after leaving. Other activities include a computer club, chess, bridge, stamp collecting, woodwork, electronics, metalwork and plastics, technical drawing, printing, photography, calligraphy and ceramics.

Careers In 1990, 50% leavers went on to degree courses; 7% to art/drama/music colleges; 2% to non-degree courses; 2% straight into careers (eg business, retailing, army); 39% other (eg reapplying to higher education, other schools). Of those going on to degree courses, 10% went to Oxbridge, 69% to other universities; 21% to poly/colleges. 3% those going on to higher education went to courses in practical art; 1% in drama/acting; 2% in music; 70% in humanities/social sciences; 4% in medicine; and 20% in science/engineering.

Uniform Modi．ed school uniform worn throughout.

Houses/prefects Competitive houses. Prefects, head boy/girl, head of house and house prefects – appointed by Head.

Religion Daily chapel and one Sunday service compulsory.

Social Geography field trips abroad, expeditions to Himalayas, cricket tours to Australia and Barbados, ski-ing etc. Some sixth form day pupils allowed to bring own car to school. Meals self-service. School tuck and games equipment shops. No tobacco allowed; licensed sixth form bar (wine and beer) for pupils 17+.

Discipline No corporal punishment. Pupils failing to produce homework once might expect detention. Smoking and drinking are met with the usual sanctions of gating, hard labour, loss of privileges and regular reporting to authority. A pupil introducing drugs into the school may expect to be expelled.

Boarding A few sixth formers have own study bedroom, most others are in dormitories. Single sex houses, of approximately 50, same as competitive houses. Resident qualified nurse and doctor. Central dining room. Pupils can provide and cook own food. 2 weekend exeats each term, and half term. Visits to local town allowed with housemaster's permission.

Alumni association run by Bill Tyrwhitt-Drake, 1 Lodge Lane, Bexley, Kent DA5 1DJ.

Former pupils Clement Attlee (former PM); Stirling Moss (racing driver); Alan Ayckbourn (playwright); Max Robertson (sports commentator); Michael Bonallack (golfer); Simon MacCorkindale (actor); Lord de Freitas (Parliamentarian); Denis Mack Smith (historian).

· Hamilton Lodge ·

Hamilton Lodge School for Deaf Children
Walpole Road
Brighton
East Sussex BN2 2ET
Tel 0273 682362

- Pupils 53
- Boys 5–18 (Day/Board)
- Girls 5–18 (Day/Board)
- Upper fifth 6

- Termly fees
  £3660 (Day)
  £4880 (Weekly)

School profile

Pupils Total age range 5–18, 53 pupils (boys and girls). Main entry ages 5, 7, 11. *Transfer from maintained schools:* 95% intake.

Entrance All pupils' fees are paid by their LEA. Weekly boarding only. Specialist school for the deaf.

Staff Principal Miss M M Moore, in post for 12 years.

Academic work *GCSE*: in 1990, 6 pupils in upper fifth, gained at least grade C in 1–4 subjects. *Computing facilities:* 10 computers. *Special provision:* All children are profoundly deaf.

338

· *Hammond* ·

Hammond School	• Pupils 170	• Termly fees
Hoole Bank House	• Boys 11–16 (Board)	£870 (Day)
Mannings Lane	• Girls 11–16 (Day/	£2500 (Board)
Hoole Bank	Board)	• ISAI
Chester CH2 2PB	• Upper sixth Not at	
Tel 0244 328542	present	

What it's like

Hammond combines the education department which offers education to girls up to GCSE level with a vocational school of dance. Senior students are presented for A-level dance. A new course is being developed which will enable senior dance students to study for more A-levels which will include music, English and art as well as dance. Hammond is a small caring school where students are encouraged to work together and be considerate to others both in school and in the community outside. A broad balanced curriculum is offered.

School profile

Pupils Age range 11–16, 170 pupils; dance pupils boys and girls; other pupils all girls. Main entry age 11. *Transfer from maintained schools:* 50% main intake.
Entrance Own entrance exam and dance audition. Grant-aided by most LEAs. Skills in classical ballet required for dance students.
Staff Principal Sybil Elliott. Head Polly Dangerfield.
Academic work *GCSE and A-levels:* 15 subjects offered to GCSE level, A-level dance for dance students. *GCSE:* On average, 87% upper fifth achieved at least grade C in 5+ subjects. *Computing facilities:* 5 BBCs; network of Nimbus computers.
European Community *Languages:* French offered: to age 14; GCSE.
Careers In 1990, 95% leavers went on to A-levels and further education.

· *Hampton* ·

Hampton School	• Pupils 875	• Termly fees
Hanworth Road	• Boys 11–18	£1100 (Day)
Hampton	(Day)	• HMC
Middlesex TW12 3HD	• Girls None	Enquiries/application to
Tel 081 979 5526	• Upper sixth 128	the Headmaster
Fax 081 941 7368		

What it's like

Founded in 1557, endowed by the will of Robert Hammond, which provided for a school room beside the parish church and for a master's salary. The present buildings, which are on a single site in a suburban area, with adjoining playing fields, date from 1939. Recent extensions and developments provide good facilities and accommodation. It is very well equipped. Staffing allows a ratio of 2:25 pupils. Academic standards are high and results are good. Very many go on to degree courses, including many to Oxbridge each year. French, German and Spanish are offered throughout the school to A-level, and in some years Italian for the Institute of Linguists. There are regular exchanges into France, Germany and Spain. An extremely strong music dept (a fine music centre was opened in 1978) and about 230 pupils learn an instrument. Considerable strength in drama and art. A high reputation in games and sports; especially rowing at which the school excels. A large number of county and international representatives in sports and games. There is a flourishing CCF and the school has a promising record in the Duke of Edinburgh's Award Scheme.

School profile

Pupils Age range 11–18; 875 day boys. Main entry ages 11, 13 and into sixth. Approx 15% are children of former pupils. *Transfer from maintained schools:* 90% intake at 11 (none at 13), plus 60% to sixth.

Entrance Common entrance and own exam used. Oversubscribed. No special skills or religious requirements. Parents not expected to buy text books; maximum extras £80 (lunches, insurance). 26 assisted places pa. 12 scholarships/bursaries pa, one-third to one-sixth remission of fees.

Parents 15+% are doctors, lawyers, etc; 15+% in industry or commerce; 15+% in the armed services, 15+% in the Church; 15+% in the theatre, media, music etc.

Staff Headmaster G G Able, in post 3 years. 68 full time staff, 5 part time. Annual turnover 8–10%. Average age 38.

Academic work GCSE, AS and A-levels offered (including A-level general studies). In 1990, 138 pupils in upper fifth, 106 in upper sixth (now 128). *GCSE:* in 1990, 116 upper fifth gained at least grade C in 8+ subjects; 18 in 5–7 subjects. *A-levels:* 81 upper sixth passed in 4+ subjects; 14 in 3; 7 in 2; and 2 in 1 subject. 33% took science A-levels; 33% arts/humanities; 33% both. *Computing facilities:* 13 and 8 station Nimbus networks, Nimbus DTP system. 12 assorted BBCs and PCs in different departments; Apple Macintosh (physics). *Special provision:* Some extra help in English where necessary.

European Community *Languages:* French offered: to age 14; GCSE; AS-level; A-level. German offered: to age 14; GCSE; AS-level; A-level. Portugese: Institute of Linguists (some years). Spanish offered: to age 14; GCSE; AS-level; A-level. 50–75% take GCSE in more than 1 EC language. *Exchanges:* Regular exchanges for pupils of all ages to France, Germany and Spain (11–14, France only; 16–18, Spain only). *Other:* Periodic talks from MEPs and senior EC civil servants. Occasional periods of study by EC pupils temporarily resident in UK.

Senior pupils' non-academic activities *Music:* 230 learn a musical instrument, 30 to Grade 6 or above, 1 accepted for Music School; 55 in school orchestra, 80 in school choir, 50 in wind bands; 4 or 5 go on to play in pop group. *Drama and dance:* 70 in school productions. Some pupils accepted for Drama/Dance Schools. *Art:* 20 sixth-formers take as non-examined subject; 25 take GCSE; 10 take A-level. 4–10 accepted for Art School. 10 belong to photographic club. *Sport:* Rugby, football, cricket, rowing, basketball, volleyball, fencing, tennis, table tennis, squash, swimming, athletics and cross-country available. 650 take non-compulsory sport. 12 represent country (rugby, football, rowing); 20 represent county (rugby, football, cricket, tennis). *Other:* 20 take part in local community schemes. 20 have bronze Duke of Edinburgh's Award, 6 have silver and 2 gold. 1 or 2 enter voluntary schemes after leaving school. Other activities include bridge, chess, war-games, debating and discussion, electronics, and whole range of subjects, societies and clubs, CCF (Army, RAF), adventure including climbing, camping, canoeing, expeditions at home and overseas.

Careers In 1990, 88% leavers went on to degree courses; 2% to art/drama/music colleges; 4% straight into careers (eg merchant banking, insurance); 7% other. Of those going on to degree courses, 11% went to Oxbridge, 60% to other universities; 18% to poly/colleges. 2% those going on to higher education went to courses in practical art; 1% in drama/acting; 2% in music; 60% in humanities/social sciences; 5% in medicine; and 30% in science/engineering.

Uniform School uniform worn throughout.

Houses/prefects No competitive houses. All upper sixth act as prefects. Head boy and 20 senior prefects.

Religion One traditional religious assembly per week, two Church services per year. Active Christian Union.

Social Drama (including joint A-level theatre studies), music, debates etc with Lady Eleanor Holles School. Exchanges with Konstanz (Germany), Orange (France). Ski-ing trips, expeditions etc. Pupils allowed to bring own bike/motorbike to school. Meals self service. School shop selling limited range of tuck. No tobacco/alcohol allowed.

Discipline No corporal punishment. Pupils failing to produce homework once might expect reprimand or perhaps lunch time detention; those caught smoking cannabis on the premises might expect expulsion.

Alumni association is run by C E Ledger, 10 Garden Close, Hampton, Middlesex.

· *Harrogate Ladies* ·

Harrogate Ladies'
College
Clarence Drive
Harrogate
North Yorkshire
HG1 2QG
Tel 0423 504543

- Pupils 400
- Boys None
- Girls 10–18
  (Day/Board)
- Upper sixth 49

- Termly fees
  £1485 (Day)
  £2230 (Board)
- GSA
Enquiries/application to
the Headmistress

What it's like

Founded in 1893, it has a most agreeable site in a quiet residential area (the Duchy estate) a few minutes' walk from the town centre and from the countryside. Harrogate itself is a pleasant and civilised town and the school's houses (7 formerly privately owned) are set in gardens. The college has an academic bias but aims to provide a very good all-round education for girls of above average and average intellectual ability. Though there are some day pupils great attention is given to create a happy and purposeful resident community. The boarding accommodation is comfortable and every modern facility is provided. A C of E school (it has its own chapel) there is a certain emphasis on religious instruction and daily worship. The teaching is good and so are results. Many sixth formers go on to degree courses. French, German and Spanish are offered up to A-level and a high proportion of girls takes GCSE in more than one European language. Very strong in music (virtually everyone is involved). Substantial successes in the Duke of Edinburgh's Award Scheme. Strong support in the local community where the school enjoys a high reputation.

School profile

Pupils Age range 10–18; 400 girls, 70 day, 330 boarding. Main entry ages 11, 12, 13 and into sixth. *Transfer from maintained schools:* 50% main intake and into sixth.

Entrance Own entrance exam used. Oversubscribed. No special skills or religious requirements. Parents not expected to buy text books (but pay a small hire charge); riding, music tuition extra. Up to 35 assisted places. 50+ scholarships/bursaries, 33%–25% of fees.

Parents 15+% in industry or commerce. 30+% live within 30 miles; 28% live overseas.

Staff Headmistress Mrs J C Lawrance, in post for 16 years. 42 full time staff, 20 part time. Annual turnover 4%. Average age 40.

Academic work GCSE and A-levels. 24 subjects offered (including A-level general studies). In 1990, 59 pupils in upper fifth, 49 in upper sixth. *GCSE:* in 1990, 38 upper fifth gained at least grade C in 8+ subjects; 17 in 5–7; and 4 in 1–4 subjects. *A-levels:* 26 upper sixth passed in 4+ subjects; 14 in 3; 5 in 2; and 2 in 1 subject. 13 took science A-levels; 17 arts/humanities; 18 both. *Computing facilities:* 2 networks (12 stations) for class use (Nimbus IBM compatible). Full school cabled network for general use. *Special provision:* Some special provision for dyslexia and English as a second language.

European Community *Languages:* French offered: to age 14; GCSE; A-level. German offered: to age 14; GCSE; A-level. Spanish offered: to age 14; GCSE; A-level. 50% take GCSE in more than 1 EC language. *Exchanges:* Regular exchanges for pupils aged 14–16 to France and Germany. *Other:* Pupils from France, Germany and Spain in school.

Senior pupils' non-academic activities *Music:* 280 learn a musical instrument, 10 to Grade 6 or above; some take GCSE and A-level; 2 accepted for Music School; 40 in school orchestra, 80 in choirs, 20 in wind band, 15 in brass group, house music competitions; 5 in local youth orchestra. *Drama and dance:* 1 major school production each year, house drama, and public speaking competitions;

8 take to Grade 6 ESB. 1–2 accepted for Drama School. *Art:* 20 take GCSE, 3 A-level. 2–3 accepted for Art School. 15 in photographic club, 25 in ceramic club; CDT taught throughout. *Sport:* Netball, lacrosse, gymnastics, swimming, athletics, squash, tennis, badminton, volleyball, basketball, aerobics, yoga available. Many take non-compulsory sport. Many take exams, eg lifesaving. Pupils represent county (athletics, tennis, swimming, badminton, lacrosse); also territorial and national teams in lacrosse. *Other:* 18 take part in local community schemes. 30 have bronze Duke of Edinburgh's Award, 20 have silver and 2–3 gold. 2–3 enter voluntary schemes after leaving school. 12 work for national charities. Other activities include a computer club, drawing, riding, amateur radio, maths, debating, sixth form society, BAYS, first aid, French club, ballet, dancing, car maintenance, pottery.

Careers In 1990, 75% leavers went on to degree courses; 6% to art/drama/music colleges; 11% to non-degree courses (eg catering, secretarial, nursing); 8% straight into careers (eg physiotherapy, nursing). Of those going on to degree courses, 4% went to Oxbridge, 70% to other universities; 24% to poly/colleges. 3% those going on to higher education went to courses in practical art; 1% in drama/acting; 67% in humanities/social sciences; 3% in medicine; and 27% in science/engineering.

Uniform School uniform worn except in sixth.

Houses/prefects Competitive houses. Prefects, head girl, head of house and house prefects – appointed by staff. Committee of form representatives elected by girls.

Religion Daily assembly and Sunday C of E services compulsory.

Social BAYS (Bristol Association of Young Scientists), sixth form society, industry conference etc with Ashville College (boys). Annual trips to France and Germany. Recent choir concerts in Russia and Czechoslovakia. Meals formal. School shop for small items. No tobacco/alcohol allowed.

Discipline Pupils failing to produce

work once might expect more work. Abuse of freedoms means restriction of privileges. Courtesy and consideration for others regarded as essential.

Boarding 50% have study bedroom, most shared with one other. Houses, of approximately 40–45 are divided by age. 2 resident qualified nurses. Central dining room. *Upper sixth* can provide and cook some food. 2 weekend exeats each term. Visits to local town allowed.

Alumni association is run by Mrs E Wheatcroft, Westfield Farm, North Wheatley, Retford DN22 9DU (3,500 members).

Former pupils Diane Leather (athlete); Henrietta Shaw (1st woman Cambridge cox); Sheila Burnford (writer – The Incredible Journey).

· Harrow ·

Harrow School
Harrow-on-the-Hill
Harrow
Middlesex HA1 3HW
Tel 081 869 1200

- Pupils 776
- Boys 13–18
- (Board)
- Girls None
- Upper sixth 166

- Termly fees
  £3725 (Board)
- HMC
Enquiries/application to
the Registrar or
individual
housemasters

What it's like

Founded in 1572 under a royal charter of Queen Elizabeth, its buildings are scattered over Harrow-on-the-Hill across some 360 acres. This superb environment includes a lake, a conservation area, a golf course and a sizeable farm. Ten million pounds have been spent in the last 7 years to create first-class accommodation and first-class facilities of every conceivable kind. The school has a notable reputation for its teaching and all-round academic achievements. Many pupils go on to degree courses including very many to Oxbridge. Very strong indeed in music and drama. Also a high standard in CCF, sport and games. Numerous extra-curricular activities. Substantial involvement with local schools and local community services.

School profile

Pupils Age range 13–18; 776 pupils, 6 day (all boys except masters' daughters), 770 boarding boys. Main entry ages 13 and into sixth. Approx 30% are children of former pupils. *Transfer from maintained schools:* 1% main intake and into sixth.

Entrance Common entrance used. Oversubscribed. No special skills or religious requirements. Parents not expected to buy text books; music tuition only extra. 17–20 scholarships/bursaries, full fees – 10% fees.

Parents 15+% in industry or commerce, 15+% are doctors, lawyers etc;

15+% in armed services. 10+% live within 30 miles; up to 10% live overseas.

Staff Head Master N R Bomford, first year in post. 80 full time staff, 36 part time. Annual turnover 3%. Average age 39.

Academic work GCSE and A-levels. 25 subjects offered (including Arabic and A-level general studies). In 1990, 136 pupils in upper fifth, 166 in upper sixth. *GCSE:* in 1990, 72% upper fifth gained at least grade C in 8+ subjects; 25% in 5–7; and 3% in 1–4 subjects. *A-levels:* 5% upper sixth passed in 4+ subjects; 69% in

3; 21% in 2; and 5% in 1 subject. 26% took science A-levels; 56% arts/ humanities; 18% both. *Computing facilities:* Nimbus networks in computer centre and technology department. Computers in most subject departments and boarding houses.

European Community *Languages:* French offered: to GCSE; A-level. German offered: to GCSE; A-level. Italian offered: to GCSE. Spanish offered: to GCSE. Under 10% take GCSE in more than 1 EC language. *Exchanges:* Regular exchanges for pupils aged 16–18 to France and Germany. *Other:* EC pupils in school. Talks from MEPs. European Business School industrial days for sixth form.

Senior pupils' non-academic activities *Music:* 300 learn a musical instrument, 40 to Grade 6 or above, 4 accepted for Music Colleges. 170 in school orchestras, 120 in choir, 20 in pop group. *Drama:* 100 in school productions, 250 in house productions, 50 in individual productions. *Art:* 225 take as non-examined subject; 50 take GCSE; 20 take A-level; 20 take history of art. 8 accepted for Art School. 25 belong to eg photographic club. *Sport:* Rugby, Harrow football, soccer, cricket, shooting (various), swimming, athletics, tennis, golf, archery, badminton, volleyball, basketball, Eton fives, rackets, squash, fencing, karate, cross-country, show jumping available. 400 take non-compulsory sport. 28 pupils represent county/country (rugby, cricket, fencing, athletics, gymnastics, golf, swimming). *Other:* 40 take part in local community schemes. 10 enter voluntary schemes after leaving school. Other activities include driving lessons, chess, bridge, farming, business companies.

Careers In 1990, 78% leavers went on to degree courses; 3% to art/drama/ music colleges; 14% to non-degree courses (eg agriculture, HND business); 4% straight into careers (eg armed services). Of those going on to degree courses, 23% went to Oxbridge, 71% to other universities; 6% to poly/colleges. 3% those going on to higher education went to courses in practical art; $1\frac{1}{2}$% in drama/acting; $1\frac{1}{2}$% in music; 63% in humanities/social sciences; 4% in medicine; and 27% in science/engineering.

Uniform School uniform worn throughout.

Houses/prefects Eleven Houses (average 70): each House Master appoints Head of House, House prefects. School prefects appointed by Head Master. Philathletic Club (senior boys organising games), Guild (senior boys organising cultural activities). Communal fagging; no personal fagging.

Religion Holy Communion and morning prayer every day; 2–3 services on Sunday. 2 C of E chaplains, 1 RC chaplain, 1 Jewish Rabbi.

Social Society meetings open to other local schools; exchanges with local comprehensive school, schools in Germany, France. Joint choral works, plays with local girls' schools, etc. Community service with girls' school, other local schools and in conjunction with NSPCC. Visits to London for concerts, plays etc. Trips this year to Bermuda (geographic expedition), Greece, Austria, France. Lunch formal, others self service. School shops sell clothes, books, tuck and photographic items. No tobacco allowed; sixth form club over 17 is licensed.

Discipline No corporal punishment. Pupils failing to produce homework once might expect to repeat it plus extra work; those caught smoking cannabis on the premises could expect expulsion.

Boarding 60% have own study bedroom, 40% share with one other. Houses, of approximately 58–70. Resident qualified nurse. Central dining room. Pupils can use house kitchens for snacks. 2 Sunday exeats per term and half-term. Visits to local town allowed with housemaster's permission.

Alumni association is run by J F Leaf, c/o Harrow School.

Former pupils Churchill; King Hussein; Crown Prince Hassan; Nehru; Lord Monckton; Duke of Westminster; Sir Keith Joseph; Earl of Lichfield; Sir William Deedes; Sir Robin Butler; Alexander of Tunis; Sir John Clark, etc.

· *Hatherop Castle* ·

Hatherop Castle School
Hatherop
Cirencester
Gloucestershire
GL7 3NB
Tel 0285 75206

- Pupils 215
- Boys $2^{1}/_{2}$–10 only (Day)
- Girls $2^{1}/_{2}$–18 (Day/Board/Weekly)
- Upper sixth 9

- Termly fees
  £1075 (Day)
  £2165 (Board)
  £2140 (Weekly)
- ISAI
  Enquiries/application to the Headmaster

What it's like

Founded in 1927 in Cambridge, it moved to its present site in 1946. This comprises what was formerly a semi-fortified Tudor country house (some parts survive from Tudor times) in a 30-acre estate in splendid Cotswold countryside. It is a delightful environment and the school provides very civilised accommodation. It has all the advantages of a small school and a friendly and happy atmosphere prevails. The staff:pupil ratio is 1:7. A sound general education is provided and results are creditable. Everyone is involved in music and drama. A good range of games and sports and a fair variety of activities. All boarders are engaged in local community services.

School profile

Pupils Total age range $2^{1}/_{2}$–18; 215 pupils, 130 day (60 boys, 70 girls), 85 boarding girls. Senior department $10^{1}/_{2}$–18, 95 girls. Main entry ages $2^{1}/_{2}$ (boys and girls), 11 and into sixth (girls). Approx 5% are children of former pupils. *Transfer from maintained schools:* 5% intake at 11, plus 5% to sixth.

Entrance Common entrance and own entrance exam used. Not oversubscribed. No special skills or religious requirements. Parents not expected to buy text books. 5 scholarships/bursaries pa, half fees to 10%.

Parents 15+% in farming; 15+% in industry or commerce. 10+% live within 30 miles; up to 10% live overseas.

Staff Headmaster Mr Brian Forster, in post for 6 years. 15 full time staff, 6+ part time. Annual turnover 5%. Average age 38.

Academic work GCSE, AS and A-levels. 18 subjects offered (including GCSE horsemanship; no A-level general studies). In 1990, 20 pupils in upper fifth, 9 in upper sixth. *GCSE:* in 1990, 5 upper fifth gained at least grade C in 8+ subjects; 6 in 5–7; and 9 in 1–4 subjects.

A-levels: 2 upper sixth passed in 3 subjects; 4 in 2 subjects. 60% took broad area of arts/humanities subjects. *Computing facilities:* Amstrad PC1640 and printers. *Special provision:* Individual tuition for mild dyslexia and EFL.

European Community *Languages:* French offered: to age 14; GCSE; A-level. German offered: to age 14; GCSE; A-level. Under 10% take GCSE in more than 1 EC language. *Exchanges:* Regular exchanges for pupils aged 14–16 to France.

Senior pupils' non-academic activities *Music:* 75 learn a musical instrument, 2 to Grade 6 or above; 18 in school orchestra, 50 in school choir. *Drama and dance:* 50 in school productions, all girls take drama, 10 take GCSE. *Art:* 12 take GCSE. 15 in art club. *Sport:* Hockey, netball, tennis, swimming, rounders, squash, gymnastics and badminton are available. Sport is compulsory. 40 take exams. *Other:* All boarders take part in local community schemes. Other activities include art, drama and gymnastic clubs.

Careers In 1990, 30% leavers went on to degree courses; 10% to art/drama/

music colleges; 30% to non-degree courses; 20% straight into careers (eg family business); 10% other. Of those going on to degree courses, 50% went to universities; 50% to poly/colleges.

Uniform School uniform worn throughout.

Houses/prefects Competitive houses. No prefects.

Religion No form of worship compulsory.

Social Organised trips abroad. Senior pupils allowed to bring own car/bike to school. Meals formal. School shop. No tobacco/alcohol allowed.

Discipline No corporal punishment. Pupils failing to produce homework once might expect to repeat it. Those caught smoking cannabis on the premises would be expelled.

Boarding 10% have own study bedroom, others share with up to 5. Resident qualified medical staff. Central dining room. Sixth form can provide and cook own food. 2 weekend exeats each term. Visits to the local town allowed for seniors only, 2 or 3 times a term.

Former pupils Nancy Mitford; Rachel and Tracy Ward (actresses); Arabella Pollen (designer).

· Heathfield (Ascot) ·

Heathfield School
London Road
Ascot
Berkshire SL5 8BQ
Tel 0344 882955

- Pupils 215
- Boys None
- Girls 11–18 (Board)
- Upper sixth 26

- Termly fees £3050 (Board)
- GSA

What it's like

Founded in 1899 with the object of giving girls a sound education within a religious framework. The buildings consist of a handsome late Georgian house in 34 acres with good teaching facilities and comfortable boarding accommodation. The chapel is physically and spiritually at the heart of the school and the Anglican traditions jealously preserved. Teaching and pastoral care are of a high standard, emphasis always being on individual achievement and breadth. All sixth formers go on to higher or further education. Danish, French, German, Italian and Spanish are all offered at A-level and private lessons are available in Italian, Greek and Danish. Considerable strength in music, drama and art. Games and sports are well catered for and there are many extra-curricular activities, especially at weekends. Frequent trips to London and elsewhere.

School profile

Pupils Age range 11–18; 215 boarding girls. Main entry ages 11 and into sixth. *Transfer from maintained schools:* 1% main intake, plus 1% to sixth.

Entrance Common entrance and own exam used.

Staff Headmistress Mrs S E Watkins, in post for 8 years.

Academic work GCSE, AS and A-levels. Approx 29 subjects offered (including languages on demand, Swedish, Japanese at present; no A-level general studies). In 1989, 38 pupils in upper fifth, 26 in upper sixth. *GCSE:* in 1989, 17 upper fifth gained at least grade C in 8+ subjects; 11 in 5–7; and 5 in 1–4 subjects. *A-levels:* 11 upper sixth passed in 3 subjects; 2 in 2 subjects. Science/arts mix of A-levels usually preferred. *Computing facilities:* 12 Apple Macintosh, 5 BBC, 8

346

Archimedes. *Special provision:* Extra English periods for EFL; little for dyslexia.
European Community *Languages:* Danish offered: to A-level. French offered: to age 14; GCSE; AS-level; A-level. German offered: to age 14; GCSE; AS-level; A-level. Italian offered: to age 14; GCSE; AS-level; A-level. Spanish offered: to age 14; GCSE; AS-level; A-level. 10–25% take GCSE in more than 1 EC language. Private lessons available in Danish, Greek and Italian. Spanish, German and Latin offered on carousel for ages 11–14. *Other:* Pupils from most EC states in school.
Careers In 1990, 100% upper sixth leavers went on to degree courses; 64% to universities; 36% to poly/colleges. 16% went to courses in practical art; 4% in music; 56% in humanities/social sciences; 4% in medicine; and 20% in science/engineering.

· *Heathfield (Pinner)* ·

Heathfield School
Beaulieu Drive
Pinner
Middlesex HA5 1NB
Tel 081 868 2346

- Pupils 530
- Boys None
- Girls 4–18
  (Day)
- Upper sixth 29

- Termly fees
  £1024 (Day)
- GSA, GPDST
  Enquiries/application to
  the Headmistress

What it's like

Founded in 1900 in Harrow, it has a 9-acre site (including playing fields) with pleasant buildings. A purpose-built junior wing was added in 1989–90. Well positioned for public transport. It has good up-to-date facilities and provides a strong all-round education. Many sixth formers go on to degree courses. The music and drama departments are strong. A range of games, sports and extra-curricular activities.

School profile

Pupils Total age range 4–18; 530 day girls. Senior department 11–18, 350 girls. Main entry ages 4, 7, 11 and into sixth. Approx 5% are children of former pupils. *Transfer from maintained schools:* 33% senior intake, plus 50% to sixth.
Entrance Own entrance exam used. Oversubscribed. No special skills or religious requirements. Maximum extras, £70 per term, plus lunches. Some scholarships/bursaries.
Parents 40% in industry or commerce, 30% are doctors, lawyers, etc.
Staff Headmistress Mrs J Merritt, in post for 3 years. 35 full time staff, 11 part time. Annual turnover 7%.
Academic work GCSE, AS and A-levels. 17 GCSE subjects offered; 3 at AS-level; 14 at A-level (no A-level general studies). In 1990, 54 pupils in upper fifth, 29 in upper sixth. *GCSE:* in 1990, 70% upper fifth gained at least grade C in 8+ subjects; 29.5% in 5–7; and 0.5% in 1–4 subjects. *A-levels:* 72% upper sixth passed in 3 subjects; 18% in 2; and 7.5% in 1 subject. 38% took science A-levels; 48% arts/humanities; 14% both. *Computing facilities:* Computing taught throughout the school, plus a computer club. *Special provision:* Extra tuition.
European Community *Languages:* French offered: to age 14; GCSE; AS-level; A-level. German offered: to GCSE. Spanish offered: to age 14; GCSE; AS-level; A-level. 25–50% take GCSE in more than 1 EC language. *Exchanges:* Regular exchanges for pupils aged 14–18 to France and Spain. *Other:* French and

Spanish nationals in school as assistants, holding regular conversation classes. Talks from MEPs and lectures from language department of King's College London.

Senior pupils' non-academic activities *Music:* 160 learn a musical instrument, 10 to Grade 6 or above, 30 in school orchestra, 50 in choir, 6 in string group, 8 in recorder group; 6 in LEA Music School. *Drama and dance:* 90 in school productions. *Art:* 3 take A-level; 2 accepted for Art School. *Sport:* Rounders, tennis, athletics, lacrosse, netball, badminton available. 15 represent county at lacrosse. *Other:* Sixth form take part in local community schemes. Other activities include a computer club, social service volunteers, public speaking group, drama group, discussion group, BAYS group.

Careers In 1990, 79% leavers went on to degree courses; 4% to art/drama/music colleges; 4% to non-degree courses (eg College of Distributive Trades); 7% straight into careers (eg banking, management training); 6% other. Of those going on to degree courses, 76% went to universities; 24% to poly/colleges. 4% those going on to higher education went to courses in practical art; 4% in drama/acting; 62% in humanities/social sciences; 9% in medicine; and 19% in science/engineering.

Uniform School uniform worn except in sixth.

Houses/prefects Competitive houses. Head girl and deputy, and head of house – elected by upper part of school.

Religion Daily assembly; weekly RE lesson.

Social Social service volunteers with local boys' school. 2nd year go to France, 3rd year exchange with school in Paris. Trips to Spain and Germany. Pupils allowed to bring own car/bike to school. Meals self service.

Discipline No corporal punishment. Punishment given by subject teacher and then in a line through Form Tutor and ultimately to Head. Serious transgressions would lead to parental involvement immediately.

Alumni association is run by Mr Barrie Haffner, c/o the School.

· *Hereford Cathedral* ·

Hereford Cathedral School
Old College
29 Castle Street
Hereford HR1 2NN
Tel 0432 273757

- Pupils 592
- Boys 11–18 (Day/Board)
- Girls 11–18 (Day/Board)
- Upper sixth 82

- Termly fees £1095 (Day) £1885 (Board)
- HMC
Enquiries/application to the Headmaster's Secretary

What it's like

There is no record of a foundation date but by 1384 a school had been long established and it is a fair presumption that some form of educational establishment had always adjoined the cathedral (founded in the 7th century). Hereford is one of the most beautiful cathedral cities in England and the school is situated right next to the cathedral and housed in a variety of fine buildings of different periods in lovely gardens very near the Wye. Large playing fields are nearby. It is a C of E foundation and religious instruction and worship are an essential part of its life. The school uses the cathedral for many services and the cathedral choristers are members of the school. Naturally, music plays a very important part in the curriculum. There is extensive participation in musical festivals. Academic standards are high and results are good. Many sixth formers go on to degree courses, including Oxbridge. Sports and games flourish and there is a fine range of extra-curricular activities.

School profile

Pupils Total age range 11–18; 592 pupils, 506 day (253 boys, 253 girls), 86 boarding (56 boys, 30 girls). Main entry ages 11, 13 and into sixth. *Transfer from maintained schools:* 50% main intake, plus 50% to sixth.

Entrance Common entrance and own entrance exam used. Oversubscribed. No special skills required. All pupils attend Christian worship. Parents not expected to buy text books; maximum extras £50 per term plus music tuition. 40 assisted places. 5 scholarships/bursaries, music exhibitions/scholarships.

Parents 80% live within 30 miles; up to 5% live overseas.

Staff Headmaster Dr Howard Tomlinson. 44 full time staff, 18 part time. Annual turnover 5%.

Academic work GCSE and A-levels. Average size of upper fifth 95; upper sixth 80 (now 82). *GCSE:* on average, 75 pupils in upper fifth pass 8+ subjects. *A-levels:* on average, 65 pupils in upper sixth pass 3 subjects. On average, 25 take science/maths A-levels; 36 take arts and humanities; 19 both. *Computing facilities:* Extensive.

European Community *Languages:* French offered: to age 14; GCSE; AS-level; A-level. German offered: to age 14; GCSE; AS-level; A-level. 25–50% take GCSE in more than 1 EC language. *Exchanges:* Regular exchanges recently started for pupils aged 14–18 to France.

Senior pupils' non-academic activities *Sport:* Rugby, cricket, rowing, hockey, netball, tennis, squash and outward bound pursuits available. Other activities include CCF, Duke of Edinburgh's Award Scheme, drama, orchestras, instrumental groups, choirs, etc.

Careers In 1990, 75% leavers went on to degree courses; 2% to art/drama/music colleges; 10% to non-degree courses (eg HND agriculture, business studies); 7% straight into careers (eg armed forces, insurance); 5% other. Of those going on to degree courses, 10% went to Oxbridge; 50% to other universities; 40% to poly/colleges. 1% those going on to higher education went to courses in practical art; 1% in drama/acting; 2% in music; 43% in humanities/social sciences; 8% in medicine; 35% in science/engineering; and 10% in business.

Uniform School uniform worn; concessions in sixth form.

Houses/prefects Competitive houses. Monitors, head boy/girl, head of house and house monitors – appointed by the Headmaster and Housemasters/mistresses. School Council.

Religion Daily services at the cathedral.

Social School participates in many Hereford festivals (3 Choirs, etc). Organised trips abroad. Pupils allowed to bring own car/bike to school. Meals self service. School shop. No tobacco/alcohol allowed.

Discipline No corporal punishment.

Boarding 20% have own study bedroom, 20% share. Houses, of approximately 40, are the same as competitive houses, divided by age group and single sex. Resident medical staff. Central dining room. Pupils can provide and cook own food. Exeats as required – some weekly boarding. Visits to local town allowed in daylight.

Former pupils Kingsley Martin; Godfrey Winn; Sir David Roberts; Peter and Dick Richardson; Paul Thorburn; Alec Rowe; Air Marshal Sir Geoffrey Dhenin.

· *Hethersett Old Hall* ·

Hethersett Old Hall
School
Hethersett
Norwich NR9 3DW
Tel 0603 810390

- Pupils 263
- Boys None
- Girls 8–18
  (Day/Board)
- Upper sixth 15

- Termly fees
  £1115 (Day)
  £2150 (Board/
  Weekly)
- GSA
  Enquiries/application to
  the Headmistress

What it's like

Founded in 1928 at Hellesdon House near Norwich, it moved to its present site in 1938. The main building is a fine early Georgian house set in beautiful gardens and grounds. It and its associated buildings have been modernised and enlarged. Boarders have comfortable accommodation in the main house. Sports and games facilities are good. The school is affiliated to the Church of England, but girls of other denominations are accepted. Each day starts with morning prayers for all and religious instruction is part of the curriculum at all levels. Girls are encouraged to develop Christian attitudes and ideals in their relationships. It has many of the advantages of being a small school and a happy 'family' atmosphere prevails. There is considerable strength in music (which is much encouraged) and also in drama and art. Many sixth form leavers go on to degree courses. French and German are offered to A-level, Spanish to GCSE. Many girls take GCSE in more than one European language. There are regular exchanges with France and Germany. A standard range of sports and games is available and there is a good variety of extra-curricular activities.

School profile

Pupils Total age range 8–18; 263 girls (173 day, 90 boarding). Senior department 11–18, 206 girls. Main entry ages, 8, 11 and into sixth. 15% are children of former pupils. *Transfer from maintained schools:* 50% main intake, 20% to sixth.

Entrance Own entrance exam used. Oversubscribed. No special skills or religious requirements. Parents of sixth form only expected to buy text books. Average extras, £50 per term. 4–9 scholarships/bursaries pa, £800-£100.

Parents 15+% are in the armed services; 15+% are doctors, lawyers, etc; 15% in industry or commerce; 15% farmers. 30+% live within 30 miles, less than 10% live overseas.

Staff Headmistress Mrs V M Redington, in post for 8 years. 20 full time staff, 14 part time. Annual turnover 5%. Average age 42.

Academic work GCSE, AS- and A-levels. 17 subjects offered at GCSE, 14 at A-level, including fashion design, history of art, textiles and A-level general studies. In 1990, 42 pupils in upper fifth, 15 in upper sixth. *GCSE:* in 1990, 50% upper fifth gained at least grade C in 8+ subjects; 26% in 5–7; and 24% in 1–4 subjects. *A-levels:* 53% sixth-form pupils passed in 3 subjects; 35% in 2; 12% in 1 subject (many with additional AS-level passes). 18% took a broad area of science/engineering and 71% arts/humanities; 11% both. *Computing facilities:* Generous facilities available. *Special provision:* Arrangements for dyslexic pupils to attend Dyslexic Institute. Extra tuition in English for overseas students.

European Community *Languages:* French offered: to age 14; GCSE; AS-level; A-level. German: to age 14; GCSE; AS-level; A-level. Spanish: to GCSE; AS-level. 25–50% take GCSE in more than 1 EC language. Extra language tuition provided. *Exchanges:* Regular exchanges for pupils aged 11–14 to France and Spain. *Other:* European studies offered to pupils aged 14–16. 2 German pupils in sixth form.

Senior pupils' non-academic activities *Music:* 38 learn a musical instrument, 5 up to Grade 6; 14 in school orchestra, 28 in school choir, 2 in South Norfolk Youth Band. 2 play in pop group after leaving school. *Drama and dance:* 55 in school productions; 8 take LAMDA exams. 10 in speech and drama; 12 in public speaking. 5 in National Theatre; 5 in National Theatre Arts Group; 40 attend theatre workshop. 3 accepted for Drama/Dance schools. 3 go on to work in theatre after leaving school. *Art:* 5 take art as non-examined subject, 32 take GCSE art; 4 A-level art. 1–2 accepted for Art School; 1 to fine art degree course; 1 to art teacher training college. 25 belong to photographic club. *Sport:* Hockey, netball, athletics, gymnastics, rounders, tennis, swimming, badminton available. 17 take aerobics; 30 basketball; 8 badminton. 8 take RLSS life saving exams; 7 take sports leaders exams. 16 represent county (swimming, hockey, athletics, cross-country). *Other:* 50 take part in local community schemes. 26 have bronze Duke of Edinburgh's Award, 4 have silver. 20 enter voluntary schemes after leaving school. Other activities include drama, riding, gym club, dance group.

Careers In 1990, 65% leavers went on to degree courses; 10% to art/drama/music colleges; 10% to non-degree courses; 5% straight into careers (eg banking); 5% other. Of those going on to degree courses, 35% went to universities; 65% to poly/colleges. 10% those going on to higher education went to courses in practical art; 10% in drama/acting; 60% in humanities/social sciences and 20% in science/engineering.

Uniform School uniform worn except in sixth.

Houses/prefects Competitive houses. Head girl, prefects, head of house and house prefects, appointed by headmistress and staff.

Religion Attendance at religious worship compulsory.

Social Quizzes/debates – Eastern area; theatre/music with local state and independent schools. Annual visits to France. Pupils may bring own cars/bike/motorbike to school. Meals formal for boarders only (evenings/weekends); otherwise self-service. No tobacco/alcohol allowed.

Discipline No corporal punishment. Those failing to produce a piece of homework for the first time, would be given pastoral guidance. Those caught smoking cannabis on the premises would expect expulsion.

Boarding 10% have own study bedrooms; 50% share; 7% in dormitories of 6+. Sixth-form can provide and cook own food. 2 weekend exeats each term and half-term. Visits to the local town allowed weekly from age 14+.

· *Highgate* ·

Highgate School
North Road
Highgate
London N6 4AY
Tel 081 340 1524
Fax 081 340 7674

- Pupils 890
- Boys 7–18
  (Day/Weekly)
- Girls None
- Upper sixth 97

- Termly fees
  £1675 (Day)
  £2845 (Weekly)
- HMC
Enquiries/application to
the Headmaster

What it's like

Founded in 1565, the main buildings are in Highgate Village and, together with the extensive grounds and playing fields adjacent to Hampstead Heath, create a very agreeable environment. The oldest buildings are Victorian. Since 1928 there has been steady expansion which has provided new and better facilities. It is now extremely well equipped by any standards. It takes boys who have skills and talents they can contribute to the community. The education is for responsibility to the individual, to the individual's talents and abilities – plus responsibility to fellow human beings. It is well known for its good teaching and high academic attainments. Many leavers go on to degree courses, including Oxbridge. Music is strong. New sports centre and very wide range of sports and games (high standards are achieved). An outstanding record in the Duke of Edinburgh's Award Scheme.

School profile

Pupils Total age range 7–18; 890 boys, 800 day, 90 weekly boarding. Senior department 13–18, 580 boys. Main entry ages 7, 8, 9, 10, 11, 13 and into sixth. Approx 5% are children of former pupils. 55% senior intake from own junior school. *Transfer from maintained schools:* Few at 11, none at 13.

Entrance Common entrance used (own entrance exam for junior school). Oversubscribed. No special skills or religious requirements but school is a C of E foundation. Main extras are individual music lessons and expeditions. 35 assisted places. 8 scholarships, 2 music awards, art award, 30 bursaries, up to full fees.

Parents Mostly professional people; wide social and ethnic mix.

Staff Headmaster R P Kennedy, 3 years in post. 57 full time staff, 2 part time.

Academic work GCSE, AS and A-levels. AS-level general studies offered. In 1989, 120 pupils in upper fifth, 103 in upper sixth (now 97). *GCSE:* in 1989, 74% upper fifth gained at least grade C in 8+ subjects; 20% in 5–7; and 6% in 1–4 subjects. *A-levels:* 3% upper sixth passed in 4+ subjects; 73% in 3; 14% in 2; and 7% in 1 subject. *Computing facilities:* Extensive Nimbus network and separate hardware in most departments; computer-aided design and desktop publishing.

European Community *Languages:* French offered: to age 14; GCSE; A-level. German offered: age 13–14; GCSE; A-level. Spanish offered: age 13–14; GCSE. 10–25% take GCSE in more than 1 EC language. *Exchanges:* Regular exchanges for pupils aged 14–18 to France and Germany. *Other:* European Studies offered to pupils aged 14–16.

Senior pupils' non-academic activities *Music:* 170 learn a musical instrument, 30 to Grade 6 or above; 40 in school orchestra with girls from Channing, 30 in Chapel choir, large choral society, chamber music, rock groups, school dance band. *Drama:* 70 in school productions. *Art:* 170 take as non-examined subject, 40 take GCSE; 10 take A-level. 40 belong to video/photographic/pottery club; entire sixth form take history of art. *Sport:* Football, rugby, Eton fives, cross-country running, athletics, cricket, swimming, basketball, fencing, golf, gymnastics, hockey, sailing, shooting, squash, tennis, water polo, canoeing, life-saving, ski-ing, weight training available. 250 take non-compulsory sport. All take exams in swimming, survival. 14 represent county, 5 represent country (Eton fives, fencing); 2 represent independent schools (soccer). *Other:* 30 take part in local community schemes. 50 have bronze Duke of Edinburgh's Award, 50 have silver and 30+ gold. Other activities include a computer club, chess club, chemistry society, school press, various historical, literary and debating societies, philatelic, zoological, astronomical societies, orchestras, bands, choirs (incl chapel choir).

Careers 2 part time careers advisers. Annual average accepted for *arts and humanities degree courses* at Oxbridge, 9; other universities, 30; polytechnics/colleges, 10. *science and engineering degree courses* at Oxbridge, 6; other universities, 20; medical schools, 6; polytechnics/colleges, 5. *art college*, 3. *HND course*, 5. Average number of pupils going straight into careers in armed services, 1; industry, 2; the City, 3; music/drama, 1.

Uniform School uniform worn throughout.

Houses/prefects Competitive houses. Prefects, head boy, head of house and house prefects – appointed by the Headmaster and Housemasters. Sixth Form Committee.

Religion Chapel once a week; separate assemblies for those of other faiths.

Social Sixth form general studies, drama, music with local girls' school. Exchange with school in Paris. Annual ski-ing and trips to Mediterranean (cruise), Greece, Italy, Russia (every other year). Pupils allowed to bring own car/bike/motorbike to school. All meals self-service. School shop. No tobacco/alcohol allowed.

Discipline No corporal punishment. Pupils failing to produce homework once might expect to be judged according to circumstances; those caught smoking cannabis on the premises could expect expulsion.

Boarding Weekly boarding only. Fifth and sixth in single or double study bedroom; others in dormitories of 6–8. Houses, of around 40, are the same as competitive houses. Resident qualified nurse. Central dining room. Pupils can provide and cook own food. Exeats every weekend.

Alumni association is run by M J Gadsden, 2 Park Avenue, St Albans AL1 4PB.

Former pupils Anthony Crosland; John Rutter; Howard Shelley; John Tavener; The Warden of All Souls; 2 Lord Justices of Appeal; Lord Garner; Bishop of Manchester; Martin Gilbert; Anthony Green RA; Patrick Procktor RA; Roland Culver; Robin Ellis; Barry Norman; Robin Ray; Geoffrey Palmer; Philip Harben; Mike Ockrent; Christopher Morahan; Robert Atkins MP.

· Holy Child ·

Holy Child Senior School
Sir Harry's Road
Edgbaston
Birmingham B15 2UR
Tel 021 440 4103/0256
Fax 021 440 3639

- Pupils 365
- Boys 3–11 only (Day)
- Girls 3–18 (Day/Weekly)
- Upper sixth 28

- Termly fees
  £1065 (Day)
  £2055 (Weekly)
- GSA
Enquiries/application to the Admissions Secretary

What it's like

Founded in 1933 by the Society of the Holy Child Jesus, it moved to its present site in 1936. It is two miles from the city centre, a very pleasant site comprising 14 acres of wooded gardens and grounds. There has been steady development since 1950 and the school is now very well equipped with up-to-date facilities. As it is a Catholic foundation it is committed to a Christian education. All pupils attend religious education lessons and school masses on Holy Days. Academically it is very well organised and results are highly creditable. Virtually all sixth form girls go on to university or other higher or further education. French and Spanish are offered right through to A-level; German to GCSE. A very high proportion of pupils takes GCSE in more than one European language. The curriculum will have a very definite European dimension by September 1992. There is considerable emphasis on science and technology. The school runs a Royal Society Project, an Understanding Industry course and a work experience course and has links with BIP Chemicals. Music, drama and art are particularly well supported by a large number of pupils. There is an impressive range of sports, games and extra-curricular activities and a substantial commitment to the Duke of Edinburgh's Award Scheme. A variety of outdoor pursuits are encouraged.

School profile

Pupils Total age range, 3–18; 365 pupils, 350 day (14 boys, 336 girls), 15 weekly boarding girls. Senior department, 11–18, 225 girls. Main entry ages 3 (boys and girls), 11 and into sixth (girls). 5% are children of former pupils. *Transfer from maintained schools:* 20% intake at 11; variable to sixth.

Entrance Common entrance and own entrance exam used. Oversubscribed in certain age groups. No special skills, but French is an advantage for 11+ entrants. Preference given to RC applications, but all religions accepted. Parents not expected to buy text books. Assisted places. Up to 4 scholarships/bursaries pa, to full fees.

Parents 15+% doctors, lawyers, etc; 15+% in industry. Most live within 30 miles; up to 5% live overseas.

Staff Head Miss J M Johnson, in post for 4 years. 27 full time staff, 11 part time. Annual turnover 8%. Average age 40.

Academic work GCSE and A-level subjects offered (including GCSE business studies and drama; AS & A-level Christian theology; A-level general studies). In 1990, 42 pupils in upper fifth, 28 in upper sixth. *GCSE:* on average, 22 upper fifth gained at least grade C in 8+ subjects; 18 in 5–7; and 2 in 1–4 subjects. *A-levels:* On average 5 upper sixth passed in 4+ subjects; 14 in 3; 7 in 2; and 2 in 1 subject. 40% took science A-levels; 40% arts/humanities; 20% both. *Computing facilities:* Apple Macintosh network; BBC masters. *Special provision:* EFL can be arranged (in the last year girls from France, Italy, Spain, Japan and Swaziland have participated).

European Community *Languages:* French offered: to age 14; GCSE; A-level. German offered: to age 14; GCSE. Spanish offered: to age 14; GCSE; A-level. 50–75% take GCSE in more than 1 EC language. *Exchanges:* Regular exchanges for pupils aged 14–16 to Germany. *Other:* Pupils from France and Spain in school (German pupils soon). Major European initiative in 1992, with increased language opportunities and overseas educational visits. Definite European dimension to curriculum planned for September 1992.

Senior pupils' non-academic activities *Music:* 75 learn a musical instrument, 10 to Grade 6 or above; 30 play in school orchestra, 60 in choir, 3 in Birmingham Schools Orchestra/Wind Band; recorder group. *Drama and dance:* 30 in school productions; 1 in National Youth Theatre, 2 in Midlands Youth Theatre, 10 in local theatre groups, 75 take grades in LAMDA. 2 accepted for Drama/Dance Schools; 2 enter competitions; 2 go on to work in theatre, 1 ESU scholarship to USA. *Art:* 55 take art as non-examined subject; 29 take GCSE; 5 A-level. 1 accepted for Art School; 16 in 1st year art club. *Sport:* Netball, hockey, tennis, rounders, basketball, volleyball, badminton, keep fit, junior swimming, senior squash/golf at local clubs, holiday hockey courses, windsurfing available. 208 pupils take part in non-compulsory sport; 30 BAGA; occasional pupil represents county (hockey, tennis). *Other:* 35 have bronze Duke of Edinburgh's Award, 22 silver, 2 gold. Other activities include a computer club, public speaking, debating, bridge, Schools' Challenge Quiz, LIFE group, art and drama clubs, ecology group, adventure weekends, self defence.

Careers 4 part time careers advisers. Annual average accepted for *arts and humanities degree courses* at Oxbridge, 1; other universities, 13; polytechnics/colleges, 2. *science and engineering degree courses* at Oxbridge, 1; other universities, 5; medical schools, 1; polytechnics/colleges, 1 (but science numbers are increasing). *BEd,* 2. *other general training courses,* 2. Virtually all girls go on to degree courses.

Uniform School uniform worn except in sixth.

Houses/prefects Competitive houses. Head girl, head of house and house prefects – elected by the school. School Council.

Religion Compulsory Roman Catholic morning assembly and Masses on Holy Days of Obligation.

Social Debates, theatre workshops. Organised trips, ski-ing and exchange systems (with Paussan in Germany and

America); developing European links. Pupils allowed to bring own car/bike to school. Lunch self service; supper formal. School shop. No tobacco/alcohol allowed. **Discipline** No corporal punishment. Pupils failing to produce homework once might expect a reprimand/order mark.

Boarding Fifth and sixth have own study bedroom; fourth form and below share. No resident medical staff but school doctor lives in same road. Central dining room. Weekly boarding. Visits to local town allowed by sixth, with permission.

Alumni association is run by Mrs S Poole, Secretary, 8 Hayward Road, Four Oaks, Sutton Coldfield B75 6SG.

Former pupils Lord Chitnis (leading Liberal Peer); Karen Armstrong (writer/broadcaster); Noelle Walsh (Editor, Good Housekeeping); Ninivah Khomo (designer).

· Holy Trinity (Bromley) ·

Holy Trinity Convent School
81 Plaistow Lane
Bromley
Kent BR1 3LL
Tel 081 313 0399

- Pupils 637
- Boys None
- Girls 5–18 (Day)
- Upper sixth 33

- Termly fees £1046 (Day)
- GSA
Enquiries/application to the Headmistress

What it's like

Founded in 1886, by a small group of Trinitarian Sisters, it moved in 1888 to 'Freelands', a big 18th-century mansion in a landscaped park of 15 acres. Since 1913 the school has expanded at regular intervals to provide increasingly up-to-date facilities and accommodation. It is now very well equipped. It has its own kindergarten and preparatory department. Pupils are predominantly Roman Catholic but others are accepted. Religious worship is compulsory and the school's prime aim is to develop the spiritual life of its pupils. Catholic doctrine is central to the teaching, and life is allied to the calendar and liturgy of the Church. A sound general education is provided and standards are high. Many sixth formers go on to degree courses. French, German and Spanish are offered to A-level and many girls take GCSE in more than one European language. There are regular exchanges with France, Germany and Spain for all age groups. There is a commitment to local community schemes.

School profile

Pupils Total age range 5–18; 637 day girls. Senior department 11–18, 345 girls. Main entry ages 5, 11, 14 and into sixth. Approx 10% are children of former pupils. *Transfer from maintained schools:* 36% main senior intake, plus 100% to sixth.

Entrance Own entrance exam used. No special skills required; most pupils Roman Catholic but others are accepted. Parents not expected to buy text books; music tuition only extra (£50). Up to 3 senior school scholarships/bursaries, full fees to one-third fees.

Parents 15+% in industry or commerce; 15+% are doctors, lawyers, etc. 60+% live within 30 miles.

Staff Headmistress Sister Bernadette, in post for 4 years. 40 full time staff, 7 part time. Annual turnover 10%. Average age 43.

Academic work GCSE and A-levels. 18 GCSE subjects offered; 22 at A-level (no A-level general studies). On average,

60 pupils in upper fifth, 33 in upper sixth. *GCSE:* on average, 67% upper fifth gain at least grade C in 8+ subjects; 27% in 5–7; and 6% in 1–4 subjects. *A-levels:* 2% upper sixth pass in 4+ subjects; 70% in 3; 26% in 2; and 2% in 1 subject. Average of 24% take science A-levels; 62% arts/humanities; 14% both. *Computing facilities:* 10 BBC. 6 Horizons, 9 Nimbus in three specialist rooms. *Special provision:* Additional help on a one-to-one basis is provided as the need arises.

European Community *Languages:* French offered: to age 14; GCSE; AS-level; A-level. German offered: to age 14; GCSE; AS-level; A-level. Spanish offered: to GCSE; AS-level; A-level. 25–50% take GCSE in more than 1 EC language. *Exchanges:* Regular exchanges for pupils aged 11–18 to France, Germany and Spain. *Other:* Attendance at EC conferences, eg sixth form conference in Paris. European evenings for parents, organised by pupils.

Senior pupils' non-academic activities *Music:* 175 learn a musical instrument, 80 to Grade 6 or above; 35 in school orchestra, 120 in choir. *Drama and dance:* 30–40 in school productions; 30 entered competitions. *Art:* 20 take GCSE art; 6 take A-level. 2 accepted for Art School. *Sport:* Hockey, netball, gym, dance, swimming, tennis, rounders, athletics and other minor games available. 160 take non-compulsory sport. 2 represent county (hockey). *Other:* 40 take part in local community schemes. Other activities include computer, science, art, chess, debating, environmental, science, language and mathematics clubs.

Careers In 1990, 80% leavers went on to degree courses; 10% to art/drama/music colleges; 5% to non-degree courses (eg HND horse studies); 5% straight into careers (eg retailing, secretarial). Of those going on to degree courses, 2% went to Oxbridge, 82% to other universities; 14% to poly/colleges. 4% those going on to higher education went to courses in practical art; 3% in drama/acting; 3% in music; 43% in humanities/social sciences; 2% in medicine; and 45% in science/engineering.

Uniform School uniform worn throughout.

Houses/prefects Competitive houses. Prefects, head girl, head of house and house prefects – appointed by Head in consultation with staff.

Religion Religious worship compulsory.

Social No organised functions with local schools. Trips to France, ski-ing, activity holidays, Venice/Rome. Pupils allowed to bring own car/bike/motorbike to school. Meals self service. No tobacco/alcohol allowed.

Discipline No corporal punishment. Pupils failing to produce homework once might expect a warning; those caught smoking cannabis on the premises could expect expulsion.

· *Howell's (Denbigh)* ·

Howell's School	● Pupils 365	● Termly fees
Park Street	● Boys None	£1564 (Day)
Denbigh	● Girls 4–18	£2500 (Board)
Clwyd LL16 3EN	(Day/Board)	● GSA
Tel 0745 813631	● Upper sixth 26	Enquiries/application to the Admissions Secretary

What it's like

Its origins date from 1540 when Thomas Howell bequeathed 12,000 gold ducats to the Drapers' Company. In 1852 an act of parliament authorised the trust to build two girls' schools in Wales. Howell's School, Denbigh was opened in 1859. The Drapers' Company provides considerable support. It has very pleasant mellow grey stone buildings in delightful grounds and gardens some 20 miles from Snowdonia; a very healthy environment amidst splendid countryside. Predominantly a boarding school, it enjoys comfortable accommodation and excellent modern facilities of all kinds. The prep department (for 5–11 year-olds) is next to the senior school. The school aims to teach the essentials of the Christian way of life and religious education (in the Anglican tradition) is part of the curriculum. It has a high academic reputation and the large staff allows a staff:pupil ratio of 1:9. The teaching is extremely good and results are first-rate. Very many leavers go on to degree courses each year, including to Oxbridge. French, German and Spanish are offered to A-level, Italian to GCSE. An exceptionally high proportion of girls takes GCSE in two or more European languages. There are regular exchanges with France and Germany. The music, drama and art departments are strong and there is a superb arts and crafts complex. Howell's is also very well equipped for sports and games and has one of the best sports halls in the country. Standards are high and girls play hockey and lacrosse at county and national level. A broad range of extra-curricular activities is provided.

School profile

Pupils Total age range 5–18; 365 girls (154 day, 211 boarding). Senior department 11–18, 295 girls. Main entry ages, 11 and into sixth. 5–10% are children of former pupils. Own prep department provides more than 20% of senior intake. *Transfer from maintained schools:* 25–30% senior intake, plus 10–15% to sixth.

Entrance Own entrance exam used. Not oversubscribed. No special skills or religious requirements. Rental charge of £20 pa for textbooks. Average charge for extras, £70. 15 assisted places pa. 9 scholarships/bursaries pa, £5,000–£100.

Parents 15+% from industry/commerce. 30+% live within 30 miles, up to 10% live overseas.

Staff Head Mrs M Steel, first year in post. 35 full time staff, 6 part time. Annual turnover less than 10%. Average age 48.

Academic work GCSE and A-levels. 20 subjects at GCSE, 16 at A-level (including Welsh). In 1990, 41 pupils in upper fifth, 26 in upper sixth. *GCSE:* in 1990, 28 upper fifth gained at least grade C in 8+ subjects; 9 in 5–7; and 4 in 1–4 subjects. *A-levels:* 8 upper sixth passed in 4+ subjects; 7 in 3; 4 in 2; and 5 in 1 subject. 27% took science A-levels; 50% arts/humanities; 23% both. *Computing facilities:* 15 Apple-Macintosh in computer centre; 6 departmental BBCs. *Special provision:* Tutor for dyslexic pupils.

European Community *Languages:* French offered: to age 14; GCSE; AS-level; A-level. German offered: to age 13–14; GCSE; AS-level; A-level. Italian offered: to GCSE. Spanish offered: to age 13–14; GCSE; AS-level; A-level. Up to 75% take GCSE in 2 or more EC languages. *Exchanges:* Regular exchanges for pupils aged 14–16 to France and Germany. *Other:* Denbigh twinned with Bierbertal (Germany); school involved in cultural and sporting activities.

Senior pupils' non-academic activities *Music:* 120 learn a musical instrument, 100 up to Grade 6; 20 in school choir; 1 plays in National Youth Orchestra; 3 take GCSE, 1 A-level. *Drama and dance:* 180 in school productions; 120 LAMDA Grades 6. *Art:* 100 take art as non-examined subject; 50 take GCSE art; 10 A-level art; 4 accepted for Art School; 10 belong to photographic club. *Sport:* Hockey, tennis, lacrosse, netball, gymnastics, squash, swimming available. 105 take non-compulsory sport. 10 represent county/country (hockey, netball, lacrosse). *Other:* 45 have bronze Duke of Edinburgh's Award. Other activities include a computer club, debating society.

Careers In 1990, 50% leavers went on to degree courses; 8% to art/drama/music colleges; 12% to non-degree courses (eg HND business and finance); 30% other (resits, Gap year). Of those going on to degree courses, 4% went to

Oxbridge; 31% to other universities; 65% to poly/colleges. 39% those going on to higher education went to courses in humanities/social sciences; 15% in medicine; and 46% in science/engineering.

Uniform School uniform worn throughout.

Houses/prefects Competitive houses. Head girl and deputy (appointed by the head), prefects (elected by the school).

Religion Attendance at religious worship compulsory.

Social Debates, dances, dinners and plays with other schools. Exchanges with Germany, Australia and the USA. Pupils allowed to bring own car/bike. Meals self-

service. School shop. No tobacco/alcohol allowed.

Discipline No corporal punishment: detention or similar sanctions. Minor infringements punished by loss of privileges; smoking by suspension; drinking alcohol by suspension and possible expulsion; drug abuse by expulsion.

Boarding 12% have own study bedrooms; 25% share (with 1 other). 63% in dormitories of 6+. Houses, of approx 50, same as competitive houses. Resident qualified nurse. Pupils can provide and cook own food. Daily visits to the local town allowed (aged 13+).

· *Howell's (Llandaff)* ·

Howell's School
Llandaff
Cardiff
CF5 2YD
Tel 0222 562019

- Pupils 680
- Boys None
- Girls 7–18
  (Day/Board)
- Upper sixth 61

- Termly fees
  £908 (Day)
  £1908 (Board/
  Weekly)
- GPDST
  Enquiries/application to
  the Administrator

What it's like

Since 1860, Howell's School, Llandaff has stood on a leafy ridge overlooking Cardiff, the capital city of Wales. The splendid mid-Victorian Gothic building has been enlarged and adapted: an Edwardian Great Hall was added in 1901 and later came modern science laboratories, a gymnasium, an indoor swimming pool and more laboratories. In 1991 a new technology centre was added; also a music department with a magnificent concert hall and a practise wing (14 practice rooms) and electronic studios. A sound education in the grammar school tradition is provided. Welsh is optionally taught as a first and as a second language. Academic standards are high and results good. Many girls go on to degree courses, including Oxbridge. French and German are offered throughout the school and many girls take GCSE in both. There are regular exchanges with France and Germany. Italian and Spanish are offered for the Institute of Linguists. Very strong in music and drama. A good range of games and sports in which high standards are achieved. A plentiful range of activities. Some involvement in local community schemes.

School profile

Pupils Total age range 7–18; 680 girls, 628 day, 52 boarding. Senior department 11–18, 582 girls. Main entry ages 7, 11 and into sixth. Approx 5–10% are children of former pupils. *Transfer from main-* *tained schools:* 5% main senior intake, plus 50% to sixth.

Entrance Own entrance exam used. Oversubscribed for day girls. No special skills or religious requirements. Parents not expected to buy text books. 194 assisted places. 16 scholarships/bursaries, £4284 to £100 pa.

Parents 15+% are doctors, lawyers, etc; 15+% in industry or commerce. 60+% live within 30 miles; up to 10% live overseas.

Staff Headmistress Mrs C J Fitz, first year in post. 41 full time staff, 13 part time. Annual turnover 5%.

Academic work GCSE and A-levels. 20 subjects offered (no A-level general studies). In 1990, 77 pupils in upper fifth, 61 in upper sixth. *GCSE:* in 1990, 65% upper fifth gained at least grade C in 8+ subjects; 24% in 5–7; and 10% in 1–4 subjects. *A-levels:* 45 upper sixth passed in 3 subjects; 11 in 2; and 3 in 1 subject. 43% took science A-levels; 24% arts/humanities; 33% both. *Computing facilities:* 14 station Nimbus network, BBC Bs in subject departments, technology workshop – CAD. *Special provision:* English language teaching.

European Community *Languages:* French offered: to age 14; GCSE; AS-level; A-level; non-examined. German offered: to age 14; GCSE; AS-level; A-level. Italian: RSA. Spanish: RSA. 25–50% take GCSE in more than 1 EC language. *Exchanges:* Regular exchanges for pupils aged 14–16 to France and Germany. *Other:* French and German pupils as boarders for 1 term–1 year. Possibility of work experience in EC for sixth form.

Senior pupils' non-academic activities *Music:* 55% learn a musical instrument (10% learn 2 or 3), most to Grade 6 or above, 2–3 accepted for Music School; 90 pupils in 2 school orchestras, 130 in 3 school choirs, 1 in National Youth Orchestra of Wales, 47 in county orchestras, choirs, windbands and ensembles. Pupils form small groups on own initiative (pop, folk, chamber). *Drama and dance:* 50% in school productions, some take Grade 6 in ESB, RAD etc; occasional pupil accepted for Drama/Dance Schools. About 15% take out-of-school drama.

Art: 20 take GCSE; 5 take A-level. 2 or 3 accepted for Art School, 1 or 2 take fine arts at university, 15 belong to photographic club. *Sport:* Lacrosse, hockey, netball, table tennis, badminton, squash, tennis, cricket, rounders, athletics and swimming available. Many take non-compulsory sport. 25 have RLSS bronze awards, 10, merit, and 5 teacher's certificate. *Other:* 30 take part in local community schemes. Many enter voluntary schemes after leaving school. Several work for national charities. Other activities include a computer club, Young Enterprise firms, debating, school book shop (run by pupils).

Careers In 1990, 72% leavers went on to degree courses; 3% to art/drama/music colleges; 9% to non-degree courses (eg bilingual secretarial, nursing, nursery nursing, HND hotel and catering, printing, management); 3% straight into careers (eg banking, employment in France); 13% other. Of those going on to degree courses, 12% went to Oxbridge, 65% to other universities; 23% to poly/colleges. 7% those going on to higher education went to courses in practical art; 4% in music; 47% in humanities/social sciences; 4% in medicine; and 38% in science/engineering.

Uniform School uniform worn except the sixth.

Houses/prefects Competitive houses. Prefects, head girl, head of house; also charity and Eisteddfod secretaries.

Social Meals self service. School shop. No tobacco/alcohol allowed.

Boarding Weekly boarding available. Pupils in houses, divided by age. 1 weekend exeat each half term.

Alumni association is run by Mrs J Crowley, 153 Pencisely Road, Llandaff, Cardiff CF4 2FQ.

Former pupils Baroness Jean McFarlane (Prof of Nursing); Dr Anne-Rosalie David (egyptologist); Audrey Bates (sport); Trudy Fraser (dress designer); Elaine Morgan (playwright).

359

· *Hulme Grammar (Boys)* ·

The Hulme Grammar
School for Boys
Chamber Road
Oldham
Lancashire OL8 4BX
Tel 061 624 4497

- Pupils 856
- Boys 7–18
  (Day)
- Girls None
- Upper sixth 85

- Termly fees
  £880 (Day)
- HMC
Enquiries/application to
the Headmaster
(Bursar for financial
enquiries)

What it's like

Founded in 1611, reconstituted in 1887, it occupies a residential urban site with its own playing fields. The present buildings date from 1895, with the addition of a science wing (1956), mathematics rooms (1966) and the acquisition of a large house near the school (1969) to form an art and sixth form study centre. Facilities are now very good. The girls' school is on the same site and there is collaboration in cultural activities. High standards of discipline and behaviour are expected. The teaching and academic attainments are highly creditable – very many go on to degree courses, many to Oxbridge. French, German and Spanish are taught to A-level and many boys take GCSE in more than one European language. There are regular exchanges into France and Germany. Strong in music, games and sports (a lot of county and national representatives). Also strong on outdoor pursuits. Vigorous participation in local community schemes.

School profile

Pupils Total age range 7–18; 856 day boys. Senior department 11–18, 740 boys. Main entry ages 7, 11 and into sixth. Approx 5% are children of former pupils. *Transfer from maintained schools:* 75% main senior intake, plus 5% to sixth.

Entrance Own entrance exam used. Oversubscribed. No special skills or religious requirements. Parents not expected to buy text books nor pay any other extras. 30 assisted places pa plus 5 in sixth form. 6 scholarships/bursaries pa, £800–£200.

Staff Headmaster G F Dunkin, in post for 4 years. 55 full time staff, 1 part time. Annual turnover 1%. Average age 35.

Academic work GCSE and A-levels. 20 GCSE subjects offered; 18 at A-level (including philosophy and A-level general studies). In 1990, 114 pupils in upper fifth, 85 in upper sixth. *GCSE:* in 1990, 84 upper fifth gained at least grade C in 8+ subjects; 19 in 5–7; and 12 in 1–4 subjects. *A-levels:* 64 upper sixth passed in 4+ subjects; 11 in 3; 5 in 2; and 5 in 1 subject. 35% took science A-levels; 40% arts/ humanities; 25% both. *Computing facilities:* One computer room with Econet system and many single computers in departments.

European Community *Languages:* French offered: to age 14; GCSE; A-level. German offered: to age 14; GCSE; A-level. Spanish offered: to GCSE; A-level. 25–50% take GCSE in more than 1 EC language. *Exchanges:* Regular exchanges for pupils aged 11–14 to France and Germany.

Senior pupils' non-academic activities *Music:* 40 learn a musical instrument (over 200 in school as a whole), 8–10 to Grade 6 or above; 2 accepted for Music School; 12 in school orchestra, 20 in choir, 10 in brass ensemble; 4 in brass bands, 4 in local orchestras, 5 in school dance band; occasionally pupils play in National Youth Orchestra, National Youth Brass Band and pop groups. *Drama and dance:* 10–12 in school productions; 12 in drama group. *Art:* 8 take as non-examined subject, 14 take GCSE; 4 take

A-level. 3 accepted for Art School. *Sport:* Soccer, cricket, squash, athletics, hockey, basketball, badminton, swimming, gymnastics, volleyball, tennis, table tennis available. 85% take non-compulsory sport. Over 70 play for competition teams at inter-school level; at least 3 international players pa (usually soccer), 10 county players (various sports). *Other:* 50 take part in local community schemes. 1 per year may work for national charity. Other activities include a computer club, debating, chess and cinema clubs, sixth form discussion group, philosophical society, science society, CCF and Duke of Edinburgh's Award Scheme.

Careers In 1990, 93% leavers went on to degree courses; 2% to art/drama/music colleges; 1% to non-degree courses (eg Dartmouth); 3% straight into careers (eg banking, insurance); 1% other. Of those going on to degree courses, 9% went to Oxbridge, 70% to other universities; 21% to poly/colleges. 2% those going on to higher education went to courses in practical art; 1% drama/acting; 57% in humanities/social sciences; 8% in medicine; and 32% in science/engineering.

Uniform School uniform worn throughout.

Houses/prefects Competitive houses. Prefects, head boy, head of house and house prefects – appointed by combination of nominations and elections.

Religion Religious worship not compulsory.

Social Co-operation in music and drama (especially chamber choir) with girls' school, on same site. Ski-ing trip, visits to Austria, and French and German exchange visits annually. Pupils allowed to bring own car to school. Meals self service. No tobacco/alcohol allowed.

Discipline Very limited corporal punishment. Pupils failing to produce homework once might expect lines; those caught smoking cannabis on the premises could expect suspension.

Alumni association is run by Mr P Savic (Secretary, OBA), 16 Walden Avenue, Oldham OL4 2PW.

Former pupils John Stapleton (TV journalist and presenter); Jack Tinker (*Daily Mail* drama critic); Andy Kershaw (TV pop music presenter); Sir Arthur Armitage (Master of Queens and Vice-Chancellor of Cambridge).

· *Hulme Grammar (Girls)* ·

The Hulme Grammar School for Girls
Chamber Road
Oldham
Lancashire OL8 4BX
Tel 061 624 2523

- Pupils 600
- Boys None
- Girls 7–18 (Day)
- Upper sixth 52

- Termly fees £940 (Day)
- GSA
Enquiries/application to the Headmistress

What it's like

Founded in 1895, it has an urban site and the main building adjoins the boys' school. The prep department is nearby and the lower sixth form house is a short distance away. Separate buildings house art and computer studies and the sports hall and indoor swimming pool. The buildings are well appointed within and facilities are up-to-date. The school is non-denominational but religious education is considered to be an important part of the curriculum, and daily worship and prayers are compulsory. Academic results are good; many sixth formers proceed to degree courses each year, including Oxbridge. There is a strong music department and a good range of sports and games and extra-curricular activities. Some commitment to local community services. An outstanding record in the Duke of Edinburgh's Award Scheme.

School profile

Pupils Total age range 7–18; 600 day girls. Senior department 11–18, 486 girls. Main entry ages 7, 11 and into sixth. Approx 25% are children of former pupils. Own prep provides approx 30% senior intake. *Transfer from maintained schools:* 90% intake to sixth.

Entrance Own entrance exam used. Oversubscribed. No special skills or religious requirements. Parents not expected to buy text books; music lessons, lunches extra. 35 assisted places pa. Bursaries offered, variable value.

Staff Headmistress Mrs Alison Groom, in post for 6 years. 39 full time staff, 11 part time. Annual turnover 5%. Average age 40.

Academic work GCSE, AS and A-levels. 17 subjects offered (including Greek and A-level general studies). In 1990, 66 pupils in upper fifth, 53 in upper sixth. *GCSE:* in 1990, 79% upper fifth gained at least grade C in 8+ subjects; 18% in 5–7; and 3% in 1–4 subjects. *A-levels:* 79% upper sixth passed in 4+ subjects; 12% in 3; 3% in 2; and 3% in 1 subject. 35% took science A-levels; 32% arts/humanities; 33% both. *Computing facilities:* One computer room containing network of 15 BBC computers. Several computers in specialist rooms. *Special provision:* Provision is based on individual need but has rarely arisen.

European Community *Languages:* French offered: to GCSE; AS-level; A-level. German offered: to GCSE; AS-level; A-level. 10–25% take GCSE in more than 1 EC language. *Exchanges:* Regular exchanges for pupils aged 14–18 to France and Germany.

Senior pupils' non-academic activities *Music:* 90 learn a musical instrument, 6 to Grade 6 or above; 50 in school orchestra, 100 in choirs. *Drama and dance:* 10 in joint productions with boys' school. *Art:* 1–5 take as non-examined subject; 25 take GCSE; 3 A-level. *Sport:* Athletics, hockey, netball, tennis, rounders, badminton, table tennis, trampolining, swimming available. 300 take non-compulsory sport; many take life-saving bronze medallion. 5–6 have represented county (hockey). *Other:* 20–30 take part in local community schemes. 45 have bronze Duke of Edinburgh's Award, 35 have silver and 29 gold. Other activities include a computer club, Christian Fellowship, Young Enterprise, Community Action.

Careers In 1990, 83% leavers went on to degree courses; 3% to art/drama/music colleges; 2% to non-degree courses (eg physiotherapy); 3% straight into careers (eg banking, retailing, ICI); 9% other (deferred entry). Of those going on to degree courses, 7% went to Oxbridge, 79% to other universities; 15% to poly/colleges. 1% those going on to higher education went to courses in practical art; 1% in drama/acting; 1% in music; 30% in humanities/social sciences; 11% in medicine; and 54% in science/engineering.

Uniform School uniform worn; separate uniform in sixth.

Houses/prefects No competitive houses. Prefects and head girl – elected by staff and senior pupils.

Religion Compulsory daily morning prayers.

Social Debates, drama, choral performances with brother school. Annual ski-ing holiday, regular French and German exchanges, frequent foreign visits to eg Florence, Venice, Rome, also educational cruises. Pupils allowed to bring own car/bike/motorbike to school. Meals self service. School tuck shops organised occasionally by pupils for charity. No tobacco/alcohol allowed.

Discipline No corporal punishment. Pupils failing to produce homework once might expect talk with form mistress, lunchtime detention if poor reason; those caught smoking cannabis on the premises might expect to be given medical/social help and to be expelled.

Alumni association c/o Headmistress.

Former pupils Olwen Hufton (Professor of History, Reading University).

· *Hunterhouse* ·

Hunterhouse College
Finaghy
Belfast
BT10 0LE
Tel 0232 612293

- Pupils 720
- Boys None
- Girls 5–19
  (Day/Board)
- Upper sixth 95

- Termly fees
  £615 (Day)
  £1315 (Board/
  Weekly)
  Enquiries/application to
  the Headmistress

What it's like

Founded in 1865, formerly called Princess Gardens, it amalgamated with neighbouring Ashleigh House school in 1987. One of the oldest grammar schools for girls in N. Ireland, it lies in a beautiful 37-acre estate of wooded parkland, gardens and playing fields 4 miles south of the centre of Belfast. The main boarding house is a large elegant 'listed' building, formerly a 'linen mansion'. The purpose-built teaching and recreational accommodation dates from 1967 and has recently undergone major renovation. The prep dept is on the same site. A cheerful relaxed, but orderly, family atmosphere prevails. The pursuit of excellence is the prime aim. Academically strong. French, German and Spanish are offered up to A-level and very many girls take GCSE in more than one European language. There are regular exchanges with not only France and Germany but Eire. Fairly strong music, art and drama depts. Very good range of sport, games and activities. Big commitment to local community schemes and education for international understanding. An impressive record in the Duke of Edinburgh's Award Scheme.

School profile

Pupils Total age range 5–19; 720 girls, 630 day, 90 boarding. Senior department 11–19, 610 girls. Main entry ages 11, 14 and into sixth. Own prep dept provides 25+% of senior intake. Approx 20–30% are children of former pupils.

Entrance Fully subscribed. No special skills or religious requirements – welcome all-rounders. Parents of fee payers expected to buy text books; maximum extras approx £45 pa. No fees for residents of Northern Ireland.

Parents 15+% in industry or commerce. 60+% live within 30 miles; 10+% live overseas (including GB).

Staff Headmistress Miss D E M Hunter, in post for 9 years. 44 full time staff, 10 part time. Annual turnover 2%. Average age 35.

Academic work GCSE and A-levels. 37 subjects offered (no A-level general studies). In 1990, 107 pupils in upper fifth, 76 in upper sixth (now 95). *GCSE:* in 1990, 50% upper fifth gained at least grade C in 8+ subjects; 27% in 5–7; and 23% in 1–4 subjects. *A-levels:* 3% upper sixth passed in 4+ subjects; 50% in 3; 25% in 2; and 22% in 1 subject. 30% took science A-levels; 50% arts/ humanities; 20% both. *Computing facilities:* Computer network to science and art departments; 15 stations; computers in most rooms. *Special provision:* Provision made as needed.

European Community *Languages:* French offered: to age 14; GCSE; A-level. German offered: to age 14; GCSE; A-level. Spanish offered: to age 14; GCSE; A-level. 50–75% take GCSE in more than 1 EC language. *Exchanges:* Regular exchanges for pupils aged 11–18 to Eire, France and Germany. *Other:* European Studies offered to pupils aged 16–18. Active in EC conferences/ competitions in Northern Ireland and beyond.

Senior pupils' non-academic activities *Music:* 130 learn a musical instru-

363

ment, 6 to Grade 6 or above; 25 take GCSE; 25 in school orchestra, 50 in school choir, 19 in wind band, 23 in choral groups, 70 in music festivals. *Drama and dance:* 60 in school productions. 30 to Grade 4 in ESB, RAD etc, 34 take GCSE drama & theatre arts. *Art:* 26 take GCSE; 5 take A-level. 26 belong to art club. 14 on community project. *Sport:* Hockey, netball, tennis, squash, badminton, table tennis, golf, riding, swimming, athletics, gymnastics, judo, karate and ice-skating available. 269 take non-compulsory sport. 4 represent province. *Other:* 60 take part in local community schemes. 34 are working for Duke of Edinburgh's bronze award, 18, silver; 8, gold. 100 in voluntary schemes in sixth form. 1 works for national charities. Other activities include computer clubs, bridge, photography, debating, public speaking, SU, stage craft + make-up club, mini-company (an in-school commercial venture), work experience programme and work shadowing.

Careers In 1990, 44% leavers went on to degree courses; $3^{1}/_{2}$% to art/drama/music colleges; 15% to non-degree courses (eg HND courses, nursing, industrial scholarship); 20% straight into careers (eg banking, civil service, police, management trainee); 18% other. Of those going on to degree courses, 3% went to Oxbridge, 88% to other universities; 9% to poly/colleges. 5% those going on to higher education went to courses in practical art; 67% in humanities/social sciences/law/business; 5% in medicine; and 23% in science/engineering.

Uniform School uniform worn except in upper sixth.

Houses/prefects Competitive houses (in sport and music). No prefects; head girl and house captains – elected by the staff and sixth form. School Council.

Religion Boarders attend church (if Christian). Morning assembly is Christian but non-denominational.

Social Regular inter-school debates, sports, fund raising for charities etc. Modern language trips, group and individual exchanges usually under auspices of Central Bureau for Educational Visits and Exchanges; ski-trips. Pupils allowed to bring own car to school. Meals formal for boarders, self service for dayschool. School shop, tuck and second-hand uniforms. No tobacco/alcohol allowed.

Discipline No corporal punishment. Pupils failing to produce homework once might expect verbal reprimand. Those caught smoking or with cannabis on the premises should expect the school to take an extremely serious view.

Boarding Most are in dormitories of 4–6. Seniors have cubicles for privacy. Sixth have own cottage in school grounds. Houses, of 40–50, divided by age group. Trained matron. Central dining room. Overseas pupils can provide and cook own food. Weekly boarding available. Visits to local town allowed.

Alumni association is run by The President, c/o the college.

Former pupils Professor Ingrid Allen (professor of neuropathology); Miss Kathleen Robb (former matron Victoria Hospital, Belfast); Miss Suzanne Lowry (Observer journalist); Miss Judith Rodgers (British Universities Record Holder in 100m hurdles); Heather Harper (international opera singer); Mrs Patricia McLaughlin MP; Miss Bessie Machonachie MP.

· *Hurstpierpoint* ·

Hurstpierpoint College
Hurstpierpoint
Hassocks
West Sussex BN6 8JS
Tel 0273 833636

- Pupils 380
- Boys 13–18
- (Day/Board)
- Girls None
- Upper sixth 70

- Termly fees
  £2285 (Day)
  £2855 (Board)
- HMC, Woodard
  Enquiries/application to
  the Headmaster

What it's like

A Woodard school, founded in 1849, it has a rural 100-acre site in the mid-Sussex countryside, 2 miles from Hurstpierpoint village and 10 miles north of Brighton. Its very attractive buildings are in the collegiate style. The original ones form two pleasant quadrangles. Many additions in the last 25 years and a new sixth form house will open in 1992. It has the advantage of being a compact and unified campus. Everything, including playing fields, is easily accessible. It is pledged to C of E tradition and practice. A friendly and orderly atmosphere prevails and there are manifold opportunities for leisure and learning. The standards of teaching and academic attainment are high. Many go on to degree courses per year. A high standard also in sport and games. A wide range of extra-curricular activities. Very strong in music, arts and crafts and drama. A flourishing army section CCF (the first such unit to be formed in England).

School profile

Pupils Age range 13–18; 380 boys, 60 day, 320 boarding. Main entry ages 13 and into sixth. Approx 4% are children of former pupils. Own junior school provides 20–25% of intake. *Transfer from maintained schools:* 2% main intake, plus 80% small intake to sixth.

Entrance Common entrance exam used; reports and tests for state school entrants. Pupils mainly, but not exclusively, C of E. Parents not expected to buy text books; maximum extras £50 pa plus music tuition and exam fees. Assisted places. 20 scholarships, 50%–25% of fees; plus bursaries if parental need is proven.

Parents 15+% in industry or commerce. 80+% live within 1 hour's drive; 10+% live overseas.

Staff Headmaster S A Watson, in post for 5 years. 44 full time staff, 15 part time. Annual turnover 5%. Average age 40.

Academic work GCSE and A-levels. 19 subjects offered (no A-level general studies). In 1990, 72 pupils in upper fifth, 70 in upper sixth. *GCSE:* in 1990, 63% upper fifth gained at least grade C in 8+ subjects; 32% in 5–7; and 4% in 1–4 subjects. *A-levels:* 1 upper sixth passed in 4+ subjects; 49 in 3; 12 in 2; and 8 in 1 subject. 22% took science A-levels; 53% arts/humanities; 25% both. *Computing facilities:* 1 Atari 4 meg. with hard disk and laser printer. 7 Atari 520 ST FM. 6 BBC videos. 1 Macintosh multi-media system and 2 Macintosh standard. *Special provision:* Some help of a minor nature only for dyslexic pupils.

European Community *Languages:* French offered: to age 14; GCSE; AS-level; A-level. German offered: to GCSE; AS-level; A-level. 25–50% take GCSE in more than 1 EC language. *Exchanges:* Regular exchanges for pupils aged 14–16. *Other:* French and German pupils welcome. European scholarship to eastern area of Germany for 1992. European Student Conference planned for 1992.

Senior pupils' non-academic activities *Music:* 100 learn a musical instrument, 25 to Grade 6 or above, 2 or 3 accepted for Music School; 42 in school orchestra, 40 in school choir, 8 in jazz

365

group, others in choral society and small choir/ensembles; 4 in county youth orchestra. *Drama and dance:* 80 in school productions; up to 7 house plays and musicals pa each involving 20–60. *Art:* 70 take as non-examined subject, 30 take GCSE, 3 take A-level; 3 accepted for Art Schools. 15 belong to art club, 30 take metal, craft, plastics and pottery GCSE. *Sport:* Rugby, hockey, cricket, athletics, squash, tennis, fencing, cross-country, shooting, swimming, water polo, basketball, badminton available. 140 take non-compulsory sport. 6 take lifesaving exams. 16 represent county (rugby, hockey, cricket). *Other:* 12 have bronze Duke of Edinburgh's Award, 3 have silver and 1 has gold. Other activities include computer, bridge, chess and engineering clubs, clay pigeon shooting, natural history society, scholars' lecture society, debating, community service, war games, learning to drive, adventure training (canoeing, rock climbing).

Careers In 1990, 50% leavers went on to degree courses; 1% to art/drama/music colleges; 15% straight into careers (eg banking, insurance, stock broking, surveying); 34% other. Of those going on to degree courses, 70% went to universities; 30% to poly/colleges. 4% those going on to higher education went to courses in practical art; 4% in music; 50% in humanities/social sciences; 4% in medicine; and 38% in science/engineering.

Uniform School uniform worn, flexible in final year.

Houses/prefects Competitive houses. Prefects and head boy appointed by Head; head of house/house prefects by housemaster. School Committee.

Religion 2 week day and 1 Sunday service compulsory; other services voluntary.

Social Theatrical and musical functions with Roedean, S Michael's Petworth, Farlington, St Mary's Hall, Brighton, Burgess Hill schools. German school exchange annually; annual trips to Alps, Dieppe, Greece; cricket team to India every fourth year; rugby team to France, Vancouver; cricketers also to Barbados. Pupils allowed to bring own bike to school. Meals self service. School shop. No tobacco allowed. There is a sixth form bar.

Discipline No corporal punishment. Sanctions of increasing severity imposed for work and misbehaviour.

Boarding 50% have own study bedroom, 10% share; 40% are in dormitories of 6+. 7 houses, of approximately 60, same as competitive houses. Resident qualified nurses. Central dining room. Prefects can provide and cook own food. Exeats every Sunday for the day and every second Saturday night. Visits to local town (Burgess Hill) and village (Hurstpierpoint) allowed daily; Brighton for special reasons only.

Former pupils Lord Plummer of Marylebone; Sir Brian Cartledge (UK Ambassador Moscow); Sir Derek Day (High Commissioner in Canada); Michael York (actor); Richard Page (MP).

· *Hutchesons'* ·

Hutchesons' Grammar School 21 Beaton Road Glasgow G41 4NW Tel 041 423 2933	• Pupils 1661 • Boys 4–18 (Day) • Girls 4–18 (Day) • Higher year 190	• Termly fees £861 (Day) • HMC Enquiries/application to the Rector

What it's like

Founded in 1641, it occupied its present site (pleasant, quiet and in a residential area, 3 miles from the city centre) in 1959. The premises are well equipped and a new science block of 15 laboratories and ancillary rooms opened in 1991. Academically it is a very high-powered school with outstanding results. Surveys suggest that it is pre-eminent in Scotland and among the most successful schools in Britain. It sends very many pupils to degree courses each year, including a few to Oxbridge which is unusual for a Scottish school. French, German and Spanish are taught up to A-level and many pupils take more than one European language at S-grade. Very strong indeed in music, drama and art. Equally strong in sports and games (a large number of representatives at county and national level and in 1990–1 four boys represented the Scottish Schools XV at rugby). A good range of extra-curricular activities. Some commitment to local community services.

School profile

Pupils Total age range 4–18; 1661 day pupils. Senior department 12–18, 1074 pupils (546 boys, 528 girls). Main entry ages 4, 9, 12. *Transfer from maintained schools:* 60% senior intake, plus 80% to sixth.

Entrance Own entrance exam used. Oversubscribed. No special skills or religious requirements. Parents expected to buy text books; maximum extras £100 pa (books, sports equipment). Some scholarships/bursaries available.

Parents 15+% are doctors, lawyers etc; 15+% in industry or commerce.

Staff Rector David R Ward, in post for 4 years. 115 full time staff, 6 part time. Annual turnover small.

Academic work O-grade/S-grade, Highers, CSYS and A-levels. 22 subjects offered. In 1990, 186 pupils in O/S-grade year, 190 in Higher year (S5), 122 in A-level/CSYS year. *O/S-grade:* in 1990, 70 pupils gained at least grade C in 7+ subjects; 110 in 5–7; and 6 in 1–4 subjects (many pupils bypass O/S-grades). *Highers:* 121 pupils in S5 passed in 5+ or more subjects, 28 in 4, 17 in 3, 14 in 2, 1 in 1 subjects. *A-levels:* 6 pupils passed in 4+ subjects; 11 in 3; 26 in 2; and 14 in 1 subject (in addition many take Highers and/or CSYS). 40% took science A-levels; 29% arts/humanities; 31% both. *Computing facilities:* Computer room with machines for 20 pupils and a number of micros per department.

European Community *Languages:* French offered: to age 14; S-grade; A-level. German offered: to age 14; S-grade; A-level. Spanish offered: to S-grade; A-level. 25–50% take S-grade in more than 1 EC language. *Exchanges:* Regular exchanges for pupils aged 14–16 to Germany. *Other:* Visited European Parliament on official sponsored visit. Choir take part in festivals in France and Germany; German school choir stayed in school for 1 week.

Senior pupils' non-academic activities *Music:* 350 learn a musical instrument, 30 to Grade 6 or above, 4 accepted for Music School; 80 play in school orchestra, 200 in school choir; 1 plays in National Youth Orchestra, 4 in National Youth Orchestra of Scotland. *Drama and* *dance:* 150 in annual opera/musical/ dramatic production. *Art:* 15 take as non-examined subject; 25 take Higher. 2 accepted for Art School. *Sport:* Boys: rugby, cricket, athletics. Girls: hockey and netball. Rowing, squash, badminton, basketball, self-defence, table tennis, swimming, curling, canoeing also available. 160 take non-compulsory sport. 10 take swimming exams. 16 represent county/country (rugby, tennis, golf, cricket). *Other:* 40+ take part in local community schemes. Other activities include a computer club, Scripture Union, gardening, chess, literary and debating.

Careers In 1990, 91% leavers went on to degree courses; 4% to art/drama/ music colleges; 1% to non-degree courses (eg HND); $1^{1}/_{2}$% straight into careers (eg Navy); $2^{1}/_{2}$% other. Of those going on to degree courses, 5% went to Oxbridge, 84% to other universities; 11% to poly/ colleges. 2% those going on to higher education went to courses in practical art; 1% in drama/acting; 4% in music; 30% in humanities/social sciences; 8% in medicine; 24% in science/engineering; 15% in law and 16% in accountancy/ business studies.

Uniform School uniform worn throughout.

Houses/prefects Competitive houses. Prefects and head boy/girl – elected by the staff. School Council.

Religion Assembly 4 mornings a week (reading, prayer, hymn). Separate Jewish assembly most days.

Social English Speaking Union debates with local schools. October trip to Paris; ski-ing trip to Switzerland; exchange with Kassel (Germany) for 20 pupils. Pupils allowed to bring own car/bike/motorbike to school. Meals self service. No tobacco/ alcohol allowed.

Discipline No corporal punishment. Detention, report card for parental signature, school based community work at weekends. For most serious offences, suspension is used, the pupil having to come in for the same number of days in the holidays.

Alumni association run by, Secretary, Hutchesons' School & Club Trust, 44 Kingarth Street, Glasgow G42 7RN.

Former pupils Ken Bruce (Radio 2 presenter); Ally Scott (Rangers footballer); Sir William Wilfred Morton (former Head of Britain's Customs and Excise); Maev Alexander (TV's That's Life); Sir Kenneth Carmichael McDonald (Ministry of Defence); Russell Hillhouse (Scottish Office); Duncan Graham (Chief Executive, National Curriculum); Lord McColl of Dulwich.

· *Huyton* ·

Huyton College	• Pupils 335	• Termly fees
Blacklow Brow	• Boys $2^{1}/_{2}$–6 only	£1085 (Day)
Huyton	(Day)	£2435 (Board)
Liverpool	• Girls $2^{1}/_{2}$–18	• GSA
L36 5XQ	(Day/Board)	Enquiries/application to
Tel 051 489 4321	• Upper sixth 20	the Headmistress

What it's like

Founded in 1894, it has a self-contained site 6 miles from Liverpool. The core of the school is Huyton Hall, a handsome 19th-century building set in 20 acres of private gardens and playing fields. A continuous programme of extension and modernisation has provided excellent up-to-date facilities for work and games. The prep school adjoins the main school. A sound general education is provided. Many sixth form leavers go on to degree courses. Religious teaching and church services are based on the doctrines of the Church of England, but the school is ecumenical.

School profile

Pupils Total age range $2\frac{1}{2}$–18; 335 pupils, 310 day (10 boys, 300 girls), 25 boarding girls. Senior department 11–18, 208 girls. Main entry ages $2\frac{1}{2}$ (boys and girls), any age including sixth (girls).

Entrance Own entrance exam used. C of E Foundation, but other denominations accepted. Extras vary. Scholarships/ bursaries (including service). Special allowance for daughters of clergy. College aid scheme in cases of hardship.

Parents 60+% live within 30 miles; 2% live overseas.

Staff Headmistress Mrs Christine Bradley (first year in post). 26 full time staff, 21 part time including 15 music staff. Annual turnover less than 2%.

Academic work GCSE and A-levels. 19 subjects offered (including A-level general studies). In 1990, 35 pupils in upper fifth, 20 in upper sixth. *GCSE:* in 1990, 14 upper fifth gained at least grade C in 8+ subjects; 8 in 5–7; and 13 in 1–4 subjects. *A-levels:* 71% upper sixth passed in 3 subjects; 12% in 2; and 17% in 1 subject. 29% took science A-levels; 65% arts/humanities; 6% both. *Computing facilities:* RML network. *Special provision:* EFL lessons for overseas students.

European Community *Languages:* French offered: to age 14; GCSE; AS-level; A-level. German offered: to age 14; GCSE; AS-level; A-level. 25–50% take GCSE in more than 1 EC language.

Senior pupils' non-academic activities *Music:* School orchestras, choirs, chamber groups, wind band, string group; pupils prepared for Music College. *Drama and art:* Pupils can be prepared for Drama and Art College. *Sport:* Lacrosse, netball, tennis, rounders, athletics, swimming, badminton, volleyball, gymnastics, judo, educational dance available. School enters Aberdare cup (tennis) and National Schools Lacrosse Tournament.

Careers On average, 80% leavers go on to degree courses; 10% to art/drama/ music colleges; 5% straight into careers; 5% other. Of those going on to degree courses, 5% go to Oxbridge, 75% to other universities; 20% to poly/colleges. 10% those going on to higher education went to courses in practical art; 2% in music; 53% in humanities/social sciences; 10% in medicine; and 25% in science/ engineering.

Uniform School uniform worn, different in sixth.

Houses/prefects Competitive houses. House prefects.

Religion C of E but other denominations welcome.

Social Visits to France, Germany and Greece.

Boarding One boarding house (mixed ages). Seniors have own study bedrooms.

· *Hymers* ·

Hymers College	● Pupils 900	● Termly fees £845
Hymers Avenue	● Boys 8–18 (Day)	● HMC
Hull HU3 1LW	● Girls 8–18 (Day)	Enquiries/application to
Tel 0482 43555	● Upper sixth 101	the Headmaster

What it's like

Founded in 1893, it is single-site and urban. Decent, solid, late Victorian and Edwardian buildings are situated on a 35-acre estate of the former Hull botanic gardens, half a mile from the centre of the city. There has been a lot of recent development and very good facilities are provided. Firm discipline and high academic standards are insisted on and the need for full parental involvement in the school is considerably stressed. The teaching and results are good, and very many pupils go on to degree courses each year, including Oxbridge. French, German and Spanish are offered up to A-level; Italian to GCSE. A high proportion of pupils takes GCSE in more than one European language. The music, drama and art depts are impressively active and a large number of people are engaged. High standards prevail in sport and games (there are a lot of county representatives). A plentiful range of extra-curricular activities and some emphasis on outdoor pursuits. A distinguished record in the Duke of Edinburgh's Award Scheme.

School profile

Pupils Total age range 8–18; 900 day pupils (fully co-educational from 1989). Senior department 11–18, 705 pupils (575 boys, 130 girls). Main entry ages 8, 9, 11 and into sixth. Approx 20% are children of former pupils. *Transfer from maintained schools:* 20% main senior intake, plus 50% to sixth.

Entrance Own entrance exam used. Oversubscribed. No special skills or religious requirements. Parents not expected to buy text books; trips, theatre etc extra. 135 assisted places.

Parents 15+% are doctors, lawyers, etc; 15+% in industry or commerce.

Staff Headmaster John Morris, 1 year in post. 56 full time staff, 5 part time staff. Turnover 5%. Average age 35–40.

Academic work GCSE and A-levels. 16 subjects offered (no A-level general studies). In 1990, 101 pupils in upper fifth, 101 in upper sixth. *GCSE:* in 1990, 75 upper fifth gained at least grade C in 8+ subjects; 20 in 5–7; and 6 in 1–4 subjects. *A-levels:* 6 upper sixth passed in 4+ subjects; 84 in 3; 11 in 2; and 4 in 1 subject. 40% took science A-levels; 50% arts/humanities; 10% both. *Computing facilities:* Large (20+ machines) computer room. Computers in all science and geography departments.

European Community *Languages:* French offered: to age 14; GCSE; A-level. German offered: to GCSE; A-level. Italian offered: to GCSE. Spanish offered: to GCSE; A-level. 50–75% take GCSE in more than 1 EC language.

Senior pupils' non-academic activities *Music:* 65 learn a musical instrument, 45 to Grade 6 or above, 2 accepted for Music School; 100+ in two school orchestras, 55 in school choir, others in various chamber groups; 20+ in local youth orchestras. *Drama and dance:* 120 in school productions. *Art:* 60 take GCSE; 12 take A-level. 2 accepted for Art School. 30 belong to art club. *Sport:* Rugby, cricket, tennis, squash, basketball, fencing, athletics, badminton, hockey, cross-country, rounders, orienteering and swimming available. 280 take non-compulsory sport. 10 represent county (rugby, cricket); 1 represents England (rugby). *Other:* 80 have bronze Duke of Edinburgh's Award, 30 taking silver and 6 taking gold. Other activities include a computer club, chess, stamps, war games, debating, Christian Union, photography, angling, bridge, outdoor pursuits (walking, climbing and camping).

Careers In 1990, 75% leavers went on to degree courses; 5% to art/drama/music colleges; 5% to non-degree courses; 5% straight into careers; 10% other. Of those going on to degree courses, 15% went to Oxbridge, 55% to other universities; 30% to poly/colleges. 5% those going on to higher education went to courses in practical art; 4% in music; 60% in humanities/social sciences; 6% in medicine; and 25% in science/engineering.

Uniform School uniform worn throughout.

Houses/prefects No competitive houses. Prefects, head boy/girl – appointed by Head in consultation with staff and senior prefects.

Religion Daily assembly for whole school.

Social No organised functions with other schools. Organised trips abroad. Pupils allowed to bring own car/bike/motorbike to school. Meals self service. School tuck shop. No tobacco/alcohol allowed.

Discipline No corporal punishment. Pupils failing to produce homework once might expect detention; those caught smoking cannabis on the premises might expect expulsion.

Alumni association is run by Mr J R Fewlass, 10 Hall Walk, Welton, Brough, North Humberside.

i

· *Ipswich* ·

Ipswich School
Henley Road
Ipswich
Suffolk IP1 3SG
Tel 0473 255313

- Pupils 625
- Boys 11–19 (Day/
  Board/Weekly)
- Girls 16–18 (Day)
- Upper sixth 97

- Termly fees
  £1210 (Day)
  £2060 (Board)
  £2000 (Weekly)
- HMC
  Enquiries/application
  to the Headmaster

What it's like

Founded in 1390 by the Ipswich Merchant Guild of Corpus Christi, its first Charter was granted by Henry VIII and subsequently confirmed by Elizabeth I. In 1852 the school moved into new and handsome buildings in the Victorian collegiate style. Many improvements and additions have been made over the years, including the fine library of 1981 and the recently reopened, refurbished and extended Performing Arts complex. The school, which has strong local support, now has excellent all-round facilities for both day-pupils and boarders (of whom, unusually, there were some from a very early stage in the school's history). The main site is on high ground overlooking Christchurch Park, with a cricket field on that site and 30 acres of other playing fields 10 minutes' walk from the school. The preparatory school has its own buildings on the same site and has the use of all the amenities of the main school. Religious education in the Anglican tradition is provided at all levels, plus daily chapel services and services on Sunday for different sections of the school. All denominations are welcome. A broad general education is provided. Academic standards are high and results good. The staff:pupil ratio is a favourable 1:10. Very many pupils go on to degree courses, many to Oxbridge. French and German are taught right through to A-level; Italian and Spanish to GCSE. A large proportion of pupils takes GCSE in more than one European language. There are regular exchanges with France and Germany. Drama and music are very well supported. There are several dramatic productions each year for all age groups. There are plentiful opportunities for music-making: with a large choral society, a chapel choir, orchestra, junior string orchestra, concert band and chamber music groups. Sports and games (in which high standards are achieved) include the normal range (with emphasis on hockey in the Lent term), plus sailing, windsurfing and riding. The CCF (a large and thriving contingent) includes Army, Navy and Air Force sections. It is a voluntary organisation; boys and sixth form girls are encouraged to belong to it or undertake some community service and many do so. A wide variety of clubs and societies cater for most needs. The school participates successfully in the Duke of Edinburgh's Award Scheme.

School profile

Pupils Total age range 11–19, 625 pupils (575 day, 50 boarding). Main entry ages 11 (boys) and into sixth (boys and girls). Own prep. *Transfer from maintained schools:* 50% main intake, plus 40% to sixth.

Entrance Own exam or common entrance used. 4% from overseas. Scholarships, including for music and art; assisted places.

Staff Headmaster Dr J M Blatchly, in post for 19 years.

Academic work GCSE and A-levels. Subjects offered include Russian; no A-level general studies although studied by all in sixth. In 1990, 80 pupils in upper fifth, 96 in upper sixth. *GCSE:* in 1990, 60 upper fifth gained at least grade C in 8+ subjects; 13 in 5–7; and 6 in 1–4 subjects. *A-levels:* 11 upper sixth passed in 4+ subjects; 70 in 3; 11 in 2; and 4 in 1 subject. 36 took science A-levels; 41 arts/humanities; 19 both. *Computing facilities:* Network of BBCs being replaced by Nimbus RM 286 system.

European Community *Languages:* French offered: to GCSE; A-level. German offered: to GCSE; A-level. Italian offered: to GCSE. Spanish offered: to GCSE. 51–75% take GCSE in more than 1 EC language. *Exchanges:* Regular exchanges for pupils aged 11–16 to France and Germany.

Careers In 1990, 85% leavers went on to degree courses; 1% to art/drama/music colleges; 14% other. Of those going on to degree courses, 17% went to Oxbridge, 70% to other universities; 13% to poly/colleges. 3% those going on to higher education went to courses in drama/acting; 62% in humanities/social sciences; 8% in medicine; and 27% in science/engineering.

· *Ipswich High* ·

Ipswich High School
Westerfield Road
Ipswich
Suffolk IP4 2UH
Tel 0473 252213

- Pupils 590
- Boys (4–7 only)
- Girls 4–18
  (Day)
- Upper sixth 50

- Termly fees
  £908 (Day)
- GSA, GPDST
  Enquiries/application to
  the Headmistress

What it's like

Founded in 1878, it moved in 1907 to its present urban site in a residential area of North Ipswich. There are 9 acres of playing fields nearby. It has pleasant buildings. Numerous modern additions including a fine library. Junior school on the same site. Its social spread is wide and it provides a good all-round education, with the emphasis on development of individual talents and the education of 'the whole person'. There is a big commitment to music; intensive dramatic activities. Overall standards are high, with many going on to degree courses, including Oxbridge. Good range of sports and games. Everyone does some voluntary service in the district from age 15 or 16.

School profile

Pupils Total age range 4–18; 590 day girls. Senior department 11–18, 415 girls. Main entry ages 4, 7, 9, 11 and into sixth. *Transfer from maintained schools:* 75% senior intake, plus 50% to sixth.

Entrance Own entrance exam used. Oversubscribed. No special skills or religious requirements. Parents not expected to buy text books. 29 assisted places pa. 3–4 scholarships awarded on academic merit, half, one-third or quarter of fees; bursaries subject to means test.

Staff Headmistress Miss P M Hayworth, in post for 20 years. 34 full time staff, 17 part time (plus 13 for 'extras'). Annual turnover very small.

Academic work GCSE and A-levels. 18 GCSE and A-level subjects offered (general studies taught but not examined). In 1990, 59 pupils in upper fifth, 50 in upper sixth. *GCSE:* in 1990, 53 upper fifth gained at least grade C in 8+ subjects; 6 in 5–7 subjects. *A-levels:* 1 upper sixth passed in 4+ subjects; 36 in 3; 12 in 2; and 1 in 1 subject. 7 took science A-levels; 16 arts/humanities; 27 both. *Computing facilities:* One room with a network of 18 computers, one with 10; clusters everywhere.

European Community *Languages:* French offered: to age 14; GCSE; AS-level; A-level. German offered: to age 14; GCSE; AS-level; A-level. Italian offered: to GCSE. 25–50% take GCSE in more than 1 EC language. *Exchanges:* Regular exchanges for pupils aged 11–16 to France and Germany. *Other:* Visit to European Parliament in Strasbourg 1992.

Senior pupils' non-academic activities *Music:* 80+ learn a musical instrument, 50 to Grade 6 or above; 3 accepted for Music School, 45 in school orchestra, 90 in school choirs; 12 in Suffolk Youth Orchestra, 14 in Suffolk Schools Choir. *Drama and dance:* Sometimes almost everyone participates in annual school play and four drama competitions; 12 to Grade 6 in ESB, RAD, etc; 1 or 2 accepted for Drama Schools. *Art:* 40 take as non-examined subject; 30 take GCSE; 10 take A-level. 6 belong to eg photographic club. 4–5 accepted for Art School. *Sport:* Hockey, tennis, netball, fencing, rounders, volleyball, squash, swimming, athletics available. Most take non-compulsory sport. 20 take exams in eg swimming. 10 represent county (hockey, tennis, netball) or country (athletics). *Other:* All 15–16

year old pupils do local voluntary service. Duke of Edinburgh's Award Scheme available for all. Other activities include chess, debating, Christian Union, games club, business/industry club, young enterprise scheme. Pupils allowed to use computers in their free time.

Careers In 1990, 64% leavers went on to degree courses; 8% to art/drama/music colleges; 12% to non-degree courses (eg accountancy foundation, diploma in rural land management); 8% straight into careers (eg insurance, retail management); 8% other. On average, of those going on to degree courses, 10% go to Oxbridge, 60% to other universities; 30% to poly/colleges. 8% those going on to higher education go to courses in practical art; 2% in drama/acting; 10% in music; 52% in humanities/social sciences; 8% in medicine; and 20% in science/engineering.

Uniform School uniform worn except in sixth.

Houses/prefects No competitive houses. All sixth form are prefects. Head girl elected by sixth form and staff. School Council.

Religion Daily assembly involves worship. Parents may withdraw their children if they wish.

Social Occasional debates and shared lectures or musical performances with local schools. Annual exchange with schools in Chevreuse and Hamburg. Annual History of Art visits to France or Italy, and ski-ing trips. Pupils allowed to bring own car/bike to school. Meals self service. Tuck shop at break. Second-hand uniform sales organised by parents. No tobacco/alcohol allowed.

Discipline No corporal punishment. Cases of pupils failing to produce homework once would be judged on their merits; those caught smoking cannabis on the premises could expect expulsion in most cases.

· *Italia Conti* ·

Italia Conti Academy of
Theatre Arts
23 Goswell Road
London EC1M 7BB
Tel 071 608 0044

- Pupils 340
- Boys 9–21 (Day)
- Girls 9–21 (Day)
- Upper sixth Yes

- Termly fees
  £1730 (Day)
- ISAI

Enquiries/application to
the Head

Staff Head C K Vote, in post for 14 years.

Entry by audition. Specialist dance and drama school.

j

· *James Allen's (JAGS)* ·

James Allen's Girls'
School
East Dulwich Grove
London SE22 8TE
Tel 081 693 1181
Fax 081 693 7842

- Pupils 725
- Boys None
- Girls 11–18
  (Day)
- Upper sixth 95

- Termly fees
  £1340 (Day)
- GSA
Enquiries to the
Headmistress/
Admissions Secretary
Application to the
Admissions Secretary

What it's like

Founded in 1741, one of three schools of the Alleyn's College foundation and the oldest girls' school in London. Commonly known as 'JAGS', it moved in 1886 to its present site of 22 acres in the pleasant inner London suburb of Dulwich. There have been massive additions since 1978 to provide excellent modern facilities. Interdenominational, it puts some stress on the inculcation of Christian ethics. Its declared aims are to encourage and promote: enthusiasm; a concern for others; a willingness to apply intelligence as a way of life; confidence and independence of mind; the pursuit of excellence (whatever the undertaking). A popular school, it is well known for its good teaching and academic achievements. Very many go on to degree courses, including many to Oxbridge. There is much emphasis on Europe. French, German, Italian and Spanish are offered for both A-level and the Institute of Linguists. Many pupils take GCSE in more than one European language. There are regular exchanges on offer to all age groups in France, Germany and Spain, and much involvement with Europe throughout the school. There is a big commitment to music and drama (it has its own theatre designed to professional standards) and art is extremely strong. Collaboration with Dulwich College in cultural enterprises. An unusually wide range of sporting and games activities. Also strong in extra-curricular activities.

School profile

Pupils Age range 11–18, 725 day girls. Main entry ages 11 and into sixth. Not many are children of former pupils. Own preparatory school provides approx 20% senior intake. *Transfer from maintained schools:* 50% senior intake, plus 50% to sixth.

Entrance Own entrance exam used. Oversubscribed. No special skills or reli-gious requirements. Parents expected to buy some sixth form text books; no other compulsory extras. 150 assisted places. 20 scholarships/bursaries, up to 80% fees according to need.

Staff Headmistress Mrs B C Davies, in post for 7 years. 58 full time staff, 23 part time. Annual turnover 5%. Average age 35.

Academic work GCSE and A-levels.

24 subjects offered (including A-level philosophy; not A-level general studies). In 1990, 101 pupils in upper fifth, 79 in upper sixth (now 95). *GCSE:* in 1990, 91 upper fifth gained at least grade C in 8+ subjects; 9 in 5–7; and 1 in 1–4 subjects. *A-levels:* 8 upper sixth passed in 4+ subjects; 66 in 3; 5 in 2 subjects. 26% took science A-levels; 54% arts/humanities; 20% both. *Computing facilities:* Computers in most departments. CAD in design and technology department; 28 computers in three computing rooms. *Special provision:* None, apart from extra general help.

European Community *Languages:* French offered: to age 14; GCSE; A-level; Institute of Linguists. German offered: to age 14; GCSE; A-level Institute of Linguists. Italian offered: to GCSE; A-level; Institute of Linguists. Spanish offered: to A-level; Institute of Linguists. 25–50% take GCSE in more than 1 EC language. *Exchanges:* Regular exchanges for pupils aged 11–18 to France, Germany, Italy and Spain (Benelux countries soon). *Other:* European Studies compulsory for pupils aged 11–14 and 16–18. 11–13 age group have adventure holiday in France annually. German pupil in lower sixth. Use radio and satellite television from EC countries and taken part in EC pupil radio link. Talks from MEPs, Sir Leon Britton etc. Much involved in European Youth Parliament.

Senior pupils' non-academic activities *Music:* 150 learn a musical instrument, 25 to Grade 6 or above. 56 in school orchestra, 25 in school choir, 8 in school pop group, 12 in wind, 3 play in pop group; 8 in youth orchestras. *Drama and dance:* 60 in school productions, 61 take ESB speech and drama lessons; All lower sixth take ESB exams in public speaking. 2 accepted for university courses. *Art:* 10 take as non-examined subject; 60 take GCSE art; 20, A-level. 6 accepted for Art School; 20 belong to photographic club. *Sport:* Hockey, netball, tennis, rounders, athletics, squash, volleyball, basketball, fencing, table tennis, indoor hockey, weight-training, keep fit, gymnastics, dance, swimming, self-defence, canoeing, sailing, gliding, riding available. 100 take non-compulsory sport. 10 represent county/country (hockey, badminton, netball, athletics, fencing, tennis). *Other:* 30 have bronze Duke of Edinburgh's Award and 10 silver. Other activities include a computer club, chess, debating, orators' contest, poetry workshop, polyglots society, design and technology club, literary society, history society, Amnesty group, Green Society.

Careers In 1990, 76% leavers went on to degree courses; 5% to art/drama/music colleges; 3% straight into careers (eg banking); 16% other. Of those going on to degree courses, 15% went to Oxbridge, 76% to other universities; 7% to poly/colleges. 6% those going on to higher education went to courses in practical art; 49% in humanities/social sciences; 10% in medicine; and 35% in science/engineering.

Uniform School uniform worn except in the sixth.

Houses/prefects Houses. 9 prefects, head girl and deputy – elected by sixth form. School Council.

Religion Interdenominational assembly 3 times a week; emphasis on Christian ethics. Non-Christians can be exempted at parents' request.

Social Semi-integrated general studies in upper sixth with Dulwich (brother school); joint theatre productions and some societies; Japanese and Arabic in lower sixth a joint venture. Windsurfing, ski-ing and adventure trips abroad. Trips and exchanges to France, Germany, Italy, Russia, USA, Egypt, Greece. Drama Tour to Australasia. Pupils allowed to bring own bike to school. Meals self service. School uniform shop. No tobacco/alcohol allowed.

Discipline No corporal punishment. Pupils failing to produce homework once might expect order mark (3 means $^1/_2$ hour detention); those caught smoking cannabis on the premises could expect suspension, possibly expulsion.

Alumni association run by Mrs Brenda Hillier, 27 Beechwood Rise, Edgebury, Chislehurst, Kent BR7 6TF and Mrs Susan Jones, 10 Eastmearn Road, London SE21 8HA.

Former pupils Anita Brookner and Lisa St Aubin de Teran (authors).

· *John Lyon* ·

The John Lyon School
Middle Road
Harrow
Middlesex HA2 0HN
Tel 081 422 2046

- Pupils 500
- Boys 11–18
  (Day)
- Girls None
- Upper sixth 68

- Termly fees
  £1130 (Day)
- HMC
Enquiries to the
Headmaster
Application to the
Headmaster's
Secretary

What it's like

Founded in 1876, it has agreeable premises on the west side of Harrow Hill amidst gardens. There are spacious playing fields nearby. There have been substantial additions and improvements over the years including a very recent suite of ten classrooms and an assembly hall. Some religious education is provided weekly for all pupils throughout the school. There are regular school assemblies. A sound general education is given and this includes Latin in the second year. Academic results are good and many pupils go on to degree courses, including Oxbridge. Music and drama are strong. A fair range of sports and games is provided and there is a plentiful variety of extra-curricular activities.

School profile

Pupils Age range 11–18; 500 day boys. Main entry ages 11, 13 and into sixth. *Transfer from maintained schools:* 70% main intake, plus 10% to sixth.

Entrance Common entrance (at 13) and own exam (at 11) used. 118 assisted places. Scholarships at 11 and 13.

Staff Headmaster Rev T J Wright, in post for 5 years. 37 full time staff, 3 part time.

Academic work GCSE and A-levels. 16 subjects offered (no A-level general studies). In 1990, 72 pupils in upper fifth, 68 in upper sixth. *GCSE:* in 1990, 44 upper fifth gained at least grade C in 8+ subjects; 20 in 5–7; and 8 in 1–4 subjects. *A-levels:* 7 upper sixth passed in 4+ subjects; 51 in 3; 8 in 2; and 3 in 1 subject. 19 took science A-levels; 38 arts/humanities; 12 both. *Computing facilities:* Computer room – network of RM Nimbus.

European Community *Languages:* French offered: to age 14; GCSE; A-level. German offered: to age 14; GCSE; AS-level; A-level. Spanish offered: non-examined. 25–50% take GCSE in more than 1 EC language. *Exchanges:* Regular exchanges for pupils aged 11–14 to France.

Careers In 1990, 84% leavers went on to degree courses; 1% to non-degree courses (eg accountancy); 3% straight into careers (eg banking); 11% other. Of those going on to degree courses, 12% went to Oxbridge, 77% to other universities; 11% to poly/colleges. 65% those going on to higher education went to courses in humanities/social sciences; 2% in medicine; and 33% in science/engineering.

k

· Keil ·

Keil School
Helenslee Road
Dumbarton
G82 4AL
Tel 0389 62003

- Pupils 213
- Boys 10–18
  (Day/Board/Weekly)
- Girls 10–18
  (Day/Board/Weekly)
- Higher year 43

- Termly fees
  £1236 (Day)
  £2169 (Board/
  Weekly)
- SHMIS
  Enquiries/application to
  the Headmaster

What it's like

Founded in 1915 at Keil House, Southend, Argyll, it moved to its present premises in 1925 where it is under the direction of governors appointed by the Mackinnon-Macneill Trust. The school is situated on the north bank of the Clyde at the gateway to the Western Highlands, a few miles away from Loch Lomond. There are marvellous views across the lower reaches of the Clyde. The school stands in very attractive grounds of some 45 acres which include lawns, woodland and playing fields – an altogether beautiful and healthy environment. The heart of the school is the handsome mansion house of Helenslee. The original buildings have been adapted and developed and the school is now well equipped. It has all the advantages of a small school and a lot of care is given to the individual. The accent, where possible, is on self-sufficiency. Much initiative and responsibility is expected of senior pupils through the prefectorial system and almost everyone has some kind of responsibility ultimately. The staff:pupil ratio is about 1:11 and classes are small (among the smallest in Scottish secondary schools); always below 20 and often smaller. Religious worship is compulsory in daily assemblies and Sunday services. A Church of Scotland foundation, it welcomes those of other faiths. Exam results are good and not a few pupils go on to degree courses each year. There is an unusually wide range of sports and games available for a school of this size and high standards are achieved. There is also a plentiful variety of extra-curricular activities and some emphasis on outdoor pursuits for which the environment is ideal. Estate work (mowing lawns, marking and preparing pitches etc) is largely in the hands of the pupils. Music, drama and art are all strong and there is regular collaboration with other schools in cultural enterprises. There has been some success in the Duke of Edinburgh's Award Scheme, and there is a rigorous army cadet force contingent.

School profile

Pupils Age range 10–18; 213 pupils, 89 day (65 boys, 24 girls), 124 boarders (106 boys, 18 girls). Main entry ages 10, 11, 12, 13 and into sixth. 4% are children of former pupils. *Transfer from maintained schools:* 90% main intake, plus 100% to sixth.

Entrance Own exam used. Not usually

oversubscribed. Skills in music, art, sport looked for and personality. Although a Church of Scotland foundation, all denominations admitted (RC monastery next door). Parents not expected to buy text books; no other compulsory extras. 6 assisted places pa. 6 scholarships and 6 bursaries pa, to £3000, both open and closed (to Highlands and Islands pupils).

Parents 30+% live within 30 miles; up to 10% live overseas.

Staff Headmaster Christopher H Tongue, in post for 7 years. 19 full time staff, 1 part time. Annual turnover 10%. Average age 34.

Academic work O/S-grade, Highers, and A-levels. 13 O/S-grade subjects, 14 Highers, 7 A-levels offered (no A-level general studies). In 1990, 43 pupils in O/S-grade year, 36 in Higher (now 43), 19 in A-level year. *O/S-grade:* in 1990, 19 pupils passed in 8+ subjects; 14 in 5–7; and 10 in 1–4 subjects. *Highers:* 9 pupils passed in 5+ or more subjects; 8 in 4; 9 in 3; 5 in 2; 3 in 1 subject. *A-levels:* 5 pupils passed in 3+ subjects. 50% took science Highers; 30% arts/humanities; 20% both. *Computing facilities:* Computer lab with 12 Commodores; 12 BBC B's spread among departments. *Special provision:* EFL taught; provision for dyslexic pupils.

European Community *Languages:* French offered: to age 14; S-grade; A-level. German offered: to age 14; S-grade. Under 10% take S-grade in more than 1 EC language. *Exchanges:* Regular exchanges for pupils aged 11–14 to France. *Other:* Pupils from Belgium, Germany and Netherlands in school.

Senior pupils' non-academic activities *Music:* 25 learn a musical instrument, 3 to Grade 6 or above; 1 accepted for Music School; 30 in school choir, 12 in orchestra, 6 in pop group. *Drama and dance:* 20 in school productions; 10 in other. 1 goes on to work in theatre. *Art:* 22 take O-grade; 10 Higher. 6 accepted for Art School. 10 belong to eg photographic club. *Sport:* Rugby, football, hockey, athletics, cross-country running, orienteering, tennis, badminton, squash, table tennis, basketball, netball, volleyball, cricket, snooker, chess, bridge available. 80 take part in non-compulsory sport. 4 pupils represent county (rugby); for last 3 years have won Thistle Award Competition (athletics) for Scottish Secondary Boys Schools. *Other:* 10 have bronze Duke of Edinburgh's Award, 4 silver, 2 gold. Other activities include a computer club (also taught to seniors), estate work is largely in the hands of the pupils; Young Enterprise; representation on crime prevention panels.

Careers In 1990, 66% leavers went on to degree courses; 5% to art/drama/music colleges; 15% straight into careers; 14% other. Of those going on to degree courses, 67% went to universities; 33% to poly/colleges. 8% those going on to higher education went to courses in practical art; 34% in humanities/social sciences; 8% in medicine; and 50% in science/engineering.

Uniform School uniform worn throughout.

Houses/prefects Competitive houses. Prefects, head boy/girl, head of house and house prefects (named chiefs, deputy chiefs and house deputies) – appointed by the Headmaster.

Religion Daily assembly and Sunday service compulsory.

Social Debates, Burns suppers, discos. Organised annual French exchange. Meals formal. 3 school shops sell uniform, stationery and tuck. No tobacco/alcohol allowed.

Discipline No corporal punishment. Pupils failing to produce homework once would receive a warning – repeated failure leads to Saturday afternoon detention; those caught smoking cannabis on or off the premises could expect expulsion.

Boarding 10% have own study bedroom, 15% share (with 2–5); 75% are in dormitories of 6+. Single sex houses, of 40 max, one junior and three senior. Resident qualified nurse. Central dining room. Pupils can provide and cook some snacks. Termly exeats (Sat lunch to Sun 9pm) up to parents. Weekly visits to local town (Dumbarton) and Glasgow allowed with permission.

Alumni association is run by Wallace Crawford, 83 Clarence Gardens, Glasgow G11 7JW.

Former pupils Rev James Currie

(minister and broadcaster); Alistair Blair (fashion designer); Professor Joseph Thomson (Regius Professor of Law, Glasgow University); Professor Andrew Skinner (Clerk to the Senate, Glasgow University).

· Kelly College ·

Kelly College
Tavistock
Devon
PL19 0HZ
Tel 0822 613005

- Pupils 330
- Boys 11–18
  (Day/Board/Weekly)
- Girls 11–18
  (Day/Board/Weekly)
- Upper sixth 70

- Termly fees
  £1195 (Day)
  £2825 (Board)
  £2700 (Weekly)
- HMC
Enquiries/application to
the Headmaster

What it's like

Founded in 1877 by Admiral Kelly, it has a magnificent site above the River Tavy on the edge of one of the most beautiful parts of Dartmoor and thus in a very healthy and invigorating environment. The pleasant market town of Tavistock is nearby. St Michael's, Tavistock, became the Junior School in 1990. There are 4 boys' boarding houses and a new boarding house for girls in the sixth form. Many additions and improvements have been made in recent years and there are plans for further developments. The school is already very well equipped and even has an Outward Bound briefing room and training centre. Numbers are kept low as a matter of policy and the large and well qualified staff allows a most favourable staff:pupil ratio of 1:8. A sound general education is provided in a friendly and happy atmosphere. Academic results are good. Many sixth formers go on to degree courses. French, German and Spanish are offered throughout the school and an exceptionally high proportion of pupils takes GCSE in more than one European language. There are regular exchanges into France and Germany. Music, drama and art are all strong. The college has unusually fine playing fields and sports facilities and there is a lot of emphasis on sports and games. High standards are attained and there have been a number of representatives at county, regional and national level. There are many clubs and societies for extra-curricular activities, which include fishing (salmon and trout), riding and printing. Every pupil is taught art and carpentry. The CCF is large, with Royal Navy, Army and Royal Marine sections. The college has maintained its nautical connections and there are close links with the navy in Dartmouth and Devonport. There is a large number of Outward Bound activities, for which the locality is ideal. Overseas trips and expeditions are a regular feature.

School profile

Pupils Age range 11–18; 330 pupils, 255 boys, 75 girls (day and boarding). Main entry ages 11 and into sixth (boys and girls); fully co-educational from 1991. *Transfer from maintained schools:* 40% main intake, plus 60% to sixth.
Entrance Common entrance and own exam used. 17 scholarships (art, music, science, naval and all-rounder); plus exhibitions and bursaries.
Staff Headmaster Christopher Hirst, in post for 5 years.
Academic work GCSE and A-levels. 22 subjects offered (including A-level general studies). In 1990, 53 pupils in upper fifth, 64 in upper sixth (now 70).

GCSE: in 1990, 16 upper fifth gained at least grade C in 8+ subjects; 13 in 5–7; and 23 in 1–4 subjects. *A-levels:* 29 upper sixth passed in 4+ subjects; 13 in 3; 14 in 2; and 6 in 1 subject. 14% took science A-levels; 33% arts/humanities; 53% both. *Computing facilities:* Computing room and computers in various departments. *Special provision:* Individual help is given.

European Community *Languages:* French offered: to age 14; GCSE; AS-level; A-level. German offered: to age 14; GCSE; AS-level; A-level. Spanish offered: to age 14; GCSE; AS-level; A-level. Over 75% take GCSE in more than 1 EC language. *Exchanges:* Regular exchanges for pupils aged 11–14 to France and Germany. *Other:* Several French, German and Spanish pupils in school.

Careers In 1990, 70% leavers went on to degree courses; 3% to art/drama/music colleges; 19% to non-degree courses (eg agricultural, secretarial, business studies); 4% straight into careers (eg family business); 4% other. Of those going on to degree courses, 5% went to Oxbridge, 45% to other universities; 50% to poly/colleges. 2% those going on to higher education went to courses in practical art; 58% in humanities/social sciences; 5% in medicine; and 33% in science/engineering.

· *Kelvinside* ·

Kelvinside Academy
33 Kirklee Road
Glasgow
G12 0SW
Tel 041 357 3376

- Pupils 685
- Boys 4–18 (Day)
- Girls None
- Higher year 71

- Termly fees £925 (Day)
- HMC

Enquiries/application to the Rector

What it's like

Founded in 1878, it has a fine site with very handsome buildings in a pleasant urban residential area. Ample playing fields are three-quarters of a mile away. It has its own junior department. Excellent modern facilities of all kinds are provided, including a well-stocked new library. One of Scotland's leading schools, it is strongly academic with a high standard of teaching and consistently good results. Many leavers go on to university each year and, in common with a number of other Scottish schools, tend to reject Oxbridge places in favour of places in a Scottish University. The music and drama departments are extremely active. There is a big range of sports and games (the school has produced a large number of international and county representatives). An equally good range of activities. There is a flourishing CCF and considerable emphasis on outdoor pursuits (the school has a base in the Cairngorms for ski-ing, hill-walking and field studies).

School profile

Pupils Total age range 4–18; 685 day boys. Senior department 11–18, 498 boys. Main entry ages 4, 7, 8, 11 and into sixth. Approx 15% are children of former pupils. *Transfer from maintained schools:* 95% senior intake, plus 90% to sixth.

Entrance Own entrance exam used. Oversubscribed. Must have academic ability and fluent English; no religious requirements. Parents pay a hire charge for text books; music lessons (£45) and lunch (£90) also extra. 50 assisted places. 7 scholarships/bursaries pa, £300–£100.

Parents 25+% in industry or commerce; 25+% are doctors, lawyers, etc. 90+% live within 30 miles.

Staff Rector J H Duff, in post for 11 years. 49 full time staff, 4 part time. Annual turnover 4%. Average age 38.

Academic work O/S-grades, Highers, A-levels and CSYS. 18 subjects offered (no A-level general studies). In 1990, 77 pupils in O/S-grade year, 71 in Higher, 48 in A-level/CSYS year (63 in 1990). *O/S-grade:* in 1990, 41 pupils passed in 8+ subjects; 24 in 5–7; and 12 in 1–4 subjects. *Highers:* 32 pupils passed in 5+ or more subjects; 13 in 4; 15 in 3; 22 in 2; 22 in 1 subject (many pupils take Highers with CSYS and A-levels). *A-levels:* On average 30 pupils passed in 4+ subjects; 12 in 3; 10 in 2; and 10 in 1 subject. 50% took science A-levels; 25% arts/humanities; 25% both. *Computing facilities:* Laboratory on network system, plus a further room with more sophisticated individual machines. *Special provision:* Help for mild dyslexics.

European Community *Languages:* French offered: to age 14; S-grade; Higher; A-level. German offered: to age 14; S-grade; Higher; A-level. 10–25% take S-grade in more than 1 EC language.

Senior pupils' non-academic activities *Music:* 40 learn a musical instrument, 5 to Grade 6 or above, 1 every 3 or 4 years accepted for Music School; 24 in school orchestra, 20+ in choir, 6 in pop group, 12 in pipe band; 10 in Strathclyde Schools orchestra and concert band. *Drama and dance:* 100 in school productions (including lighting and stage staff). 1 accepted for Royal Ballet school; occasionally pupils go on to work in theatre. *Art:* 5 take as non-examined subject; 25 take O-grade; 20 Higher. 2 accepted for Art School. *Sport:* Rugby football, cricket, athletics, shooting (full and small bore), cross-country running, golf, tennis, sailing, curling, ski-ing, badminton, hill walking and climbing, windsurfing, canoeing, swimming, squash, basketball, volleyball, wrestling, gymnastics available. 300+ take non-compulsory sport. Approx 5 take exams. 14 represent Scotland and 20+ Glasgow/West (rugby, cricket, golf, athletics, shooting, cross-country running, badminton, squash, tennis, swimming). *Other:* 30 take part in local community schemes. Other activities include a computer club, CCF, chess, debating, Scripture Union, model railway club, business games, 'Dungeons and Dragons', electronics society and many others.

Careers In 1990, 81% leavers went on to degree courses; 2% to art/drama/music colleges; 9% to non-degree courses; 6% straight into careers (eg banking); 2% other. Of those going on to degree courses, 61% went to universities; 39% to poly/colleges. 2% those going on to higher education went to courses in practical art; 49% in humanities/social sciences; 9% in medicine; and 40% in science/engineering.

Uniform School uniform worn throughout.

Houses/prefects Competitive houses. Prefects, head boy, head of house and house prefects – appointed by the Rector.

Religion Daily morning assembly – non-Christians in senior school may opt out. Timetabled RE classes – all attend.

Social Joint debates, mixed badminton team, social functions with local schools. Organised rugby and cricket tours, ski trips, 'interest' trips eg Israel/France, CCF camps with BAOR, some exchanges. Pupils allowed to bring own car/bike/motorbike to school. Meals self service. School tuck shop. No tobacco/alcohol allowed.

Discipline Corporal punishment exists in theory (Rector and Deputy only); rarely used. Pupils failing to produce homework once might expect extra work or detention; those caught smoking cannabis on the premises could expect expulsion.

Alumni association run by John A Welsh, Secretary, Kelvinside Academical Club, 18 Grange Road, Bearsden, Glasgow G61.

Former pupils Sir T Risk (Governor of Bank of Scotland); Sir Hugh Fraser (Lord Fraser); Colin Mackay (TV political commentator) and many leading figures in the professions.

· Kent College (Canterbury) ·

Kent College
Canterbury
Kent
CT2 9DT
Tel 0227 763231

- Pupils 637
- Boys 7–18
  (Day/Board)
- Girls 7–18
  (Day/Board)
- Upper sixth 79

- Termly fees
  £1500 (Day)
  £2678 (Board)
- HMC
  Enquiries/application to
  the Headmaster

What it's like

Founded in 1885 and in 1920 acquired by the board of management for Methodist Residential Schools. It stands on a fine site overlooking the city of Canterbury. The junior school, Vernon Holme, is a mile away. The main campus comprises about 20 acres, with additional playing fields nearby. There is also the school farm on the beautiful Moat Park estate of about 90 acres. The school is about 1.5 miles from the city centre and 4.5 miles from the sea. In recent years there have been major development programmes and the school is now very well equipped. No particular religious affiliation is required but there is an emphasis on regular worship, morning prayers etc. A sound general education is provided and results are consistently good. Many sixth formers go on to degree courses, including Oxbridge. French, German and Spanish are offered to A-level and many pupils take GCSE in more than one European language. There are regular exchanges with France and Germany. There is a good range of sports and games and high standards are attained. A plentiful variety of clubs and societies for extra-curricular activities, including the Duke of Edinburgh's Awards.

School profile

Pupils Total age range 7–18; 637 pupils, 362 day (199 boys, 163 girls), 275 boarders (164 boys, 111 girls). Senior department, 11–18; 560 pupils, 318 boys, 242 girls. Main entry ages 7, 11, 13 and into sixth. *Transfer from maintained schools:* 60% senior intake, plus 50% to sixth.

Entrance Own entrance exam used. Oversubscribed for day pupils. No special skills or religious requirements. Assisted places available. Scholarships available (incl music and sixth form), also bursaries for some boarders.

Staff Headmaster R J Wicks.

Academic work GCSE and A-levels. 19 GCSE subjects offered; 21 at A-level (including AS-level general studies, not A-level). In 1990, 84 pupils in upper fifth, 79 in upper sixth. *GCSE:* in 1990, 40 upper fifth gained at least grade C in 8+ subjects; 34 in 5–7; and 9 in 1–4 subjects. *A-levels:* 8 upper sixth passed in 4+ subjects; 47 in 3; 12 in 2; and 8 in 1 subject.

24 took science A-levels; 32 arts/humanities; 23 both. *Computing facilities:* Two purpose-built rooms, network extending throughout school. *Special provision:* Dyslexia unit for pupils of sound ability.

European Community *Languages:* French offered: to age 14; GCSE; AS-level; A-level. German offered: to age 14; GCSE; AS-level; A-level. Spanish offered: to age 14; GCSE; AS-level; A-level. 25–50% take GCSE in more than 1 EC language. *Exchanges:* Regular exchanges for pupils aged 11–18 to France and Germany. *Other:* European Studies offered to pupils aged 16–18. European programme in sixth form, attracting young people from different countries for 1–2 years. Exchange programme includes joint musical activities and exchanges with European schools eg orchestra combining with German orchestra to tour France.

Senior pupils' non-academic activities *Music:* 50 pupils in school orchestra. There is a choir, brass group, wind band, recorder group, madrigal group and choral society. *Drama and dance:* Many in school productions and house plays. *Art:* Many take art as non-examined subject, GCSE; a fair number take A-level. Some accepted each year for Art School. *Sport:* Rugger, hockey, cricket, tennis, athletics, swimming, sailing, netball, squash, badminton, basketball, fencing, table tennis, riding, wind-surfing, outdoor pursuits, cross-country, orienteering available. *Other:* Other activities include a computer club, crafts, needlework, photography, printing, chess, bridge, debating, Christian Union, scouts and farming (has own 25-acre farm), arts society.

Careers In 1990, 70% leavers went on to degree courses; 5% to art/drama/music colleges; 15% to non-degree courses; 10% straight into careers. Of those going on to degree courses, 15% went to Oxbridge, 65% to other universities; 20% to poly/colleges. 5% those going on to higher education went to courses in practical art; 2% in drama/acting; 3% in music; 30% in humanities/social sciences; 5% in medicine; and 30% in science/engineering.

Houses/prefects Prefects, head of house and house prefects – prefects appointed by Head, house prefects by housemaster/housemistress.

Social Tours abroad – arts, music, sport, social.

· *Kent College (Pembury)* ·

Kent College
Pembury
Tunbridge Wells
Kent TN2 4AX
Tel 0892 82 2006

- Pupils 393
- Boys None
- Girls 4–18
  (Day/Board/Weekly)
- Upper sixth 37

- Termly fees
  £1470 (Day)
  £2465 (Board)
  £2275 (Weekly)
- GSA
  Enquiries/application to
  the Headmistress

What it's like

Noted for a friendly atmosphere and a strong sense of community, the school is situated on an attractive open site half a mile from the village of Pembury, three miles from Tunbridge Wells. The main building is a fine Victorian house but in the last twenty years there has been considerable expansion and the facilities now are impressive, including modern purpose-built boarding houses, an indoor heated swimming pool and a music school (1990). A wide range of courses is offered and special attention is given to individual needs. Many sixth form leavers go on to degree courses. French, German and Spanish are offered to A-level. Girls are encouraged to aim for high standards in academic studies, and in music, drama and sport. There is a strong emphasis on extra-curricular activities and girls are expected to contribute to the school community and accept responsibility.

School profile

Pupils Total age range 4–18; 393 girls, 200 day, 193 boarding. Senior department 11–18, 273 girls. Main entry ages, up to 11; 13 and into sixth. *Transfer from maintained schools:* 35% senior intake, plus 10% to sixth.

Entrance Own exam used (common entrance accepted). Average extras £50

Day Girls, £100 Boarders. Text books supplied by the school. 7 scholarships pa.

Parents 5+% in the armed services. 10+% live overseas.

Staff Headmistress Miss Barbara J Crompton, 1 year in post. 30 full time staff, 16+ part time. Annual turnover 5%. Average age 35–40.

Academic work GCSE and A-levels. 19 subjects offered to GCSE; 15 to A-level (including general studies). In 1990, 50 pupils in upper fifth, 37 in upper sixth. *GCSE:* in 1990, 88% upper fifth gained at least grade C in 5+ subjects. *A-levels:* 51% took arts/humanities A-levels; 49% took science or a mixture of science and arts. *Computing facilities:* Computer room, plus computers in science, maths, geography, English depts and library. *Special provision:* EFL tuition available; help for dyslexic pupils.

European Community *Languages:* French offered: to age 14; GCSE; A-level. German offered: to age 14; GCSE; A-level. Spanish offered: to age 14; GCSE; A-level. 10–25% take GCSE in more than 1 EC language. *Exchanges:* Regular exchanges for pupils aged 16–18 to Germany. *Other:* Regular 1–2 term visits from European students usually aged 16. Welcomes foreign students who play a full part in the life of the school; EFL tuition available.

Senior pupils' non-academic activities *Sport:* Netball, hockey, tennis, rounders, swimming, athletics, badminton, gymnastics, trampolining, riding and fencing available. Other activities include debating societies, drama clubs, computing, craft club, Duke of Edinburgh's Award, CDT club, silk printing, art club, choirs, wind band, orchestra etc.

Careers In 1990, 69% leavers went on to degree courses; 13% to art/drama/music colleges; 2% straight into careers; 14% other. Of those going on to degree courses, 2% went to Oxbridge, 50% to other universities; 48% to poly/colleges. 5% those going on to higher education went to courses in practical art; 2% in drama/acting; 2% in music; 63% in humanities/social sciences; 2% in medicine; and 24% in science/engineering.

Uniform School uniform worn except in the sixth.

Houses/prefects Competitive houses. Head girl and 2 deputies elected by school; house captains and deputies elected by houses. School Council and Senior Council.

Religion Methodist foundation, now inter-denominational. Morning assembly and Sunday services; everyone attends.

Social Day and short trips to France. Other visits abroad and field study visits in U.K. Regular theatre visits to London. Debates, dances, matches with other schools. Meals: central dining-room, self service. School tuck shop. No tobacco/alcohol allowed.

Discipline Detention for poor work. For a serious breach of school rules e.g. smoking, alcohol offences, parents are informed and the girl is 'gated' for 2–3 weeks including weekends. Day girls would be expected to report to school on Saturdays and Sundays. Extra work/community service set.

Boarding 1st and 2nd Form in Junior House. 3rd to 6th Form in 3 Senior Houses. Upper 6th in separate House. 2 fixed exeats per term. Pupils visit Tunbridge Wells on Saturdays, from 3rd year upwards.

· *Kilgraston* ·

Kilgraston School
Convent of the Sacred
Heart
Bridge of Earn
Perthshire PH2 9BQ
Tel 0738 812257

- Pupils 274
- Boys None
- Girls 8–18
  (Day/Board/Weekly)
- Higher year 35

- Termly fees
  £1125 (Day)
  £2185 (Board/
  Weekly)
- GSA, BSA, SHA,
  HAS
  Enquiries/application to
  the Headmistress

What it's like

Founded in 1920, it moved in 1930 from Edinburgh to its present splendid site, a little south of Perth, which comprises 70-odd acres of beautiful gardens, woodlands and playing fields. The main building and focal point of the school is a particularly handsome Georgian house designed by Robert Adam for the Grants of Strathspey. Since the 1930s there has been a steady programme of building and modernisation which now provides, among other things, comfortable accommodation for boarders (60% have their own study bedroom) and first-rate teaching facilities. Kilgraston is a Roman Catholic foundation and is part of the Society of Sacred Heart network of some 200 schools and colleges throughout the world. Its pupils may be of any religious persuasion and the aim is to create an environment in which Christian ideals and principles may thrive. The chapel is the centre of its spiritual life. Prayer and reflection are regarded as important in the development of the pupils. It has many of the advantages of a small school. There is a large full-time staff (and a large part-time staff) and the school enjoys an unusually favourable staff:pupil ratio of roughly 1:7.5. Very few schools in Britain can better this. A sound, general education is provided, with some strength in modern languages (Italian and Spanish as well as French and German), and results are consistently good. Very many leavers proceed to degree courses. Music is strong and drama flourishes. A standard range of sports and games is available, for which there are excellent provisions; plus ski-ing, riding, karate, judo and golf. Community services are particularly well supported and there has been a good deal of success in the Duke of Edinburgh's Award Scheme. Girls have many contacts with other schools for the purpose of debating, dances and public speaking competitions. Extensive use is made of the cultural amenities of neighbouring cities and towns.

School profile

Pupils Total age range 8–18; 274 girls (85 day, 189 boarding). Senior department 12–18, 238 girls. Main entry ages, 11, 13 and into sixth. 10% are children of former pupils. Own junior school provides more than 20% of senior intake. *Transfer from maintained schools:* 30% main intake, 80% to sixth.

Entrance Common entrance and own exam used. Oversubscribed. No special skills or religious requirements. Parents not expected to buy text books. Average extras, £150 per term. 50 assisted places pa. 12 scholarships/bursaries pa, £1800-£500.

Parents 15+% in industry or commerce; 15% farmers/landowners. 30+% live within 30 miles, 10+% live overseas.

Staff Headmistress Sister Barbara F Farquharson, in post for 4 years. 36 full time staff, 22 part time. Annual turnover 3%.

Academic work S-grade, Highers and A-levels. 18 subjects offered. In 1990, 36 pupils in S-grade year, 35 in main Higher year, 28 in upper sixth. *S-grade:* in 1990, 15 upper fifth gained at least grade C in 7+ subjects; 8 in 5–6; and 12 in 1–4 subjects. *A-levels and/or Highers:* 15 sixth-form pupils passed in 4+ subjects; 20 in 3; 14 in 2; and 7 in 1 subject. All took a mixture of science/engineering and arts/humanities. *Computing facilities:* Nimbus network with 16 stations in computing room. Nimbus and BBCs in other departments. *Special provision:* Classes in English as a foreign language for overseas students.

European Community *Languages:* French offered: to age 14; S-grade; Higher; A-level. German: to S-grade; Higher; A-level. Italian: to S-grade; Higher; A-level. Spanish: to S-grade; Higher; A-level. 10–25% take S-grade in more than 1 EC language. *Exchanges:* Regular exchanges for pupils aged 11–16 to France and Germany. *Other:* Small number of EC pupils each year. Extra language tuition offered. Contact both with French sister school and German school in Perth's twin town.

Senior pupils' non-academic activities *Music:* 25 learn a musical instrument, 10 up to Grade 6; 15 in school orchestra, 18 in school choir, 3 in National Youth Orchestra Repertoire Group, 2 in Perth Youth Orchestra. *Drama and dance:* 25 in school productions; 5 in Perth Theatre Studio Workshop; 2 in Scottish Youth Theatre Festival. 20 take LAMDA exams. *Art:* 2 take art as non-examined subject, 20 take S-grade art; 14 Higher; 2 A-level art. 4 accepted for Art School. *Sport:* Tennis, hockey, netball, volleyball, rounders, badminton, swimming, ski-ing, skating, riding, golf, gymnastics, athletics, karate, aerobics available. 70 take part in non-compulsory sport. 20 take exams, eg karate, riding, ski-ing. 3 represent county/country (ski-ing, riding). *Other:* 70 take part in local community schemes. 37 have bronze Duke of Edinburgh's Award, 13 silver and 7 have gold. 3 enter voluntary schemes after leaving school. Other activities include computer and debating clubs, public speaking, sixth form discussion groups, theatre outings, driving lessons.

Careers In 1990, 92% leavers went on to degree courses; 8% to non-degree courses. Of those going on to degree courses, 50% went to universities; 50% to poly/colleges. 7% those going on to higher education went to courses in practical art; 73% humanities/social sciences and 20% in science/engineering.

Uniform School uniform worn, including the sixth form during class hours.

Houses/prefects Competitive houses. Head girls, prefects, head of house and house prefects, elected by school and ratified by the staff.

Religion Attendance at religious worship compulsory on Sunday.

Social ESU and Britannic Assurance debates, local newspaper's debates, dances/discos, police quiz competitions, senior citizens' functions, sporting fixtures, Multiple Sclerosis Society and Save the Children Fund functions/flag-selling and fund-raising with other local schools. Yearly exchange visit with sister school in France; exchange with German school; annual ski trips to France/Switzerland. Sixth-form day pupils may bring cars; all day girls may bring bikes. Meals formal on special occasions, usually self-service. School shop. No tobacco; wine allowed at some special functions.

Discipline No corporal punishment. For those failing to produce a piece of homework for the first time, punishment would be a rebuke or detention, depending on the circumstances. Those caught smoking cannabis on the premises might expect expulsion.

Boarding 60% have own study bedrooms; 1% share with 1 other. 39% in dormitories of 6+. Resident qualified nurse; weekly visit by doctor. Pupils can occasionally provide and cook own food, eg for house events. 2 weekend exeats (2 nights) plus half-term (5–11 days). Visits to the local town allowed on Saturday afternoon, from age 14; evening outings for sixth formers at weekends, as arranged.

Alumni association is run by Miss Anne Jarvie, 10 Dungoil Road, Claddens, Lenzie, Glasgow G66 5PG

· King Alfred (Hampstead) ·

King Alfred School	• Pupils 490	• Termly fees
Manor Wood	• Boys 4–18 (Day)	£1465 (Day)
North End Road	• Girls 4–18 (Day)	Enquiries/application to
London NW11 7HY	• Upper sixth 22	the Admissions
Tel 081-905 5599		Secretary

What it's like

Founded in 1898, it is single-site, urban, in 6 acres of woodland gardens on the edge of Hampstead Garden Suburb. Strictly undenominational. It is kept deliberately small and enjoys a high staff:pupil ratio (1:9). Many sixth formers go on to degree courses. It provides a good range of sport and games and extra-curricular activities.

School profile

Pupils Total age range 4–18; 490 day pupils (248 boys, 242 girls). Senior department 11–18, 257 pupils (139 boys, 118 girls). Main entry ages 4, 7, a few at 11, 14 and into sixth. Approx 5–7% are children of former pupils. *Transfer from maintained schools:* 27% senior intake, plus 1% to sixth.

Entrance Own entrance exam, 2 day visit and interview used. Oversubscribed. No special skills or religious requirements. Parents expected to buy text books. Several sixth form bursaries, subject to means.

Staff Head Francis Moran, in post for 8 years. 38 full time staff, 15 part time. Annual turnover 5–10%. Average age thirties.

Academic work GCSE and A-levels. 16 GCSE subjects offered; 13 at A-level (including photography; no A-level general studies). In 1990, 37 pupils in upper fifth, 23 in upper sixth (now 22). *GCSE:* in 1990, 18 upper fifth gained at least grade C in 8+ subjects; 11 in 5–7; and 8 in 1–4 subjects. *A-levels:* 10 upper sixth passed in 3 or 4 subjects; 7 in 2; and 6 in 1 subject. 4 took science A-levels; 10 arts/humanities; 9 both. *Computing facilities:* Eliot-Medway Computalab for class teaching; computers in main subject areas. *Special provision:* Special subjects dept; mild dyslexia only.

European Community *Languages:* French offered: to age 14; GCSE; A-level. German offered: to GCSE; A-level. Under 10% take GCSE in more than 1 EC language. *Other:* One of three British schools taking part in European competition, 'Go Down in Legend' (involving pupils writing their own play and visiting Paris to watch other schools' plays).

Senior pupils' non-academic activities *Music:* 10+ learn a musical instrument, 7 to Grade 6 or above. 10 play in pop group after school; 5 in instrumental groups. *Drama and dance:* 9 in school productions; 2 accepted for Drama/Dance Schools. *Art:* 24 take GCSE; 9, A-level; 6 accepted for Art School; 9 belong to photographic club. *Sport:* Football, netball, volleyball, basketball, table tennis, badminton, cricket, tennis, rounders, squash, gymnastics, American football, five-a-side, weights available. 30+ take non-compulsory sport. *Other:* Activities include computer clubs, Bulletin editorial group, French club, explorers, maths, chess.

Careers In 1990, 70% leavers went on to degree courses; 8% to art/drama/music colleges; 12% straight into careers; 8% other. Of those going on to degree courses, 7% went to Oxbridge, 73% to other universities; 20% to poly/colleges. 15% those going on to higher education went to courses in practical art; 5% in drama/acting; 65% in humanities/social sciences; 5% in medicine; and 10% in science/engineering.

Uniform School uniform not worn.

Houses/prefects No competitive houses. Prefects – elected by the school. School Council.

Religion No compulsory worship.

Social Organised trips abroad. Pupils allowed to bring own car/bike/motorbike to school. No tobacco/alcohol allowed.

Discipline No corporal punishment. Pupils failing to produce homework once would have no punishment. Those caught smoking cannabis on the premises would probably be offered professional help; but sanctions might well be invoked, depending on circumstances and severity of case.

Alumni association is run by Mrs X Bowlby, Boundary House, Wyldes Close, London NW11.

Former pupils Anthony Pleeth, Janet Craxton and Pamela Moisewitch (musicians); Maggie Norden (radio); Zoe Wanamaker, Stacey Tendeter, Catherine Harrison (actresses); Mamoun Hassan (films).

· King Edward's (Bath) ·

King Edward's School
North Road
Bath
Avon
BA2 6HU
Tel 0225 464313

- Pupils 685
- Boys 11–18 (Day)
- Girls 16–18 (Day)
- Upper sixth 120

- Termly fees £990 (Day)
- HMC

Enquiries/application to the Admissions Secretary

What it's like

Founded in 1552 by royal charter of Edward VI, the school occupied its present premises in 1961 which lie on a fine site of 14 acres on the southern slope of the city, just below the university. The Old Building (c1830) houses part of the school, but there are many new buildings from 1961. Modern facilities and accommodation are first-class. There is a high standard of teaching and academic achievement. Very many pupils go on to degree courses each year, many to Oxbridge. French and German are offered throughout the school, also Spanish up to GCSE. Many pupils take GCSE in more than one European language and there are regular exchanges with France and Germany. The music, art and drama departments are very strong. A good range of sports and games and much emphasis on outdoor pursuits. Full use is made of the city's cultural amenities and also those of Bristol.

School profile

Pupils Age range 11–18; 685 day pupils (640 boys, 45 girls). Main entry ages 11 and 13 (boys) and into sixth (boys and girls). Approx 5% are children of former pupils. Own junior school provides 50% of intake. *Transfer from maintained schools:* 45% main intake, plus 50% to sixth.

Entrance Own entrance exam used. Oversubscribed. No special skills or religious requirements. Parents not expected to buy text books; lunch (£63), music tuition (£70 per term) optional extras. 18 assisted places. 3 first year and 2 sixth form scholarships, half fees. Bursaries according to need.

Staff Headmaster J P Wroughton, in post for 9 years. 48 full time staff, 2 part time. Annual turnover 5%. Average age 38.

Academic work GCSE and A-levels. 19 subjects offered (general studies offered but not examined). In 1990, 98 pupils in upper fifth, 107 in upper sixth (now 120). *GCSE:* in 1990, 75% upper fifth gained at least grade C in 8+ subjects; 21% in 5–7; and 4% in 1–4 subjects. *A-levels:* 6% upper sixth passed in 4+ subjects; 74% in 3; 15% in 2; and 2% in 1 subject. 26% took science A-levels; 56% arts/humanities; 18% both. *Computing facilities:* A computer centre with 22 Acorn Archimedes A3000 computers linked by Econet system; also computers in most subject areas and in library. *Special provision:* Help arranged for dyslexic pupils.

European Community *Languages:* French offered: to age 14; GCSE; A-level. German offered: to age 14; GCSE; A-level. Spanish offered: to age 14; GCSE. 25–50% take GCSE in more than 1 EC language. *Exchanges:* Regular exchanges for pupils to France and Germany.

Senior pupils' non-academic activities *Music:* 45 learn a musical instrument, 8 to Grade 6 or above. 1 accepted for Music School. 25 in school orchestra, 90 in school choir, 6 in school pop group, 5 in wind band, 40 in string ensembles; 1 in Avon Schools' Orchestra, 8 in Bath Society of Young Musicians. *Drama and dance:* 30 in school productions, 12 in public speaking classes; 1 goes on to work in theatre. The school organises an annual arts festival. *Art:* 30 take as non-examined subject; 70 take GCSE; 30 A-level; 12 printmaking option; 6 pottery option; 4 accepted for Art School, 3 for architecture courses; 12 belong to art club. *Sport:* Rugby, hockey, cricket, tennis, athletics, badminton, squash, swimming, soccer, cross-country, orienteering, golf, table tennis, fencing, rockclimbing, judo available. All senior pupils play sport. About 10 represent county (rugby, athletics, hockey, cricket, badminton, squash or golf). *Other:* 6 take part in local community schemes. 30 have bronze Duke of Edinburgh's Award, 6 silver and 12 gold. Other activities include a computer club and societies: astronomical, chess, Christian Union, war games, radio-controlled cars, craft/design/technology, ornithology, wildlife,

outdoor pursuits, rock climbing, ski-ing. For sixth form – car maintenance, bedsit cookery, typing, word processing, photography, Arts Society, English Society, theatre club.

Careers In 1990, 80% leavers went on to degree courses; 5% to art/drama/music colleges; 10% to non-degree courses (eg HND engineering); 5% straight into careers (eg retail management). Of those going on to degree courses, 10% went to Oxbridge, 70% to other universities; 20% to poly/colleges. 5% those going on to higher education went to courses in practical art; 2% in drama/acting; 2% in music; 58% in humanities/social sciences; 3% in medicine; and 30% in science/engineering.

Uniform School uniform worn except in the sixth form.

Houses/prefects Competitive houses. Prefects, elected by staff, after poll of school. Head boy/girl – appointed by the Head. School Improvements Committee can make suggestions.

Religion Morning assembly compulsory; voluntary communion services twice a term.

Social Pupils belong to joint Sixth Form Societies (eg economics, science) and the Bath Society of Young Musicians with other local schools. Exchange visits to France and Germany; expeditions to a community in Kenya; three ski trips a year; music tours abroad. Pupils allowed to bring own car/bike to school. Meals self service. School shop. No tobacco/alcohol allowed.

Discipline No corporal punishment. Pupils failing to produce homework once might expect extra work during the lunch break; those caught smoking cannabis on the premises could expect expulsion.

Alumni association is run by Mr H M Kenwood, c/o the School.

Former pupils Viscount Simon, Chancellor of Exchequer 1937–40 and Lord Chancellor 1940–45.

· *King Edward's (Birmingham; Boys)* ·

King Edward's School
Edgbaston Park Road
Birmingham
B15 2UA
Tel 021 472 1672

- Pupils 749
- Boys 11–18
  (Day)
- Girls None
- Upper sixth 100

- Termly fees
  £1085 (Day)
- HMC
  Enquiries/application to
  the Chief Master

What it's like

Founded in 1552 by royal charter of Edward VI, it moved from the city centre to its present site at Edgbaston in 1936 to occupy a purpose-built establishment of pleasing design in a big area of parkland and spacious playing fields. The site is shared with King Edward's High School for Girls and there is plenty of collaboration between them. High academic standards are needed for entry. Academically it is one of the leading schools in England. Very many pupils go on to degree courses, including Oxbridge. It is strong in music, drama and the visual arts and has an excellent all-round record in sports and games.

School profile

Pupils Age range 11–18; 749 day boys. Main entry ages 11, 13 and into sixth.

Entrance Own entrance exam used. Oversubscribed. A high academic standard required for entry. No religious requirements. Parents not normally expected to buy text books. 280 assisted places. Up to 20 academic, music and art scholarships, full fees to £200.

Staff Chief Master Martin Rogers. 58 full time staff, 3 part time. Annual turnover 5%.

Academic work GCSE and A-levels. Average size of upper fifth 100; upper sixth 100. *GCSE:* on average, 96 pupils in upper fifth pass 8+ subjects; 3, 5–7 subjects; 1 pupil passes 1 subject. *A-levels:* on average, 91 pupils in upper sixth pass 4 subjects; 4, 3 subjects and 2 pass 2 subjects. On average, 45% take science/engineering A-levels; 45% take arts and humanities; 10% a mixture. *Computing facilities:* A well equipped computer laboratory. Computers in most departments.

Senior pupils' non-academic activities Music, drama and the visual arts are strong and flourishing.

Careers Over 90% of all pupils attend universities. They are encouraged to spend a year between school and university, preferably working abroad. Over a third of all boys go to Oxford or Cambridge.

Uniform School uniform worn throughout.

Houses/prefects 8 competitive houses. School prefects.

Social No tobacco/alcohol allowed.

Discipline No corporal punishment. Any contact with drugs would result in expulsion.

· King Edward (Birmingham; Girls) ·

King Edward VI High
School for Girls
Edgbaston Park Road
Birmingham B15 2UB
Tel 021 472 1834

- Pupils 551
- Boys None
- Girls 11–18
  (Day)
- Upper sixth 85

- Termly fees
  £980 (Day)
- GSA
  Enquiries/application to
  the Headmistress

What it's like

Founded in 1883, it moved to its present urban site in Edgbaston (next to the boys' school) in 1940. Purpose-built and well equipped, it has spacious playing fields. Non-denominational, it enjoys good teaching and high academic achievement. Very many leavers go on to degree courses, including many to Oxbridge. French, German, Italian and Spanish are offered at GCSE and a high proportion of girls takes GCSE in more than one European language. Plentiful collaboration with the neighbouring boys' school. Strong in music, drama and art and design. A good range of sport, games and extra-curricular activities. Considerable commitment to local community schemes.

School profile

Pupils Age range 11–18; 551 day girls. Main entry ages 11 and into sixth. Approx 2% are children of former pupils. *Transfer from maintained schools:* 69% main intake, plus 29% to sixth.

Entrance Own entrance exam used. Oversubscribed. No special skills or religious requirements. Parents not expected to buy text books; lunch, outings, music tuition extra. 185 assisted places. 25 scholarships/bursaries, 100–25% fees.

Staff Headmistress Miss E W Evans, in post for 14 years. 38 full time staff, 9 part time. Annual turnover 3%.

Academic work GCSE and A-levels. 17 subjects offered (including Greek and A-level general studies). In 1990, 77 pupils in upper fifth, 86 in upper sixth. *GCSE:* in 1990, 73 upper fifth gained at least grade C in 8+ subjects; 4 in 5–7 subjects. *A-levels:* 81 upper sixth passed in 4+ subjects; 3 in 3; 2 in 2 subjects. 30% took science A-levels; 49% arts/humanities; 21% both. *Computing facilities:* Nimbus network plus a variety of isolated micros (mainly BBC).

European Community *Languages:* French offered: to age 14; GCSE; A-level. German offered: to GCSE; A-level.

Italian offered: to GCSE. Spanish offered: to GCSE. 25–50% take GCSE in more than 1 EC language. *Exchanges:* Regular exchanges for pupils aged 14–18 to France and Germany.

Senior pupils' non-academic activities *Sport:* Gymnastics, hockey, netball, tennis, rounders, dance, fencing, badminton, squash rackets, swimming, athletics, lacrosse, basketball, volleyball, golf, self-defence, aerobics available. A wide variety of other activities including community service.

Careers In 1990, 94% leavers went on to degree courses; 1% to non-degree courses; 2% straight into careers; 3% other. Of those going on to degree courses, 18% went to Oxbridge, 73% to other universities; 9% to poly/colleges. 72% those going on to higher education went to courses in humanities/social sciences; 18% in medicine; and 10% in science/engineering.

Uniform School uniform worn except in the sixth.

Houses/prefects Competitive houses. School Council.

Social Many joint activities with brother school (King Edward's). Organised trips

abroad. Pupils allowed to bring own car/ bike to school. Meals self service. School shop. No tobacco/alcohol allowed.
Discipline No corporal punishment. Rules are kept to the minimum necessary for good order and a purposeful working environment. Atmosphere and tradition play an important part in the maintenance of discipline.

· King Edward (Lytham) ·

King Edward VII School
Lytham St Anne's
Lancashire
FY8 1DT
Tel 0253 736459

- Pupils 640
- Boys 7–18
- (Day)
- Girls None
- Upper sixth 64

- Termly fees
  £784 (Day)
- HMC
Enquiries/application to
the Headmaster

What it's like

Founded in 1908, it has a 40-acre site by the seaside, close to sandhills and dunes. It is semi-rural and suburban in an open and bracing position. Non-denominational, it has good facilities and playing fields. The standards of teaching are high and results are good. Many sixth formers go on to degree courses including many to Oxbridge. French and German are offered throughout the school and a high proportion of pupils take both at GCSE. There are regular exchanges arranged into France and Germany. It collaborates with its sister school Queen Mary. Strong sporting tradition. Use is made of an outdoor pursuit centre at Ribblehead in the Dales. Some community service and participation in the Duke of Edinburgh's Award Scheme. Many active clubs and societies. Regular musical and dramatic productions in conjunction with Queen Mary's.

School profile

Pupils Total age range 7–18; 640 day boys. Senior department 11–18, 550 boys. Main entry ages 11 and into sixth. Approx 8% are children of former pupils. Own junior school provides 30% of senior intake. *Transfer from maintained schools:* 60% senior intake.

Entrance Own entrance exam and common entrance used. Oversubscribed. Overall academic ability required; no religious requirements. Parents not expected to buy text books; no essential extras. 30 assisted places pa. 1 or 2 open scholarships pa, 50% fees. 5 or 6 bursaries, 27.5% fees.

Staff Headmaster D Heap, in post for 9 years. 45 full time staff, 4 part time. Annual turnover 8%. Average age 36.

Academic work GCSE and A-levels. 16 GCSE subjects offered; 3 at AS-level; 16 at A-level (all students take A-level general studies). On average, 85 pupils in upper fifth, 60+ in upper sixth. *GCSE:* on average, 46 upper fifth gained at least grade C in 8+ subjects; 30 in 5–7; and 9 in 1–4 subjects. *A-levels:* on average 35 upper sixth passed in 4+ subjects; 12 in 3; 8 in 2; and 5 in 1 subject. On average, 36% took science A-levels; 35% arts/ humanities; 29% both. *Computing facilities:* Network allowing access to computer facilities from every room, plus a main computer base, equipped with Archimedes computers. Software loaded from large capacity disk; plotters and laser colour printers used for output.

European Community *Languages:* French offered: to age 14; GCSE; AS-level; A-level. German offered: to age 14; GCSE; AS-level; A-level. 25–50% take GCSE in more than 1 EC language. *Exchanges:* Regular exchanges for pupils aged 14–18 to France and Germany. *Other:* Satellite television.

Senior pupils' non-academic activities Include computer club, chess club, driving club, aviation society, caving, canoeing, fell-walking and climbing clubs, Duke of Edinburgh's Award. Sport and drama well supported.

Careers In 1990, 84% leavers went on to degree courses; 6% to art/drama/music colleges; 10% straight into careers (eg banking, insurance, RAF). Of those going on to degree courses, 13% went to Oxbridge, 61% to other universities; 26% to poly/colleges. 3% those going on to higher education went to courses in practical art; 1% in music; 47% in humanities/social sciences; 9% in medicine; and 40% in science/engineering.

Uniform School uniform worn throughout.

Houses/prefects Competitive houses. Prefects, head boy, head of house and house prefects – appointed by the Head after consultation.

Religion School assemblies, non-denominational.

Social Many activities with sister school, Queen Mary. Organised trips abroad. Pupils allowed to bring own car/bike/motorbike to school. Meals self service. School shop. No tobacco/alcohol allowed.

Alumni association is run by M Nield, 9 Cambridge Road, Ansdell, Lytham St Anne's.

Former pupils Sir Alan Leslie (Past Pres, Law Soc.); Peter Shaffer (playwright); Sir Peter Harrop KCB (Permanent Secretary DOE).

· *King Edward (Southampton)* ·

King Edward VI School
Kellett Road
Southampton
Hampshire SO9 3FP
Tel 0703 704561

- Pupils 965
- Boys 11–19 (Day)
- Girls 16–19 (Day)
- Upper sixth 134

- Termly fees
  £1100 (Day)
- HMC

What it's like

Founded in 1553 under Letters Patent of King Edward VI. The first headmaster was appointed the following year. It has occupied four different sites and is now housed in buildings erected in 1938 about a mile and a half from the centre of Southampton. Good playing fields adjoin it and there are other playing fields at Swaythling. There have been considerable additions and improvements to the buildings over the years (major developments in 1962, 1980 and 1982) and they are now well equipped. The assembly hall seats the whole school. Pupils of all religious persuasions are accepted, but there is a close association (dating from the 16th century) with St Mary's, Southampton. Assemblies include worship, and religious education forms part of the curriculum. There is a staff:pupil ratio of about 1:12. Academic standards are high and results consistently good. Very many sixth formers go on to degree courses, including many to Oxbridge. French, German and Spanish are offered and a high proportion of pupils takes GCSE in more than one European language. There are regular exchange arrangements with France, Germany and Spain. Music and drama are well supported. A broad range of games and sports is provided (including squash racquets and Winchester fives). Rugby, hockey and cricket are strong. A very large number of clubs and societies (30 or more) cater for most conceivable extra-curricular needs and interests.

School profile

Pupils Age range 11–19, 965 day pupils. Main entry ages 11 and 13 (boys) and into the sixth (boys and girls). *Transfer from maintained schools:* 55% main intake, plus 40% to sixth.

Entrance Own entrance exam used. Scholarships, bursaries and 40 assisted places pa.

Staff Headmaster T R Cookson, 1 year in post.

Academic work GCSE and A-levels. 20 subjects offered (no A-level general studies). In 1990, 145 pupils in upper fifth, 134 in upper sixth. *GCSE:* in 1990, 124 upper fifth gained at least grade C in 8+ subjects; 21 in 5–7 subjects. *A-levels:* 14 upper sixth passed in 4 subjects; 111 in 3; 8 in 2 subjects. 63 took science A-levels; 71 arts/humanities. *Computing facilities:* A suite of 25 networked BBCs. 10 mobile facilities for use in other classrooms.

European Community *Languages:* French offered: to age 14; GCSE; A-level. German offered: to GCSE; A-level. Spanish offered: to GCSE; A-level. 25–50% take GCSE in more than 1 EC language. *Exchanges:* Regular exchanges for pupils aged 11–18 to France, Germany and Spain.

Careers In 1990, 92% leavers went on to degree courses; 5% straight into careers; 4% other. Of those going on to degree courses, 17% went to Oxbridge, 74% to other universities; 9% to poly/colleges. 1% those going on to higher education went to courses in practical art; $1/2$% in drama/acting; $1/2$% in music; 58% in humanities/social sciences; 4% in medicine; and 36% in science/engineering.

· *King Edward's (Witley)* ·

King Edward's School
Witley
Godalming
Surrey
GU8 5SG
Tel 042 879 2572

- Pupils 520
- Boys 11–18
  (Day/Board)
- Girls 11–18
  (Day/Board)
- Upper sixth 61

- Termly fees
  £1652 (Day)
  £2237 (Board)
- HMC
Enquiries to the Head
Application to the
Head's Secretary

What it's like

Founded in 1553 by King Edward VI, it was formerly at the Bridewell Palace and in 1867 moved to its present splendid site of 100 wooded acres near the Surrey/Sussex/Hampshire borders where it is easily accessible by road and rail. It retains strong links with the City and the Lord Mayor of London. The Bridewell Foundation is well endowed and several million pounds have been spent on facilities in the last 20 years. Now extremely well equipped in every respect. Pupils come from a wide social background. It is a C of E school and there is pronounced emphasis on religious instruction, and worship in its fine Victorian Gothic chapel. Academically it is quite distinguished and many sixth formers go on to degree courses. The music and art departments are tremendously strong. There is a good range of sport, games and activities and the school has an outstanding record in the Duke of Edinburgh's Award Scheme.

School profile

Pupils Age range 11–18; 520 pupils, 113 day (64 boys, 49 girls), 407 boarding (195 boys, 212 girls). Senior department 13–18, 404 pupils (204 boys, 200 girls). Main entry ages 11, 13 and into sixth. Very few are children of former pupils. *Transfer from maintained schools:* 50% main intake, plus 5% to sixth.

Entrance Own entrance exam used. Not oversubscribed. No special skills required. Parents not expected to buy text books; music (£60) extra. 15 assisted places. Boarding bursaries, few small forces bursaries, sixth form scholarship – £1740–£400.

Parents 15+% in industry or commerce; 15+% are doctors, lawyers, etc; 15+% in the armed services. 30+% live within 30 miles; 10+% live overseas.

Staff Head R J Fox. 46 full time staff, 21 part time. Annual turnover 5%. Average age 40.

Academic work GCSE and A-levels. 27 subjects offered (including A-level general studies). In 1990, 91 pupils in upper fifth, 61 in upper sixth. *GCSE:* in 1990, 60 upper fifth gained at least grade C in 8+ subjects; 24 in 5–7; and 6 in 1–4 subjects. *A-levels:* 28 upper sixth passed in 4+ subjects; 18 in 3; 10 in 2; and 8 in 1 subject. 30% took science A-levels; 55% arts/humanities; 15% both. *Computing facilities:* Large computer department; computers used in many departments; GCSE information technology.

European Community *Languages:* French offered: to age 14; GCSE; AS-level; A-level. German offered: to age 14; GCSE; AS-level; A-level. 10–25% take GCSE in more than 1 EC language. *Exchanges:* Regular exchanges for pupils aged 11–18 to France and Germany.

Senior pupils' non-academic activities *Music:* 72 learn a musical instrument or study singing, 27 to Grade 6 or above. 1 accepted for Music School; 3 for university music courses. 29 in school orchestra, 30+ in school choir, 2 in pop group, 10 in flute choir and saxophone and guitar group; 1 in Surrey Youth Orchestra, 6 in Holiday Youth Orchestra. *Drama and dance:* 30 in school productions. *Art:* 203 take as non-examined subject; 30–40 take GCSE; 12 study GCSE after school; 12+, A-level art (with art history); 40–50 take general studies in several media; 4–6 accepted for Art School; 52 in art clubs. *Sport:* Soccer, hockey, basketball, tennis, rounders, netball, swimming, squash, cricket, athletics, canoeing, shooting, badminton, etc available. Most take non-compulsory sport. 10 represent county/country (athletics, swimming). *Other:* 50 have bronze Duke of Edinburgh's Award; 4 silver and 17 gold. Other activities include a computer club, outside driving teachers, aerobics, pottery, cooking, etc.

Careers In 1990, 73% leavers went on to degree courses; 14% to art/drama/music colleges; 10% to non-degree courses (eg secretarial, travel and tourism, agriculture, hotel and catering); 3% straight into careers (eg banking, estate agency). Of those going on to degree courses, 1% went to Oxbridge, 59% to other universities; 40% to poly/colleges. 9% those going on to higher education went to courses in practical art; 1% in drama/acting; 1% in music; 35% in humanities/social sciences; and 37% in science/engineering.

Uniform School uniform worn throughout.

Houses/prefects Competitive houses. Prefects, head boy and girl, head of house and house prefects – elected by school, approved by Head. School Council.

Religion Religious worship compulsory.

Social Debates, contests, etc with other local schools. Organised trips to France and Germany. Pupils allowed to bring own bike to school. Meals self service. School shop. No tobacco/alcohol allowed.

Discipline No corporal punishment. Pupils failing to produce homework once might expect detention; those caught smoking cannabis on the premises could expect expulsion.

Boarding Sixth formers have own study bedroom; fifth formers share with one

397

other; only juniors are in dormitories of 6+. Single sex houses, of approximately 55, same as competitive houses. Resident qualified nurse. Central dining room. One overnight exeat every 3 weeks. Visits to local town allowed at weekends. **Alumni association** run by Mr P Whittle, c/o the School.

· King's (Bruton) ·

King's School
Bruton
Somerset
BA10 0ED
Tel 0749 813326

- Pupils 337
- Boys 13–18 (Day/Board)
- Girls 16–18 (Day/Board)
- Upper sixth 54

- Termly fees £1995 (Day) £2820 (Board)
- HMC
Enquiries/application to the Headmaster

What it's like

Founded in 1519, it occupies the original site in a very pretty small town (2000 inhabitants). The old school house (1519) is still in use. Modern buildings provide very good accommodation and the school is well equipped with modern facilities. Delightful playing fields adjoin it by the parish church. There are strong, long-standing links with the town and the parish. A balanced all-round education is provided within a strong Christian framework. Academic results are good and many sixth form leavers go on to university, polytechnic or college of higher education. The music, drama and art departments are very active. A good range of games and sports (a number of representatives at county level). A big commitment to local community schemes.

School profile

Pupils Age range 13–18; 337 pupils, 36 day (boys), 301 boarding (278 boys, 23 girls). Main entry ages 13 (boys) and into sixth (boys and girls). Approx 7–10% are children of former pupils. *Transfer from maintained schools:* 2% main intake, plus 3% to sixth.

Entrance Common entrance; other exam rarely used. Oversubscribed. No special skills or religious requirements but expected to attend C of E services. Parents not expected to buy text books; personal accident insurance (£4.05 per term) only compulsory extra. 2 assisted places pa at 13. 10 scholarships/bursaries, from half fees to £245.

Parents 15+% in industry or commerce. 30+% live within 30 miles.

Staff Headmaster A H Beadles, in post for 6 years. 32 full time staff. Annual turnover 3. Average age 36.

Academic work GCSE and A-levels.

14 GCSE subjects offered (no A-level general studies). In 1990, 67 pupils in upper fifth, 56 in upper sixth (now 54). *GCSE:* in 1990, 33 upper fifth gained at least grade C in 8+ subjects; 19 in 5–7; and 20 in 1–4 subjects. *A-levels:* 1 upper sixth passed in 4+ subjects; 27 in 3; 15 in 2; and 8 in 1 subject. 20% took science A-levels; 50% arts/humanities; 30% both. *Computing facilities:* 16 Booth Research machines, Nimbus system. *Special provision:* Learning difficulties unit for small number of pupils with mild dyslexia and to teach EFL.

European Community *Languages:* French offered: to GCSE; A-level. German offered: to GCSE; A-level. Italian: non-examined subject. Spanish offered: to GCSE. 10–25% take GCSE in more than 1 EC language. *Exchanges:* Regular exchanges for pupils aged 14–16 to France and Germany.

Senior pupils' non-academic activities *Music:* 110 learn a musical instrument, 12 to Grade 6 or above; 25 in school orchestra, 30 in school choir. *Drama and dance:* 120–160 in school productions. *Art:* 110 take as non-examined subject; 28 take GCSE; 6 take A-level. 30 do photography as an activity. *Sport:* Rugby, hockey, cricket, athletics, cross-country, tennis, swimming, basketball, judo, badminton, squash, fives, gymnastics, soccer, volleyball, indoor hockey and soccer available. 8 pupils represent county/country (athletics, hockey). *Other:* 35 take part in local community schemes. Other activities include a computer club, canoeing, pot holing, sailing, chess, riding, driving, etc.

Careers In 1990, 73% leavers went on to degree courses; 4% to art/drama/music colleges; 12% to non-degree courses (eg business, agriculture, catering, leisure, hotel management); 11% other. Of those going on to degree courses, 5% went to Oxbridge, 56% to other universities; 39% to poly/colleges. 7% those going on to higher education went to courses in practical art; 50% in humanities/social sciences; 5% in medicine; and 38% in science/engineering.

Uniform School uniform worn throughout.

Houses/prefects Competitive houses. Prefects, head boy/girl, head of house and house prefects – appointed by the Head and housemaster.

Religion Compulsory C of E services on Wednesday and Sunday.

Social Many organised local events, trips and exchanges abroad. Meals self service. School shop. No pupils allowed tobacco/alcohol.

Discipline No corporal punishment. Pupils failing to produce homework once would be treated according to teacher; those caught smoking cannabis on the premises might expect expulsion.

Boarding 15% have own study bedroom. 25% share with others, 60% in dormitories of 6+. Single sex houses, of 55–65, same as competitive houses. Resident qualified nurse; 2 doctors in town. Central dining room. 2 weekend exeats each term. Visits to the local town allowed.

Alumni association is run by J Tyndall, c/o the school.

· *King's (Canterbury)* ·

The King's School
Canterbury
Kent
CT1 2ES
Tel 0227 475501

- Pupils 705
- Boys 13–18
  (Day/Board)
- Girls 13–18
  (Day/Board)
- Upper sixth 180

- Termly fees
  £2170 (Day)
  £3100 (Board)
- HMC
  Enquiries/application to
  the Headmaster

What it's like

Founded in 597, the school was first a part of the 6th century Benedictine monastery. It has been associated with the cathedral for most of its life. Nearly all the buildings are in the cathedral precincts or at St Augustine's Abbey nearby. Many of them date from the middle ages, some belong to the 16th and 17th centuries. Thus, the school is blessed with an unusually civilised environment and some of the finest architecture in England. Modern facilities are first-class and include exceptionally good libraries, well-equipped laboratories and new sports centre. A very well run school, it reveals high standards in virtually every enterprise. Religious worship and instruction form an important part of the curriculum. Academically it is high-powered and achieves excellent results. Many sixth form leavers go on to degree courses, including many to Oxbridge. French and German are taught throughout the school and there are regular exchange arrangements with France and Germany. In addition, Spanish is taught to GCSE level, and Italian is offered as a non-examined subject. The music in the school is of outstanding quality and vigour. Drama is also very strong. Each year the school presents its own festival of music and drama which is attended by thousands. A wide variety of sports and games is available and standards are very high. Thirty or more clubs and societies cater for most extra–curricular activities. There is a flourishing CCF contingent and considerable emphasis on outdoor pursuits. A fine record in the Duke of Edinburgh's Award Scheme.

School profile

Pupils Age range 13–18; 705 pupils, 131 day (102 boys, 29 girls), 574 boarding (446 boys, 128 girls). Main entry ages 13 and into sixth (fully co-educational from 1990). Own junior school provides more than 20% of intake. *Transfer from maintained schools:* Minimal; 5% to sixth.

Entrance Common entrance and own sixth form entrance exam used. Sometimes oversubscribed. No special skills or religious requirements. Extras include account at school shop. Numerous academic, art and music awards.

Staff Headmaster Canon A C J Phillips, in post for 5 years. 80 full time staff, 5 part time. Annual turnover 5%.

Academic work GCSE and A-levels. 25 subjects offered (including Russian and A-level general studies). In 1990, 112 pupils in upper fifth, 180 in upper sixth. *GCSE:* in 1990, 87% upper fifth gained at least grade C in 8+ subjects. *A-levels:* 92% upper sixth passed in 3 or more subjects. *Computing facilities:* Excellent computing facilities, recently upgraded.

European Community *Languages:* French offered: to age 14; GCSE; A-level. German offered: to age 14; GCSE; A-level. Italian offered: to age 14; GCSE. Spanish offered: to age 14; GCSE; A-level. 50–75% take GCSE in more than 1 EC language. *Exchanges:* Regular exchanges for pupils aged 14–18 to France and Germany. *Other:* Membership of Europe Youth Parliament.

Senior pupils' non-academic activities *Sport:* Rugby, soccer, cricket, tennis, rowing, swimming, basketball, hockey, fencing, lacrosse, netball available. *Other:* Some pupils take part in local community schemes; some participate in Duke of Edinburgh's Award scheme. Other activities include a computer club, music, drama, crafts, debating, gardening, writing and literary appreciation, chess, printing, CCF etc.

Careers In 1990, 84% leavers went on to degree courses; 1% to art/drama/music colleges; 1% to non-degree courses (eg agriculture, business studies – mostly HNDs); 7% straight into careers (eg Lloyds, design, tree surgery, army, civil service, PR, banking); 7% other. Of those going on to degree courses, 20% went to Oxbridge, 67% to other universities; 13% to poly/colleges. 1% those going on to higher education went to courses in practical art; 1% in music; 68% in humanities/social sciences; 4% in medicine; and 26% in science/engineering.

Uniform School uniform worn throughout.

Houses/prefects Prefects (monitors), head boy and girl (captain of school and senior girl), house and house monitors – appointed by Headmaster and housemasters. Various school committees.

Religion Compulsory attendance at cathedral or other religious establishments on alternate Sundays.

Social Concerts, debates, dances, quiz programmes with other schools. Organised trips abroad. Pupils allowed to bring own bike to school. Meals self service. School shop. No tobacco/alcohol allowed.

Discipline No corporal punishment.

Boarding Single sex houses, of approximately 60. Resident qualified medical staff. Central dining room. Pupils can provide and cook own food on a small scale. Half-term plus 2–3 weekend exeats as required. Visits to local town allowed.

Alumni association run by Mr M Hodgson, Headmaster, St Martin's School, Northwood HA6 2DJ.

· King's (Chester) ·

The King's School
Wrexham Road
Chester
CH4 7QL
Tel 0244 680026

- Pupils 590
- Boys 8–18 (Day)
- Girls None
- Upper sixth 60

- Termly fees £1205 (Day)
- HMC

Enquiries/application to the Headmaster

What it's like

Founded in 1541, it was originally in the cathedral precinct. In 1960 it moved to a semi-rural site on the Wrexham Road, 1 mile from the city. This is an agreeable purpose-built establishment in 32 acres of grounds and playing fields. In 1989 new labs and classrooms, a music school, art room, sixth form centre, sports hall, kitchen, administration rooms. The junior school is combined. A C of E foundation, worship and religious instruction are of some importance. Very strong in music and drama. The academic standards are high and very many sixth formers go on to degree courses, including many to Oxbridge. French, German and Spanish are offered throughout the school and a high proportion of pupils takes GCSE in more than one EC language. A good range of sports and games and numerous extra-curricular activities. Quite a big commitment to local community services.

School profile

Pupils Total age range 8–18; 590 day boys. Senior department 11–18, 475 boys. Main entry ages 8, 9, 11 and into sixth.

Entrance Own entrance exam used. Oversubscribed. Pupils should have all-round intellectual ability; Anglican foundation but all denominations and creeds accepted. Parents not expected to buy text books. 100 assisted places. Several means-tested scholarships/bursaries.

Parents 15+% are doctors, lawyers etc. 90+% live within 30 miles.

Staff Headmaster A R D Wickson, in post for 10 years. 41 full time staff, 2 part time. Annual turnover 5%. Average age 26–50.

Academic work GCSE and A-levels. Average size of upper fifth 60+; upper sixth 60+. Most pass at least 7 GCSE and 3 A-levels. On average, 35 take science/ engineering A-levels; 15 take arts and humanities; 10, both. *Computing facilities:* A well-equipped computer room; several departments have their own computers. *Special provision:* Mildly visually handicapped pupils are assimilated into normal teaching groups.

European Community *Languages:* French offered: to age 14; GCSE; AS-level; A-level. German offered: to age 14; GCSE; AS-level; A-level. Spanish offered: to age 14; GCSE; AS-level; A-level. 25–50% take GCSE in more than 1 EC language.

Senior pupils' non-academic activities *Music:* 100–150 learn a musical instrument, 10 to Grade 6 or above, 1 or 2 accepted for Music School, 40 in school orchestras; 60 in school choirs. *Drama and dance:* Many in school productions. *Art:* About 6 take GCSE, 2 or 3 take A-level. 2 or 3 accepted for Art School. *Sport:* Rowing, soccer, hockey, basketball, table tennis, squash, swimming, athletics, cross-country, cricket, tennis available. Large numbers take non-compulsory sport. Several represent county/country (rowing, cricket, football). *Other:* 30 take part in community schemes. Lively chess club.

Careers In 1990, 89% leavers went on to degree courses; 1% to art/drama/ music colleges; 2% to non-degree courses; 3% straight into careers; 5% other. Of those going on to degree courses, 17% went to Oxbridge; 75% to other universities; 8% to poly/colleges.

44% those going on to higher education went to courses in humanities/social sciences; 10% in medicine; 42% in science/engineering; and 4% others.

Uniform School uniform worn throughout.

Houses/prefects No competitive houses. All sixth form perform prefectorial duties. Head boy appointed by the Headmaster with sixth form advice. Sixth form Council.

Religion Daily services, 4 cathedral services a year, plus voluntary communion services in school and cathedral.

Social A variety of activities with Queen's School eg debating society, Christian Union, Gilbert & Sullivan. Regular trips and exchanges abroad. Meals self service. No tobacco/alcohol allowed.

Discipline Pupils failing to produce homework once might expect a talking to; those caught smoking cannabis on the premises would be asked to leave immediately. Serious or repeated offences, are punished by community service of various sorts.

Former pupils Ronald Pickup; Nicholas Grace; others in academic or medical spheres.

· King's (Ely) ·

The King's School
Ely
Cambridgeshire
CB7 4DB
Tel 0353 662824

- Pupils 824
- Boys 4–18 (Day/ Board/Weekly)
- Girls 4–18 (Day/ Board/Weekly)
- Upper sixth 65

- Termly fees
  £1943 (Day)
  £2896 (Board)
  £2826 (Weekly)
- HMC
  Enquiries/application to the Admissions Secretary or Headmaster's Secretary

What it's like

Founded in 970, refounded in 1541 by Henry VIII, it has a superb position on the edge of one of the most beautiful cathedral cities in Europe. Much of the school is housed in the buildings of the old Benedictine monastery and these are of great architectural and historical interest. They include Prior Crauden's chapel, the 14th-century Monastic Barn (now the school dining hall), the Porta (gateway of the monastery) which is now the art centre, and the Norman Undercroft in School House which contains the library. Since 1960 there has been a massive development and modernisation programme which has included the creation of the Hayward Theatre. Facilities and accommodation are excellent. The school combines a kindergarten and a junior school, thus providing continuous education for boys and girls from 4–18. Ely is C of E orientated and pupils are expected to attend services. A high standard of teaching prevails and results are very good. Many sixth formers go on to degree courses, including Oxbridge. French, German and Spanish are offered at GCSE, AS-level and A-level and a high proportion of pupils takes more than one of them at GCSE. There are regular exchange arrangements with France, Germany and Spain but many children prefer to make their own family arrangements. Very strong indeed in music and drama. A wide range of sports and games (standards are high). A lot of emphasis on outdoor pursuits and adventure training. Full use is made of the city's facilities, and those of Cambridge, fifteen miles away.

School profile

Pupils Total age range 4–18; 824 pupils, 577 day (318 boys, 259 girls), 247 boarding (145 boys, 102 girls). Senior department 13–18, 405 pupils (220 boys, 185 girls). Main entry ages 4, 9, 11, 13 and into sixth. Approx 5% are children of former pupils (increasing). Own junior school provides more than 70% senior intake. *Transfer from maintained schools:* 25% intake at 11, plus a few at 13, 14 and into sixth.

Entrance Common entrance and own exam used. Oversubscribed. No special skills required. Church of England orientated school; pupils are expected to attend a school service. Parents buy text books; other extras include expeditions, music lessons etc. Many scholarships/bursaries, up to 50% fees.

Parents 30+% live within 30 miles; up to 10% live overseas.

Staff Headmaster H Ward, in post for 21 years. 70 full time staff, few part time. Annual turnover 5–10%. Average age about 40.

Academic work GCSE and A-levels. 15 GCSE subjects offered; 19 at A-level (general education course in sixth form, no A-level general studies). In 1990, 103 pupils in upper fifth, 62 in upper sixth (now 65). *GCSE:* in 1990, 71 upper fifth gained at least grade C in 8+ subjects; 22 in 5–7; and 8 in 1–4 subjects. *A-levels:* 7 upper sixth passed in 4+ subjects; 36 in 3; 12 in 2; and 4 in 1 subject. 25% took science A-levels; 51% arts/humanities; 24% both. *Computing facilities:* Computer centre plus computers in most departments. *Special provision:* none, to any extent.

European Community *Languages:* French offered: to age 14; GCSE; AS-level; A-level. German offered: to GCSE; AS-level; A-level. Italian offered: to AS-level. Spanish offered: to GCSE; AS-level; A-level. 25–50% take GCSE in more than 1 EC language. *Exchanges:* Regular exchanges for pupils aged 11–18 to France, Germany and Spain (many pupils prefer to make their own family arrangements).

Senior pupils' non-academic activities *Music:* 200 learn a musical instrument, 30 to Grade 6 or above. Several accepted for Music School. 25 in school orchestra, 40 in school choir, 10 in school pop group; occasional pupil in National Youth Orchestra. *Drama and dance:* 15–20 in school productions, 80–100 in house and form plays; 1 accepted for Drama/Dance School. *Art:* 20 take GCSE; 3–4, A-level. 1–2 accepted for Art School. *Sport:* Rugby, hockey, cricket, athletics, rowing, tennis, netball, rounders, sailing, swimming, squash, badminton, golf available. 10–12 represent county/country (rowing, rugby, cricket, hockey). *Other:* 25 have bronze Duke of Edinburgh's Award, several have silver. Other activities include a computer club, chess club, driving lessons can be arranged.

Careers In 1990, 75% leavers went on to degree courses; 1% to art/drama/music colleges; 17% to non-degree courses (eg technician, photographic); 5% straight into careers; 2% other. Of those going on to degree courses, 10% went to Oxbridge, 67% to other universities; 23% to poly/colleges. 2% those going on to higher education went to courses in practical art; 2% in music; 65% in arts/humanities/social sciences; 4% in medicine; and 27% in science/engineering.

Uniform School uniform worn on formal occasions; school dress on other occasions.

Houses/prefects Houses predominantly pastoral. Prefects, head of school and deputies, head of house and house prefects – some elected by fifth and sixth form, others appointed by the Headmaster or housemaster/mistress. Sixth form committee.

Religion 2 morning services per week. Sunday service for boarders.

Social Annual French exchange. Pupils allowed to bring own car/bike/motorbike to school. Some meals formal, some self service. School book and tuck shops. No tobacco/alcohol allowed.

Discipline No corporal punishment. Pupils failing to produce homework once may be put into detention; work-force for minor offences of behaviour; suspension for 1 week if more serious.

Boarding About 10 per house have own

study bedroom; most share with 2 or 3 others; few in dormitory of 6+. Single sex houses, of 40–50, same as competitive houses. Resident qualified nurse; doctor local. Central dining room. Pupils can provide and cook own snacks. Exeats each weekend (weekly boarding increasingly popular). Visits to local town allowed out of school time.

Alumni association is run by Hon Sec, Old Elean's Club, c/o the School.

· *King's (Gloucester)* ·

The King's School
Pitt Street
Gloucester
GL1 2BG
Tel 0452 21251

- Pupils 650
- Boys 4–18
  (Day/Board/Weekly)
- Girls 4–18
  (Day/Board/Weekly)
- Upper sixth 50

- Termly fees
  £1354 (Day)
  £2296 (Board)
  £2111 (Weekly)
- SHMIS, CSA
  Enquiries/application to
  the Headmaster

What it's like

The first reference to some kind of school attached to the cathedral dates from 1072. The present school was refounded by Henry VIII in 1541. It lies in the cathedral close in the middle of Gloucester and is a pleasant combination of ancient and modern buildings with good up-to-date facilities. It provides a sound general education in the context of the Christian faith. The cathedral is the spiritual and cultural centre of the school. Most days begin with worship in it. Its strong music dept has for its core the cathedral choristers who get free tuition. The drama dept is also active. Academically, results are good and many sixth form leavers go on to degree courses, including some to Oxbridge. A range of games and sports and an adequate number of clubs and societies. A good record in the Duke of Edinburgh's Award Scheme.

School profile

Pupils Total age range 4–18; 650 pupils, 574 day (410 boys, 164 girls), 76 boarding (69 boys, 7 girls). Senior department 11–18, 477 pupils (360 boys, 117 girls). Main entry ages 4, 11 and into sixth. Approx 20% are children of former pupils. Own junior school provides more than 50% of senior intake. *Transfer from maintained schools:* 50% senior intake, plus 10% to sixth.

Entrance Common entrance and own entrance exam used. Oversubscribed. Musical skills looked for. Parents expected to buy text books; maximum extras £100. 15 scholarships, for choristers, academic and music, full fees to 40%.

Parents 45+% in industry or commerce; 17% are doctors. 60+% live within 30 miles; 10% live overseas.

Staff Headmaster Rev Alan C Charters, in post for 8 years. 47 full time staff, 9 part time. Annual turnover 4%. Average age 36.

Academic work GCSE and A-levels. 17 subjects offered (including Greek; no A-level general studies). In 1991, 78 pupils in upper fifth, 50 in upper sixth. *GCSE:* in 1990, 37 upper fifth gained at least grade C in 8+ subjects; 19 in 5–7; and 13 in 1–4 subjects. *A-levels:* 4 upper sixth passed in 4+ subjects; 25 in 3; 14 in 2; and 9 in 1 subject. 40% took science A-levels; 30% arts/humanities; 30% both. *Computing facilities:* Computer centre; computers in most departments. *Special provision:* Mild dyslexia; 1 trained EFL teacher.

European Community *Languages:* French offered: to age 14; GCSE; AS-level; A-level. German offered: to age 14; GCSE; AS-level; A-level. 10–25% take GCSE in more than 1 EC language. *Exchanges:* Regular exchanges for pupils aged 11–16 to France. *Other:* French and German pupils in sixth form. Regular choir visit to Brittany.

Senior pupils' non-academic activities *Music:* 220 learn a musical instrument, 30+ to Grade 6 or above, 4 accepted for Music School; 65 in school orchestra, 90 in school choir, 12 in madrigal group, 6 in school pop group; 1 in National Youth Orchestra, 1 organ scholar, 1 choral scholar. *Drama and dance:* 15 in school productions, 30 in theatre workshops. *Art:* 35 take as non-examined subject; 6 take A-level; 4–5 accepted for Art School. 8 belong to photographic club. *Sport:* Rugby, hockey, rowing, cricket, athletics, cross-country, squash, tennis, basketball, netball, and rounders available, plus badminton and soccer. 50–60 take non-compulsory sport. 7–8 represent county/country (rugby, cross-country, hockey). *Other:* 25 have bronze Duke of Edinburgh's Award, 6 have silver. 3–4 enter voluntary schemes after leaving school. Other activities include computer and chess clubs, literary and debating society, theatre workshop, astronomy society and numerous smaller clubs.

Careers In 1990, 72% leavers went on to degree courses; 8% to art/drama/music colleges; 2% to non-degree courses (eg agriculture); 15% straight into careers (eg army, banking, building society); 5% other. Of those going on to degree courses, 7% went to Oxbridge, 56% to other universities; 27% to poly/colleges. 6% those going on to higher education went to courses in practical art; 6% in music; 38% in humanities/social sciences; and 45% in science/engineering.

Uniform School uniform worn throughout.

Houses/prefects Competitive houses. Prefects, head boy/girl, head of house and house prefects – appointed by the Head and housemasters. School Council.

Religion Compulsory daily worship in cathedral. Sunday morning service. Voluntary participation in cathedral services.

Social Joint theatre workshops, choral society productions, dances/discos with local girls' schools. Annual choir trip to Brittany, exchange with France (Metz), European trip (Iceland in 1989); Pyrenees annual climbing holiday. Pupils allowed to bring own car/bike/motorbike to school. Meals formal. School shop. No tobacco/alcohol allowed.

Discipline No corporal punishment. Pupils failing to produce homework once might expect to complete it by the next day; those caught smoking cannabis on the premises would be asked to leave.

Boarding Sixth formers have own study bedroom, fourth and fifth share with 1 or 2 others; only one dormitory has 6+. Single sex houses, of approximately 36, divided by age. Resident nurse; visiting doctor. Central dining room. Pupils can provide and cook a small amount of their own food. 2 exeats of 24 hours each term. Visits to the local town allowed.

Alumni association is run by The Secretary, The King's School Society, c/o the School.

Former pupils Terry Biddlecombe (champion jockey); Dr Herbert Sumsion (organist); Dr Donald Hunt (organist); Dr Bernard Wood (Professor of Anatomy); Ivan Lampkin (artist); Richard Shephard (composer).

· *King's (Macclesfield)* ·

The King's School
Cumberland Street
Macclesfield
Cheshire SK10 1DA
Tel 0625 22505

- Pupils 1030
- Boys 7–18 (Day)
- Girls 16–18 (Day)
- Upper sixth 146

- Termly fees
  £1155 (Day)
- HMC
  Enquiries/application to
  the School Secretary

What it's like

Founded in 1502, re-established in 1552 by Royal Charter of Edward VI, the school moved in 1855 to its present site in the centre of Macclesfield. It has attractive surroundings and the new developments include a very large library, a fine science block and Matchmaker artificial playing surface. The playing fields are on two sites and the junior school is combined. A strongly academic school, it lays considerable stress on the encouragement of pupils to develop confidence in their own judgement and to develop their own particular interests to the full within a broad and balanced curriculum. In a secure and supportive environment, the active involvement of parents is much encouraged. Academic standards are high and many leavers go on to degree courses, including many to Oxbridge. Very strong in music, drama and art. Wide range of sports and games (again standards are high) and activities. Substantial commitment to local community schemes.

School profile

Pupils Total age range 7–18; 1030 day pupils (950 boys, 80 girls). Senior department 11–18, 900 pupils (820 boys, 80 girls). Main entry ages 7–11, 13 (boys) and into sixth (boys and girls). Approx 15% are children of former pupils. Own junior provides about 50% senior intake. *Transfer from maintained schools:* 50% senior intake, plus 50% to sixth.

Entrance Common entrance (at 13) and own exam used (any age). Oversubscribed. Welcomes all talents; no religious requirements. Parents not expected to buy text books; maximum extras £50 per term (rare). 35 assisted places. 5 scholarships/bursaries pa, half fees to £300.

Parents 15+% in industry or commerce. 60+% live within 30 miles.

Staff Head A G Silcock, 4 years in post. 74 full time staff, 14 part time. Annual turnover 2%. Average age late thirties.

Academic work GCSE and A-levels. 18 GCSE and A-level subjects offered (A-level general studies rarely taken). In 1991, 145 pupils in fifth, 143 in upper sixth (now 140). *GCSE:* in 1990, 66 fifth gained at least grade C in 8+ subjects; 30 in 5–7; and 9 in 1–4 subjects. *A-levels:* 103 upper sixth passed in 3 subjects; 15 in 2; and 12 in 1 subject. 41 took science A-levels; 65 arts/humanities; 28 both. *Computing facilities:* Fully equipped laboratory with 24 stations. *Special provision:* Extra tuition in English in early years.

European Community *Languages:* French offered: to age 14; GCSE; A-level. German offered: to age 14; GCSE; A-level. Spanish: non-examined subject. 10–25% take GCSE in more than 1 EC language. *Exchanges:* Regular exchanges for pupils aged 14–18 to France and Germany.

Senior pupils' non-academic activities *Music:* 160 learn a musical instrument, 37 to Grade 6 or above, 2–3 accepted for Music School; 45 in school orchestra, 75 in school choir, 8 in school pop group; 1 in National Youth Orchestra, 12 in local orchestras/bands. *Drama and dance:* 70 in school productions; 20 take GCSE; 20 in theatre arts. *Art:* 55 take GCSE; 12 take A-level. 8 accepted for Art School. 10 in recreational art, 10 belong to eg photographic club, 10 in art club. Most

A-level art pupils are placed in foundation courses. *Sport:* Rugby, hockey, cricket, soccer, athletics, cross-country, swimming, badminton, tennis, squash, table tennis, sailing, orienteering, hill-walking, rock-climbing, caving, abseiling, basketball, netball, canoeing available. 300 take non-compulsory sport. 50 represent county (rugby, hockey, swimming, athletics, cricket, tennis, squash and table tennis). *Other:* 20–30 take part in local community schemes. Activities include a computer club, chess, ornithology, railways, debating, DIY, car maintenance, aviation, Christian Union, botany, historical society.

Careers In 1990, 67% leavers went on to degree courses; 5% to art/drama/music colleges; 12% to non-degree courses (eg BTEC, HND, agriculture); 5% straight into careers (eg armed forces, secretarial, banking, management trainee); 10% other, eg deferred entry. Of those going on to degree courses, 19% went to Oxbridge, 53% to other universities; 28% to poly/colleges. 5% those going on to higher education went to courses in practical art; $1/2$% in music; 44% in humanities/social sciences; 7% in medicine; and 43% in science/engineering.

Uniform School uniform worn except the sixth.

Houses/prefects No competitive houses. Prefects and head of school appointed by the Head.

Religion C of E worship encouraged.

Social No organised events with local schools. 5–6 foreign trips and exchanges per year. Pupils allowed to bring own car/bike/motorbike to school. Meals self service. School shop. No tobacco/alcohol allowed.

Discipline No corporal punishment. Pupils failing to produce homework once might expect to explain why; those caught smoking cannabis on the premises would probably expect expulsion.

Alumni association is run by P R Mathews, c/o the School.

Former pupils Alan Beith; Christian Blackshaw; Forbes Robinson; Steve Smith; Hewlett Johnson; Sir Arthur Smith Woodward; A A Golds; G G Hulme; F N Golding; E A Wrigley; Comm J R Porter; F E Knowles; G N Sanderson; C Booth; A Garner; R J Johnson; R J Hewitt.

· *King's (Rochester)* ·

King's School
Rochester
Kent
ME1 1TE
Tel 0634 843913

- Pupils 380
- Boys 13–18 (Day/Board/Weekly)
- Girls 16–18 (Day)
- Upper sixth 70

- Termly fees £1741 (Day) £2904 (Board/Weekly)
- HMC, CSA Enquiries/application to the Headmaster

What it's like

The school traces its foundation to the early 7th century, having been refounded after the dissolution of the monastery in 1542. It has a fine site in the precinct of the cathedral, close by the castle and very near the river Medway. The older buildings are very agreeable and there has been considerable expansion and modernisation since 1955 to produce excellent modern facilities. Naturally there are strong links with the cathedral and its life. Religious education is important in the curriculum. Attendance at services and chapel is compulsory. Academic standards are good and many leavers go on to degree courses each year. Strong music, art and drama depts. A wide range of sports and games (high standards achieved) and a good range of activities. A vigorous CCF and a lively commitment to local community services.

School profile

Pupils Age range 13–18; 380 pupils, 320 day (280 boys, 40 girls), 60 boarding boys. Main entry ages 13 (boys) and into sixth (boys and girls).

Entrance Common entrance and own exam used. No special skills or religious requirements. Parents not expected to buy text books. 54 assisted places. 83 scholarships/bursaries, £1000 to £70 per term.

Parents 15+% are doctors, lawyers, etc; 15+% in industry or commerce. 60+% live within 30 miles; up to 10% live overseas.

Staff Headmaster Dr I R Walker, in post for 4 years. 41 full time staff, 12 part time. Annual turnover 2%. Average age 40.

Academic work GCSE and A-levels. 17 subjects offered (no A-level general studies). In 1990, 75 pupils in upper fifth, 70 in upper sixth. *GCSE:* in 1990, 36 upper fifth gained at least grade C in 8+ subjects; 28 in 5–7; and 11 in 1–4 subjects. *A-levels:* 12% upper sixth passed in 4+ subjects; 62% in 3; 13% in 2; and 4% in 1 subject. 15 took science A-levels; 50 arts/humanities; 5 both. *Computing facilities:* Computer centre – Nimbus network.

European Community *Languages:* French offered: to age 14; GCSE; A-level. German offered: to age 14; GCSE; A-level. 25–50% take GCSE in more than 1 EC language. *Exchanges:* Regular exchanges for pupils aged 16–18 to France and Germany. *Other:* Number of German pupils spend 2–3 terms in school; plans for pupils to spend similar period in German boarding school. Long weekend pupil (and teacher) exchanges with Deutsche Schule in London planned. Number of contacts with eg ministries in Germany, EC bodies; visits to eg European School in Culham, Deutsche Schule in London and various schools in the Netherlands.

Senior pupils' non-academic activities *Music:* 60 learn a musical instrument, 40 to Grade 6 or above. 3 accepted for Music School, 30 in school orchestra, 28 in school choir, 15 in instrument groups, 2 in Kent Youth Orchestra, 1 in Rochester Arts Orchestra, 4 play in pop group. *Drama and dance:* 120 in school productions. 1 accepted for Drama/Dance school. 10 entered competitions. *Art:* 60 take as non-examined subject; 20 take GCSE; 10 take A-level. 2 accepted for Art School, 3 for foundation course. 10 belong to photographic club. *Sport:* Boys; Rugby, hockey, cricket, fencing, rowing, athletics, basketball, badminton, squash, tennis, swimming, shooting, cross-country available. Girls; Hockey, netball, rowing, tennis, athletics, swimming and fencing. Most take non-compulsory sport. 12 represent county/country (rugby, hockey, cricket, fencing). *Other:* 54 take part in local community schemes. 1 enters volunteer scheme after leaving school. Other activities include a computer club, debating, geographical, art, historical, Christian Fellowship, chess, technical, ornithology, law, jazz and science societies.

Careers In 1990, 72% leavers went on to degree courses; 1% to art/drama/music colleges; 11% to non-degree courses (eg agriculture, computer studies, business administration); 16% straight into careers (eg armed forces, insurance). Of those going on to degree courses, 4% went to Oxbridge, 57% to other universities; 39% to poly/colleges. 4% those going on to higher education went to courses in practical art; 2% in drama/acting; 2% in music; 59% in humanities/social sciences; 4% in medicine; and 29% in science/engineering.

Uniform School uniform worn throughout.

Houses/prefects Competitive houses. Prefects, head boy/girl, head of house and house prefects – appointed by the Head after vote/consultation.

Religion Compulsory C of E services and chapel.

Social Organised local events including theatre/music, etc. Organised trips to France, Germany and Russia. Pupils allowed to bring own car/bike to school. Meals self service. School shop. No tobacco/alcohol allowed.

Discipline No corporal punishment. Pupils failing to produce homework once

might expect a verbal warning; detention system; anyone involved with drugs can expect expulsion.

Boarding 20% have own study bedroom, 80% share with others; all in one house. Resident qualified nurse. Central dining room. Pupils can provide and cook own food. 4 weekend exeats each term. Visits to the local town allowed after school.

Alumni association is run by Mr J A

Clay, Greenmount, White Post Lane, Cobham, Gravesend, Kent DA13 9AX.

Former pupils John Selwyn Gummer; Richard Dadd (artist); Russell Thorndike (novelist); Percy Whitlock (composer); Sir H A Atkinson (PM of New Zealand); Sir Francis Head KCH (privy councillor); Dinsdale Landen (actor); Sir Lionel Dakers (composer); Clive King (children's author).

· King's (Taunton) ·

King's College	● Pupils 475	● Termly fees
South Road	● Boys 13–18	£2150 (Day)
Taunton	(Day/Board)	£2880 (Board)
Somerset	● Girls 13–18	● HMC, Woodard
TA1 3DX	(Day/Board)	Enquiries/application to
Tel 0823 272708	● Upper sixth 104	the Headmaster

What it's like

Its historical links go back to the medieval grammar school which was refounded by Bishop Fox of Winchester in 1522. In 1869 it was moved from what are now the municipal buildings in Taunton to its present site half a mile south of the city. It is the oldest school in the Western Division of the Woodard Corporation, and stands in a well wooded and spacious setting of 110 acres. There are fine playing fields and splendid views of the Blackdown and Quantock Hills. All told, a very attractive and civilised environment. There is a prep and pre-prep school, King's Hall, housed in a handsome Georgian mansion north of the city. A lot of excellent facilities have been added in recent years and the school is very well equipped. The chapel and its services are an integral part of school life and religious education plays an important part. A full range of academic subjects is available, the teaching is good and standards and results are high. Many leavers go on to degree courses each year. Music, drama and art are very strong indeed. Full use is made of the two theatres and there are excellent art and design and CDT centres which produce impressive results. Much use is made, too, of a sophisticated video production unit. Facilities for sports and games are first-rate and there is a high standard of performance (numerous representatives at county and regional level; 4 international rugby caps in recent years). Many clubs and societies cater for most extra–curricular activities. The CCF is a flourishing contingent and there is a good deal of emphasis on outdoor pursuits. A large number of pupils are involved in local community services.

School profile

Pupils Age range 13–18; 475 pupils, 60 day boys, 415 boarders (372 boys, 43 girls). Main entry age 13 and into the sixth (boys and girls; fully co-educational since 1991). 5% are children of former pupils. *Transfer from maintained schools:* 2% main intake, plus 6% to sixth.

Entrance Common entrance and own

entrance scholarship used. Oversubscribed. No special skills or religious requirements although Anglican foundation. Parents not expected to buy text books. 20 academic and music scholarships/bursaries pa at 13 and sixth form, £8640–£1440.

Parents 15+% in the armed services, 15+% doctors, lawyers, etc. 10+% live within 30 miles; 10+% live overseas.

Staff Headmaster R S Funnell, 3 years in post. 52 full time staff, 2 part time. Annual turnover 5%. Average age 35.

Academic work GCSE and A-levels. 20 subjects offered (including social biology, classical civilisation, economics; no A-level general studies). In 1990, 93 pupils in upper fifth, 110 in upper sixth (now 104). *GCSE:* in 1990, 67 upper fifth gained at least grade C in 8+ subjects; 17 in 5–7; and 9 in 1–4 subjects. *A-levels:* 3 upper sixth passed in 4+ subjects; 77 in 3; 19 in 2; and 10 in 1 subject. 33 took science A-levels; 41 arts/humanities; 36 both. *Computing facilities:* Computer department; other computers in academic departments and houses. CAD/CAM facilities in CDT centre. *Special provision:* EFL tuition available. Arrow learning system.

European Community *Languages:* French offered: to age 14; GCSE; A-level. German offered: to age 14; GCSE; A-level. Spanish offered: to age 14; GCSE; AS-level; A-level. 10–25% take GCSE in more than 1 EC language. *Exchanges:* Regular exchanges for pupils aged 14–18 to France, Germany and Spain. *Other:* French, German and Spanish pupils in school full-time; hosting groups of French pupils (from Bordeaux and Normandy) for 2–3 weeks.

Senior pupils' non-academic activities *Music:* 110 learn a musical instrument, 60 to Grade 6 or above; 4 pa accepted for Music School. 40 pupils play in school orchestra, 50 in choir, 80 in choral society, 10 in school pop group, 40 in wind band, 10 in school string orchestra. 2 on Eton Choral course, 5 in County Youth Orchestra. *Drama and dance:* 250 involved in school and house productions; 2 accepted for Drama/Dance Schools; 3 go on to work in theatre, 2 in TV. *Art:* 15 take art as non-examined subject, 35 take GCSE; 20 A-level. 6 accepted for Art School. 80 belong to eg photographic club. *Sport:* Rugby football, hockey, cricket, squash, tennis, fencing, swimming, water polo, athletics, cross-country running, association football, badminton, basketball, shooting, canoeing, sailing available. All pupils take part in a variety of sports, eg gymnastics. 4 international rugby caps in last 5 years. Numerous county/regional representatives (rugby, cricket, tennis, cross-country, athletics, squash). *Other:* 285 in CCF. 70 in local community schemes. 20 enter voluntary schemes after leaving school; 5 work for national charities. Other activities include a computer club, video studio, CCF (including rock climbing, parachuting, Marines, power boating), debating, music, drama, chess; driving lessons by arrangement.

Careers In 1990, 75% leavers went on to degree courses; 6% to art/drama/music colleges; 3% to non-degree courses (eg HND agriculture, rural land management); 2% straight into careers; 14% other. Of those going on to degree courses, 5% went to Oxbridge, 55% to other universities; 40% to poly/colleges. 6% those going on to higher education went to courses in practical art; 1% in drama/acting; 3% in music; 60% in humanities/social sciences; 5% in medicine; and 25% in science/engineering.

Uniform School uniform worn, except in sixth.

Houses/prefects Competitive houses. Head boy; heads of houses and house prefects; prefects (selected after going on a training scheme) – all appointed by the Head.

Religion Compulsory services on two weekdays and on Sundays. Voluntary candlelit communion weekly.

Social Science weekends of lectures and seminars, historical association meetings, general knowledge competitions, debates, geographical meetings. Exchanges and trips to France, Belgium, Germany and Spain. Organised trips to rain forests of Sierra Leone, South America, India, Russia, Israel, Egypt, Greece, Italy. Pupils allowed to bring own bike to school. Meals self service. School shop. No tobacco/alcohol allowed; there is a senior social club open on particular evenings.

Discipline No corporal punishment. Pupils failing to produce homework once would be expected to produce it as soon as possible; those caught smoking cannabis on the premises could expect immediate expulsion. The school takes a specially strong line on stealing, bullying and all forms of drugs.

Boarding 25% have own study bedroom, 20% share (with 1 other); 55% are in dormitories of 6+. Single sex houses, of approx 60, same as for competitive purposes. Resident qualified sister; non-resident doctor. Central dining room. Pupils can provide and cook snacks. 1–2 weekend exeats per term, Sunday exeats after chapel. Visits to local town allowed 2 afternoons a week – all ages; Saturday nights – sixth form.

Alumni association is run by B Sykes, c/o the School.

Former pupils Lord Rippon PC; Professor Anthony Hewish (Nobel prize winner); Simon Jones (actor – *Brideshead Revisited*); Ian Smith (BBC *Newsnight*); Gerald Butt (BBC Jerusalem correspondent).

· *King's (Warwick)* ·

King's High School for Girls
Smith Street
Warwick CV34 4HJ
Tel 0926 494485

- Pupils 550
- Boys None
- Girls 11–18 (Day)
- Upper sixth 57

- Termly fees £915 (Day)
- GSA

Enquiries/application to the Headmistress

What it's like

Founded in 1879, it has an interesting urban site in the town of Warwick, near Warwick Preparatory School and the Warwick School for Boys. It is particularly fortunate in its beautiful buildings which span 600 years and include the town's Eastgate. A sound general academic education is provided and results are impressive. Very many sixth formers go on to degree courses each year, including Oxbridge. There is a new language centre. French, German and Spanish are offered at GCSE, AS-level and A-level. A high proportion of girls takes more than one European language at GCSE and there are regular exchange arrangements with France and Germany. Music and drama are particularly well supported. There is a fine range of sports and games (in which high standards are attained) and a good variety of clubs and societies. Joint events with the boys' school are frequent. A feature of the school is its vigorous participation in local community schemes.

School profile

Pupils Age range 11–18; 550 day girls. Main entry ages 11 and into sixth. 4–5% are children of former pupils. Warwick Prep provides 20% pupils. *Transfer from maintained schools:* 50% intake at 11 and into sixth.

Entrance Own entrance exam used. Oversubscribed. No special skills or religious requirements. Parents not expected to buy text books. 220 assisted places. 9 scholarships/bursaries (at 11 and 16), 50% fees.

Parents 15+% in education, 15+% in industry. 60+% live within 30 miles.

Staff Head Mrs J M Anderson, in post for 4 years. 37 full time staff, 13 part time. Annual turnover 6%. Average age 40.

Academic work GCSE and A-levels. 16 GCSE subjects offered; 19 at A-level (including Russian and Greek; general studies taught in sixth form, but A-level not taken). In 1990, 79 pupils in upper fifth, 57 in upper sixth. *GCSE:* in 1990, 79 upper fifth gained at least grade C in 8+ subjects; 3 in 5–7; and 2 in 1–4 subjects. *A-levels:* 51 upper sixth passed in 3 subjects; 7 in 2 subjects. 33% took science A-levels; 33% arts/humanities; 33% both. *Computing facilities:* RML Nimbus network.

European Community *Languages:* French offered: to age 14; GCSE; AS-level; A-level. German offered: to GCSE; AS-level; A-level. Spanish offered: to GCSE; AS-level; A-level. 25–50% take GCSE in more than 1 EC language. *Exchanges:* Regular exchanges for pupils aged 14–16 to France and Germany. *Other:* New language centre (opened by MEP, Sir Henry Plumb).

Senior pupils' non-academic activities *Music:* 90 learn a musical instrument, 11 take GCSE, 3 take A-level, 45 take Associated Board, 10 take part in 6th form musical activities. Orchestra, string orchestra, choir, madrigal group, chamber ensembles and wind band provide opportunities for all. *Drama and dance:* 50+ in school productions. *Art:* 27 take GCSE; 4 A-level; 2 accepted for Art School. 10 take sixth form art activities; lunch-time art club. *Sport:* Athletics, netball, hockey, rounders, tennis, gymnastics, dance available, plus badminton, golf, table tennis, basketball, volleyball for sixth. 70 take part in non-compulsory sport. 12 pupils represent county (hockey, swimming, netball). *Other:* Duke of Edinburgh's Award Scheme. 100 in local community schemes. Other activities include a computer club,

science clubs (inc electronic and radio), religious affairs discussion group, classical society, modern languages society, Russian and chess clubs, debating society.

Careers In 1990, 91% leavers went on to degree courses; 3% to art/drama/music colleges; 2% to non-degree courses; 4% straight into careers (eg accountancy, physiotherapy). Of those going on to degree courses, 9% went to Oxbridge, 68% to other universities; 23% to poly/colleges. 3% those going on to higher education went to courses in practical art; 2% in music; 52% in humanities/social sciences; 9% in medicine; and 34% in science/engineering.

Uniform School uniform worn except in sixth (own clothes within guide lines).

Houses/prefects No competitive houses. Prefects, head girl – elected by staff and school. School Council.

Religion Christian and/or inter-denominational assembly daily – not compulsory but all girls choose to attend.

Social BAYS with sixth formers from local schools; joint music, drama, discussion group, expeditions, social with Warwick Boys' School. Regular trips to Russia, ski-ing, exchange visits with French, German, Russian and American schools. Pupils allowed to bring own car/bike/motorbike to school. Meals self service. No tobacco/alcohol allowed.

Discipline No corporal punishment.

Alumni association is run by Mrs J Duffy, 35 Cliffe Way, Warwick.

Former pupils Kim Hartman (Helga in *'Allo 'Allo*); Dr Barbara Ansell (specialist in rheumatology, MRC); Harriet Castor (children's author).

· *King's (Wimbledon)* ·

King's College School
South Side
Wimbledon Common
London SW19 4TT
Tel 081 947 9311

- Pupils 670
- Boys 13–18
  (Day)
- Girls None
- Upper sixth 132

- Termly fees
  £1495 (Day)
- HMC
Enquiries/application to
the Registration
Secretary

What it's like

Founded in 1829, originally in the Strand, it moved to its present site at the end of the 19th century and occupies 17 acres of grounds on the south side of Wimbledon Common in a very pleasant residential area. Good playing fields; a further 15 acres of fields at West Barnes Lane. Junior and Senior Schools share the same campus. Well-designed and comfortable buildings provide first-rate facilities. High standards are expected in work and behaviour. Integrity and tolerance are regarded as important qualities. A well-run school, it has strong academic traditions. Very many leavers go to Oxbridge; three-quarters of the rest go to degree courses. European languages on offer include at various levels French, German, Modern Greek, Italian and Spanish. A high proportion of boys takes more than one European language at GCSE and there are regular exchanges arranged with France, Germany and Spain. In 1990, a group of sixth formers represented the UK in the fifth session of the European Youth Parliament in Lisbon. Very strong music, drama and art depts. A very good range of sports and games (high standards are achieved) and a large number of activities. There is considerable emphasis on outdoor pursuits and the CCF is a flourishing contingent.

School profile

Pupils Age range 13–18; 670 day boys. Main entry ages 13 and into sixth. Own junior school provides about 60% of intake. *Transfer from maintained schools:* 100% intake to junior school at 11, 1% main intake at 13, 40% to sixth.

Entrance Common entrance used. Oversubscribed. Academic scholarships for music, classics, and modern languages. C of E school but boys not required to be of any particular persuasion. Parents expected to buy text books but is a loan scheme; maximum extras lunches (£90), books and stationery (£40). 8 assisted places pa. Up to 12 scholarships, 50% to 10% of fees.

Parents 15+% in the theatre, media, music, etc; 15+% are doctors, lawyers; 15+% in industry or commerce.

Staff Headmaster R M Reeve, in post for 11 years. 70 full time staff, 3 part time. Annual turnover 5%. Average age 38.

Academic work GCSE, AS and A-levels. 20 GCSE and A-level subjects offered (no A-level general studies). In 1991, 131 pupils in upper fifth, 132 in upper sixth. *GCSE:* in 1990, 130 upper fifth gained at least grade C in 8+ subjects; 1 in 5–7; and 1 in 1–4 subjects. *A-levels:* 25 upper sixth passed in 4+ subjects; 101 in 3; 5 in 2; and 1 in 1 subject. 32 took science and maths A-levels; 48 arts/humanities; 43 both. *Computing facilities:* 30 BBC computers of various sorts, mostly networked using Amcom E-Net.

European Community *Languages:* French offered: to age 14; GCSE; AS-level; A-level. German offered: to age 14; GCSE; A-level. Greek (modern) offered: to age 14; GCSE; A-level. Italian offered: to GCSE. Spanish offered: to age 14; GCSE; A-level. 50–75% take GCSE in more than 1 EC language. *Exchanges:* Regular exchanges for pupils aged 13–16

413

to France, Germany and Spain. *Other:* 13 sixth formers represented UK at European Youth Parliament in Lisbon, November 1990.

Senior pupils' non-academic activities *Music:* 166 learn a musical instrument, 104 to Grade 6 or above; 60 in school orchestra, 32 in school choir, 40 in wind band; 2 in Stoneleigh Orchestra. *Drama and dance:* 75 in school productions. 1 accepted for Drama/Dance Schools; 1 now works in theatre. *Art:* 10 take as non-examined subject; 110 take GCSE; 10 take A-level. 4 accepted for Art School. *Sport:* Rugby, hockey, cricket, athletics, archery, badminton, basketball, cross-country, fencing, golf, rowing, sailing, shooting, soccer, squash, swimming, table tennis and tennis available. 300 take non-compulsory sport. 100 take exams eg swimming. 22 represent county (rugby, hockey, cricket and cross-country). *Other:* Chess, computer, debating, English and history societies.

Careers In 1990, 87% leavers went on to degree courses; 2% to art/drama/ music colleges; 9% to non-degree courses; 1% straight into careers. Of those going on to degree courses, 21% went to Oxbridge, 71% to other universities; 8% to poly/colleges.

Uniform School uniform worn; dark suit in sixth form.

Houses/prefects Competitive houses. Prefects, head boy, head of house and house prefects – recommended by committee of housemasters for approval by Headmaster. School Council.

Religion 3 religious assemblies plus one divinity period per week; opting out is possible.

Social Joint debating union with Wimbledon High. Girls recruited from local schools for theatrical productions. Trips and exchanges abroad. Pupils allowed to bring own car/bike/motorbike to school. Meals self service. School shop. No tobacco/alcohol allowed.

Discipline No corporal punishment. Pupils failing to produce homework once might expect a prefect-supervised period at lunchtime; those caught smoking cannabis on the premises might expect to be asked to leave.

Alumni association is run by Alan Wells, Secretary, Old King's Club.

Former pupils Roy Plomley; Alvar Liddell; Jimmy Edwards; Richard Pascoe; Tim Luscombe.

· *King's (Worcester)* ·

The King's School	● Pupils 858	● Termly fees
Worcester	● Boys 7–18	£1480 (Day)
WR1 2LH	(Day/Board)	£2428 (Board)
Tel 0905 23016	● Girls 7–18	● HMC
	(Day/Board)	Enquiries to the
	● Upper sixth 134	Headmaster
		Application to the
		Headmaster's
		Secretary

What it's like

Refounded in 1541 by Henry VIII, it comprises an enclave of very fine buildings grouped round College Green on the south side of the cathedral and on the banks of the Severn. The oldest structure is the 14th-century College Hall. There are many 17th, 18th and 19th-century buildings and a large number of modern ones, all in fine grounds and gardens. The Junior School occupies separate premises, St Albans, in its own grounds near the main school. Academic standards are very high and the teaching is good. Very many go on to degree courses including many to Oxbridge. French, German and Spanish are offered throughout the school and there are regular exchange arrangements with France, Germany and Spain. Spanish is also offered as a non-examined subject. Basic Christian ethics and doctrine are taught and the cathedral is an important part of the school's life. A very strong music dept which gains much from its association with the cathedral. Strong, too, in art and drama (9 or 10 productions each year). Excellent sport and games and an enormous range of activities. The CCF is vigorous. A fair commitment to local community schemes and to the Duke of Edinburgh's Award Scheme.

School profile

Pupils Total age range 7–18; 858 pupils, 738 day (658 boys, 80 girls), 120 boarding (104 boys, 16 girls). Senior department 11–18, 706 pupils (626 boys, 80 girls). Main entry ages 7, 8, 11, 13 and into sixth (boys and girls); fully co-educational from 1991. Approx 20% are children of former pupils. *Transfer from maintained schools:* 80% at 11, 20% at 13, 30% to sixth.

Entrance Own entrance exam used; some admission by common entrance. Oversubscribed. No special skills or religious requirements. Parents not expected to buy text books. 34 assisted places pa. 20 scholarships/bursaries, half fees to £475.

Parents 60+% live within 30 miles; up to 10% live overseas.

Staff Headmaster Dr J M Moore, in post for 7 years. 61 full time staff, 7 part time. Annual turnover 7%.

Academic work GCSE and A-levels. 17 GCSE subjects offered; 22 at A-level (no A-level general studies). In 1990, 100 pupils in upper fifth, 134 in upper sixth. *GCSE:* in 1990, 75% upper fifth gained at least grade C in 8+ subjects; 21% in 5–7; and 4% in 1–4 subjects. *A-levels:* 10% upper sixth passed in 4+ subjects; 87% in 3; 2% in 2; and 1% in 1 subject. 30% took science A-levels; 40% arts/humanities; 30% both. *Computing facilities:* Computers in all departments. *Special provision:* Mildly visually handicapped accepted. EFL taught. (No provision for dyslexia.)

European Community *Languages:* French offered: to age 14; GCSE; A-level. German offered: to age 14; GCSE; A-level. Italian offered: to GCSE. Spanish offered: to age 14; GCSE; A-level. 10–25% take GCSE in more than 1 EC language. *Exchanges:* Regular exchanges for pupils aged 14–18 to France, Germany and Spain.

Senior pupils' non-academic activities *Music:* 300 learn a musical instrument, many to Grade 6 or above, few accepted for Music School, some go on to play in pop group; 90 in school orchestra, 100 in school choir, 8–14 in school pop group; occasional pupil in National Youth Orchestra, 22 choristers in cathedral choir. Much other musical activity. *Drama and dance:* Many pupils in school productions, 9 or 10 productions a year, school/house/group plays. *Art:* Many take as non–examined subject; 30 take GCSE; 8 take A-level. A few accepted for Art School. 20 belong to photography club. *Sport:* Rugby, football, hockey, rowing, cricket, athletics, badminton, canoeing, cross-country running, fencing, fives, sailing, squash, swimming and tennis available. Very many take non-compulsory sport. A lot of pupils represent county/country (eg rugby, cricket, rowing, canoeing, tennis, fencing, hockey, netball, pentathlon). *Other:* 10–20 take part in local community schemes. 20+ have silver Duke of Edinburgh's Award, 5 have gold. Some enter voluntary schemes after leaving school. Other activities include a computer club, craft workshop, swimming club, nature club, chess club, .22 rifle shooting, model engineering, drama workshop, wind band, Christian Union, literary society, Keys Society, debates, printing, ice skating, rock climbing, cinema club, theatre visits, golf, basketball, dry ski-ing, rounders, sub-aqua and confirmation classes.

Careers In 1990, 94% leavers went on

to degree courses; 2% to art/drama/ music colleges; 4% straight into careers. Of those going on to degree courses, 12% went to Oxbridge, 78% to other universities; 10% to poly/colleges. 1% those going on to higher education went to courses in drama/acting; 6% in music; 60% in humanities/social sciences; 8% in medicine; and 25% in science/ engineering.

Uniform School uniform worn except upper sixth.

Houses/prefects Pastoral rather than competitive houses. Prefects, head boy/ girl, head of house and house prefects – appointed by the Head.

Religion Worship is encouraged.

Social No organised local events.

French/German/Spanish exchanges, skiing trips, geography field trips, other trips to Italy, France and Spain. Pupils allowed to bring own car/bike/motorbike to school. Some meals formal, some self service. School shop. No tobacco/alcohol allowed.

Discipline No corporal punishment.

Boarding Seniors in own or shared studies; juniors in dormitories of 6+. Single sex houses are pastoral units, approx 35, divided by age group. Resident qualified nurse. Central dining room. Pupils can provide and cook their own food. Regular exeats usually of 36 hours. Visits to local town allowed.

Alumni association is run by Mr M R Craze, c/o the School.

· *Kingsley* ·

The Kingsley School
Beauchamp Avenue
Leamington Spa
Warwickshire
CV32 5RD
Tel 0926 425127

- Pupils 561
- Boys None
- Girls 3–18 (Day)
- Upper sixth 40

- Termly fees £990 (Day)
- GSA

Enquiries/application to the Admissions Secretary

What it's like

Founded in 1884 by Rose Kingsley, daughter of the writer Charles Kingsley and by Joseph Wood, who became Headmaster of Harrow. Its present site on Beauchamp Avenue is close to the centre of the elegant Regency spa town. The senior school is in Beauchamp Hall (a fine listed building). A separate building – Dilke House – accommodates the junior school and there is a well-equipped sixth form centre at Claremont House. The school has close links with Holy Trinity church and candidates may be prepared for confirmation. However, other faiths are welcomed. It enjoys a favourable staff:pupil ratio of about 1:12 and provides a sound general education. Academic standards are good and results creditable. Each year a number of girls go on to degree courses. French, German and Spanish are offered to GCSE and a high proportion of girls take more than one GCSE in a European language. French is offered at AS-level and both French and German at A-level. There are regular exchange arrangements with France and Germany. There is a fair amount of musical and dramatic activity (plays are regularly presented in conjunction with Warwick Boys' School). Sports and games are well catered for, and include (apart from the usual range) Olympic gymnastics and show jumping. Regular representation by pupils at county level; the show jumping team have twice won the National Schools' Championship at Hickstead. There is a wide variety of clubs and societies and substantial commitment to the Duke of Edinburgh's Award Scheme (many silver and gold awards), which involves community services and expeditions in Britain and overseas.

School profile

Pupils Total age range 3–18; 561 girls. Senior department 11–18, 415 girls. Main entry ages 3, 8, 11 and into sixth. Approx 10% are children of former pupils. *Transfer from maintained schools:* 25% main intake at 11, plus 5% to sixth.

Entrance Own entrance exam used. Often oversubscribed. No special skills or religious requirements. Standard charge for text books; maximum extras usually £65. 5 assisted places. 4 scholarships/bursaries pa, £1500–£500.

Parents 15+% in industry or commerce; 15+% are doctors, lawyers, etc; 15+% in farming.

Staff Headmistress Mrs M A Webster, in post for 3 years. 32 full time staff, 20 part time. Annual turnover 5%. Average age 40.

Academic work GCSE and A-levels; RSA, Pitman and Teeline. 27 GCSE subjects offered (including Latin, Greek, PE, Spanish, drama and separate sciences); 21 at A-level (including theatre studies, business studies and general studies). In 1990, 69 pupils in upper fifth, 30 in upper sixth (now 40). *GCSE:* in 1990, 33 upper fifth gained at least grade C in 8+ subjects; 23 in 5–7; and 13 in 1–4 subjects. *A-levels:* 14 upper sixth passed in 4 subjects; 7 in 3; 6 in 2; and 2 in 1 subject. 50% took science A-levels; 25% arts/humanities; 25% both. *Computing facilities:* Access to computers at all levels. *Special provision:* Lessons for dyslexic pupils.

European Community *Languages:* French offered: to age 14; GCSE; AS-level; A-level. German offered: to age 14; GCSE; A-level. Spanish offered: to GCSE. 25–50% take GCSE in more than 1 EC language. *Exchanges:* Regular exchanges for pupils aged 11–16 to France and Germany.

Senior pupils' non-academic activities *Music:* 35 learn a musical instrument, 15 to Grade 6 or above. 30 in senior choirs, 25 in school orchestra and other musical groups. *Drama and dance:* 18 in school productions; 30 take LAMDA, 25 Associated Board exams. 1 in National Youth Theatre. *Art:* 6 take as non-examined subject, 6 take GCSE; 6 A-level. 4 accepted for Art School. *Sport:* Fencing, golf, badminton, tennis, aerobics, hockey, swimming, squash, judo, ballroom dancing available. All pupils take sport. 5% take exams. *Other:* Many pupils take part in local community schemes. In 1991, 110 took bronze Duke of Edinburgh's Award, 18 silver and 20 gold. 20 work for national charities. 6 will enter voluntary schemes after leaving school. Other activities include a computer club, BAYS, Young Enterprise, chess and bridge clubs, school newspaper, riding competitions eg Hickstead.

Careers In 1990, 47% leavers went on to degree courses; 2% to art/drama/music colleges; 6% to non-degree courses (eg nursery nursing, secretarial); 45% other. Of those going on to degree courses, 4% went to Oxbridge, 58% to other universities; 38% to poly/colleges. $3^1/_2$% those going on to higher education went to courses in practical art; $3^1/_2$% in drama/acting; 79% in humanities/social sciences; and 14% in science/engineering.

Uniform School uniform worn, except in sixth.

Houses/prefects Competitive houses. Head girls, heads of houses and Sports Captain – elected by the school. School Council.

Religion Religious worship compulsory unless specifically requested by parents.

Social BAYS, French Society, theatrical productions with local boys' independent schools. German and French exchanges; ski-ing, cruises, trips to Russia, etc. Pupils allowed to bring own car/bike/motorbike to school. No tobacco/alcohol allowed.

Discipline No corporal punishment. Pupils failing to produce homework once might expect an order mark (3 order marks in a half-term means detention); possession of tobacco or alcohol leads to suspension; students are aware that smoking cannabis would mean expulsion.

Former pupils Jean Brooker (RSC); Dennis Matthews (pianist); Maria Edgar (1988 European Junior Show Jumping Champion).

· *Kingston Grammar* ·

Kingston Grammar
School
70 London Road
Kingston upon Thames
Surrey KT2 6PY
Tel 081 546 5875

- Pupils 590
- Boys 10–18
  (Day)
- Girls 10–18
  (Day)
- Upper sixth 79

- Termly fees
  £1255 (Day)
- HMC
  Enquiries/application to
  the Registrar

What it's like

The origins of the school are traceable to the Charter issued by Queen Elizabeth in 1561 which provided endowments, including the Chapel of St Mary Magdalen and land and building attached to it. Historical evidence suggests that it is more than likely that the school existed c1300 or earlier. 'King's Town' had been a settlement of importance since Saxon times. The present site lies on the London Road, opposite the Chapel of St Mary Magdalen, and has an interesting range of buildings representing architectural styles from the 1870s to the present day. It has excellent up-to-date facilities and ample playing fields (22 acres) near Hampton Court Palace. Academic standards are high and results are impressive. Many pupils proceed to degree courses, including many to Oxbridge. French, German and Spanish are taught at GCSE level and a high proportion of pupils takes GCSE in more than one European language. French and German are offered at A-level and there are regular exchange arrangements with France and Germany. The pastoral organisation is particularly efficient, and pupils are given encouragement to develop their individual talents. Music and drama are strong. There are several orchestras and ensembles, plus a choral society. Several dramatic performances are presented each year. Sports and games are very well catered for, and the school has a strong tradition in cricket, rowing and hockey. Kingston is famous for its hockey (played in both winter terms) and has a long list of 'blues' and international players. Numerous clubs and societies provide for most extra-curricular needs. Computing, printing, photography and handicrafts have special facilities. The CCF contingent is large and flourishing and comprises Army and Air Force sections.

School profile

Pupils Age range 10–18, 590 day pupils. Main entry ages 10, 11, 13 and into sixth. *Transfer from maintained schools:* 80% main intake, plus 75% to sixth.

Entrance Common entrance and own exam used. Scholarships, bursaries, assisted places.

Staff Headmaster Mr A B Creber, in post for 4 years.

Academic work GCSE and A-levels. 18 subjects offered (no A-level general studies). In 1990, 84 pupils in fifth, 70 in upper sixth (now 79). *GCSE:* in 1990, 48 fifth gained at least grade C in 8+ subjects; 24 in 5–7; and 12 in 1–4 subjects. *A-levels:* 3 upper sixth passed in 4+ sub-

jects; 49 in 3; 12 in 2; and 6 in 1 subject. 28 took science A-levels; 27 arts/humanities; 15 both. *Computing facilities:* Nimbus network; BBC network; assorted BBC's and Apples in classrooms. *Special provision:* No special provisions, but extra help available.

European Community *Languages:* French offered: to age 14; GCSE; A-level. German offered: to age 14; GCSE; A-level. Spanish offered: to GCSE. 25–50% take GCSE in more than 1 EC language. *Exchanges:* Regular exchanges for pupils aged 14–16 to France and Germany. *Other:* Talks from MEPs. Use of European satellite television.

Careers In 1990, 70% upper sixth leavers went on to degree courses; 7% to art/drama/music colleges; 1% to non-degree courses (eg secretarial); 10% straight into careers; 11% other. Of those going on to degree courses, 17% went to Oxbridge, 62% to other universities; 21% to poly/colleges. 8% those going on to higher education went to courses in practical art; 2% in drama/acting; 35% in humanities/social sciences; 12% in medicine; and 43% in science/engineering.

· *Kingswood* ·

Kingswood School	• Pupils 487	• Termly fees
Lansdown	• Boys 11–18	£1730 (Day)
Bath	(Day/Board)	£2660 (Board)
Avon	• Girls 11–18	• HMC
BA1 5RG	(Day/Board)	Enquiries/application to
Tel 0225 311 627	• Upper sixth 85	the Headmaster's secretary

What it's like

Founded in 1748 by John Wesley who created its first curriculum and compiled its first text books. It has a particularly splendid position on the slopes of Lansdown Hill, overlooking Bath. The main buildings are Victorian Gothic (1851) and these remain the heart of the modern school which has a vast campus of 218 acres. Many new buildings have been added, including a Georgian mansion, a big library, a sixth form centre, a superb sports hall, and Art and CDT centres. In these very civilised surroundings, the facilities and accommodation are first-class. Though ecumenical, the school retains especially strong links with the Methodist Church. An excellent academic education is given and results and standards are high: many go on to degree courses each year, including Oxbridge. Very strong music and art departments. An exceptionally fine range of sports, games, clubs, societies and extra-curricular activities. Strong commitment to local community services and an impressive record in the Duke of Edinburgh's Award Scheme. The prep school, Prior's Court, is near Newbury, Berkshire.

School profile

Pupils Age range 11–18; 487 pupils, 180 day (98 boys, 82 girls), 307 boarding (178 boys, 129 girls). Main entry ages 11, 13 and into sixth. Prior's Court school provides more than 20% of intake. Approx 8% are children of former pupils. *Transfer from maintained schools:* 25% main intake plus 15% to sixth.

Entrance Common entrance and own entrance exam used. Oversubscribed. No special skills or religious requirements, but school has strong links with the Methodist Church. Parents not expected to buy text books; other extras agreed with parents. 37 assisted places. 11 scholarships/bursaries pa, 33–20% fees.

Parents 30+% live within 30 miles; 10+% live overseas.

Staff Headmaster G M Best, in post for 4 years. 46 full time staff, 4 part time. Annual turnover 5% (including retirement). Average age 36.

Academic work GCSE, AS and A-levels; 16 GCSE subjects offered; 28 A-level (including general studies). Average size of upper fifth 76; upper sixth 84. *GCSE:* on average, 48 pupils in upper fifth pass 8+ subjects; 18, 5–7 subjects; 15 pass 1–4 subjects. *A-levels:* on average, 26 pupils in upper sixth pass 4 subjects; 30, 3 subjects; 8, 2 subjects and 14 pass 1 subject. On average, 21 take science/engineering A-levels; 37 arts and humanities; 26 a mixture. *Computing facilities:* Computer room (Macintosh system). *Special provisions:* Visiting specialists offer help with special needs, including dyslexia.

Senior pupils' non-academic activities *Music:* 140 learn a musical instrument, 20 to Grade 6 or above. 2 accepted for Music School; 1 choral/organ scholar. 50 in school orchestra, 70 in school choir, 10 in school pop group, 8 in jazz/swing and 30 in wind bands. *Drama and dance:* 60 participate in school productions; 20 in informal theatre; 1 accepted for Drama/Dance Schools, 1 goes on to work in theatre. *Art:* 24 take as non-examined subject, 34 take GCSE art, 15, A-level, 22, A-level history of art. 8 accepted for Art School, 2 for university fine art courses, 4, history of art and 1, architecture; 20 belong to photographic club. *Sport:* Archery, athletics, badminton, basketball, cricket, cross-country, golf, hiking, hockey, horse-riding, karate, multi-gym, netball, orienteering, rounders, rugby, sailing, self-defence, shooting, squash, swimming, tennis, trampolining, volleyball, windsurfing available. 200 take non-compulsory sport. 25 represent county/country (rugby, hockey, cricket, tennis, cross-country, athletics, orienteering). *Other:* 50 take part in local community schemes. 25 have bronze Duke of Edinburgh's Award, 20, silver and 15, gold. 2 are D of E Award Panel Members; 10 enter voluntary schemes after leaving school, 5 work for national charities. Other activities include 3 computer clubs, astronomy, bridge, CB radio, canal group, chess, Christian Fellowship, community service, current affairs, dance, debating, drama, electronics, film, history, model making, model railway, politics, printing, video making, war-games and many others.

Careers 3 part time advisers. Average number of pupils accepted for *arts and humanities degree courses* at Oxbridge, 4; other universities, 25; polytechnics or CHE, 4. *science and engineering degree courses* at Oxbridge, 6; other universities, 17; medical schools, 6; polytechnics or CHE, 11. *BEd*, 6. *other general training courses*, 3. Average number of pupils going straight into careers in the armed services, 2; the Church, 1; industry, 2; the City, 1; music/drama, 1; commerce/banking, 2.

Uniform School uniform worn except in the sixth.

Houses/prefects Competitive houses. Prefects, head boy/girl, head of house and house prefects – appointed by the Head.

Religion Daily morning assembly (religious) for all. Sunday service for boarders.

Social Local schools joint cricket tour abroad, choral production (annually), debating competitions and joint sixth form activities occasionally. Annual ski trip abroad. Occasional small group trips (history, art, visit to Taize, Kenya, Russia etc); annual exchange with German school. Pupils allowed to bring own car to school. Meals self service. School shop. No tobacco/alcohol allowed.

Discipline No corporal punishment. Pupils failing to produce homework once might be required to produce it within 24 hours; those caught smoking cannabis on the premises could expect expulsion.

Boarding All sixth form share (2 or 3); 50% are in dormitories of 6+. Houses, of approximately 40, 2 junior, 7 senior, single sex. Resident qualified nurse, visiting doctor. Central dining room. Pupils can provide and cook own snacks. 2 weekend exeats each term plus some day exeats. Visits to local town allowed.

Alumni association run by Mr W B Mountford, c/o the School.

· *Kirkham Grammar* ·

Kirkham Grammar
School
Ribby Road
Kirkham
Preston
Lancashire PR4 2BH
Tel 0772 684264

- Pupils 600
- Boys 7–18
  (Day/Board)
- Girls 7–18
  (Day/Board)
- Upper sixth 45

- Termly fees
  £830 (Day)
  £1520 (Board)
- SHMIS
  Enquiries/application to
  the Headmaster

What it's like

Founded in 1549, it occupies an agreeable 20-acre rural site in the Fylde close to Kirkham. The main school buildings date from 1910, but there have been many additions since the 1930s. A programme of expansion is still under way and a multipurpose hall opened in 1990. Accommodation and facilities are now very good. It retains old and traditional links with the Drapers' Company and provides a traditional grammar school education. Results are good. Many sixth former go on to degree courses. French and German are offered throughout the school and a high proportion of pupils takes both at GCSE. In addition Italian is offered to A-level and there are regular exchange arrangements with Belgium, France, Germany and Italy for all age groups. Kirkham sets out to be a Christian school and to prepare its pupils for a Christian life in the world. A well-organised establishment, it has a purposeful and motivated atmosphere. Very strong music and drama departments. An impressive range of sport, games and activities.

School profile

Pupils Total age range 7–18; 600 pupils, 526 day (316 boys, 210 girls), 74 boarding (38 boys, 36 girls). Main entry ages 7, 11 and into sixth. Approx 4% are children of former pupils. *Transfer from maintained schools:* 2% at 11, plus 10% to sixth.

Entrance Own entrance exam used. No special skills or religious requirements. Parents not expected to buy text books. 10 assisted places pa. 10 scholarships/bursaries, half fees to £100 per term.

Parents 15+% in industry or commerce; 15+% are doctors, lawyers, etc. 60+% live within 30 miles; up to 10% live overseas.

Staff Headmaster B Stacey, first year in post. 39 full time staff, 3 part time. Annual turnover 3%. Average age 35.

Academic work GCSE and A-levels. 18 subjects offered (including A-level general studies). In 1991, 84 pupils in upper fifth, 45 in upper sixth. *GCSE:* in 1990, 35 upper fifth gained at least grade C in 8+ subjects; 27 in 5–7; and 15 in 1–4

subjects. *A-levels:* 17 upper sixth passed in 4+ subjects; 14 in 3; 3 in 2; and 8 in 1 subject. 40% took science A-levels; 40% arts/humanities; 20% both. *Computing facilities:* Eight computers; specialist room. *Special provision:* Test in English exam arranged for sixth formers for whom English is not native tongue.

European Community *Languages:* French offered: to age 14; GCSE; AS-level; A-level. German offered: to age 14; GCSE; AS-level; A-level. Italian offered: to age 14; A-level. 25–50% take GCSE in more than 1 EC language. *Exchanges:* Regular exchanges for pupils aged 11–18 to Belgium, France, Germany and Italy.

Senior pupils' non-academic activities *Music:* 58 learn a musical instrument, 8 to Grade 6 or above. 28 in school orchestra, 150 in school choir; 1 on RSCM cathedral course; 2 in RSCM cathedral singers; 2 in Lancashire School Training Orchestra; 1 finalist in national electronic organ championships. *Drama* *and dance:* 60 in school productions; 20 in junior workshop; 23 in GCSE drama course; 21 to Grade 6 and above in LAMDA; 12 in dance class; 200 (years 1–3) take drama once a week. 1 goes on to work in theatre. *Art:* 30 take GCSE; 7 A-level. 4 accepted for Art School; 2 for architecture courses. 20 belong to photographic club. *Sport:* Badminton, squash, athletics, cricket, tennis, rugby, swimming, netball, hockey, gymnastics, dance available. 100 take non-compulsory sport. Some take exams in gymnastics and swimming. 11 represent county (tennis, swimming, rugby, squash); some county champions; 1 represents country at rugby plus 7 in trials. *Other:* 10 take part in local community schemes. 6 enter voluntary schemes after leaving school; 20 work for national charities. Other activities include a computer club, angling society (local fishing), fell-walking society, electronics, bridge club, astronomical and science fiction societies, natural history.

Careers In 1990, 75% leavers went on to degree courses; 15% to art/drama/music colleges; 10% to non-degree courses; 10% straight into careers. Of those going on to degree courses, 2% went to Oxbridge, 82% to other universities; 16% to poly/colleges. 5% those going on to higher education went to courses in practical art; 5% in drama/acting; 2% in music; 48% in humanities/social sciences; 10% in medicine; and 30% in science/engineering.

Uniform School uniform worn throughout.

Houses/prefects Competitive houses. Prefects, head boy/girl, head of house and house prefects – appointed by the Head or housemasters.

Religion Church of England worship encouraged.

Social No organised events with local schools. Trips to Germany and France. Pupils allowed to bring own car/bike/motorbike to school. Meals self service. School shop. No tobacco/alcohol allowed.

Discipline No corporal punishment. Pupils failing to produce homework once might expect a second chance. Detention system operates.

Boarding 40% have own study bedroom, 20% share with one other; 40% in dormitories of 6+. Resident qualified medical staff. Central dining room. One weekend exeat every 3 weeks. Visits to local town allowed.

Alumni association run by David Stirzaker, 112 Thorn Court, Salford M6 5EL.

Former pupils Prof E R Laithwaite (Imperial College, London); David W H Walton (Director of Research, British Antarctic Survey); Graham Clark (English National Opera); Ian Byatt (Director of Water Services); G Sagar (Professor of Botany, Bangor University).

!

· La Sagesse ·

La Sagesse Convent
High School
North Jesmond
Newcastle upon Tyne
NE2 3RJ
Tel 091 281 3474

- Pupils 350
- Boys None
- Girls 11–18
  (Day)
- Upper sixth 22

- Termly fees
  £940 (Day)
- GSA
Enquiries/application to
the Headmistress

What it's like

Founded in 1912, by the Sisters of La Sagesse it is now run by a board of governors. The premises lie on the fringe of the city overlooking Jesmond Dene. It is single-site (with 9 acres of grounds) but housed in 3 buildings; the senior and nursery departments are on the same site. A Roman Catholic foundation, religious education is an essential part of the curriculum. Most pupils are Christian but girls of all religious denominations are welcomed. A sound general academic education is provided and results are good. Many sixth formers go on to degree courses. French and Spanish are taught throughout the school and many girls take GCSE in both. German is offered for the Institute of Linguists. Great deal of emphasis is on careers in sixth form (eg Understanding Industry course). Music, drama and art and a range of sports, games, clubs and societies. Some involvement in local community schemes.

School profile

Pupils Age range 11–18; 350 day girls. Main entry ages 11 and into sixth. Approx 5% are children of former pupils. Own junior school provides over 30% intake. *Transfer from maintained schools:* 40% main intake.

Entrance Own entrance exam used (junior pupils have automatic entrance). Parents not expected to buy text books or stationery. 171 assisted places. 6 scholarships/bursaries per year, one-third fees.

Parents 15+% are doctors, lawyers, etc; 15+% in industry or commerce.

Staff Headmistress Mrs D Parker, in post for 2 years. 29 full time staff. Annual turnover 2%. Average age 45.

Academic work GCSE and A-levels. 16 subjects offered (including A-level general studies). In 1990, 51 pupils in upper fifth, 22 in upper sixth. *GCSE:* in 1990, 36 upper fifth gained at least grade C in 8+ subjects; 9 in 5–7; and 6 in 1–4 subjects. *A-levels:* 10 upper sixth passed in 4+ subjects; 5 in 3; 4 in 2; and 3 in 1 subject. 5 took science A-levels; 12 arts/humanities; 6 both. *Computing facilities:* Computer rooms with 20 computers. Computers used in science labs, geography and home economics. *Special provision:* Dyslexic lessons in lunchtime in school.

European Community *Languages:* French offered: to age 14; GCSE; AS-

423

level; A-level. German: Institute of Linguists. Spanish offered: to age 14; GCSE; A-level. 25–50% take GCSE in more than 1 EC language. *Exchanges:* Regular exchanges for pupils aged 14–18 to France. *Other:* Sixth form attended recent Paris conference.

Senior pupils' non-academic activities *Music:* Important throughout the school. 40 in school choir, 20 in orchestra – both successfully take part in local festivals. *Drama and dance:* 80 involved in annual dance/drama production or fashion show. Entries to dance competitions; speech and drama exams. *Sport:* Netball, hockey, tennis, badminton, swimming, squash, rounders available. Some represent county; one represented country in International Catholic Schools Games. *Other:* Many voluntary concerns given active support. Community work in sixth. Typing course, needlework, computer studies and clubs for dance, drama, chess, debating. Pupils enter gymnastics, art and general knowledge contests.

Careers and business liaison In 1990, 69% leavers went on to degree courses; 7% to art/drama/music colleges; 14% to non-degree courses (eg BTEC sport, secretarial); 10% straight into careers (eg civil service, banking, legal executive). Of those going on to degree courses, 6% went to Oxbridge, 50% to other universities; 44% to poly/colleges. 8% those going on to higher education went to courses in practical art; 8% in drama/acting; 43% in humanities/social sciences; 8% in medicine; and 30% in science/engineering.

Uniform School uniform worn, except the sixth.

Houses/prefects Competitive houses. Prefects, head girl, head of house and house prefects – appointed by the school. School Council.

Religion School prays together twice a week (RC) and daily in forms.

Social Public speaking and geographical quiz with other local schools. Language and ski-ing trips abroad, individual sixth formers visit Spain and France; Exchange programme. Pupils allowed to bring own car/bike to school. Meals, most bring own food. School shop. No tobacco/alcohol allowed.

Discipline No corporal punishment. Pupils failing to conform to acceptable standards of behaviour are warned. In a case of a serious breach of discipline a pupil would be suspended. Detention very occasionally used (eg repeated lateness, lack of homework) but in general the warning system and clear rules are sufficient.

· *Lady Eleanor Holles* ·

Lady Eleanor Holles School
Hanworth Road
Hampton
Middesex TW12 3HF
Tel 081 979 1601

- Pupils 810
- Boys None
- Girls 7–18 (Day)
- Upper sixth 82

- Termly fees £1125 (Day)
- GSA

Enquiries to the Head Mistress
Application to the Registrar

What it's like

Founded in the Cripplegate Ward of the City of London in 1711 under the will of the Lady Eleanor Holles, daughter of the second Earl of Clare. It is now housed in modern buildings in Hampton where it moved from North London in 1936 (having left the City in 1878). It stands on a pleasant 33–acre site surrounded by gardens and playing fields. All sports facilities are on site. Within the last eight years there has been an extensive building programme which has included four new science laboratories, an additional sixth-form common room, a music wing, a drama room, an art block and a video room. Altogether it is very well equipped. It is a C of E foundation and has its own chapel where worship in the Anglican tradition is encouraged. Academic standards are high and results are consistently creditable. Each year very many girls go on to degree courses, including many to Oxbridge. French, German and Spanish are offered to A-level. A high proportion of pupils takes GCSE in more than one European language and there are regular exchanges with France, Germany and Spain. Music is very strong (a wind band, string orchestra and chamber groups) and drama is also very strong with 200 or more pupils being involved in annual dramatic competitions and in the productions of neighbouring boys' schools. A good range of sports and games is provided and standards are high (many representatives at county and regional level, especially in netball, rowing and lacrosse). There is much regular social and academic liaison with Hampton Boys' school next door. Some commitment to local community services and a modest record in the Duke of Edinburgh's Award Scheme.

School profile

Pupils Total age range 7–18; 810 day girls. Senior department 11–18, 620 girls. Main entry ages 7, 11 and into sixth. 10% are children of former pupils. *Transfer from maintained schools:* 30% senior intake, plus 10% to sixth.

Entrance Own entrance exam used. Oversubscribed. No special skills required, although music and sport are encouraged; no religious requirements. Parents not expected to buy text books. 56 assisted places. Scholarships (academic and music) at 11 and 16; means tested bursaries at 11, full to one-third fees.

Staff Head Mistress Miss E M Candy, in post for 10 years. 62 full time staff, 33 part time. Annual turnover 7%. Average age 43.

Academic work GCSE, AS and A-levels. 19 GCSE subjects offered; 9 at AS; 26 at A-level (including theatre studies, Russian; no A-level general studies). In 1991, 91 pupils in upper fifth, 82 in upper sixth. *GCSE:* in 1990, 84 upper fifth gained at least grade C in 8+ subjects; 5 in 5–7 subjects. *A-levels:* 7 upper sixth passed in 4+ subjects; 67 in 3; 6 in 2; and 2 in 1 subject. 20% took science A-levels; 68% arts/humanities; 12% both. *Computing facilities:* Set of 10 BBC2 computers. New 12 place Nimbus network. *Special provision:* Additional individual coaching available.

European Community *Languages:* French offered: to age 14; GCSE; AS-level; A-level; Flic; non-examined. German offered: to age 14; GCSE; AS-level; A-level; Flic; non-examined. Spanish offered: to GCSE; AS-level; A-level; non-examined. 50–75% take GCSE in more than 1 EC language. Flic (Foreign Languages for Industry and Commerce) and non-examined language courses both available to sixth form. *Exchanges:* Regular exchanges for pupils aged 16–18 to France, Germany and Spain. *Other:* European Studies offered to pupils aged 16–18 (unexamined). Outside speakers, often jointly with Hampton, include Sir Geoffrey Howe, local MEP. Occasional German and French girls in sixth form for 1 term–1 year.

Senior pupils' non-academic activities *Music:* 200+ learn a musical instrument, over 50 to Grade 6 or above; 2 accepted for Music School; 30+ play in school orchestra, 40 in choir; some in wind band, string orchestra, dance band, jazz band, chamber groups; 20 play in local youth orchestras. *Drama and dance:* 50–60 in school productions; 250 in annual drama competition; 20 in productions with neighbouring boys' schools; 20 take A-level theatre studies; 50 LAMDA exams; 1 accepted for Drama/Dance Schools; 4 to university media/drama courses. *Art:* 30 take GCSE; 15 A-level. 3 accepted for Art School, 1 for art related degree courses; 40 take life drawing, theatre design, vacation courses in eg millinery. *Sport:* Netball, lacrosse, swimming, badminton, tennis, athletics, rowing, competition gymnastics, fencing available. 50 take part in non-compulsory sport; 30 take exams, eg swimming; 20 RLSS bronze; 10 ASA PTA. 30 pupils represent county (lacrosse, rowing, netball, tennis, swimming, athletics). *Other:* 38 have bronze Duke of Edinburgh's Award. 20 in local community schemes. 1 on Project Trust; 2 on Operation Raleigh. Other activities include clubs for computers, chess, photography, drama, languages, pottery, gardening, science, sign language classes for communication with the deaf.

Careers In 1990, 86% leavers went on to degree courses; 5% to art/drama/music colleges; 2% to non-degree courses (eg secretarial); 7% other. Of those going on to degree courses, 20% went to Oxbridge, 73% to other universities; 7% to poly/colleges. 5% those going on to higher education went to courses in practical art; 5% in drama/acting; 60% in humanities/social sciences; 15% in medicine; and 15% in science/engineering.

Uniform School uniform worn, except in sixth.

Houses/prefects No competitive houses. Head girl, elected by the school. School Council.

Religion Religious worship encouraged. C of E chapel and chaplain.

Social Service volunteers, drama productions, orchestral and choral performances, debating with neighbouring boys' school. Organised exchange with German school; French, Spanish, Russian, classical trips; 2 ski-ing holidays pa. Pupils allowed to bring own car/bike/motorbike to school. Meals in cafeteria. No tobacco/alcohol allowed.

Discipline No corporal punishment. Pupils failing to produce homework once might expect to stay in during lunch recess and do the work; those caught smoking cannabis on the premises could expect expulsion.

Alumni association is run by Mrs M Sharman, Derryallen, Shere Road, West Horsley, Surrey KT24 6EW.

Former pupils Charlotte Attenborough; Anne Nightingale; Saskia Reeves; Beattie Edney; Lucy Irvine; Christina Hardyment; Jane Thynne; Joan Hopkins.

· *Lancing* ·

Lancing College	● Pupils 555	● Termly fees
Lancing	● Boys 13–18	£2139 (Day)
West Sussex	(Day/Board)	£3009 (Board)
BN15 0RW	● Girls 16–18	● HMC, Woodard
Tel 0273 452213	(Day/Board)	Enquiries/application to
Fax 0273 464720	● Upper sixth 111	the Head Master's
		Secretary

What it's like

Founded in 1848 by the Rev Nathaniel Woodard and the first of the Woodard schools. It has a splendid site by any standards on a spur of the South Downs overlooking the sea to the south and the Weald to the north. The superb grounds comprise about 550 acres and include the college farm. The main buildings – handsome examples of the collegiate style of architecture – are grouped round two main quadrangles. There have been many improvements and developments in recent years, including a music school, a sixth-form residence, a sports hall, study bedrooms and a new theatre. The boys are comfortably accommodated in 8 houses; the girls have 2 purpose-built boarding houses. Lancing is intended primarily for Church of England pupils, but pupils of other Christian denominations may be accepted. The college has a magnificent chapel which is used a great deal. There is considerable emphasis on religious instruction and worship. A large and well-qualified staff allows a staff:pupil ratio of about 1:10. A broad general education is provided. Academic standards are high and results consistently good. Many pupils go on to higher education, including many to Oxbridge. French, German, Italian and Spanish are taught up to A-level and an exceptionally high proportion of pupils take GCSE in more than one European language. Music and art are an important part of the education of all pupils. Quite a lot of dramatic work is also done. A good range of sports and games is available and standards are high. There is also a fair variety of extra–curricular activities. The flourishing CCF contingent contains Army, Naval and RAF sections. The college also has a farming group which helps to run the school farm. There is a particularly active social services organisation which helps the local community and also people in the Camberwell district of London.

School profile

Pupils Age range 13–18; 555 pupils, 480 boys, 75 girls. Main entry ages 13 (boys) and into sixth (boys and girls). *Transfer from maintained schools:* 2% main intake, plus 2% to sixth.

Entrance Common entrance used. 30 scholarships and exhibitions pa.

Staff Head Master J S Woodhouse, in post for 9 years.

Academic work GCSE and A-levels. Approx 20 subjects offered (no A-level general studies). In 1990, 105 pupils in upper fifth, 111 in upper sixth. *GCSE:* in 1990, 51 upper fifth gained at least grade C in 8+ subjects; 52 in 5–7; and 2 in 1–4 subjects (boys take 1–3 GCSE a year early). *A-levels:* 11 upper sixth passed in 4+ subjects; 86 in 3; 12 in 2; and 1 in 1 subject. 19 took science A-levels; 62 arts/humanities; 30 both. *Computing facilities:* Two RML Nimbus networks, 20 machines. *Special provision:* Dealt with individually. No general provision.

European Community *Languages:* French offered: to age 14; GCSE; AS-level; A-level. German offered: to age 14; GCSE; AS-level; A-level. Italian offered: to GCSE; AS-level; A-level. Spanish offered: to GCSE; AS-level; A-level. Over 75% take GCSE in more than 1 EC language. *Exchanges:* Regular exchanges for pupils aged 13–16 to France and Germany. *Other:* Euro-days for fifth and sixth form to stimulate interest in Europe and give information (careers, political institutions, etc). Work experience for lower sixth linguists being planned.

Careers In 1990, 76% leavers went on to degree courses; 24% other. Of those going on to degree courses, 17% went to Oxbridge, 72% to other universities; 11% to poly/colleges. 3% those going on to higher education went to courses in music; 70% in humanities/social sciences; 4% in medicine; and 23% in science/engineering.

· *Langley* ·

Langley School
Langley Park
Norwich
NR14 6BJ
Tel 0508 20210

- Pupils 210
- Boys 11–18
  (Day/Board/Weekly)
- Girls 11–18
  (Day/Board/Weekly)
- Upper sixth 29

- Termly fees
  £1305 (Day)
  £2485 (Board)
  £1960 (Weekly)
- SHA
Enquiries/application to
the Headmaster's
Secretary

What it's like

Founded in 1910 in St Giles, Norwich, in 1946 the school moved to Langley Park and was renamed. Langley Hall – between Norwich and the pleasant town of Beccles – is a handsome red-brick Georgian mansion in Palladian style and is a Grade I listed building set in 50 acres of grounds. With the admission of girls at all levels 2 years ago, the school is implementing an expansion programme to provide a fully co-educational school community. It is already well equipped, with six science laboratories, a computer room, home economics laboratory, a CDT workshop, art and pottery rooms, a lecture theatre, an assembly hall and a large sports hall. There are extensive playing fields, 10 tennis courts, a nine-hole golf course and an assault course. The school is in membership of local squash and sailing clubs. The main boys' games are rugby, hockey, athletics and cricket, and for the girls hockey, netball and rounders. To accommodate the increasing numbers of pupils, additional study bedrooms for boys and girls, a girls' changing room, a day-pupils' centre, five classrooms and staff accommodation have been built. Boarders live in study bedrooms catering for one to seven occupants according to age. The staff:pupil ratio is 1:11. The aim of the school is to provide a full education, academically, socially and culturally, to encourage pupils to develop their talents and personality, to use time wisely, to achieve a high standard of self-discipline and to draw out and train the qualities of leadership. Langley is proud of the education it gives to pupils of wide ranging ability. Careers guidance, study skills and ethical studies are taught to all pupils. A number of sixth form leavers to on to degree courses. French, German and Spanish are offered to A-level and also with Portuguese for the Institute of Linguists exams. The school offers a caring, secure and disciplined environment. Some 25 clubs and societies cater for most needs. Langley Preparatory School is located in Norwich.

School profile

Pupils Age range 11–18, 210 pupils, 134 day (111 boys, 23 girls), 76 boarders (59 boys, 17 girls). Main entry ages 11, 12, 13 and into sixth. *Transfer from maintained schools:* 15% main intake, plus 2% to sixth.

Entrance Common entrance and own exam used. Parents expected to buy text books in sixth. Academic and music scholarships and bursaries; discounts for boarding pupils from service families.

Parents 30+% live within 30 miles; 10+% live overseas.

Staff Headmaster S J W McArthur, in post 2 years. 25 full time staff, 8 part time. Annual turnover 5%.

Academic work GCSE, AS- and A-levels. 20 GCSE subjects offered including some at AS-level. In 1990, 39 pupils in upper fifth, 16 in upper sixth. *GCSE:* in 1990, 11 upper fifth gained at least grade C in 8+ subjects; 10 in 5–7 subjects.

Classes are small and a tight monitoring and tutoring system operates at all levels. *Computing facilities:* 26 computers (BBC, IBM and Archimedes). All pupils study information technology to age 14. *Special provision:* Teachers qualified to teach both dyslexic pupils and English as a foreign language.
European Community *Languages:* French offered: to age 14; GCSE; AS-level; A-level; Institute of Linguists. German offered: to age 14; GCSE; AS-level; A-level; Institute of Linguists. Italian offered: to age 14; GCSE; Institute of Linguists. Portuguese: Institute of Linguists. Spanish offered: to age 14; GCSE; AS-level; A-level. 10–25% take GCSE in more than 1 EC language. *Exchanges:* Regular exchanges being established to France and Germany. *Other:* EC pupils regularly attend (eg from France, Germany, Spain and Denmark). Developing links with schools and businesses in EC.
Careers In 1990, 50% leavers went on to degree courses; 21% to non-degree courses (eg hotel and catering); 29% other. Of those going on to degree courses, 71% went to universities; 29% to poly/colleges. 73% those going on to higher education went to courses in humanities/social sciences; and 27% in science engineering.
Social No tobacco/alcohol allowed.

· *Latymer* ·

Latymer Upper School	● Pupils 1060	● Termly fees
King Street	● Boys 9–18	£1495 (Day)
London	(Day)	● HMC
W6 9LR	● Girls None	Enquiries/application to
Tel 081 741 1851	● Upper sixth 130	the Headmaster

What it's like

Founded by the will of Edward Latymer in 1624, the modern school lies between King Street and the Thames in Hammersmith (West London). In 1969 an extensive rebuilding programme was started and in 1981 the modernisation of the older buildings began. It is now a very well equipped establishment, which runs down to the River Thames and has fine views over Hammersmith Reach. The playing fields are about one and a half miles away. For many years it was one of London's leading direct grant schools and this tradition is continued in the generous number of assisted places available. No able boy need be denied a place on financial grounds. It draws on boys from a wide area of London and is known as a friendly, welcoming and tolerant community. The teaching is well known to be good and academic standards are high. Results are excellent and each year a very large number of boys go on to degree courses, including very many to Oxbridge. French, German, Italian and Spanish are offered at GCSE and many boys take GCSE in more than one European language. French and German are taught to AS- and A-level, and there are regular exchanges with France and Germany. Music is tremendously strong: 250 learn an instrument; 175 are involved in school orchestras, and about 150 in the choirs. All boys are encouraged to take part in musical activities. Drama and art are well supported. There is a good deal of collaboration with Godolphin and Latymer Girls' School in cultural enterprises and there is a joint orchestra. Many sports and games are provided and standards of achievement are high (a large number of representatives at county and regional level). There is a wide range of extra-curricular activities, including scouts. A lot of camps, expeditions and field courses are organised. The school has also participated very successfully indeed in the Duke of Edinburgh's Award Scheme (each D of E boy does a course with the Metropolitan Police).

School profile

Pupils Total age range 9–18; 1060 day boys. Main entry ages 9, 11 and into sixth. Some are children of former pupils. *Transfer from maintained schools:* 65% at 11, plus 50% to sixth.

Entrance Own entrance exam used. Oversubscribed (3–4 applicants per place). Good academic potential looked for. No religious requirements. Parents not expected to buy text books. 50 assisted places pa. Scholarships and bursaries.

Parents 15+% are doctors, lawyers, etc. 15+% in the theatre, media, music, etc., 15+% in industry.

Staff Headmaster Martin Pavey, in post for 2 years. 80 full time staff, 22 music staff. Annual turnover 6%. Average age 38.

Academic work GCSE and A-levels. 21 GCSE subjects offered; 22 at A-level (including Russian; general studies taught but not examined). In 1989, 147 in upper fifth, 130 in upper sixth. *GCSE:* in 1989, 105 upper fifth gained at least grade C in 8+ subjects; 35 in 5–7; and 7 in 1–4 subjects. *A-levels:* 6 upper sixth passed in 4+ subjects; 84 in 3; 13 in 2; and 4 in 1 subject. 42% took science A-levels; 58% arts/humanities. *Computing facilities:* 30 BBCs, 4 Archimedes, 40 networked PC 286 Nimbus.

European Community *Languages:* French offered: to age 14; GCSE; AS-level; A-level; non-examined subject. German offered: to age 14; GCSE; AS-level; A-level; non-examined subject. Italian offered: to GCSE. Spanish offered: to GCSE. 25–50% take GCSE in more than 1 EC language. *Exchanges:* Regular exchanges for pupils aged 14–18 to France and Germany. *Other:* Special programme to arrange courses and work experience in local culture and language for fifth and sixth forms.

Senior pupils' non-academic activities *Music:* 250 learn a musical instrument, over 75 to Grade 6 or above; 50 accepted for Music School; 5 for Junior College, Academy/Guildhall. 150 in school choir, 175 in school orchestra; others in local youth orchestras and choirs. *Drama and dance:* 35 in school productions; 15 in others. 1 goes on to work in theatre. *Art:* 30 take art as non-examined subject; 21 take GCSE; 3–11 A-level; 9 history of art A-level. Most who take art A-level go on to Art School or university. 25 belong to eg photographic club; 30 to art/pottery club. *Sport:* Winter: football, rugby, rowing, squash, badminton, basketball, golf, swimming, water polo. Summer: cricket, tennis, athletics, swimming, squash, sailing available. 460 take part in non-compulsory sport. 252 take exams, eg swimming. 30 pupils represent county (rugby, soccer, rowing, cricket, athletics, cross-country). *Other:* 80 have silver Duke of Edinburgh's Award, 25 gold. 20 enter voluntary schemes after leaving school. School has annual charity drive – for eg a generator for Kenyan Secondary School. Other activities include flourishing chess club (wins challenging matches); driving instruction arranged; long-established drama and arts society; economics, debating, political sciences. Computer clubs for Junior, Middle and Senior pupils.

Careers In 1990, 83% leavers went on to degree courses; 7% to art/drama/music colleges; 10% other. Of those going on to degree courses, 25% went to Oxbridge, 60% to other universities; 15% to poly/colleges.

Uniform School uniform worn except in sixth.

Houses/prefects No competitive houses. Prefects, head boy, head of house and house prefects – appointed by the Head after a trial period of duties. Sixth form Liaison Committee.

Religion All boys whose parents do not request their absence are obliged to attend School Assembly (main assembly Christian plus Jewish assembly). Communion encouraged for those who have been confirmed (Confirmation classes offered).

Social Regular French and German exchanges, joint orchestra and other activities (eg athletics training) with Godolphin and Latymer School. Many organised trips abroad; links with leading schools in Paris and Hamburg. Pupils allowed to bring own bike to school. Meals self service. Uniform and tuck shops. No tobacco/alcohol allowed.

Discipline No corporal punishment. Pupils failing to produce homework once would certainly be given an imposition by teacher; thereafter, the weekly school detention system most likely punishment; those caught smoking cannabis on the premises would be expelled.

Alumni association is run by B J Southcott, 9 Kewferry Drive, Northwood HA6 2NT.

Former pupils Peter Walker MP; Ian Percival MP (formerly Solicitor General); Mel Smith (actor, comedian); Andy Holmes (Olympic rowing gold medallist).

· Laurel Bank ·

Laurel Bank School
4 Lily Bank Terrace
Glasgow
G12 8RX
Tel 041 339 9127

- Pupils 408
- Boys 3–4 only (Day)
- Girls 3–18 (Day)
- Higher year 40

- Termly fees £1050 (Day)
- GSA
Enquiries/application to the Headmistress

What it's like

Founded in 1903, it moved to its present site in 1910. This consists of converted terraced houses in the west end of the city and near the university. The nursery, junior school and senior school are combined. Good modern facilities are provided. Religious education is given throughout the school. Academic standards are high and results good. Very many go on to degree courses each year. French and German are offered through to CSYS level; Spanish to Highers. Many girls take more than one European language. There are regular exchange arrangements with Belgium, France and Spain for the 11–14 age group. Strong in drama, music and art. Considerable strength in sports and games and high standards. A promising record in the Duke of Edinburgh's Award Scheme. Plentiful use is made of the cultural amenities of Glasgow.

School profile

Pupils Total age range 3–18; 408 day pupils (8 boys, 400 girls). Senior department 11–18, 264 girls. Main entry age 12. *Transfer from maintained schools:* 90+% main senior intake, variable number to sixth.

Entrance Own entrance exam used. Not oversubscribed. No special skills or religious requirements. 50+ assisted places. 8 scholarships, half fees to £100.

Parents 15+% are in industry or commerce, 15+% are doctors, lawyers, etc.

Staff Headmistress Miss L G Egginton, in post for 7 years. 34 full time staff, 11 part time. Annual turnover 5%. Average age 40s.

Academic work S-grades, Highers, CSYS. 16 subjects offered (including Higher modern studies). On average, 40 pupils in S-grade year, 40 in Higher, 30 in CSYS year. *S-grade:* on average, 26 upper fifth gain passes in at least 8+ subjects; 8 in 5–7; and 6 in 1–4 subjects. *Highers:* on average, 18 pupils pass in 5+ subjects; 4 in 4; 9 in 3; 5 in 2; 1 in 1. *Computing facilities:* Extensive – lab; computers in most departments. *Special provision:* Permanent full time learning support teacher.

European Community *Languages:* French offered: to age 14; S-grade; Higher; CSYS. German offered: to age 14; S-grade; Higher; CSYS. Spanish offered: to S-grade; Higher. 25–50% take S-grade in more than 1 EC language. *Exchanges:* Regular exchanges for pupils aged 11–14 to Belgium, France and Spain. *Other:* Spanish pupils in school on termly basis.

Senior pupils' non-academic activities *Music:* 80+ learn a musical instrument, 8 to Grade 6 or above; 36 in school orchestra, 60 in choir, 13 in wind band; 2 in Glasgow Schools wind group, 2 in Glasgow Schools orchestra, 1 Junior RSAM, 4 Junior SNO choir, 6 in Dunbartonshire wind band. *Drama and dance:* Many participate in school productions. *Art:* 8 take art as non-examined subject; 10 take S-grade; 5 Higher; 3 CSYS art. 2 accepted for Art School; 6 go on to art-based HND courses. *Sport:* Athletics, tennis (main summer sports), badminton, gymnastics, netball, short tennis, squash, table tennis, swimming, netball, trampoline, volleyball, hockey available. 50 take non-compulsory sport – skiing, squash, aerobics. School successfully competes annually in schools (Glasgow and Scottish) athletics and swimming competitions, Midland Bank and Scottish Cup tennis competitions, and all West District Hockey Tournaments. *Other:* 20 have bronze Duke of Edinburgh's Award, 20 have silver and 2 have gold. Other activities include a computer club, drama, debating and public speaking.

Careers In 1990, 82% leavers went on to degree courses; 7% to art/drama/music colleges; 11% to non-degree courses (eg food technology, communication skills, further Highers or CSYS). Of those going on to degree courses, 4% went to Oxbridge, 74% to other universities; 22% to poly/colleges. 15% those going on to higher education went to courses in practical art/architecture; 52% in humanities/social sciences; 11% in medicine; 15% in science/engineering; and 7% in eg business studies, hotel management.

Uniform School uniform worn throughout.

Houses/prefects Competitive houses. Prefects, head girl, head of house and house prefects – elected by the school. School Council.

Religion Morning assembly (some opt out).

Social Mixed badminton, debates, social events, shared conferences with other schools. Organised tours abroad, especially ski-ing. Meals self service. No tobacco/alcohol allowed.

Discipline No corporal punishment. Pupils failing to produce homework once might expect a warning; those caught smoking cannabis on the premises could expect expulsion (after consideration of all circumstances).

Alumni association run by Miss Julia Blake, c/o the school.

Former pupils Frances Cairncross (editor of Economist); Paddy Higson (film producer); Sally Magnusson (TV presenter); Gudrun Ure (actress – Supergran); Moira McLeod (International British Olympic hockey player).

· *Lavant House* ·

Lavant House School
Lavant
Chichester
West Sussex
PO18 9AB
Tel 0243 527211

- Pupils 145
- Boys None
- Girls 7–18
- (Day/Board/Weekly)
- Upper sixth 8

- Termly fees
  £1440 (Day)
  £2415 (Board)
- GSA
  Enquiries/application to
  the Headmistress

What it's like

Founded in 1952, the main building is Lavant House, formerly the property of the Duke of Richmond, in a pleasant estate of 15 acres. It is a small school with a happy family atmosphere and has many of the advantages of being small. The modern facilities are good. A sound general education is provided and there is considerable emphasis on character values. Academic results are often excellent and half the leavers go on to degree courses each year, some to Oxbridge. Dutch, French, German and Spanish are offered up to A-level. An exceptionally high proportion of girls takes GCSE in more than one European language, and there are regular exchange arrangements with France and Spain. Virtually everyone is involved in music and plays an instrument. There are active drama and art clubs. A good range of games and sports and plentiful activities. The school has an enviable record in the Duke of Edinburgh's Bronze and Silver Awards Schemes.

School profile

Pupils Total age range 7–18; 145 girls, 120 day, 25 boarding. Senior department 11–18, 117 girls. Main entry ages 7, 11, 13 and into sixth. Approx 2% are children of former pupils. Own junior school provides 80+% senior intake. *Transfer from maintained schools:* 5% at 11.

Entrance Common entrance and own exam used. Not oversubscribed. No special skills or religious requirements. Parents expected to buy certain GCSE English text books and some A-level books; maximum extras £70 (day), £130 (boarding) for music, riding, dancing, etc. 6 scholarships/bursaries, £500 to £250.

Parents 15+% in industry or commerce. 65% live within 30 miles; up to 10% live overseas.

Staff Headmistress Mrs Y G Graham, first year in post. 9 full time staff, 11 part time. Annual turnover 10%.

Academic work GCSE and A-levels. 15 GCSE subjects offered; 16 at A-level (including A-level general studies). In 1990, 20 pupils in upper fifth, 3 in upper sixth (now 8). *GCSE:* in 1990, 13 upper fifth gained at least grade C in 8+ subjects; 4 in 5–7; and 3 in 1–4 subjects. *Computing facilities:* 8 BBC Masters in computer room. *Special provision:* EFL teaching (extra); teacher from Winchester Dyslexia Institute.

European Community *Languages:* Dutch offered: to age 14; GCSE; A-level. French offered: to age 14; GCSE; A-level. German offered: to age 14; GCSE; A-level. Spanish offered: to age 14; GCSE; A-level. Over 75% take GCSE in more than 1 EC language. *Exchanges:* Regular exchanges for pupils aged 11–16 to France and Spain. *Other:* European Studies offered to pupils aged 14–16. Pupils from Denmark, France, Germany and Spain spend half a term to a year in the school.

Senior pupils' non-academic activities *Music:* 107 learn a musical instrument, 1 to Grade 6 or above; 50 in 2 school choirs. *Drama and dance:* 10 in school productions, 6 take LAMDA exams. 1 accepted for Drama School. 4 entered competitions. *Art:* 15 take GCSE;

2 take A-level; 7 take A-level history of art. *Sport:* Lacrosse, netball, swimming, athletics, tennis, squash, badminton, volleyball, gymnastics, rounders and cricket available. All girls take part in sport. 4 represent county (lacrosse). *Other:* Sixth form take part in local community schemes. 18 have bronze Duke of Edinburgh's Award, 9 have silver. Other activities include a computer club, art club, science club, orchestra, pottery club, aerobics.

Careers On average, 60% leavers went on to degree courses; 10% to art/drama/music colleges; 20% to non-degree courses; 10% straight into careers (eg banking, stable management, theatre box office). Of those going on to degree courses, 15% went to Oxbridge, 35% to other universities; 50% to poly/colleges. 30% those going on to higher education went to courses in practical art; 10% in drama/acting; 40% in humanities/social sciences; 10% in medicine; and 10% in science/engineering.

Uniform School uniform worn except the sixth.

Houses/prefects Competitive houses. Prefects, head girl, head of house and house prefects – appointed by Head and staff.

Religion Religious worship at assembly, 3 times per week. Attendance at church, or service in school on Sunday for boarders. Carol Service; Confirmation.

Social Debates, sixth form dances and dinner parties with other schools. Organised trips abroad. Pupils allowed to bring own car/bike/horse to school. Meals self service. School shop. No tobacco allowed.

Discipline No corporal punishment. Pupils failing to produce homework once might expect a warning; those caught smoking cannabis on the premises would face expulsion.

Boarding 5 have own study bedroom, the remainder share. Central dining room. *Upper sixth* can provide and cook their own food. Exeats possible any weekend, except first and last in any term. Weekly boarding available. Visits to local town allowed.

· *Lawnside* ·

Lawnside	● Pupils 105	● Termly fees
Albert Road South	● Boys None	£1500 (Day)
Great Malvern	● Girls 11–18	£2620 (Board/
Worcestershire	(Day/Board)	Weekly)
WR14 3AJ	● Upper sixth 13	● GSA
Tel 0684 575504		Enquiries/application to the Registrar

What it's like

Founded c1818–20 by Caroline Cooper who rented a room and started a school with three pupils. It has unusually attractive Victorian buildings in beautiful landscaped gardens, and lies near the centre of the delightful town of Great Malvern on the slopes of the Malvern Hills. Recent developments include art and music schools, two libraries, laboratories and a design technology department. There is some emphasis on religious education and worship in the Anglican tradition (morning prayers, Sunday services, etc). A sound general education is provided and results are creditable; many sixth formers go on to degree courses. French, German and Spanish are offered to A-level, Italian to GCSE. There are regular exchanges to France, occasional exchanges to Spain. Music is particularly strong, partly because of a long-standing association with Edward Elgar. Most of the girls are involved in making music; there are three choirs, an orchestra and smaller ensembles. Drama is well supported as are arts and crafts. Lawnside has all the advantages of a small school: it aims at all-round development of abilities and close attention to individual needs. Sympathetic treatment and training is provided for those with learning difficulties. Sports and games are well catered for – there is a standard variety, including riding. Extensive use is made of local cultural facilities and events. Local community services are especially active; most girls are involved in these in the town.

School profile

Pupils Age range 11–18, 105 girls (5 day and 100 boarding). Main entry ages, 11, 12, 13 and into sixth. 5–10% are children of former pupils. *Transfer from maintained schools:* 5% main intakes.

Entrance Common entrance used (own exam if this is not possible). Not oversubscribed. No special skills or religious requirements (worship follows the Anglican tradition but girls of other faiths are accepted). Parents expected to buy only those text books pupils wish to retain. Average extras and sundries per term £235. 5 scholarships/bursaries pa (including art, music and sixth form), 33%–10% fees.

Parents 15+% from industry/commerce. 10+% live within 30 miles, 10+% live overseas.

Staff Head Miss J A Harvey, 1 year in post. 17 full time staff, 12 part time. Annual turnover less than 5%. Average age 43.

Academic work GCSE and A-levels. 25 subjects offered (not including A-level general studies). In 1990, 29 pupils in upper fifth, 13 in upper sixth. *GCSE:* in 1990, 13% upper fifth gained at least grade C in 8+ subjects; 71% in 5–7; and 16% in 1–4 subjects. *A-levels:* 40% upper sixth passed in 3 subjects; 55% in 2; and 5% in 1 subject. 10% took science A-levels; 70% arts/humanities; 20% both. *Computing facilities:* RM Nimbus network and some BBC Masters. *Special provision:* Individual help available for mildly dyslexic pupils; EFL classes available to Cambridge First Certificate level.

European Community *Languages:* French offered: to age 14; GCSE; AS-level; A-level. German offered: to age 14; GCSE; AS-level; A-level. Italian offered: to age 14; GCSE. Spanish offered: to age 14; GCSE; AS-level; A-level. 10–25% take GCSE in more than 1 EC language. *Exchanges:* Regular exchanges for pupils aged 14–16 to France and occasionally Spain. *Other:* Always have some EC pupils (3 weeks to 3 years).

Senior pupils' non-academic activities *Music:* Junior and senior choirs, chamber choir and orchestra. *Drama and dance:* Drama club, public speaking competition, LAMDA exams and local festivals. *Art:* Craft club. *Sport:* Hockey, netball, rounders, tennis, keep fit, swimming and many minority sports are available as extras. *Other:* All expected to participate in community service in town. Girls may join the Malvern Boys College CCF Unit.

Careers In 1990, 70% leavers went on to degree courses; 20% to non-degree courses (eg Montessori, agriculture); 10% other. Of those going on to degree courses, 57% to universities; 43% to poly/colleges. All those going on to higher education went to courses in humanities/social sciences.

Uniform School uniform worn except in sixth.

Houses/prefects Competitive houses. Head girl, prefects, head of house and house prefects, appointed by the head. School Council.

Religion Attendance at religious worship compulsory.

Social Social events with other Malvern schools (including maintained schools). Annual French trip. Upper sixth pupils allowed to bring own cars. Meals formal. Tuck shop. No tobacco allowed; alcohol only allowed to sixth form at specific social functions.

Discipline No corporal punishment. Punishment for pupils failing to produce homework once would be at the discretion of individual staff; those caught smoking cannabis on the premises could expect immediate suspension/ expulsion depending on circumstances.

Boarding Upper sixth have own study bedrooms; lower sixth share. Some juniors in dormitories of 6+. Houses divided by age, of up to 32. Resident qualified nurse. Some seniors may provide and cook own food. Half-term plus 1 or 2 exeats each term. Visits to the local town allowed for all pupils.

Alumni association is run by Miss M Dixey, 9 St James Road, Malvern, Worcestershire.

· *Laxton* ·

Laxton School
North Street
Oundle
Peterborough PE8 4AR
Tel 0832 73569

- Pupils 185
- Boys 11–18 (Day)
- Girls 11–18 (Day)
- Upper sixth 30

- Termly fees £1125
Enquiries/application to
the Headmaster's
secretary

What it's like

Founded in 1556 by Sir William Laxton as the town grammar school. In 1876 the Grocers' Company decided to divide the school and so founded Oundle School. Both are grouped together under the Oundle Group of Schools and governed by the Grocers' Company. It is C of E and became co-educational in 1989. There is close association with Oundle and academic integration at all levels. Indoor and outdoor facilities are shared but Laxton has its own Headmaster. In essence local boys and girls are accepted into Laxton and integrated into Oundle – just as any other day pupils would be. *SEE OUNDLE*

School profile

Pupils Age range 11–18; 185 pupils (128 boys, 57 girls). Main entry ages 11, 13 and into sixth (fully co-educational since 1989).

Entrance Own exam (at 11) or common entrance (at 13). Scholarships including 1 for music.

Staff Headmaster R I Briggs.

Alumni assocation is run by Keith Diggle, Greenfield House, 24 Cotterstock Road, Oundle, Peterborough PE8 5HA.

· *Leeds Grammar* ·

Leeds Grammar School	● Pupils 1155	● Termly fees
Moorland Road	● Boys 8–18	£1107 (Day)
Leeds	(Day)	● HMC
LS6 1AN	● Girls None	Enquiries/application to
Tel 0532 433417	● Upper sixth 140	the Headmaster's
		Secretary

What it's like

Founded in 1552 by Sir William Sheafield, priest of the Clarell Chantry in the city of Leeds, for the 'Education of Youths in the Learned Languages', and enlarged in 1624 by John Harrison. It grew steadily in size and reputation and in 1859 moved to its present site near the university. It has a traditional and respected role as the city's grammar school and is well sited to serve a wide surrounding area. It occupies an agreeable site with spacious grounds and playing fields plus other fields at Lawnswood three miles north. Since 1958 there has been a steady programme of development and extension: laboratories, classrooms, assembly hall, music centre, language labs, sports centre and design centre. Recently, an award–winning library has been constructed, a new theatre, and a £2 million science block. A distinguished school, it is very strongly supported in the city of Leeds. Academically high-powered, it has a long record of Oxbridge successes as well as a reputation for excellent results with average candidates. Each year very many pupils go on to university (including Oxbridge). Music, drama and art are all vigorously supported and in cultural enterprises there is a good deal of collaboration with the local Leeds Girls' High School. There is a wide range of sports and games and high standards are attained. Some 25 clubs and societies cater for most extra-curricular activities. There are also an active scout group and a venture scout unit, plus a large voluntary CCF (RAF and Army). Much emphasis is put on outdoor pursuits and for these the school has a well-equipped outdoor centre in the Pennines near Teesdale. All boys in the lower sixth (ie 140) are involved in local community services. Recently, there has been extensive participation in the Duke of Edinburgh's Award Scheme.

School profile

Pupils Total age range 8–18; 1155 day boys. Senior department 10–18; 1023 boys. Main entry ages 8, 10, 11, 13 and into sixth. *Transfer from maintained schools:* 50% senior intake, plus 50% to sixth.

Entrance Own entrance exam used. Oversubscribed. No special skills or religious requirements. Parents not expected to buy text books; maximum extras £70 (including lunches). 191 assisted places. 25 scholarships/bursaries per year.

Parents 15+% are doctors, lawyers, etc, 15+% in industry, 15+% academics.

Staff Headmaster B W Collins, in post for 5 years. 84 full time staff, 11 part time. Annual turnover 5%. Average age 30–40.

Academic work GCSE and A-levels. 18 GCSE subjects offered; 21 at A-level (including A-level business studies, Russian, general studies). In 1990, 143 pupils in upper fifth, 133 in upper sixth (now 140). *GCSE:* in 1990, 130 upper fifth gained at least grade C in 8+ subjects; 11 in 5–7; and 2 in 1–4 subjects. *A-levels:* 98 upper sixth passed in 4+ subjects; 30 in 3; 2 in 2; and 3 in 1 subject. 29% took science A-levels; 50% arts/humanities; 21% both. *Computing facilities:* Station network for CAL, IT, computer studies and private use plus computers in many departments for CAL, 'electronic blackboard'.

European Community *Languages:* French offered: to age 14; GCSE; AS-level; A-level. German offered: to age 14; GCSE; AS-level; A-level. 25–50% take GCSE in more than 1 EC language. *Exchanges:* Regular exchanges for pupils aged 14–18 to France and Germany.

Senior pupils' non-academic activities *Music:* Many learn a musical instrument, some to Grade 6 or above; 5 organ scholarships in last 8 years. 54 play in school orchestras, 60 in choirs, others in school concert band/other ensembles, some in National Youth Orchestra. *Drama:* Over 200 in school productions; 20 in sixth form course in theatre skills; others in Middle School and Junior drama clubs; 10 accepted for Drama Schools, National Youth Theatre/TV productions. 2 go on to work in theatre. *Art:* 25 take as non-examined subject; 41 take GCSE; 2 A-level; 10 take other exams. 2 accepted for Art School. *Sport:* Rugby, cricket, soccer, swimming, tennis, squash, badminton, athletics, golf, basketball, ski-ing, hockey, harriers, volleyball, weight-training, health–related fitness, cycling. 420 take part in non-compulsory sport. All juniors take swimming and gymnastic exams. *Other:* 75 boys participate in Duke of Edinburgh's Award Scheme. All lower sixth take part in local community schemes. Other activities include a computer club, astronomy, bird-watching, bridge, chess, debating, literary, model railways, outdoor pursuits, philosophy, war-games, CCF, scouts, etc.

Careers In 1990, 88% leavers went on to degree courses; 1% to art/drama/music colleges; 1% to non-degree courses (eg journalism); 8% straight into careers (eg army); 2% other. Of those going on to degree courses, 18% went to Oxbridge, 65% to other universities; 18% to poly/colleges. 1% those going on to higher education went to courses in practical art; 1% in drama/acting; 1% in music; 62% in humanities/social sciences; 8% in medicine; and 27% in science/engineering.

Uniform School uniform worn, own suit in sixth.

Houses/prefects Competitive houses. Prefects, head boy, head of house and house prefects – appointed by the Head. Sixth form committee.

Religion Non-denominational Christian assemblies/separate Jewish assemblies. Sunday chapel optional.

Social Arts programme with Leeds High (joint-foundation). Many organised trips abroad and exchange systems. Pupils allowed to bring own car/motorbike/bike to school. Meals cafeteria service. School shop. No tobacco/alcohol allowed.

Discipline No corporal punishment. Pupils failing to produce homework once might expect a warning and requirement to complete; those caught smoking cannabis on the premises could expect expulsion.

Alumni association is run by M J Buswell, Hon Secretary, Old Leodiensian Association, 22 Wynmore Avenue, Bramhope, Leeds LS16 9DE.

Former pupils Tony Harrison; Gerald Kaufman; Lord Diamond; Barry Cryer; Colin Montgomerie.

· *Leeds High* ·

Leeds Girls' High
School
Headingley Lane
Leeds LS6 1BN
Tel 0532 744000
Fax 0532 752217

- Pupils 980
- Boys 3–8 only
  (Day)
- Girls 3–18
  (Day)
- Upper sixth 85

- Termly fees
  £1043 (Day)
- GSA
  Enquiries/application to
  the Admissions
  Secretary

What it's like

The school is situated in Headingley, 2–3 miles from Leeds city centre and within walking distance of the university. Founded in 1876, it has elegant and well-equipped buildings in 10 acres of pleasant grounds with lawns and gardens. The junior school, Ford House, is 3 minutes' walk away. The prep school, Rose Court, is on the same site as the senior school. The teaching is good and academic standards are high; each year very many pupils go on to degree courses. Talent is encouraged across a wide range of activities. Self confidence, independence and a spirit of enquiry are developed, together with the promotion of co-operation and team-work. A personal and social education programme is in operation for all pupils. The school's Industrial Liaison Officer fosters links with local businesses, runs courses/conferences and arranges work experience/shadowing. Music and drama are strong and the Elinor Lupton Centre provides excellent facilities for work in these subjects, including a suite of individual practice rooms. There is also a modern sports complex with swimming pool on site. Extra-curricular activities are well catered for.

School profile

Pupils Total age range 3–18; 980 day pupils, (12 boys, 968 girls). Senior department, 11–18, 623 day girls. Main entry ages 3, 4 (boys and girls), 11 and into sixth (girls). Small proportion are children of former pupils. Junior school provides 50% of senior school. *Transfer from maintained schools:* 20% senior intake, plus 3% to sixth.

Entrance Own entrance exam used. Oversubscribed. No special skills or religious requirements. Parents not expected to buy text books. 142 assisted places. 7–10 scholarships pa (including 2 music), full to one-sixth fees.

Parents 15+% are doctors, lawyers, etc. 15+% in industry.

Staff Headmistress Miss P A Randall, in post for 14 years. 60 full time teaching staff, 13 part time.

Academic work GCSE, A-levels and S-levels. 20 subjects offered (including further maths, classical Greek, home economics and A-level general studies). In 1991, 90 pupils in upper fifth, 85 in upper sixth. *GCSE:* in 1990, 83 upper fifth gained at least grade C in 8+ subjects; 9 in 5–7; and 2 in 1–4 subjects. *A-levels:* 63 upper sixth passed in 4+ subjects; 12 in 3; 5 in 2; and 4 in 1 subject. 33% took science A-levels; 48% arts/humanities; 19% both. *Computing facilities:* Purpose-designed computer room with 35 machines with networking facilities, plus computers situated in several departments.

European Community *Languages:* French offered: to age 14; GCSE; AS-level; A-level. German offered: to age 14; GCSE; AS-level; A-level. 25–50% take GCSE in more than 1 EC language. *Exchanges:* Regular exchanges for pupils aged 14–18 to France and Germany. *Other:* 11–12 year olds spend 1 week in France. Many pupils have pen-friends in France/Germany. Visits and twinning with schools in eg France, Germany, Italy. **Senior pupils' non-academic activities** Music, sport, drama and art are all popular activities. The school has a flourishing choir and orchestra. Approx 52 senior school pupils take Guildhall exams. In 1991, 21 taking GCSE art, 6 A-level. 3 accepted for Art School. *Sport:* Hockey, netball, tennis, rounders, swimming, athletics, badminton, volleyball, keep fit, trampolining available. Many teams; pupils in city and county teams. Other activities include drama, electronics, debating, Christian Union, life saving, regular walking/conservation weekends. Young Enterprise. Computer room open to all during lunch period and to seniors when free.

Careers In 1990, 83% leavers went on to degree courses; 2% to art/drama/music colleges; 8% to non-degree courses (eg agriculture, BTEC leisure, secretarial, nursing); 3% straight into careers (eg banking, management); 4% other. Of those going on to degree courses, 7% went to Oxbridge, 77% to other universities; 16% to poly/colleges.

Uniform School uniform worn, except in sixth.

Houses/prefects Competitive houses. Head girl, head of house and house prefects – elected by staff and sixth. School Council.

Religion Non-denominational assemblies daily. Pupils may opt for separate Jewish assemblies.

Social Joint social activities, clubs, musical and drama events with other schools particularly Leeds Grammar. Annual skiing trip. Pupils allowed to bring own car/bike to school. Meals self service. No tobacco/alcohol allowed.

Alumni association is run by Mrs B L Askey, 40 Spennithorne Avenue, Leeds, LS16 6JA.

· *Leicester Grammar* ·

Leicester Grammar School 8 Peacock Lane Leicester LE1 5PX Tel 0533 621221	• Pupils 550 • Boys 10–18 (Day) • Girls 10–18 (Day) • Upper sixth 60	• Termly fees £980 (Day) Enquiries/application to the Headmaster

What it's like

Founded in 1981 as a direct result of the loss of the city's grammar schools through reorganisation. It is housed in two late Victorian buildings in the cathedral precinct in the middle of Leicester. These buildings have been extensively modernised to provide up-to-date facilities. The school's growth has been remarkable: from an original 90 pupils to 550 in nine years; a success story which reflects much credit on those involved – and highlights the needs of the community. The curriculum is geared to the academic rather than the average pupil (good staff:pupil ratio of 1:11). French and German are taught right through the school to A-level; Italian to GCSE and Spanish to 14. A large proportion of pupils takes GCSE in more than one European language and there are regular exchange arrangements with France and Germany. Fees are kept low. Exceptionally strong departments in music, drama and art. A good standard of general education is provided. A full range of games, sports (civic amenities are used) and activities. The school enjoys vigorous local support and has a substantial commitment to local community schemes.

School profile

Pupils Total age range 10–18; 550 day pupils (284 boys, 266 girls). Senior department 11–18, 510 pupils (264 boys, 246 girls). Main entry ages 10, 11, 13 and into sixth. *Transfer from maintained schools:* 70% senior intake, plus 30% to sixth.

Entrance Common entrance and own entrance exam mainly used. Oversubscribed. No special skills or religious requirements; open to all faiths. Meals and non-curricular excursions extra. Assisted places. Scholarships/bursaries, up to full fees.

Parents 15+% in industry or commerce.

Staff Headmaster John B Sugden, 1 year in post. 40 full time staff, 12 part time. Annual turnover 4%. Average age 36.

Academic work GCSE and A-levels. 21 GCSE subjects offered; 21 at A-level (including A-level general studies). In 1990, 74 pupils in upper fifth, 48 in upper sixth (now 60). *GCSE:* in 1989, 61 upper fifth gained at least grade C in 8+ subjects; 12 in 5–7; and 1 in 1–4 subjects. *A-levels:* 9 upper sixth passed in 4+ subjects; 31 in 3; 5 in 2; and 3 in 1 subject. 31% took science A-levels; 27% arts/humanities; 42% both. *Computing facilities:* Computer laboratory; IT servicing for other departments.

European Community *Languages:* French offered: to age 14; GCSE; AS-level; A-level. German offered: to age 14; GCSE; AS-level; A-level. Italian offered: to GCSE. Spanish offered: to age 14. 25–50% take GCSE in more than 1 EC language. *Exchanges:* Regular exchanges for pupils aged 14–18 to France and Germany.

Senior pupils' non-academic activities *Music:* 322 learn a musical instrument, 33 to Grade 7 or above; 68 in school orchestras, 74 in school choirs, jazzband, 15 in school pop groups; dance band; chamber ensembles; wind band; recorder groups; 20 in Leicestershire schools orchestras. *Drama and dance:* 205 in school productions. *Art:* 275 take as non-examined subject; 36 take GCSE; 5 take A-level. 24 belong to eg photographic club and 26 in sketch club. *Sport:* Rugby football, hockey, basketball, netball, tennis, cricket, athletics, squash, swimming and badminton available. 255 take non-compulsory sport. *Other:* 65 take part in local community schemes. Other activities include a computer club, gymnastics, fitness club, chess, bridge, table tennis and dramatic societies.

Careers In 1990, 94% leavers went on to degree courses; 4% to non-degree courses (eg HND); 2% straight into careers (eg retail management). Of those going on to degree courses, 13% went to Oxbridge, 62% to other universities; 26% to poly/colleges. 2% those going on to higher education went to courses in music; 42% in humanities/social sciences/law/languages; 4% in medicine; 34% in science/engineering; and 18% in business/economics.

Uniform School uniform worn except the sixth.

Houses/prefects Competitive houses. Prefects, head boy and girl, head of house and house prefects – appointed by the Headmaster in consultation with staff and prefects.

Religion Daily assembly, monthly cathedral services for all.

Social Pupils take part in local competitions for debating and academic activities (eg science, geography, classical reading). French, German, Russian exchanges, classical tours and ski trips abroad. Pupils allowed to bring own bike to school. Meals self service. School shop. No tobacco/alcohol allowed.

Discipline Extensive pastoral care through heads of year and houses. Major sanctions: detention and extra work. Bullying and drugs would invite expulsion.

Alumni association is run by C L Duckworth, 12 Plantation Avenue, Leicester.

· *Leighton Park* ·

Leighton Park School
Shinfield Road
Reading
Berkshire
RG2 7DH
Tel 0734 872065

- Pupils 360
- Boys 11–18
  (Day/Board)
- Girls 16–18
  (Day/Board)
- Upper sixth 58

- Termly fees
  £2217 (Day)
  £2958 (Board)
- HMC
  Enquiries/application to
  the Headmaster

What it's like

Founded in 1890, it is not far from the middle of Reading but enjoys a most peaceful environment of 70 acres of lovely wooded grounds, formerly the estates of two large country houses. Some of the well-designed school buildings are 19th-century, some 20th. A considerable development programme currently includes 2 new boarding houses, a science and technology centre, a library and study centre and an all-weather pitch. The junior school is combined and the facilities are excellent. A Quaker school, it lays considerable emphasis on Quaker philosophy and adheres to the principles and practice of Quakerism which, of its nature, is ecumenical and tolerant. The teaching is good and academic standards are high. Many sixth formers proceed to degree courses, including Oxbridge. Part of the GCSE course in all subjects is taught at Lycée St Stanislas, Nantes, France. There are five European languages on offer at GCSE level – French, German, Italian, Portuguese and Spanish. Many pupils take GCSE in more than one European language, and there are regular exchange arrangements with France and Germany. Extremely strong in music; good drama and art. High level in sports and games (a lot of representatives of county standard). Much emphasis on outdoor pursuits and adventure training. Big commitment to local community services (a lot of post-school voluntary work). Wide range of activities, including an unusual number of hobby interests, and an impressive record in the Duke of Edinburgh's Award Scheme.

School profile

Pupils Age range 11–18; 360 pupils, 125 day (121 boys, 4 girls), 235 boarding (210 boys, 25 girls). Main entry ages 11, 13 (boys) and into sixth (boys and girls). Approx 10% are children of former pupils. *Transfer from maintained schools:* 90% intake at 11, 20% at 13, plus 40% to sixth.

Entrance Common entrance and own entrance exam used. Fully subscribed. Pupils must be in top 25% of ability range; no religious requirements. Parents only expected to buy sixth form text books; music tuition extra (£96 per term). 50 scholarships/bursaries, 75%-25% of fees.

Parents 15+% in industry or commerce. 30+% live within 30 miles; 10+% live overseas.

Staff Headmaster John A Chapman, in post for 5 years. 37 full time staff, 25 part time (including music). Annual turnover 7%. Average age 35–40.

Academic work GCSE and A-levels. 17 GCSE and A-level subjects offered (no A-level general studies). In 1990, 58 pupils in upper fifth, 58 in upper sixth. *GCSE:* in 1990, 35% upper fifth gained at least grade C in 8+ subjects; 40% in 5–7; and 25% in 1–4 subjects. *A-levels:* 3% upper sixth passed in 4+ subjects; 64% in 3; 27% in 2; and 6% in 1 subject. 33% took science A-levels; 33% arts/humanities; 33% both. *Computing facili-*

442

ties: 2 computer rooms; computers in each boarding house, and in each academic department. *Special provision:* Special classes.

European Community *Languages:* French offered: to age 14; GCSE; A-level. German offered: to GCSE; AS-level; A-level. Italian offered: to GCSE. Portuguese offered: to GCSE. Spanish offered: to GCSE. 25–50% take GCSE in more than 1 EC language. *Exchanges:* Regular exchanges for pupils aged 14–18 to France and Germany. *Other:* Part of GCSE course (all subjects) taught at Lycée St Stanislas, Nantes, France; French pupils will be taught their syllabus at Leighton Park.

Senior pupils' non-academic activities *Music:* 175 learn a musical instrument, 25 to Grade 6 or above, 2–4 pa accepted for Music School, 10–20 play in pop group beyond school; 25 in school orchestra, 20 in choir, 10 in pop group, 60+ in brass, jazz and big bands; 2 in National Youth Orchestra; 10 in local orchestras. *Drama and dance:* 50 in school productions. 2 take to Grade 6 in ESB, RAD etc. 2–3 accepted for Drama/Dance Schools. *Art:* 20 take GCSE; 12, A-level. 2–3 accepted for Art School; 2–3 accepted for foundation art courses. 20 belong to printing or other art clubs. *Sport:* Rugby, soccer, basketball, canoeing, athletics, cross-country, swimming, tennis, cricket, hockey, squash, golf available. 180 take non-compulsory sport. 12 represent county/country at various sports. *Other:* 20 take part in local community schemes. 20 have bronze Duke of Edinburgh's Award, 10 have silver and 5 gold. 20 enter voluntary schemes after leaving school; 30 work for national charities eg Amnesty. Other activities include a computer club and 58 other hobbies/interests.

Careers In 1990, 80% sixth form leavers went on to degree courses; 15% to art/drama/music colleges; 5% to non-degree courses (eg repeating A-levels) or straight into careers. Of those going on to degree courses, 5% went to Oxbridge, 75% to other universities; 20% to poly/colleges. 12% those going on to higher education went to courses in practical art; 3% in drama/acting; 7% in music; 42% in humanities/social sciences; 7% in medicine; and 29% in science/engineering.

Uniform School dress code followed throughout.

Houses/prefects Competitive houses. Prefects, head boy/girl, head of house and house prefects – appointed by the Head and school. School Council.

Religion Some compulsory worship in the Quaker manner.

Social Regular conferences at sixth form level and discos with other schools, also Challenge of Industry events. Organised trips abroad and exchange systems. Meals formal. School shop. No tobacco/alcohol allowed.

Discipline No corporal punishment. Pupils failing to produce homework once might expect extra prep or detention work; anyone caught smoking cannabis on the premises would be asked to leave.

Boarding 10% have own study bedroom, 20% share; 20% are in dormitories of 6+. Houses, of approximately 65–75. Resident qualified medical staff. Pupils can provide and cook own food. Weekly exeats, if required. Visits to the local town allowed.

Former pupils Michael Foot; David Lean; Richard Rodney Bennett; Laurence Gowing; Lord Caradon; Bishop Newbigin; Peter Cadbury; Karel Reisz; Tony Baldry; Basil Bunting; Lord Seebohm.

· *Leys* ·

The Leys School
Cambridge
CB2 2AD
Tel 0223 355327

- Pupils 400
- Boys 13–18
  (Day/Board)
- Girls 16–18
  (Day/Board)
- Upper sixth 77

- Termly fees
  £2190 (Day)
  £2960 (Board)
- HMC
  Enquiries/application to
  the Headmaster

What it's like

Founded in 1875, it has a compact site on the edge of the city, bounded by common land on two sides and close to the river. The main buildings are late Victorian and very pleasing, and lie in 50 acres of delightful grounds and playing fields. Modern extensions provide excellent facilities, including a big design and technology centre. It is a Methodist foundation but inter-denominational. A large staff allows a staff:pupil ratio of about 1:9. An informal and friendly atmosphere characterises the school. The standard of teaching is high (there is a particularly good tutorial system) and results are good. Very many leavers go on to university each year. Very strong in music, drama and art. A wide range of sports and games and a very good variety of activities. Plentiful use is made of the cultural amenities of Cambridge. A substantial commitment to local community schemes and an outstanding record in the Duke of Edinburgh's Award Scheme.

School profile

Pupils Age range 13–18; 400 pupils, 100 day (96 boys, 4 girls), 300 boarding (234 boys, 56 girls). Main entry ages 13, 14 (boys) and into sixth (boys and girls). Approx 14% are children of former pupils. St Faith's Prep School provides more than 20% of intake. *Transfer from maintained schools:* 2.5% main intake, plus 10% to sixth.

Entrance Common entrance and own entrance exam used. Oversubscribed (for sixth form girls' places). Fairly high academic attainment and extra-curricular interests looked for. No special religious requirements, Methodist foundation with ecumenical tradition. Parents expected to buy text books. 12 assisted places. 18 scholarships/bursaries, 50% to 10% of fees.

Parents 15+% are doctors, lawyers, etc; 15+% in industry or commerce. 30+% live within 30 miles; up to 10% live overseas.

Staff Headmaster John Barrett, first year in post. 45 full time staff, 8 part time. Annual turnover 5%. Average age 40.

Academic work GCSE and A-levels. 19 subjects offered (including business studies, theatre studies, design and technology; no A-level general studies). In 1990, 74 pupils in upper fifth, 77 in upper sixth. *GCSE:* in 1990, 50 upper fifth gained at least grade C in 8+ subjects; 18 in 5–7; and 6 in 1–4 subjects. *A-levels:* 4 upper sixth passed in 4+ subjects; 61 in 3; 6 in 2; and 5 in 1 subject. 26 took science A-levels; 40 arts/humanities; 11 both. *Computing facilities:* Laboratory of 20 computers. Computers in all departments. *Special provision:* Private tuition can be arranged for pupils with eg dyslexia.

European Community *Languages:* French offered: to GCSE; A-level. German offered: to GCSE; A-level. 25–50% take GCSE in more than 1 EC language. *Other:* Regularly have German pupils in lower sixth, mostly for 1 year.

Senior pupils' non-academic activities *Music:* 87 learn a musical instrument, 29 to Grade 6 or above; 31 in school orchestra, 21 in school choir, 7 in school pop group; 3 in county orchestra. 9 in jazz band. *Drama and dance:* 80 in school productions, 50 in house plays, 58 in first year activities. 32, GCSE; 25, A-level. 3 accepted for Drama/Dance Schools, 2 go on to work in theatre. *Art:* 175 take as non–examined subject; 30 take GCSE; 16 take A-level. 8 accepted for Art School; 4 for architecture. 10 belong to photographic club; 50 calligraphy and mixed crafts. Ceramics included for senior year group. *Sport:* Rugby, football, cricket, hockey, squash, water-polo, swimming, fencing, soccer, tennis, athletics, shooting, sailing, rowing, canoeing, jazz and contemporary dance, clay-pigeon shooting available. All 270 take part in compulsory sport. 14 pupils represent county/country (rugby, hockey and cricket). *Other:* 80 take part in local community schemes. 24 have bronze Duke of Edinburgh's Award, 32 have silver and 16 gold. Other activities include a computer club, debating and public speaking, local history society, philosophical society, science society, Christian Union, chess club, CCF (100 Army and 45 RAF cadets) etc.

Careers In 1990, 77% leavers went on to degree courses; 4% to art/drama/ music colleges; 5% to non-degree courses (eg Sandhurst, HND horticulture); 6% straight into careers (eg nursing, banking, RAF); 8% other. Of those going on to degree courses, 7% went to Oxbridge, 62% to other universities; 31% to poly/ colleges. 8% those going on to higher education went to courses in practical art; 3% in drama/acting; 57% in humanities/ social sciences; 4% in medicine; and 28% in science/engineering.

Uniform School uniform worn, modified in the sixth.

Houses/prefects Competitive houses. Prefects, head boy/girl, head of house and house prefects – appointed by the Head or housemasters.

Religion Services on Wednesdays and Sundays, 'religious' assembly on Fridays.

Social Organised local events include inter-school debates and public speaking competitions (eg ESU); combined choral concerts; Schools Challenge (inter– schools quiz contests). Visits to classical sites abroad, cultural visits (art and art history); individual language exchanges; ski trips, walking holidays in Alps; choir tours. Pupils allowed to bring own bike to school. Meals self service. School shop. No tobacco/alcohol allowed.

Discipline No corporal punishment. Pupils failing to produce homework once might expect work to be re-done and seen by the housemaster; those caught smoking cannabis on the premises can expect expulsion.

Boarding 30% have own study bedroom, 25% share with others; 45% are in dormitories of 6+. Single sex houses, of 50–65, same as competitive houses. Resident qualified medical staff. Central dining room. Pupils can provide and cook their own food. Two exeats each term. Visits to the local town allowed once or twice a week.

Alumni association is run by The Secretary, OLU: Mr P R Chamberlain; editor of the OL Directory: Mr M Howard – both c/o the school.

Former pupils Sir Alastair Burnet; Martin Bell (BBC TV correspondent); J G Ballard (fiction writer); Richard Heffer (actor).

· *Licensed Victuallers' (Ascot)* ·

Licensed Victuallers'
School
London Road
Ascot
Berkshire SL5 8DR
Tel 0344 882770
Fax 0344 884703

- Pupils 714
- Boys 5–18
  (Day/Board/Weekly)
- Girls 5–18
  (Day/Board/Weekly)
- Upper sixth 43

- Termly fees
  £1350 (Day)
  £2400 (Board)
  £2350 (Weekly
- SHMIS
  Enquiries/application to
  the Admissions
  Secretary

What it's like

Founded in London in 1803, the school has enjoyed royal patronage since 1830. It moved to Slough in 1921, and thence in 1989 to new premises on a 26-acre site at Ascot. The new buildings include boarding houses, a self-contained junior school, sports complex, theatre, chapel and re-equipped teaching facilities. There are extensive outdoor facilities for games and recreation including a fishing lake. The new school is well equipped for information technology. The founders' intention was to cater for pupils of all abilities and this remains the case today. The junior department (5–10) provides a firm grounding in the basic skills of literacy and numeracy within a framework which closely reflects the national curriculum. All subjects in the senior school are taught in setted groups with pupils expected to take GCSE examinations in all subjects followed. All pupils follow a core curriculum of mathematics, English, balanced science, technology and modern European languages. In addition the option system requires all pupils to follow courses in humanities, creative studies, PE and careers to the age of 16. The underlying aim is to encourage self-motivation and independence across a wide ability range. For this reason the school has a wide range of GCSE and A-level subject options including PE, Drama, Technology and Music. At GCSE level, Dutch, French, German, Italian and Spanish are offered; at A-level French, Italian and Spanish. There are regular exchange arrangements with France, Germany and Spain for all age groups. The sixth form courses include A-levels and a General Studies course for all.

School profile

Pupils Total age range 5–18; 714 pupils, 507 day (345 boys, 162 girls), 207 boarding (138 boys, 69 girls). Senior department 11–18, 511 pupils (346 boys, 165 girls). Main entry ages 5, 7, 11 and into sixth (boys and girls) plus 13 (boys). Very few are children of former pupils. 40% senior intake from own junior school. *Transfer from maintained schools:* 60% of main intake 11+ and over, plus 50+% into sixth.

Entrance Oversubscribed at certain ages (especially junior). No special skills or religious requirements. Parents expected to buy text books; maximum extras, £80.

12 scholarships/bursaries pa, £1000–£500.

Parents 20+% are licensees. 60+% live within 30 miles; 10+% live overseas.

Staff Headmaster Mr W J Powell, in post for 2 years. 68 full time staff, 4 part time. Annual turnover 10%. Average age 36.

Academic work GCSE, AS and A-levels. 25 subjects offered (including general studies at GCSE and AS level). In 1990, 90 pupils in year 11 (GCSE year), 43 in upper sixth. *GCSE:* in 1990, 18 pupils in year 11 gained at least grade C in 8+ subjects; 27 in 5–7; and 45 in 1–4 subjects. *A-levels:* in 1990 6 upper sixth passed in 3 subjects; 11 in 2; and 13 in 1 subject. 16 took science A-levels; 16 arts/humanities; 10 both. *Computing facilities:* 3 rooms of 20 stations plus numerous stand alone computers and department networks. *Special provision:* Special unit for learning difficulties.

European Community *Languages:* Dutch offered: to GCSE (self-help). French offered: to age 14; GCSE; A-level. German offered: to age 14; GCSE. Italian offered: to GCSE (self-help); A-level. Spanish offered: to age 14; GCSE; A-level. All pupils choose their first European language from French, German or Spanish after short introductory course. *Exchanges:* Regular exchanges for pupils aged 11–18 to France, Germany and Spain. *Other:* Number of local EC residents have children in school.

Senior pupils' non-academic activities *Music:* 240 learn a musical instrument, 8 to Grade 6 or above. 40 in school orchestra, 50 in school choir, 6 in school pop group. *Drama and dance:* 50+ in school productions; 1 accepted for Drama/Dance School. *Art:* 14 take as non-examined subject, 25 take GCSE; 9, A-level. 2 accepted for Art School. *Sport:* Football, rugby, basketball, volleyball, tennis, cross-country, table tennis, netball, hockey, indoor and outdoor rounders, weight training, cricket, athletics, swimming, gymnastics, badminton available. 70% take non-compulsory sport. 25 take exams. 5–6 represent county. *Other:* 36 have bronze Duke of Edinburgh's Award, 7 gold. Other activities include clubs for computers, all sporting activities, chess, board games, flying, fishing, rowing, art, metalwork, scuba diving, water polo, trampoline, etc.

Careers In 1990, 7% leavers went on to degree courses; 6% to art/drama/music colleges; 75% to non-degree courses (eg BTEC business and finance, catering); 12% straight into careers (eg catering, retailing). Of those going on to degree courses, 38% went to universities; 62% to poly/colleges. 36% those going on to higher education went to courses in practical art; 9% in drama/acting; 36% in humanities/social sciences; and 18% in science/engineering.

Uniform School uniform worn, modified in sixth.

Houses/prefects Competitive houses. Prefects, head boy and girl, head of house and house prefects – appointed by the Head.

Religion Attendance at religious worship compulsory.

Social Sports fixtures for all sports with local schools. French exchange (year 9 two GCSE pupils and lower sixth); German exchange (GCSE pupils). Meals self service. School shop. No tobacco/alcohol allowed.

Discipline No corporal punishment. Pupils failing to produce homework once might expect extra work or detention depending on circumstances. Those caught smoking cannabis on premises would expect to be expelled.

Boarding 10% have own study bedroom, 40% share; 25% in dormitories of 6+. Houses (single sex senior, mixed junior) up to 60, same as for competitive purposes. Resident qualified nurse. 6 exeats per year – Friday afternoon to Sunday evening. Weekend visits to local town allowed at 13 and over.

Former pupils John Moore MP.

· *Lime House* ·

Lime House School
Holm Hill
Dalston, Carlisle
Cumbria
CA5 7BX
Tel 0228 710 225

- Pupils 308
- Boys 4–18
  (Day/Board/Weekly)
- Girls 4–18
  (Day/Board/Weekly)
- Upper sixth 35

- Termly fees
  £750 (Day)
  £1750 (Board)
  £1400 (Weekly)
- ISAI
Enquiries/application to
the Chairman of the
Board of Governors

What it's like

Founded in 1899 at Wetheral, it moved in 1947 to its present site near Dalston where it lies in 100 acres of its own very agreeable grounds which are surrounded by a large private estate. The main building (a fine country house built in 1638) has been extensively modernised to provide good accommodation. Other facilities and buildings are nearby. It has all the advantages of a small school and enjoys a high staff:pupil ratio. French and German are offered throughout the school up to A-level; Dutch and Spanish are also taught to pupils aged 11–14 and Spanish may be taken as a non-examined subject at a greater age. There are regular exchange arrangements with France, Italy and Spain. Strong music, art and drama depts. A range of sports, games and activities. Some commitment to local community schemes and the Duke of Edinburgh's Award Scheme and school farm.

School profile

Pupils Total age range 4–18; 308 pupils, 88 day (40 boys, 48 girls), 220 boarding (140 boys, 80 girls). Senior department 11–18, 209 pupils (109 boys, 100 girls). Entry at any age. Approx 31% are children of former pupils.

Entrance Common entrance and own entrance exam used. Not oversubscribed. No special skills or religious requirements. Parents not expected to buy text books; maximum extras £87 per term. No assisted places. 12 scholarships/bursaries per year.

Parents 15+% in industry or commerce; 15+% in the armed services. 10+% live within 30 miles; 10+% live overseas.

Staff Headmaster N A Rice, in post for 8 years. 40 full time staff, 8 part time. Annual turnover 1%. Average age 36.

Academic work GCSE and A-levels. Chinese, technical drawing, Dutch, pottery, PE offered to GCSE/A-level. Average size of upper fifth, 40; upper sixth, 25 (currently 35). *GCSE:* on aver-

age, 4 pupils in upper fifth pass 8+ subjects; 30, 5–7 subjects; 6 pass 1–4 subjects. *A-levels:* on average, 20 pupils in the upper sixth pass 2–3 subjects; 5 pass 2 subjects. An even spread across science/engineering, and arts/humanities A-levels. *Computing facilities:* 20 interlinked Spectrums with disc drives, 12 BBC B interlinked into Prestel, 6 Commodore PCs. *Special provision:* Dyslexic unit; some EFL provision.

European Community *Languages:* Dutch offered: to age 14. French offered: to age 14; GCSE; AS-level; A-level. German offered: to age 14; GCSE; AS-level; A-level. Spanish offered: to age 14; non-examined subject. 50–75% take GCSE in more than 1 EC language. *Exchanges:* Regular exchanges for pupils aged 14–18 to France, Italy and Spain.

Senior pupils' non-academic activities *Music:* 60% learn a musical instrument, 31% to Grade 6 or above; 20% in school orchestra, 20% in school choir. *Drama and dance:* All in school productions. 2–3 accepted for Drama/Dance schools per year. *Art:* 12% take as non-examined subject; 15 take GCSE; 4 take A-level. 4–6 accepted for Art School per year. 20 belong to eg photographic club. *Sport:* All sports available. 50% take non-compulsory sport. 20% take exams eg swimming. Some represent county (hockey, football, rugby, athletics, netball, swimming, golf, tennis). *Other:* Pupils involved in local community schemes, and Duke of Edinburgh's Award, at all levels. Pupils enter voluntary schemes after leaving school. Other activities include a computer club, driving instruction, ski-ing, chess and train clubs.

Careers 1 full time and 1 part time adviser. Average number of pupils accepted for *arts and humanities degree courses* at universities, 3; polytechnics or CHE, 3. *other general training courses*, 12. Average number of pupils going straight into careers in the armed services, 20–25; industry, 11; the City, 2; the civil service, 4; music/drama, 1.

Uniform School uniform worn throughout.

Houses/prefects Competitive houses. Prefects, head boy/girl, head of house and house prefects – appointed by the Head, School Governors and the School.

Religion Religious worship compulsory.

Social No organised events with local schools. Organised trips abroad. Pupils allowed to bring own car/bike/motorbike to school. Some meals formal, some self service. School shop. No tobacco/alcohol allowed.

Discipline Pupils failing to produce homework once might expect detention; those caught smoking on the premises might expect removal of privileges.

Boarding Fifth and sixth formers have own bedroom, most others share with 2 others; 10% are in dormitories of 6+. Houses, of approximately 38, are divided by age group and sex. Resident qualified nurse. Central dining room. Three half terms per year. Visits to local town allowed.

Former pupils Michael Rodd; James Fox; E Kaunda.

· *Liverpool College* ·

Liverpool College	● Pupils 695	● Termly fees
Mossley Hill	● Boys 5–18 (Day)	£1025 (Day)
Liverpool L18 8BE	● Girls 16–18 (Day)	● HMC
Tel 051 724 1563	● Upper sixth 70	Enquiries/application to the Headmaster

What it's like

Founded in 1840, it moved to its present premises at Mossley Hill in the 1930s. It is single-site and suburban in 26 acres of grounds and playing fields in a pleasant area. The buildings are mostly modern and well-equipped. Three schools (preparatory, lower and upper) are separate but all on the same campus. A C of E foundation (but thoroughly ecumenical) it has high academic standards and good results (many go on to degree courses each year, including Oxbridge). Strong in music, games and sports. The CCF is very active. Some participation in local community schemes, and quite a lot in the Duke of Edinburgh's Award Scheme. The school has a good reputation and enjoys vigorous local support.

School profile

Pupils Total age range 5–18; 695 day pupils (669 boys, 26 girls). Senior department 11–18, 398 pupils (372 boys, 26 girls). Main entry ages 5, 11 (boys) and into sixth (boys and girls). *Transfer from maintained schools:* 35% senior intake, plus 10% to sixth.

Entrance Own entrance exam used. Oversubscribed (though not all pass exam). No special skills or religious requirements. Parents expected to buy text books in sixth only. 175 assisted places. 8 scholarships/bursaries, £100 to half fees; plus 4 music scholarships and bursaries pa, up to half fees.

Parents 15+% in industry or commerce; 15+% are doctors and lawyers, etc.

Staff Headmaster R V Haygarth, in post for 11 years. 52 full time staff, 2 part time. Annual turnover 5%. Average age 40.

Academic work GCSE and A-levels. 15 GCSE subjects offered; 20 at A-level (including A-level general studies). In 1989, 77 pupils in upper fifth, 70 in upper sixth. *GCSE:* in 1989, 33 upper fifth gained at least grade C in 8+ subjects; 28 in 5–7; and 16 in 1–4 subjects. *A-levels:* 3 upper sixth passed in 4+ subjects; 42 in 3; 21 in 2; and 4 in 1 subject. 40% took science A-levels; 37% arts/humanities; 23% both. *Computing facilities:* 4-room IT centre.

Senior pupils' non-academic activities *Music:* 100+ learn a musical instrument, 10 to Grade 6 or above. 1 accepted for Music School; some play in pop group beyond school. 40 in school orchestra, 50+ in choir; 5 in local youth orchestra. *Drama and dance:* 150 in school productions; 1 accepted for Drama/Dance School. *Art:* 400+ take as non-examined subject; 20 take GCSE; 5, A-level. 2 accepted for Art School; 10+ belong to photographic club. *Sport:* Rugby, cricket, hockey, athletics, cross-country, tennis, swimming, badminton, golf, cycling available. 50 in lower school take swimming exams. 11 represent county/country (rugby, hockey, tennis). *Other:* 15 take part in local community schemes. 30 have bronze Duke of Edinburgh's Award, 10 have silver. Other activities include a computer club, plus over 20 different societies, CCF and debating especially strong.

Careers 6 part time advisers. Annual average accepted for *arts and humanities degree courses* at Oxbridge, 2; other universities, 14; polytechnics/colleges, 4. *science and engineering degree courses* at Oxbridge, 3; other universities, 25; medical schools, 5; polytechnics/colleges, 6. *BEd,* 1. *other general training courses,* 1. Average going straight into careers in the armed services, 1; industry, 2; music/drama, 1. Traditional school careers, medicine, engineering.

Uniform School uniform worn throughout.

Houses/prefects Competitive and pastoral houses. All sixth formers have prefectorial duties. Head boy/girl, head of house and house prefects – appointed by the Head and Common Room.

Religion A C of E foundation. All pupils attend unless parents wish them not to.

Social No organised events with local schools. Organised trips abroad. Pupils allowed to bring own car/bike/motorbike to school. Meals self service. No tobacco/alcohol allowed.

Discipline No corporal punishment. Pupils failing to produce homework once might expect detention; those caught smoking cannabis on the premises could expect probable expulsion.

Alumni association run by The Bursar, c/o the College.

· *Llandovery* ·

Llandovery College
Llandovery
Dyfed
SA20 0EE
Tel 0550 20315

- Pupils 225
- Boys 11–18 (Day/ Board)
- Girls 11–18 (Day/ Board)
- Upper sixth 37

- Termly fees
  £1423 (Day)
  £2181 (Board/ Weekly)
- HMC
  Enquiries/application to the Warden

What it's like

Founded and endowed by Dr Thomas Phillips in 1847, it has a fine site amidst magnificent countryside in the small market town of Llandovery. The extensive grounds and playing fields run alongside 2 miles of the River Towy. It was founded to provide a classical and liberal education in which the Welsh language and the study of Welsh literature and history were to be cultivated. The original buildings are handsome and well appointed and there have been a number of good additions and improvements. It is now very well equipped. There is a daily morning service for all pupils and Eucharist on Sundays for boarders. Academically – as in other respects – Llandovery is one of the most distinguished schools in Wales. The staff:pupil ratio is about 1:11. Academic standards are high and results consistently good. Very many pupils go on to degree courses, including Oxbridge. Welsh is compulsory for all boys in the first two years and special provision is made for beginners. In addition to Welsh, French is offered to A-level, German to GCSE. An exceptionally high proportion of pupils takes GCSE in more than one of these three European languages. The college is strong in music and drama and the majority of the pupils are involved in these. There is an annual programme of visiting artists and lecturers. Sports and games are compulsory and the college has an outstanding record in these (especially rugby), with many representatives at county, regional and national level. There is considerable emphasis on outdoor pursuits which include fishing, canoeing, CCF and fell-walking. The college takes part in the Duke of Edinburgh's Award Scheme with considerable success (some 12 pupils gain gold standard each year).

School profile

Pupils Age range 11–18; 225 pupils, 56 day (28 boys, 28 girls), 169 boarding (126 boys, 43 girls). Main entry ages, 11, 13 and into sixth. 5% are children of former pupils. *Transfer from maintained schools:* 80% main intakes, 90% to sixth.

Entrance Common entrance and own exam used. Slightly oversubscribed (particularly to sixth). No special skills or religious requirements. Parents not expected to buy text books. Average extras, £100 per term. 12 assisted places pa. 10 scholarships/bursaries pa, half fees to £500.

Parents 30+% live within 30 miles, less than 10% live overseas.

Staff Headmaster Dr C E Evans, 3 years in post. 23 full time staff, 4 part time. Annual turnover 10%. Average age 45.

Academic work GCSE and A-levels. 18 subjects offered (including Welsh and A-level general studies). In 1990, 48 pupils in upper fifth, 37 in upper sixth. *GCSE:* in 1990, 48% upper fifth gained at least grade C in 8+ subjects; 28% in 5–7; and 24% in 1–4 subjects. *A-levels:* 22% upper sixth passed in 4+ subjects; 38% in 3; 20% in 2; and 20% in 1 subject. 20% took science A-levels; 41% arts/ humanities; 39% both. *Computing facili-*

ties: A range of IBM compatible, BBC, RM Nimbus and Atari machines. *Special provision:* Some provision for dyslexic children; EFL for pupils from overseas.

European Community *Languages:* French offered: to GCSE; A-level. German: to GCSE. Welsh: to GCSE; AS-level; A-level. Over 75% take GCSE in more than 1 EC language. *Exchanges:* Regular exchanges for pupils aged 14–18 to France. *Other:* Few EC pupils in school.

Senior pupils' non-academic activities *Music:* 13 learn a musical instrument, 10 up to Grade 6; 9 in school orchestra, 11 in school choir. *Drama and dance:* 12 in school productions. *Art:* 6 take art as non-examined subject, 13 take GCSE art; 3 A-level art; 2 accepted for art school; 6 belong to photographic club. *Sport:* Rugby, hockey, cricket, tennis, badminton, netball available. 63 take part in non-compulsory sport. 8 represent county/country (rugby, shooting). *Other:* 2 take part in local community schemes. 25 have bronze Duke of Edinburgh's Award, 22 silver and 10 have gold. Other activities include computer club, driving lessons, parachuting, clay-pigeon shooting, canoeing, rock-climbing.

Careers In 1990, 85% leavers went on to degree courses; 4% to art/drama/music colleges; 6% to non-degree courses; 2% straight into careers; 3% other. Of those going on to degree courses, 5% went to Oxbridge; 62% to other universities; 33% to poly/colleges. 2% those going on to higher education went to courses in practical art; 2% in music; 50% in humanities/social sciences; 7% in medicine; and 39% in science/engineering.

Uniform School uniform worn throughout.

Houses/prefects Competitive houses. A head boy and head girl (in some years), appointed by Head. Heads of houses appointed by Head and Housemasters; house prefects by Housemaster.

Religion Attendance at religious worship compulsory.

Social Local Rotary clubs debating competitions with other local schools. Exchange scheme with French school in Valognes. Regular visits to twinned town in Brittany. Pupils allowed to bring own car/bike/motorbike. Some meals formal, some self-service. School shop. No tobacco; alcohol allowed only in sixth-form common room.

Discipline No corporal punishment. Pupils failing to produce a piece of homework once might be asked to repeat it in own free time by next day; those caught smoking cannabis on the premises can expect expulsion.

Boarding Sixth form have own study bedrooms or share with one other. Houses, of about 50, same as competitive houses except for 11 and 12 year-olds who have own house; girls accommodated separately but are attached to boys' houses. Resident qualified nurse. Pupils can provide and cook own food to limited extent. One exeat, 2 leave-out weekends each term. Visits to the local town allowed, frequency depending on age from once/week in forms 1 and 2.

Alumni association is run by J H Thomas, c/o Llandovery College.

Former pupils A M Rees, Cliff Jones, Vivian Jenkins (International rugby players); Major General P M Davies (GOC, Wales); Peter Morgan (Director General of Institute of Directors).

· *Lomond* ·

Lomond School	• Pupils 553	• Termly fees
Stafford Street	• Boys 3–18	£928 (Day)
Helensburgh	(Day/Board/Weekly)	£1187 (Board)
Dunbartonshire	• Girls 3–18	£1100 (Weekly)
G84 9SX	(Day/Board/Weekly)	Enquiries/application to
Tel 0436 2476	• Higher year 55	the Headmaster

What it's like

Founded in 1977 as a result of the amalgamation of Larchfield School for Boys (1845) and St Bride's School for Girls (1895). It has an agreeable split site in the upper part of Helensburgh, a dormitory town a few miles from Loch Lomond and 40 minutes' drive from Glasgow. The three main buildings are quite near each other and have pleasant gardens. The staff:pupil ratio is 1:8. Academic standards are high and results very good; Very many sixth formers go on to degree courses. French and German are taught right through the school to A-level; Spanish to GCSE. An exceptionally high proportion of pupils takes GCSE in more than one European language. There are regular exchange arrangements with France and Germany. The music, drama and art departments are all strong. There is a high standard of public performance in drama and music. Sports and games are well catered for (a large number of representatives at county and national level). An unusually wide range and large number of extra-curricular activities (about 70 are on offer). Good facilities for outdoor pursuits and adventure training for which the neighbouring environment is ideal. Some commitment to local community schemes and an outstanding record in the Duke of Edinburgh's Award Scheme.

School profile

Pupils Total age range 3–18; 553 pupils, 488 day (240 boys, 248 girls), 65 boarding (28 boys, 37 girls). Senior department 12–18, 321 pupils (145 boys, 176 girls). Main entry ages 12 and into sixth. Approx 20% are children of former pupils. *Transfer from maintained schools:* 20% main senior intake, plus 50% to sixth.

Entrance Own entrance exam used. Oversubscribed in some areas. No special skills or religious requirements. Parents not expected to buy text books. 44 assisted places. 15 scholarships/bursaries, £730–£387.

Parents 15+% are doctors, lawyers, etc. 60+% live within 30 miles; up to 10% live overseas.

Staff Headmaster A D Macdonald, in post for 4 years. 46 full time staff, 8 part time. Annual turnover less than 10%.

Academic work O-, S-grades, Highers, A-levels. Average size of O/S-grade year,

60 (now 55); Higher year, 60; A-level year, 45. *O/S-grades:* on average, 89% pass 8+ subjects. *Highers:* on average, 74% pass 5+ subjects. *A-levels:* on average, 50% pass 3 subjects. (Many pupils take Highers instead.) On average, 6 take science/engineering A-levels; 10 take arts and humanities; 16 a mixture. *Computing facilities:* Computer lab, 10 BBC micros with Econet system. *Special provision:* Specialised help in cases of need.

European Community *Languages:* French offered: to age 14; S-grade; A-level. German offered: to age 14; S-grade; A-level. Spanish offered: to S-grade. Over 75% take S-grade in more than 1 EC language. *Exchanges:* Regular exchanges for pupils aged 14–18 to France and Germany. *Other:* French and German assistants in school. EC pupils on bursaries every year. S5 pupils on work experience in Germany. Well established

European dimension and tradition.

Senior pupils' non-academic activities *Music:* 6–7 learn a musical instrument to Grade 6 or above; 20–30 in school orchestra, 40–50 in school choir, 5 in school pop group. *Drama and dance:* 20–30 in school productions. 5 productions pa. *Art:* 25 take O-grade; 12 Higher; 2–3 A-level. 2–3 accepted for Art School. 10 belong to eg photographic club. *Sport:* Rugby, hockey, athletics, tennis, squash, golf, sailing, badminton, table tennis, swimming, cricket, netball available. Over 75% participate in team games. 50 take swimming tests. 12 represent county/country (rugby, hockey, athletics, tennis, squash, sailing). *Other:* 8–10 take part in local community schemes. 50 have bronze Duke of Edinburgh's Award, 20 have silver and 20 gold. Other activities include a computer club, square dancing, dog training, electronics, chess, bridge, microwave cookery, rifle shooting, first aid, piping, strategic simulations, 3D art, soft toy making, car maintenance, knitting, keep fit, architectural studies.

Careers In 1990, 95% leavers went on to degree courses; 2% to art/drama/music colleges; 2% to non-degree courses; 1% other. Of those going on to degree courses, 2% went to Oxbridge, 85% to other universities; 8% to poly/colleges. 6% those going on to higher education went to courses in practical art; 38% in humanities/social sciences; 16% in medicine; and 45% in science/engineering.

Uniform School uniform worn throughout.

Houses/prefects Competitive houses. Prefects, head boy/girl, head of house and house prefects – elected by Head and school.

Religion Religious worship encouraged.

Social No organised events with local schools. Exchange visits to France and Germany. Pupils allowed to bring own car/bike/motorbike to school. Meals self service. School shop. No tobacco/alcohol allowed.

Discipline No corporal punishment. Pupils failing to produce homework once might expect extra prep; those caught smoking cannabis on the premises will be expelled.

Boarding 10% have own study bedroom, 20% share; remainder in dormitories of 6+. Single sex houses, of approximately 30. Resident qualified nurse and doctor. Central dining room. Pupils can provide and cook own food. 2 exeats (2 days) each term. Visits to local town allowed.

Alumni association run by Mrs McIntyre, Secretary, Lomond Society, c/o the School.

· *Longridge Towers* ·

Longridge Towers School Berwick upon Tweed Northumberland TD15 2XH Tel 0289 307584	• Pupils 240 • Boys 4–18 (Day/Board/Weekly) • Girls 4–18 (Day/Board/Weekly) • Upper sixth 7	• Termly fees £995 (Day) £1990 (Board) £1880 (Weekly) • SHA, ISAI Enquiries/application to the Headmaster's Secretary

What it's like

Founded in 1983, it occupies an impressive Victorian mansion on a fine estate of 80 acres in very beautiful surroundings. A good staff:pupil ratio of 1:11. It provides a sound general education and results are creditable. A few sixth formers go on to degree courses. There is some music and quite a lot of drama and art. A good range of sports and games and a fair range of other activities. A promising record in the Duke of Edinburgh's Award Scheme.

School profile

Pupils Total age range 4–18; 240 pupils, 170 day (62 boys, 108 girls), 70 boarding (35 boys, 35 girls). Senior department 11–18, 165 pupils (70 boys, 95 girls). Main entry ages 4, 8, 11, 13 and into sixth. *Transfer from maintained schools:* 50% senior intake, plus 80% to sixth.

Entrance Common entrance and own exam used (tests in English and maths). Not oversubscribed. Parents not expected to buy text books; maximum extras £10. 6 scholarships pa, to half fees. Scholarships, bursaries and concessions for children of HM Forces, £150–£200 per term.

Parents 15+% in the armed services; 15+% in industry or commerce; 15+% are farmers. 60+% live within 30 miles; 10+% live overseas.

Staff Headmaster Dr M J Barron, in post for 8 years. 22 full time staff, 1 part time. Annual turnover 10%. Average age 38.

Academic work GCSE, Highers and A-levels. 15 subjects offered (no A-level general studies). In 1990, 23 pupils in upper fifth, 8 in upper sixth (now 7). *GCSE:* in 1990, 14 upper fifth gained at least grade C in 8+ subjects; 5 in 5–7; and 4 in 1–4 subjects. *A-levels:* 5 upper sixth passed in 3 subjects; 3 in 2 subjects. 40% took science A-levels; 40% arts/humanities; 20% both. *Computing facilities:* Computer lab with 16 BBC model B's in Econet.

European Community *Languages:* French offered: to age 14; GCSE; A-level. German offered: to age 14; GCSE; A-level. 10–25% take GCSE in more than 1 EC language. *Exchanges:* Regular exchanges for pupils aged 11–14 to France.

Senior pupils' non-academic activities *Music:* 8 learn a musical instrument; 15 in school choir; 1 goes on to play in pop group. *Drama and dance:* 50 in school productions. *Art:* 2 take as non-examined subject; 12 take GCSE; 2–3 take A-level. 1–2 accepted for Art School. *Sport:* Athletics, tennis, cricket, rifle shooting, rounders, swimming (own pool), rugby, hockey, netball, cross-country, archery, rowing, and gymnastics available. 20 take non-compulsory sport. 50 take exams. 6 represent county/country (athletics, cricket, hockey). *Other:* 15 have bronze Duke of Edinburgh's Award, 5 have silver. 1 works for national charity. Other activities include a computer club, gym, country dancing, stamps, judo, statistics, chess, squash and shooting.

Careers In 1990, 73% leavers went on to degree courses; 18% straight into careers (eg family business); 9% other. Of those going on to degree courses, 86% went to universities; 14% to poly/colleges. 43% those going on to higher education went to courses in humanities/social sciences; 14% in medicine; and 43% in science/engineering.

Uniform School uniform worn except the sixth.

Houses/prefects Competitive houses. Prefects, head boy (School Captain), head of house and house prefects – appointed by Head after consultation with staff.

Religion Morning prayers held Mon–Thurs. Sunday service in school chapel.

Social Performance of Verdi opera in Edinburgh with other schools; debating in competitions. Regular trips abroad eg Morgins (Switzerland). Some meals self service. School tuck shop for boarders and book shop for all. No tobacco/alcohol allowed.

Discipline No corporal punishment. Pupils failing to produce homework once might expect a verbal warning; those caught smoking cannabis on the premises would be expelled.

Boarding 7% have own study bedroom, 83% share with others, 10% are in dormitories of 6+. Houses, of approx 35, are single sex. Resident matron. Central dining room. Four weekend exeats each term. Visits to the local town allowed.

Alumni association is run by Mrs C Fletcher, c/o the School.

· *Lord Wandsworth* ·

Lord Wandsworth
College
Long Sutton
Basingstoke
Hampshire RG25 1TB
Tel 0256 862482

- Pupils 440
- Boys 11–18
  (Day/Board/Weekly)
- Girls 16–18
  (Day/Board/Weekly)
- Upper sixth 58

- Termly fees
  £1836 (Day)
  £2352 (Board/
  Weekly)
- HMC
  Enquiries/application to
  the Headmaster's
  Secretary or
  Foundation Registrar

What it's like

Founded in 1920 and endowed by Lord Wandsworth. It has very agreeable buildings in a beautiful part of Hampshire on an estate of 1000 acres. One could hardly hope for a better position or finer surroundings. Early links between the school and agriculture have now virtually disappeared but the rural environment remains a strong feature of the school. It is extremely well equipped in a 'village' environment and provides a sound education. Academic results are highly credi- table. Many sixth form leavers go on to degree courses, including Oxbridge. A non-denominational foundation, religious education and attendance at chapel is more or less compulsory. The staff: pupil ratio is good – 1:11. There is a CCF and a good range of games, sports and activities. Day fees are high; weekly boarding popular.

School profile

Pupils Age range 11–18; 440 pupils, 61 day (55 boys, 6 girls), 379 boarding (355 boys, 24 girls). Main entry ages 11, 13 (boys) and into sixth (boys and girls). *Transfer from maintained schools:* 85% at 11, 4% at 13, 10% to sixth.

Entrance Common entrance and own exam used. Oversubscribed. No special skills or religious requirements. Parents not expected to buy text books. 75 assisted places. 26 scholarships; Foundation Awards for sons of widows, widowers or single parents, one-third to full fees, according to means.

Parents 50+% live within 30 miles; up to 10% live overseas.

Staff Headmaster G A G Dodd, in post for 8 years. 40 full time staff, 3 part time. Annual turnover 1 or 2. Average age 38.

Academic work GCSE and A-levels (no A-level general studies). In 1990, 77 pupils in upper fifth, 58 in upper sixth. *GCSE:* in 1990, 48 upper fifth gained at least grade C in 8+ subjects; 20 in 5–7; and 9 in 1–4 subjects. *A-levels:* 68% upper

sixth passed in 3 subjects; 19% in 2; and 7% in 1 subject. 39% took science A-levels; 36% arts/humanities; 25% both. *Computing facilities:* Computer centre – BBC and Archimedes, networked. Many BBC's around the school.

European Community *Languages:* French offered: to GCSE; A-level. German: non-examined subject. Spanish offered: to GCSE; A-level. 25–50% take GCSE in more than 1 EC language. *Exchanges:* Regular exchanges for pupils aged 11–18 to France and Spain. *Other:* French trading venture run by pupils and staff.

Senior pupils' non-academic activi- ties *Music:* Choral Society, choir, orchestra, band. *Sport:* Hockey, rugby, cricket, athletics, cross-country, swim- ming, tennis, badminton, squash, shoot- ing, golf available. *Other:* Activities include a computer club, Duke of Edinburgh's Award Scheme, community service pro- ject, sixth form society.

Careers In 1990, 70% leavers went on

to degree courses; 2% to art/drama/ music colleges; 10% to non-degree courses (eg agriculture, HND courses); 4% straight into careers (eg insurance, sailing instruction); 14% other. Of those going on to degree courses, 10% went to Oxbridge, 72% to other universities; 18% to poly/colleges. 60% those going on to higher education went to courses in humanities/social sciences; and 40% in science/engineering.

Uniform School uniform worn throughout.

Houses/prefects Mildly competitive houses. Prefects, head boy, head of house and house prefects – appointed by the Head and housemaster in consultation with senior pupils.

Religion Attendance at religious worship compulsory.

Social Many dramatic and choral functions, dances/discos with local girls' schools. Organised trips abroad and exchange systems. Meals self service. School shop. No tobacco allowed; some beer in sixth form centre.

Discipline No corporal punishment.

Boarding Houses of 75 pupils (including day). Resident qualified nurse. Central dining room. Exeats each term. Visits to the local town allowed.

Alumni association The Old Sternian Association, c/o the School.

· *Loretto* ·

Loretto School	● Pupils 300	● Termly fees
Musselburgh	● Boys 13–18	£1966 (Day)
Midlothian	(Day/Board)	£2950 (Board)
EH21 7RE	● Girls 16–18 (Board)	● HMC
Tel 031 665 5003	● Upper sixth 70	Enquiries/application to the Headmaster

What it's like

Founded in 1827 by the Rev Thomas Langhorne, it was bought in 1862 by Hely Hutchinson Almond, a distinguished scholar of strong and unconventional convictions. He built up the school and was its Head until he died in 1903. Since then it has become one of the most distinguished schools in Britain. It has a fine site on the outskirts of the small town of Musselburgh on the Firth of Forth, 6 miles from Edinburgh. This comprises 80 acres of lawns, trees and playing fields. The junior school is a separate unit on the same site. The buildings are handsome, especially Pinkie House – an historic building (partly because of its connections with the Battles of Prestonpans and Pinkie). Many recent developments have produced excellent facilities (including good boarding accommodation). An interdenominational school, chapel plays an important part in its life. The policy has always been to keep the school small and pupils are expected to give their loyalty and make a general all-round contribution. They are given authority and responsibility from an early age. There is a staff:pupil ratio of 1:9. Academic standards are high and results consistently good. A high proportion of pupils (for a school of this size) go on to degree courses, including Oxbridge. Very strong in music, drama and art. Much use is made of the cultural amenities of Edinburgh. Loretto has long had a reputation for excellence in sports and games of which there is a wide variety. Many clubs and societies cater for most conceivable extra-curricular needs. There is a very strong CCF (compulsory for every boy for at least 3 years) with its own Pipes and Drums. Physical fitness and regular exercise are high priorities and there is an

457

emphasis on adventure training. A substantial commitment to local community services. An outstanding record in the Duke of Edinburgh's Award Scheme.

School profile

Pupils Total age range 13–18; 300 pupils, 10 day (all boys), 290 boarding (254 boys, 36 girls). Main entry ages 13 (boys) and into sixth (boys and girls). Own junior school (The Nippers) provides more than 20% of intake. Approx 25% are children of former pupils.

Entrance Common entrance, own entrance and scholarship exams used. Oversubscribed at most levels. General all-round contribution looked for; non-denominational. Parents expected to buy some specialist sixth form text books; other extras variable. 30 assisted places. Various scholarships/bursaries pa.

Parents 15+% are doctors, lawyers, etc; 15+% in industry or commerce. A number live overseas.

Staff Headmaster Rev Norman W Drummond, in post for 7 years. 31 full time staff, 8 part time.

Academic work GCSE, Highers and A-levels. Average size of upper fifth 53; upper sixth 70. *GCSE:* on average, 26 pupils in upper fifth pass 8+ subjects; 19, 5–7 subjects; 8 pass 1–4 subjects. *Highers and A-levels:* pupils do a mixture: on average, 7% pass 4 A-levels, or 3 A-levels and 2 Highers; 62% pass 3 A-levels and 1 Higher; 26% pass 2 A-levels, or 1 A-level and 2–3 Highers. On average 22 take science/engineering A-levels; 26 take arts and humanities; 25 a mixture. *Computing facilities:* Computer centre in new Industry and Business Centre; departmental computers/word processors. *Special provision:* For mild dyslexia; cystic fibrosis.

European Community *Languages:* French offered: to age 14; GCSE; A-level. German offered: to age 14; GCSE; A-level. 25–50% take GCSE in more than 1 EC language. *Exchanges:* Regular exchanges for pupils aged 14–16 to France and Germany. *Other:* Pupils from France, Germany and Spain in school for varying periods of time. European language tapes available for those not studying academic languages.

Senior pupils' non-academic activities *Music:* 33+% learn a musical instrument, 30 to Grade 6 or above, 1 diploma candidate, 1–2 accepted for Music School, 2 go on to play in pop group; 31 in school orchestra, 35 in chamber choir, whole school regularly sings as a choir in chapel, 7 in pop group, 5 in jazz band, 25 in concert band, 16 in pipe band, 1 in Edinburgh Youth Orchestra. *Drama and dance:* New award-winning theatre; 3 full length productions annually, several others. *Art:* 50 take as non-examined subject; 20 take GCSE, 10 take A-level. 2 accepted for Art School, 1 for course in architecture, landscape architecture or photography. 10 belong to eg photographic club. *Sport:* Rugby, cricket, hockey, tennis, golf, squash, fives, badminton, athletics, lacrosse, fencing, swimming, curling, cycling, horse riding, miniature range and clay pigeon shooting, sailing, skiing available. 120 take non-compulsory sport. 43 take exams. 8 represent county/country (rugby, hockey, cricket). *Other:* 65 take part in local community schemes. 54 have gold Duke of Edinburgh's Award. 14 enter voluntary schemes after leaving, 5 work for national charities. Other activities include computer club, art and crafts, debating, chess, bridge, Scottish country dancing, industrial and political societies.

Careers In 1990, 84% leavers went on to degree courses; 6% to art/drama/music colleges; 1·5% to non-degree courses (eg agriculture); 7% straight into careers (eg army, family business); 1·5% other (eg resits). Of those going on to degree courses, 10% went to Oxbridge; 60% to other universities; 30% to poly/colleges. 4% those going on to higher education went to courses in practical art; 2% in drama/acting; 52% in humanities/social sciences; 8% in medicine; and 34% in science/engineering.

Uniform School uniform worn throughout.

Houses/prefects No competitive houses. Prefects, head boy (head of school), head of house/room/table (graduated system of responsibility) and house prefects – appointed by Head and house-masters. Committees for eg messing, charities. Regular leadership seminars on service and management.

Religion Sunday chapel and mid-week services compulsory.

Social Joint community service committee with Musselburgh Grammar School; involved with local club for disabled. Sharing of school and local facilities eg sports hall, swimming pool, squash club, theatre. Carol service for town. Some organised trips abroad. Pupils allowed to bring own bike to school (summer term). Meals formal. School shop. No tobacco/alcohol allowed.

Discipline No corporal punishment. Pupils failing to produce homework once might expect to do it in their own time and detention; rigorous framework of discipline leading to suspension and expulsion for the most serious of offences.

Boarding 25% have own study bed-room, lower sixth girls share; 75% are in dormitories of 6+. Houses, of approximately 60 (boys), 36 (girls) are single sex. Resident qualified sanatorium sister. Central dining room. 2 overnight exeats each term plus half-term. Visits to local town (Musselburgh) at specific times allowed according to age.

Former pupils Jim Clark (motor racing); Sir Hector Laing (Chairman, United Biscuits); Sir Denis Forman (Chairman, Granada TV); Sandy Carmichael (Scotland XV – 50 caps); Peter Fraser QC (Lord Advocate); Michael Mavor (Headmaster, Gordonstoun); David McMurray (Headmaster, Oundle); Norman Lamont MP; Nicholas Fairbairn QC, MP; Professor John Hunter (Grant Professor of Dermatology, Edinburgh University); Professor I M Murray-Lyon (Consultant Physician and Gastroenterologist, Charing Cross Hospital).

· *Loughborough Grammar* ·

Loughborough
Grammar School
6 Burton Walks
Loughborough
Leicestershire
LE11 2DU
Tel 0509 233233

- Pupils 900
- Boys 10–18 (Day/Board/Weekly)
- Girls None
- Upper sixth 135

- Termly fees
  £1079 (Day)
  £2067 (Board)
  £1708 (Weekly)
- HMC
  Enquiries/application to the Headmaster

What it's like

Founded by tradition in 1495 by Thomas Burton, Merchant of the Staple of Calais, though it is likely that the Trustees of the Town Charity were managing a school well before that date. In any event, it is one of the oldest schools in the country. It moved to its present site away from the centre of the town in 1852 where it is blessed with most attractive grounds, gardens and playing fields. The buildings of the Victorian period are handsome and in the collegiate style. Three main buildings form three sides of a quadrangle. There has been much recent building between 1961 and the present day. These include an assembly hall, laboratories, classrooms, a library, sixth form centre, art & design centre, refectory and sports hall. The school is in general exceptionally well equipped and the playing fields are outstanding. It prides itself on its 'family' atmosphere, and its very active house system. There is a staff:pupil ratio of about 1:12.5. Academic results are consistently good or excellent. Very many pupils go on to university each year, including many to

Oxbridge. Music and drama are very strongly supported and there is much enterprise in these cultural activities (frequent collaboration with the sister school). A wide range of sports and games is available and the school has long been known for its excellence in these. It has provided a substantial number of representatives at county, regional and national level. A large variety of clubs and societies cater for most conceivable needs. The big CCF (Army, Navy and Air Force) is voluntary but has about 250 senior members. There is considerable emphasis on outdoor pursuits and the school has a distinguished record in the Duke of Edinburgh's Award Scheme.

School profile

Pupils Age range 10–18; 900 boys (830 day, 70 boarding). Main entry ages 10, 11, 13 and into sixth. Small proportion are children of former pupils. *Transfer from maintained schools:* 50% main intake, plus 40% to sixth.

Entrance Common entrance and own entrance exam used. Oversubscribed. No special skills or religious requirements. Parents not expected to buy text books. 23 assisted places pa (at 11, 13, 16). A number of scholarships (including music), exhibitions, boarding bursaries, armed forces and clergy.

Parents 60+% live within 30 miles; up to 15% live overseas.

Staff Headmaster D N Ireland, in post for 7 years. 70 full time staff, 3 part time. Annual turnover 5%. Average age 38.

Academic work GCSE and A-levels. 18 subjects offered (including A-level general studies). In 1990, 135 pupils in upper fifth, 135 in upper sixth. *GCSE:* in 1990, 109 upper fifth gained at least grade C in 8+ subjects; 26 in 5–7 subjects. *A-levels:* 94 upper sixth passed in 4+ subjects; 29 in 3; 11 in 2; and 1 in 1 subject. 35% took science A-levels; 35% arts/ humanities; 30% both. *Computing facilities:* Computer laboratory containing 26 Acorn Archimedes; 8 BBC Masters in other departments and the library (2 BBC's on network).

European Community *Languages:* French offered: to age 14; GCSE; AS-level; A-level. German offered: to age 14; GCSE; AS-level; A-level. Italian offered: to GCSE. Spanish offered: to GCSE; AS-level; A-level. *Exchanges:* Regular exchanges for pupils aged 11–16 to France and Germany.

Senior pupils' non-academic activities *Music:* 45 learn a musical instrument, 15 to Grade 6 or above; 2 take A-level, 1 accepted for Music School, 1 to university music course; 1 in pop group; 12 pupils play in school orchestra, 16 in choir, 20 in concert band, 15 in big band, 30 opera/musical. *Drama and dance:* School produces plays, operas, musicals; numbers vary according to production. 2 accepted for Drama/Dance Schools. 2 go on to work in theatre. *Art:* 21 take art as non-examined subject; 20 take GCSE; 13 A-level. 2 accepted for Art School, 3 to university, 1 to polytechnic course. 16 belong to eg photographic club, 12 to ceramics club. *Sport:* Rugby, cricket, hockey, athletics, swimming, badminton, squash, basketball, cross-country, tennis, fencing available. 150–200 take non-compulsory sport. 60 pupils represented county or region (rugby, hockey, cross-country, tennis, cricket, athletics, decathlon), 3 represented country (U16 rugby, U18 cricket), 4 in national schools championships. *Other:* 15 have bronze Duke of Edinburgh's Award, 20 silver, 25 gold. Other activities include choir, chess, board games, canoeing, karting, science society, debating society, swimming, wind ensemble, music, ceramics, big band, CCF Corp of Drums, Young Enterprise, art club, scouts, runners, dancing, orchestra, CDT, concert band, video, film club, etc. 3 computer clubs (senior, intermediate, junior).

Careers In 1990, 95% leavers went on to degree courses; 2% to art/drama/ music colleges; 3% straight into careers. Of those going on to degree courses, 15% went to Oxbridge; 60% to other universities; 25% to poly/colleges. 2% those going on to higher education went to courses in practical art; 2% in drama/ acting; 1% in music; 45% in humanities/

social sciences; 8% in medicine; and 40% in science/engineering.

Uniform School uniform worn throughout.

Houses/prefects Competitive houses. Head boy, Deputy Head boy, head of house and house prefects – appointed by Head and staff.

Religion Assembly compulsory – Sunday chapel for boarders.

Social Debates, music and drama, clubs and societies, are joint with sister school (Loughborough High). Many organised trips abroad and exchange systems. Pupils allowed to bring own car/bike to school. Meals formal. School shop. No tobacco/alcohol allowed.

Discipline No corporal punishment. Pupils failing to produce homework once might expect a warning.

Boarding Sixth have own study bedroom, fourth and fifth share (2–4); others in dormitories of 6+. Houses, of 25–35, Junior and Senior. Resident qualified medical staff. Central dining room. 2 exeats each term. Daily visits to local town allowed. Weekly boarding allowed.

Former pupils include: 1 Vice-Chancellor, 1 General, 1 Air Marshal, Editor of *Guardian*, 5 FRS, 1 Government Minister.

· *Loughborough High* ·

Loughborough High
School
Burton Walks
Loughborough
Leicestershire
LE11 2DU
Tel 0509 212 348

- Pupils 540
- Boys None
- Girls 11–18
  (Day/Weekly)
- Upper sixth 82

- Termly fees
  £972 (Day)
  £1578 (Board)
- GSA
Enquiries/application to
the Headmistress

What it's like

The school is part of the foundation originally provided by Thomas Burton who, in 1495, endowed a chantry with which was connected a grammar school for boys. The foundation was extended to girls in 1849. The girls' upper school was at Rectory Place and moved to its present site in 1879. There are spacious and very pleasant grounds on the edge of the town. There have been many modern additions to the late Victorian buildings and facilities are now excellent. Religious instruction is non-denominational but the school has a Christian basis and all pupils are expected to attend RE lessons and assembly. The aim is to provide an academic education of the traditional grammar school type in a disciplined atmosphere of steady work. Standards are high and results very good. Many girls go on to degree courses each year, including Oxbridge. French, German and Spanish are offered at GCSE and a high proportion of girls takes GCSE in more than one European language. The school is very strong in music, drama and art. There are also high standards in sports and games (there are always representatives at county and international level). There is a full range of extra-curricular activities. There is a strong commitment to local community schemes and a good record in the Duke of Edinburgh's Award Scheme.

School profile

Pupils Age range 11–18; 540 girls (day and weekly board). Main entry ages 11 and into sixth. Own junior school, shared with Loughborough Grammar. *Transfer from maintained schools:* 40% main intake.
Entrance Own exam used. Assisted places. Academic scholarships and bursaries, including some music awards.
Staff Headmistress Miss J E L Harvatt, in post for 13 years.
Academic work GCSE and A-levels. (A-level general studies offered.) In 1990, 82 pupils in upper fifth, 71 in upper sixth (now 82). *GCSE:* in 1990, 74 upper fifth gained at least grade C in 8+ subjects; 8 in 5–7 subjects. *A-levels:* 46 upper sixth passed in 4+ subjects; 19 in 3; 2 in 2; and 3 in 1 subject. 19 took science A-levels; 39 arts/humanities; 12 both. *Computing facilities:* Computer room and network. Various computers in certain departments.
European Community *Languages:*

French offered: to age 14; GCSE; A-level. German offered: to GCSE; A-level. Spanish offered: to GCSE. 50–75% take GCSE in more than 1 EC language. *Exchanges:* Many regular exchanges for pupils aged 14–18 to France and Germany. *Other:* European Studies offered to pupils aged 11–14. Several sixth formers work in EC countries in holidays. French assistants each year.
Careers In 1990, 84% leavers went on to degree courses; 4% to art/drama/music colleges; 4% to non-degree courses; 8% other. Of those going on to degree courses, 11% went to Oxbridge; 76% to other universities; 13% to poly/colleges. 4% those going on to higher education went to courses in practical art; 58% in humanities/social sciences; 7% in medicine; and 31% in science/engineering.

· Lycée ·

Lycée Francais Charles de Gaulle
35 Cromwell Road
London SW7 2DG
Tel 071-584 6322

- Pupils 2500
- Boys 4–20 (Day)
- Girls 4–20 (Day)
- Upper sixth 56 + 131

- Termly fees £524 (Day)
  Enquiries/application to the Headmaster

What it's like

Founded in 1915 and closely associated with the French Institute, it first opened in Buckingham Palace Road and in 1932 moved to a bigger site in a small area of South Kensington. It is one of over 400 Lycées set in 120 different countries. Most of the pupils are British or French, but it is a remarkably cosmopolitan school with pupils from as many as 70 different countries. Its fees are among the lowest anywhere. One of the largest schools in Britain, it has a huge staff of 180 (140 French and 40 British) which allows a staff:pupil ratio of about 1:14. Its main asset lies in the virtual guarantee of bi- or tri-lingualism which all pupils achieve under the French system up to the end of the third year of the secondary school. They may then opt for either the English or French streams. An exceptionally high proportion of pupils takes GCSE in more than one European language, of which there are four on offer at all levels throughout the school – French, German, Italian and Spanish. Owing to its size it is divided into four different buildings according to the ages of the pupils: the primary school; the first to third years of the secondary school in the 'Petit Lycée'; the fourth and fifth secondary school years are in the 'Grand Lycée'; sixth formers are in a separate block. Everyone is in a highly concentrated area which has well-equipped buildings. The teaching is well known to be of a high standard and results are excellent in both GCSE and A-levels and in the Baccalauréat. Very many leavers go on to degree courses, including Oxbridge. There are close links with French cultural organisations and the Lycée is run by the French Ministry of Foreign Affairs. Sports and games are a part of the curriculum and the playing fields are at Raynes Park in South London. A wide range of activities, including drama, music and art is available on specified days. Many outings are organised each year.

School profile

Pupils Total age range 4–20; 2500 day pupils (1250 boys, 1250 girls). Senior department 11–20; 1350 pupils (650 boys, 700 girls). Main entry ages 4, 14 and into sixth. 10% are children of former pupils.

Entrance Own entrance exam used. Oversubscribed. Fluency in French looked for. No special religious requirements. Parents only expected to buy A-level sixth form text books; maximum extras £50.

Parents 15+% in industry. Up to 10+% live overseas.

Staff Headmaster Monsieur Yves de Saint Do, in post for 7 years (retiring soon). 180 full time staff, 20 part time. Annual turnover less than 10%. Average age 35.

Academic work GCSE, A-levels or French Baccalauréat. 17 subjects offered at AS- and A-level (including Arabic; no A-level general studies). In 1990, 60 pupils in upper fifth, 56 in upper sixth in the English section; 131 in French section preparing for French Baccalauréat. *GCSE:* in 1990, 43 upper fifth gained at least grade C in 8+ subjects; 13 in 5–7 subjects. *A-levels:* 8 upper sixth passed in 4+ subjects; 21 in 3; 10 in 2; and 7 in 1 subject. 45% took science A-levels; 55% arts/humanities. *Baccalauréat:* 95% pass.

European Community *Languages:* French offered: to age 14; GCSE; AS-level; A-level. German offered: to age 14; GCSE; AS-level; A-level. Italian offered: to age 14; GCSE; AS-level; A-level. Spanish offered: to age 14; GCSE; AS-level; A-level. Over 75% take GCSE in more than 1 EC language. *Exchanges:* Regular exchanges for pupils aged 14–18 to Belgium, France, Italy and Spain.

Careers In 1990, 80% leavers went on to degree courses; 15% to art/drama/music colleges; 5% other. Of those going on to degree courses, 10% went to Oxbridge; 80% to other universities; 10% to poly/colleges. 15% those going on to higher education went to courses in practical art; 60% in humanities/social sciences and others; 5% in medicine; and 20% in science/engineering.

Uniform School uniform not worn.

Houses/prefects No competitive houses or prefects. School Council, with elected pupil representatives.

Religion No compulsory worship.

Social Organised local events from time to time. Organised trips abroad and exchange systems. Pupils allowed to bring own bike to school. Meals self service. No tobacco/alcohol allowed.

Discipline No corporal punishment. Pupils failing to produce homework once might expect school to contact the parents so they may co-operate in ensuring that work is done; those caught smoking cannabis on the premises could expect probable expulsion.

m

· *Magdalen College School* ·

Magdalen College
School
Oxford
OX4 1DZ
Tel 0865 242191

- Pupils 500
- Boys 11–18
  (Day/Board)
- Choristers from 9
- Girls None
- Upper sixth 74

- Termly fees
  £1114 (Day)
  £2114 (Board)
- HMC, CSA
  Enquiries/application to
  the Master

What it's like

Founded in 1478 by William of Waynflete as part of Magdalen College. It was a distinguished school in Tudor times and produced some famous grammarians. William Tyndale was a pupil and so, in all probability, were Thomas More and Richard Hooker. Cardinal Wolsey was one of its masters. Formerly, the famous choristers had their own separate school but from the nineteenth century or earlier have been incorporated in the grammar school. It is situated near Magdalen Bridge and is well-equipped with up-to-date facilities, most buildings having been built during a period of steady expansion in the last thirty years. A wide range of subjects is provided for a sound general education. French and German are offered to A-level (also non-examined) and also Spanish at GCSE – many boys take GCSE in more than one. Academic standards and results are consistently very good and very many pupils go on to universities each year, very many to Oxbridge. Music is very strong, and there is some strength, too, in art, drama and chess. A good range of sports and games is provided on the large playing fields surrounded by the River Cherwell. Standards in sports and games are high. There is also a plentiful variety of extra-curricular activities.

School profile

Pupils Age range 11–18, choristers from 9; 500 boys (475 day, 25 boarding). Main entry ages 11, 13 and into sixth. *Transfer from maintained schools:* 60% main intake, plus 30% to sixth.

Entrance Common entrance and own exam used. 24 assisted places pa. 57 scholarships (including music) and bursaries.

Staff Master P M Tinniswood, first year in post.

Academic work GCSE and A-levels. 21 subjects offered (including Russian; no A-level general studies). In 1990, 74 pupils in upper fifth, 80 in upper sixth (now 74). *GCSE:* in 1990, 62 upper fifth gained at least grade C in 8+ subjects; 9 in 5–7 subjects. *A-levels:* 16 upper sixth passed in 4+ subjects; 50 in 3; 10 in 2; and 2 in 1 subject. 28 took science A-levels; 32 arts/humanities; 20 both. *Computing facilities:* Full-sized laboratory equipped with 15 Acorn Archimedes machines on an SJ Research Network.

European Community *Languages:* French offered: to age 14; GCSE; A-level; non-examined subject. German offered: to age 14; GCSE; AS-level; A-level; non-examined subject. Spanish offered: to GCSE. 25–50% take GCSE in more than 1 EC language. *Exchanges:* Regular exchanges for pupils aged 14–16 to France. *Other:* Frequently have 1 or 2 German boys for 1 term at lower sixth. **Careers** In 1990, 80% leavers went on to degree courses; 20% other. Of those going on to degree courses, 22% went to Oxbridge; 68% to other universities; 10% to poly/colleges. 1% those going on to higher education went to courses in drama/acting; 2% in music; 54% in humanities/social sciences; 3% in medicine; and 40% in science/engineering.

· *Malvern (Boys)* ·

Malvern College
Malvern
Worcestershire
WR14 3DF
Tel 0684 892333
Fax 0684 572398

- Pupils 600
- Boys 13–18
  (Day/Board)
- Girls None
- Upper sixth 130

- Termly fees
  £2235 (Day)
  £3070 (Board)
- HMC
Enquiries/application to
the Registrar

What it's like

Founded in 1865, it has always been a boys' school but there is now a plan to merge with Ellerslie, the girls' school which already has a joint 6th with Malvern. It could therefore be co-educational from 1992. Malvern has one of the most beautiful and civilised settings in England. The elegant, well-appointed buildings are arranged in a horse-shoe around the grounds on the eastern slope of the Malvern Hills, with magnificent views over the Severn Valley and the Vale of Evesham. It has first-class facilities of every kind, including excellent boarding accommodation. The town is 10 minutes' walk away and the college benefits greatly from its position by a town which has become an important centre of education. It also benefits through close co-operation with the four independent girls' boarding schools in the area. The aims of the house system and the tutorial arrangements are to ensure that each boy learns to live in a community and develops his potential. It is an Anglican foundation and boys are obliged to attend certain chapel services. Academic standards are very high. Results are first-rate and very many leavers go on to university each year, including many to Oxbridge. French, German and Spanish are offered from the third to the sixth form, also some Italian and Portuguese at GCSE level. Many pupils take GCSE in more than one language. It is very strong indeed in music (many pupils learn an instrument), drama, art and information technology. Also very strong in sport and games. All take part in a sporting programme (compulsory), but there are a large number of options. The CCF is optional; there are Army, Navy, RAF and Marine sections. Adventure training is compulsory in the lower sixth. There is a substantial commitment to local community services for the old, disabled and homeless. A fine record in the Duke of Edinburgh's Award Scheme (39 golds).

School profile

Pupils Age range 13–18; 600 boys, 40 day, 560 boarding. Main entry ages 13 and into sixth. Approx 8–10% are children of former pupils. *Transfer from maintained schools:* 1% main intake, plus 20% to sixth.

Entrance Common entrance and own entrance exam used. Oversubscribed. No special skills or religious requirements. Parents expected to buy text books; no other extras. 66 assisted places. 20 scholarships/bursaries, £7500–£500.

Parents 15+% are doctors, lawyers, etc. Up to 10% live within 30 miles; up to 10% live overseas.

Staff Head R de C Chapman, in post for 8 years. 67 full time staff, 10 part time.

Academic work GCSE and A-levels. 23 GCSE subjects offered; 24 at A-level (including GCSE Greek, drama, photography & graphic communication; A-level: electronics, Greek, design and technology, general studies). In 1990, 119 pupils in upper fifth, 119 in upper sixth (now 130). *GCSE:* in 1990, 76% upper fifth gained at least grade C in 8+ subjects; 21% in 5–7; and 3% in 1–4 subjects. *A-levels:* 14% upper sixth passed in 4+ subjects; 69% in 3; 13% in 2; and 3% in 1 subject. 18% took science A-levels; 57% arts/humanities; 25% both. *Computing facilities:* Extensive facilities available – 24 Apple Macintosh, 2 Nimbus and 12 BBC computers. *Special provision:* Extensive English courses on the timetable for boys with special writing difficulties in lower English sets; qualified part time SLD and EFL teachers who will teach on one-to-one basis.

European Community *Languages:* French offered: to age 14; GCSE; AS-level; A-level. German offered: to age 14; GCSE; AS-level; A-level. Spanish offered: to age 14; GCSE; AS-level; A-level. Some pupils also take Italian and Portuguese GCSE. 25–50% take GCSE in more than 1 EC language. *Exchanges:* Regular exchanges for pupils aged 16–18 to Germany. *Other:* Pupils regularly visit France and Spain. Healthy minority of EC pupils, particularly in sixth form.

Senior pupils' non-academic activities *Music:* 230 learn a musical instrument, 50 to Grade 6 or above, 3 accepted for Music School; 80 in school orchestra, 100 in choir. *Drama and dance:* 150 in school productions; 200 in house plays. *Art:* 60–70 take GCSE; 30 A-level. 2–10 accepted for Art School. *Sport:* Soccer, rugby and cricket are major games; also athletics, cross-country running, squash, lawn tennis, rackets, Winchester fives, hockey, swimming, sailing, rifle shooting, wind-surfing, golf, badminton, fencing, gymnastics, judo available. Sport is compulsory, but with large number of options. 20 take exams eg gymnastics, swimming. *Other:* 50 take part in local community schemes. 39 have Duke of Edinburgh's Gold Award. About 5 enter voluntary schemes beyond school. Other activities include a computer club, adventure training, chess, natural history, science, debating, language, architecture, music societies.

Careers In 1990, 75% leavers went on to degree courses; 2% to art/drama/music colleges; 3% to non-degree courses (eg agriculture); 5% straight into careers (eg army, retailing); 15% other (eg resits or reapply). Of those going on to degree courses, 25% went to Oxbridge; 50% to other universities; 25% to poly/colleges. 10% those going on to higher education went to courses in practical art; 3% in music; 64% in humanities/social sciences; 6% in medicine; and 17% in science/engineering.

Uniform School uniform worn throughout.

Houses/prefects Competitive houses. Prefects and head boy – appointed by the Head; head of house and house prefects – appointed by housemasters.

Religion Some compulsory chapel services.

Social Joint general studies classes, debates, dances, discos, plays, concerts with local schools. Organised trips abroad (eg to USA). Exchanges with French/German pupils on individual basis. Pupils allowed to bring own bike to school. Meals formal. School shop. Sixth form bar. No smoking.

Discipline No corporal punishment.

Boarding 40% have own study bedroom, 60% are in dormitories of 6+. Houses, of approximately 60, same as competitive houses. Resident qualified nurse, doctor on call. No central dining room. Pupils can provide and cook own food at times. 2 weekend exeats each term plus half-term. Visits to the local town allowed.

Alumni association run by G H Chesterton, c/o the School.
Former pupils Bernard Weatherill (Speaker of the House of Commons); Denholm Elliott (actor); Sir Ian Maclaurin (Chairman of Tesco); Jeremy Paxman (Newsnight).

· Malvern (Girls) ·

Malvern Girls' College
Avenue Road
Malvern
Worcestershire
WR14 3BA
Tel 0684 892288
Fax 0684 566204

- Pupils 525
- Boys None
- Girls 11–18
  (Day/Board)
- Upper sixth 80

- Termly fees
  £1880 (Day)
  £2820 (Board)
- GSA
  Enquiries/application to
  the Registrar

What it's like

Founded in 1893, it has a splendid site at the foot of the Malvern Hills in the town. Eight school houses are scattered near the main buildings. It is extremely well equipped and has excellent sports facilities including an all-weather games pitch. There is a high standard of teaching and academic standards and results are excellent. Very many pupils go on to degree courses each year, many to Oxbridge. French, German, Italian and Spanish are offered at GCSE and an exceptionally large proportion of girls takes GCSE in more than one European language. It is tremendously strong in music and 390–400 girls learn an instrument. Games and sports are of a high standard and in 1989 alone there were 40 representatives at county and district level. A plentiful range of extra-curricular activities and quite a lot of emphasis on outdoor pursuits. Full use is made of Malvern's cultural and festival events. Worship and prayer in the Anglican tradition are encouraged.

School profile

Pupils Age range 11–18; 520 girls, 60 day, 460 boarding. Main entry ages 11, 12, 13 and into sixth. Approx 8% are children of former pupils.
Entrance Common entrance and own scholarship exam used. Oversubscribed. No special skills or religious requirements but majority C of E. Parents expected to buy some text books. 10 scholarships/exhibitions (including music scholarship), half fees.
Parents 15+% are doctors, lawyers, etc; 15+% in industry or commerce; 15+% in armed services. 10+% live within 30 miles; 10+% live overseas.
Staff Headmistress Dr V B Payne, in post for 5 years. 70 full time staff, 30 part time. Annual turnover 5%.
Academic work GCSE and A-levels.

Average size of upper fifth 80; upper sixth 80. *GCSE:* on average, 70 pupils in upper fifth gain at least grade C in 8+ subjects; 10 pass 6–7 subjects. *A-levels:* on average, 32 pupils in upper sixth pass 4 subjects; 43, 3 subjects; 3, 2 subjects; 3 pass 1 subject. On average, 26 take science/engineering A-levels; 42 take arts and humanities; 12 take a mixture. Excellent computing facilities.
European Community *Languages:* French offered: to age 14; GCSE; AS-level; A-level. German offered: to age 14; GCSE; AS-level; A-level. Italian offered: to GCSE. Spanish offered: to age 14; GCSE; A-level. Over 75% take GCSE in more than 1 EC language. *Exchanges:* Regular exchanges for pupils aged 14–16 to France.

Senior pupils' non-academic activities *Music:* 394 learn a musical instrument, 112 to Grade 6 or above; 132 in school orchestra, 74 in school choir. *Drama and dance:* Middle school performs in house plays competition annually. Popular dance club; annual dance festival. *Art:* 20 take as non-examined subject; 25+ take GCSE; 10 take A-level. 5 accepted for Art School. *Sport:* Lacrosse, hockey, netball, swimming, squash, badminton, golf, tennis, athletics, rounders, cricket, aerobics, volleyball, riding, table tennis, dance, gymnastics and fencing available. 120 take non-compulsory sport. 45 represent county/district (lacrosse, hockey, swimming, tennis, athletics). *Other:* Pupils have bronze, silver and gold Duke of Edinburgh's Award. Other activities include outdoor pursuits (eg canoeing, climbing, sailing, white water rafting and walking), numerous clubs (computing, classics, drama, life drawing, public speaking, animal, mini-enterprise, electronics, creative writing, Earth action, British Association of Young Scientists, Amnesty International). Strong emphasis on community and charity work: pupils host weekly coffee morning for Senior Citizens; fortnightly sports club for the disabled; sixth form spend a week doing social service; large sums are raised for charity through special events.

Careers In 1990, 90% leavers went on to degree courses; 5% to art/drama/music colleges; 5% to non-degree courses (eg secretarial, fine arts, valuation, business studies, food and consumer studies). Of those going on to degree courses, 13% went to Oxbridge; 70% to other universities; 17% to poly/colleges. On average 5% those going on to higher education go to courses in practical art; 2·5% in music; 70% in humanities/social sciences; 10% in medicine; and 12% in science/engineering.

Uniform School uniform worn except the sixth.

Houses/prefects No competitive houses. Prefects, head girl, head of house and house prefects – appointed by Head after consultation with staff and School Council.

Religion Worship encouraged.

Social Joint choral and theatrical productions with Malvern College. Debating societies, sixth form general studies with local schools participating; regular discos and rock concerts. Organised trips abroad. Sixth form allowed to bring own bike to school. Meals formal; self service in sixth. School shop sells books and second-hand uniform. No tobacco/alcohol allowed.

Discipline No corporal punishment. Pupils caught smoking cannabis on the premises would expect instant dismissal. Each girl is given a copy of the code of conduct expected, essential rules and sanctions for offences.

Boarding Sixth form mainly have own study bedroom (many share if they wish). 15% middle school have own study bedrooms, 85% share with 1–3 others. 9 houses, of 40–60, including 2 sixth form houses. 2 resident qualified nurses. Sixth form can provide and cook own food. Half-term plus 2 weekend or 6 day exeats each term. Visits to local town allowed.

Alumni association is run by the Old Girls' Secretary, Mrs P Wilkinson, Syke House, Saddleworth Road, Greelland, Halifax.

· Manchester Grammar ·

The Manchester
Grammar School
Rusholme
Manchester M13 0XT
Tel 061 224 7201

- Pupils 1450
- Boys 11–18
  (Day)
- Girls None
- Upper sixth 201

- Termly fees
  £1000 (Day)
- HMC
Enquiries/application to
the High Master's
Secretary

What it's like

Founded in 1515 by Hugh Oldham, Bishop of Exeter. In 1931 it moved from its original site in Long Millgate to Fallowfield and grew to nearly 1450 boys, its present size. The original buildings have been constantly added to and facilities are first-class. The playing fields are adjacent and the whole area covers 28 acres. As its founder intended, it is a predominantly academic school and has long been one of the most distinguished in the country. Each year over 200 boys join it from widely differing backgrounds and from a wide area of the north-west. Intellectually and academically very high-powered, its results are consistently fine. Each year a very high proportion of pupils go on to university (a very large number to Oxbridge). Almost all the other leavers go on to some form of higher education. Religious worship is encouraged and religious studies form a fundamental part of the curriculum. Very strong in music, drama and art. An excellent range of games and sports in which high standards are attained. There is an immense range of out-of-school activities – many carried to remarkable levels of achievement. Considerable emphasis on outdoor pursuits; the school owns two sites (one in Cheshire and one near Grasmere) where these are followed; in addition several other camp sites are used each year. Local community schemes are active. One of the most outstanding features of the school is its vigorous corporate life, and its prestige is enhanced by its very high reputation locally and far afield.

School profile

Pupils Age range 11–18; 1450 day boys. Main entry ages 11 and into sixth. *Transfer from maintained schools:* 66% main intake, plus 33% to sixth.

Entrance Common entrance and own entrance exam used. Oversubscribed. High ability in English and numbers looked for; no religious requirements. Parents not expected to buy text books. 290 assisted places. Bursaries, on scale similar to government assisted places scheme.

Parents 15+% are in industry or commerce.

Staff High Master J G Parker, in post for 6 years. 104 full time staff, 12 part time. Annual turnover 5%. Average age 35.

Academic work GCSE and A-levels. 17 subjects offered (including Russian; no A-level general studies). In 1990, 205 pupils in fifth, 201 in upper sixth. *GCSE:* in 1990, 200 fifth gained at least grade C in 8+ subjects; 5 in 5–7. *A-levels:* 2 upper sixth passed in 4+ subjects; 189 in 3; 6 in 2; and 3 in 1 subject. 39% took science A-levels; 47% arts/humanities; 14% both. *Computing facilities:* Micro-computer laboratory; mini-computer facilities.

European Community *Languages:* French offered: to age 14; GCSE; A-level. German offered: to age 14; GCSE; A-level. Greek (modern): non-examined subject. Italian: non-examined subject. Spanish offered: to GCSE. 25–50% take GCSE in more than 1 EC language.

Senior pupils' non-academic activities *Music:* 60 learn a musical instrument. 40 in school orchestra, 100 in choir.

Drama and dance: 30 in school productions. *Art:* 10 take as non-examined subject. 40 take GCSE, 13 A-level. 7 accepted for Art School; 15 in eg photographic club. *Sport:* Soccer, rugby, cross-country, swimming, squash, badminton, cricket, tennis, athletics available. 120 take non-compulsory sport; 10 take exams. 10 represent county/country (soccer, rugby, cricket, cross-country, badminton). *Other:* 30 take part in local community schemes; 5 work for national charities after leaving. Other activities include chess, camping, fell walking, trekking.

Careers In 1990, 90% leavers went on to degree courses; 1% to art/drama/music colleges; 1% straight into careers; 8% other. Of those going on to degree courses, 30% went to Oxbridge; 63% to other universities; 7% to poly/colleges. 1% those going on to higher education went to courses in practical art; 45% in humanities/social sciences; 12% in medicine; and 42% in science/engineering.

Uniform School uniform; specific dress regulations in the sixth.

Houses/prefects No competitive houses. Prefects, head boy – appointed by High Master. Sixth Form Committee.

Religion Religious worship encouraged. School is multi-faith community, which is reflected in all aspects of religion within it. Religion is taught as an academic subject. Weekly assemblies for the major religious traditions represented.

Social Joint society meetings, productions, other activities with local schools. Trips abroad, exchange systems. Pupils allowed to bring own car/bike/motorbike to school. Meals self service. No tobacco/alcohol allowed.

Discipline No corporal punishment. Pupils failing to produce homework once might expect verbal warning. For more serious offences there is a staff supervised Punishment School, both after school and on Saturday mornings. Drug offences are treated seriously, and are likely to result in suspension/expulsion.

Alumni association run by Mr W T Hall, c/o the School.

Former pupils Sir William Barlow; Lord Sieff; Lord Winstanley; Lord Tordoff; Lord Lever; Ben Kingsley; Robert Powell; Robert Bolt; Sir Joseph Cantley.

· *Manchester Jewish Grammar* ·

Manchester Jewish
Grammar School
Charlton Avenue
Prestwich
Greater Manchester
M25 8PH
Tel 061 773 1789

- Pupils 140
- Boys 10–18
  (Day)
- Girls None
- Upper sixth 15

- Termly fees
  £870 (Day)
  Enquiries/application to
  the Head

What it's like

Founded in its present form in 1961, this small school gives high priority to Hebrew studies and daily worship. It provides a sound education based on the Jewish tradition. Many of the boys stay on for A-levels; and many of upper sixth formers go on to degree courses. Some music and a standard range of sports and games. A fair variety of clubs and societies is available. There is a community service unit and the pupils participate in the Duke of Edinburgh's Award Scheme.

School profile

Pupils Age range 10–18, 140 day boys. Main entry age 10 and into sixth. *Transfer from maintained schools:* 85% main intake, plus 95% to sixth.

Entrance Own entrance exam used. Fees based on parental income; Greater Manchester Education Trust bursaries available.

Staff Head P Pink, in post for 15 years.

Academic work GCSE and A-levels. 10 subjects offered (including biblical Hebrew; no A-level general studies). In 1989, 25 pupils in upper fifth, 15 in upper sixth. *GCSE:* in 1989, 17 upper fifth gained at least grade C in 8+ subjects; 6 in 5–7; and 2 in 1–4 subjects. *A-levels:* 1 upper sixth passed in 4+ subjects; 10 in 3; 3 in 2; and 1 in 1 subject. 25% took science A-levels; 50% arts/humanities; 25% both. *Computing facilities:* Dedicated computing room with 11 BBC Master/Archimedes on network.

· *Marlborough* ·

Marlborough College
Marlborough
Wiltshire
SN8 1PA
Tel 0672 515511
Fax 0672 516234

- Pupils 863
- Boys 13–18 (Day/Board)
- Girls 13–18 (Day/Board)
- Upper sixth 187

- Termly fees
  £2610 (Day)
  £3480 (Board)
- HMC, SHA
  Enquiries/application to the Registrar

What it's like

Founded in 1843 as a school 'for the Sons of Clergy of the Church of England', it has a delightful setting on the edge of one of the most agreeable country market towns in southern England. The Marlborough Downs lie to the north, Savernake Forest to the east, and the Kennet runs through the school grounds. Its elegant and well-appointed buildings lie amidst fine lawns and gardens. Very large playing fields adjoin them. All facilities are of a high standard. It pioneered the admission of girls into the sixth form in 1968, and in September 1989 became fully co-educational. By September 1993 the school will comprise 300 girls and 600 boys. One of the most distinguished schools in the country, it is said to combine strenuous activity with relaxed personal relations. In line with the terms of its foundation, there is quite a lot of emphasis on Anglican worship and instruction. Worship is encouraged and some services are compulsory. A great range of choice of subjects and different combinations for A-level. A very large full time staff (plus 28 part timers) allows a ratio of 1:8 pupils. Academic standards are extremely high and results are consistently impressive. The great majority of leavers go on to degree courses each year (78% in 1990), many to Oxbridge. French, German and Spanish are offered at GCSE and A-level and a high proportion of pupils takes more than one European language at GCSE. Russian is also taught to A-level. There are regular exchange arrangements with France, Germany and Spain. Tremendously strong involvement in music (about 350 pupils learn an instrument) and very strong also in art. Over 20 dramatic productions each year, at every level of the school. There are 34 different sports and games on offer and the college has an outstanding record in these (especially hockey) with many county and national representatives. An outstanding range of extra-curricular activities is provided: 42 clubs and societies cater for virtually everyone's needs. The CCF is a flourishing contingent of some 180 volunteers, and the Duke of Edinburgh's Award Scheme is also run. There is splendid provision for outdoor activities (eg canoeing, climbing, trekking, sub aqua) with centres both in the college and Snowdonia. Other outdoor pursuits (eg fishing, clay pigeon shooting) are encouraged and the college owns a pack of beagles which is managed entirely by pupils. There is a very substantial commitment to local community schemes. The organisation of pastoral care includes the Chaplain's staff and the nursing staff in addition to Housemasters/mistresses and tutors.

School profile

Pupils Age range 13–18; 863 pupils, 8 day, 855 boarding (636 boys, 219 girls). Main entry ages 13 and into sixth. Approx 14% are children of former pupils. *Transfer from maintained schools:* Less than 1% main intake, plus 6% to sixth.

Entrance Common entrance used; own exam for sixth form entrance. Oversubscribed. No special skills but students are encouraged in extra-curricular activities; no religious requirements but is an Anglican foundation. Parents expected to buy text books; average extras £170 per term. Large number of scholarships/bursaries, depending on quality of candidates; special scholarships for art, music and technology. Scholarships up to 50% of fees on merit; can be supplemented by bursaries up to 90% of fees.

Parents 20% live overseas.

Staff Master David Cope, in post for 5 years. 112 full time staff, 34 part time. Annual turnover 6%. Average age 38.

Academic work GCSE and A-levels. 19 GCSE subjects offered; 21 at A-level (including design, theatre studies, business studies, Arabic, Mandarin Chinese and Japanese; no A-level general studies). In 1991, 159 pupils in upper fifth, 187 in upper sixth. *GCSE:* in 1990, 138 upper fifth gained at least grade C in 8+ subjects; 9 in 5–6; and 6 in 1–4 subjects. *A-levels:* 2 upper sixth passed in 5 subjects; 20 in 4 subjects; 158 in 3; 21 in 2; and 5 in 1 subject. 13% took science A-levels; 55% arts/humanities; 32% both. *Computing facilities:* 28 station RML Nimbus network centre; also micros in many departments; facilities available to pupils in and outside curriculum six days a week. *Special provision:* Individual remedial help with dyslexia.

European Community *Languages:* French offered: to GCSE; AS-level; A-level. German offered: to GCSE; A-level. Spanish offered: to GCSE; A-level. 25–50% take GCSE in more than 1 EC language. *Exchanges:* Regular exchanges for pupils aged 14–18 to France, Germany and Spain. *Other:* EC pupils from most EC states, for 1–5 years. Periodic talks by MEP.

Senior pupils' non-academic activities *Music:* 350 learn a musical instrument, 180 Grade 6 or above, 100+ play in 3 school orchestras, 170 in choir, 50 in chamber music, 35 in school pop group, also jazz groups and 100 in wind and brass bands; 36 music scholars and exhibitioners, 20 take singing lessons; 60 in school musicals, 4 play in pop group, 4 going on to conservatoires, 3 to study music at university. *Drama and dance:* 90 in school productions, 200 others participate. *Art:* Whole school takes as non-examined subject, 50 A-level, 420 attend upper school art lectures; 30 in eg photographic club; 20 accepted for Art School; 12 to foundation courses. *Sport:* Cricket, rugger, soccer, hockey, athletics, squash, fencing, rackets, cross-country, tennis, basketball, netball, badminton, fives, gymnastics, canoeing, climbing, swimming, judo, shooting, volleyball, water polo, table tennis, lacrosse, golf, weight training available among others. Some sport compulsory; approx 500 take non-compulsory sport. Regular county representation (rugby, hockey, tennis, athletics, swimming, cricket, fencing, lacrosse). *Other:* 140 take part in local community schemes. Other activities include driving lessons, Duke of Edinburgh's Award Scheme. 42 diverse clubs and societies eg languages, wine making, philosophy, literature, archaeology.

Careers In 1990, 78% leavers went on to degree courses; 12% to art/drama/music colleges; 6% to non-degree courses (eg agriculture, accountancy); 4% straight into careers (eg armed forces, retail management, commerce). Of those going on to degree courses, 13% went to Oxbridge; 69% to other universities; 17% to poly/colleges. 5% those going on to higher education went to courses in practical art; 2% in drama/acting; 3% in music; 65% in humanities/social sciences; 5% in medicine; and 19% in science/engineering.

Uniform School uniform worn by lower school; dress regulations in upper school.

Houses/prefects Prefects, head boy/girl, head of house and house prefects – appointed by the Head. School Council (Forum).

Religion Religious worship encouraged; a few compulsory services each term.

Social 'Day School' organised periodically with St John's Comprehensive; week-long exchanges annually with a Comprehensive School in Birmingham; Third World Development link with the Gambia. A number of trips abroad and exchanges (eg France, Germany, Russia, Spain); growing contact with Latvia. Pupils allowed to bring own bike to school. Meals self service. School shop. No tobacco allowed; some supervised house bars.

Discipline No corporal punishment. Pupils failing to produce homework once might expect a warning, thereafter extra work; certain expulsion for any drugs offence, or sexual misconduct.

Boarding About 300 have own study bedroom, about 280 share with 1 other, 320 are in small dormitories. 15 houses, of about 60; 5 boys, 5 girls (twinned), and 5 mixed (55 boys and 10 sixth form girls). 4 qualified nurses in sanatorium; doctors local. Central dining room. Pupils can provide and cook own supplementary food. 2 weekend exeats each term plus half-term. Afternoon visits into town allowed.

Alumni association run by Robert Smith, c/o the College.

Former pupils Captain Mark Phillips; Sir John Betjeman; Norris McWhirter; The Hon Peter Brooke; Lord Hunt; Norman Del Mar; Sir Nicholas Goodison; Julian Pettifer; Chris De Burgh; Christopher Martin-Jenkins.

· *Mary Erskine* ·

The Mary Erskine
School
Ravelston
Edinburgh EH4 3NT
Tel 031 337 2391

- Pupils 600
- Boys None
- Girls 12–18
  (Day/Board)
- Higher year 92

- Termly fees
  £1122 (Day)
  £1782 (Board)
- GSA
  Enquiries/application to
  the Principal

What it's like

Founded in 1694 as the Merchant Maiden Hospital by Mary Erskine and the Company of Merchants of the City of Edinburgh. It was one of the first (possibly the first) schools in Britain to be endowed specifically for girls. After three different locations it occupied its present site at Ravelston in 1966. The plain, modern and well-equipped buildings are set in pleasant grounds. A new technology centre opened in 1991. Morning assemblies are held regularly and these take the form of non-denominational religious services. There is a full time specialist teacher of religious, moral and social education – a subject which forms part of the curriculum at all levels. Academic results are most creditable and two-thirds of the leavers go on to university or colleges of higher education. French, German, Modern Greek and Spanish are offered at GCSE, and a very high proportion of girls takes GCSE in more than one European language. Music is very strong indeed and plays an important part in the life of the school. There are several orchestras, ensembles and bands. Over two hundred girls learn a musical instrument. Drama and art are well supported. There are fine playing fields and other excellent facilities for sports and games in which good standards are attained. Sports include shooting, riding, curling, fencing, rowing and skiing. There is much emphasis on other open-air activities (eg orienteering, mountaineering and Outward Bound training). There are two Girl Guide companies and extensive participation in the Duke of Edinburgh's Award Scheme. The CCF contingent is very strong and the girls combine with the boys of Melville College and Daniel Stewart's School. A large number of activities are run in conjunction with these two schools. Full use is made of the cultural amenities of Edinburgh.

School profile

Pupils Age range 12–18, 600 girls. Main entry age 12. Junior school shared with Daniel Stewart's.

Entrance Own entrance exam used. Assisted places; 4 scholarships and some bursaries.

Staff Head P F J Tobin, 2 years in post.

Academic work O-grade/S-grade/Highers/CSYS. 25 subjects offered. In 1989, 94 pupils in O/S-grade year, 92 in Higher, 65 in CSYS year. *O/S-grade:* in 1989, 58 pupils gained at least grade C in 8+ subjects; 28 in 5–7; and 8 in 1–4 subjects. *Highers (+ 6th year):* 29(+1) passed in 5+ subjects; 25(+4) in 4; 10(+9) in 3; 12(+22) in 2; 7(+13) in 1 subject. *CSYS:* 1 pupil passed in 4+ subjects; 8 in 3; 7 in 2; 12 in 1 subject. *Computing facilities:* Good computing facilities in school for all year groups.

European Community *Languages:*
French offered: to age 14; S-grade; Highers; CSYS. German offered: to age 14; S-grade; Highers; CSYS. Greek (Modern) offered: to age 14; S-grade. Spanish offered: to age 14; S-grade; Highers; CSYS. 50–75% take S-grade in more than 1 EC language. *Exchanges:* Regular exchanges for pupils aged 14–16 to France and Germany.

Careers In 1990, 60% leavers went on to degree courses; 10% to art/drama/music colleges; 5% to non-degree courses; 5% straight into careers (eg bank trainee). Of those going on to degree courses, 3% went to Oxbridge; 82% to other universities; 16% to poly/colleges. 1% those going on to higher education went to courses in practical art; 25% in humanities/social sciences; 5% in medicine; and 3% in science/engineering.

· *Marymount* ·

Marymount International School George Road Kingston upon Thames Surrey KT2 7PE Tel 081 949 0571 Fax 081 336 2485	• Pupils 192 • Boys None • Girls 11–18 (Day/Board/Weekly) • Upper sixth 43	• Termly fees £2000 (Day) £4800 (Board) £4600 (Weekly) Enquiries/application to the Admissions Officer

What it's like

Founded in 1955, it derives from an educational movement inaugurated by the Roman Catholic Institute of the Religious of the Sacred Heart of Mary in Beziers which established international schools in four continents. Known as Marymount schools, the first was in New York. This one in Surrey, like its sister schools in Rome and Paris, has as its goal the provision of continuity in the academic careers of students whose education has been interrupted by family moves abroad. Many pupils have parents in the diplomatic corps. Representatives of 40 nations are currently on the roll at Kingston. Its 7-acre campus of pleasant grounds lies on the outskirts of the town. The original main building is a mock-Tudor private house. Recent buildings adjoin it. It is extremely well equipped and provides very comfortable boarding accommodation. It is one of only a handful of schools in the UK which offers the International Baccalaureat. French, German, Italian, Portuguese and Spanish are all offered for the I.B. The academic curriculum is designed to meet the needs of an international student body and it provides a wide selection of courses at all levels. It enjoys an excellent staff:pupil ratio of 1:10. High academic standards are achieved and for such a small school the number of pupils going on to degree courses is impressive. It has compulsory religious study programmes which include the study of world religions: a multi-faith approach. The school maintains strong international links with educational bodies and with other Marymount schools. Its cosmopolitanism is pervasive and very constructive.

School profile

Pupils Age range 11–18; 192 girls, 95 day, 97 boarding. Entry age, 12–16. 1% are children of former pupils.

Entrance Not oversubscribed. Good working knowledge of English required; no religious requirements. Parents expected to buy some specialist text books. Limited financial help at Principal's discretion.

Parents 15+% are from the diplomatic service; 15+% in industry or commerce. 30+% live within 30 miles; 30+% live overseas.

Staff Principal Sister Rosaleen Sheridan, 1 year in post. 23 full time staff, 7 part time. Annual turnover 4%. Average age 38.

Academic work International Baccalaureat (offers any IB language). Average size of upper fifth (10th grade) 40; upper sixth (12th grade) 43. School offers no external examination at 16 years. Twelfth grade students sit for IB Diploma and IB Certificate (Higher and Subsidiary level) exams. 17 pupils gain full IB Diploma; 12 IB Certificates at subsidiary and higher level. The IB programme covers 6 subjects to be chosen from 5 subject areas including science, maths, arts, humanities. School will arrange tutorials in Arabic, Urdu, Japanese, Dutch, etc for native speakers in preparation for IB. *Computing facilities:* Laboratory with 10 BBC and Apple computers. Computer studies is a compulsory

part of all student programmes in first 3 years. *Special provisions:* EFL.

European Community *Languages:* French offered: to age 14; IB. German offered: to age 14; IB. Italian offered: to IB. Portuguese offered: to IB. Spanish offered: to age 14; IB. *Other:* Educational tours to European countries.

Senior pupils' non-academic activities *Music:* 13 learn a musical instrument, 3 take voice training; 3 take IB higher level music. 1 accepted for Music School every 2 years. *Drama and dance:* 100 in school productions; 15 in Independent Schools Theatre Association; 1 accepted for Drama/Dance Schools every few years. *Art:* 25 take as non-examined subject; 6 take IB Higher Level; 3 accepted for Art School; 6 belong to eg photographic club. *Sport:* Badminton, basketball, volleyball, softball, soccer, tennis available. 100 take non-compulsory sport; 60 in ISST & AIST tournaments as varsity and junior varsity basketball, volleyball and soccer teams. *Other:* 50 take part in local community schemes. Other activities include various once-a-week club activities, occasional discos, film evenings and other social activities.

Careers In 1990, 82% leavers went on to degree courses; 18% other (eg Gap year, crammer courses, returning to home country). Of those going on to degree courses, 3% went to Oxbridge; 97% to other universities. 91% those going on to higher education went to courses in humanities/social sciences; 3% in medicine; and 6% in science/engineering.

Uniform School uniform worn throughout.

Houses/prefects No competitive houses. Student Council elected by the school.

Religion Compulsory religious studies programme includes study of world religions: a multi-faith approach. Students are encouraged to bear witness to their own faith and to learn to respect and understand the beliefs of others.

Social Drama, sports and maths competitions with other European Council of International Schools members all over Europe; sports tournaments with other members of London American-International Schools Sports Tournament Association; participate in the Model United Nations in The Hague. Annual educational tours week in February in which all students participate. Several destinations each year eg Russia, Egypt, Turkey, France, Italy, Austria. Pupils allowed to bring own bike to school. Meals self service. School tuckshop. No tobacco/alcohol allowed.

Discipline No corporal punishment. Punishment for pupils failing to produce homework dependent on individual teachers; those caught smoking cannabis on the premises could expect immediate expulsion.

Boarding All share with 1, 2, or 3. Qualified nurse during school hours, then on call; as is school doctor. Central dining room. Pupils can provide and cook snacks. Exeats any weekend. Visits to local town allowed, but not alone.

Alumni association run by Sister Mary Catherine Walsh, c/o the School.

· *Mayfield* ·

Mayfield College	• Pupils 200	• Termly fees
Mayfield	• Boys 10–18	£1915 (Day)
East Sussex	(Day/Board/Weekly)	£2835 (Board)
TN20 6PL	• Girls None	£2765 (Weekly)
Tel 0435 872041	• Upper sixth 20	• ISAI
		Enquiries/application to the Headmaster

What it's like

Founded in 1868 it has a fine site of 40 acres in the Sussex weald, a mile from Mayfield. Agreeable buildings and good modern facilities. A sound education is provided and results are creditable (10 plus university entrants per year). Adequate music, drama and art. Good range of games and sports. Some commitment to local community schemes and some participation in the Duke of Edinburgh's Award Scheme.

School profile

Pupils Age range 10–18; 200 boys, 100 day, 100 boarding. Main entry ages 11, 13 and into sixth. Approx 1% are children of former pupils.

Entrance Common entrance and own entrance exam used. Not oversubscribed. No special skills or religious requirements. Parents not expected to buy text books. Scholarships, up to 50% of fees, awarded on results of competitive examination. Bursaries, in cases of special need, are income-related.

Parents 15+% in industry or commerce. 31–60% live within 30 miles; 10+% live overseas.

Staff Headmaster D P Bannister, 1 year in post. 24 full time staff, 2 part time. Annual turnover 8%. Average age 41.

Academic work GCSE and A-levels. Average size of upper fifth 36; upper sixth 20. *GCSE:* on average, 7 pupils in upper fifth pass 8+ subjects; 11, 5–7 subjects; 13 pass 1–4 subjects. *A-levels:* on average, 2 pupils in upper sixth pass 4 subjects; 5, 3 subjects; 5, 2 subjects and 4 pass 1 subject. On average, 5 take science/engineering A-levels; 6 take arts and humanities; 8 a mixture. *Computing facilities:* Network of RM Nimbus machines. Tuition and experience is available through all age groups. *Special provisions:* EFL and assistance for dyslexics of good ability.

Senior pupils' non-academic activities *Music:* 12 learn a musical instrument, 1 or 2 to Grade 6 or above; 20 in school choir, 6 in school pop group. *Drama and dance:* 25 in school productions. *Art:* 15 take GCSE; 2, A-level. 1 accepted for Art School. *Sport:* Team games: rugby, soccer, cricket, basketball; racquet sports: tennis, squash, badminton; water sports: swimming, canoeing, sailing; individual sports: athletics, fencing, archery available. 50 take non-compulsory sport. 12 represent county (rugby, athletics). *Other:* 10 take part in local community schemes. 6 have bronze Duke of Edinburgh's Award. Other activities include a computer club, debating, choral singing.

Careers 2 part time advisers. Average number of pupils accepted for *arts and humanities degree courses* at universities, 4; polytechnics or CHE, 6. *science and engineering degree courses* at universities, 6; polytechnics or CHE, 2. Average number of pupils going straight into careers in industry, 4; commerce, 10.

Uniform School uniform worn except in the sixth.

Houses/prefects Competitive houses. Prefects, head boy, head of house and house prefects – appointed after consultation.

Religion Compulsory daily assembly for all. One service of worship midweek for all Christians and Sunday mass.

Social Sports fixtures, debates, music and drama, socials with local schools. Visits to France (to support language studies), skiing (once a year), sports camp in Majorca (once a year). Pupils allowed to bring own car/motorbike to school. Meals self service. School shop. No tobacco/alcohol allowed.

Discipline No corporal punishment. Pupils failing to produce homework once might expect a detention; those caught smoking cannabis on the premises could expect suspension, leading to probable expulsion.

Boarding Prefects have own study bedroom, all other sixth formers share with one other; 8 in each dormitory cubicle. House dormitories of 25, subdivided into cubicles divided by competitive houses and age group. Resident SRN. Central dining room. 2 weekend exeats each term. Visits to the local town allowed.

Alumni association run by M R Cullnane, 31 Rosemont Road, Acton, London W3.

· *Maynard* ·

The Maynard School	● Pupils 550	● Termly fees
Denmark Road	● Boys None	£953 (Day)
Exeter	● Girls 7–18	● GSA
Devon EX1 1SJ	(Day)	Enquiries/application to
Tel 0392 73417	● Upper sixth 51	the Headmistress

What it's like

Founded in 1658, it moved to its present site in 1882. A short distance from the centre of Exeter, it occupies high ground overlooking the Barnfield. The main and commodious building is a handsome house in the Victorian collegiate style. It enjoys fine gardens and grounds, in which also stands Traceyville, the junior school. There are in addition a splendid sixth-form centre, a sports hall (Bradley Hall) and (1991) a new purpose-built block housing six laboratories, a computer room, an economics room and a suite of five mathematics rooms. Overall, the school's facilities are good. The Maynard is non-denominational but is committed to the inculcation of sound Christian principles. Every opportunity is given for the development of talents and aptitudes and for the maturing of social skills. The curriculum in the main school is academically biased, with a good balance between arts and sciences. A well-qualified staff (augmented by a large number of part-time staff and visiting music teachers) provides a thorough general education. The staff:pupil ratio is about 1:11. Each year many girls go on to degree courses (including Oxbridge). Many pupils take GCSE in more than one European language. Music, art and drama are particular strengths (a large number of girls are involved in theatrical presentations). There are excellent facilities for sports and games (street hockey has been added to the games available) and the school has a distinguished reputation, especially in tennis, netball, hockey and indoor hockey. The school regularly reaches the national finals in hockey, and in all three games has provided an impressive number of representatives at county and national level. A fair range of clubs and societies and some participation in social services and the Duke of Edinburgh's Award Scheme.

School profile

Pupils Total age range 7–18; 550 day girls. Senior department 11–18, 440 girls. Main entry ages 7, 10, 11 and into sixth. *Transfer from maintained schools:* 50% main intake at 11, plus 50% to sixth.

Entrance Own entrance exam used. Oversubscribed. No special skills or religious requirements. Parents not expected to buy text books; maximum extras, £60 per term (1 extra per pupil). 31 assisted places pa. 4+ bursaries at sixth form level for isolated cases of hardship, £2000–£150.

Parents 60+% live within 30 miles.

Staff Headmistress Miss F Murdin, in post for 11 years. 38 full time staff, 15 part time. Annual turnover 6%. Average age 41.

Academic work GCSE and A-levels. 10 GCSE subjects offered; 23 at A-level (including Russian; no A-level general studies). In 1990, 62 pupils in upper fifth, 41 in upper sixth (now 51). *GCSE:* in 1990, 58 upper fifth gained at least grade C in 8+ subjects; 3 in 5–7; and 1 in 1–4 subjects. *A-levels:* 32 upper sixth passed in 3 subjects, of whom 4 added 1 AS-level; 8 in 2; and 1 in 1 subject. 25% took science A-levels; 34% arts/humanities; 41% both. *Computing facilities:* 1 fully equipped room for computer studies classes, plus single computers in junior form rooms, specialist department rooms (eg geography) and staff room. *Special provision:* Sympathetic attention and help given as required to any pupil in special difficulties (must be able to pass selective entrance test).

European Community *Languages:* French offered: to age 14; GCSE; AS-level; A-level; non-examined subject. German offered: to GCSE; A-level. Spanish offered: to A-level. 25–50% take GCSE in more than 1 EC language. *Exchanges:* Regular exchanges for pupils aged 11–16 to France and Germany.

Senior pupils' non-academic activities *Music:* 45 learn a musical instrument, 40 to Grade 6 or above. 1 accepted for Music School. 24 in school orchestra, 37 in school choir, 8 in chamber choir, 7 in school jazz band. *Drama and dance:* 100 in school productions; 1 accepted for Drama/Dance School. 3 enter public speaking, 12 drama, 6 ballroom dancing competitions. *Art:* 80 take as non-examined subject, 55 take GCSE; 4 A-level. 2 accepted for Art School. *Sport:* Hockey, indoor hockey, netball, badminton, swimming, tennis available. 40 pupils take non-compulsory sport. 18 achieve bronze medal (swimming). 19 pa represent county (tennis, hockey, netball, swimming), 5 represent country (tennis, hockey). *Other:* 30 take part in local community schemes. 26 have bronze Duke of Edinburgh's Award, 1 pa has gold. Other activities include a computer club, inter-school SCU, drama clubs for all ages. Many interest groups for younger pupils.

Careers In 1990, 76% leavers went on to degree courses; 2% to art/drama/music colleges; 5% to non-degree courses; 8% straight into careers; 9% other. Of those going on to degree courses, 10% went to Oxbridge; 69% to other universities; 21% to poly/colleges. 6% those going on to higher education went to courses in practical art; 50% in humanities/social sciences; 15% in medicine; and 29% in science/engineering.

Uniform School uniform worn except in sixth.

Houses/prefects Competitive houses for sports activities. No prefects; head girl – appointed by the Head, from sixth form shortlist. House captains elected by house members. School Council.

Religion Attendance at religious worship compulsory.

Social Annual inter-school public-speaking, modern languages, classical reading events with local schools, many local quizzes, etc sponsored by eg fire service, local radio and TV, road safety; sports fixtures. Exchanges with schools in Moscow, Rennes, Hildesheim. Regular ski trips (Alps), classical trips (Greece, Rome), history of art (Paris, Amsterdam), activities holidays (Mediterranean). Pupils allowed to bring own bike/moped to school. Second-hand uniform shop. Meals self service. No tobacco/alcohol allowed.

Discipline No corporal punishment. Pupils failing to produce homework once might expect a reprimand by teacher and early deadline for production of work; those caught smoking cannabis on school premises would be sent to the Headmistress and kept out of lessons and from all contact with other pupils until the matter had been discussed with parents, preferably at school and with the offender present. Further action would be unlikely to be necessary (a persistent offender would be regarded as a medical rather than a moral problem).

Alumni association is run by Mrs J P Gray, 9 Marlborough Road, Exeter.

Former pupils Professor Margaret Turner-Warwick (first woman President of Royal College of Physicians); Penelope Campbell, Rosemary Goodridge, Heather Wakefield (hockey internationals); Alison Hill (tennis international).

· Merchant Taylors' (Crosby) ·

Merchant Taylors'
School
Crosby
Liverpool L23 0QP
Tel 051 928 3308

- Pupils 830
- Boys 7–18
  (Day)
- Girls None
- Upper sixth 88

- Termly fees
  £963 (Day)
- HMC
Enquiries/application to
the Secretary

What it's like

Founded in 1620 by John Harrison, citizen and Merchant Taylor of London, it moved to its present site in 1878. This is urban and well equipped with modern facilities. A separate junior school is attached to the main school. Academic standards are high and results are good. Many sixth formers go on to degree courses, including Oxbridge. Strong music, drama and art departments. Good range of sports and games (high standards and a lot of county representatives) plus activities. Some participation in the Duke of Edinburgh's Award Scheme.

School profile

Pupils Total age range 7–18; 830 day boys. Senior department 11–18, 720 boys. Main entry ages 7, 11, 13 and into sixth. *Transfer from maintained schools:* 75% main senior intake, plus 90% to sixth.

Entrance Own entrance exam used. Oversubscribed. No special skills or religious requirements. Parents not expected to buy text books; maximum extras, £62. 185 assisted places. 50 grants, to full fees.

Parents 15+% in industry or commerce; 15+% are doctors, lawyers, etc.

Staff Headmaster S J R Dawkins, in post for 4 years. 54 full time staff, 4 part time. Annual turnover 7%. Average age 40.

Academic work GCSE and A-levels. 22 subjects offered (including A-level philosophy and general studies). On average, 106 pupils in upper fifth, 88 in upper sixth. *GCSE:* on average, 90% upper fifth gained at least grade C in 8+ subjects; 7% in 5–7; and 3% in 1–4 subjects. *A-levels:* 70% upper sixth passed in 4+ subjects; 20% in 3; 8% in 2; and 2% in 1 subject. 40% took science A-levels; 40% arts/humanities; 20% both. *Computing facilities:* 32 BBC Masters, 8 Archimedes; 12 Masters in separate departments. *Special provision:* Dyslexic counselling.

European Community *Languages:* French offered: to age 14; GCSE; A-level. German offered: to age 14; GCSE; A-level. Spanish offered: to age 14; GCSE. 25–50% take GCSE in more than 1 EC language. *Exchanges:* Regular exchanges for pupils aged 11–18 to France and Germany.

Senior pupils' non-academic activities *Music:* 210 learn a musical instrument, 20 to Grade 6 or above, 1 accepted for Music School; 31 in school orchestra, 35 in choir, 10 in pop group; 4 in Merseyside youth orchestra. *Drama and dance:* 70 in school productions; 50 in house plays; 10 in lower sixth play; 12 sixth form drama course. *Art:* 24 take as non-examined subject; 12 take GCSE; 4–6, A-level; art history is a compulsory short course for general studies. Occasional pupil accepted for Art School. *Sport:* Rugby, hockey, rowing, cross-country, swimming, tennis, cricket, softball, basketball, table tennis, golf, sailing, wind-surfing available. 60 take exams eg gymnastics, swimming. 30 represent county/country (rugby, hockey). *Other:* 6 have silver Duke of Edinburgh's Award, 2 have gold. Other activities include a computer club, CCF (voluntary), Scouts; societies: Amnesty, Christian, classical, debating, economics, railway, science, French play reading.

Careers In 1990, 85% leavers went on to degree courses; 5% to art/drama/

480

music colleges; 5% straight into careers (eg armed forces); 5% other. Of those going on to degree courses, 10% went to Oxbridge; 65% to other universities; 25% to poly/colleges. 2% those going on to higher education went to courses in practical art; 45% in humanities/social sciences; 10% in medicine; and 43% in science/engineering.

Uniform School uniform worn throughout.

Houses/prefects Competitive houses. Prefects, head boy, head of house and house prefects – appointed by the Head.

Religion Non-denominational Christian assemblies involve prayers and readings and RS classes explain (amongst other things) the meaning and purpose of Christian worship. Parents may 'opt out'; very few do.

Social Drama, music, several societies with sister girls' school. Organised trips abroad. Pupils allowed to bring own car/ bike/motorbike to school. Meals formal. School shop. No tobacco/alcohol allowed.

Discipline No corporal punishment. Pupils failing to produce homework once might expect a verbal warning; those caught smoking cannabis on the premises would be expelled.

Alumni association run by R R R Fisher, 25 Little Crosby Road, Crosby, Liverpool L23.

· *Merchant Taylors' (Girls)* ·

Merchant Taylors' School for Girls Crosby Liverpool L23 5SP Tel 051 924 3140	● Pupils 858 ● Boys None ● Girls 4–18 (Day) ● Upper sixth 63	● Termly fees £963 (Day) ● GSA Enquiries/application to the Headmistress

What it's like

Founded in 1888, it is suburban, single-site, in the centre of Crosby which is on the coast, 10 miles from Liverpool and 12 from Southport. Its well designed and pleasant buildings lie in gardens, with playing fields nearby. The junior school is close. It is non-denominational. There are strong traditional links with Merchant Taylors' Boys' School, Crosby, especially in cultural activities. It is a well run school with high academic standards and very good results. Nearly all girls do A-levels. Each year many pupils go on to degree courses, including Oxbridge. The music department is extremely strong. There is a good range of extra-curricular activities and sports, where high standards are achieved. In the sixth form there is a very substantial commitment to local community services.

School profile

Pupils Total age range 4–18; 858 day girls. Senior department 11–18, 591 girls. Main entry ages 4, 11 and into sixth. Approx 3% are children of former pupils. Own junior school, Stanfield, provides approx 25% of senior intake. *Transfer from maintained schools:* 75% main senior intake, plus few to sixth.

Entrance Own entrance exam used. Oversubscribed. No special religious requirements; music and sports skills looked for. Parents not expected to buy text books; dinner (£52) and music (£72) per term extra. 164 assisted places. 6–7 scholarships/bursaries, some depending upon parents' income.

Parents 15+% are doctors, lawyers, etc; 15+% in industry or commerce.

Staff Headmistress Miss E J Panton, 3 years in post. 46 full time staff, 30 part time (including music). Annual turnover 3%. Average age 40.

Academic work GCSE and A-levels. 20 subjects offered (including Russian, Theatre Studies and A-level general studies). In 1990, 85 pupils in upper fifth, 58 in upper sixth (now 63). *GCSE:* in 1990, 80 upper fifth gained at least grade C in 8+ subjects; 5 in 5–7 subjects. *A-levels:* 40 upper sixth passed in 4+ subjects; 10 in 3; 5 in 2; and 2 in 1 subject. 40% took science A-levels; 40% arts/ humanities; 20% both. *Computing facilities:* Acorn Archimedes networked (19 terminals) and Acorn Masters networked. *Special provision:* A preliminary screening test for dyslexia is available and examination concessions arranged; all-round awareness of the condition though no specific dyslexia unit.

European Community *Languages:* French offered: to age 14; GCSE; AS-level; A-level. German offered: to age 14; GCSE; AS-level; A-level. Spanish offered: to age 14; GCSE. 25–50% take GCSE in more than 1 EC language. *Other:* Investigating work experience links for sixth formers through Lingua programme.

Senior pupils' non-academic activities *Music:* Very many learn a musical instrument, 10–12 to Grade 6, 1–2 accepted for Music School; brass and wind ensembles in school, 2 orchestras of about 50 each, 3 school choirs; 1 or 2 in National Youth Orchestra, several in local youth orchestras, several enter local music festivals. *Drama and dance:* Variable number in school productions. Some grades of ESB taken in first–third forms and GCSE drama. 4 or 5 known to enter local dance competitions. *Art:* 40+ take GCSE; 5 or 6 take A-level. 3 accepted for Art School.

Sport: Swimming, hockey, netball, tennis, athletics are available. Sixth form use a sports centre. 2 or 3 represent county (athletics, hockey, swimming, tennis). *Other:* Voluntary service is a sixth form option. Other activities include a computer club, gymnastics, science, history and drama.

Careers In 1990, 72% leavers went on to degree courses; 5% to art/drama/ music colleges; 6% to non-degree courses (eg HND courses, resitting A-levels); 2% straight into careers. Of those going on to degree courses, 12% went to Oxbridge; 63% to other universities; 25% to poly/ colleges. 57% those going on to higher education went to courses in humanities/ social sciences; 7% in medicine; and 36% in science/engineering.

Uniform School uniform worn, modified in sixth.

Houses/prefects No house system or prefects – school affairs run by sixth form committees. Head girl and 2 deputies, elected by staff and seniors, confirmed by Head. School Council.

Religion Compulsory, non-denominational morning assembly.

Social Work closely with brother school. Regular trips abroad, though not in exchange. Pupils allowed to bring own car/bike/motorbike to school (but not use car park). Meals self service. Tuck facilities at break. No tobacco/alcohol allowed.

Discipline No corporal punishment. Those involved in serious breaches of rules (eg caught smoking on the premises) might expect immediate suspension until facts were verified.

Alumni association is run by Mrs S Duncan, Fairhaven, Serpentine South, Blundellsands, Liverpool L23 6UQ.

Former pupils Beryl Bainbridge.

· *Merchant Taylors' (Northwood)* ·

Merchant Taylors'
School
Sandy Lodge
Northwood
Middlesex HA6 2HT
Tel 09274 21850

- Pupils 725
- Boys 11–18
  (Day/Board)
- Girls None
- Upper sixth 120

- Termly fees
  £1680 (Day)
  £2680 (Board)
- HMC
  Enquiries/application to
  the Headmaster

What it's like

Founded in 1561 by the Merchant Taylors' Company, its first Headmaster was Richard Mulcaster. It moved to its present premises at Sandy Lodge in 1933 where it occupies a superb 300-acre estate of gardens, wooded grounds and lakes. The Merchant Taylors' Company continues to support the school financially. The handsome, well-equipped brick buildings are dominated by the Great Hall. Facilities are excellent and the libraries very good. It provides a highly academic and competitive environment and results are consistently impressive. Many leavers go on to degree courses, including a high proportion to Oxbridge. A high proportion of pupils takes GCSE in more than one European language. French and German are offered at all levels, Spanish at GCSE, and both Italian and Modern Greek as non-examined subjects. Music, drama and art are all very well supported. A wide range of games and sports is available and standards are high. Also a wide range of activities including a very big CCF and a flourishing Scout group. A fair commitment to local community services and a fine record in the Duke of Edinburgh's Award Scheme.

School profile

Pupils Age range 11–18; 725 boys, 655 day, 70 boarding. Main entry ages 11, 13 and into sixth. Approx 5% are children of former pupils. *Transfer from maintained schools:* 5% main intake, few to sixth.

Entrance Common entrance (at 13) used and own entrance exam (at 11 and for scholarships at 13). Oversubscribed. Excellence in all fields is welcomed; no religious requirements. Parents not expected to buy text books; extras rarely exceed £50. 20 assisted places pa. 14 scholarships (including 2 music) pa. Various bursaries available in case of need, supplementing up to full day fees.

Parents 15+% in industry or commerce; 15+% are doctors, lawyers, etc. 60+% live within 30 miles; 10+% live overseas.

Staff Headmaster J R Gabitass, first year in post. 61 full time staff, 14 part time. Annual turnover 8%. Average age 40.

Academic work GCSE and A-levels offered (including Ancient Greek, Latin and Russian). On average, 130 pupils in upper fifth, 120 in upper sixth. *GCSE:* on average, 96 upper fifth gained at least grade C in 8+ subjects; 31 in 5–7; and 12 in 1–4 subjects. *A-levels:* 6 upper sixth passed in 4+ subjects; 81 in 3; 20 in 2; and 10 in 1 subject. 45 took science A-levels; 41 arts/humanities; 32 both. *Computing facilities:* A computer centre with 14 computers. Almost every department uses computers. *Special provision:* Academically suitable children with special educational needs accepted (medical advice sought as appropriate). Pupils must be able to cope with teaching in English without remedial help.

European Community *Languages:* French offered: to age 14; GCSE; A-level. German offered: to age 14; GCSE; A-level. Greek (Modern): non-examined subject. Italian: non-examined subject. Spanish offered: to GCSE. 50–75% take

483

GCSE in more than 1 EC language. *Exchanges:* Regular exchanges for pupils aged 14–18 to France and Germany.

Senior pupils' non-academic activities *Music:* 70 learn a musical instrument, 25 to Grade 6 or above; 45 in school orchestra; 20 in choir; 12 in pop group; 1 in National Youth Orchestra. *Drama and dance:* 30 participate in school productions; 100+ in house plays; 1 accepted for Drama/Dance School; 1 competes in ice dancing. *Art:* 26 take GCSE; 12 A-level. 3 accepted for Art School. 1 belongs to photographic club. *Sport:* Athletics, badminton, basketball, chess, cricket, cross-country, canoeing, fencing, fishing (fly and coarse), fives, golf, hockey, judo, multigym, rock climbing, rugby, sailing, shooting, soccer, squash, swimming, table tennis, tennis, volleyball, windsurfing available. 40% take non-compulsory sport. 2 represent country (golf, ice dance); 6 represent county (rugby, athletics, cricket). *Other:* 36 take part in local community schemes. 25 have bronze Duke of Edinburgh's Award, 15 have silver. 30 in scouts. 10 enter voluntary schemes after leaving school. Other activities include a computer club; driving lessons.

Careers In 1990, 77% leavers went on to degree courses; 1% to art/drama/music colleges; 15% to non-degree courses (eg tutorial, agricultural); 2% straight into careers (eg electrical contracting); 5% other. Of those going on to degree courses, 24% went to Oxbridge; 67% to other universities; 9% to poly/colleges. 1% those going on to higher education went to courses in practical art; 60% in humanities/social sciences; 8% in medicine; and 31% in science/engineering.

Uniform School uniform worn throughout.

Houses/prefects Competitive houses. Prefects, head boy, head of house and house prefects – appointed by the Head and housemasters after consultation.

Religion Daily assembly.

Social Choral works, concerts, debates, drama, field work, careers conventions, industrial conferences, academic lectures with local schools. Organised French/German exchanges; German orchestral exchange visit. Ski trips. Sports tours. Pupils allowed to bring own car/bike/motorbike to school. Meals self service. School shop. No tobacco/alcohol allowed.

Discipline No corporal punishment. Pupils failing to produce homework once might expect to have to do it by the following day; those persistently refusing to obey school rules could expect expulsion.

Boarding 25 have own study bedroom, 36 share (2); 17 are in dormitories (12, 5). 1 House. Resident qualified nurse; doctor visits regularly and always on call. Central dining room. Pupils can provide and cook their own food. 3 weekend exeats each term. Visits to the local town allowed in sixth form.

Alumni association is run by N J Foley, Chairman OMT Society, St Benets, Northfield Avenue, Pinner, Middlesex.

Former pupils Rt Rev Donald Coggan; Reginald Maudling; Michael Peschardt; Lynn Chadwick.

· *Merchiston* ·

Merchiston Castle
School
Colinton
Edinburgh EH13 0PU
Tel 031 441 1722
Fax 031 441 6060

- Pupils 380
- Boys 11–18
  (Day/Board)
- Girls None
- Upper sixth 65

- Termly fees
  £1840 (Day)
  £2860 (Board)
- HMC
Enquiries to the
Headmaster
Applications to the
Registrar

What it's like

Founded in 1833 in the centre of Edinburgh, it moved in 1930 to Colinton House and the ruins of Colinton Castle. These lie 4 miles south-west of Edinburgh in a fine estate of gardens, sports fields and parkland bordered on two sides by the Water of Leith and are close to the Pentland Hills. Apart from the original house (now the science block) all the buildings are purpose-built and date from the 1930s or the development programmes since the 1960s, including in the 1980s a theatre, computer and electronics departments, a careers centre, art and design centre, sports hall, indoor rifle range and a new classroom block. The environment is healthy and facilities very good (including comfortable boarding accommodation currently undergoing major refurbishment). The school prides itself on its adherence to Scottish values and traditions, and there is emphasis on striving for excellence, a belief in the value of the individual, in hard work, integrity and good manners. The 'Scottishness' is exemplified in the wearing of a kilt on Sundays and formal occasions, the fine pipe band, and social occasions such as a Highland Ball and Scottish country dancing. There is also emphasis on the practice of Christianity and the importance of service to the community. The school regularly raises considerable sums for charity, and has a substantial commitment to local community services. Religious education is part of the curriculum: Merchiston is interdenominational but services are based on those of the Church of Scotland. Academic standards are high and the teaching very good. A staff:pupil ratio of 1:9. Results are consistently impressive. For a small school, a high proportion of pupils go on to degree courses, including Oxbridge. French, German and Spanish are offered at all levels throughout the school and also as non-examined subjects. European exchange arrangements are currently being re-organised. Music is particularly strong and the choir have recorded for the BBC and regularly go on tour abroad. Art, design, drama and debating are also strong. A wide range of sports and games is available and the school has long had a reputation for excellence in these, particularly rugby. Cricket, athletics, swimming and shooting also strong. Also a good range of extra-curricular activities with emphasis on outdoor pursuits for which the environment is ideal. A flourishing CCF in which each boy spends 2 years and an impressive record in the Duke of Edinburgh's Award Scheme.

School profile

Pupils Age range 11–18; 380 boys, 65 day, 315 boarding. Senior department 13–18, 320 boys. Main entry ages 11, 12, 13 and into sixth. Approx 25% are children of former pupils. *Transfer from maintained schools:* 25% main intake, plus 10% to sixth.

Entrance Common entrance and own exam used. Oversubscribed at most levels. A breadth of interest and talents looked for; interdenominational. Parents charged £20 per term towards text books; maximum extras approx £80 for eg music. 30 assisted places. Various scholarships/bursaries, 75%–10% of fees.

Parents 40% are doctors, lawyers, etc; 40% in industry or commerce. 20% live within 30 miles; 20% expatriates.

Staff Headmaster D M Spawforth, in post for 9 years. 46 full time staff, 4 part time. Annual turnover 6%. Average age 35.

Academic work GCSE, Highers, AS and A-levels. 16 GCSE subjects offered; 13 at Higher; 17 at A-level (including AS electronics; A-level computing; general studies taught but not examined). In 1990, 60 pupils in GCSE year, 63 in A-level/Higher year (now 65). *GCSE:* in 1990, 44 upper fifth gained at least grade C in 8+ subjects; 12 in 5–7; and 4 in 1–4 subjects. *Highers:* 6 passed in 5+ subjects; 6 in 4; 5 in 3; 3 in 2 subjects. *A-levels:* 4 passed in 4+ subjects; 29 in 3; 7 in 2; and 3 in 1 subject. 38% took science A-levels; 42% arts/humanities; 21% both. *Computing facilities:* Purpose-built – 2 'Lab' computing department. All pupils undergo basic computing – age 11–13 and also available as GCSE, A-level and as activity. *Special provision:* Extra English classes, and tutoring.

European Community *Languages:* French offered: to age 14; GCSE; A-level; non-examined subject. German offered: to age 14; GCSE; A-level; non-examined subject. Spanish offered: to age 14; GCSE; A-level; non-examined subject. 50–75% take GCSE in more than 1 EC language. *Exchanges:* Exchanges currently being reorganised for linguists and others in lower sixth. *Other:* A number of EC boys (eg Belgian, French, German, Dutch). Conference every second year on EC/NATO. Regular study trips mainly to France and Germany.

Senior pupils' non-academic activities *Music:* 125 learn a musical instrument, 10 to Grade 6 or above; 33 in school orchestra, 94 in choir, 6 in pop group, 12 in close harmony group, 15 in pipe band; 1 in National Youth Orchestra. Choir has recently recorded for BBC Radio and gone on tour to the Far East. *Drama and dance:* 80 in school production, 80 in house drama productions; 1 production to Edinburgh Fringe; 100 in Scottish reels clubs. 2 go on to work in theatre. *Art:* 22 take art or design as non-examined subject; 43 GCSE art and CDT; 4 A-level. 3 accepted for Art School; 3 for design. 2 participate in Design Council Awards competition for schools. 20 belong to photographic club. *Sport:* Rugby, cricket, athletics, swimming, fencing, tennis, shooting, squash, fives, badminton, hockey, crosscountry running available. 250 take non-compulsory sport. 12 represent county/country (rugby, athletics, biathlon, fencing). *Other:* 30 take part in local community schemes. 10 have bronze Duke of Edinburgh's Award, 10 have silver and 4 gold. 4 enter voluntary schemes and 2 work for national charities after leaving. Other activities include a computer club, electronics, debating, science, travel, drama, photography, ornithology, chess, bridge, video filming, driving lessons, skiing, Outward Bound (hill walking); leadership course; links with industry; work experience. Gold and silver awards in both British Pupils Olympiad and National Mathematics Competition (under 19s).

Careers In 1990, 75% leavers went on to degree courses; 5% to art/drama/music colleges; 11% to non-degree courses (eg agriculture, HND hotel and catering management); 4% straight into careers (eg retail, food industry); 4% other. Of those going on to degree courses, 14% went to Oxbridge; 78% to other universities; 8% to poly/colleges. 5% those going on to higher education went to courses in practical art; 3% in drama/acting; 47% in humanities/social sciences; 5% in medicine; and 41% in science/engineering.

Uniform School uniform worn except the upper sixth.

Houses/prefects No competitive houses. Prefects, head boy, head of house and house prefects – appointed by the Head. Various committees and councils, eg food, charities, chapel.

Religion Daily morning act of worship; Sunday morning service for whole school.

Social Debates, plays, concerts, charity

fundraising events, dances, Scottish reel evenings and some guest speakers organised with local girls' schools. Tours to France, Germany, Spain, Italy; skiing; rugby tours eg recently to Japan; choir recently toured Far East; expeditions. Meals self service. School shops sell sports equipment, books and second-hand school wear. No tobacco allowed; sixth form club with beer bar at weekends under housemaster's control.

Discipline No corporal punishment. Pupils failing to produce homework once might expect to re-do; also detentions, suspensions or expulsion for very serious offences.

Boarding 33% have own study bedroom, 30% are in dormitories of 6+.

Houses, of approximately 60, divided by age. Resident nurse and assistant matron; doctor on call. Central dining room. Pupils can provide and cook own food in house kitchen. 1 exeat of 3 days to a week each term. Visits to local town allowed though controlled and dependent on age.

Alumni association run by President of the Merchistonian Club, c/o the School.

Former pupils Rt Hon John MacGregor MP; Lord Craigavon; Sir James Robertson; Sir Donald Acheson (Government Chief Medical Officer); Lt Gen Sir Alexander Boswell; John Jeffrey, Roger Baird (Scotland XV); Sir Eric Campbell Geddes.

· Methodist College ·

The Methodist College
1 Malone Road
Belfast
BT9 6BY
Tel 0232 669558

- Pupils 2195
- Boys 4–19 (Day/Board)
- Girls 4–19 (Day/Board)
- Upper sixth 270

- Termly fees
  £650 (Day)
  £1419 (Board)
- HMC
  Enquiries/application to the Principal

What it's like

Founded in 1868, it is urban, single-site in landscaped grounds close to Queen's University and a mile from the city centre. It has two large prep schools. The principal buildings are Victorian Gothic, with suggestions of Scottish 'baronial' and hotel de ville. There are many modern buildings including a splendid chapel. It is a superbly well equipped establishment with very high academic attainments. Many leavers go on to degree courses, including Oxbridge. Tremendously strong in music and drama. Very high standards in sport and games. An enormous number of clubs and societies catering for virtually every need. Big commitment to local community schemes and an outstanding record in the Duke of Edinburgh's Award Scheme. Fees are very low.

School profile

Pupils Total age range 4–19; 2195 pupils, 2018 day (1010 boys, 1008 girls), 177 boarding (106 boys, 71 girls). Senior department 11–19, 1653 pupils (831 boys, 822 girls). Main entry ages 11, 16 and into sixth. Approx 30% are children of former pupils.

Entrance Common entrance not used. Oversubscribed. No special skills or religious requirements. Parents expected to buy text books; maximum extras, £100 pa. 10 scholarships/bursaries available, from £400 to £300.

Parents 15+% are doctors, lawyers, etc;

15+% in industry or commerce; 15+% are teachers/lecturers. 60+% live within 30 miles; 5% live overseas.

Staff Principal Mr T W Mulryne, in post for 2 years. 123 full time staff, 13 part time. Annual turnover 5%. Average age 38.

Academic work GCSE and A-levels. (Russian, Classical Greek are offered to GCSE/A-level.) Average size of upper fifth 230; upper sixth 270. *GCSE:* on average, 190 pupils in upper fifth pass 8+ subjects; 25, 5–7 subjects; 15 pass 1–4 subjects. *A-levels:* on average, 28 pupils in the upper sixth pass 4 subjects; 174, 3 subjects; 42, 2 subjects; 26 pass 1 subject. On average, 90 take science/engineering A-levels; 80 take arts and humanities; 100 take a mixture. *Computing facilities:* 18 Station 480Z network, three 15 Station Nimbus networks and BBC computers in various departments. 16 station Nimbus network for word processing and business studies.

European Community *Languages:* French offered: to age 14; GCSE; A-level. German offered: to age 14; GCSE; A-level. Spanish offered: to age 14; GCSE; A-level. 10–25% take GCSE in more than 1 EC language. *Exchanges:* Regular exchanges for pupils aged 11–16 to France. *Other:* European Studies offered to pupils aged 16–18. Member of European Studies Project.

Senior pupils' non-academic activities *Music:* 90 learn a musical instrument, 45 to Grade 6 or above, 4+ accepted for Music School; 50 in school orchestra, 300 in choir, 80 in band; 15 in City of Belfast Youth Orchestra, 8 in SE Ed & Library Board Orchestra. *Drama and dance:* 120 in school productions including musicals. 6 accepted for Drama/Dance Schools, 2 go on to work in theatre, 1 recent pupil is theatrical musical director. 15 AEB Drama, 16 take General Drama Studies. *Art:* 25 take A-level. 6 accepted for Art School, 1 for art history at university, 12 belong to photographic club, 8 in art club, 11 take history & appreciation of Art. *Sport:* Rugby, cricket, hockey, rowing, judo, swimming, fencing, squash, badminton, netball, cross-country, athletics, golf and tennis avail-

able. 270 take non-compulsory sport. Pupils have represented county and country in rugby, hockey, rowing, squash, badminton, swimming, athletics. Others have judo belts (testing and awards). *Other:* 86 take part in local community schemes. 140 take bronze and silver Duke of Edinburgh's Award; 30 have gold. A few enter voluntary schemes after leaving school. Other activities include a computer club, very lively chess club recently (won 3 Ulster School Leagues, Irish Schools Individual Champion, 4th in Times British Schools Tournament), driving lessons, over 60 clubs and societies.

Careers In 1990, 69% leavers went on to degree courses; 2% to art/drama/music colleges; 1% to non-degree courses; 16% straight into careers (eg banking, insurance, nursing, civil service); 12% other. Of those going on to degree courses, 14% went to Oxbridge; 72% to other universities; 14% to poly/colleges. 3% those going on to higher education went to courses in practical art; 1% in drama/acting; 1% in music; 51% in humanities/social sciences; 9% in medicine; and 35% in science/engineering.

Uniform School uniform worn throughout.

Prefects Prefects, head boy and girl, deputy head boy and girl – appointed by the Head in consultation with staff. Sixth form Council.

Religion Sunday evening service compulsory for boarders (in school chapel); brief act of worship at morning assemblies for all pupils.

Social 2 community relations co-ordinators for work in sixth forms are based in school; current affairs, debates, public speaking, Christian Union, chess and sports generally. Pupils allowed to bring own car/bike/motorbike to school. Meals self service. Small school tuck shops. No tobacco/alcohol allowed.

Discipline No corporal punishment. Pupils failing to produce homework once might expect reprimand; those caught smoking cannabis on the premises might expect expulsion.

Boarding 40 girls, 36 boys have own study bedroom; 24 girls and 10 boys share with 1 or 2 others; 22 girls and 74 boys in dormitories of 6+. Houses, of approximately 11–30, are divided by age and are single sex. Resident qualified medical staff. Central dining room. Pupils can provide and cook their own food (senior girls at supper, boys in specified rooms). 2 weekend exeats each term. Visits to local town allowed.

Alumni association Old Boys' Association, Mr Gerald Beamish, 37 Quarry Road, Belfast, Northern Ireland. Old Girls' Association: Mrs Pat Arneill, 73 Skyline Avenue, Lambeg, Lisburn, Northern Ireland.

Former pupils Barry Douglas (winner of Tchaikovsky Piano Competition); James Ellis (actor); Dr Robin Eames (present Primate of All Ireland); George Hamilton (sports commentator); Jack Siggins (British Lions Manager); Roger Young (British Lion); Prof Ernest Walton (winner of Nobel Prize 1951); Sir Ewart Bell (ex-head NI Civil Service); Field Marshal Sir John Dill (CIGS World War II); Edith Major (Mistress of Girton).

· *Michael Hall* ·

Michael Hall Rudolf
Steiner School
Kidbrooke Park
Forest Row
East Sussex RH18 5JB
Tel 0342 822275

- Pupils 540
- Boys 4–18
  (Day/Board)
- Girls 4–18
  (Day/Board)
- Upper sixth 25

- Termly fees
  £975 (Day)
  £2250 (Board)
  £2050 (Weekly)
- Steiner
  Enquiries/application to
  the Secretary for
  Admissions

What it's like

Founded in 1925, this is the oldest, biggest and most established of the Rudolf Steiner schools in the UK. It has a fine rural site in its own parkland on the edge of Ashdown Forest and a mile from the village centre of Forest Row. It offers a very broad education to boys and girls 4–18, which is based on the educational philosophy of Steiner. The curriculum embodies cultural studies, foreign languages (a high proportion of pupils takes GCSE in more than one European language and, for late entrants, a knowledge of French and/or German is an advantage), sciences, general arts and humanities, crafts, music and movement. Art, music and drama are very important elements in the school life. A remedial dept and EFL is available. Steiner's fascinating educational theories, philosophy and methods need to be looked at in detail by prospective parents. The teaching is of a high standard. A fair range of sports, games and extra-curricular activities is offered.

School profile

Pupils Total age range 4–18; 540 pupils, 450 day (225 boys, 225 girls), 90 boarding (45 boys, 45 girls). Senior department 11–18, 257 pupils (128 boys, 129 girls). Open entry. Approx 10% are children of former pupils. *Transfer from maintained schools:* Less than 5% senior intake and to sixth.

Entrance Not oversubscribed. Knowledge of French and/or German an advantage; no particular religious requirements. Parents expected to buy text books; maximum extras, £275. Means-tested bursaries available (after first year of school).

Parents 60+% live within 30 miles; up to 10% live overseas.

Staff Chairman of the College of Teachers, currently Peter Bark (changes annually). 44 full time staff, 9 part time. Annual turnover 10%. Average age 36.

Academic work GCSE and A-levels. 16 subjects offered (including integrated science and integrated humanities; no A-level general studies). In 1990, 43 pupils in upper fifth, 25 in upper sixth. *GCSE:* in 1990, 15 upper fifth gained at least grade C in 5–7 subjects; and 4 in 1–4 subjects. *A-levels:* 2 upper sixth passed in 3 subjects; 2 in 2; and 7 in 1 subject. 8% took science A-levels; 52% arts/humanities; 4% both. *Computing facilities:* BBC and Archimedes; laboratory with 8 computers. *Special provision:* Special EFL programme; remedial one-to-one coaching.

European Community *Languages:* French offered: to age 14; GCSE; A-level. German offered: to age 14; GCSE; A-level. Spanish offered: to age 14; GCSE; A-level. 25–50% take GCSE in more than 1 EC language. *Exchanges:* Regular exchanges for pupils aged 11–16 to France and Germany.

Senior pupils' non-academic activities *Music:* 25 learn a musical instrument, 1 accepted for Music School, 2 go on to play in pop group; 25 in school orchestra, 30 in school choir. *Drama and dance:* 40 in school productions. 1 accepted for Drama/Dance School. *Art:* 120 take as non-examined subject; 35 take GCSE; 10, A-level. 1 accepted for Art School. *Sport:* Hockey, cricket, tennis, swimming, basketball, archery, sailing, rock climbing and athletics available. 25 take non-compulsory sport. Other activities include a computer club and a very lively drama section.

Careers 1 part time adviser. Annual average accepted for *arts and humanities degree courses* at Oxbridge, 1; other universities, 4; polytechnics/colleges, 2. *science and engineering degree courses* at universities, 2. *other general training courses*, 4. Average going straight into careers in the armed services, 1.

Uniform School uniform not worn.

Houses/prefects No competitive houses, no prefects, or head boy/girl.

Religion Non-denominational Sunday service in school is encouraged.

Social Some musical productions with other local schools. Art history trip to Italy, and opportunities for exchanges with sister schools on the continent. Pupils allowed to bring own bike/motorbike to school. Meals in hostel formal, self service at lunch. No tobacco/alcohol allowed.

Discipline No corporal punishment.

Boarding One hostel of 30 pupils, very few have own study bedroom; rooms are shared with a few others; also boarding in homes of families with children at the school. No resident qualified medical staff. Exeats by arrangement. Visits to local town allowed.

Alumni association is run by Ivor Revere, c/o Michael Hall.

Former pupils Martyn Boysens (mountaineer); Oliver Tobias (actor); Sean Yates (international cyclist).

· *Micklefield* ·

Micklefield School	● Pupils 222	● Termly fees
Sutton Avenue	● Boys 4–8 only	£1400 (Day)
Seaford	(Day)	£2400 (Board)
East Sussex	● Girls 4–18	£2250 (Weekly)
BN25 4LP	(Day/Board/Weekly)	● GSA, BSA
Tel 0323 892457	● Upper sixth up to	Enquiries/application to
	15	the Headmaster

What it's like

Founded in 1910 at Reigate it moved to its present site between Newhaven and Eastbourne in 1920. The pleasant modern buildings lie in 7 acres of gardens and playing fields in a residential area of the small seaside town. The boarding houses are in the same road within a few minutes' walk of each other. A large number of developments in the last 15 years have provided excellent modern facilities. A good general education is given in a happy and stimulating environment and the school has all the advantages of being a small establishment (staff:pupil ratio of 1:12). Results are creditable. Each year a few pupils go on to degree courses. Many pupils take GCSE in both French and Spanish. There are strong music, drama and art departments and a satisfactory range of sports, games and extra-curricular activities.

School profile

Pupils Total age range 4–18; 222 pupils, 118 day (20 boys, 98 girls), 104 boarding girls. Senior department 11–18, 140 girls. Main entry ages 5–6 (boys and girls), 10, 11 and into sixth (girls). Approx 2% are children of former pupils. *Transfer from maintained schools:* 15% main intake, plus 10% to sixth.

Entrance School's own assessments sometimes used. Not oversubscribed. Skills in music, drama, sports and creative arts looked for; no special religious requirements. Parents not expected to buy text books; maximum extras, £200. 2 major, 2 minor scholarships, two third fees to one third fees. Bursaries for service children.

Parents 15+% in the armed services. 30+% live within 30 miles; 10+% live overseas.

Staff Headmaster Mr Eric Reynolds, in post for 3 years. 20 full time staff, 14 part time. Annual turnover 10–15%. Average age 43.

Academic work GCSE, AS and A-levels. 17 subjects offered (no A-level general studies). In 1989, 28 pupils in upper fifth, 4 in upper sixth (an exceptional year). *GCSE:* in 1989, 25% upper fifth gained at least grade C in 8+ subjects; 35% in 5–7; and 33% in 1–4 subjects. *A-levels:* 75% upper sixth passed in 3 subjects; 25% in 2 subjects. 50% took science A-levels; 50% arts/humanities. *Computing facilities:* Computer laboratory – 6 RKM Nimbus and 2 BBC B's. *Special provision:* Special needs unit; specialist EFL teacher.

European Community *Languages:* French offered: to age 14; GCSE; AS-level; A-level. Spanish offered: to GCSE; AS-level; A-level. 25–50% take GCSE in more than 1 EC language. *Exchanges:* Regular exchanges for pupils aged 11–14 to France.

Senior pupils' non-academic activities *Music:* 60 learn a musical instrument, 4 to Grade 6 or above; 15 in school orchestra, 25 in school choir. *Drama and dance:* 90 in school productions. 2 take Grade 6 in ESB, RAD, etc. *Art:* 5 take as non-examined subject; 20 take GCSE; 5 take A-level. 3 accepted for Art School. 10 belong to eg photographic club. *Sport:* Lacrosse, netball, volleyball, badminton, swimming, tennis, athletics, gymnastics, trampolining and self-defence available. 50 take non-compulsory sport. 40 take exams. Other activities include a computer club, guides, pottery and ballet.

Careers In 1990, 60% leavers went on to degree courses; 30% to art/drama/music colleges; 10% to non-degree courses. Of those going on to degree courses, 30% went to universities; 70% to poly/colleges. 10% those going on to higher education went to courses in practical art; 60% in humanities/social sciences; 10% in medicine; and 20% in science/engineering.

Uniform School uniform worn except the sixth.

Houses/prefects Competitive houses. Prefects – appointed by staff; head girl – appointed by Head; head of house and house prefects. School Council.

Religion Morning Assembly. Regular Sunday services.

Social No organised local events. Annual trip abroad organised. Meals self service. School shop. No tobacco/alcohol allowed.

Discipline No corporal punishment. Pupils failing to produce homework once might expect detention; those caught smoking cannabis on the premises might expect expulsion.

Boarding 20% have their own study bedroom, 10% share with one other; 12% in dormitories of 6+. Pupils divided into houses, approx 20–30, by age. Resident nurse. Central dining room. Pupils occasionally allowed to provide and cook own food. 2 weekend exeats per term.

Visits to local town allowed. **Alumni association** is run by Mrs A Golledge, 29 Chesterton Drive, Seaford, East Sussex.

· *Mill Hill* ·

Mill Hill School
The Ridgeway
London
NW7 1QS
Tel 081 959 1176

- Pupils 540
- Boys 13–18
  (Day/Board)
- Girls 16–18
  (Day/Board)
- Upper sixth 112

- Termly fees
  £1875 (Day)
  £2850 (Board/
  Weekly)
- HMC
  Enquiries/application to
  the Headmaster

What it's like

Founded in 1807 by a group of non-conformist Christian ministers and City merchants. In 1827 it moved to the buildings which form the central part of the main school. These, palatial, neo-classical, magnificently designed within and without, lie in 120 acres of wooded parkland in the green belt 10 miles from the middle of London. There has been much development in recent years and facilities and accommodation are first-class. Belmont, the junior school, is a few hundred metres away. A well-run school with long-established high standards, it regards hard work, self-criticism, enthusiasm and loyalty as paramount virtues. Chapel services are compulsory for all. Academic results are good. Many pupils go on to degree courses, including Oxbridge. French, German and Spanish are offered throughout the school and a high proportion of pupils take GCSE in more than one European language. There is a large business studies centre, pioneering business and IT. Strong in music, drama and art. Very broad range of games and sports (the standards are high). Substantial commitment to local community schemes. Appreciable success in the Duke of Edinburgh's Award Scheme.

School profile

Pupils Age range 13–18; 540 pupils, 290 day (270 boys, 20 girls), 250 boarding (210 boys, 40 girls). Main entry ages 13 (boys) and into sixth (boys and girls). Approx 5% are children of former pupils. Belmont, Mill Hill Junior provides 40% of intake. *Transfer from maintained schools:* 5–10% main intake, plus 25% to sixth.

Entrance Common entrance and own entrance exam used. Oversubscribed (not for boarding). No special skills or religious requirements but all are expected to attend chapel services. Parents not expected to buy text books; average extras £50. 15 assisted places pa. 12 scholarships/bursaries, musical and aca-

demic, up to half fees. 15% fees reduction for service children.

Parents 30% in industry or commerce. 60% live within 30 miles; 10+% live overseas.

Staff Headmaster Mr A C Graham, in post for 11 years. 55 full time staff, 15 part time. Annual turnover 2–4%. Average age 35.

Academic work GCSE and A-levels. 16 GCSE subjects offered; 21 at A-level (including design technology, GCSE & A-level; business studies with information technology, A-level; no A-level general studies). In 1989, 89 pupils in upper fifth, 112 in upper sixth. *GCSE:* in 1990, 58 upper fifth gained at least grade C in 8+ subjects; 17 in 5–7; and 14 in 1–4 subjects. *A-levels:* 14 upper sixth passed in 4+ subjects; 63 in 3; 23 in 2; and 9 in 1 subject. 30% took science A-levels; 30% arts/humanities; 40% both. *Computing facilities:* 20 Archimedes networked with file store in main computer room. Business studies has 12 Zenith with modem and Times network system; plus 35 BBC micros distributed around the departments; Doomsday system. *Special provision:* Extra English for boys with eg slight dyslexia; EFL available in first year.

European Community *Languages:* French offered: to age 14; GCSE; A-level. German offered: to age 14; GCSE; A-level. Spanish offered: to age 14; GCSE; A-level. 50–75% take GCSE in more than 1 EC language. *Exchanges:* Regular exchanges for pupils aged 13–18 to France, Germany and Spain. *Other:* Pupils from all over Europe in school. Party of sixth formers to Alden Biesen in Belgium for European seminar week.

Senior pupils' non-academic activities *Music:* 85 learn a musical instrument, 30 to Grade 6 or above; 40 in school orchestra, 60 in school choir, 20 in school jazz band. *Drama and dance:* 100 in school productions, large numbers in house plays. *Art:* 35 take as non-examined subject; 20 take GCSE; 10 take A-level. 1 or 2 accepted for Art School. 20 in art society. *Sport:* Rugby, cricket, hockey, squash, Eton fives, tennis, badminton, basketball, netball, swimming, shooting, fencing, athletics, cross-country, golf, sailing, karate and horse-riding available. 200 take non-compulsory sport. 10 take exams in eg swimming, 10 represent county (rugby, cricket). *Other:* 30 take part in local community schemes. 20 have silver Duke of Edinburgh's Award. Other activities include an informal computer club in the computer room, CCF (Army and Navy), chess club (usually wins every competition in Barnet) and cinema society.

Careers In 1990, 70% leavers went on to degree courses; 10% to art/drama/ music colleges; 5% to non-degree courses (eg secretarial, HND); 5% straight into careers (eg financial, such as Lloyd's, banking); 10% other. Of those going on to degree courses, 10% went to Oxbridge; 55% to other universities; 35% to poly/ colleges. 3% those going on to higher education went to courses in practical art; 2% in drama/acting; 5% in music; 45% in humanities/social sciences; 15% in medicine; and 25% in science/ engineering.

Uniform School uniform worn, modified in sixth.

Houses/prefects Competitive houses. Prefects, head boy/girl, head of house and house prefects – appointed by the Head and House Masters, advice accepted from upper sixth. School Council.

Religion Chapel compulsory for all (about 3 times per week).

Social Extensive use of our Field Study Centre at Dent in Cumbria. Exchanges with France, Germany and Spain; involves about 100 boys per year. Pupils allowed to bring own car/bike to school. Meals self service. School shop. No tobacco allowed. Alcohol on occasion.

Discipline Pupils failing to produce homework once might expect a warning; those caught smoking cannabis on the premises might expect expulsion.

Boarding All upper sixth have own study bedroom, most lower sixth and fifth forms share with one other; most juniors in dormitories of 6+. Houses, of approximately 50, same as competitive houses; some single sex, some mixed. Resident SRN, doctor visits daily. Central dining room. Pupils can provide and cook own snacks. Exeats most weekends (weekly boarding allowed). Visits to local town allowed.

Alumni association is run by Mrs Janet Scott, c/o the School.

Former pupils Dennis Thatcher; Francis Crick (Nobel prize – structure of DNA); Simon Jenkins (Editor of *The Times*); Richard Dimbleby; Lord Salmon of Sandwich.

· *Millfield* ·

Millfield School
Street
Somerset
BA16 0YD
Tel 0458 42291

- Pupils 1250
- Boys 13–18 (Day/Board)
- Girls 13–18 (Day/Board)
- Upper sixth 217

- Termly fees
  £1860 (Day)
  £3185 (Board)
  Enquiries/application to
  P H Vaughan, Tutor for
  Admissions

What it's like

Founded in 1935 by R J O Meyer, it has a fine campus of 67 acres, plus 97 acres of playing fields. It is in beautiful countryside, with 26 boarding houses in the town of Street and surrounding villages. The junior school is in nearby Glastonbury. In 1984 the convent school in Glastonbury was acquired in order to create a pre-prep school. Large, diverse and complex, Millfield is an extremely well run school which enjoys a very high staff:pupil ratio (about 1:7), and this is one of its many strengths. Since 1970 a massive building programme has provided facilities which are second to none in Britain. It caters for virtually every need and displays energy, organisation and purposefulness in every activity. Academically strong, it sends many pupils to degree courses each year, including many to Oxbridge. The range of European languages offered at GCSE level is exceptionally large and includes Danish, Dutch, Modern Greek and Portuguese as well as French, German, Italian and Spanish. Many pupils take GCSE in more than one European language. Over 40 sports and games are available and the school has excelled in these. In the last 20 years well over 200 pupils have gained international selection in 19 different sports. Since 1960 it has produced over 20 Olympic competitors. The school turns itself into an activity holiday centre during the summer.

School profile

Pupils Age range 13–18; 1250 pupils, 289 day (180 boys, 109 girls), 961 boarding (608 boys, 353 girls). Main entry ages 13 and into sixth. Approx 5% are children of former pupils. Edgarley Hall, Millfield Junior School, provides approx 50% of intake. *Transfer from maintained schools:* 10% main intake, plus 25% to sixth.

Entrance Common entrance and own entrance exam used. Oversubscribed. Good all-round academic and sporting abilities looked for; no special religious requirements. Parents not expected to buy text books; stabling of horses etc extra. No assisted places. 160+ scholarships/bursaries, 100–5% of fees.

Parents 15+% are doctors, lawyers, etc; 65+% in industry or commerce. 30+% live within 30 miles; 15+% live overseas.

Staff Head C S Martin, first year in post.

165 full time staff. Annual turnover 11%. Average age 30–35.

Academic work GCSE and A-levels (including Chinese, Japanese; no A-level general studies). In 1990, 228 pupils in upper fifth, 218 in upper sixth. *GCSE:* on average, 80 upper fifth gained at least grade C in 8+ subjects; 75 in 5–7; and 80 in 1–4 subjects. *A-levels:* 20 upper sixth passed in 4+ subjects; 130 in 3; 35 in 2; and 25 in 1 subject. 65 took science A-levels; 80 arts/humanities; 65 both. *Computing facilities:* Computer centre with (a) classroom, (b) office layout. *Special provision:* Language Development Unit for dyslexics; FE department for English as a foreign language.

European Community *Languages:* Danish offered: to GCSE. Dutch offered: to GCSE. French offered: to GCSE; AS-

494

level; A-level. German offered: to GCSE; AS-level; A-level. Greek offered: to GCSE. Italian offered: to GCSE; AS-level; A-level. Portuguese offered: to GCSE. Spanish offered: to GCSE; A-level. 25–50% take GCSE in more than 1 EC language. *Exchanges:* Regular exchanges for pupils aged 14–16 to France, Germany and Spain. *Other:* Study scholarships for languages other than French.

Senior pupils' non-academic activities *Music:* 288 learn a musical instrument, 74 to Grade 6 or above, 2 accepted for Music School; 80 in school orchestra, 70 in school choir, 80 in chamber groups; 2 in National Youth Orchestra, 1 in National Youth Wind Orchestra, 10 in county orchestra. *Drama and dance:* Annual plays and French play; new dance studio in constant use for all forms of dance. 2 pupils in National Youth Theatre. *Art:* 200 take as non-examined subject; 60 take GCSE; 30 take A-level. 8 accepted for Art School, 2 for architecture. 20 in art society, 80+ in Millfield Activities Programme. *Sport:* Over 40 sports available. 500 take sports of their choice. 20 take exams. 60+ represent country/county at a variety of sports. *Other:* 85 have bronze Duke of Edinburgh's Award, 29 have silver and 14 have gold. Other activities include a computer club, debating club, driving lessons, a chess club (competitive) and many varied activities.

Careers In 1990, 70% leavers went on to degree courses; 5% to art/drama/music colleges; 15% to non-degree courses (eg nursing, secretarial, cordon bleu, tutorial college); 10% straight into careers (eg business). Of those going on to degree courses, 15% went to Oxbridge; 65% to other universities; 20% to poly/colleges. 8% those going on to higher education went to courses in practical art; 3% in drama/acting; 3% in music; 35% in humanities/social sciences; 8% in medicine; and 43% in science/engineering.

Uniform Suits, sports jackets for boys; school skirt/trousers and jumper for junior girls.

Houses/prefects Competitive houses. Prefects, head boy/girl, head of house and house prefects – appointed by prefect committee and staff. School Council.

Religion Worship is compulsory on special occasions eg carol service, start of term multi-faith service plus regular services for Catholics, Jews, Muslims, etc.

Social No organised local events. German/French exchange, games tours (Germany/France/Hong Kong/Barbados and Australia, Argentina – rugby). Cultural tour to China in 1988, Russia in 1990. Pupils allowed to bring own bike/horse to school. Meals self service. School shop. No tobacco/alcohol allowed.

Discipline No corporal punishment. Pupils failing to produce homework once might expect a warning and a deadline; those caught smoking cannabis on the premises can expect immediate expulsion.

Boarding Few seniors have own study bedroom, most share double study bedrooms; juniors in dormitories of 3+. Single sex houses, 10–50 (most small), same as competitive houses. Resident qualified nurse. Central dining room. 3 weekend exeats each term. Visits to the local town allowed.

Alumni association is run by Mr E J C Bromfield, The Millfield Society, c/o the School.

Former pupils Sir John L Standing (actor); John Sargeant (BBC parliamentary correspondent); Charles Burton (explorer: circumnavigated world via North and South Poles); Gareth Edwards (international rugby); Duncan Goodhew and Mary Rand (Olympic Gold Medallists); Jeremy Thomas (film producer *Last Emperor*).

· Milton Abbey ·

Milton Abbey School
Blandford
Dorset
DT11 0BZ
Tel 0258 880484

- Pupils 275
- Boys 13–18
  (Board)
- Girls None
- Upper sixth 52

- Termly fees
  £2856 (Board)
- SHMIS
  Enquiries/application to
  the Headmaster

What it's like

Founded in 1954, it has an exceptionally beautiful site (one that has been settled for at least 1000 years) in a large area of parkland near Blandford. The main building is a very large 18th-century country house which incorporates some of the buildings of the original Benedictine monastery and abbey of the middle ages. The magnificent medieval abbey church is the outstanding architectural feature. The main block of the school has a fine quadrangle. There are many modern additions and extensions and the accommodation and facilities are first-rate. It is a C of E school with its own chaplain and the abbey church is the co-ordinating focus of the life of the community and a considerable influence on it. Worship and religious instruction are an important part of the general curriculum. Self-discipline, courtesy, self-respect and a sense of responsibility are deemed to be of prime importance in a pupil's development. A sound general education is provided and results are good. Drama is strong; music and art flourish. Natural history has a particularly keen following. The CCF is very strong and there are close links with service units in the region. A good range of sports and games and outdoor pursuits (these include a lot of sailing). The school's local community services are long established.

School profile

Pupils Age range 13–18; 275 boarding boys. Main entry ages 13 and into sixth. Approx 3% are children of former pupils. *Transfer from maintained schools:* 3% main intake, plus 20% to sixth.

Entrance Common entrance exam used. Not oversubscribed. No special skills or religious requirements. Parents expected to buy text books; maximum extras, £250. 8 scholarships/bursaries pa (academic, music, art), 75–25% of fees.

Parents 10+% live within 30 miles; up to 10% live overseas.

Staff Headmaster R H Hardy, in post for 3 years. 32 full time staff, 9 part time. Annual turnover 3%. Average age 41.

Academic work GCSE, AS and A-levels. 18 GCSE subjects offered; 14 at A-level (AS-level general studies). In 1990, 58 pupils in upper fifth, 40 in upper sixth. *GCSE:* in 1990, 20 upper fifth gained at least grade C in 8+ subjects; 22 in 5–7; and 16 in 1–4 subjects. *A-levels:*

On average, 1 upper sixth passed in 4+ subjects; 11 in 3; 16 in 2; and 8 in 1 subject. 11 took science A-levels; 21 arts/humanities; 11 both. *Computing facilities:* Main centre: 13 RM Nimbus computers linked on network to file-server. Separate facilities in individual departments eg CAD, science dept. *Special provision:* Remedial English and mathematics; EFL.

European Community *Languages:* French offered: to GCSE; AS-level; A-level. Spanish offered: to GCSE; A-level. 10–25% take GCSE in more than 1 EC language. *Exchanges:* Regular exchanges for pupils aged 14–16 to France. *Other:* French for business studies at AO-level for sixth form. MEP visits occasionally. Sixth form French pupils have school trip to Paris. Regularly take German and Spanish pupils.

Pupils' non-academic activities (whole school) *Music:* 62 learn a musical instrument, 1 to Grade 8; pupils also take GCSE, AS, and A-level music. 38 in school choir, 8 in school pop group, 6 in chamber group, 16 in theatre orchestras; brass ensemble; chamber choir; 3 play in pop group and 2 go on to writing and composing after leaving. *Drama and dance:* 150 in school productions, musicals, Music Festival, house plays, etc; drama classes but not exams. 1 accepted for Drama/Dance Schools, 1 goes on to work in theatre. *Art:* 10 take GCSE; 4, A-level; 2, A-level photography. 3–6 accepted for Art School. 15 belong to photographic, 20 to pottery, and 15+ to art clubs. *Sport:* Rugby, hockey, cricket, athletics, cross-country, sailing, canoeing, squash, golf, tennis, shooting, swimming, fencing, archery, basketball available. Some games or sport compulsory. 80 take non-compulsory sport. 16 pupils represent county (rugby, hockey, cross-country, athletics, cricket). *Other:* 12 take part in local community schemes. 78 taking silver Duke of Edinburgh's Award, and 6 have gold. 2 enter voluntary schemes after leaving school. 141 go on annual sponsored walk. Other activities include a computer club, strong CCF; natural history society. Many clubs. Adventure training.

Careers On average, 37% leavers go on to degree courses; 14% to art/drama/music colleges; 18% to non-degree courses (eg agricultural, boatyard management, business management); 16% straight into careers (eg insurance, civil engineering, timber business); 14% other (eg armed forces). Of those going on to degree courses, 56% went to universities; 44% to poly/colleges. 13% those going on to higher education went to courses in practical art; 7% in drama/acting; 3% in music; 47% in humanities/social sciences; 3% in medicine; and 27% in science/engineering.

Uniform School uniform worn throughout.

Houses/prefects Competitive houses. Prefects, head boy, head of house and house prefects – appointed by the Head.

Religion Religious worship compulsory.

Social Theatrical productions and dances with other local schools. Modern languages trips abroad, Himalayan adventures. Prefects allowed to bring own car/bike to school. Meals self service. School shop. No tobacco allowed; alcohol allowed in sixth form club.

Discipline No corporal punishment. Pupils failing to produce homework once might expect warning and repeat work; those caught smoking cannabis on the premises could expect expulsion.

Boarding 22% have own study bedroom, 50% share with up to 3 others; 18% are in dormitories of 6+. Houses, of approximately 55, same as competitive houses. Resident qualified nurse. Central dining room. 2 weekend exeats per term plus half-term. Visits to local town allowed at weekends.

Alumni association run by A P Nicholson, c/o the School.

Former pupils Alastair Boyd (who parachuted off the Empire State Building); Anthony Geffen (BBC producer).

· Moira House ·

Moira House School
Upper Carlisle Road
Eastbourne
East Sussex
BN20 7TD
Tel 0323 644144

- Pupils 370
- Boys None
- Girls 3–18
  (Day/Board/Weekly)
- Upper sixth 40

- Termly fees
  £1802 (Day)
  £2695 (Board/
  Weekly)
- GSA, BSA
  Enquiries/application to
  the Headmaster

What it's like

Founded in 1875 and established on its present site in 1887. It is near Beachy Head with grounds and gardens opening on to the Downs. The buildings are well designed and comfortable and provide good accommodation and facilities. Religious education and worship are compulsory. Academic standards are high and results are good. For a school of this size a high proportion of pupils go on to degree courses, including Oxbridge. French, German and Spanish are offered throughout the school and many girls take GCSE in more than one European language. It enjoys a high staff:pupil ratio. The music and drama depts are flourishing and the school particularly prides itself on its very strong careers counselling service. Good sports and games, plus an enormous range of activities. Some commitment to local community schemes.

School profile

Pupils Total age range 3–18; 370 girls, 200 day, 170 boarding. Senior department 11–18, 300 girls. Main entry ages 11, 12, 13 and into sixth. Approx 5% are children of former pupils. *Transfer from maintained schools:* 30% senior intakes, plus 2% to sixth.

Entrance Common entrance and own exam used. Oversubscribed. No special skills or religious requirements. Parents not expected to buy text books; maximum extras £100 approx. No assisted places. 12 scholarships/bursaries per year, 75%–50% of fees.

Parents 60+% live within 30 miles; 30+% live overseas.

Staff Headmaster Adrian Underwood, in post for 15 years. 43 full time staff, 34 part time. Annual turnover 7%. Average age 30.

Academic work GCSE, AS and A-levels. 20 GCSE and A-level subjects offered; 15 at AS-level (no A-level general studies). In 1990, 49 pupils in upper fifth, 40 in upper sixth. *GCSE:* in 1990, 17 upper fifth gained at least grade C in 9+ subjects; 23 in 7–8; and 9 in 3–6 subjects. *A-levels:* 30 upper sixth passed in 3 subjects; 6 in 2; and 4 in 1 subject. 50% took science A-levels; 40% arts/humanities; 10% both. *Computing facilities:* Olivetti computer room (16 units). *Special provision:* Special tutoring for dyslexic pupils and EFL.

European Community *Languages:* French offered: to age 14; GCSE; AS-level; A-level. German offered: to age 14; GCSE; AS-level; A-level. Spanish offered: to age 14; GCSE; AS-level; A-level. 25–50% take GCSE in more than 1 EC language. *Exchanges:* Regular exchanges for pupils aged 11–18 to France and Germany.

Senior pupils' non-academic activities *Music:* 100+ learn a musical instrument, 20 to Grade 6 or above. 45 in school orchestra, 60 in choir. *Drama and dance:* 120 in school productions. 16 to Grade 6 in ESB, RAD, etc. *Art:* 15 take GCSE; 10, A-level. 2 accepted for Art School. *Sport:* Hockey, netball, swimming, tennis, squash, badminton, riding, sailing, windsurfing, skiing, judo, dance, table tennis, aerobics, cricket and golf available. 130 take non-compulsory sport. 100 take exams. 9 represent county (hockey and athletics). *Other:* 50 take part in local community schemes. 20 have bronze Duke of Edinburgh's Award, 5 have silver. 20 enter voluntary schemes after leaving school. 10 work for national charities. Other activities include a computer club, debate and public speaking, pottery, electronics, community service, and driving lessons.

Careers On average, 60% leavers go on to degree courses; 15% to art/drama/music colleges; 15% to non-degree courses; 10% other. Of those going on to degree courses, 10% go to Oxbridge; 60% to other universities; 30% to poly/colleges. 10% those going on to higher education go to courses in practical art; 5% in drama/acting; 5% in music; 40% in humanities/social sciences; 15% in medicine; and 25% in science/engineering.

Uniform School uniform worn except the sixth.

Houses/prefects Competitive houses.

Prefects, 2 head girls, House Councils – elected by girls and staff.

Religion Morning prayers and Sunday church compulsory; confirmation, Christian Union.

Social Public speaking, Eastbourne Festival of Music and Arts with other local schools. Organised trips abroad. Pupils allowed to bring own car/bike to school. Some meals formal, some self service. School shop. No tobacco/alcohol allowed.

Discipline No corporal punishment. Pupils failing to produce homework once will repeat their work; those caught smoking cannabis on the premises will be expelled.

Boarding 50% have own study bedroom, 50% share with others. Houses, of approximately 55, divided by age. Resident SRN. Central dining room. Sixth form pupils can provide and cook their own food. 2 weekend and half-term exeats. Visits to local town allowed at weekends.

Former pupils Rumer Godden (novelist); Prunella Scales (actress); Joy Finzi (artist).

· *Monkton Combe* ·

Monkton Combe School Monkton Combe Bath Avon BA2 7HG Tel 0225 721102	● Pupils 330 ● Boys 11–19 (Day/Board) ● Girls 11–19 (Day/Board) ● Upper sixth 66	● Termly fees £2135 (Day) £2895 (Board) ● HMC Enquiries/application to the Head Master

What it's like

Founded in 1868, it lies in a very pretty village 2.5 miles from Bath and overlooking the Avon valley. There are most attractive buildings in Cotswold stone, and there have been many modern extensions which are very well equipped. Delightful playing fields adjoin the school. Considerable emphasis on Christian teaching and worship. Academic standards are high and results are good. There is a staff:pupil ratio of 1:10. A high proportion of pupils for a school of this size go on to degree courses each year, many to Oxbridge. Strong in music, drama, art and computing. An impressive record in sports and games (a large number of representatives at county level). The CCF contingent is large and active. There are numerous clubs and societies. Creditable commitment to local community services.

School profile

Pupils Age range 11–19; 330 pupils, 45 day (35 boys, 10 girls), 285 boarding (235 boys, 50 girls). Main entry ages 11, 13 and into sixth (fully co-educational from 1992). Approx 6% are children of former pupils. Own junior school provides more than 25% of intake. *Transfer from maintained schools:* 5% main intake, plus 40% to sixth.

Entrance Common entrance and own entrance exam used. Ability to contribute to the school community looked for at entry; no religious requirements but must be willing to attend chapel. Parents expected to buy text books which can be sold back after use; maximum extras, £150. 10 assisted places pa. 8 scholarships pa, 50–10% fees (can be increased in cases of need). 6–8 bursaries pa for children of clergy and missionaries, up to third fees.

Parents 15+% in the armed services. 10+% live within 30 miles; 10+% live overseas.

Staff Head M J Cuthbertson, 1 year in post. 35 full time staff, 15 part time. Annual turnover 3%. Average age 38.

Academic work GCSE and A-levels. 18 subjects offered (no A-level general studies). In 1990, 65 pupils in upper fifth, 66 in upper sixth. *GCSE:* in 1990, 39 upper fifth gained at least grade C in 8+ subjects; 17 in 5–7; and 9 in 1–4 subjects. *A-levels:* 1 upper sixth passed in 4+ subjects; 51 in 3; 11 in 2; and 3 in 1 subject. 28% took science A-levels; 41% arts/ humanities; 31% both. *Computing facilities:* 12 IBM compatible machines in lab, others in departments; CDT dept with 10 BBC's. *Special provision:* Specialist EFL teacher; teacher from Bath Dyslexic Institute.

European Community *Languages:* French offered: to GCSE; AS-level; A-level. German offered: to GCSE; AS-level; A-level. Spanish offered: to A-level. 10–25% take GCSE in more than 1 EC language. *Exchanges:* Regular exchanges for pupils aged 16–18 to France and Germany. *Other:* Occasional EC pupils in sixth form.

Senior pupils' non-academic activities *Music:* 65 learn a musical instrument, 12 to Grade 6 or above; 30 in school orchestra, 25 in school choir, 15 in school dance band, 30 in wind band. 5–6 take music beyond school. *Drama and dance:* 60 in school productions. 1 accepted for Drama School. *Art:* 80 take as non-examined subject; 35 take GCSE; 15 take A-level. 6–8 accepted for Art School. 15 belong to eg photographic club. *Sport:* Archery, athletics, badminton, cricket, cross-country running, cycling, hockey, judo, netball, rowing, rugby football, shooting, squash, swimming and tennis available. Pupils have represented county/ country (rowing, hockey, judo, tennis, cricket). *Other:* 24 take part in local community schemes. 10 enter voluntary schemes after leaving school, 2 work for national charities. Other activities include bridge, canoeing, a computer club, chess, CCF, debating (enter local and regional competitions), fishing (in local river and brook), life-saving, Christian Union and Bible Study groups, war gaming.

Careers In 1990, 84% leavers went on to degree courses; 5% to art/drama/ music colleges; 5% to non-degree courses; 6% straight into careers (eg city, banking). Of those going on to degree courses, 10% went to Oxbridge; 60% to other universities; 30% to poly/colleges. 5% those going on to higher education went to courses in practical art; 2% in music; 59% in humanities/social sciences; 4% in medicine; and 30% in science/engineering.

Uniform School uniform worn, modified in the sixth.

Houses/prefects Competitive houses. Prefects, head boy, head of house and house prefects – appointed by the Head or housemaster. All new boys help with general chores.

Religion Attendance at chapel is compulsory and Christian activities are encouraged.

Social Debates with other schools, sponsored Activity Day in support of a local or national charity. Ski trip abroad each year. Pupils allowed to bring own bike to school. Meals, self service. School shop. No tobacco/alcohol allowed.

Discipline No corporal punishment.

Report card system for pupils failing to produce homework. Expulsion for any offence involving drugs.
Boarding 15% have own study bed-room, 20% share with one other; 40% in dormitories of 6+. Single sex houses, of 40–50, same as competitive houses. 2 qualified nurses. Central dining room. Pupils can provide and cook own food. Termly exeats, 3 Saturday nights and half-term. Visits to local town allowed once a week.

Alumni association is run by C J H Rogers, Tabora, Shaft Road, Monkton Combe, Bath BA2 7HA.
Former pupils Rt Rev G Leonard (former Bishop of London); Rt Rev J Bone (Bishop of Reading); Rt Rev W Persson (Bishop of Doncaster); Rt Rev S Sykes (Bishop of Ely); Rt Rev M A P Wood (former Bishop of Norwich); Richard Stilgoe; Martin Adeney.

· Monmouth ·

Monmouth School
Monmouth
Gwent
NP5 3XP
Tel 0600 3143

- Pupils 535
- Boys 11–18 (Day/Board/Weekly)
- Girls None
- Upper sixth 78

- Termly fees
  £1190 (Day)
  £2033 (Board/Weekly)
- HMC
  Enquiries/application to the Headmaster

What it's like

Founded in 1614, single-site on the edge of the town by the Wye; a very fine position. The present buildings, in the collegiate style, date from 1865 when the 17th-century school was demolished. There has been much modernisation in the last twenty years. A C of E foundation it follows the rites of the Church in Wales. A distinguished and well-run school, with a high reputation locally and further afield. It benefits from strong links with the Haberdashers' Company and provides excellent facilities and a first-rate education on terms that few schools can match. Closely integrated with the town (itself a most attractive place) there is a strong local flavour with half the pupils coming from Monmouth itself or the neighbouring villages. This close relationship between 'town and gown' has created considerable local pride in the school and has enabled many musical and sporting collaborations to flourish. Academic results are first-class. Many leavers go on to degree courses, many to Oxbridge. Strong in music, drama and art. Also very strong in sports and games (especially rugby and rowing); a large number of county and international representatives. Notable emphasis on extra-curricular activities of which there is a wide range. Strong participation in the Duke of Edinburgh's Award Scheme.

School profile

Pupils Age range 11–18; 535 boys, 350 day, 185 boarding. Main entry ages 11, 13 and into sixth. Approx 10–20% are children of former pupils. Own junior day school, The Grange, provides about 20% of intake. *Transfer from maintained schools:* 25% main intakes, plus 75% to sixth.

Entrance Common entrance and own entrance exam used. Oversubscribed. Good academic standard and good all-round contributors, especially in music and sport. No religious barriers. Parents not expected to buy text books; maximum extras £50, including music lessons. 26

assisted places pa. Scholarships/bursaries, up to 75% fees.

Parents 30+% live within 30 miles; up to 10% live overseas.

Staff Headmaster R D Lane, in post for 8 years. 51 full time staff, 5 part time. Annual turnover 7%. Average age 35–40.

Academic work GCSE and A-levels. 20 GCSE subjects offered; 19 at A-level (including Russian, geology A-level; general studies compulsory for sixth but not examined at A-level). In 1990, 85 pupils in upper fifth, 82 in upper sixth (now 78). *GCSE:* in 1990, 69 upper fifth gained at least grade C in 8+ subjects; 10 in 5–7; and 5 in 1–4 subjects. *A-levels:* 8 upper sixth passed in 4+ subjects; 54 in 3; 12 in 2; and 6 in 1 subject. 45% took science A-levels; 40% arts/humanities; 15% both. *Computing facilities:* Computer room with 24 Amstrad 1640's, 2 Archimedes machines; about 24 other machines/word processors in departments.

European Community *Languages:* French offered: to age 14; GCSE; AS-level; A-level. German offered: to AS-level; non-examined subject. Spanish offered: to age 14; GCSE; AS-level; A-level. 10–25% take GCSE in more than 1 EC language. *Exchanges:* Regular exchanges for pupils aged 11–18 to France, Germany and Spain. *Other:* Relevant talks on contemporary European issues. Sixth form may undertake work experience in France.

Senior pupils' non-academic activities *Music:* 200 learn a musical instrument, 20 to Grade 6, 10 to Grade 8, a number of pupils accepted for Music School; 50 in school orchestra; 100 in choir; numerous pop groups; 60 in concert band. *Drama and dance:* 40 participate in school productions; 150 in others. 3 take exams in drama and dance. *Art:* 10 take art as non-examined subject; 70 take GCSE; 18, A-level; 6, A-level art history; 3, subsidiary art; 4 accepted for Art School; 3 for architecture courses and art history degree courses. *Sport:* Rugby, rowing, cricket, shooting, swimming, squash, badminton, sub-aqua, cross-country, orienteering, sailing, fishing, canoeing, athletics, tennis, golf, skiing and croquet available. 300 take non-compulsory sport.

30 take exams eg diving, gymnastics, swimming. 27 represent county/country (rugby, rowing, swimming, tetrathlon, badminton, squash, cross-country, cricket). *Other:* 10 take part in local community schemes. 45 take gold Duke of Edinburgh's Award. 300 involved in fund raising for charity. Other activities include a computer club, photography, radio satellite club, Christian Fellowship, drama workshop, horse riding, modelling, junior debating, chess, bridge, electronics, stage craft, art club, astronomy, stamp club.

Careers In 1990, 80% leavers went on to degree courses; 6% to art/drama/music colleges; 14% straight into careers. Of those going on to degree courses, 18% went to Oxbridge; 60% to other universities; 22% to poly/colleges. 5% those going on to higher education went to courses in practical art; 40% in humanities/social sciences; 10% in medicine; and 40% in science/engineering.

Uniform School uniform worn throughout.

Houses/prefects Competitive houses. Prefects, head boy, head of house and house prefects – appointed by the Headmaster or housemaster.

Religion Religious worship encouraged.

Social Plays, concerts, Challenge of Industry Conference with local schools. Organised exchanges with both French and Spanish schools, also with Japan. Pupils allowed to bring own bike to school. Meals self service. School shop. No tobacco/alcohol allowed.

Discipline No corporal punishment. Pupils failing to produce homework once might expect to have to explain why; those caught smoking cannabis on the premises could expect expulsion.

Boarding All sixth form share study bedroom, 33% are in dormitories of 6+. Houses, of approximately 45, divided by age. Resident qualified nurse. Central dining room. Pupils can provide and cook their own food. 3 weekend exeats each term. Visits to the local town allowed.

Alumni association is run by H C Toulouse, 3 Monkswell Close, Monmouth, Gwent NP5 3PH.

Former pupils Lord Ezra of Horsham (former Chairman NCB); Lord Brecon; K

Jarrett, A M Jorden and E T Butler (rugby internationals); F J Davies (managing director, Rockware); R J Herd (engineer, racing car designer); G M J Worsnip (TV presenter); V G A Spinetti (actor); M W Barnes QC; Hon C B Moynihan (Minister for Energy); David Broome (showjumper).

· Moreton Hall ·

Moreton Hall
Weston Rhyn
Oswestry
Shropshire SY11 3EW
Tel 0691 773671
Fax 0691 778 552

- Pupils 350
- Boys None
- Girls 11–18
  (Day/Board)
- Upper sixth 45

- Termly fees
  £1815 (Day)
  £2735 (Board)
- GSA
  Enquiries/application to
  the Principal

What it's like

Founded in 1913 it occupies an attractive rural site with excellent access to the north and the south by road and rail. The campus is a village-like community in 75 acres of splendid grounds and gardens and the buildings are a mixture of the modern and the venerable. Completely refurbished within the last 10 years, extremely well equipped with modern facilities. A sports complex with three adjacent floodlit tennis courts and a theatre centre for the performing arts are the latest additions. The school looks for all-round ability and a happy purposeful atmosphere prevails. It is neither consciously progressive nor traditional in its approach. It is not academically exclusive but all girls are expected to be able to make a positive contribution to their own growth and that of the school. It is therefore a balanced community where each pupil feels valued and where growth in self-confidence develops naturally. All pupils are actively and sympathetically encouraged to achieve their best. The teaching is good (a high staff:pupil ratio of 1:9) and results are creditable (many sixth form leavers go on to degree courses including Oxbridge). French, German and Spanish are offered throughout the school and many girls take GCSE in more than one European language. The school prides itself on its careers dept which is a leader among girls' schools. Strong music and drama depts. A good range of sports and games (high standards) and a wide range of activities. 'Moreton Enterprises' and 'Moreton Travel' give girls opportunities to learn business and entrepreneurial skills.

School profile

Pupils Age range 11–18; 350 girls, 25 day, 325 boarding. Main entry ages 11, 12, 13 and into sixth. Approx 3–5% are children of former pupils. *Transfer from maintained schools:* 10–15% main intake, plus 5% to sixth.

Entrance Own entrance exam used. Well subscribed. All-round abilities looked for; no particular religious requirements. Parents not expected to buy text books or stationery; maximum extras £200 including music tuition. No assisted places. Up to 4 scholarships (academic and music) for half fees at 11+ to 13+; one sixth form. Bursaries for clergy and school teachers' children.

Parents 15+% in industry or commerce. 30+% live within 50 miles; 15+% live overseas (expatriates).

Staff Principal M J Maloney, first year in post. 38 full time staff, 21 part time. Annual turnover 5%. Average age 38.

Academic work GCSE and A-levels. 24 GCSE subjects offered; 20 at A-level (general studies taught but not examined). On average, 55 pupils in upper fifth, 45 in upper sixth. *GCSE:* in 1990, 46% upper fifth gained at least grade C in 8+ subjects; 44% in 5–7; and 10% in 1–4 subjects. *A-levels:* 12 upper sixth passed in 4+ subjects; 12 in 3; 14 in 2; and 7 in 1 subject. 20% took science A-levels; 40% arts/humanities; 40% both. *Computing facilities:* Technology (as in National Curriculum) introduced in year 1; optional courses to GCSE and in sixth form. Two specialist IT rooms (Archimedes and Amstrad); most departments have their own (or ready access to) computing facilities. *Special provision:* Learning support teacher on staff (dyslexia and related disorders).

European Community *Languages:* French offered: to age 14; GCSE; A-level; Institute of Linguists. German offered: to age 14; GCSE; A-level. Italian offered: to GCSE; Institute of Linguists; non-examined subject. Spanish offered: to age 14; GCSE; A-level. 25–50% take GCSE in more than 1 EC language. *Other:* Second and fourth years visit France annually.

Senior pupils' non-academic activities *Music:* 220 learn a musical instrument; 1 accepted for Music School; 40 in school orchestras, 60 in school choir. *Drama and dance:* 100+ in school productions. 9 to Grade 6 in ESB, RAD etc, 64 Spoken English (ESB, LAMDA, and festivals); GCSE dance offered. 1 accepted for Drama School, 1 a BBC trainee. *Art:* some take as non-examined subject; 38 take GCSE; 10 take A-level. 6 accepted for Art School. 6 take history of art, 3 fashion. *Sport:* Lacrosse, hockey, tennis, netball, rounders, athletics, golf, badminton, table tennis, aerobics, self-defence, gymnastics, dance, sailing and volleyball available. Many represent county in lacrosse, some at junior international level. 200 take tennis coaching, 20 sail. *Other:* 60 take part in local community schemes. 5 have silver Duke of Edinburgh's Award and 1 has gold. 2–3 each year enter voluntary schemes after leaving school. Most pupils work for national charities. Other activities include Moreton Enterprises, Moreton Travel,

driving, ice skating, self-defence, weaving, wine making plus some 50 others.

Careers On average, 50% leavers go on to degree courses; 20% to art/drama/music colleges; 20% to non-degree courses (eg secretarial, agricultural); 10% other. Of those going on to degree courses, 7% go to Oxbridge; 60% to other universities; 33% to poly/colleges. 20% those going on to higher education go to courses in practical art; 10% in drama/acting; 5% in music; 40% in humanities/social sciences; 5% in medicine; and 20% in science/engineering.

Uniform School uniform worn except the sixth.

Houses/prefects No competitive houses. Prefects, including head and second prefects – appointed by the Principal after consultation. School Council and sixth form Council.

Religion Compulsory daily assembly and Sunday church in the Anglican tradition. Some relaxation of Sunday requirements for sixth form.

Social Many joint social activities/outings with Shrewsbury. Annual skiing trip, organised visits to Germany and France to stay with families. Pupils allowed to bring own bike to school. Meals self service. School shop. No tobacco allowed; alcohol only permitted on very restricted basis, in sixth form club (to which girls may invite visitors, including boys).

Discipline No corporal punishment. Pupils failing to produce homework at any time would expect an enquiry as to why and be expected to remedy the situation at once.

Boarding All sixth formers have single or double bedrooms. 6 houses of 50–55; 2 junior, 3 senior, 1 upper sixth. Resident qualified nurse; separate sanatorium. Central dining room. Sixth form pupils can provide and cook own snacks. 2–4 weekend exeats each term. Visits to local towns allowed, according to age.

Alumni association Secretary is Miss D Gittins, 42 Roman Road, Shrewsbury, Shropshire.

Former pupils Thea Musgrave (composer).

· *Morrison's* ·

Morrison's Academy
Ferntower Road
Crieff
Perthshire
PH7 3AN
Tel 0764 3885

- Pupils 780
- Boys 5–18
  (Day/Board)
- Girls 5–18
  (Day/Board)
- Higher year 107

- Termly fees
  £857 (Day)
  £2225 (Board)
- HMC, GSA
  Enquiries to the Rector
  Application to the
  Director of Admissions

What it's like

Founded in 1860, it has a pleasant, semi-rural, 10-acre site on the lower slopes of the Knock in Crieff. Regular development over the years has produced a fine and well-equipped campus. It became fully co-educational in 1979. The primary school is an integral part of the Academy. A thorough, traditional Scottish education is provided and academic results are very good. Most pupils go on to degree courses each year. French, German and Spanish are offered at S-level and Highers and many pupils take more than one European language at S-level. Very strong indeed in music, and there are flourishing drama groups. A good range of sports and games (high standards achieved). About 34 clubs and societies cater for most conceivable needs. A vigorous CCF. A lot of emphasis on outdoor pursuits for which the environment is very suitable. A good record in the Duke of Edinburgh's Award Scheme.

School profile

Pupils Total age range 5–18; 780 pupils, 600 day (300 boys, 300 girls), 180 boarding (90 boys, 90 girls). Senior department 12–18, 600 pupils (300 boys, 300 girls). Main entry ages 5, 12 and into sixth. Approx 20% are children of former pupils. *Transfer from maintained schools:* 43% main senior intake, plus 20% to sixth.
Entrance Own entrance exam used. Oversubscribed for day places. No special skills or religious requirements. Parents not expected to buy text books, stationery, etc. 153 assisted places. 6 scholarships/bursaries, up to half fees.
Parents 60+% live within 30 miles; up to 10% live overseas.
Staff Rector H Ashmall, in post for 12 years. 68 full time staff, 4 part time. Annual turnover 1%. Average age 42.
Academic work O-grade, S-grade, CSYS, Highers and A-levels. 17 subjects offered (no A-level general studies). In 1990, 113 pupils in O/S-grade year, 107 in Higher year, 75 in A-level/CSYS year.

O/S-grade: in 1990, 92 pupils passed in 5–9 subjects; and 19 in 1–4 subjects. *Highers:* 35 pupils passed in 5 subjects; 16 in 4; 15 in 3; 18 in 2; 17 in 1 subject (counting 55 only). *A-levels:* 2 pupils passed in 3 subjects; 14 in 2; and 15 in 1 subject. 35% took science A-levels; 62% arts/humanities; 3% both. *Computing facilities:* 4 networked labs plus individual machines in some departments. *Special provision:* Small groups tuition for English as a second language. Special examination.
European Community *Languages:* French offered: to age 14; S-grade; Higher. German offered: to age 14; S-grade; Higher. Spanish offered: to S-grade; Higher. 25–50% take S-grade in more than 1 EC language. *Exchanges:* Regular exchanges for pupils aged 14–16 to Germany. *Other:* German pupils spend 1 or more terms in school.
Senior pupils' non-academic activities include CCF, chess, computing, cookery, country dancing, curling, debat-

ing, Duke of Edinburgh's Award, electronics, fencing, Gaelic, geography, hill walking, model-making, woodwork, orienteering, theatre, sailing, Scripture Union, sewing and handcraft, skiing and Quest, table-tennis, pipe band, karate, drama and music.

Careers In 1990, 77% leavers went on to degree courses; 2% to art/drama/music colleges; 4% to non-degree courses (eg hotel management, agriculture, sport and recreation); 11% straight into careers (eg services, commerce, banking); 6% other. Of those going on to degree courses, 73% went to universities; 27% to poly/colleges. 57% those going on to higher education went to courses in humanities/social sciences; 11% in medicine; and 32% in science/engineering.

Uniform School uniform worn throughout.

Houses/prefects Competitive houses. Prefects, head boy and girl, head of house and house prefects.

Religion Morning prayers.

Social Discos and debates with other schools. Organised trips and exchange systems with schools abroad. Lunch self service; others formal. No tobacco/alcohol allowed.

Discipline No corporal punishment.

Boarding Various sleeping arrangements in single sex accommodation. Central dining room. Seniors can provide and cook own supper. 7 weekend exeats during session. Visits to local town allowed.

Former pupils Sir Andrew McCance; Sir James Henderson Stewart; Dr Gavin Strang; Air Vice-Marshal MacGregor; Dr A R Belch; Dennis Lawson.

· Mount (York) ·

The Mount School
Dalton Terrace
York
YO2 4DD
Tel 0904 654823

- Pupils 280
- Boys None
- Girls 11–18
  (Day/Board/Weekly)
- Upper sixth 40

- Termly fees
  £1690 (Day)
  £2540 (Board/
  Weekly)
- GSA
  Enquiries/application to
  the Headmistress's
  Secretary

What it's like

Founded in 1831, it moved to its present site in 1857. A very pleasant compact wooded campus with splendid gardens, mature trees and playing fields. The buildings are a combination of 19th-century architecture and brand new blocks including new maths and science block. Facilities are good. A Quaker school, it aims to develop 'the whole person' and to care for everyone as an individual. It prides itself on a welcoming atmosphere but aims, also, for academic excellence. It has all the advantages of a small school, with a good staff:pupil ratio and an unusual number of part-time staff. Each year very many leavers go on to degree courses, including Oxbridge. French, German, Spanish and Italian (by arrangement) are offered at GCSE and many pupils take GCSE in more than one language. Very strong in music, drama and art (talent in these is looked for in candidates). Much involvement in local cultural activities and full use is made of the city's amenities. A wide range of sport and games and extra-curricular activities. Big commitment to local community services and an outstanding record in the Duke of Edinburgh's Award Scheme.

School profile

Pupils Age range 11–18; 280 girls, 50 day, 230 boarding. Main entry ages 11 (also 12, 13 and 14) and into sixth. Approx 7% are children of former pupils. *Transfer from maintained schools:* 50% main intakes, plus 50% to sixth.

Entrance Own entrance exam used. No special skills or religious requirements but school is Quaker. Parents not expected to buy text books; minimum of extras. Assisted places. Scholarships (academic) up to 50% fees; smaller scholarships for music, art and drama. Bursaries for Quakers according to need and limited help to old scholars.

Parents 10+% are doctors, lawyers, etc; 10+% in industry or commerce; 10+% in the armed services, 10+% are farmers. 10+% live within 30 miles; 15% live overseas.

Staff Headmistress Miss Barbara J Windle, in post for 4 years. 29 full time staff, 41 part time. Annual turnover 5%. Average age 38.

Academic work GCSE and A-levels. 20 subjects offered at A-level (including general studies). In 1990, 51 pupils in upper fifth, 40 in upper sixth. *GCSE:* in 1990, 35 upper fifth gained at least grade C in 8+ subjects; 9 in 5–7; and 6 in 1–4 subjects. *A-levels:* 22 upper sixth passed in 4+ subjects; 21 in 3; 6 in 2; and 3 in 1 subject. 25% took science A-levels; 75% arts/humanities (science numbers increasing with new facilities). *Computing facilities:* Computer room with access at all times; computers in certain departments also. *Special provision:* Assessed by local Dyslexia Institute and attend as advised. Extra English provided by qualified EFL teacher (limited number only).

European Community *Languages:* French offered: to age 14; GCSE; AS-level; A-level. German offered: to age 14; GCSE; AS-level; A-level. Italian offered: to GCSE (by arrangement). Spanish offered: to GCSE. 25–50% take GCSE in more than 1 EC language. *Other:* Regular visits to Europe in third and fourth year plus sixth form groups. Classical trips to Italy periodically. Girls from EC accepted, visits 1 term–1 year.

Senior pupils' non-academic activi- ties *Music:* 77 learn a musical instrument, 23 to Grade 6 or above, 3 accepted for Music School; 40 in school orchestra, 40 in school choir, 20 in school pop group. 1 in County Youth Orchestra; 2 in National Youth Orchestra, 3 in National Children's Orchestra, 1 Northern Children's Wind Orchestra, 1 a member of Guildhall orchestra, 1 plays in pop group. 1 a concert pianist. *Drama and dance:* 60 in school productions. 6 to Grade 6 in ESB, RAD, etc, 20 learn drama as an individual subject. 2–4 go on to work in theatre. *Art:* 35 take as non-examined subject; 8 A-level. 2–3 pa accepted for Art School. 16 belong to photographic club. *Sport:* Hockey, netball, tennis, badminton, squash, swimming, rounders, horse-riding, ballet, fencing, volleyball, athletics and gymnastics available. 80 take non-compulsory sport. 12 take exams. *Other:* 65 take part in local community schemes. 50 have bronze Duke of Edinburgh's Award, 70 have silver and 3 gold. 2–6 enter voluntary schemes after leaving school. Other activities include a computer club, arts society, linguists society, debating, poetry, creative writing (poet in residence 1987), several music groups, science societies, Amnesty International, community service groups, life-saving, pets group, chess club, driving lessons.

Careers In 1990, 75% leavers went on to degree courses; 5% to art/drama/music colleges; 15% to non-degree courses (eg Montessori teaching, nursery nursing, nursing, occupational therapy); 2·5% straight into careers (eg retail management); 2·5% other. Of those going on to degree courses, 14% went to Oxbridge; 57% to other universities; 29% to poly/colleges. 8% those going on to higher education went to courses in practical art; 4% in drama/acting; 81% in humanities/social sciences; and 8% in science/engineering.

Uniform School uniform worn except the sixth.

Houses/prefects No competitive houses. School prefects and head girl elected by the school. House prefects, appointed by house staff. School Council.

Religion Quaker, attendance at daily act of worship and Sunday evening meetings.
Social Social events with other local schools. Debates, theatrical productions with Bootham (sibling school) and joint meeting for worship, dances. Foreign language exchanges; trips abroad for language study, art and art history, ski-ing, religious education. Older pupils allowed to bring own bike to school. Some meals formal, family service, some self service. Sunday breakfast. School shop. No tobacco/alcohol allowed.
Discipline No corporal punishment. Pupils failing to produce homework once might expect discussion and completion of work; if anyone were caught smoking cannabis on the premises they would be expelled.

Boarding 16% share with 2–6 others, 15% are in dormitories of 6+. Houses, of 20–75, divided broadly by age. Resident qualified medical staff. Central dining room. Sixth formers sometimes allowed to cook own food. Flexible system of exeats. Visits to local town allowed.
Alumni association is run by The Secretary, MOSA, c/o The Mount School.
Former pupils Dame Judi Dench; Margaret Drabble; A S Byatt; Isobel Barnett; Dame Elaine Kellett-Bowman; Jocelyn Burnell (astronomer); Mary Ure; Jenny Killick; Hilary Wainwright; Rose Neil (Ulster TV); Anna Walker (ITV Weather); Kate Bellingham (*Tomorrow's World*).

· *Mount Carmel* ·

Mount Carmel School
Wilmslow Road
Alderley Edge
Cheshire SK9 7QB
Tel 0625 583028

- Pupils 410
- Boys None
- Girls 11–18
  (Day)
- Upper sixth 45

- Termli fees
  £865 (Day)
- ISAI
  Enquiries/application to
  the Headmistress

What it's like

Founded in 1945 by the Congregation of the Sisters of St Joseph of the Apparition, the main school building is a large house in very agreeable surroundings in the village of Alderley Edge. Since 1945 extensive additions have been made and it is well equipped with modern facilities. Children of all faiths are welcome. Separate provision is made for religious instruction for Catholic pupils. There is some emphasis on regular worship, prayers, mass, etc. A broad general education is given. Not a few of the staff are Sisters of the Congregation, and there is a favourable staff:pupil ratio of about 1:10. Academic results are creditable. Many sixth form leavers go on to degree courses. Music is very well supported and there are several choirs, plus orchestras, ensembles, etc. Drama and dance are popular and flourishing and are taught as part of the curriculum. There are good facilities for sports and games of which there is the usual range. Plenty of societies and clubs cater for extra-curricular activities. There is an active Guide group, and some participation in the Duke of Edinburgh's Award Scheme. Senior girls are involved in local community services.

School profile

Pupils Total age range 11–18, 410 day girls. Main entry age 11. *Transfer from maintained schools:* 40% main intake.
Entrance Own entrance exam used.

Bursaries and assisted places.
Staff Headmistress Mrs M Moss, in post for 6 years.
Academic work GCSE and A-levels.

18 subjects offered (including A-level general studies). In 1990, 64 pupils in upper fifth, 32 in upper sixth (now 45). *GCSE:* in 1990, 51 upper fifth gained at least grade C in 8+ subjects; 12 in 5–7; and 2 in 1–4 subjects. *A-levels:* 12 upper sixth passed in 4+ subjects (of whom 1 had an additional AS-level); 12 in 3 (of whom 1 had an additional AS-level); 4 in 2; and 4 in 1 subject and/or 1 AS-level. 42% took science A-levels; 25% arts/ humanities; 33% both.

European Community *Languages:* French offered: to age 14; GCSE; AS-level; A-level. German offered: to age 14; GCSE; AS-level; A-level. 10–25% take GCSE in more than 1 EC language. *Exchanges:* Regular exchanges for pupils aged 11–18 to France and Germany. *Other:* Work experience for girls aged 16–18 in French or German speaking countries.

Careers In 1990, 69% leavers went on to degree courses; 12·5% to art/drama/ music colleges; 12·5% to non-degree courses; 6% straight into careers (eg banking). Of those going on to degree courses, 10% went to Oxbridge; 59% to other universities; 31% to poly/colleges.

· *Mount St Mary's (Exeter)* ·

Mount St Mary's
Convent School
Wonford Road
Exeter
Devon EX2 4PF
Tel 0392 436770

- Pupils 350
- Boys None
- Girls 11–18 (Day)
- Upper sixth 20

- Termly fees £750 (Day)
  Enquiries/application to the Headmistress

What it's like

Established on its present site in 1949, in a quiet residential area of Exeter. It is run by the Sisters of the Presentation of Mary who have been involved in education in Exeter since the 1890s. The convent and school buildings are all modern, well equipped and include new facilities for art, pottery and textiles. They occupy spacious grounds with beautiful gardens and tennis courts. It is a Roman Catholic school and thus religious education, which is according to the doctrines of the Church, is an essential element of the curriculum. The aim of the school is to promote Christian values recognising that each pupil is gifted in a unique way; 'building confidence' is one of its strengths. It is an academically challenging but also very happy school.

School profile

Pupils Total age range 11–18; 350 day girls. Main entry ages 11 and into sixth. Own junior school (Presentation Convent) provides more than 20% of intake. Many pupils from maintained schools.

Entrance Own entrance exam used. Oversubscribed. Roman Catholic establishment but other persuasions are accepted. Parents not expected to buy text books; trips, etc extra, maximum £50 per term.

Staff Headmistress Sister Eileen Dalaney, in post for 5 years. 27 full time staff, 3 part time. Annual turnover 3%. Average age 40.

Academic work GCSE and A-levels. Average size of upper fifth 60; upper sixth 20 (growing). *A-levels:* on average, 9 pupils in upper sixth pass 3 subjects. On average, 33% take science/engineering A-levels; 33% take arts/humanities; 33%, a mixture. *Computing facilities:* Computers are used as an integrated part of the curriculum as an aid to teaching; computer clubs.

European Community *Languages:* French offered: to age 14; GCSE; AS-level; A-level. German offered: to age 14; GCSE; AS-level; A-level. Spanish offered: to age 14; GCSE; AS-level; A-level. 50–75% take GCSE in more than 1 EC language. *Exchanges:* Regular exchanges for pupils aged 11–18 to France, Germany and Spain. *Other:* European Studies offered to pupils aged 16–18.

Senior pupils' non-academic activities *Music:* Strong music department; all pupils learn music; many play in school orchestra or sing in school choir; regular school concerts. *Drama and dance:* All in school productions; speech and drama lessons available. *Sport:* Netball, basketball, hockey, volleyball, tennis, badminton, swimming, rounders and athletics are available. All take non-compulsory sport. Some pupils have represented county in cross-country, netball and tennis. *Other:* Large proportion of pupils take Duke of Edinburgh's Award Scheme. Other activities include a computer club, Young Enterprise scheme, a school bank, keep-fit, and community service in a local hospital, Ten Tors expedition.

Careers In 1990, 90% leavers went on to degree courses; 5% to art/drama/music colleges; 5% to non-degree courses (eg bilingual secretarial). Of those going on to degree courses, 67% went to universities; 33% to poly/colleges. 10% those going on to higher education went to courses in practical art; 10% in drama/acting; 10% in music; 30% in humanities/social sciences; 20% in medicine; and 20% in science/engineering.

Uniform School uniform worn except the sixth.

Houses/prefects No competitive houses. Prefects and head girl – appointed by the staff.

Religion Roman Catholic establishment.

Social Inter-school sport; sixth form resources shared with a local independent boys' school. Organised trips abroad include ski holidays; exchanges with France, Germany and Spain; visit to Russia. Meals: packed lunches. No tobacco/alcohol allowed.

Discipline No corporal punishment. Pupils failing to produce homework once might expect detention at lunchtime.

Alumni association is run by Mrs P Gorin, c/o the School.

· *Mount St Mary's (Sheffield)* ·

Mount St Mary's	● Pupils 322	● Termly fees
College	● Boys 13–18	£1460 (Day)
Spinkhill	(Day/Board/Weekly)	£2162 (Board)
Sheffield	● Girls 13–18	£1825 (Weekly)
S31 9YL	(Day/Board/Weekly)	● HMC, SHA
Tel 0246 433388	● Upper sixth 55	Enquiries/application to the Headmaster

What it's like

Founded in 1842 and run under the direction of the Society of Jesus, which had a presence at Spinkhill from 1580 when priests were obliged to work in secrecy. In 1756 the manor of Spinkhill was bought by the Jesuits. The present school lies in the village and has a fine estate of playing fields and farmlands. Most pupils are Roman Catholics. There is strong emphasis on religious instruction in Catholic doctrine; mass and some other services are compulsory for Catholic pupils. It has a good staff:pupil ratio of 1:11. Academic standards are high and results are good. Many leavers go on to degree courses each year, including Oxbridge. French, German, Italian and Spanish are offered at A-level. Many pupils take GCSE in more than one European language and there are regular exchange arrangements for that age group with France. There are strong music, drama and art depts. Considerable strength in sport and games. A very good variety of clubs and societies. About a quarter of the pupils are involved in local community services and the school has an outstanding record in the Duke of Edinburgh's Award Scheme.

School profile

Pupils Age range 13–18; 322 pupils, 75 day (45 boys, 30 girls), 247 boarding (173 boys, 74 girls). Main entry ages 13 and into sixth. Approx 15% are children of former pupils. Own prep school, Barlborough Hall, provides more than 20% of intake. *Transfer from maintained schools:* 10% main intake, plus 20% to sixth.

Entrance Common entrance and own exam used (with interviews and IQ tests). Not oversubscribed. Sport and music skills looked for; pupils expected, but not required, to be RC. Parents not expected to buy text books. 55 assisted places. 10 scholarships, £100 to full fees. Bursaries added to assisted places to enable such pupils to board.

Parents 15+% are doctors, lawyers, etc; 15+% in industry or commerce; 15+% in the armed services. 10+% live within 30 miles; up to 10% live overseas.

Staff Headmaster P B Fisher, first year in post. 30 full time staff, 4 part time. Annual turnover 5%. Average age 36.

Academic work GCSE and A-levels. 23 GCSE subjects offered; 20 at A-level (including GCSE sports studies; no A-level general studies). In 1990, 57 pupils in upper fifth, 52 in upper sixth (now 55). *GCSE:* in 1990, 46% upper fifth gained at least grade C in 8+ subjects; 39% in 5–7; and 15% in 1–4 subjects. *A-levels:* 7% upper sixth passed in 4+ subjects; 51% in 3; 25% in 2; and 17% in 1 subject. 40% took science A-levels; 40% arts/ humanities; 20% both. *Computing facilities:* Computer laboratory and desk-top publishing facilities. *Special provision:* Specialist teaching for dyslexia and EFL.

European Community *Languages:* French offered: to age 14; GCSE; AS-level; A-level. German offered: to age 14; GCSE; AS-level; A-level. Italian offered: to AS-level; A-level. Spanish offered: to age 14; GCSE; AS-level; A-level. 25– 50% take GCSE in more than 1 EC language. *Exchanges:* Regular exchanges for pupils aged 14–16 to France (school in Lille). *Other:* Regular boys from St Louis de Gouzagne in Paris, boys and girls from Spain, particularly Barcelona. Contact with activity/outdoor centre in south of France.

Senior pupils' non-academic activities *Music:* 30% learn a musical instrument, 8 to Grade 6 or above, 2 accepted for Music School; some in school choir; others in Sheffield Youth Orchestra; GCSE Music Lab offered. *Drama and dance:* 30% in school productions. 2 accepted for Drama/Dance Schools, 2 go on to work in theatre. *Art:* 50% take as non-examined subject; 50% take GCSE; 8 take A-level. 10 belong to eg photographic club. *Sport:* Rugby, cricket, swimming, athletics, squash, riding, hockey and basketball, tennis available. All take non-compulsory sport. Some take lifesaving exams; GCSE and A-level sports studies recently introduced. Pupils represent county/country (rugby, cricket, hockey). Winners of 1988 National Schools Sevens Open Tournament. *Other:* All have bronze Duke of Edinburgh's Award and 12 have gold. Other activities include driving lessons, and about 20 clubs from sailing to chess and computers.

Careers In 1990, 70% leavers went on to degree courses; 10% straight into careers (eg nursing, tourism); 20% other. Of those going on to degree courses, 11% went to Oxbridge; 78% to other universities; 11% to poly/colleges. 3% those going on to higher education went to courses in music; 27% in humanities/ social sciences; 10% in medicine; and 60% in science/engineering.

Uniform School uniform worn in lower school.

Houses/prefects Competitive houses. Prefects, head boy, head of house and house prefects – appointed by the Head.

Religion Compulsory mass for Catholics. Other denominations welcomed.

Social No organised local events. Exchanges with Jesuit schools in Australia, Zimbabwe and France. Day pupils allowed to bring own car/bike/motorbike to school. Meals self service; lunch separate sittings. School shop. No tobacco/alcohol allowed.

Discipline Strong emphasis throughout the school on growth to self-discipline. No corporal punishment.

Boarding Sixth form have own study bedrooms; remainder in study cubicles. Single sex houses, approximately 50–60, divided by age. Resident SRN. Central dining room. 2 weekend exeats each term. Visits to local town allowed for upper school.

Former pupils Rt Hon Lord Wheatley PC; Sir Martin Melvin; Air Marshal Sir Francis Fresanges; Rt Hon Sir Denis Henry; Sir David Rose; Sir Diarmaid Conroy; Major General McGuiness.

n

· Nativity School ·

Nativity School	• Pupils 320	• Termly fees
West Street	• Boys 3–11 only	£900 (Day)
Sittingbourne	(Day)	• ISAI
Kent ME10 1AE	• Girls 3–18 (Day)	Enquiries/application to
Tel 0795 423713	• Upper sixth 12	the Headmaster

What it's like

Founded in 1895 by the Sisters of the Nativity (and now maintained by the Sisters of Christ) it has a pleasant site in the centre of the attractive town of Sittingbourne. Games facilities are on site. It has many of the advantages of a small school, with a friendly and co-operative atmosphere. There is particular emphasis on individual attention and support. It is a Roman Catholic foundation and spiritual and religious education are considered important, including prayer, mass, worship, etc according to the liturgy of the Church. A sound general education is provided and results are creditable. Each year a number of sixth formers go on to degree courses. Some music, drama and art. An adequate range of sports, games and extra-curricular activities. Some local community service and participation in the Duke of Edinburgh's Award Scheme.

School profile

Pupils Total age range 3–18; 320 day pupils (25 boys, 295 girls). Senior department 11–18, 150 girls. Main entry ages 3 (boys and girls), 11 and into sixth (girls). 20% are children of former pupils. *Transfer from maintained schools:* 50% senior intake, plus 50% to sixth.

Entrance Own entrance exam used for seniors. Not oversubscribed. Range of skills are recognised and encouraged; pupils expected to be Christian (school is Roman Catholic foundation). Parents not expected to buy text books; maximum extras £100. Scholarships available at 11, 13 and sixth, £900–450 per term.

Parents 15+% are doctors, lawyers, etc; 15+% in industry. 60+% live within 30 miles.

Staff Head Geoffrey Tierney, 2 years in post. 24 full time staff, 12 part time. Annual turnover 10%. Average age 35–45.

Academic work GCSE, AS and A-levels. 15 subjects offered. In 1990, 24 pupils in upper fifth, 8 in upper sixth (now 12). *GCSE:* in 1989, 6 upper fifth gained at least grade C in 8+ subjects; 4 in 5–7; and 14 in 1–4 subjects. *A-levels:* on average, 4 upper sixth pass in 3 subjects; 4 in 2 subjects. 2 take science A-levels; 4 arts/humanities; 2 both. *Computing facilities:* New network of RM Nimbus computers. *Special provision:* Individual/small group teaching.

European Community *Languages:* French offered: to age 14; GCSE; AS-level; A-level. Spanish offered: to age 14; GCSE; AS-level; A-level. 25–50% take

GCSE in more than 1 EC language. *Exchanges:* Regular exchanges for pupils aged 14–18 to France and Spain.

Senior pupils' non-academic activities *Music:* 20 learn a musical instrument, 9 to Grade 6 or above; 1 accepted for Music School, 15 play in school orchestra, 6 in other groups. *Drama and dance:* 20 in school productions; 2 accepted for Drama/Dance Schools; 2 go on to work in theatre. *Art:* 3 take art as non-examined subject; 20 take GCSE; 6 A-level. 3 accepted for Art School. *Sport:* Hockey, netball, rounders, tennis, gymnastics available. 12 take non-compulsory sport. 6 take exams eg gymnastics. *Other:* 12 have bronze Duke of Edinburgh's Award. 12 in local community schemes. Other activities include clubs for stamps, chess, computing, gymnastics, etc.

Careers In 1990, 50% leavers went on to degree courses; 20% to art/drama/music colleges; 10% to non-degree courses; 20% straight into careers. Of those going on to degree courses, 50% went to universities; 50% to poly/colleges. 40% those going on to higher education went to courses in practical art; 15% in drama/acting; 30% in humanities/social sciences; and 15% in science/engineering.

Uniform School uniform worn throughout.

Houses/prefects Competitive houses. Prefects, head girl, head of house and house prefects – elected by school. School Council.

Religion Compulsory assemblies; voluntary attendance at services. Open to all Christian students.

Social Debates and sports with other local schools. Organised trips abroad to France and Belgium. Tuck shop. No tobacco/alcohol allowed.

Discipline No corporal punishment. Pupils failing to produce homework once might expect a warning and repeat.

· New Hall ·

New Hall	• Pupils 560	• Termly fees
Boreham	• Boys None	£1745 (Day)
Chelmsford	• Girls 11–18	£2725 (Board)
Essex CM3 3HT	(Day/Board)	• GSA
Tel 0245 467588	• Upper sixth 59	Enquiries/application to
Fax 0245 467188		the Registrar

What it's like

Founded at Liège in 1642, the school is run by the English Canonesses of the Holy Sepulchre. The nuns were compelled to leave during the French Revolution and reopened the school at its present site in 1798–99, where it is administered by nuns of the Order of the Holy Sepulchre. The main building is New Hall, formerly a Tudor palace (once the home of Mary Tudor). There is probably a house on the site before 1066. The present buildings are handsome and provide excellent facilities. The private estate of 120 acres is beautiful and there are excellent playing fields and sporting amenities. It is a Catholic school centred on a religious community and with a cosmopolitan intake. Its essential aim is that staff and pupils should experience Christian community together. Most of the pupils are Roman Catholics but others are welcomed and the school is enriched by them. The life of the school is closely associated with the liturgy of the Church, of which Sunday Mass is an important element. Religious instruction is an essential part of the curriculum. A very large staff allows a staff:pupil ratio of 1:8. Academic standards are high and results impressive. Most leavers go on to degree courses each year. Five European languages are available at GCSE (French, German, Modern Greek, Italian and Spanish) and many girls take more than one. French, German and Spanish are taught to A-level and there are regular exchanges with France, Germany and Spain. There is a massive commitment to music (350+ girls learn an instrument). Very strong indeed in drama (many productions) and art. A wide range of sport and games (high standards attained). A wide variety of activities caters for most needs. A lot of social work is done by pupils locally and there is an impressive record in the Duke of Edinburgh's Award Scheme. Justice and peace issues are important to the school's ethos.

School profile

Pupils Age range 11–18; 560 girls, 190 day, 370 boarding (weekly boarding available in sixth form). Main entry ages 11 and into sixth (also 12, 13, 14). Small number are children of former pupils (but school grown 5-fold in last 30 years). *Transfer from maintained schools:* 25% main intake, plus 50% to sixth.

Entrance Own entrance exam used. Variety of skills looked for. Commitment to Christian values expected, large proportion are RC (although many other Christians and a few non-Christians welcomed). Parents expected to buy only a few text books that are to be kept; maximum extras £250 per term although usually under £100. Some scholarships and bursaries.

Parents 20+% in industry or commerce. 40% live within 30 miles; 20% live overseas.

Staff Headmistress Sister Margaret Mary Horton, in post for 5 years. 64 full time staff. Annual turnover 5%.

Academic work GCSE, AS and A-levels; some EFL and LCCI. Approx 20 GCSE subjects offered; 6 at AS; 20 at A-level (AS-level general studies offered, no A-level). In 1990, 91 pupils in upper fifth, 59 in upper sixth. *GCSE:* in 1990, 52 upper fifth gained at least grade C in 8+ subjects; 19 in 5–7; and 18 in 1–4 subjects. *A-levels:* 36 upper sixth passed in 3+ subjects; 15 in 2; and 7 in 1 subject (mixed ability in sixth; other courses also offered). Approx 7% took science A-levels; 73% arts/humanities; 20% both. *Computing facilities:* Considerable – BBC, Amstrad, desktop publishing; School Net – art and design computers, etc. *Special provision:* Special teaching and ancillary help for physically handicapped.

European Community *Languages:* French offered: to age 14; GCSE; AS-level; A-level. German offered: to age 14; GCSE; A-level. Greek (modern) offered: to GCSE. Italian offered: to GCSE. Spanish offered: to age 14; GCSE; A-level. 25–50% take GCSE in more than 1 EC language. *Exchanges:* Regular exchanges for pupils aged 11–16 to France, Germany and Spain. *Other:* Various 1992 initiatives planned including choir visit to Europe.

Senior pupils' non-academic activities *Music:* 352 learn a musical instrument, 25 to Grade 6 or above; 1 accepted for Music School; 60 in school orchestra, 140 in school choir, 22 in school pop group; membership of Youth Orchestras in some years. *Drama and dance:* on average, approx 150 in school productions, 80 in workshops. 40 take GCSE theatre arts, 10 A-level. 3 accepted for Drama/Dance Schools, 8 for BA drama, 5 go on to work in theatre, 10 in media. *Art:* 120 take art and craft activities; 40 take GCSE art; 12 A-level. 5 accepted for Art School, 2 work in art galleries. *Sport:* Netball, hockey, gymnastics, cross-country, tennis, athletics, swimming, trampolining, aerobics, volleyball, badminton, squash, table tennis and other minority sports available. 155 take non-compulsory sport. 150 in teams. 5 represent county (athletics, hockey, netball, tennis); 1 country (athletics). *Other:* Many take part in local community schemes. Pupils take part in Duke of Edinburgh's Award, bronze, silver and gold. Some enter voluntary schemes after leaving school, others work for national charities. Other activities include a computer club, bridge club, driving lessons, public speaking, debating, voluntary service, drama, fencing and karate, technology club; natural science club.

Careers In 1990, 46% leavers went on to degree courses; 5% to art/drama/music colleges; 16% to non-degree courses (eg commercial college, pilot, nursing); 8% straight into careers (eg banking, tourism); 34% other (Gap year). Of those going on to degree courses, 4% went to Oxbridge, 70% to other universities; 26% to poly/colleges. 7% those going on to higher education went to courses in practical art; 18% in drama/acting; 53% in humanities/social sciences; and 22% in science/engineering.

Uniform School uniform worn; formal occasions only in sixth.

Houses/prefects All members of upper sixth have positions of responsibility.

Religion Compulsory attendance at Eucharist on Sundays, Assemblies, House Prayers, etc. Many other opportunities.

Social Debates, choirs, social events with other schools. Trips abroad arranged most half-terms and holidays. Pupils allowed to bring own car/bike/caged pet to school. Meals self service. School shop.

No tobacco allowed; sixth form permitted limited alcohol under supervision and on special occasions.

Discipline No corporal punishment. Pupils failing to produce homework once might expect help from tutor; any involvement in illegal drugs can lead to expulsion.

Boarding Upper sixth have own study bedroom, lower sixth share; all others in individual cubicles in dormitories. Houses for 50 boarders, 30 day pupils approx; vertical groups plus separate sixth form house. Resident SRN. Central dining room. Pupils can provide and cook some own food at weekends. Exeats each term – vary with age group (principle being: some weekend time at school allows pupils to benefit from boarding but contact with home through exeats, etc is encouraged). Weekend visits to local town allowed, dependent on age.

Former pupils Cindy Buxton (natural history film maker); Ciaran Madden (actress); Nadine Beddington (past president ARIBA); Anya Hindmarch (businesswoman); several doctors.

· Newcastle Church High ·

Newcastle upon Tyne	● Pupils 623	● Termly fees
Church High School	● Boys None	£900 (Day)
Tankerville Terrace	● Girls 4–18	● GSA
Jesmond	(Day)	Enquiries to the
Newcastle upon Tyne	● Upper sixth 32	Headmistress
NE2 3BA		Application to the
Tel 091 281 4306		School Secretary

What it's like

Founded in 1885 it stands in a pleasant residential district in one of the older suburbs, close to the city centre and university. The original buildings (completed in 1890) are well designed and there are many modern additions. These are surrounded by pleasant gardens and grounds. The senior and junior schools are on the same site. It caters for varying degrees of academic ability and lays considerable stress on a Christian atmosphere and education. Exam results are good and many sixth formers go on to degree courses each year. There are flourishing music, art and drama depts and a fair range of sports, games and activities. Strong commitment to local community schemes.

School profile

Pupils Total age range 4–18; 623 day girls. Senior department 11–18, 376 girls. Main entry ages 4, 7, 9, 11 and into sixth. Approx 5% are children of former pupils. *Transfer from maintained schools:* 65% senior intake, plus minimal proportion to sixth.

Entrance Own entrance exam used. No special skills or religious requirements. Parents not expected to buy text books. Assisted places. 9 scholarships/exhibitions pa (including 1 music), one-half to one-sixth fees.

Parents 15+% are doctors, lawyers, etc. 80% live within 30 miles.

Staff Headmistress Miss P E Davies, in post for 15 years. 41 full time staff, 19 part time. Annual turnover 3%.

Academic work GCSE and A-levels. 18 GCSE and A-level subjects offered. In 1990, 57 pupils in upper fifth, 32 in upper sixth. *GCSE:* in 1990, 80+% upper fifth gained at least grade C in 8+ subjects. *A-levels:* 70+% upper sixth passed in 3+ subjects. *Computing facilities:* Labs in senior and junior school – 27 computers. *Special provision:* EFL tutor (senior school).

European Community *Languages:* French offered: to age 14; GCSE; AS-level; A-level. German offered: to age 14; GCSE; AS-level; A-level. 10–25% take GCSE in more than 1 EC language. *Exchanges:* Regular exchanges for pupils aged 14–18 to France and Germany. *Other:* European Theme week in 1990.

Senior pupils' non-academic activities *Music:* 224 learn a musical instrument; choir, barbershop group, junior wind group, wind octet, flute, clarinet and brass ensembles, recorder consort, recorder trio, junior string orchestra, string quartet. Pupils strongly encouraged to form their own variable small ensembles with their friends. Some put on lunch-time recitals and concerts; 7 girls joined the Royal Grammar (Newcastle) Big Band. *Drama and dance:* 50 in school productions, 100 in other. 1 accepted for Drama/Dance School. *Art:* 17 take GCSE; 3 take A-level. 1 accepted for Art School. *Sport:* Netball, hockey, swimming, gymnastics, volleyball, dance, tennis, athletics, rounders available. Most take part in non-compulsory sport. Some take exams in swimming, gymnastics and athletics. 14 represent city, 10 the county. *Other:* 30 take part in local community schemes. Other activities include public speaking, Duke of Edinburgh Award Scheme, Christian Union, chess, house drama and music, computer club, school magazine. Sixth form car maintenance.

Careers In 1990, 70% leavers went on to degree courses; 4% to art/drama/music colleges; 8% to non-degree courses (eg building, catering); 12% straight into careers (eg computing, accountancy); 6% other. Of those going on to degree courses, 4% went to Oxbridge, 66% to other universities; 33% to poly/colleges. 8% those going on to higher education went to courses in practical art; 4% in music; 40% in humanities/social sciences; 8% in medicine; and 40% in science/engineering.

Uniform School uniform worn, optional in the sixth.

Houses/prefects Competitive houses. Prefects and head girl, appointed by sixth form and staff; head of house and house prefects by girls.

Religion Daily assembly. 3 church services a year.

Social Charity fair, ballroom dancing available, debates and music with local schools. Trips for ski–ing, art and languages. Pupils allowed to bring own car to school. Meals cafeteria style. No tobacco/alcohol allowed.

Discipline No corporal punishment. Detention is given for three consecutive pieces of work not produced.

Alumni association is run by Mrs J Harris, 7 Bemersyde Drive, Jesmond, Newcastle upon Tyne NE2 2HL.

· *Newcastle High* ·

Central Newcastle High
School
Eskdale Terrace
Newcastle upon Tyne
NE2 4DS
Tel 091 281 1768

- Pupils 790
- Boys None
- Girls 4–18
  (Day)
- Upper sixth 75

- Termly fees
  £908 (Day)
- GSA, GPDST
  Enquiries/application to
  the Headmistress

What it's like

Opened in 1895, a member of The Girls' Public Day School Trust, it has occupied the same premises in Eskdale Terrace since 1900. Numerous additions over the last twenty years include a science wing, library extension, assembly hall, computer room, lecture rooms, a sixth form block, a gym and very recently a new art department with CDT laboratory. It serves a wide catchment area and draws its pupils from many different backgrounds; a varied social 'mix' is a feature of its philosophy. It enjoys a high reputation in the region and gets good results. Very many girls go on to degree courses, many to Oxbridge. French, German and Spanish are offered at GCSE; many pupils take more than one GCSE European language. Non-examined Italian and Spanish are also available. Good in music and an impressive range of extra-curricular activities. Strong local support. The junior school is in Gosforth, 3 miles away.

School profile

Pupils Total age range 4–18; 790 day girls. Senior department 11–18, 560 girls. Main entry ages 4, 7, 9, 11 and into sixth. *Transfer from maintained schools:* 50% senior intake, plus 15% to sixth.

Entrance Own entrance exam used. No special skills or religious requirements. Parents not expected to buy text books; music tuition extra (£50). Assisted places. Approx 4 scholarships pa (quarter fees); bursaries.

Parents 15+% in industry or commerce; 15+% are doctors, lawyers, etc. 60+% live within 30 miles.

Staff Headmistress Mrs Angela Chapman, in post for 7 years. 48 full time staff, 25 part time.

Academic work GCSE and A-levels (including Russian, Greek and A-level general studies). In 1990, 76 pupils in upper fifth, 75 in upper sixth. *GCSE:* in 1990, 71 upper fifth gained at least grade C in 8+ subjects; 4 in 5–7; and 1 in 1–4 subjects. *A-levels:* 20 upper sixth passed in 4+ subjects; 50 in 3; 4 in 2; and 1 in 1 subject. 30 took science A-levels; 28 arts/

humanities; 17 both. *Computing facilities:* A computer room equipped with 2 computer networks with a total of 20 micros, plus various departmental computers. Special provision: some available for dyslexic pupils.

European Community *Languages:* French offered: to age 14; GCSE; AS-level; A-level. German offered: to age 14; GCSE; AS-level; A-level. Italian: non-examined subject. Spanish offered: to GCSE; non-examined subject. 25–50% take GCSE in more than 1 EC language. *Exchanges:* Regular exchanges for pupils aged 11–18 to France and Germany. Lower sixth involved in European work experience exchange scheme. *Other:* Talks from people involved in Europe.

Senior school non-academic activities *Music:* 210 learn a musical instrument, 60 to Grade 6 or above. 2 accepted for Music School; 1 or 2 play in pop group beyond school, 50 in school orchestra, 125 in 2 school choirs, 30 in chamber groups. *Drama and dance:* 20 in school productions, all at some time in drama productions; 1 accepted for Drama/Dance School. *Art:* 14 take A-level. *Sport:* Hockey, netball, tennis, athletics, rounders, swimming, lacrosse, pony trekking, gymnasium, volleyball, basketball, badminton, cricket, basketball, fencing available. Good attendance for non-compulsory sport; others have tennis coaching, hockey, netball and judo. 6 take exams eg gymnastics, swimming. 28 represent county/country (hockey, tennis, badminton, swimming, cross country, athletics). *Other:* 20 help at sheltered accommodation. Sixth formers regularly enter voluntary schemes after leaving school. Other activities include a computer club, debating, maths, science, electronics, aerobics, judo, French, poetry, drama, chess, LATE (Looking at the Environment).

Careers In 1990, 85% leavers went on to degree courses; 8% to non-degree courses (eg art foundation, further A-levels, accountancy, equestrian management); 7% other (Gap year). Of those going on to degree courses, 13% went to Oxbridge, 65% to other universities; 22% to poly/colleges. 3% those going on to higher education went to courses in music; 62% in humanities/social sciences; 8% in medicine; and 27% in science/engineering.

Uniform School uniform worn except in the sixth.

Houses/prefects 4 houses compete in sport, music and drama. Prefects, head girl and heads of house – elected by the girls. School Council.

Religion Non-denominational assembly, non-Christians can opt out. Occasional Jewish assembly.

Social Senior debates, sixth form drama and musical productions with Royal Grammar School for boys. Organised exchange to France, Germany; ski trips, trips to Greece. Pupils allowed to bring own car/bike to school. Meals self service. School shop sells uniform and tuckshop. No tobacco/alcohol allowed.

Alumni association is run by Mrs Helen Turnbull, 86 Polwarth Road, Brunton Park, Gosforth, Newcastle upon Tyne NE3 5NE.

Former pupils Miriam Stoppard.

· *Newcastle-under-Lyme* ·

Newcastle-under-Lyme School
Mount Pleasant
Newcastle-under-Lyme
Staffordshire ST5 1DB
Tel 0782 633604

- Pupils 1353
- Boys 8–18 (Day)
- Girls 8–18 (Day)
- Upper sixth 162

- Termly fees £787 (Day)
- HMC
Enquiries/application to the Principal

What it's like

Founded in 1874. The present school is a result of an amalgamation (in 1981) of Newcastle High School and Orme's Girls' School (founded in 1876) nearby. Both lie in a residential area of the Potteries and have some 30 acres of grounds and playing fields. The original buildings are still part of the school. There have been a number of extensions to provide good modern facilities. The school enjoys vigorous local support. Good teaching is provided and academic standards are high. Results are impressive and very many pupils go on to degree courses, including Oxbridge. Many pupils take more than one of the three European languages available (French, German, Spanish) at GCSE. The music department is very strong. A good range of sports and activities. There is a vigorous CCF and a scout troup. Some commitment to the Duke of Edinburgh's Award Scheme.

519

School profile

Pupils Total age range 8–18; 1353 day pupils (654 boys, 699 girls). Senior department 11–18; 1211 pupils (589 boys, 622 girls). Main entry ages 8, 11 and into sixth. Approx 10% are children of former pupils. *Transfer from maintained schools:* 80% senior intake, plus 20% to sixth.

Entrance Common entrance and own exam used. Oversubscribed. No special skills or religious requirements. Parents not expected to buy text books. 73 assisted places. 6 scholarships/bursaries, £400–£100.

Parents 15+% in industry or commerce; 15+% are doctors, lawyers, etc.

Staff Principal R M Reynolds, 1 year in post. 94 full time staff, 12 part time. Annual turnover 8%. Average age 40.

Academic work GCSE and A-levels. 22 subjects offered at A-level (including Greek and Russian; all sixth form take A-level general studies). In 1990, 180 pupils in fifth, 163 in upper sixth. *GCSE:* in 1990, 148 fifth gained at least grade C in 8+ subjects; 19 in 5–7; and 13 in 1–4 subjects. *A-levels:* 107 upper sixth passed in 4+ subjects; 29 in 3; 21 in 2; and 7 in 1 subject. 40% took science A-levels; 50% arts/humanities; 10% both. *Computing facilities:* 2 computer rooms.

European Community *Languages:* French offered: to age 14; GCSE; AS-level; A-level. German offered: to age 14; GCSE; AS-level; A-level. Spanish offered: to GCSE. 25–50% take GCSE in more than 1 EC language. *Exchanges:* Regular exchanges for pupils aged 14–16 to France.

Senior pupils' non-academic activities *Music:* 300 learn a musical instrument, 40 to Grade 6 or above, 3–4 accepted for Music School. *Drama and dance:* 4 school productions a year. 2 accepted for Drama/Dance Schools. *Art:* 40 take GCSE; 21 A-level. 20 belong to photographic club. 7 accepted for Art School. *Sport:* Rugby, hockey, cricket, cross-country, swimming, water polo, judo, shooting, netball, athletics available. Many take non-compulsory sport. *Other:* Some pupils have gold Duke of Edinburgh's Award. Other activities include a computer club, chess, Christian Fellowship, CCF, Scouts.

Careers In 1990, 85% leavers went on to degree courses; 4% to art/drama/music colleges; 6% to non-degree courses (eg re-taking A-levels, HND business studies, nursing); 4% straight into careers (eg banking, legal executive); 1% other. Of those going on to degree courses, 11% went to Oxbridge, 51% to other universities; 38% to poly/colleges. 5% those going on to higher education went to courses in practical art; 2% in drama/acting; 1% in music; 58% in humanities/social sciences; 7% in medicine; and 27% in science/engineering.

Uniform School uniform worn throughout.

Houses/prefects Competitive houses. Prefects, head boy and girl – elected by the school. School Council.

Religion Daily assemblies.

Social 6 organised trips abroad and exchange systems with schools abroad every year. Pupils allowed to bring own car/bike/motorbike to school. Meals self service. School shop. No tobacco/alcohol allowed.

Discipline No corporal punishment. Pupils failing to produce homework once might expect a repeat or detention; those caught smoking cannabis on the premises could expect expulsion.

Former pupils Sir Richard Bailey; Sir David Barritt; 6 professors; 2 generals; 1 admiral.

· *Normanton (Buxton)* ·

Normanton School	● Pupils 120	● Termly fees
Buxton	● Boys 10–18	£900 (Day)
Derbyshire	(Day/Board/Weekly)	£1950 (Board)
SK17 6SJ	● Girls 10–18	£2325 (Overseas)
Tel 0298 22745	(Day/Board/Weekly)	● ISAI
	● Upper sixth 10	Enquiries/application to
		the Headmaster

What it's like

Founded in 1877, it has well-appointed buildings in the centre of the attractive town of Buxton which itself is situated in one of the most beautiful parts of the Peak District of Derbyshire. The school is non-denominational and has all or most of the advantages of a small school. A sound general education is provided and results are good. Sports and games are well catered for and the school has the use of the town's facilities (eg swimming pool and sports hall). There is a fair range of open-air and other extra-curricular activities.

School profile

Pupils Age range 10–18, 120 pupils. Main entry ages 10 and into sixth. *Transfer from maintained schools:* 10% main intake, plus 50% to sixth.

Staff Headmaster S B Smith, in post for 3 years.

Academic work GCSE and A-levels. 10 subjects offered (no A-level general studies). In 1990, 25 pupils in upper fifth, 9 in upper sixth. *GCSE:* in 1990, 4 upper fifth gained at least grade C in 8+ subjects; 10 in 5–7; and 9 in 1–4 subjects. *A-levels:* 6 upper sixth passed in 3 subjects; 1 in 2; and 1 in 1 subject. 6 took science A-levels; 3 a mixture of science and arts. *Computing facilities:* Computer awareness course to GCSE (option).

Special provision: Timetabled ESL; teacher for dyslexics.

European Community *Languages:* French offered: to age 14; GCSE; AS-level; A-level. German offered: to age 14; GCSE; AS-level; A-level. Under 10% take GCSE in more than 1 EC language.

Careers In 1990, 75% leavers went on to degree courses; 10% straight into careers (eg banking, finance); 15% other (eg Services). Of those going on to degree courses, 50% went to universities; 50% to poly/colleges. 50% those going on to higher education went to courses in humanities/social sciences; and 50% in science engineering.

· *North Foreland Lodge* ·

North Foreland Lodge
Sherfield-on-Loddon
Basingstoke
Hampshire RG27 0HT
Tel 0256 882431

- Pupils 185
- Boys None
- Girls 11–18 (Board)
- Upper sixth 25

- Termly fees £2700 (Board)
- GSA
Enquiries/application to the Headmistress

What it's like

Founded 1909. It occupies a pleasant rural site near Basingstoke. The buildings are pleasant but not luxurious. Facilities and accommodation are up to date. A sound education is given, based on the teaching of the Church of England. Many sixth form leavers go on to degree courses. There is a staff:pupil ratio of 1:9. A standard range of sports, games and extra-curricular activities.

School profile

Pupils Age range 11–18; 185 boarding girls. Main entry ages 11–12. *Transfer from maintained schools:* None.

Entrance Common entrance exam used plus own assessment day. Oversubscribed. No special skills or religious requirements. Parents not expected to buy text books; music and sport coaching extra. 2 sixth form science scholarships, half fees.

Staff Head Miss D L Matthews, in post for 8 years. 24 full time staff, 10 part time. Annual turnover 10%. Average age 42.

Academic work GCSE and A-levels (A-level general studies offered). In 1990, 30 pupils in upper fifth, 25 in upper sixth. *GCSE:* in 1990, 27 upper fifth gained at least grade C in 8+ subjects; 3 in 6–8 subjects. *A-levels:* 19 upper sixth passed in 3+ subjects; 3 in 2; and 1 in 1 subject. 80% took A-levels in arts/humanities; 8% broad area of science/engineering; 12% both. *Computing facilities:* RM Nimbus network – BBC Master SJ network.

European Community *Languages:* French offered: to age 14; GCSE; AS-level; A-level. German offered: to age 14. Spanish offered: to age 14; GCSE; AS-level; A-level. 25–50% take GCSE in more than 1 EC language. *Exchanges:* Regular exchanges for pupils aged 16–18 to Spain. *Other:* French, Danish and German pupils in school for 1 year. Talks from MEPs. School visits to Europe most years, eg to France, Italy or Spain.

Careers In 1990, 80% leavers went on to degree courses; 20% to non-degree courses (eg secretarial). Of those going on to degree courses, 75% went to universities; 25% to poly/colleges. 72% those going on to higher education went to courses in humanities/social sciences; and 8% in science/engineering.

Senior pupils' non-academic activities *Sport:* Swimming, tennis, rounders, lacrosse, netball, basketball, trampolining, squash, gymnastics available. *Other* activities include music, art, needlework, Duke of Edinburgh Award Scheme, first aid, road safety.

Uniform Juniors wear uniform, not in sixth.

· North London Collegiate ·

North London
Collegiate School
Canons
Edgware
Middlesex HA8 7RJ
Tel 081 952 0912
Fax 081 905 6979

- Pupils 900
- Boys None
- Girls 7–18
  (Day)
- Upper sixth 100

- Termly fees
  £1140 (Day)
- GSA
  Enquiries/application to
  the Headmistress

What it's like

Founded in 1850 by Miss Frances Buss, the first woman to use the title 'headmistress'. In 1929 it bought 'Canons', the former home of the Duke of Chandos, a magnificent 18th-century house with fine terraces and gardens. This is the heart of the school for the sixth form. A modern school has since been built in the 30 acres of parkland. This includes a music school, a drawing school, a theatre and the junior school. A C of E foundation, it is strong in music (300 girls learn an instrument), and in drama. An energetic, purposeful school, its facilities are very good and it provides an excellent education. A very high proportion of pupils go to university including very many to Oxbridge. Four European languages are offered at various levels and all of them (French, German, Italian and Spanish) for the Institute of Linguists. A high proportion of girls take more than one European language at GCSE. A range of sports, games and extra-curricular activities, including the Duke of Edinburgh's Award Scheme.

School profile

Pupils Total age range 7–18; 900 day girls. Senior department 11–18, 700 girls. Main entry ages 7, 11 and into sixth. Approx 10% are children of former pupils.

Entrance Own entrance exam used. Oversubscribed. No special skills or religious requirements. Parents not expected to buy text books. 73 assisted places. 77 bursaries, 11 scholarships, £3360 pa.

Parents 100% live within 30 miles.

Staff Headmistress Mrs J L Clanchy, in post for 4 years. 54 full time staff, 22 part time. Annual turnover 6%.

Academic work GCSE and A-levels. On average, 100 pupils in upper fifth, 100 in upper sixth. *GCSE:* on average, 100 upper fifth gained at least grade C in 8+ subjects. *A-levels:* 6 upper sixth pass in 4+ subjects; 90 pass 3; 5 pass 2 subjects. *Computing facilities:* Network of 12 BBC + 4 stand alone BBC; a network of 14 Nimbus (RM) + plotters, printers, etc.

European Community *Languages:* French offered: to age 14; GCSE; AS-level; A-level; Institute of Linguists. German offered: to age 14; GCSE; AS-level; A-level; Institute of Linguists. Italian offered: to AS-level; Institute of Linguists. Spanish offered: to GCSE; AS-level; A-level; Institute of Linguists. 50–75% take GCSE in more than 1 EC language. *Exchanges:* Regular exchanges for pupils aged 11–16 to France and Germany. *Other:* Membership of Young Europeans. Regular information on Erasmus.

Senior pupils' non-academic activities *Music:* 300 learn a musical instrument. 2 or 3 accepted for Music School. 130 in school orchestra, 160 in school choir, 80 in chamber music groups; 20 in Harrow youth orchestra and other local orchestras. *Drama and dance:* 70–80 in school productions, about 20 participate in other productions. 1 accepted for Drama/Dance School. *Sport:* Lacrosse, netball, tennis, rounders, swimming, athletics, judo, fencing, self-defence, volleyball, badminton available. 80 take non-compulsory sport; 10 take exams. 6 represent county/country (lacrosse, netball, swimming, athletics). *Other:* 37 have bronze Duke of Edinburgh's Award, 13 have silver and 7 gold. Other activities include a computer club, driving, typing, chess, bridge, debating, Scottish dancing, pottery, photography.

Careers In 1990, 96% leavers went on to degree courses; 4% straight into careers (eg retailing, banking). Of those going on to degree courses, 24% went to Oxbridge, 80% to other universities; 6% to poly/colleges. 6% those going on to higher education went to courses in practical art; 2% in drama/acting; 4% in music; 56% in humanities/social sciences; 12% in medicine; and 20% in science/engineering.

Uniform School uniform worn except in the sixth.

Houses/prefects Head girl elected by the school. School Council.

Religion Religious worship compulsory.

Social Some debates, drama, lectures with other schools. Exchange with a German school, ski-ing trips, visits to France, Russia, Italy, Greece, etc. Pupils allowed to bring own car/bike to school. Meals self service. No tobacco/alcohol allowed.

Discipline No corporal punishment. Anyone abusing any drug on the premises could expect expulsion.

Former pupils Esther Rantzen; Eleanor Bron.

· *Northampton High* ·

Northampton High School for Girls Derngate Northampton NN1 1UN Tel 0604 38095	• Pupils 520 • Boys None • Girls 11–18 (Day) • Upper sixth 65	• Termly fees £1035 (Day) • GSA Enquiries/application to the Headmistress

What it's like

Founded in 1878 by a committee of local church people, it has long educated girls from a large area of the county and a wide social range. It occupied its present site in 1921. Its nucleus is the former All Saints Vicarage to which, over the years, have been added laboratories, a computer room, an assembly hall, libraries, a gym and art and domestic science centres. Thus the school comprises a conglomerate of houses and purpose-built structures which are well equipped. It is an Anglican school, ecumenical in spirit and practice, with some emphasis on Christian values and teaching. A broad, traditional grammar-school education is provided and results are creditable. A number of sixth formers go on to degree courses. Music is well supported, with orchestra, choirs, recorder and brass groups. Drama and dance are also popular. A standard range of sports and games is available (the playing fields are a few minutes' drive away). There is a fair variety of clubs and societies.

School profile

Pupils Total age range 3–18. Senior department 11–18, 520 day girls. Main entry ages 3, 11 and into sixth. *Transfer from maintained schools:* 80% of new girls joining the 60 girls from own junior school.

Entrance Own exam used. Assisted places.

Staff Headmistress Mrs L A Mayne, in post for 3 years.

Academic work GCSE, AS and A-levels (no A-level general studies offered). In 1989, 89 pupils in upper fifth, 40 in upper sixth (rising to 65 over next few years). *GCSE:* in 1989, 50 upper fifth gained at least grade C in 8+ subjects; 31 in 5–7; and 8 in 1–4 subjects. *A-levels:* 1 upper sixth passed in 4+ subjects; 26 in 3; 7 in 2; and 5 in 1 subject. 10 took science A-levels; 15 arts/humanities; 15 both. *Computing facilities:* Computer room and computers in some other areas.

· *Northamptonshire Grammar* ·

Northamptonshire
Grammar School
Pitsford
Northamptonshire
NN6 9AX
Tel 0604 880306

- Pupils Rising to 500
- Boys 11–18
  (Day)
- Girls None
- Upper sixth 80 likely

- Termly fees
  £964 (Day)
- ISAI

Enquiries/application to the Headmaster's Secretary

What it's like

Founded in 1989, this brand new school has for its premises Pitsford Hall, in a fine 26-acre park 4 miles north of Northampton. The school was created to fill a gap, as there was no academic boys' day school in Northamptonshire. It aims eventually to have 500 pupils and is described as a 'boarding school without the boarding' since it has an unusually long day (8.45 am–5.20 pm). It is interdenominational but 'strives to portray a living Christianity that reflects the whole range of denominations and is sympathetic to other faiths'. A full range of subjects is provided, from classics to technology. At present three European languages are offered at GCSE – French and German and, somewhat unusually Dutch in the sixth form. There is particular emphasis on a tutorial care system. Most pupils are expected to go on to higher education and the first A-level leavers will be in the academic year 1993–94. Music and drama are already well supported. There is a standard range of sports and games and a burgeoning number of clubs and societies.

School profile

Pupils Age range currently 11–14, 11–18 by 1994; 200 day boys, rising to 500. Main entry ages 11 and 13. *Transfer from maintained schools:* Main intake 50% at 11+.

Entrance Common entrance and own exam used. Academic ability to reach A-levels looked for. Christian foundation; sympathetic to others. Parents not expected to buy text books; maximum extras, £100 for lunches. 3 scholarships pa, 4 bursaries pa, value 100%–10% fees.

Staff Headmaster Dr Malcolm D W Tozer, in post for 2 years. 17 full time staff, 3 part time. Average age 35.

Academic work GCSE and A-levels. 12 GCSE subjects offered. Planning to have 80 in fifth and upper sixth. All expected to pass 5–7 GCSE at grade C or above and 2 A–levels. Expect 60% to take science A-levels; 30% arts/humanities; 10% both. *Computing facilities:* BBC Masters (1 for every 6 pupils), Archimedes (1 for every 100 pupils). *Special provision:* Specialist help with study skills.

European Community *Languages:* Dutch offered: to GCSE (in sixth form). French offered: to age 14; GCSE. German offered: to age 14; GCSE. 21% take GCSE in more than 1 EC language. *Exchanges:* Regular exchanges for pupils aged 11–16 to France and Germany. *Other:* Special initiation during 1991/2, which is European year at the school.

Non-academic (whole school) activities *Music:* 50% learn a musical instrument, 2% to Grade 6 or above. 30% in school orchestra, 20% in school choir.

Drama and dance: 30% in school productions. *Art:* 100% take as non-examined subject, 10% take GCSE. *Sport:* Rugby, hockey, cross-country, badminton, cricket, tennis, athletics, golf, sailing available. 90% pupils take non-compulsory sport. 10 represent county (rugby, cricket, golf, badminton, archery). *Other:* 60% take part in local community schemes. Recently started Duke of Edinburgh's Award Scheme. Other activities include a computer club, magazine, model cars, archive research, ecology, board games, steam engines, bridge.

Careers 1 full time adviser. Most pupils expected to go on to degree courses, first A-level leavers will be in academic year 1993–94.

Uniform School uniform worn, varied in sixth.

Houses/prefects Competitive houses.

There will be prefects, head boy, head of house and house prefects – appointed by the Head.

Religion Religious worship compulsory, except for those of other faiths. Voluntary Sunday services.

Social Musical, debating, general knowledge, dances with Northampton High School. French and German exchanges, with Northampton High School. Annual visits to Hadrian's Wall and Italy/Greece. Pupils allowed to bring own bike to school. Meals formal. School shop. No tobacco/alcohol allowed.

Discipline No corporal punishment. Pupils failing to produce homework once would be asked to produce it next day; failure to do so results in 1 hour's detention; those caught smoking cannabis on the premises would be expelled.

· *Northfield* ·

Northfield School
Church Road
Watford
Hertfordshire WD1 3QB
Tel 0923 229758

- Pupils 180
- Boys 3–7 only (Day)
- Girls 3–18 (Day)
- Upper sixth up to 6

- Termly fees £1155 (Day)
- ISAI

Enquiries/application to the Secretary

What it's like

Founded c1870, it occupied its present premises, urban and single-site, in 1944. It combines a nursery class and kindergarten. The main building is a large private house with very agreeable gardens. Modern extensions provide good facilities. A pleasant, happy school which has all the advantages of being small. It prides itself on a 'caring and supportive atmosphere' and has very small learning groups. Results are good. All girls in the upper school are expected to take 8 or 9 subjects to GCSE level. Sixth form courses fall into 3 categories: Advanced/Advanced supplementary in wide range of subjects; GCSE one year courses, eg. business studies, sociology, child care, human biology; Vocational courses, eg. Pitman foundation course, typing, office practice, bookkeeping, pre-nursery nursing course. A decent range of sports, games and activities.

School profile

Pupils Total age range 3–18; 180 day pupils (20 boys, 160 girls). Senior department 11–18, 94 girls. Main entry ages 3 (boys and girls), 7, 11 and into sixth (girls).

Transfer from maintained schools: 75% senior intake.

Entrance Own entrance exam used. Oversubscribed. No special skills or religious requirements. Parents expected to buy text books. Sixth form scholarships/ bursaries.

Staff Headmistress Mrs P Hargreaves in post 1 year. 8 full time staff, 20 part time. Annual turnover 4%.

Academic work GCSE and A-levels plus vocational courses. 16 subjects offered (no A-level general studies). In 1990, 29 pupils in upper fifth, 2 in upper sixth. *GCSE:* in 1990, 25% upper fifth gained at least grade C in 8+ subjects; 25% in 5–7; and 50% in 1–4 subjects. *A-levels:* 100% upper sixth passed in 2 subjects. *Computing facilities:* 4 in senior school.

European Community *Languages:* French offered: to age 14; GCSE; AS-level; A-level. German offered: to GCSE; AS-level; A-level. Under 10% take GCSE in more than 1 EC language.

Senior pupils' non-academic activities *Music:* 18 learn a musical instrument, 1 to Grade 6 or above. 12 in school orchestra, 18 in school choir. *Drama and dance:* All pupils are encouraged to take part in school productions; some pupils take LAMDA exams, GCSE drama. *Art:* 2 take as non-examined subject, 11 take GCSE; 4, A–level; 3 accepted for Art School. *Sport:* Hockey, netball, volleyball, badminton, tennis, rounders, swimming, athletics available. *Other:* 8 have bronze Duke of Edinburgh's Award and 4 have silver. Other activities include a computer club, sports club, supporting a child in Kenya through Save the Children and charity work (through classes and through houses; sixth form support local soup kitchen).

Careers On average, 30% leavers went on to degree courses; 10% to art/drama/ music colleges; 30% to non-degree courses (eg HND business studies, accountancy); 30% straight into careers (eg civil service, legal secretary, BBC, retail management). Of those going on to degree courses, all go to poly/colleges. 40% those going on to higher education went to courses in practical art; 40% in humanities/social sciences; and 20% in science/engineering.

Uniform School uniform worn except in the sixth.

Houses/prefects Competitive houses. Prefects, head girl, head of house and house prefects – elected by the school and staff. School Council (head girl chairs meetings of class reps and some staff; broad range of non-curricular matters discussed).

Religion Daily prayers.

Social Public speaking and road safety competitions with other local schools. Week in France for fourth and fifth forms. Pupils allowed to bring own car/bike to school. No tobacco/alcohol allowed.

Discipline No corporal punishment.

· *Northwood* ·

Northwood College	● Pupils 535	● Termly fees
Maxwell Road	● Boys None	£1095 (Day)
Northwood	● Girls 4–18	● GSA
Middlesex HA6 2YE	(Day)	Enquiries/application to
Tel 09274 25446	● Upper sixth 31	the Head Mistress

What it's like

Founded in 1878, it is single-site on the outskirts of London. The college consists of the original main building (1892) and several modern buildings erected during the last 25 years. These provide good up-to-date facilities in a pleasant environment. The aim of the school is to give a thorough all-round education which enables a girl to develop her gifts and personality and fit her for a worthwhile career in a changing world. Academic standards and results are good. Many sixth form leavers go on to degree courses each year, including Oxbridge. Four European languages are offered at GCSE. Girls have the opportunity to participate in music and drama. There is a good range of sports and games, a standard variety of activities and some commitment to local community schemes; the Duke of Edinburgh's Award Scheme is open to members of the Air Training Corps.

School profile

Pupils Total age range 4–18; 535 day girls. Senior department 11–18, 315 girls. Main entry ages 4, 7, 11 and into sixth. Approx 5% are children of former pupils. *Transfer from maintained schools:* 25% senior intake, plus 25% to sixth.

Entrance Own entrance exam used. Oversubscribed. No special skills or religious requirements. Parents not expected to buy text books; maximum extras, £200. Four sixth form scholarships, £1095 pa.

Parents 30% in industry or commerce; 30% are doctors, lawyers, etc.

Staff Head Mistress Mrs D K Dalton, in post for 5 years. 40 full time staff, 9 part time. Annual turnover 10%. Average age 38.

Academic work GCSE and A-levels. 28 subjects offered (no A-level general studies). In 1990, 45 pupils in upper fifth, 29 in upper sixth (now 31). *GCSE:* in 1990, 31 upper fifth gained at least grade C in 8+ subjects; 8 in 5–7; and 6 in 1–4 subjects. *A-levels:* 2 upper sixth passed in 4+ subjects; 21 in 3; 5 in 2; and 1 in 1 subject. 4 took science A-levels; 14 arts/humanities; 11 both. *Computing facilities:* 12 BBC's on Econet system and 8 BBC's with peripherals in senior school; 9 BBC's in junior school.

European Community *Languages:* French offered: to age 14; GCSE; AS-level; A-level. German offered: to age 14; GCSE; AS-level; A-level. Italian offered: to GCSE. Spanish offered: to GCSE. 25–50% take GCSE in more than 1 EC language. *Exchanges:* Regular exchanges for pupils aged 14–18 to France and Germany. *Other:* 14-year olds spend 6 days with French families annually; sixth form attend language courses in France.

Senior pupils' non-academic activities (age 11–18) *Music:* 66 learn a musical instrument, 10 to Grade 6 or above; 35 in school orchestra, 65 in choir. *Drama and dance:* 85 participate in school productions; 170 in drama competition; 120 take Poetry Society exams. 20 take Grade 6 GSM and D; 8 GCSE drama, 6 A-level theatre studies. *Art:* 20 take GCSE; 4, A-level. 2 accepted for Art School. *Sport:* Tennis, swimming, rounders, gymnastics, table tennis, badminton, squash, volleyball, netball, hockey, aerobics, golf, judo, dance, stoolball available. 150 take non-compulsory sport. 9 represent county/borough (hockey, netball, swimming). *Other:* 30 take part in local community schemes. Other activities include computer, science, languages and mathematics clubs, Christian Union, Jewish Heritage.

Careers On average, 85% leavers go on to degree courses; 5% to art/drama/music colleges; 5% to non-degree courses; 5% straight into careers (eg police, banking). Of those going on to degree courses, 10% go to Oxbridge, 50% to other universities; 40% to poly/colleges. 5% those going on to higher education go to courses in practical art; 5% in music; 45% in humanities/social sciences; 15% in medicine; and 30% in science/engineering.

Uniform School uniform worn except in the sixth.

Houses/prefects Competitive houses. Prefects, head girl, heads of houses – appointed by Head Mistress, nominated by senior pupils.

Religion Assembly compulsory for all.

Social Joint productions and conferences with local independent boys' schools, debates, choral concerts. Organised ski-ing trips, Mediterranean cruises, classical tours, exchange with a school in France and in USA, sailing course, hockey course, geography field trips. Pupils allowed to bring own car/bike to school. Meals self service. No tobacco/ alcohol allowed.

Discipline No corporal punishment. Pupils failing to produce homework once might expect a detention; those caught smoking cannabis on the premises could expect expulsion.

Former pupils Dame Margaret Booth (judge).

· *Norwich* ·

Norwich School	• Pupils 763	• Termly fees
The Close	• Boys 8–18	£1075 (Day)
Norwich	(Day/Board)	£1975 (Board/
NR1 4DQ	• Girls None	Weekly)
Tel 0603 623194	• Upper sixth 91	• HMC, CSA
		Enquiries/application to the Headmaster

What it's like

An ancient foundation, mentioned in Bishop Suffield's will of 1256; it was re-founded and granted a charter by Edward VI in 1547. About six years later it moved to its present site in the Cathedral Close. It has very handsome, in some cases magnificent, buildings – including the early 14th-century Chapel – in most civilised surroundings in the middle of the city. Fairly recent buildings include the fine Reynolds Library, three blocks of classrooms, several laboratories, a large centre for Advanced Practical Studies, a lecture theatre and sixth-form facilities in the former Bishop's Palace. Overall, the school is very well equipped with modern facilities and since 1949 has been strongly supported by the Worshipful Company of Dyers. It is non-denominational but has a C of E chaplain and enjoys daily assemblies in the superb cathedral. Cathedral choristers are educated at the school and there is a certain amount of emphasis on ecumenical religious instruction. A broad, general education is provided and standards are high. A high percentage of leavers go on to a degree course , some to Oxbridge. French and German are offered to A-level, Spanish to GCSE. Many boys take GCSE in more than one European language. There are regular exchanges with France and Germany. Music is very strong indeed and very well organised. All pupils are encouraged to take part. A large number is involved in orchestras, choirs and bands and roughly 285 pupils learn a musical instrument. Drama is also strong and there is close co-operation with the Girls' High School in theatrical activities. There are excellent facilities next to the school for sport and games which are compulsory for all. High standards are attained in rugby, cricket and hockey (numerous representatives at county level). Many clubs and societies cater for most conceivable needs. There is considerable emphasis on outdoor activities which include cycling, shooting, sailing, and rowing. There is a flourishing group of Sea Scouts and the Duke of Edinburgh's Award Scheme has been well supported over the years. Plentiful use is made of Norwich's cultural amenities.

School profile

Pupils Total age range 8–18; 763 boys (753 day, 10 boarding). Senior department 13–18, 601 boys. Main entry ages, 8, 9, 11, 12 and into sixth. 5% are children of former pupils. *Transfer from maintained schools:* 50% main intake, plus 20% to sixth.

Entrance Common entrance and own

exam used. Oversubscribed. No special skills or religious requirements. Parents not expected to buy text books; no other extras charged. 18 assisted places pa. 8 scholarships/bursaries pa, full tuition fees–£300 (means tested).

Parents 15+% are doctors, lawyers, etc. 60+% live within 30 miles, up to 10% live overseas.

Staff Headmaster C D Brown, in post for 7 years. 56 full time staff, 17 part time. Annual turnover 8%. Average age 38.

Academic work GCSE and A-levels. 19 subjects offered (no A-level general studies). In 1990, 104 pupils in upper fifth, 91 in upper sixth. *GCSE:* in 1990, 83 upper fifth gained at least grade C in 8+ subjects; 18 in 5–7; and 3 in 1–4 subjects. *A-levels:* 5 upper sixth passed in 4+ subjects; 70 in 3; 12 in 2; and 3 in 1 subject. 25% took science A-levels; 20% arts/humanities; 55% both. *Computing facilities:* Over 50 BBC Micros and Masters, Archimedes and IBM computers; moving to RM machines.

European Community *Languages:* French offered: to age 14; GCSE; A-level. German offered: to age 14; GCSE; A-level. Spanish offered: to GCSE. 25–50% take GCSE in more than 1 EC language. *Exchanges:* Regular exchanges for pupils aged 11–18 to France and Germany.

Senior pupils' non-academic activities *Music:* 285 learn a musical instrument, 19 up to Grade 6; 1 accepted for Music School; 2 per year study music at university. 57 in school orchestra, 200 in school choir, 25 in pop group, 115 in band/jazz band, 43 in recorder/guitar groups. 10 in County Youth Orchestra and Band. *Drama and dance:* 100 approx in school productions. 1 to National Youth Theatre. *Art:* 40 take art as non-examined subject; 35 take GCSE art; 6 A-level art; 6 history of art. 2–3 accepted for Art School. 100 belong to photographic club. *Sport:* Rugby, hockey, cricket; also tennis, rowing, fencing, sailing, athletics, badminton, cross country, golf, soccer, squash, swimming, cycling, self-defence available. 50

represent county (rugby, hockey, cricket, cross country, squash); 4 represent country (rugby, squash, fencing). *Other:* 4 take part in local community schemes. 36 have bronze Duke of Edinburgh's Award, 12 silver and 6 gold. Other activities include computer and chess clubs, debating, drama, electronics, United Nations, sea scouts, fencing and many more.

Careers In 1990, 74 leavers went on to degree courses; 9 to to non-degree courses; 8 straight into careers (eg banking, insurance, flying); 9 other. Of those going on to degree courses, 8% went to Oxbridge; 76% to other universities; 16% to poly/colleges. 3% those going on to higher education went to courses in practical art; 3% in music; 63% in humanities/social sciences; 5% in medicine; and 26% in science/engineering.

Uniform School uniform worn throughout.

Houses/prefects Competitive houses. Head boy, prefects, head of house and house prefects, appointed by the head. School consultative committee.

Religion Attendance at religious worship not compulsory.

Social Debating, theatre, music, Young Enterprise with other schools. German and French exchanges and music trips abroad. Pupils allowed to bring own bike/motorbike. Meals self-service. School shop. No tobacco/alcohol allowed.

Discipline No corporal punishment. Pupils failing to produce homework once could expect detention; those caught smoking cannabis on the premises could expect expulsion.

Boarding 25% have own study bedrooms, others share with 2–3 others. 2 long weekend exeats, also weekly boarding. Visits to the local town allowed daily, within reason.

Alumni association is run by Mr D Conway, Hon Sec, Old Norvicensian Club, Beech House, Town House Road, Old Costessey, Norwich NR8 5BY.

Former pupils John Quinton (Barclays Bank), Lord Blake, Clive Radley (England cricketer).

· *Norwich High* ·

Norwich High School
for Girls
Eaton Grove
95 Newmarket Road
Norwich NR2 2HU
Tel 0603 53265

- Pupils 841
- Boys None
- Girls 7–18
  (Day)
- Upper sixth 86

- Termly fees
  £908 (Day)
- GSA, GPDST
  Enquiries/application to
  the Admissions
  Secretary

What it's like

Founded in 1875, it is single-site in the middle of the city. The senior school is housed in a fine Georgian mansion in spacious wooded grounds and beautiful gardens. There are numerous purpose-built extensions and facilities are excellent. It enjoys a wide social spread from the whole of Norfolk and north Suffolk. Non–denominational, it provides a very good education in the grammar school tradition. Results are impressive and very many leavers proceed to degree courses, including many to Oxbridge. A large number of girls take more than one of the three European languages taught at GCSE level and regular exchanges are offered with France and Germany throughout the senior department of the school. Tremendously strong in music (most are involved) and also strong in drama and art. High standards in sport and games. An outstanding record in the Duke of Edinburgh's Award Scheme. Full advantage is taken of the city's cultural amenities. It has a high reputation locally and is well supported.

School profile

Pupils Total age range 7–18; 841 day girls. Senior department 11–18, 629 girls. Main entry ages 7, 11 and into sixth. *Transfer from maintained schools:* 65% senior intake, plus 40% to sixth.
Entrance Own entrance exam used. Oversubscribed. All-rounders welcome; no religious requirements. Parents not expected to buy text books; no other extras. 220 assisted places. Scholarships, including music: 25–50% fees. Also bursaries.
Staff Headmistress Mrs Valerie Bidwell. 48 full time staff, 10 part time.
Academic work GCSE and A-levels. 18 subjects offered (including A-level general studies). In 1989, 90 pupils in upper fifth, 86 in upper sixth. *GCSE:* in 1989, 81 upper fifth gained at least grade C in 8+ subjects; 8 in 5–7; and 1 in 1–4 subjects. *A-levels:* 10 upper sixth passed in 4+ subjects; 57 in 3; 15 in 2; and 4 in 1 subject. 32 took science A-levels; 23 arts/humanities; 31 both. *Computing facilities:* Network and freestanding machines.

European Community *Languages:* French offered: to age 14; GCSE; AS-level; A-level. German offered: to age 14; GCSE; AS-level; A-level. Spanish offered: to GCSE. 50–75% take GCSE in more than 1 EC language. *Exchanges:* Regular exchanges for pupils aged 11–18 to France and Germany.
Senior pupils' non-academic activities *Music:* 250 learn a musical instrument, 24 to Grade 6 or above. 3 go on to music degree courses. 150 in school orchestra, 220 in school choir, 6 in school boogie group, 25 in madrigal group, 4 in string quartet; 10 in brass group, 12 in woodwind ensemble; 1 in National Youth Orchestra. *Drama and dance:* 40 in school productions, 45 in company drama, 30 in drama club, 90 in pantomimes; 2 go on to work in theatre; others as leisure activity after leaving. *Art:* 30 take as non-examined subject, 20–30 take GCSE. 4 accepted for Art School; 20 belong to photographic club. *Sport:* Lacrosse, netball, life-saving, swimming, badminton,

volleyball, tennis, athletics, rounders available. 60 take non-compulsory sport. 10 take exams in swimming and Royal Life Saving Society Award. 17 represent county (lacrosse, netball, swimming, tennis, athletics). *Other:* Some take part in local community schemes. 48 have bronze Duke of Edinburgh's Award, 42 have silver and 53 have gold. Other activities include a computer club, science club, stamp club, rowing club, fencing.

Careers In 1990, 94% leavers went on to degree courses; 2% to art/drama/music colleges; 1% to non-degree courses; 1% straight into careers; 2% other. Of those going on to degree courses, 12% went to Oxbridge, 68% to other universities; 20% to poly/colleges. 3% those going on to higher education went to courses in practical art; 1% in music; 40% in humanities/social sciences; 8% in medicine; and 48% in science/engineering.

Uniform School uniform worn except in the sixth.

Houses/prefects Competitive houses. Prefects, head girl, head of house and house prefects – elected by staff and sixth form.

Religion Morning assembly. Parents may withdraw their children on religious grounds.

Social Debates, Young Enterprise, theatrical productions, BAYS with other local schools. Organised trips abroad. Pupils allowed to bring own car/bike/motorbike to school. Meals self service. School shop sells uniform. No tobacco/alcohol allowed.

Discipline No corporal punishment. Pupils failing to produce homework once might expect to make up work promptly; those caught smoking cannabis on the premises could expect suspension, probable expulsion.

Alumni association run by Mrs E Taylor, 16 The Avenues, Norwich NR2 3PH.

Former pupils Beryl Bryden (international jazz singer); Pat Barr (novelist); Anne Weale (authoress); Jane Manning (opera singer); Jenny Lane (BBC); Ann Tyrell (dress designer); Dr Jennifer Moyle (scientist).

· *Notre Dame (Cobham)* ·

Notre Dame Senior
School
Burwood House
Cobham
Surrey KT11 1HA
Tel 0932 63560

- Pupils 400
- Boys None
- Girls 11–18
  (Day)
- Upper sixth 27

- Termly fees
  £1095 (Day)
  Enquiries/application to
  the Headmistress

What it's like
Founded in 1937 and run by the Sisters of the Company of Mary, an international teaching order. The original building is Burwood House, a mansion on a fine estate. A large number of modern additions provide good facilities and equipment. Both senior and junior schools are on the same site, approximately 1 mile from Cobham. A sound general education is provided and results are pleasing. Departments of music and art are strong. Very many sixth formers go on to degree courses. There is a range of sports and games and good facilities for these are on site.

School profile

Pupils Age range 11–18; 400 day girls. Main entry ages 11 and into sixth.

Entrance Own entrance exam used. No special skills or religious requirements. Parents not expected to buy text books. No assisted places at present but some scholarships/bursaries.

Staff Headmistress Sister Faith Ede, in post for 4 years. 33 full time staff, 26 part time. Annual turnover 5%. Average age 43.

Academic work GCSE, A-levels, LCCI and Pitmans secretarial exams. Average size of fifth year 70; upper sixth 27. All fourth year girls take RE. *Computing facilities:* 15 Nimbus network system.

European Community *Languages:* French offered: to age 14; GCSE; AS-level; A-level. German offered: to age 14; GCSE; AS-level; A-level. Spanish offered: to age 14; GCSE; AS-level; A-level. 11–25% take GCSE in more than 1 EC language.

Senior pupils' non-academic activities *Music:* 47 learn a musical instrument, 32 in school orchestra; 50 in choir. *Drama and dance:* 50 in school productions. *Art:* 30 take GCSE; 6 take A-level. *Sport:* Netball, badminton, squash, tennis, swimming, basketball, volleyball, hockey, gymnastics available. 16 take exams. 3 represent county (tennis, badminton, swimming). *Other:* Senior girls take part in local community schemes and many participate in Duke of Edinburgh's Award Scheme. Other activities include computer club, drama and debating societies.

Careers In 1990, 95% sixth form leavers went on to degree courses; 5% to non-degree courses. Of those going on to degree courses, 90% went to universities; 10% to poly/colleges. 5% those going on to higher education went to courses in practical art; 90% in humanities/social sciences; and 5% in science/engineering.

Uniform School uniform worn except in sixth.

Houses/prefects Competitive houses. Prefects, head girl, head of house and house prefects – appointed by Head and staff.

Religion All girls attend mass twice a term; assemblies reflect Christian beliefs.

Social Joint theatrical productions with local boys' school and social events in sixth form. Organised trips abroad. Sixth formers allowed to bring own car to school. Meals self service. School tuckshop. No tobacco/alcohol allowed.

Discipline No corporal punishment. Pupils failing to produce homework once might expect parents to be informed, threatening detention.

Alumni association run by the Headmistress.

· *Notre Dame (Lingfield)* ·

Notre Dame School
St Piers Lane
Lingfield
Surrey RH7 6PH
Tel 0342 833176

- Pupils 500
- Boys 3–11 only (Day)
- Girls 3–18 (Day)
- Upper sixth 12

- Termly fees £1055 (Day)
- ISAI

Enquiries/application to the Principal

What it's like

Founded in 1940 by the Sisters of Notre Dame as a boarding and day school conducted by the Sisters. They withdrew from the school in 1987 and it is now a corporate charity under lay management. It combines nursery, infant, junior and senior schools on the edge of the attractive village of Lingfield. The pleasant buildings are well equipped and occupy a campus which comprises about 20 acres of lawns, formal gardens, orchards and playing fields. An historic country house on site is being developed as a sixth form centre (the sixth form is expanding). The philosophy of the school is based on a firm belief in the development of 'the whole person'. Roman Catholic doctrine, morality and liturgical celebrations are an integral part of its life. There is a flourishing tradition of maximum care and support for the individual. A sound general education is provided and from what is still a relatively small sixth form, quite a high proportion of girls now go on to degree courses. Strong in music and drama and a range of sports, games and extra-curricular activities. Some recent commitment to the Duke of Edinburgh's Award Scheme.

School profile

Pupils Total age range 3–18; 500 day girls. Senior department 11–18, 315 girls. Main entry ages 3 (boys and girls), 11, 12 and into sixth (girls). Approx 5% are children of former pupils. *Transfer from maintained schools:* 15% senior intake.

Entrance Own entrance exam used. Not oversubscribed at present. No special skills required but pupils must be Christian. Parents not expected to buy basic text books; maximum extras, £50. 2 bursaries, 50%.

Parents 15% in industry or commerce.

Staff Principal Mr Gerald Davies, in post for 4 years. 25 full time staff, 14 part time. Annual turnover 5%.

Academic work GCSE and A-levels. 16 GCSE and A-level subjects offered (general studies taught but not examined). In 1990, 64 pupils in upper fifth, 12 in upper sixth. *GCSE:* in 1990, 25 upper fifth gained at least grade C in 8+ subjects; 22 in 5–7; and 16 in 1–4 subjects. *A-levels:* 3 upper sixth passed in 3 subjects; 4 in 2; and 4 in 1 subject. 30% took science A-levels; 20% arts/humanities; 50% both. *Computing facilities:* 10 BBC computers, 5 printers. *Special provision:* Part time specialist tutors for dyslexia and EFL.

European Community *Languages:* French offered: to age 14; GCSE; A-level. German offered: to age 14; GCSE; A-level. 10–25% take GCSE in more than 1 EC language. *Exchanges:* Regular exchanges for pupils aged 14–18 to France and Germany.

Senior pupils' non-academic activities *Music:* 53 learn a musical instrument, 14 to Grade 6 or above, 5 accepted for Music School; 14 in school orchestra, 15 in choir; 4 in local orchestras, 3 in wind bands. *Drama and dance:* 30 in school productions, 13 in drama club for GCSE. 1 goes on to work in theatre. *Art:* 300 take as non–examined subject; 25 take GCSE. 2 accepted for Art School. *Sport:* Netball, tennis, hockey, rounders, cross-country, squash, swimming, gymnastics and dance available; sailing, canoeing, rock-climbing in sixth. 200 take non–compulsory sport. 100 take exams. 10 represent county/country.

Careers In 1990, 75% leavers went on to degree courses; 15% to non-degree courses (eg agriculture, nursery nursing); 10% straight into careers (eg food research, airport management trainee). Of those going on to degree courses, 60% went to universities; 40% to poly/colleges. 10% those going on to higher education went to courses in music; 70% in humanities/social sciences; and 20% in science/engineering.

Uniform School uniform worn, modified in sixth.

Houses/prefects Competitive houses. Prefects, head girl and heads of houses – appointed in consultation with staff. School Council and Sixth Form Council.

Religion Compulsory morning assembly, occasional masses and ecumenical service.

Social Drama, debates, orchestral and choral concerts with Worth School; sixth form social events with local independent schools. Ski-ing holidays; exchanges arranged through AIJ. Pupils allowed to bring own bike/car to school. Meals self service. School shop selling exercise books, etc. No tobacco/alcohol allowed.

Discipline No corporal punishment.

Pupils failing to produce homework once might expect to repeat it plus extra work on same topic; detention for persistent offender; parental involvement in disciplinary procedure is regarded as very important; those caught smoking cannabis on the premises would be expelled.
Alumni association contact School Secretary.

· Notting Hill & Ealing High ·

Notting Hill & Ealing
High School
2 Cleveland Road
Ealing
London W13 8AX
Tel 081 997 5744

- Pupils 768
- Boys None
- Girls 5–18
  (Day)
- Upper sixth 72

- Termly fees
  £1228 (Day)
- GSA, GPDST
  Enquiries/application to
  the Headmistress

What it's like

Founded in 1873 by the Girls' Public Day School Company, now the Girls' Public Day School Trust in Notting Hill. The move to Ealing took place in 1931. Suburban and single-site it lies in a pleasant and quiet residential area. The core consists of several large (formerly private) houses to which modern blocks have been added. There are playgrounds and large gardens. It has its own junior school. A sound general education is provided and, from a large sixth form, the great majority of pupils go on to degree courses, including many to Oxbridge. European links are strong. French, German and Spanish are taught right through to A-level and regular exchanges with France, Germany and Spain are offered to all age groups. Many girls take more than one European language at GCSE. A range of games, sports and activities. Good commitment to local social services.

School profile

Pupils Total age range 5–18; 768 day girls. Senior department 11–18, 562 girls. Main entry ages 5, 7, 11 and into sixth. Approx 5–10% are children of former pupils. *Transfer from maintained schools:* 60% senior intake, plus 10% to sixth.

Entrance Own entrance exam and interview used. Oversubscribed. Academic ability looked for; no religious requirements. Parents not expected to buy text books. Assisted places. 3 scholarships (1 academic, 1 music, 1 sixth form), $1/2$ and $1/7$ fees. Bursaries, depending on family income.

Parents 15+% in industry or commerce; 15+% are doctors, lawyers, etc and 15+% in the theatre, media, music, etc. 70+% live within the Borough of Ealing.

Staff Headmistress Mrs S M Whitfield, first year in post. 45 full time staff, 16 part time. Annual turnover 5%.

Academic work GCSE and A-levels. 16 GCSE subjects offered; 17 at A-level In 1991, 85 pupils in upper fifth, 72 in upper sixth. *GCSE:* in 1990, 73 upper fifth gained at least grade C in 8+ subjects; 7 in 5–7 subjects. *A-levels:* 3 upper sixth passed in 4+ subjects; 53 in 3; 13 in 2; and 4 in 1 subject. 19 took science A-levels; 38 arts/humanities; 12 both. *Computing facilities:* New computer room: 8 station RML 480Z network, 8 station Nimbus network and desktop printer; 5 BBC's in subject specialist rooms. *Special provision:* Visiting teacher gives assistance to mild dyslexics.

European Community *Languages:* French offered: to age 14; GCSE; A-level. German offered: to age 14; GCSE;

A-level. Spanish offered: to age 14; GCSE; A-level. 25–50% take GCSE in more than 1 EC language. *Exchanges:* Regular exchanges for pupils aged 11–18 to France, Germany and Spain.

Senior pupils' non-academic activities *Music:* 60% learn a musical instrument, 60% to Grade 6 or above; 15% in school orchestra, 30% in school choir; comprehensive concert programme. Madrigal choir tours in Europe every summer. *Drama and dance:* 25% participate in school productions. 12% belong to dance clubs; 8% and 15% (dance and drama respectively) up to Grade 8 in RAD. 5% entered competitions. *Art:* 15% take as non-examined subject, 30% take GCSE; 8% take A-level painting, drawing, graphics, collage, printing (lino, screen, drypoint, monoprints). *Sport:* Netball, hockey, tennis, athletics, gym, dance, badminton, windsurfing, dry skiing, trampolining, volleyball, riding, weight training, squash, table tennis available plus golf in sixth form. 25% take non-compulsory sport. 5% represent county/country (gym, netball, tennis, badminton or mixture). *Other:* 20% take part in local community schemes. Each form has charity week to raise money (total last year – £5500). Other activities include a computer club, literary society, BAYS,

school bank (Midbank scheme for schools), lighting club, school shop (mini-enterprise), junior speakers club, Duke of Edinburgh's Award Scheme, photographic club, life drawing class.

Careers In 1990, 72% leavers went on to degree courses; 1% to art/drama/music colleges; 4% to non-degree courses (eg art foundation course); 4% straight into careers (eg retail, television); 18% other. Of those going on to degree courses, 12% went to Oxbridge, 75% to other universities; 14% to poly/colleges. 9% those going on to higher education went to courses in practical art; 66% in humanities/social sciences; 9% in medicine; and 16% in science/engineering.

Uniform School uniform worn except in the sixth.

Houses/prefects No competitive houses. No prefects; head girl and deputies elected by the sixth form. School Council.

Religion Morning assembly.

Social Trips to Spain, France, Germany, Italy and Austria, ski-ing in Switzerland and activity holidays in the UK. Pupils allowed to bring own car/bike/motorbike to school. Meals self service.

Former pupils Angela Rumbold; Eve Matheson (actress).

· Nottingham High (Boys) ·

Nottingham High School Waverley Mount Nottingham NG7 4ED Tel 0602 786056	• Pupils 850 • Boys 11–18 (Day) • Girls None • Upper sixth 114	• Termly fees £945 (Day) • HMC Enquiries/application to the Headmaster

What it's like

Founded in 1513 by Dame Agnes Mellers, widow of Richard Mellers – a bell founder and Mayor of Nottingham. She got a royal charter from Henry VIII. For the first 300 years it was a small school, but had early links with Oxford and Cambridge to which many boys went as scholars. From the turn of the 19th century it expanded steadily to its present size. In 1868 it was moved to its present position between the Arboretum and the Forest where it enjoys a very agreeable bosky, urban site with fine gardens (the main playing fields are 2 miles away). The campus is compact and well designed and is unusually well equipped. There have been many developments in the last 10 years including a design and technology workshop and a magnificent science block which is regarded as one of the best in the country. The libraries are also very good. Pupils come from a wide catchment area (some 20 miles radius). None needs to be of any particular religious persuasion. The staff:pupil ratio is in the region of 1:14. It is a well-run school with motivated pupils and staff. Its academic standards are high and results are impressive. Very many leavers proceed to degree courses, including many to Oxbridge. French and German are offered to A-level, Italian and Spanish as non-exam languages. There are regular exchanges with France and Germany. Music is very strong: two orchestras, a number of choirs, two bands and other ensembles. There is much activity in drama throughout the school. Sports and games are compulsory for everyone and high standards are attained each year (the school has an outstanding record at county and national level). Numerous clubs and societies cater for most conceivable needs. Chess is especially strong and Nottingham is one of the premier chess schools in the country (it has won the zonal final of 'The Times' competition nine years running; runner-up in the national final twice). A large and flourishing CCF has been successful in many enterprises. Also a small, but very active, scout group. At any one time there are well over a hundred pupils taking part in the Duke of Edinburgh's Award Scheme for silver and gold awards. Outdoor pursuits in general are widely encouraged (eg orienteering, canoeing, rock-climbing). Expeditions and foreign trips are frequent. The school combines with Nottingham Girls' High School in joint theatrical productions etc. A large number of boys are actively engaged in local community services.

School profile

Pupils Age range 11–18; 850 day boys. Main entry ages, 11 and into sixth. 10% are children of former pupils. Own prep provides more than 20% of intake. *Transfer from maintained schools:* 45% main intake, 70% to sixth.

Entrance Own entrance exam used. Oversubscribed. All skills besides academic ability are recognised; no special religious requirements. Parents expected to buy text books. 30 assisted places pa. 15 scholarships/ bursaries pa, one-third full fees.

Staff Headmaster Dr D T Witcombe, in post for 20 years. 66 full time staff, 16 part time (including peripatetic music teachers). Annual turnover 5%. Average age 38.

Academic work GCSE and A-levels. 14 GCSE subjects offered, 18 A-level (general studies offered but not as an A-level subject). In 1990, 118 pupils in upper fifth, 114 in upper sixth. *GCSE:* in 1990, 97% upper fifth gained at least grade C in 8+ subjects; 3% in 5–7 subjects. *A-levels:* 3% upper sixth passed in 4+ subjects; 85% in 3; 8% in 2; and 4% in 1 subject. 56% took science A-levels; 23% arts/humanities; 21% both. *Computing facilities:* Laboratory containing 22 Archimedes computers; access to other computers in various departments.

European Community *Languages:* French offered: to age 14; GCSE; A-level. German: to age 14; GCSE; A-level. Italian and Spanish offered as non-examined subjects. *Exchanges:* Regular exchanges for pupils to France and Germany.

Senior pupils' non-academic activities *Music:* 75 learn a musical instrument, 28 up to Grade 6; 60 in school orchestra, 30 in school choir. 11 in Nottingham Youth Orchestra. *Drama and dance:* 27 in school productions. *Art:* 40 take art as non-examined subject, 21 take GCSE art; 9 A-level art. 2 accepted for Art School. *Sport:* Rugby, cricket, tennis, athletics, swimming, badminton, squash, hockey, football, cross-country, golf available. Games are compulsory for all. 9 have preliminary RFU coaching award. 27 represent county/country (rugby, athletics, cricket, hockey, cross-country). *Other:* 100+ take part in local community schemes. 80 have silver Duke of

Edinburgh's Award and 38 have gold. Other activities include computer club, thriving chess club (one of premier chess schools – Marlwood Trophy winners three years in succession), war games, dungeons and dragons, natural history society, fantasy role play, swimming, politics society, CCF, scouts.

Careers In 1990, 85% leavers went on to degree courses; 2% to art/drama/music colleges; 1% to non-degree courses; 4% straight into careers (eg banking, retail management); 8% other. Of those going on to degree courses, 12% went to Oxbridge; 70% to other universities; 18% to poly/colleges. 2% those going on to higher education went to courses in practical art; 46% in humanities/social sciences; 12% in medicine; and 40% in science/engineering.

Uniform School uniform worn throughout.

Houses/prefects Competitive houses. Head boy, prefects, head of house and house prefects, appointed by the Headmaster based on recommendations from housemasters and prefects.

Religion Attendance at religious worship not compulsory.

Social Joint theatrical productions, politic society, venture scouts with Nottingham High School for Girls. French and German exchange visits; Mediterranean educational cruise; trip to Moscow. Pupils allowed to bring own car/bike. Meals formal. School shop. No tobacco/alcohol allowed.

Discipline No corporal punishment. Pupils failing to produce a piece of prep/homework once would receive a warning; those caught smoking cannabis on the premises would be suspended or expelled.

Alumni association is run by J D Powell, 30 Villiers Road, Woodthorpe, Nottingham NG5 4FB.

Former pupils Kenneth Clarke, Lord Richardson, Reg Simpson, Sir Peter Gregson, Sir Douglas Wass.

· Nottingham High (Girls) ·

Nottingham Girls' High School
9 Arboretum Street
Nottingham NG1 4JB
Tel 0602 417663

- Pupils 1079
- Boys None
- Girls 4–18 (Day)
- Upper sixth 117

- Termly fees £908 (Day)
- GSA, GPDST
Enquiries/application to the Headmistress

What it's like
Founded in 1875, single-site in the middle of Nottingham. The original Victorian houses have been modernised and there have been extensive additions to create a well-equipped school. The junior school is housed in new buildings separate from but adjacent to the senior school. Pupils come from a wide range of backgrounds. Religious worship is encouraged. An academic education is given in all areas, including technology. Results are very good and very many girls go on to degree courses, many to Oxbridge. Strong in music, art and drama, and high standards are achieved in games and sports. A substantial commitment to local community schemes and an outstanding record in the Duke of Edinburgh's Award Scheme. Frequent collaboration with Nottingham High (Boys) in drama, debating, joint community service and Christian Union.

School profile
Pupils Total age range 4–18; 1079 day girls. Senior department 11–18, 812 girls. Main entry ages 4, 7, 11 and into sixth.

Transfer from maintained schools: 60% senior intake, plus 58% to sixth.

Entrance Own entrance exam used.

538

Oversubscribed. No special skills or religious requirements. Lessons from peripatetic staff and meals charged extra. 35 assisted places (11+ and 16+) pa. Scholarships up to half fees. Bursaries in cases of financial need.

Staff Headmistress Mrs C Bowering, in post for 7 years. 63 full time staff, 51 part time including visiting musicians. Annual turnover 5–10%.

Academic work GCSE, AS and A-levels. 23 GCSE subjects offered; 12 at AS; 23 at A-level (including GCSE Russian/Greek and A-level general studies). In 1990, 112 pupils in upper fifth, 115 in upper sixth (now 117). *GCSE:* in 1990, 100 upper fifth gained at least grade C in 8+ subjects; 10 in 5–7 subjects. *A-levels:* 58 upper sixth passed in 4+ subjects; 41 in 3; 8 in 2; and 5 in 1 subject. 29% took science A-levels; 37% arts/humanities; 34% both. *Computing facilities:* A networked computer room and departmental computers (BBC, Archimedes).

European Community *Languages:* French offered: to age 14; GCSE; AS-level; A-level. German offered: to age 14; GCSE; AS-level; A-level. Spanish offered: to age 14; GCSE; AS-level; A-level. 25–50% take GCSE in more than 1 EC language. *Exchanges:* Regular exchanges for pupils aged 11–16 to France and Germany. *Other:* European Studies offered to pupils aged 16–18 as part of general studies course.

Senior pupils' non-academic activities *Music:* 100+ learn a musical instrument, 30+ to Grade 6 or above. 40+ in school orchestra, 80+ in school choirs, 10+ in Nottingham Youth Orchestra. Tradition of chamber music and music-theatre productions. *Drama and dance:* Annual school productions, drama festival each year in which most participate; drama clubs at various ages leading to productions; theatre trips. 20+ to Grade 6 in ESB, RADA, Spoken English and Public Speaking exams, several act with theatre groups, 2 or 3 accepted for Drama School or drama degrees, 1 or 2 enter competitions. *Art:* A few take as non-examined

subject, art clubs at varying ages; 40+ take GCSE; 8+ take A-level pa; several take A-level fashion/fabric design. 4 or 5 accepted for art foundation courses. *Sport:* Hockey, netball, athletics, swimming and tennis available plus other recreational activities. 30 represent county (netball, hockey, tennis, squash, badminton, swimming); 3 represent country (archery, sailing, netball). *Other:* 50+ take part in local community schemes. 37 are involved in Duke of Edinburgh's Award scheme at bronze level, 30 at silver and 30+ at gold. Some take part in Conservation Group. Several enter voluntary schemes after leaving school on individual basis. Other activities include computer clubs.

Careers In 1990, 76% leavers went on to degree courses; 4% to art/drama/music colleges; 10% to non-degree courses (eg HND accountancy, nursing, rural estate management); 3% straight into careers (eg retail management, accountancy); 7% other. Of those going on to degree courses, 13% went to Oxbridge, 72% to other universities; 15% to poly/colleges. 5% those going on to higher education went to courses in practical art; 2% in drama/acting; 60% in humanities/social sciences; 13% in medicine; and 20% in science/engineering.

Uniform School uniform worn except in the sixth.

Houses/prefects No competitive houses. No prefects. Head girl and deputies elected by the school. Elected Sixth Form Executive Committee and School Council.

Religion Religious worship encouraged (assembly).

Social Debating and drama activities with Nottingham High (Boys), also joint community service and Christian Union. Annual ski-ing holiday. Exchanges with schools in both France and Germany. Cruises. Pupils allowed to bring own cars to school. Meals self service. No tobacco/alcohol allowed.

Discipline No corporal punishment. Pupils failing to produce homework once might expect possible detention.

O

· *Oakdene* ·

Oakdene School	● Pupils 220	● Termly fees
Wilton Road	● Boys 4–8 only	£1290 (Day)
Beaconsfield	● Girls 4–18	● GSA
Buckinghamshire	(Day)	Enquiries/application to
HP9 2BS	● Upper sixth 17	the Headmistress
Tel 0494 675114		

What it's like

Founded in 1911, it is single-site on the edge of the town; a compact and well-equipped campus in pleasant semi-rural surroundings, including good playing fields. Good modern facilities. A C of E school but ecumenical. A sound general education is provided and results are creditable. A number of sixth formers go on to degree courses. Quite a good range of games and sports. Reasonable range of activities. It has a promising record in the Duke of Edinburgh's Award Scheme. Boarding is being phased out over the next few years.

School profile

Pupils Total age range 4–18 220 day pupils, (218 girls, 2 boys). Senior department 11–18, 188 girls. Main entry ages 4, 8, 11, 12 and into sixth. Very few are children of former pupils. *Transfer from maintained schools:* 50% senior intake.

Entrance Own entrance exam used. Not oversubscribed. No special skills. C of E school; other religions accepted but should be prepared to attend assembly, RE lessons, etc. Purchase of text books included in fees. 16 scholarships/bursaries, £1000–£200 pa.

Parents 10+% in the armed services; 25+% in industry or commerce; 20+% are doctors, lawyers, etc. More than 80% live within 30 miles; 5+% live overseas.

Staff Headmistress Miss A M Tippett, in post for 4 years. 23 full time staff, 12 part time. Annual turnover 10%. Average age 40.

Academic work GCSE and A-levels.

15 GCSE subjects offered; 16 at A-level (no A-level general studies). In 1990, 48 pupils in upper fifth, 17 in upper sixth. *GCSE:* on average, 44% upper fifth gain at least grade C in 8+ subjects; 35% in 5–7; and 19% in 1–4 subjects. *A-levels:* on average, 50% upper sixth pass in 3 subjects; 20% in 2; and 20% in 1 subject. On average, 30% take science A-levels; 40% arts/humanities; 30% both. *Computing facilities:* 12 BBC B's. *Special provision:* Some EFL teaching and specialist teaching available as an extra for pupils with mild dyslexic problems.

European Community *Languages:* French offered: to age 14; GCSE; A-level. German offered: to age 14; GCSE; A-level. Spanish: non-examined subject. 10–25% take GCSE in more than 1 EC language.

Senior pupils' non-academic activities *Music:* 40 learn a musical instru-

540

ment, 12 to Grade 6 or above; 15 in school orchestra; 25 in choir. *Drama and dance:* 45 participate in school productions; 2 take Grade 6 in ESB, RAD, etc. *Art:* 10 take as non-examined subject; 25 take GCSE; 8, A-level; 1 accepted for Art School; 5 belong to photographic club. *Sport:* Lacrosse, netball, athletics, tennis, swimming, rounders, badminton available. 30 take non-compulsory sport; 4 take exams eg gymnastics, swimming. 6 pupils represent county or district (athletics, lacrosse). *Other:* 20 have bronze Duke of Edinburgh's Award, 10 have silver.

Careers In 1990, 57% upper sixth leavers went on to degree courses; 29% to non-degree courses (eg HND, re-taking A-levels); 14% straight into careers (eg civil service). Of those going on to degree courses, 25% went to universities; 75% to poly/colleges. 80% those going on to higher education went to courses in humanities/social sciences; and 20% in science/engineering.

Uniform School uniform worn except sixth.

Houses/prefects Competitive houses. Head girl and head of house – appointed by the Head after consultation. School Council.

Religion Weekly boarders chapel. Assembly. Boarders evening service on Sunday.

Social Dances/discos with other local schools from time to time. Organised ski trips regularly; others occasionally. Pupils allowed to bring own car/bike to school. Meals cafeteria system. No tobacco allowed; under some circumstances sixth form may have some alcohol in a staff-controlled situation.

Discipline No corporal punishment. Pupils failing to produce homework once might expect a verbal warning and be required to hand in work the next day. The parents of a pupil found in possession of or smoking cannabis on school premises would be asked to remove her from the school.

Alumni association run by Mrs B Douglas, c/o the School.

· *Oakham* ·

Oakham School
Chapel Close
Oakham, Rutland
Leicestershire
LE15 6DT
Tel 0572 755238
Fax 0572 755786

- Pupils 990
- Boys 11–18
  (Day/Board)
- Girls 11–18
  (Day/Board)
- Upper sixth 150

- Termly fees
  £1600 (Day)
  £2895 (Board)
- HMC
  Enquiries/application to
  the Registrar

What it's like

Founded in 1584 by Robert Johnson, Archdeacon of Leicester, it remained, until about 1960, a small and comparatively local boys' school. In the next 10 years the number of boys almost doubled and then co-education was introduced. To meet this rapid expansion the amenities were transformed and a massive building programme undertaken. There was further expansion after 1970 and it is now one of the best-equipped schools in England. It has two theatres, one of which is in the original school building. The houses are scattered in the very attractive, mellow, small country town of Oakham and extend into the countryside. There are fine gardens and playing fields. There is, inevitably, a close 'town and gown' relationship. The practice of Christianity is an essential part of the life of the community and there are regular chapel services. A happy friendly school in which a lot of attention is given to the individual. The large staff allows a staff:pupil ratio of 1:9. Academic standards are very high and results consistently good. Each year very many pupils go on to degree courses (many to Oxbridge). French, German, Italian and Spanish are offered at GCSE (no Italian at A-level) and an exceptionally high proportion of pupils take GCSE in more than one European language. It is very strong indeed in music and drama (each year there is a spring drama festival). There is a very high standard in sports and games (a large number of county and national representatives in hockey, rugby, cricket, squash and shooting). Numerous extra-curricular activities cater for most interests. There is a large and flourishing CCF for boys and girls. An exploration society has sent expeditions to Iceland, the Sahara and Papua New Guinea. A substantial commitment to local community services and a phenomenal record in the Duke of Edinburgh's Award Scheme.

School profile

Pupils Age range 11–18; 990 pupils, 419 day (228 boys, 191 girls), 571 boarding (270 boys, 301 girls). Main entry ages 11, 13 and into sixth. Approx 7% are children of former pupils. *Transfer from maintained schools:* 5% main intake, plus 5% to sixth.

Entrance Common entrance and own exam used. Oversubscribed. Skills in music and art welcomed; no particular religious requirements. Parents not expected to buy text books; maximum extras, £150 per term. Assisted places available. 35 scholarships/bursaries pa, full fees to one-third tuition.

Parents 30+% live within 30 miles; 10+% live overseas.

Staff Head Graham Smallbone, in post for 6 years. 108 full time staff, 30 part time. Annual turnover 3%. Average age 35.

Academic work GCSE and A-levels. 28 subjects offered (including Russian, theatre studies, textiles; no A-level general studies). Average number of pupils in upper fifth 140; 150 in upper sixth. *GCSE:* on average, 124 upper fifth gain at least grade C in 8+ subjects; 9 in 5–7; and 8 in 1–4 subjects. *A-levels:* 6 upper sixth pass in 4+ subjects; 107 in 3; 26 in 2; and 11 in 1 subject. On average, 40 take science A-levels; 46 arts/humanities; 45 both. *Computing facilities:* Comprehensive networked and stand alone computers in all departments. *Special provision:* Some specialised teaching.

European Community *Languages:* French offered: to age 14; GCSE; AS-level; A-level. German offered: to age 14; GCSE; A-level. Italian offered: to GCSE. Spanish offered: to age 14; GCSE; A-

level. Over 75% take GCSE in more than 1 EC language. *Exchanges:* Regular exchanges for pupils aged 14–18 to Germany; planned for France and Spain. *Other:* French for business studies (post GCSE). Frequent cultural visits to France and Spain. Over 20 German nationals studying in school.

Senior pupils' non-academic activities *Music:* 100 learn a musical instrument, 60 to Grade 6 or above; 40 in school orchestra; 30, choir; 12, pop group; 25, concert band; 8, jazz band; 3 National Youth Orchestra. *Drama and dance:* 80 in school productions. 1 accepted for Drama/Dance School; 3 work in theatre. *Art and Design:* 20 take as non-examined subject; 30 GCSE; 20 A-level. 8 accepted for Art School. 12 belong to eg photographic club. *Sport:* Rugby, cricket, tennis, netball, athletics, swimming, shooting, fencing, water polo, fives, table tennis, squash, basketball, soccer available. 150 take non-compulsory sport (at least 1 game option compulsory). 20 pupils represent county/country (hockey, rugby, cricket, squash, shooting). *Other:* 80 have bronze Duke of Edinburgh's Award, 90 have silver and 130 gold. Many other activities include computer club, chess, exploration, observing, debating.

Careers In 1990, 88% leavers went on to degree courses; 4% to art/drama/music colleges; 4% to non-degree courses; 4% straight into careers. Of those going on to degree courses, 15% went to Oxbridge, 53% to other universities; 32% to poly/colleges. 6% those going on to higher education went to courses in practical art; 2% in drama/

acting; 2% in music; 43% in humanities/ social sciences; 6% in medicine; and 40% in science/engineering.

Uniform School uniform worn except in upper sixth.

Houses/prefects Competitive houses. Prefects, head boy and girl, head of house and house prefects – elected. School Council.

Religion Regular chapel services.

Social Debating in local and national competitions. Regular German school exchange. Pupils allowed to bring own bike to school. Meals self service. School shop. No tobacco allowed; supervised licensed bar for upper sixth.

Discipline No corporal punishment. Pupils failing to produce homework once might expect detention; those caught smoking cannabis on the premises will be expelled.

Boarding 90% share a study bedroom with 1 or 2, 10% are in dormitories of 3. 7 single sex houses, of approximately 70, divided by age. Resident qualified nurse. 2 central dining rooms. Pupils can provide and cook own snacks. 1 termly exeat, 4–7 days. Visits to local town allowed in free time.

Alumni association run by Rev G Treanor, c/o the school.

Former pupils Thomas Merton (religious philosopher); A P F Chapman (cricketer); R Jacobs (rugby); Matthew Manning (psychic).

· Old Palace ·

Old Palace School
Old Palace Road
Croydon
Surrey CR0 1AX
Tel 081-688 2027

- Pupils 750
- Boys None
- Girls 7–18
- (Day)
- Upper sixth 70

- Termly fees
  £933 (Day)
  Enquiries/application to
  the Headmistress

What it's like

Founded in 1887 by the Sisters of the Church, an Anglican community, to provide for girls a similar education to that provided for boys by the then Middle Whitgift School. The Old Palace was a former residence of the Archbishops of Canterbury and some of the buildings are exceptionally handsome and dignified. They include the Chapel, the Great Hall and the Library which date from the 15th century. These historic buildings are complemented by modern developments, including accommodation for computing, technology, textiles design and a sixth-form suite, which provide good facilities. The school's aim is to provide a sound general education based on a Christian way of life. The scheme of work has been adapted to cover the National Curriculum in the core subjects; technology is introduced early and continued to the fourth year of the senior school. Academic standards are high and the majority of girls go on to degree courses, including a number each year to Oxbridge. French, German and Spanish are offered to A-level and an exceptionally high proportion of girls takes GCSE in more than one European language. There are regular exchanges with France, Germany and Spain. The senior school is combined with the preparatory school on the same site. There is some drama and art and lively musical activity (the choir has recently given concerts in major venues such as St John's Smith Square). There is a standard range of sports and games (the netball and tennis teams have achieved some local success), plus a variety of clubs and societies for extra-curricular activities.

School profile

Pupils Total age range 7–18; 750 day girls. Senior department 11–18, 600 girls. Main entry ages, 11 and into sixth. Own prep school. *Transfer from maintained schools:* 60% main intake, 12% to sixth.

Entrance Own entrance exam used. Oversubscribed. No special skills or religious requirements. Parents not expected to buy text books. 35 assisted places pa; variable number of scholarships and bursaries, full fees to £100.

Parents 15+% doctors, lawyers; 15+% in industry/commerce.

Staff Headmistress Miss K L Hilton, in post for 14 years. 51 full time staff, 10 part time. Annual turnover 5–10%. Average age 35–40.

Academic work GCSE and A-levels. 26 subjects offered (including A-level general studies). In 1990, 86 pupils in upper fifth, 70 in upper sixth. *GCSE:* in 1990, 84 upper fifth gained at least grade C in 8+ subjects; 7 in 5–7; and 1 in 1–4 subjects. *A-levels:* 52 upper sixth pupils passed in 4+ subjects; 19 in 3; 7 in 2 and 3 in 1 subject. 40% took science A-levels; 40% arts/humanities; 20% both. *Computing facilities:* Computers in all science laboratories, and well-equipped computer room.

European Community *Languages:* French offered: to age 14; GCSE; AS-level; A-level. German: to age 14; GCSE; AS-level; A-level. Spanish: to age 14; GCSE; AS-level; A-level. Over 75% take GCSE in more than 1 EC language.

Exchanges: Regular exchanges for pupils aged 11–16 to France, Germany and Spain. *Other:* European studies offered to pupils aged 11–14.

Senior pupils' non-academic activities *Music:* 400 learn a musical instrument; 110 in 2 school orchestras, 220 in 2 choirs. 3 accepted for Music School. *Art:* 3 accepted for Art School. *Sport:* Netball, swimming, tennis, cross-country, squash, badminton available. *Other:* 25 have bronze Duke of Edinburgh's Award.

Careers In 1990, 89% leavers went on to degree courses; 11% straight into careers. Of those going on to degree courses, 20% went to Oxbridge; 68% to other universities; 12% to poly/colleges. 3% those going on to higher education went to courses in music; 11% in humanities/social sciences; 4% in medicine; 33% in science/engineering and 38% in arts.

Uniform School uniform worn except in sixth.

Houses/prefects Competitive houses. Head girl, prefects, head of house and house prefects, elected by the school.

Religion Attendance at religious worship compulsory.

Social Young Enterprise; debates with local schools. Organised trips to Russia, Greece, Italy, France, Spain, Germany and Switzerland. Pupils may bring own bike to school. School shop. No tobacco or alcohol allowed.

Discipline No corporal punishment.

· *Old Swinford Hospital* ·

Old Swinford Hospital	• Pupils 550	• Termly fees
Stourbridge	• Boys 11–18	Nil (Day)
West Midlands	(Day/Board)	£825 (Board/
DY8 1QX	• Girls None	Weekly)
Tel 0384 370025	• Upper sixth 74	• SHMIS
		Enquiries/application to
		the Admissions'
		Secretary

What it's like

Founded in 1667 by Thomas Foley, a local industrialist, descendants of Foley are actively involved with the school. Old Swinford is still sometimes known locally as the Bluecoat School (though the traditional uniform was abandoned in 1928). It has a fine site on the edge of Stourbridge on a spacious campus with excellent playing fields: handsome and extremely well-equipped and comfortable buildings. The boarding accommodation is particularly good and all sixth formers have their own study/bedrooms. There has been rapid development over the last 10 years and in April 1990, a fourth new boarding house, and a new technology centre were completed. The school has grant maintained status and parents pay nothing for education costs; the boarding fees are low. It is a very energetic, well-run school with a civilised and purposeful atmosphere. Religious worship and instruction is in the Anglican tradition. The staff:pupil ratio is about 1:13. Academic standards are high and results good; many boys go on to degree courses each year. Tremendously strong in music, drama and art. A wide range of sports and games is provided and an unusually large number of clubs and societies cater for most conceivable needs. The CCF contingent is very strong (all boys belong to it from their third to their fifth year). There is also much emphasis on adventure training of various kinds. The school has a phenomenal record in the Duke of Edinburgh's Award Scheme.

School profile

Pupils Age range 11–18; 550 boys (154 day, 390 boarding). Main entry ages 11, 13 and into sixth. *Transfer from maintained schools:* 15% main intakes, plus 40% to sixth.

Entrance Boarders chosen after day's interview at school; prep school candidates take common entrance. Always oversubscribed. Skills in music, drama and sport an advantage. No religious requirements. Parents not expected to buy text books, no other extras. 12 scholarships pa, £1880–£120; also means tested bursaries up to two-thirds boarding fee.

Parents 16+% in the armed services.

Staff Headmaster C F R Potter, in post for 12 years. 42 full time staff, 15 part time plus artist in residence, musician in residence, games coaches, etc. Annual turnover 5%. Average age approx 35.

Academic work GCSE and A-levels. 23 subjects offered (including GCSE & A-level archaeology and A-level general studies). In 1990, 79 pupils in fifth, 74 in upper sixth. *GCSE:* in 1990, 49 fifth gained at least grade C in 8+ subjects; 19 in 5–7; and 10 in 1–4 subjects. *A-levels:* 45 upper sixth passed in 4+ subjects; 17 in 3; 9 in 2; and 2 in 1 subject. 20% took science A-levels; 40% arts/humanities; 40% both. *Computing facilities:* ST research level 3 Econet linking BBC model B Master 128 and Archimedes A3000 micro-computer, over $4^1/_2$km in length and with 100+ stations; most sixth form study bedrooms on line. *Special provision:*

Some special needs support within and outside the classroom.

European Community *Languages:* French offered: to age 14; GCSE; A-level. German offered: age 13–14; GCSE; A-level. Spanish non-examined subject. 10–25% take GCSE in more than 1 EC language. All sixth form take introductory Spanish course.

Senior pupils' non-academic activities *Music:* At least 100 pupils learn a musical instrument. School orchestra, choir, string ensemble, brass band/ensemble, wind band/ensemble. *Drama:* Large numbers participate in school productions. *Art:* Some pupils given art scholarships. *Sport:* Rugby, soccer, cricket, hockey, football, shooting, badminton, table tennis, cross-country, squash, golf, tennis, athletics, sailing, judo, riding, swimming, fencing, basketball, snooker available. *Other:* 100+ take gold Duke of Edinburgh's Award. Other activities include CCF, range of 35 activities including computer club, war games, industrial society.

Careers In 1990, 75% leavers went on to degree courses; $1^1/_2$% to art/drama/music colleges; 10% to non-degree courses (eg sports studies); 9% straight into careers (eg management training, insurance); $4^1/_2$% other. Of those going on to degree courses, 6% went to Oxbridge, 75% to other universities; 19% to poly/colleges. 5% those going on to higher education went to courses in practical art; 2% in music; 37% in humanities/social sciences; 10% in medicine; and 46% in science/engineering.

Uniform School uniform worn, modified in sixth.

Houses/prefects Competitive houses. Prefects, head boy, head of house and house prefects – appointed by Headmaster or housemaster.

Religion All boys go to assemblies. All boarders attend Sunday service.

Social Girls take part in drama productions. Organised trips abroad include adventure week. Sixth form day boys allowed to bring car; over 14's, bikes. Meals self service. School shop. No tobacco on premises. Sixth form club licensed bar for 17+ boys with permission.

Discipline No corporal punishment. Pupils failing to produce homework once would expect a warning by subject teacher, and report to personal tutor; anyone caught being involved with drugs, etc on the premises could expect expulsion, even for first offence, regardless of previous record in school.

Boarding All sixth form have own study bedroom; others are in dormitories of 6+. Houses, of 60–70 (11 year olds separately). Resident qualified nurse; doctor visits. Central dining room. Pupils can provide and cook snacks within boarding houses to a limited extent (some have microwave cookers.) Number and length of exeats varies. Visits to local town allowed with restrictions.

· *Oratory* ·

The Oratory School	● Pupils 370	● Termly fees
Woodcote	Boys 11–18	£2012 (Day)
Reading	(Day/Board)	£2877 (Board)
Berkshire RG8 0PJ	● Girls None	● HMC
Tel 0491 680207	● Upper sixth 75	Enquiries/application to the Headmaster

What it's like

Founded in 1859 to meet the educational needs of the Catholic laity. The Venerable John Henry Newman himself was very much responsible for establishing the school and his views and beliefs about education are still its driving force. It was originally founded in Birmingham, moved to Caversham after the First World War and settled at Woodcote during the Second World War. It has a very agreeable rural site with spacious grounds and purpose-built accommodation. Facilities are excellent. Religious education is an important part of the curriculum. Sunday mass and daily house prayers are compulsory. Very good teaching is provided and academic standards are high. Virtually all proceed to degree courses each year, many to Oxbridge. European links are exceptionally strong. The Oratory runs a property in Normandy and has links with a Jesuit College in Paris. French, German, Italian, Portuguese and Spanish are all offered at GCSE and A-level. Many boys take more than one European language at GCSE. It is outstandingly strong in music and there is a considerable commitment to drama and art. A big range of games and sports is available (a lot of representatives at county level) and the newly constructed sports centre includes a real tennis court, the first to be built in Great Britain for eighty years. Also a wide variety of extra-curricular activities and a strong CCF. A promising record in the Duke of Edinburgh's Award Scheme.

School profile

Pupils Age range 11–18; 370 boys, 80 day, 290 boarding. Senior department 13–18, 332 boys. Main entry ages 11, 13 and into sixth. Approx 7% are children of former pupils. Own prep school provides more than 20% of intake. *Transfer from maintained schools:* 3% main intakes, plus 1% to sixth.

Entrance Common entrance exam and informal tests used. Oversubscribed. No special skills required; overwhelming majority of boarders are Roman Catholic, some day boys not. Parents expected to pay a termly flat rate charge for books. Scholarships/bursaries available.

Parents 15+% in the armed services, 15+% are doctors, lawyers, etc; remainder are overwhelmingly professional, commercial and industrial. 10+% live within 30 miles; up to 10% live overseas.

Staff Headmaster M Lynn, in post for 3 years. 37 full time staff, 17 part time. Annual turnover under 5%. Average age 37.

Academic work GCSE and A-levels. 22 subjects offered (including GCSE photography; English language; no A-level general studies). In 1991, 70 pupils in upper fifth, 75 in upper sixth. *GCSE:* in 1990, 93% upper fifth gained at least grade C in 8+ subjects; 7% in 5–7 subjects. *A-levels:* 2% upper sixth passed in 4+ subjects; 95% in 3; 3% in 2 subjects. 33% took science A-levels; 47% arts/humanities; 20% both. *Computing facilities:* Computer centre (Nimbus), two computer study rooms. *Special provision:* Specialist tuition for mildly dyslexic children only.

European Community *Languages:* French offered: to age 14; GCSE; A-level. German offered: to GCSE; A-level. Italian: to GCSE; A-level. Portuguese: to GCSE; A-level. Spanish offered: to GCSE; A-level. 50–75% take GCSE in more than 1 EC language. *Exchanges:* Regular exchanges for pupils aged 14–18 to France and Spain. *Other:* Strong links with a Jesuit college in Paris. School has range of European pupils, full-time and for termly stays. Property in Normandy, used for language visits, lay pupils, history study groups, geography field work and base for musical and sporting pursuits.

Senior pupils' non-academic activities *Music:* 200 learn a musical instrument, 40 to Grade 6 or above, 1 accepted for Music School; 3 take music degrees (Oxford); 50 in 2 school orchestras, 40 in choir, 15 in string orchestra, 16 in chamber music groups; 2 go on to London choirs (eg RPO); 40 take music courses in holidays. *Drama and dance:* 50 in school productions. 7 took Grade 8 RAD in recent years. 1 accepted for Drama School. *Art:* 15 take as non-examined subject; 75 take GCSE; 26 A-level; 10 take other exams. 4–5 accepted for Art School; 5–6 for architecture; 2–3 for university art degree. 20 belong to school arts society. *Sport:* Rugby, cricket, soccer, rowing, lawn tennis, hockey, athletics, cross-country running, real tennis, squash, swimming, sailing, canoeing, table tennis, badminton, basketball, windsurfing, golf available. 20 take non-compulsory sport. 75 take exams eg gymnastics, swimming, life-saving. 10 pupils represent county (rugby, hockey, table tennis, squash, golf) and country (judo, shooting). *Other:* 40 have bronze Duke of Edinburgh's Award, 2 have silver (recently reintroduced). Other activities include a computer club, chess, judo, music, debating, cultural, law, science, arts, current affairs societies, thriving car mechanics club.

Careers In 1990, 94% leavers went on to degree courses; 2% to art/drama/ music colleges; 2% to non-degree courses; 2% straight into careers. Of those going on to degree courses, 11% went to Oxbridge, 79% to other universities; 10% to poly/colleges. 2% those going on to higher education went to courses in practical art; 1% in drama/ acting; 2% in music; 55% in humanities/ social sciences; 3% in medicine; and 37% in science/engineering.

Uniform School uniform worn, modified in the sixth.

Houses/prefects Competitive houses. Prefects, school captain, house captains and house prefects – appointed by the Headmaster with housemasters. Community orderlies only in second year.

Religion Sunday mass and twice termly house mass compulsory; weekday masses optional; daily house prayers compulsory.

Social Debates, dances, other social/ educational ventures with other local schools. Organised ski trips, sailing trips, some exchanges – usually to Spain and France. Pupils allowed to bring own bike to school. Meals self service. School tuck shop and paperback bookshop. Smoking is not permitted. Boys over 18 may visit local inns; some social functions and informal occasions where boys between 16 and 18 may be allowed alcohol under staff supervision.

Discipline Pupils failing to produce homework once might expect additional work to be set; those caught smoking cannabis on the premises or off would be asked to leave. The essential approach of the school is encapsulated in the words of Newman, its founder; 'The young for the most part cannot be driven, but on the other hand are open to persuasion and the influence of kindness and personal attachment. They are to be kept straight by indirect contrivances rather than by authoritative enactments.'

Boarding 25% have own study bedroom, 35% share double studies; 20% share with 2–4 others; 20% are in dormitories of 6+, 1 junior house, 4 senior approximately 60 boarders (and 15 day). 2 resident qualified nurses, 1 non-resident; doctor lives very close. Central dining room. Pupils can provide and cook own food. Exeats to suit parental convenience. Occasional visits to the local town allowed for sixth form for specified reasons.

Former pupils Sir James Comyn (High Court judge); Sir Michael Levey (National Gallery); Mgr V F J Morgan (Vicar General of Royal Navy); J J Hayes MP; Michael Berkeley (composer); Christopher Hurford (Australian government minister); Joseph Connolly (Times columnist); Nicholas Bicat (composer); Igor Judge QC; Paul Purnell QC; Nicholas Purnell QC; E Leigh MP.

· *Oswestry* ·

Oswestry School
Oswestry
Shropshire
SY11 2TL
Tel 0691 655711

- Pupils 484
- Boys 8–18
  (Day/Board)
- Girls 8–18
  (Day/Board)
- Upper sixth 44

- Termli fees
  £1320 (Day)
  £2225 (Board)
- SHMIS
  Enquiries/application to
  the Headmaster

What it's like

Founded in 1407 and one of the oldest continuous foundations in England. The agreeable, well-designed, red-brick buildings occupy pleasant grounds and playing fields on the edge of the market town of Oswestry and overlooking the Shropshire Plain. The junior school and pre-prep are combined nearby. Facilities are very good. A good all-round education is provided in a supportive family atmosphere and every effort is made to accommodate families' needs. Academic standards and results are good and many leavers go on to degree courses each year. Lively music, drama and art. Sport and games are encouraged and high standards are attained (a lot of county representatives). A very large number of clubs and societies cater for every need. The CCF is vigorous and the school has an impressive record in the Duke of Edinburgh's Award Scheme.

School profile

Pupils Total age range 8–18; 484 pupils, 299 day (173 boys, 126 girls), 185 boarding (117 boys, 68 girls). Senior department 13–18, 306 pupils (200 boys, 106 girls). Main entry ages 11, 13 and into sixth. *Transfer from maintained schools:* 50% senior intakes, plus 80% to sixth.

Entrance Common entrance and own exam used. Places generally available. No religious requirements. Parents expected to buy text books. 10 scholarships/bursaries available (including sport and music), £2300–£500.

Parents 15+% in the armed services. 60+% live within 30 miles; 10+% live overseas.

Staff Headmaster Ian G Templeton, in post for 6 years. 31 full time staff, 4 part time. Annual turnover 5%. Average age 40.

Academic work GCSE, AS and A-levels. 15 subjects offered (including sports studies, AS-level philosophy). In 1990, 69 pupils in upper fifth, 44 in upper sixth. *GCSE:* in 1990, 32 upper fifth gained at least grade C in 8+ subjects; 16 in 5–7; and 17 in 1–4 subjects. *A-levels:* 23

upper sixth passed in 3 subjects; 10 in 2; and 8 in 1 subject. 30% took science A-levels; 50% arts/humanities; 20% both. *Computing facilities:* Mainly Amstrad/BBC in computer room, others in individual departments. *Special provision:* EFL teaching, help for dyslexic pupils on 'withdrawal from classes' basis usually three times a week.

European Community *Languages:* French offered: to age 14; GCSE; AS-level; A-level. German offered: to GCSE; AS-level; A-level. Spanish offered: to age 14; GCSE; AS-level; A-level. 25–50% take GCSE in more than 1 EC language. *Exchanges:* Regular exchanges for pupils aged 16–18 to France and Germany. *Other:* Attended Europe post 1992 seminar in Paris. German and Spanish pupils in school. Sir Christopher Prout MEP was 1991 guest speaker.

Senior pupils' non-academic activities *Music:* 6 learn a musical instrument to Grade 6 or above. 1 accepted for Music School. 5 play in pop group beyond school. 30 in school orchestras, 70 in choirs, 5 in pop group, 2 in county orchestra. *Drama and dance:* Most pupils in school productions. *Art:* 30 take GCSE; 6, A-level. 4 accepted for Art School, 1 for architecture, 1 for interior design. 10 belong to photographic club. *Sport:* Boys: rugby, soccer, cricket. Girls: hockey, netball. Both: athletics, cross-country, swimming, badminton, tennis, squash available. 90 take non-compulsory sport; 20 take exams eg gymnastics, swimming. 25 represent county/country (cricket, swimming, athletics, hockey/football). *Other:* 6 have bronze Duke of Edinburgh's Award, 24 have silver and 16 gold. Other activities include a computer club, chess club, angling.

Careers In 1990, 55% leavers went on to degree courses; 10% to art/drama/music colleges; 25% to non-degree courses (eg agriculture, drama, catering); 10% straight into careers (eg banking, retailing). Of those going on to degree courses, 4% went to Oxbridge, 50% to other universities; 46% to poly/colleges. 15% those going on to higher education went to courses in practical art; 6% in drama/acting; 3% in music; 45% in humanities/social sciences; 9% in medicine; and 22% in science/engineering.

Uniform School uniform worn except in the sixth.

Houses/prefects Competitive houses. Prefects, head boy and girl, head of house and house prefects – appointed after consultation.

Religion Compulsory chapel. Boarders must attend unless attending own (eg Roman Catholic) church.

Social Organised exchanges in France, Germany, trips to Russia, France, Spain, Italy, etc. Pupils allowed to bring own bike to school. Meals self service. School shop. No tobacco allowed; beer allowed in sixth form club supervised by staff.

Discipline No corporal punishment. Pupils failing to produce homework once might expect a reminder then work detention for persistent failure. Should anyone be caught with drugs, they would be expelled (has never arisen).

Boarding 5% have own study bedroom, 50% share (1 or 2); 45% in dormitories of 5–8. Single sex houses, of approximately 50, same as competitive houses. Resident qualified medical staff. Central dining room. Pupils can provide and cook own snacks. 3 or 4 overnight exeats each term. Visits to local town allowed.

Alumni association run by J F Tilley, Herschell House, Whittington, Oswestry, Shropshire SY11 4DB.

· *Oundle* ·

The School
Oundle
Peterborough PE8 4EN
Tel 0832 273536

- Pupils 840
- Boys 11–18 (Board)
- Girls 13–18 (Board)
- Upper sixth 163

- Termly fees
  £3275 (Board)
- HMC
Enquiries/application to
the Headmaster

What it's like

It originated from the bequest of Sir William Laxton, a native of Oundle, to the Grocers' Company in 1556, and by this he re-endowed a grammar school already in existence in 1485. In 1876 the Grocers' Company divided the school, founding Oundle (and leaving the grammar school as Laxton School in close association): Oundle's 17th, 18th and 19th-century buildings (plus the many additions made in the 20th century) are scattered through the small and very agreeable township. Thus, the school is an integral part of the town, and vice versa, and there is a close 'town and gown' relationship. It is extremely well equipped with all that a school needs including a fine 1914–18 memorial chapel. There are 14 houses which are all independent units. Religious instruction accords with the teaching of the Church of England and there is some emphasis on regular worship. A very large staff allows a staff:pupil ratio of 1:8. The teaching is well known to be good and academic standards are high. Results are consistently impressive and each year large numbers of leavers go on to university (including to Oxbridge) and other places of higher education. There is an extremely strong music department and many of the boys are involved in numerous musical activities in the school and beyond it. There is also an excellent and very active art department. Large numbers of pupils are also engaged in dramatic activities, many of which are presented in the Stahl Theatre. Professional companies often visit to give performances. Oundle has long had a reputation for high achievements in sports and games and a wide variety of clubs and societies caters for virtually every conceivable need. The CCF is one of the largest contingents in the country and it has an ambitious and enterprising programme each year. There is also emphasis on outdoor pursuits and the school runs a large adventure training section whose members have made expeditions to Ecuador, Afghanistan, Ladakh, China, Pakistan and Belize (1989). Over 100 boys and girls are engaged in local community services.

School profile

Pupils Age range 11–18; 840 boarding pupils, 720 boys, 120 girls. Main entry ages 11 and 13 (boys, and girls from 1990); small number into sixth. *Transfer from maintained schools:* 10% main intake.

Entrance Common entrance and own exam used. Some scholarships (including art and music).

Staff Headmaster D B McMurray, in post for 6 years.

Academic work GCSE and A-levels; (no A-level general studies offered). In 1990, 159 pupils in upper fifth, 163 in upper sixth. *GCSE:* in 1990, 110 upper fifth gained at least grade C in 8+ subjects; 42 in 5–7; and 7 in 4 subjects. *A-levels:* 4 upper sixth passed in 4+ subjects; 146 in 3; 9 in 2; and 4 in 1 subject. 39% took science A-levels; 51% arts/humanities; 10% both. *Computing facilities:* Extensive: 4 room block with 100 machines. An IT room, CAD and CAM. Computers in all departments. *Special provision:* Extra English. Dyslexic tuition by qualified person (very limited number).

Exchanges with Poland, Hungary and Russia, apart from EC.

European Community *Languages:* French offered: to age 14; GCSE; A-level. German offered: to GCSE; A-level. Spanish offered: to GCSE; A-level. 25–50% take GCSE in more than 1 EC language. *Exchanges:* Regular exchanges for pupils aged 14–18 to France, Germany and Spain. *Other:* 'Europe Day' for 14 year olds.

Careers In 1990, 90% leavers went on to degree courses; 1% to art/drama/music colleges; 1% to non-degree courses (eg HND business studies); 3% straight into careers (eg armed services); 5% other. Of those going on to degree courses, 17% went to Oxbridge; 73% to other universities; 10% to poly/colleges. 1% those going on to higher education went to courses in practical art; 1% in music; 51% in humanities/social sciences; 6% in medicine; and 41% in science/engineering.

· *Our Lady's (Abingdon)* ·

Our Lady's Convent
Senior School
Radley Road
Abingdon
Oxfordshire OX14 3PS
Tel 0235 524658

- Pupils 370
- Boys None
- Girls 11–18
  (Day/Board/Weekly)
- Upper sixth 33

- Termly fees
  £834 (Day)
  £1884 (Board)
  £1879 (Weekly)
- ISAI
  Enquiries/application to
  the Headmistress

What it's like

Founded in 1860 and administered by the Sisters of Mercy. It is situated in the market town on a single site with playing fields opposite. Pleasant buildings and good modern facilities. A new building programme in the 1970s provided extensive additions. There is a junior school. It has a reputation for a friendly and caring approach and aims to provide a thorough education by a combination of traditional and modern methods, in the atmosphere of a Catholic community and according to Christian principles. All boarders are Roman Catholics but day girls may be of other Christian denominations. Standards of teaching are good and so are results. Each year some girls go on to degree courses. French, German, Italian and Spanish are offered at A-level. Very strong in music; a third of the school is involved. Some drama and art. A wide range of sports and games and plentiful activities. Some commitment to local community schemes and an impressive record in the Duke of Edinburgh's Award Scheme.

School profile

Pupils Age range 11–18; 370 girls, 323 day, 47 boarding. Main entry ages 11 and into sixth. Approx 2% are children of former pupils. *Transfer from maintained schools:* 30% main intake, plus 2% to sixth.

Entrance Own entrance exam used. No special skills required. Boarders must be Roman Catholic; other Christian denominations for day girls. Parents not expected to buy text books; no extras. Some scholarships.

Parents 15+% in the armed services; 15+% in industry or commerce. More than 60% live within 30 miles; up to 10% live overseas.

Staff Head Sister Monica Sheehy, in post for 10 years. 23 full time staff, 16 part time. Annual turnover 1%. Average age mid-40s.

Academic work GCSE and A-levels (no A-level general studies). In 1990, 58 pupils in upper fifth, 29 in upper sixth (now 33). *GCSE:* in 1990, 30 upper fifth gained at least grade C in 8+ subjects; 15 in 5–7; and 13 in 1–4 subjects. *A-levels:* 1 upper sixth passed in 4+ subjects; 13 in 3; 12 in 2; and 3 in 1 subject. 20% took science A-levels; 60% arts/humanities; 20% both. *Computing facilities:* Fully-equipped computer room with 12 BBC computers.

European Community *Languages:* French offered: to age 14; GCSE; AS-level; A-level. German offered: to GCSE; AS-level; A-level. Italian offered: to A-level if requested. Spanish offered: to GCSE; AS-level; A-level. 10–25% take GCSE in more than 1 EC language. *Exchanges:* Regular exchanges for pupils aged 14–16 to France and Germany.

Senior pupils' non-academic activities *Music:* 33% of pupils learn a musical instrument; school orchestra and 2 choirs. *Art:* 10 take GCSE; 11 A-level; 3 accepted for Art School. *Sport:* Hockey, badminton, squash, tennis, netball, gymnastics, keep fit, weight lifting, SCUBA

552

(sixth form only), swimming, modern dance available. Almost all take non-compulsory sport. At least 2 represent county (badminton, hockey, squash). *Other:* 25 take part in local community schemes. 60+ have bronze Duke of Edinburgh's Award, 5 have silver and 1 has gold. Other activities include computer, French, ceramics, needlework, drama, debating, jewellery and art clubs.

Careers In 1990, 33% upper sixth leavers went on to degree courses; 10% to art/drama/music colleges; 6% to non-degree courses (eg French courses in France); 2% straight into careers (eg retail management); 48% other. Of those going on to degree courses, 80% went to universities; 20% to poly/colleges. 24% those going on to higher education went to courses in practical art; 51% in humanities/social sciences; 1% in medicine; and 24% in science/engineering.

Uniform School uniform worn, modified in the sixth.

Houses/prefects Competitive houses. Prefects, head girl and head boarding prefect – appointed by Head following suggestions by staff and sixth form. School Council.

Religion Sunday mass for boarders. All pupils join in school services, held once or twice a term, and assembly daily.

Social Lectures, dances, SCUBA, inter-sixth form society with other local schools (sixth form social committee). French exchange scheme organised through Dragons International and a German exchange with a school in Hanover. Pupils allowed to bring own car/bike/motorbike to school (but no parking provided). Meals formal. School shop. No tobacco/alcohol allowed.

Discipline No corporal punishment. Pupils failing to produce homework once might expect to be kept in to make it up at break, lunch time or after school; those caught smoking cannabis on the premises could expect expulsion.

Boarding Upper sixth only have own study bedroom; fourth to lower sixth share; juniors in dormitories of 6+. Houses, of 20+, are divided into class groups. Qualified nurse. Central dining room. Older pupils can provide and cook own food. Exeats any weekend. Visits to the local town and Oxford allowed. Educational/pleasure trips organised regularly.

· *Our Lady's (Loughborough)* ·

Our Lady's Convent
School
Burton Street
Loughborough
Leicestershire
LE11 2DT
Tel 0509 263901

- Pupils 630
- Boys 3–5 only (Day)
- Girls 3–18 (Day)
- Upper sixth 26

- Termly fees £780 (Day)
Enquiries/application to the Headmistress

What it's like

Established in 1845 by the Sisters of Providence – the Rosminians. It has a pleasant urban site with four independent buildings for four departments: Montessori, infant, junior and senior. The staff is both religious and secular and there is an excellent range of facilities. A Roman Catholic school, it teaches religious education in all departments. A cheerful and friendly atmosphere prevails. The girls are given as much liberty as is compatible with good discipline. A strong sense of responsibility is inculcated. It provides a sound general education. Almost all sixth formers go on to degree courses. Quite a good range of sport, games and activities. A substantial commitment to local community schemes and the Duke of Edinburgh's Award Scheme.

School profile

Pupils Total age range 3–18; 630 day pupils (7 boys, 623 girls). Senior department 11–18, 393 girls. Main entry ages 3 (boys and girls), 5, 7, 11 and into sixth (girls). Approx 10% are children of former pupils. *Transfer from maintained schools:* 90% intake at 11.

Entrance Own entrance exam used. Oversubscribed. No special skills or religious requirements. Parents not expected to buy text books; music tuition and outings extra. Some assisted places.

Staff Head Sister Mary Mark, in post for 5 years. 38 full time staff, 35 part time. Annual turnover 2%. Average age 40.

Academic work GCSE and A-levels. 18 GCSE subjects offered; 16 at A-level (A-level general studies being introduced). In 1990, 64 pupils in upper fifth, 26 in upper sixth. *GCSE:* in 1990, 25 upper fifth gained at least grade C in 8+ subjects; 24 in 5–7; and 15 in 1–4 subjects. *A-levels:* 16 upper sixth passed in 3+ subjects; 7 in 2; and 2 in 1 subject. 8% took science A-levels; 58% arts/humanities; 33% both. *Computing facilities:* 10 BBC computers on a network in computer room and 3 Archimedes; 1 BBC + 7 Amstrad WPs in commercial room; 3 Archimedes in design and technology; mobile BBC in science department. *Special provision:* No special provision for dyslexic or EFL; there are special lessons outside school.

European Community *Languages:* French offered: to age 14; GCSE; AS-level; A-level. German offered: to age 14; GCSE; AS-level; A-level. Italian offered: to age 14; GCSE; AS-level; A-level; Institute of Linguists. 10–25% take GCSE in more than 1 EC language. *Exchanges:* Regular exchanges for pupils aged 11–18 to France and Germany. *Other:* Educational visits to France.

Senior pupils' non-academic activities *Music:* many learn a musical instrument to grade 8. Occasional pupil accepted for Music School; 50 in school orchestra, 30 in school choir, 10 in chamber group, a number in Leicester Schools Orchestra. *Drama and dance:* 40 in school productions, 5 in various productions in Leicester area; some up to Grade 6 in elocution. *Art:* 56 take GCSE; 12, A-level; 5 accepted for Art School. *Sport:* Swimming, hockey, netball, athletics, tennis, squash, gymnastics, badminton available (fifth and sixth canoeing, dry slope ski-ing). 22 take non-compulsory sport. 12 pupils represent county/country (cricket, hockey, athletics). *Other:* Number in local community schemes. 25 have bronze Duke of Edinburgh's Award, 6 have silver, 6 working towards gold. Other activities include choir, orchestra, cross-country, gymnastics, board games, debating society, science society.

Careers In 1990, 99% sixth form leavers went on to degree courses; 1% to art/drama/music colleges. Of those going on to degree courses, 3% went to Oxbridge, 47% to other universities; 50% to poly/colleges.

Uniform School uniform worn throughout.

Houses/prefects Competitive houses. Prefects, head girl, head of house and house prefects – appointed by the Head.

Religion Daily assembly and termly services compulsory.

Social Science society, debating society with other schools. Organised trips abroad. Pupils allowed to bring own car/bike/motorbike to school. Cold lunch. School shop. No tobacco/alcohol allowed.

Discipline No corporal punishment. Pupils failing to produce homework once might expect warning; those caught smoking on the premises could expect suspension or discipline 'cards'.

Alumni association is run by Mrs Brenda West, 76 Warwick Way, Loughborough, Leicestershire.

· *Oxford High* ·

Oxford High School
Belbroughton Road
Oxford
OX2 6XA
Tel 0865 59888

- Pupils 650
- Boys None
- Girls 9–18
- (Day)
- Upper sixth 75

- Termly fees
  £908 (Day)
- GPDST
  Enquiries/application to
  the Headmistress

What it's like

Founded in 1875, in the decade which saw the foundation of the first women's colleges at Oxbridge. Its early pupils were among the first women to obtain university degrees. The early history of the school is bound up with the development of North Oxford. College Fellows, newly permitted to marry, were keen to avail themselves of the opportunity to have their daughters educated. It has expanded steadily during the 20th century and now occupies a large, well-equipped urban site two miles from the city centre. All playing fields are on site. Assemblies are frequently (but not always) in the form of religious worship. There is some emphasis on religious instruction and the Christian Union is a flourishing organisation. A sound general education is provided, in the high school tradition, and academic results are most creditable. Very many girls go on to degree courses each year, including a very high proportion to Oxbridge. Four European languages are taught to A-level and a high proportion of pupils takes more than one European language at GCSE. Music, drama and art are very strong. So are sports and games (there have been a large number of representatives at county level). The school provides some local community service volunteers and it has an outstanding record in the Duke of Edinburgh's Award Scheme. In various activities there is quite a lot of collaboration with other schools (such as Magdalen College School in the centre of the city).

School profile

Pupils Total age range 9–18; 650 day girls. Senior department, 11–18, 550 girls. Main entry ages 9, 11 and into sixth. Small number are children of former pupils.

Entrance Own entrance exam used. Oversubscribed. Academic ability looked for. No religious requirements. Parents not expected to buy text books. 25 assisted places pa (20 at 11+, 5 at 16+). Up to 6 scholarships pa (including music) at 11 and 16, $\frac{1}{4}$ to $\frac{1}{8}$ fees.

Parents 15+% are doctors, lawyers etc. 15+% university dons.

Staff Headmistress Mrs Joan Townsend, in post for 10 years.

Academic work GCSE and A-levels. Russian taught to GCSE and A-level, ceramics to GCSE. Average size of upper fifth 80; upper sixth 75. *GCSE:* on aver-age, 75 pupils pass 8+ subjects; 4, 5–7 subjects; 1, 1–4 subjects. *Computing facilities:* RML Nimbus network; stand alone Nimbuses, BBCs. *Special provision:* No formal provision; can provide for pupils with eg hearing aids, crutches (difficult because of stairs), mild dyslexia if academically sound.

European Community *Languages:* French offered: to age 14; GCSE; AS-level; A-level. German offered: to age 14; GCSE; A-level. Italian offered: to GCSE (in sixth); A-level. Spanish offered: to age 14; GCSE; A-level. 50–75% take GCSE in more than 1 EC language. *Exchanges:* Many regular exchanges for pupils aged 14–18 to France, Germany and Spain. Periodically, German students from exchange school in Bonn spend a term in lower sixth in school.

Senior pupils' non-academic activities *Music:* 310 learn a musical instrument, 70 to Grade 6 or above; 150 pupils play in orchestra, string orchestra and highly strung orchestra, 200 in choirs, 30 in wind band. *Drama and dance:* 50 in school productions; 47 Guildhall Speech and Drama, Grade 4–7 exams. *Art:* 40 take GCSE; 8 A-level, 4 A-level ceramics; 5 take Chinese brush painting, 15 needlecraft, 14 pottery and general art. 26 belong to eg photography club. 4 accepted for Art School. *Sport:* Hockey, netball, tennis, athletics, swimming, badminton, dance, trampolining, aerobics, volleyball, judo, sailing, rowing available. Outdoor activity week in holidays for 11–12 year-olds. 17 pupils represent county (netball, hockey, swimming, tennis, badminton). *Other:* 70 taking bronze Duke of Edinburgh's Award, 30 silver, 10 gold. 7 in local community schemes. Some work in OXFAM shops beyond school. Other activities include a chess club (1 pupil represents Britain), very lively drama, theatre outings club, computer club, conservation society.

Careers On average, 82% leavers go on to degree courses; 4% to art/drama/music colleges; $^{1}/_{2}$% to non-degree courses or straight into careers (eg retail management). Of those going on to degree courses, 31% went to Oxbridge, 62% to other universities; 7% to poly/colleges. 4% those going on to higher education went to courses in practical art; 4% in music; 69% in humanities/social sciences; 8% in medicine; and 15% in science/engineering.

Uniform School uniform worn except in sixth.

Houses/prefects No competitive houses. Prefects, head girl and deputy – elected by sixth and staff. School Council.

Religion Religious worship encouraged. Assemblies frequently in form of religious worship. Christian Union flourishes.

Social Debates with eg Magdalen College School and joint theatrical productions; parents organise dances. Organised trips abroad to Russia, France, Germany, Spain and Italy. Pupils allowed to bring own bike to school. Meals self service. Parents organise sale of second-hand uniforms. No tobacco/alcohol allowed.

Discipline No corporal punishment. Pupils failing to produce homework once might expect a reprimand and to produce work later; those caught smoking cannabis on the premises could expect expulsion.

Alumni association Miss Jean Watson, The Secretary, Oxford High School Old Girls' Association, c/o the School.

Former pupils Maggie Smith; Miriam Margolyes; Sian Edwards (conductor); Elizabeth Jennings (poet); Lucinda Leech (furniture designer); Emma Bridgewater (potter); Ursula Buchan (journalist); Sophie Grigson; Louise Williams (violinist).

p

· Pangbourne ·

Pangbourne College
Pangbourne
Reading
Berkshire RG8 8LA
Tel 0734 842101
Fax 0734 845443

- Pupils 395
- Boys 11–18
- (Day/Board)
- Girls None
- Upper sixth 50

- Termly fees
  £1950 (Day)
  £2780 (Board)
- HMC
  Enquiries/application to
  the Headmaster

What it's like

Although founded as a nautical college in 1917 Pangbourne has been a conventional independent school for the last 22 years. Even so, it still retains some aspects of the naval ethos and nautical tradition, including the wearing of uniform. It has a very fine site indeed of 275 acres in beautiful Berkshire countryside a mile from Pangbourne village and near the river. There have been many improvements and additions in recent years and the college is now extremely well equipped. Pupils live in 6 boarding houses; after the first year they share study bedrooms. A broad general education is provided and there is a favourable staff:pupil ratio of 1:10. Academic standards are high and results are good. Quite a lot of leavers go on to degree courses. The college has a strong tradition of success in music and drama. There is a chapel choir, a choral society, an orchestra and a military band. Each year there is a major annual dramatic production plus a house drama festival and work by the modern theatre group. Sports and games are well provided for (rugby and hockey are strong) and the school has a reputation for rowing and sailing. The CCF is voluntary but there are army and naval contingents and a Royal Marine section. There is an emphasis on outdoor pursuits for which the environment is most suitable. A good range of clubs and societies caters for most extra-curricular activities. Pupils are engaged in a lot of charity fund-raising.

School profile

Pupils Age range 11–18; 395 boys (95 day, 300 boarding). Main entry ages 11, 13 and into sixth. 3% are children of former pupils. *Transfer from maintained schools:* 20% main intakes, plus 1% to sixth.

Entrance Common entrance and own entrance exam used. Not oversubscribed. No special skills or religious requirements, but C of E predominates. Parents not expected to buy text books. 5 assisted places pa. 12 scholarships (academic, music and art) at 11+, 13+, 16+, value £4,940–£900.

Parents 15+% in the armed services. 15+% in industry or commerce. 30+% live within 30 miles; up to 10% live overseas.

Staff Headmaster A B E Hudson, in post for 2 years. 34 full time staff, 15 part time (including music). Annual turnover 10%. Average age 41.

Academic work GCSE and A-levels. 16 GCSE subjects offered; 18 at A-level (including drama & theatre arts and A-level general studies). On average, 61 pupils in upper fifth, and over the last 3 years 50 in upper sixth. *GCSE:* in 1990, 37 upper fifth gained at least grade C in 8+ subjects; 18 in 5–7; and 5 in 1–4 subjects. *A-levels:* On average 4% upper sixth pass in 4+ subjects; 40% in 3; 28% in 2; and 17% in 1 subject. On average 27% take science A-levels; 44% arts/humanities; 29% both. *Computing facilities:* Research machine 480Z of 10 terminals for computer science teaching; PC compatible network of 10 terminals for computer science and other subjects; various departments have computers as teaching aids. *Special provision:* Full-time specialist supervises a number of part-time teachers providing extra tuition in English and maths for dyslexics and EFL for foreigners.

European Community *Languages:* French offered: to age 14; GCSE; A-level. German offered: to age 14; GCSE; A-level. Boys also took GCSE in Italian, Spanish and Portuguese. 10–25% take GCSE in more than 1 EC language (100% take French, some 20% German). *Exchanges:* Some exchanges for pupils aged 14–16 to France. *Other:* European Studies to be offered soon. Some 10 European boys in school.

Senior pupils' non-academic activities *Music:* 50 learn a musical instrument, 15 to Grade 6 or above; 1 accepted for Music School. 40 play in school orchestra, 25 in choir, 10 in jazz band, 6 in folk group. *Drama and dance:* 85 in school productions; 110 in house drama; 1 accepted for Drama/Dance School. 1 goes on to work in theatre, 1 to BBC/media. *Art:* 22 take GCSE; 10 A-level. 4 accepted for Art School. 15 belong to eg photographic club. *Sport:* Rugby, hockey, cricket, rowing, sailing, tennis, squash, fencing, badminton, basketball available. Some sport compulsory; 80 take part in non-compulsory sport. 10 take exams (STAA). 8 pupils represent county (rowing, hockey, rugby, athletics), 2 represent Britain. *Other:* 12 take part in local community schemes. Considerable amount of charity fund-raising is done. Other activities include 25 clubs and societies (mostly functioning in the 'Central Hour', after lunch, specially set aside) ranging from computer club, photography, newspaper production and printing, to vehicle maintenance, weaving and wine tasting, across a whole spectrum of interests. Strong CCF (Naval, Army and Royal Marine sections).

Careers In 1990, 50% leavers went on to degree courses; 25% to art/drama/music colleges; 10% straight into careers; 15% other. Of those going on to degree courses, 5% went to Oxbridge, 45% to other universities; 50% to poly/colleges. 20% those going on to higher education went to courses in practical art; 5% in drama/acting; 50% in humanities/social sciences; 5% in medicine; and 20% in science/engineering.

Uniform School uniform worn throughout.

Houses/prefects Competitive houses. Prefects, head boy, head of house and house prefects – appointed by the Head. There is no fagging.

Religion Daily morning prayers for the whole school, or by houses. Sunday chapel.

Social Debates, music, dancing, drama frequently organised jointly with local girls' schools. Organised choir and orchestra tours abroad; also sports tours, ski trips, French language trips. Sixth formers allowed to bring bike to school. Meals self service. School shop. Some alcohol allowed in upper sixth social club.

Discipline No corporal punishment. Pupils failing to produce homework once might expect detention, ie one hour of compulsory extra study time; those caught smoking cannabis on the premises could expect expulsion.

Boarding 30% have own study bedroom, 50% share (from 1–4); 20% are in dormitories of 6+. Houses, of approximately 65, same as for competitive purposes. Resident qualified nurse. Central dining room. Pupils can provide own food (no cooking). 2 weekend exeats termly and any Sunday. Visits to local village allowed when free – all ages.

Alumni association is run by L C

Stephens, Hon Secretary O.P. Society, c/o the College.

Former pupils Ken Russell (film director); Mike Hailwood (racing motor cyclist); Lord Vinson (life peer and industrialist); John Ridgway (transatlantic oarsman).

· *Park* ·

The Park School for Girls
25 Lynedoch Street
Glasgow G3 6EX
Tel 041 332 0426

- Pupils 400
- Boys None
- Girls 5–18 (Day)
- Higher year 60

- Termly fees £981 (Day)
- GSA
Enquiries/application to the Headmistress

What it's like

The Girls' School Company Ltd was founded in 1879 and is responsible for administering this school and St Columba's Kilmacolm. The Park School lies in the middle of the city in the Park Circus Conservation Area. There are big playing fields at Anniesland and pupils also have the use of the Allander Sports Centre in Bearsden. The school is well equipped with modern facilities and a sound general education is provided. A family atmosphere, small teaching sets (the staff:pupil ratio is about 1:10) and efficient pastoral care produce good results academically and otherwise. There is much emphasis on self-discipline and acceptance of responsibility for oneself. Close liaison exists between school and parents. Each year many sixth formers go on to degree courses. French, German and Spanish are offered to A-level. Quite strong in music, drama and art. A good record in sports and games (a lot of representatives at county level) and a promising record in the Duke of Edinburgh's Award Scheme.

School profile

Pupils Total age range 5–18; 400 day girls. Senior department 12–18, 300 girls. Main entry ages 5, 12 and into sixth. Approx 10% are children of former pupils.

Entrance Own entrance exam used. Oversubscribed at some stages. No special skills or religious requirements. Parents expected to buy text books. 51 assisted places. 4 scholarships/bursaries available, £350 per term.

Parents 15+% in industry or commerce; 15+% are doctors, lawyers, etc.

Staff Headmistress Mrs M E Myatt, in post for 5 years. 31 full time staff, 15 part time. Annual turnover 4%. Average age 30–40.

Academic work O-grade, S-grade, Highers, CSYS, A-levels. Average number in O-grade year, 47; Higher year, 60; A-level/CSYS year, 40. *O/S-grades:* on average, 45 pupils pass 8+ subjects; 11, 5–7 subjects; 8 pass 1–4 subjects. *Highers:* on average 17 pupils pass 5+ subjects; 10, 4 subjects; 10, 3 subjects; 9, 2 subjects; 2 pass 1 subject. On average, 8 take science/ engineering A-levels; 6 take arts and humanities; 2 a mixture. *Computing facilities:* 20 BBC computers, disks, printers etc. *Special provision:* special teaching as needed.

European Community *Languages:* French offered: to age 14; S-grade; A-level. German offered: to age 14; S-grade; A-level. Spanish offered: to S-grade; A-level. 10–25% take S-grade in more than 1 EC language.

Senior pupils' non-academic activities *Music:* 17 learn a musical instrument, 5 to Grade 6 or above; 12 in school orchestra, 37 in choir; 1 in National Youth Orchestra. *Drama and dance:* 20 in school productions. 2 take Grade 6 in ESB, RAD etc. 1 accepted for Drama/Dance School; 1 goes on to work in theatre. *Art:* 60 take art appreciation as non-examined subject; 33 take GCSE; 6 A-level; 16 Higher. 3 accepted for Art School; 1 for architecture, 2 for college of textiles, 3 to technical colleges. 10 belong to art club. *Sport:* Hockey, swimming, tennis, athletics, squash, badminton, curling, judo, ski-ing, golf, aerobics, gymnastics available. 50 take non-compulsory sport. 24 represent county/country (tennis, hockey, gym, showjumping, athletics, netball). *Other:* 6 take part in local community schemes. 3 have bronze Duke of Edinburgh's Award, 3 have silver and 3 have gold. Other activities include a computer club, electronics club, theatre-goers club, debating and public speaking, Young Enterprise scheme.

Careers In 1990, 50% leavers went on to degree courses; 25% to art/drama/music colleges; 20% to non-degree courses; 5% straight into careers. Of those going on to degree courses, 75% went to universities; 25% to poly/colleges. 30% those going on to higher education went to courses in practical art; 40% in humanities/social sciences; 5% in medicine; and 25% in science/engineering.

Uniform School uniform worn throughout.

Houses/prefects Competitive houses. Prefects, head girl, head of house and house prefects – elected by the school. School Council.

Religion Compulsory daily assembly.

Social ESU debates, sport, Young Enterprise with other local schools. Organised trips abroad and exchange systems. Meals self service. School shop. No tobacco/alcohol allowed.

Discipline No corporal punishment. Pupils failing to produce homework once might expect lunch time detention, extra work and communication to parents.

Alumni association run by Mrs G L Mackay, Camallt, Dumgoyne, by Killearn, G63 9LA.

Former pupils Siobhan Redmond (actress); Joanna Isles (artist).

· *Parsons Mead* ·

Parsons Mead School
Ottways Lane
Ashtead
Surrey KT21 2PE
Tel 03722 76401

- Pupils 485
- Boys None
- Girls 3–18
  (Day/Board/Weekly)
- Upper sixth 23

- Termly fees
  £1150 (Day)
  £2135 (Board)
  £1975 (Weekly)
- GSA
  Enquiries/application to
  the Headmistress

What it's like

Founded in 1897, it is greenbelt with well-designed modern buildings and good facilities on a 12-acre site. Senior and junior schools combined. It is C of E by tradition but girls of all faiths are welcome. There is close cooperation between parents and staff. A sound education is given and exam results are good. Art, music and drama are popular and well supported. A decent range of sports (new sports hall), games, clubs and societies.

School profile

Pupils Total age range 3–18; 485 girls, 435 day, 50 boarding. Senior department 11–19, 300 girls. Main entry ages 3, 8, 11 and into sixth. Approx 5% are children of former pupils. *Transfer from maintained schools:* 10% intake at 11.

Entrance Own entrance exam used. Oversubscribed. No special skills or religious requirements. Parents not expected to buy text books; extras include ballet, piano etc. Up to 5 scholarships/bursaries per year at 11+, 30–25% of fees; also scholarships in sixth. Bursaries to existing pupils.

Parents 15+% in industry or commerce. 80+% live within 30 miles.

Staff Headmistress Miss E B Plant, in post for 1 year. 36 full time staff, 10 part time. Annual turnover up to 10%. Average age 35–40.

Academic work GCSE and A-levels. 18 GCSE subjects offered; 24 at A-level (including A-level general studies). In 1990, 55 pupils in upper fifth, 18 in upper sixth (average 23). *GCSE:* in 1990, 37 upper fifth gained at least grade C in 8+ subjects; 13 in 5–7; and 5 in 1–4 subjects. *A-levels:* 10 upper sixth passed in 3 subjects; 2 in 2; and 6 in 1 subject. 6 took science A-levels; 5 arts/humanities; 7 both. *Computing facilities:* Computer room with 12+ Nimbus network. *Special provision:* Extra coaching possible.

European Community *Languages:* French offered: to age 14; GCSE; A-level. German offered: to age 14; GCSE; A-level. Spanish offered: to GCSE. 25–50% take GCSE in more than 1 EC language. *Exchanges:* Regular exchanges for pupils aged 14–16 to France and Germany.

Senior pupils' non-academic activities *Music:* Many learn a musical instrument, quite a few to Grade 6 or above. A few apply for Music School. *Drama and dance:* Many in school productions; a few up to Grade 6 in ESB, RAD. Very rare for pupils to be accepted for Drama/Dance Schools. *Art:* All pupils take as non-examined subject, 20 take GCSE; 1–5, A-level; 1–2 accepted for Art School. *Sport:* Hockey, netball, tennis, rounders, swimming, athletics, badminton, volleyball, squash available at local club. A lot take non-compulsory sport; many younger girls take exams, eg gymnastics, swimming; a few pupils represent county (tennis, swimming). *Other:* 15 take part in local community schemes. School supports charities. Other activities include 5 computer clubs, 20 other clubs. Duke of Edinburgh's Award Scheme thrives.

Careers In 1990, 50% leavers went on to degree courses; 10% to art/drama/music colleges; 10% to non-degree courses; 10% straight into careers; 20% other. Of those going on to degree courses, 50% went to universities; 50% to poly/colleges. 10% those going on to higher education went to courses in practical art; 55% in humanities/social sciences; and 35% in science/engineering.

Uniform School uniform worn except in the sixth.

Houses/prefects No competitive houses or prefects. Head girl – elected by sixth form. School Council.

Religion Religious worship encouraged.

Social Various organised local events. Ski-ing and other educational trips abroad. Day pupils allowed to bring own bike to school. Meals self service. No tobacco/alcohol allowed.

Discipline No corporal punishment. Pupils failing to produce homework once might expect 1 report (3 in 1 term means detention); those caught smoking cannabis on the premises could expect suspension/expulsion.

Boarding Nearly half have own study bedroom, 6 in pairs; 20 are in dormitories of 4–6. Qualified nurse during day, then on call. Central dining room. Sixth form can provide and cook own food. 3–5 exeats each term. Visits to local town allowed.

Alumni association is run by Mrs D Peacock, c/o the School.

· Penrhos ·

Penrhos College
Colwyn Bay
Clwyd
LL28 4DA
Tel 0492 530333

- Pupils 440
- Boys 4–11 only (Day)
- Girls 4–18 (Day/Board/Weekly)
- Upper sixth 37

- Termly fees
  £1630 (Day)
  £2380 (Board/Weekly)
- GSA
  Enquiries/application to the Head Master

What it's like

Founded in 1880, it has a pleasant campus in the resort of Colwyn Bay, by the sea. Well designed and comfortable buildings with good boarding accommodation. The junior school is half a mile away. A forward looking school with a happy atmosphere, it is interdenominational but basically Christian. A sound general education is provided and academic standards are good. Many pupils go on to degree courses each year. It is very strong indeed in music, drama and art. Considerable strength in sport and games (a number of county representatives). Its activities programmes are outstanding. Between 25–30 activities are available each term and everyone's needs are catered for. There is also a comprehensive programme for outdoor pursuits (eg sailing, canoeing, mountaineering). A lot of overseas trips are organised. A high proportion of pupils takes both French and German at GCSE. All second years spend a week in France and third years, a week in Germany.

School profile

Pupils Total age range 4–18; 440 pupils, 254 day (30 boys, 224 girls), 186 boarding girls. Senior department 11–18, 290 girls. Main entry ages 4 (boys and girls), 11, 12, 13 and into sixth (girls). Approx 5% are children of former pupils. *Transfer from maintained schools:* 50% senior intake, plus 50% to sixth.

Entrance Own entrance exam used. Not oversubscribed. No special skills or religious requirements. Parents not expected to buy text books; no compulsory extras. 12 assisted places. 5 scholarships/bursaries available, 50% of fees.

Parents 30+% live within 30 miles; 10+% live overseas.

Staff Head Master N C Peacock, in post for 16 years. 30 full time staff, 13 part time. Annual turnover 1 or 2. Average age 42.

Academic work GCSE and A-levels (A-level general studies offered but prefer to do it as a non-examined subject). On average, 42 pupils in upper fifth, 36 in upper sixth. *GCSE:* on average, 24 upper fifth gain at least grade C in 8+ subjects; 12 in 5–7; and 6 in 1–4 subjects. *A-levels:* on average 1 upper sixth passes in 4+ subjects; 18 in 3; 12 in 2; and 4 in 1 subject. On average 8 take science A-levels; 21 arts/humanities; 6 both. *Computing facilities:* 13 Nimbus plus various computers in subject rooms. *Special provision:* Specialist one-to-one tuition for dyslexics. EFL available.

European Community *Languages:* French offered: to age 14; GCSE; A-level. German offered: to age 14; GCSE; A-level. 50–75% take GCSE in more than 1 EC language. *Exchanges:* Regular exchanges for pupils to Germany. *Other:* Second year spend one week at chateau in Normandy annually (included in fees; not charged extra). School hosts 1 EP European student each year. Various European pupils have spent 1 term in school.

Senior pupils' non-academic activities *Music:* 130 learn a musical instrument, 17 to Grade 6 or above, 1 accepted for Music School; 30 in school orchestra, 36 in choir, 4 in string quartet; 2 in county youth orchestra. *Drama and dance:* 40 in school productions; 100% in house plays; 50 in drama festivals. 10 take New Era, Guildhall exams. 1 accepted for Drama/Dance School; 1 goes on to work in theatre; 1 audition for Opportunity Knocks. *Art:* 17 take GCSE; 9 A-level. 2–3 accepted for Art School. 30 belong to ceramics club. *Sport:* Hockey, netball, tennis, athletics, rounders, swimming, squash, badminton available. 40% of pupils involved in sailing (school is RYA Centre) climbing, canoeing, mountain walking, squash. All take exams. 7 represent county/country (hockey, athletics, judo). *Other:* Wide ranging service programme – old people, handicapped children; sixth form give holiday for handicapped children; inshore rescue boat. Comprehensive programme of sailing, canoeing, mountaineering etc with expeditions away from school. 25–30 other activities each term from ballet to welding; driving lessons arranged; CDT workshop.

Careers In 1990, 60% leavers went on to degree courses; 25% to art/drama/music colleges; 19% to non-degree courses; 2% other. Of those going on to degree courses, 6% went to Oxbridge, 50% to other universities; 44% to poly/colleges. 20% those going on to higher education went to courses in practical art; 20% in drama/acting; 30% in humanities/social sciences; 10% in medicine; and 20% in science/engineering.

Uniform School uniform worn throughout.

Houses/prefects Competitive houses. Prefects, head girl, head of house and house prefects – some appointed, some volunteer. There is a Pupil/Staff Rules Committee.

Religion Range of visiting lay and clerical people – 'Jesuits to Jews' for Sunday service (compulsory unless specific request by parents).

Social Social functions – sports, dances, debates, sixth form dinner with local boys and co-ed schools. Organised ski trips, cultural trips, individual exchanges for staff and pupils from time to time. Pupils allowed to bring own bike to school. Meals self service. Pupils run school shop. No tobacco/alcohol allowed.

Discipline No corporal punishment. Pupils failing to produce homework once would not receive punishment; those caught smoking cannabis on the premises could expect expulsion.

Boarding 6 have own study bedroom, most upper sixth share (2, 3, 4). None in large dormitories. Houses, of approx 50, as for competitive purposes. Resident qualified nurse. Central dining room. *Upper sixth* pupils can provide and cook own food. Exeats: special system of 'long weekends' at pupils' choice, 1 per term; unlimited short weekends. Visits to local town allowed.

Former pupils Paula Yates; Prof Alison Fairlie (Professor of French, Cambridge); Janet Hargreaves (actress); Roberta Lamming (author); Dr Kathleen Sherry (gynaecologist); Marjorie Young (golf); Moya Jackson (social work, Philippines).

· *Perse (Boys)* ·

The Perse School	● Pupils 485	● Termly fees
Hills Road	● Boys 11–18	£1087 (Day)
Cambridge	(Day/Board)	£2187 (Board)
CB2 2QF	● Girls None	● HMC
Tel 0223 248127	● Upper sixth 70	Enquiries/application to the Headmaster's Secretary

What it's like

Founded in 1615, originally in Free School Lane, then Gonville Place (1890), it moved to its present 30-acre green field site on the outskirts of Cambridge in 1960. The whole school was constructed as new between 1958–60. It has pleasant buildings and excellent modern facilities. Further extensions were made in the 1980s and a new development programme is underway which includes replacing the two boarding houses with a new purpose-built house. A new 180-seater drama studio/lecture theatre, art and design centre and modern languages block has been completed. It is Christian but non-denominational. It has all the advantages of being a comparatively small school. There is much emphasis on management by the boys and it runs a very efficient pastoral care scheme. Naturally, there are strong links with the university. The teaching is good, academic standards are high and results impressive. Very many leavers go on to degree courses and a large proportion to Oxbridge. There is a staff:pupil ratio of about 1:12. French and German are offered to A-level and an eceptionally large proportion of boys take both at GCSE. (Spanish is also offered as a non-examined language.) There are regular exchanges with France and Germany. Very strong indeed in music and drama, which are undertaken as a joint venture with the Perse (Girls). Also strong in art. The school operates a TWIN (Teachers Within Industry) scheme. The Perse has always had a notable record in sports and games (a very large number of representatives at county and national level). An excellent range of extra-curricular activities, including an unusually large and energetic CCF. Some commitment to local community services. Much use is made of Cambridge's cultural amenities.

School profile

Pupils Age range 11–18; 485 boys, 455 day, 30 boarding. Main entry ages 11, 13 and into sixth. Own prep school provides 66% of intake at 11. *Transfer from maintained schools:* 33% at 11, few at 13.

Entrance Own entrance exam used. Oversubscribed. No special skills or religious requirements. Parents not expected to buy text books. 57 assisted places. Variable number of scholarships/bursaries, honorary except where proven financial need.

Parents 15+% are doctors, lawyers etc; 15+% in industry or commerce. Up to 10% live overseas.

Staff Headmaster Dr G M Stephen, in post for 3 years. 35 full time staff, 3 part time. Annual turnover 5%.

Academic work GCSE and A-levels. Average size of upper fifth 70+; upper sixth 70. *GCSE:* on average, 70 upper fifth gained at least grade C in 8+ subjects; 6 in 5–7; 1 in 1–4 subjects. *A-levels:* on average, 4 upper sixth pass in 4 subjects; 61 in 3; 5 in 2; 1 pupil in 1 subject. On average, there is a 50/50 split between science/engineering and arts/humanities. *Computing facilities:* 30+ networked BBCs plus various others. Whole school on Econet network system.

European Community *Languages:* French offered: to age 14; GCSE; A-level. German offered: to age 14; GCSE; A-level. Spanish: non-examined subject. Over 75% take GCSE in more than 1 EC language. *Exchanges:* Regular exchanges for pupils aged 11–16 to France and Germany. *Other:* Significant number of sons of visiting academics in school for 1 term to 1 year. Establishing Young Enterprise Scheme with French schools.

Senior pupils' non-academic activities *Music:* 80 learn a musical instrument, 12 to Grade 6 or above; 30 in first school orchestra, 30 in choir; some pupils in own groups, small ensembles and operas; occasional pupils in National Youth Orchestra; 12 take GCSE music; 2 A-level. Occasional pupils go on to play in jazz bands; 2 Cambridge music scholarships. *Drama and dance:* 60 in school productions, most with Perse (Girls); 150 in other productions. *Art:* 50–67% take as non-examined subject; 6 A-level; 2 history of art. 5 accepted for Art School; 4 for university. 20 in eg photographic club. *Sport:* Rugby, hockey, cricket, tennis, fives, basketball, athletics available; off site – golf, squash, swimming, cross-country available. 95 take non-compulsory sport. 36+ represent county/country (rugby, hockey, tennis). *Other:* Some take part in local community schemes. Duke of Edinburgh's Award available through Scouts. 5–10 enter voluntary schemes after school; others work for national charities. Other activities include a computer club, chess, Scouts, CCF, Young Enterprise Scheme.

Careers In 1990, 95% leavers went on to degree courses; 5% other. Of those going on to degree courses, 30% went to Oxbridge; 60% to other universities; 10% to poly/colleges. 40% those going on to higher education went to courses in humanities/social sciences; 10% in medicine; and 50% in science/engineering.

Uniform School uniform worn, modified in sixth.

Houses/prefects No competitive houses. Prefects, head boy, head of (boarding) house and house prefects – appointed by the Head after nomination by staff and pupils. School Council.

Religion Compulsory religious worship (unless opted out).

Social All music and drama (including master classes) joint with Perse (Girls) plus debates, discos, plays, a combined orchestra, general chamber music groups. Organised trips abroad. Pupils allowed to bring own car/bike to school. Meals self service. School tuckshop. No tobacco/alcohol allowed.

Discipline No corporal punishment. Pupils failing to produce homework once may not be punished.

Boarding No single study bedrooms but new house planned; most are in dormitories of 6+. Resident qualified nurse, doctor on call. No central dining room. Exeats any weekend unless involved in Saturday matches. Visits to local town allowed (Saturday).

Alumni association run by Mr K Barry.

Former pupils Sir Peter Hall; 2 Nobel prizewinners; many notable university figures.

· *Perse (Girls)* ·

Perse School for Girls
Union Road
Cambridge
CB2 1HF
Tel 0223 359589

- Pupils 703
- Boys None
- Girls 7–18
- (Day)
- Upper sixth 72

- Termly fees
  £1048 (Day)
- GSA
  Enquiries/application to
  the Headmistress

What it's like

Founded in 1881 under the scheme for the management of the Perse Trust, it is well sited in the centre of Cambridge, in agreeable and very well equipped buildings. Recent developments include a music wing and new science and technology facilities. The junior school is nearby. There is time-tabled religious education up to the end of the fifth year and daily school prayers. The Perse has a high reputation academically; it prides itself on providing for girls from all sectors of society a first-class balanced general education and the opportunity to develop talent and individuality in any field. Pupils come not only from Cambridge and Cambridgeshire but also from the neighbouring counties. The GCSE and A-level results are consistently excellent, and each year many girls go on to degree courses, including a very high proportion to Oxbridge. Four European languages are offered right through to A-level and an unusually high proportion of girls take more than one at GCSE. Regular exchanges for girls aged 14–16 are offered into France, Germany, Italy and Spain. Music, drama and art are all strong, especially music. The senior school has three choirs, two orchestras, a wind band and several chamber music groups. The school combines with other schools in Cambridge for various extra-curricular activities (of which there are many), in drama, music, The British Association for Young Scientists, Young Enterprise, and Youth Action which involves many girls. Sports and games are played to a high standard (the playing fields are ten minutes from the school). Hockey and tennis are especially strong (a high number of representatives at county and regional level). Much enterprise is shown in exchange visits with several European countries. The Duke of Edinburgh's Award Scheme is well supported. Extensive use is made of Cambridge's cultural amenities.

School profile

Pupils Total age range 7–18; 703 day girls. Senior department 11–18, 543 girls. Main entry ages 7, 8, 9, 10, 11 and into sixth. Very few are children of former pupils. *Transfer from maintained schools:* 35% of main intake at 11, and 50% into sixth.

Entrance Own entrance exam used. Oversubscribed. All-round ability looked for; no religious requirements. Parents not expected to buy text books; maximum extras, £70 (for individual music/speech lessons). 20 assisted places pa. 15 scholarships/bursaries pa, £1,800–£600.

Parents Up to 10% live overseas.

Staff Headmistress Miss H S Smith, in post for 1 year. 51 full time staff, 16 part time. Annual turnover 10%. Average age 40.

Academic work GCSE and A-levels. 22 GCSE subjects offered; 23 at A-level (including Russian; no A-level general studies). In 1990, 78 pupils in upper fifth, 70 in upper sixth (now 72). *GCSE:* in 1990, 68 upper fifth gained at least grade C in 8+ subjects; 7 in 5–7; and 3 in 1–4 subjects. *A-levels:* 7 upper sixth passed in 4+ subjects; 55 in 3; 8 in 2 subjects. 22% took science A-levels; 46% arts/ humanities; 32% both. *Computing facili-*

566

ties: Well equipped computer room; individual computers in specialist rooms. *Special provision:* Any necessary provision arranged on individual basis.

European Community *Languages:* French offered: to age 14; GCSE; AS-level; A-level. German offered: to age 14; GCSE; A-level. Italian offered: to age 14; GCSE; A-level. Spanish offered: to age 14; GCSE; A-level. Over 75% take GCSE in more than 1 EC language. *Exchanges:* Regular exchanges for pupils aged 14–16 to France, Germany, Italy and Spain. *Other:* Occasional pupil from Germany and Spain in school.

Senior pupils' non-academic activities *Music:* 91 learn a musical instrument, 44 to Grade 6 or above. 2 accepted for Music School. 60 in school orchestra, 35 in school choir, 5 in school pop group, 30 in chamber groups, 1 in National Youth Orchestra, 2 play in pop group after leaving, 2 obtain choral awards (7 currently applying). *Drama and dance:* 40 in school productions; 40 in house drama; 1 accepted for Drama/Dance School, 30 take LAMDA/Poetry Society exams, 15 enter competitions/festivals/speech training, 1 goes on to work in theatre. *Art:* 50 take as non-examined subject, 22 take GCSE, 6 AS-level, 6–10 A-level. 1–3 accepted for Art School. *Sport:* Hockey, netball, rounders, tennis, swimming, aerobics available, plus badminton, squash, trampoline, golf, weights, archery, basketball, using outside school facilities. Approx 50 take non-compulsory sport. Approx 20 pa take BAGA/MILK in action awards in gymnastics; 20 take exams in athletics, 80 in swimming. 18 represent county (hockey, netball, tennis, cricket), 4 represent region (tennis, hockey, cricket). *Other:* 15 take part in local community schemes. 15 are working for silver Duke of Edinburgh's Award, 22 for gold. Other activities include several computer clubs.

Careers In 1990, 76% leavers went on to degree courses; 4% to art/drama/music colleges; 6% to non-degree courses; 4% straight into careers; 10% other. Of those going on to degree courses, 26% went to Oxbridge, 68% to other universities; 6% to poly/colleges. 2% those going on to higher education went to courses in practical art; 2% in drama/acting; 2% in music; 60% in humanities/social sciences; 14% in medicine; and 20% in science/engineering.

Uniform School uniform worn, except in sixth.

Houses/prefects Competitive houses. Prefects, head girl, head of house and house prefects – elected by the school. School Council.

Religion Attendance at religious worship compulsory, except for conscientious objectors.

Social Joint with Perse (Boys): orchestra, theatrical productions, debates, Young Enterprise, some societies. Exchanges with schools in France, Germany, Italy, Spain, Russia. Organised trips to Pompeii, Italy (ski-ing), France, Russia. Pupils allowed to bring own bike (car in sixth). Meals self-service. No tobacco/alcohol allowed.

Discipline No corporal punishment. Pupils failing to produce homework once might expect discussion with relevant staff; those caught smoking cannabis on the premises could expect to be expelled.

Alumni association Old Persean Guild, Mrs J Waters, 12 Garner Close, Milton, Cambridge CB4 6DY.

· *Pierrepont* ·

Pierrepont School
Frensham
Farnham
Surrey GU10 3DN
Tel 025 125 2110

- Pupils 240
- Boys 11–18 (Day/ Board/Weekly)
- Girls 11–18 (Day)
- Upper sixth 20

- Termly fees
  £1517 (Day)
  £2523 (Board)
  £2376 (Weekly)
- SHMIS
  Enquiries/application to the Headmaster

What it's like

Founded in 1947 its main building is a house designed by Norman Shaw and built in 1876. Later additions have helped to create a compact campus on a pleasant wooded site with ample playing fields and gardens (46 acres in all). The boarding accommodation is comfortable. Religious worship in the Anglican tradition is encouraged. Academic standards are creditable and some pupils go on to degree courses each year. A good range of sports and games is available and standards are quite high. There is a flourishing CCF contingent and some commitment to the Duke of Edinburgh's Award Scheme since 1983.

School profile

Pupils Age range 11–18; 240 pupils, 150 day (140 boys, 10 girls), 90 boarding (all boys). Main entry ages 11, 12, 13 and into sixth. Approx 1% are children of former pupils.

Entrance Common entrance and own entrance exam used. Oversubscribed at some ages. No special skills or religious requirements. Parents not expected to buy text books; music tuition extra. 14 scholarships/bursaries, 60% to 20% day fees.

Staff Headmaster J D Payne, in post for 8 years. 22 full time staff, 4 part time. Annual turnover 6%. Average age 40.

Academic work GCSE and A-levels. Average size of upper fifth 58; upper sixth 20. *Computing facilities:* Network of Opus PC IVs. *Special provision:* for EFL and dyslexia.

European Community *Languages:* French offered: to age 14; GCSE; AS-level; A-level. German offered: to age 14; GCSE; A-level. Spanish offered: to GCSE; A-level. 10–25% take GCSE in more than 1 EC language. *Exchanges:* Regular exchanges for pupils aged 11–14 to France, Germany and Spain. *Other:* EC

pupils encouraged to spend time in school (half term to 3 years).

Senior pupils' non-academic activities *Art:* 12–15 take GCSE; 3–5, A-level. *Sport:* Rugby, hockey, cricket, athletics, basketball, squash, badminton, volleyball, gymnastics, sailing, swimming, shooting, riding, tennis available. *Other:* Activities include a computer club, drama, CCF, Duke of Edinburgh's Award Scheme, chess, bridge, electronics, model railway, photography, orchestra, Young Engineers.

Careers In 1990, 40% leavers went on to degree courses; 10% to art/drama/music colleges; 10% to non-degree courses (eg agriculture); 20% straight into careers; 20% other. Of those going on to degree courses; 50% went to universities; 50% to poly/colleges. 10% those going on to higher education went to courses in practical art; 30% in humanities/social sciences; and 60% in science/engineering.

Uniform School uniform worn except the sixth.

Houses/prefects Competitive houses. Prefects, head boy/girl, head of house and house prefects – appointed by Headmaster and housemasters.

Religion Religious worship encouraged.

Social Occasional debates with other schools. Annual ski-ing party, regular trips to France; rugby tours. Pupils allowed to bring own car/bike/motorbike to school. Meals self service. School tuckshop and bookshop. No tobacco allowed; beer or wine only in social club for 17+.

Discipline No corporal punishment. Pupils caught smoking cannabis on the premises might expect expulsion.

Boarding One-third have own study bedroom, one-third share with 1 or 2; very few in dormitories of 6+. Houses, of approximately 30–35, are the same as competitive houses. Resident SRN. Central dining room. Pupils can provide and cook own food to some extent. Number and length of exeats varies each term; weekly boarding available. Visits to local town allowed.

· *Pipers Corner* ·

Pipers Corner School	● Pupils 379	● Termly fees
Great Kingshill	● Boys None	£1235 (Day)
High Wycombe	● Girls 8–18	£2225 (Board)
Buckinghamshire	(Day/Board/Weekly)	£2185 (Weekly)
HP15 6LP	● Upper sixth 33	● GSA
Tel 0494 718255		Enquiries/application to the Headmistress

What it's like

Founded in 1930, it has been on its present site since 1945. It stands in most agreeable, rural surroundings, high in the Chilterns, with some 36 acres of grounds and gardens. The main building reflects the 17th-century farmhouse out of which the school has grown. It is well equipped with good modern facilities and comfortable accommodation. A C of E foundation, it is ecumenical in spirit and policy. Boarders are expected to attend Sunday service either in the school chapel or at the local parish church of Hughenden with which the school has close links. The school aims to provide a complete education leading to GCSE and A-level. There is a favourable staff:pupil ratio with 30 full time teachers and 15 part-timers. Exam results are creditable. Many sixth formers go on to degree courses. French and German are offered to A-level and many girls take GCSE in both. They are also offered under the FLAW scheme at sixth form level. Drama and art are especially strong. A variety of sports and games is available and there are plentiful extra-curricular activities. Local community services flourish and the school achieves success at bronze level in the Duke of Edinburgh's Award Scheme.

School profile

Pupils Total age range 8–18; 379 girls (276 day, 103 boarding). Senior department, 12–18, 268 girls. Main entry ages 8–14 and into sixth. 5% are children of former pupils. *Transfer from maintained schools:* 20% senior intake.

Entrance Own entrance exam used. No special skills or religious requirements.

Parents not expected to buy text books. Sixth form scholarships, service and academic bursaries available.

Parents 15+% in the armed services. 60+% live within 30 miles; up to 10% live overseas.

Staff Headmistress Dr M M Wilson, in post for 5 years. 30 full time staff, 15 part time. Annual turnover 8%. Average age 40.

Academic work GCSE and A-levels. General studies offered at AS-level, not A-level. In 1991, 43 pupils in upper fifth, 33 in upper sixth. *GCSE:* in 1990, 15 upper fifth gained at least grade C in 8+ subjects; 18 in 5–7; and 10 in 1–4 subjects. *A-levels:* 14 upper sixth passed in 3 subjects; 3 in 2; and 3 in 1 subject. 10% took science A-levels; 70% arts/ humanities; 20% both. *Computing facilities:* 10 computers in computer room. 6 others in classrooms; 1 in reprographics. *Special provision:* Private EFL.

European Community *Languages:* French offered: to age 14; GCSE; A-level. German offered: to age 14; GCSE; A-level. 25–50% take GCSE in more than 1 EC language. FLAW (Foreign Languages at Work) in French and German in sixth form. *Exchanges:* Regular exchanges for pupils aged 14–16 to France and Germany.

Senior pupils' non-academic activities *Music:* 150 learn a musical instrument, 10 to Grade 6 or above; 20 play in school orchestra, 25 in choir, 10 in chamber groups, 4 in music centre. *Drama:* 85–90 in school productions; 40 take exams to Grade 6 in ESB, RAD, 100 perform in festivals, 100 in competitions (local and area), 24 take GCSE drama, 8–10 propose A-level; 2–3 accepted for Drama Schools. 4 enter National Youth competitions; 8 to theatre summer schools. *Art:* 30 take GCSE; 18 A-level. 6 accepted for Art School. 12 belong to eg photographic club, 6 take pottery. *Sport:* Netball, hockey, tennis, rounders, athletics, swimming available. 25 take part in non-compulsory sport. 5 take exams, eg swimming. 3 represent county (netball). *Other:* 22 have bronze Duke of Edinburgh's Award, 3 silver. Other activities include a computer club; driving lessons can be arranged out of school hours.

Careers In 1990, 70% leavers went on to degree courses; 15% to art/drama/ music colleges; 5% to non-degree courses (eg cookery course); 10% straight into careers (eg nursing). Of those going on to degree courses, 20% went to Oxbridge, 50% to other universities; 30% to poly/ colleges. 15% those going on to higher education went to courses in practical art; 60% in humanities/social sciences; 5% in medicine; and 20% in science/ engineering.

Uniform School uniform worn except in sixth.

Houses/prefects Competitive houses. Prefects, head girl, head of house and house prefects – selected by Headmistress, staff and sixth form. School Council. Charity Committee.

Religion C of E foundation; confirmation, church and chapel.

Social Occasional debates, dances with local boys' schools; public speaking, Youth Speaks (Rotary) and English Speaking Union, Observer Mace Debating. Some organised trips abroad and exchange systems. Pupils allowed to bring own car to school. Lunch, self service; other meals formal. No tobacco/alcohol allowed.

Discipline No corporal punishment. Pupils failing to produce homework once would be asked to produce work by next day to tutor.

Boarding 15% have own study bedroom, 20% share (2 or 3); 30% share (4); remainder are in dormitories of 6. Houses divided by year groups. Resident nurse; doctor visits. Central dining room. Sixth form can provide and cook snacks. 3 exeats for full boarders, weekly boarding available. Visits to local town allowed by sixth form in groups of 2 or 3 at the weekend.

· *Pocklington* ·

Pocklington School	● Pupils 700	● Termly fees
West Green	● Boys 7–18	£1112 (Day)
Pocklington	(Day/Board)	£2173 (Board)
York	● Girls 7–18	● HMC
YO4 2NJ	(Day/Board)	Enquiries/application to
Tel 0759 303125	● Upper sixth 90	the Headmaster

What it's like

Founded in 1514, the school was largely rebuilt in 1850 and its fine buildings are sited on the outskirts of the small market town in ample grounds. The senior school is single site; the junior department is separate. There have been extensive modern developments and facilities are very good. The standard of teaching is high and the academic results are impressive. Very many pupils go on to degree courses. Flourishing music, CDT and drama depts. Good range of sports and games and high standards achieved (a lot of county players). Numerous societies and clubs. Well supported in the area.

School profile

Pupils Total age range 7–18; 700 pupils, 560 day (460 boys, 100 girls), 140 boarding (130 boys, 10 girls); boarding available from age 11 only. Senior department, 11–18, 600 pupils. Main entry ages 11, 13 and into sixth. Approx 15% are children of former pupils. *Transfer from maintained schools:* 50% senior intake, plus 40% to sixth.

Entrance Common entrance and own exam used. Oversubscribed at 11. No special skills required. C of E school but accepts all denominations. Parents not expected to buy text books; maximum extras, £100. 137 assisted places. Various scholarships for academic excellence. Bursaries awarded subject to means test, full tuition fees to £150.

Parents 15+% are doctors, lawyers, etc; 15+% in armed services, 15+% in agriculture. 60+% live within 30 miles; up to 10% live overseas.

Staff Headmaster A D Pickering, in post for 10 years. 52 full time staff, 4 part time. Annual turnover 5%. Average age 30–35.

Academic work GCSE and A-levels. 18 GCSE subjects offered; 20 at A-level (including A-level general studies). In 1990, 89 pupils in upper fifth, 98 in upper sixth. *GCSE:* in 1990, 56 upper fifth gained at least grade C in 8+ subjects; 28 in 5–7; and 5 in 1–4 subjects. *A-levels:* 62 upper sixth passed in 4+ subjects; 22 in 3; 8 in 2; and 5 in 1 subject. 30% took science A-levels; 55% arts/humanities; 15% both. *Computing facilities:* Computer lab with 16 IBM compatible 286 VGA systems, 15 BBC, 4 Archimedes, Apple, Amstrad, 2 Acorns. *Special provision:* EFL for foreign students; some dyslexic help.

European Community *Languages:* French offered: to age 14; GCSE; AS-level; A-level. German offered: to age 14; GCSE; AS-level; A-level. Spanish offered: to age 14; GCSE. 10–25% take GCSE in more than 1 EC language. *Exchanges:* Regular exchanges for pupils aged 14–18 to France and Germany.

Senior pupils' non-academic activities *Music:* 60 learn a musical instrument, 12 to Grade 6 or above, 28 in school orchestra, 20 in school choir, 10 in school pop group, 6 in chamber group and 36 in ensemble/band/brass group; 3 in area youth orchestra. *Drama:* 25–50 in school productions, 80 in house plays. *Art/Design:* 15–20 take as non-examined subject; 75 take GCSE in CDT; 30 take A-level art or CDT. 6–10 accepted for Art School. 20 belong to eg photographic club. *Sport:*

Rugby, cricket, football, athletics, tennis, hockey, cross-country, squash, basketball, volleyball, netball, badminton, swimming and golf available. 150 take non-compulsory sport. Some take exams in swimming, karate, judo, sailing. 12 represent county (squash, cross-country, rugby, hockey and athletics), 5 country (rugby, hockey) and 1 international (rugby). Other activities include a computer club, numerous societies, and clubs from board games to electronics, woodwork to high technology.

Careers In 1990, 93% sixth form leavers went on to degree courses; 1% to art/drama/music colleges; 2% to non-degree courses (eg HND, agricultural college); 2% straight into careers (eg Inland Revenue, armed forces); 1% other. Of those going on to degree courses, 3% went to Oxbridge, 64% to other universities; 33% to poly/colleges. 2% those going on to higher education went to courses in practical art; 55% in humanities/social sciences; 3% in medicine; and 40% in science/engineering.

Uniform School uniform worn throughout.

Houses/prefects Competitive houses. Prefects, head boy/girl, head of house and house prefects – appointed by the Headmaster and housemasters.

Religion Sunday morning service and daily assembly.

Social No organised events with local schools. Organised trips abroad to France and Germany. Day pupils allowed to bring own car/bike/motorbike to school. Meals self service. School shop. Sixth formers allowed some alcohol; no tobacco allowed.

Discipline No corporal punishment. Pupils failing to produce homework once might expect to re-write it or get detention. Those caught smoking cannabis on the premises might expect expulsion, but would be helped to move to another school to make a new start if this was appropriate.

Boarding 15% have own study bedroom, 45% share with others; 40% are in dormitories of 6+. Houses, of approximately 50, are divided by age group and sex. Resident qualified nurse. Central dining room. Pupils can provide and cook own food. 2 weekend exeats and half-term. Visits to local town allowed frequently.

Alumni association is run by M G Milne Esq, c/o the School.

Former pupils Sir James Cobban; Tom Stoppard; Adrian Edmondson.

· Polam Hall ·

Polam Hall School	● Pupils 475	● Termly fees
Grange Road	● Boys None	£1010 (Day)
Darlington	● Girls 4–18	£2060 (Board)
Durham	(Day/Board/Weekly)	£2035 (Weekly)
DH1 5PA	● Upper sixth 28	● GSA
Tel 0325 463383		Enquiries/application to the Headmistress

What it's like

Originally a Friends' school under personal ownership (1884); the present school dates from 1888. The main building (and the heart of the place) is a very elegant late 18th century house in a beautiful garden and wooded part of 19 acres on the edge of Darlington. Kindergarten and junior school are combined with the main school. During the last 20 years many developments have taken place and the buildings much improved and extended. Facilities and accommodation are now excellent. Great importance is attached to pastoral life and to the creation of a happy family atmosphere. All boarders go to the parish church (or church of their own denomination) each Sunday. A good general academic education is given and many sixth formers proceed to degree courses. Very strong music and drama depts. Good range of sports, games and activities. Substantial commitment to local community service. Quite an impressive record in the Duke of Edinburgh's Award Scheme.

School profile

Pupils Total age range 4–18; 475 girls, 368 day, 107 boarding. Senior department 11–18, 333 girls. Main entry ages 9, 11, 13 and into sixth. Approx 5–10% are children of former pupils. *Transfer from maintained schools:* 30% senior intakes, plus 10% to sixth.

Entrance Own entrance exam used. No special skills or religious requirements. Parents not expected to buy text books; maximum extras, £50 plus £40 per term lunch for day girls. 5 assisted places at 11 years. Scholarships/bursaries available, 50%–10% of fees.

Parents 10+% live within 30 miles; up to 10% live overseas.

Staff Headmistress Mrs H C Hamilton, in post for 4 years.

Academic work GCSE and A-levels. 20 GCSE subjects offered; 18 at A-level (including A-level statistics, craft, design and practice and general studies). In 1990, 64 pupils in upper fifth, 28 in upper sixth. *GCSE:* in 1990, 35 upper fifth gained at least grade C in 8+ subjects; 10 in 5–7; and 14 in 1–4 subjects. *A-levels:* 7 upper sixth passed in 4+ subjects; 13 in 3; 5 in 2; and 1 in 1 subject. 18% took science A-levels; 29% arts/humanities; 53% both. *Computing facilities:* 10 BBC micros. *Special provision:* Dyslexia Institute visits; English as a second language – lessons provided in school.

European Community *Languages:* French offered: to age 14; GCSE; AS-level; A-level. German offered: to age 14; GCSE; AS-level; A-level. Spanish offered: to GCSE; AS-level; A-level. 10–25% take GCSE in more than 1 EC language.

Senior pupils' non-academic activities *Music:* 150 learn a musical instrument, 30 to Grade 6 or above, 1 accepted for Music degree; 24 in school orchestra, 100 in school choirs, 24 in wind band; 2 in National Children's Orchestra; 2 in Independent Schools' Orchestra. *Drama and dance:* 100 in school productions; 25 take modern dance; 5, ballet. 6 take Grade 6 in ESB, RAD etc. 2 accepted for Drama/Dance Schools. *Art:* 25 take GCSE; 14 A-level. *Sport:* Hockey, lacrosse, netball, tennis, rounders, athletics, horse riding, swimming, golf, self-defence, basketball, volleyball, squash available. 100 take non-compulsory sport. 20 take exams in eg swimming. 3 represent county. *Other:* 6 take part in local community schemes. 25 taking bronze Duke of Edinburgh's Award and 6 gold. 15 pupils are guides. Outdoor pursuits weekends arranged. Other activities at weekends for boarders, including dry skiing.

Careers In 1990, 59% leavers went on to degree courses; 8% to art/drama/music colleges; 5% to non-degree courses (eg HND hotel management); 11% straight into careers (eg trainee chemist); 16% other. Of those going on to degree courses, 5% went to Oxbridge, 77% to other universities; 18% to poly/colleges. 11% those going on to higher education went to courses in practical art; 7% in music; 41% in humanities/social sciences; 4% in medicine; and 37% in science/engineering.

Uniform School uniform worn except the sixth.

Houses/prefects Competitive houses. No prefects, head girl and head of house elected by school and staff.

Religion Morning assembly (reading) compulsory, as is church for boarders.

Social Social functions and occasional joint musical activities with local independent schools. Organised trips abroad. Pupils allowed to bring own car/bike to school. Some meals formal, some self service. No tobacco/alcohol allowed.

Discipline No corporal punishment. Pupils failing to produce homework once

might expect a late mark; those caught smoking cannabis on the premises may expect expulsion.

Boarding 2% have own study bedroom, 98% share, up to 5. Houses, of 25–40, divided by age. Resident qualified nurse. Central dining room. Pupils can provide and cook limited food. 2 weekend exeats each term. Limited visits to local town allowed.

Alumni association run by Mrs D Bateman, Honey Cottage, 6 West Street, Gayles, Richmond, N Yorkshire DL11 7JA.

· *Portora Royal* ·

Portora Royal School	● Pupils 350	● Termly fees
Enniskillen	● Boys 11–18	£760 (Day)
County Fermanagh	(Day/Board/Weekly)	£1560 (Board)
BT74 7HA	● Girls 11–18	£1418 (Weekly)
Tel 0365 22658	(Day/Board/Weekly)	● HMC
	● Upper sixth 55	Enquiries/application to the Headmaster

What it's like

Founded in 1608 it is a Church of England and Protestant school – and one of the most distinguished in Ireland. Its alumni include Oscar Wilde and Samuel Beckett. The first buildings were at the village of Ballybalfour near Enniskillen. In 1641 the school moved to Enniskillen itself. In 1777 the school took new premises on Portora Hill where it has a magnificent 70-acre site in unusually beautiful and unspoilt countryside on the shores of Lough Erne. In its earlier days Portora's government was in the hands of the King and the Viceroy but from 1890 was managed under the provisions of the Irish Educational Endowments Act. Modern buildings include classrooms and an observatory, plus biology and engineering departments. The boarding accommodation is very comfortable. The school chaplain is in charge of religious education for all and there are weekly services in the chapel for all boarders. Academic standards are high and results are good. Many pupils go on to degree courses each year; many of those who do not, go on to agricultural college. Music and drama are strongly supported and there are regular public performances. The environment is ideal for outdoor pursuits which are many and varied and include sailing, canoeing, caving and fishing. Sports and games are pursued to a high standard – especially cricket, rugby and rowing. The school has produced many outstanding oarsmen. Considerable success has been achieved in the Duke of Edinburgh's Award Scheme.

School profile

Pupils Total age range 11–18, 350 pupils. Main entry age 11. *Transfer from maintained schools:* 98% main intake.

Entrance LEA exam or common entrance used. 2 entry and 2 leaving scholarships pa.

Staff Headmaster R L Bennett, in post for 6 years.

Academic work GCSE and A-levels. 15 subjects offered (including Chinese; no A-level general studies). In 1990, 57 pupils in upper fifth, 55 in upper sixth. *GCSE:* in 1990, 51% upper fifth gained at least grade C in 8+ subjects; 39% in 5–7; and 10% in 1–4 subjects. *A-levels:* 21% upper sixth passed in 4+ subjects; 29% in 3; 29% in 2; and 17% in 1 subject. 50% took science A-levels; 10% arts/

humanities; 40% both. *Computing facilities:* 1 micro per 20 pupils. *Special provision:* Special tuition available.

European Community *Languages:* French offered: to age 14; GCSE; A-level. German offered: to age 14; GCSE; A-level. 10–25% take GCSE in more than 1 EC language. *Exchanges:* Regular exchanges for pupils aged 14–16 to Germany.

Careers In 1990, 72% leavers went on to degree courses; 20% to non-degree courses (mainly agricultural); 8% straight into careers (eg armed services). Of those going on to degree courses, 5% went to Oxbridge, 65% to other universities; 30% to poly/colleges. 40% those going on to higher education went to courses in humanities/social sciences; 10% in medicine; and 50% in science/engineering.

· *Portsmouth Grammar* ·

The Portsmouth
Grammar School
High Street
Portsmouth
Hampshire PO1 2LN
Tel 0705 819125

- Pupils 740
- Boys 11–18
  (Day)
- Girls 11–18
  (Day)
- Upper sixth 110

- Termly fees
  £985 (Day)
- HMC
Enquiries/application to
the Headmaster

What it's like

Founded in 1732 by Dr William Smith, it was remodelled by the Endowed Schools Commission in buildings erected on the site of the old fortifications in 1879. It became fully co-educational in 1991. The present buildings, in an agreeable, plain design, were opened in 1927 and stand in the High Street of Old Portsmouth. Recent developments (from 1982) include modern languages laboratories, a CDT centre, a computer centre, a multi-gym, a sports hall, theatre, music school, pottery and Old Pupils' room. The school is closely connected with Portsmouth Cathedral (whose choristers are mainly pupils), but religious instruction (in accordance with the principles of the Christian faith) is non-denominational. Lower and upper schools are combined; a pre-prep department was opened in 1977. A sound general education is provided. A large, well-qualified staff allows a favourable staff:pupil ratio of 1:10. There is a very large sixth form. Academic standards are high and results consistently good. Many pupils proceed to degree courses (a high proportion to Oxbridge) and other places of higher education. Music and drama are quite strong. There is a good range of sports and games for which the facilities are first-rate. A customary variety is available, plus judo, fencing, rowing (at sea) and sailing. A strong CCF contingent comprises Navy, Army and Air Force sections. Considerable emphasis on open-air pursuits and in the Duke of Edinburgh's Award Scheme (which involves local community services and charity work). The school has vigorous local support; the 'town and gown' relationship amicable.

School profile

Pupils Age range 11–18, 740 day pupils. Main entry age 11 (including girls from 1991). Own junior school. *Transfer from maintained schools:* 35% main intake, plus 20% to sixth.

Entrance Common entrance or own exam (including pupils of own junior). Assisted places; scholarships (including art and music) and bursaries.

Staff Headmaster A C V Evans, in post for 8 years.

Academic work GCSE and A-levels

(general studies taught but not as examination subject). In 1990, 108 pupils in fifth, 110 in upper sixth. *GCSE:* in 1990, 89% fifth gained at least grade C in 8+ subjects; 10% in 5–7; and 1% in 1–4 subjects. *A-levels:* 10% upper sixth passed in 4+ subjects; 66% in 3; 15% in 2; and 8% in 1 subject. 30% took science A-levels; 40% arts/humanities; 30% both. *Computing facilities:* Well equipped IT centre and computers in various departments.

European Community *Languages:* French offered: to age 14; GCSE; AS-level; A-level. German offered: to age 14; GCSE; A-level. Spanish offered: to age 14; GCSE; AS-level; A-level. 25–50% take GCSE in more than 1 EC language. *Exchanges:* Regular exchanges for pupils aged 11–18 to France, Germany and Spain.

Careers In 1990, 71% leavers went on to degree courses; 4% to art/drama/music colleges; 7% straight into careers (eg armed services, accountancy); 8% other. Of those going on to degree courses, 17% went to Oxbridge, 63% to other universities; 20% to poly/colleges. 2% those going on to higher education went to courses in practical art; 1% in drama/acting; 1% in music; 51% in humanities/social sciences; 13% in medicine; and 32% in science/engineering.

· *Portsmouth High* ·

Portsmouth High School
25 Kent Road
Southsea
Hampshire PO5 3EQ
Tel 0705 826714

- Pupils 520
- Boys None
- Girls 11–18 (Day)
- Upper sixth 50

- Termly fees £908 (Day)
- GSA, GPDST
Enquiries/application to the Headmistress

What it's like

Founded in 1882, it has pleasant premises close to Southsea Common and the sea which have been greatly extended over the years. Modern facilities are good and include a fine sports hall, excellent labs and art accommodation. The junior school at Dovercourt is a few minutes away. Administratively the schools form one unit. Pupils are drawn from all parts of Portsmouth and surrounding districts. The staff:pupil ratio is about 1:13. Academic standards are high and results impressive; very many of the sixth form go on to degree courses each year, many to Oxbridge. Many girls take more than one European language at GCSE. French, German and Spanish are taught right through to A-level and there are regular exchanges with France, Germany and Spain. Music, drama and art departments are strong. A good range of sports and games (quite a few representatives at county and national level) and an adequate range of extra-curricular activities. A promising record in the Duke of Edinburgh's Award Scheme.

School profile

Pupils Age range 11–18; 520 day girls. Main entry ages, 11, 14 and into the sixth. Small number are children of former pupils. Own junior school provides over 20%. *Transfer from maintained schools:* 60% main intakes, plus 80% to sixth.
Entrance Own entrance exam used.

Oversubscribed. No special skills or religious requirements. Parents not expected to buy text books. 29 assisted places each year. 5 scholarships/bursaries pa, half to one-third fees.
Parents 15+% are doctors, lawyers etc; 15+% in industry or commerce.

Staff Headmistress Mrs J M Dawtrey, in post for 7 years. 32 full time staff, 11 part time. Annual turnover 4%.

Academic work GCSE and A-levels. 17 subjects offered (no A-level general studies). In 1990, 85 pupils in upper fifth, 52 in upper sixth (now 50). *GCSE:* in 1990, 76 upper fifth gained at least grade C in 8+ subjects; 9 in 5–7 subjects. *A-levels:* 4 upper sixth passed in 4+ subjects; 44 in 3; 3 in 2; and 1 in 1 subject. 45% took science A-levels; 50% arts/ humanities; 5% both. *Computing facilities:* RM Nimbus network. *Special provision:* Coaching as necessary.

European Community *Languages:* French offered: to age 14; GCSE; AS-level; A-level. German offered: to age 14; GCSE; A-level. Spanish offered: to age 14; GCSE; A-level. 25–50% take GCSE in more than 1 EC language. *Exchanges:* Regular exchanges for pupils aged 11–16 to France, Germany and Spain. *Other:* European work experience in sixth form.

Senior pupils' non-academic activities *Music:* 37 learn a musical instrument in school, 25 out of school, 22 to Grade 6 or above, 2 accepted for Music School; 16 in school orchestra, 45 in choir, 16 wind band, 9 string group; 5 in county youth orchestra, 9 in area youth orchestras and bands. *Drama and dance:* 30–50 in school productions. Pupils take Associated Board, New Era Academy or Guildhall exams; 15 participate in speech festivals. *Art:* 45 take GCSE in fine art, textiles or pottery; 10 A-level (pupils able to build a portfolio even if they are not taking A-level). 3 accepted for Art School. *Sport:* Lacrosse, netball, tennis, cricket, volleyball, badminton, table tennis, swimming, rounders, athletics available. 13 represent county/country (gym, swimming, lacrosse, netball, sailing, cricket). *Other:* 25 have bronze Duke of Edinburgh's Award, 2 have silver and 2 gold. Other activities include electronics, debating, Christian Fellowship, gymnastics, running, chess and board games.

Careers In 1990, 94% leavers went on to degree courses; 4% to art/drama/ music colleges; 2% to non-degree courses (eg nursery nursing). Of those going on to degree courses, 15% went to Oxbridge, 84% to other universities; 1% to poly/ colleges. 4% those going on to higher education went to courses in practical art; 2% in music; 50% in humanities/social sciences; 10% in medicine; and 30% in science/engineering.

Uniform School uniform worn except the sixth.

Houses/prefects No competitive houses or prefects. Head girl and 2 deputies, elected by senior girls.

Religion Morning assembly unless withdrawn for religious reasons.

Social Concerts, debates, musicals, lectures with local boys' schools; BAYS, Young Enterprise etc. Exchanges with France, Germany, Spain; group cultural visits; ski-ing trips. Pupils allowed to bring own car/bike to school. Meals self service. School tuckshop. No tobacco/alcohol allowed.

Discipline No corporal punishment. Pupils failing to produce homework once will be required to do it; those caught smoking cannabis on the premises can expect immediate suspension and probable expulsion.

Alumni association run by Mrs J Gauntlett, Windy Ridge, Portsdown Hill Road, Cosham, Portsmouth, Hampshire.

· Princess Helena ·

The Princess Helena
College
Temple Dinsley
Preston
Hitchin
Hertfordshire SG4 7RT
Tel 0462 432100

- Pupils 150
- Boys None
- Girls 11–18
  (Day/Board)
- Upper sixth 17

- Termly fees
  £1750 (Day)
  £2480 (Board)
- GSA, BSA
  Enquiries/application to
  the Headmistress

What it's like

Founded in 1820, the first academic school for girls (day or boarding). After a series of moves it settled at Temple Dinsley, near Hitchin. The main building is a delightful Queen Anne mansion (1712), enlarged by Lutyens in 1909. This and the Dower House lie in fine Gertrude Jekyll gardens and 183 acres of parkland. Considerable modern developments now provide first-rate accommodation and all-round facilities. It has all the advantages of a small school and a happy family atmosphere prevails. Worship is compulsory at morning prayers and Sunday services. A good staff:pupil ratio of 1:14 (plus an unusual number of part-time staff). A good all-round education is given and four European languages are offered right through to A-level. Results are impressive (many sixth formers proceed to degree courses). Very strong indeed in music (especially orchestral). A good range of sports, games and activities. Substantial commitment to local community schemes and an impressive record in the Duke of Edinburgh's Award Scheme.

School profile

Pupils Age range 11–18; 150 girls (40 day, 110 boarding). Main entry ages 11 and into sixth. Approx 4–5% are children of former pupils. *Transfer from maintained schools:* 10% main intake, plus 8% to sixth.

Entrance Common entrance used. Oversubscribed. Music skills looked for. Parents expected to buy text books; maximum extras £150. 4 scholarships pa (including 2 sixth form), 50% fees; minor income-related awards; bursaries for clergy and armed forces, 15% fees.

Parents 15+% in industry or commerce. 10+% live within 30 miles; up to 15% live overseas.

Staff Headmistress Miss Helen Davidson-Wall, in post for 1 year. 15 full time staff, 23 part time.

Academic work GCSE and A-levels. 16 subjects offered (no A-level general studies). In 1991, 37 pupils in upper fifth, 17 in upper sixth. *GCSE:* in 1990, 60% upper fifth gained at least grade C in 8+ subjects. *A-levels:* 1 upper sixth passed in 4+ subjects; 11 in 3; 2 in 2; and 2 in 1 subject. *Computing facilities:* 14 computers (1 to a girl in each set). *Special provision:* Cambridge First Certificate and Certificate of Proficiency offered.

European Community *Languages:* French offered: to age 14; GCSE; AS-level; A-level. German offered: to age 14; GCSE; AS-level; A-level. Italian offered: to age 14; GCSE; AS-level; A-level. Spanish offered: to age 14; GCSE; AS-level; A-level. 10–25% take GCSE in more than 1 EC language. *Exchanges:* Regular exchanges for pupils aged 14–16 to France. *Other:* French, German and Spanish girls visit school (1 term–1 year). German, Italian and Spanish teachers are native speakers; Head of Modern Languages is native French speaker.

Senior pupils' non-academic activities *Music:* 100+ learn a musical instrument, many to Grade 5 or above, 2–3 accepted for Music School; 30+ in school orchestra, 30 in school choir; 1 in Hertfordshire Youth Orchestra. *Drama and dance:* 50+ in school productions. *Art:* 18 take GCSE. 2 accepted for Art School. Glass engraving, photography and ceramics. *Sport:* Lacrosse, netball, field and track athletics, cross-country, tennis, swimming, gymnastics, many indoor games including badminton and volleyball available. 100 take non-compulsory sport. 5 represent county and 2 country (lacrosse). *Other:* Other activities include a computer club, cookery and the Duke of Edinburgh's Award Scheme.

Careers In 1990, 78% leavers went on to degree courses; 16% to art/drama/music colleges; 5% straight into careers. Of those going on to degree courses, 6% went to Oxbridge, 80% to other universities; 14% to poly/colleges. 11% those going on to higher education went to courses in practical art; 5% in music; 42% in humanities/social sciences; and 42% in science/engineering.

Uniform School uniform worn throughout, modified in sixth.

Houses/prefects Competitive houses. Prefects, head girl, head of house and house prefects – appointed by the Head, consulting colleagues and head girl. School Council.

Religion Attendance at religious worship compulsory: daily prayers; church on Sunday (church in village, Catholic church in Hitchin).

Social Participation in social events with other schools. Regular visits abroad plus Outward Bound. Sixth form allowed to bring own bike to school. Meals combination of self service and formal. School shop. No tobacco or alcohol allowed.

Discipline Pupils failing to produce prep might expect an order mark; anyone caught smoking cannabis on the premises would be removed (although this has never had to happen); for smoking cigarettes, removal after first and final warning.

Boarding Sixth form have own study bedroom (new sixth form house); others in small dormitories. New sixth form house, 70 single study-bedrooms in 1991. Resident qualified nurse. Central dining room. Flexible exeats. Visits to local town allowed for senior girls.

Alumni association is run by Mrs Sue Prince, c/o the school.

Former pupils Governesses to the children of Queen Victoria and the Kaiser; Dr Helena Wright (pioneer of birth control); Mary Allen (founder of Women's Auxiliary Police); Dorothea Lambert Chambers (six times Wimbledon champion); Kathleen Archer (MI5, who rumbled Philby); Lady Trumpington (Government minister); Cindy Shelley (actress).

· *Prior Park* ·

Prior Park College
Ralph Allen Drive
Bath
Avon
BA2 5AH
Tel 0225 835353

- Pupils 416
- Boys 11–18
  (Day/Board)
- Girls 11–18
  (Day/Board)
- Upper sixth 60

- Termly fees
  £1432 (Day)
  £2590 (Board)
- HMC

What it's like

Founded in 1830 by Bishop Peter Augustine Baines, it was governed for most of the 19th century by the bishops of Clifton. In 1924 it was taken over by the Congregation of Christian Brothers. It changed to lay administration in 1981 and is one of the few lay Roman Catholic coeducational schools in the country. Its particularly beautiful and well-appointed 18th-century Georgian buildings (designed by John Wood and high on the schedule of listed buildings in Britain) are set in 57 acres of fine grounds and playing fields. The school enjoys a splendid position on the southern hills of Bath, looking down on the city. A major programme of modernisation in 1980–1 provided purpose-built accommodation for resident staff and their families, plus comfortable quarters for boarding pupils. In 1986 the Priory House was acquired as a boarding and day house for girls. In 1987 a sixth-form annexe was opened. A sixth-form centre, theatre and technology centre are in preparation. The college is now very well equipped. It provides an education rooted in the values of the Catholic Church, and a priest serves as full-time chaplain. Considerable importance is attached to religious education (all pupils study this to GCSE level) and practice: Sunday Mass, daily voluntary Mass, prayer, the opportunity for weekly confession and so forth. Much importance is attached to the family atmosphere produced by a resident headmaster and resident house staff. It thus has many of the advantages of a small school whose life is based on the family life of residential house staff. The staff:pupil ratio is a favourable 1:11. Academic standards are high. Many sixth formers go on to degree courses. French, German and Spanish are offered to A-level. Music is strong (over 50% of pupils receive individual tuition in at least one instrument) and there are two orchestras, a choir and a band. Drama is also strong, and both drama and debating feature prominently. The college has a notable sporting tradition, and games and sports (which include hockey, judo and volleyball) are well provided for. A wide range of extra-curricular societies and clubs (including those for estate conservation, archery and shooting). A flourishing CCF includes all three services, plus a REME platoon and a signals platoon. There is keen participation in the Duke of Edinburgh's Award Scheme and an extensive community service programme which runs its own 'Young Enterprise' scheme.

School profile

Pupils Age range 11–18; 416 pupils, 257 boys, 159 girls (day and boarding; boarding for girls only from age 12/13). Main entry age 11, 13 and into sixth. Own prep school. *Transfer from maintained schools:* 40% main intakes, plus 15% to sixth.

Entrance Common entrance and own exam used. Assisted places. Academic, Music and Art Scholarships.

Staff Headmaster J W R Goulding in post 2 years.

Academic work GCSE and A-levels. 19 subjects offered (including philosophy, history of art, classical civilisation, politics and A-level general studies). In 1989, 73 pupils in upper fifth, 60 in upper sixth. *GCSE:* in 1989, 35 upper fifth gained at least grade C in 8+ subjects; 18 in 5–7; and 20 in 1–4 subjects. *A-levels:* 5 upper sixth passed in 4+ subjects; 38 in 3; 13 in 2; and 4 in 1 subject. 13 took science A-levels; 37 arts/humanities; 10 both. *Computing facilities:* Computing Department and computers within departments. *Special provision:* Private lessons at local Dyslexic Centre; extra English lessons for foreign pupils.

European Community *Languages:* French offered: to age 14; GCSE; A-level. German offered: to age 14; GCSE; AS-level; A-level. Spanish offered: to age 14; GCSE; AS-level; A-level. *Exchanges:* Regular exchanges for pupils aged 11–16 to France and Spain.

Careers In 1990, 71% leavers went on to degree courses; 4% to art/drama/music colleges; 2% straight into careers; 23% other (retaking A-levels, reapplying). Of those going on to degree courses, 3% went to Oxbridge, 74% to other universities; 23% to poly/colleges. 6% those going on to higher education went to courses in practical art; 2% in music; 56% in humanities/social sciences; 2% in medicine; and 4% in science/engineering.

· *Prior's Field* ·

Prior's Field School
Godalming
Surrey
GU7 2RH
Tel 0483 810551

- Pupils 245
- Boys None
- Girls 11–18
- (Day/Board/Weekly)
- Upper sixth 21

- Termly fees
  £1495 (Day)
  £2395 (Board/
  Weekly)
- GSA
  Enquiries/application to
  the Headmistress

What it's like

Founded in 1902 by Mrs Leonard Huxley, mother of Julian and Aldous Huxley. It retains links with the Huxley family which has been a guiding influence since the foundation. The main buildings, which include a Voysey house, are in a delightful and peaceful rural site of 25 acres (including formal gardens) in the green belt outside Guildford. Apart from sixth form houses, the whole school is under one roof. Being a small school it has a congenial family atmosphere and enjoys comfortable accommodation and good modern facilities. The staff:pupil ratio is about 1:7.5. Academic standards and results are creditable. Many sixth formers go on to degree courses each year. All girls play some sport on a regular basis. An adequate range of extra-curricular activities. The Duke of Edinburgh's Award Scheme was started in 1988.

School profile

Pupils Age range 11–18; 245 girls, 75 day, 170 boarding. Main entry ages 11, 12, 13 and into sixth. 1% are children of former pupils. *Transfer from maintained schools:* 12% main intakes, plus 5% to sixth.

Entrance Common entrance and own entrance exam used. Oversubscribed. No special skills or religious requirements. Parents not expected to buy text books. 4 scholarships including art and drama 50% to 25% fees; plus some sixth form bursaries according to ability and need, 30% to 10% fees.

Parents 15+% are doctors, lawyers etc; 15+% are in industry or commerce. 60+% live within 30 miles; 10+% live overseas.

Staff Headmistress Mrs J M McCallum, in post for 4 years. 22 full time staff, 12 part time. Annual turnover 8%. Average age 40.

Academic work GCSE and A-levels. 17 subjects offered (no A-level general studies). In 1990, 40 pupils in upper fifth, 20 in upper sixth (now 21). *GCSE:* on average, 35% upper fifth gain at least grade C in 8+ subjects; 53% in 5–7; and 12% in 1–4 subjects. *A-levels:* on average, 28% upper sixth pass in 3 subjects; 56% in 2; and 16% in 1 subject. On average, 36% take science A-levels; 56% arts/ humanities; 8% both. *Computing facilities:* BBC micros networked. *Special provision:* One-to-one tuition for dyslexics with teacher who comes in once a week.

European Community *Languages:* French offered: to age 14; GCSE; AS-level; A-level. Spanish offered: to age 14; GCSE; AS-level; A-level. 10–25% take GCSE in more than 1 EC language. *Exchanges:* Regular exchanges for pupils aged 11–14 to France. *Other:* Visiting French and Spanish pupils each year.

Senior pupils' non-academic activities *Music:* 46 learn a musical instrument, 13 to Grade 6 or above. 16 in school choir. *Drama and dance:* 15 in school productions; 8 take A-level theatre arts. *Art:* 20 take GCSE; 8 A-level art; 3 history of art A-level; 3 accepted for Art School. 7 belong to eg photographic club. *Sport:*

Lacrosse, hockey, netball, rounders, tennis, swimming, athletics, basketball, badminton available; sixth form options: golf, fencing, squash, aerobics. Sport compulsory for all. 4 represent county/country (lacrosse, tennis). *Other:* 25 have bronze Duke of Edinburgh's Award, 2 silver (started 1988). Other activities include clubs for computers, crafts, bridge, drama.

Careers In 1990, 69% leavers went on to degree courses; 8% to art/drama/music colleges; 6% to non-degree courses (eg nursing, secretarial); 17% straight into careers (eg advertising, fashion). Of those going on to degree courses, 51% went to universities; 49% to poly/colleges. 12% those going on to higher education went to courses in practical art; 6% in drama/acting; 52% in humanities/social sciences; 6% in medicine; and 24% in science/engineering.

Uniform School uniform worn except the sixth.

Houses/prefects Competitive houses. Prefects and head girl – appointed by the Head after secret ballot of school and staff. School Council.

Religion Compulsory church on some Sundays for all Christians.

Social Ski-ing holidays and exchange with school in France. Sixth form allowed to bring own bike to school. Lunch self service, other meals formal. School shop. No tobacco/alcohol allowed.

Discipline No corporal punishment. Pupils failing to produce homework once might expect to do it in their own time by the following day; those caught smoking cannabis on the premises might expect expulsion.

Boarding 50% have own study bedroom, 50% share with 1 or 2, occasionally 4. Houses, of 40–65, divided by age group. Resident qualified nurse. Central dining room. Sixth form can provide and cook own food. 2 weekend exeats each term. Visits to local town allowed (weekly for seniors, twice a term for juniors).

Alumni association run by Mrs V Wright, 10 Putney Heath Lane, London SW15 3JG.

Former pupils Baroness Warnock; Jill Bennett, actress.

· *Purcell* ·

The Purcell School
Mount Park Road
Harrow-on-the-Hill
Middlesex
Tel 081 422 1284

- Pupils 148
- Boys 8–18
  (Day/Board)
- Girls 8–18
  (Day/Board)
- Upper sixth 32

- Termly fees
  £2063 (Day)
  £3488 (Board)
- SHMIS, NAGC
  Enquiries/application to
  the Registrar

What it's like

Founded in 1962 it has an agreeable semi-rural site in pleasant grounds on Harrow Hill. It is a coeducational specialist school for young musicians and was the first of its kind in Britain. It began in Conway Hall, then moved to Morley College, thence to Hampstead and finally in 1975 to its present site. It is the only specialist music school in the Greater London area. Many of its pupils go on through the colleges of music or universities to a career in music. It is a multi-racial and non-denominational school with a very high staff:pupil ratio. It can therefore pay particular attention to the needs – musical, academic or pastoral – of the individual and reduce to a minimum the pressures which often threaten a musically gifted child. Drama is strong and there is a fair range of sports and games and extra-curricular activities.

School profile

Pupils Total age range 8–18; 148 pupils, 63 day (23 boys, 40 girls), 85 boarders (30 boys, 55 girls). Senior department, 12–18; 130 pupils (49 boys, 81 girls). Main entry ages 8, 12 and into sixth.

Entrance By musical audition only. Oversubscribed. Exceptional musical promise looked for. Non-denominational (international pupil intake). Parents only expected to buy text books in the sixth. Government aided pupil scheme; LEA awards from some authorities, some school bursaries and scholarships, income related.

Parents 15+% are doctors, lawyers, teachers; 15+% in industry; 15+% in music. 10+% live within 30 miles; up to 10% live overseas.

Staff Head John Bain, in post for 8 years. 21 full time staff, 5 part time. Annual turnover 4%. Average age 35.

Academic work GCSE and A-levels. Average size of upper fifth 27; upper sixth 30 (now 32). *GCSE:* on average, 20 pupils in upper fifth pass 5–7 subjects; 7, 1–4 subjects (because of emphasis on music there is a maximum of 7 subjects per pupil). *A-levels:* on average, 3 pupils in upper sixth pass 3 subjects; 20, 2 subjects; 2, 1 subject (norm is for pupils to take 2 subjects). Most take arts and humanities A-levels including A-level music course. *Computing facilities:* Computer studies may be taken to GCSE on request. Facilities being developed. *Special provision:* EFL teaching as required.

European Community *Languages:* French offered: to age 14; GCSE; A-level. German offered: to age 14; GCSE; A-level. 25–50% take GCSE in more than 1 EC language.

Senior pupils' non-academic activities *Music:* All learn a musical instrument to Grade 6 or above. 70% accepted for Music College. *Drama and dance:* Whole school in 1 production pa. *Art:* 6 take A-level. *Sport:* Swimming, squash, badminton, football available. *Other:* Activities include a computer and chess club. Most extra-curricular activities are musical.

Careers In 1990, 20% leavers went on to degree courses; 60% to art/drama/music colleges; 20% other. Of those going on to degree courses, 50% went to Oxbridge, 50% to other universities. All those going on to higher education go to courses in music.

Uniform School uniform not worn.

Houses/prefects No competitive houses. Prefects ('deputies') – most sixth formers will be a team leader at some stage; head boy/girl ('senior deputies') – appointed by the Headmaster, in consultation with sixth form tutors. School Council.

Religion Religious worship on a private basis.

Social Occasionally provides whole orchestra or some players for other schools' productions. Regular organised trips abroad. Pupils allowed to bring own car/bike/motorbike to school, by arrangement. Meals self service. School tuck shop. No tobacco/alcohol allowed.

Discipline No corporal punishment.

Boarding Most share in groups of 4. Houses are divided by age group, juniors – mixed, senior girls – single sex. Resident matron. Central dining room. Pupils can provide own snacks. 2 weekend exeats termly. Visits to local town allowed with permission, in pairs or small groups.

Former pupils Robert Cohen (cellist); Oliver Knussen (composer and conductor); Nicholas Daniel (oboist).

· *Putney High* ·

Putney High School
35 Putney Hill
London
SW15 6BH
Tel 081 788 4886

- Pupils 825
- Boys None
- Girls 5–18
- (Day)
- Upper sixth 80

- Termly fees
  £1224 (Day)
- GPDST
  Enquiries/application to
  the Headmistress

What it's like

Founded in 1893, it is single-site on Putney Hill and has the bonus of unusually beautiful gardens. The main buildings are three large late Victorian houses to which there have been important additions in recent years, including a technology/computing centre and a large new classroom block with a floor for each of three major departments. The junior school is separate in Lytton House within the school grounds. Facilities are good. Netball and tennis courts are on site, and pupils attend local leisure centres for other sports such as squash, swimming and dry ski-ing. It is a well-run school, academically very competitive and with a high reputation locally. Academic results are impressive and very many girls go on to degree courses each year, including Oxbridge. French, German and Spanish are offered at GCSE and a small (rising) proportion of girls takes GCSE is more than one European language. Italian is taught at A-level, and there are regular exchanges with France, Germany, Italy and Spain. It is very strong indeed in music and also has considerable strength in drama and art. Joint social and cultural functions occasionally with King's College Wimbledon, Tiffins and Emanuel. The school has a high standard in sports and games and a commitment to local community schemes.

School profile

Pupils Total age range 5–18; 825 day girls. Senior department 11–18, 605 girls. Main entry ages 5, 7, 11+ and into sixth. *Transfer from maintained schools:* 20% senior intake, plus 1% to sixth.

Entrance Own entrance exam used. Oversubscribed. No special religious requirements or skills (but academically competitive). Parents not expected to buy text books; music tuition extra, £80 per term. 20 assisted places pa. 5 scholarships and 5 in sixth form, 50–25% fees.

Parents Mainly professional, many from the media.

Staff Headmistress Mrs E Merchant, first year in post. 39 full time staff, 14 part time in the senior school.

Academic work GCSE and A-levels. 21 subjects offered (including Italian and history of art; no A-level general studies; Chinese taught but not examined). In 1990, 81 pupils in upper fifth, 63 in upper sixth (now 80). *GCSE:* in 1990, 53 upper

fifth gained at least grade C in 8+ subjects; 24 in 5–7; and 4 in 1–4 subjects. *A-levels:* 44 upper sixth passed in 3 subjects; 13 in 2; and 5 in 1 subject. 24% took science A-levels; 63% arts/humanities; 13% both. *Computing facilities:* Large computing room with network for whole class. Computers also in departments.

European Community *Languages:* French offered: to age 14; GCSE; A-level. German offered: to GCSE; A-level. Italian: A-level. Spanish offered: to GCSE. 10–25% take GCSE in more than 1 EC language at present; more often 1991 when first pupils take Spanish GCSE. *Exchanges:* Regular exchanges for pupils aged 14–18 to France, Germany, Italy and Spain.

Senior pupils' non-academic activities *Music:* 300+ learn musical instruments, 50 to Grade 6 or above, 6 accepted for Music School, 4 for university music degree; 2 choral scholarships; 50 in senior school orchestra, 60 in junior, 120 in senior choir, 80 in junior choir, 30 in school band, 80 in chamber groups; 1 in National Youth Orchestra, 3 in Stonleigh youth orchestra; 12 pupils in orchestras outside school. *Drama and dance:* 150+ in musical productions. *Art:* 9 take A-level. 4 accepted for Art School. *Sport:* Netball, tennis, hockey (indoor and playground), badminton, fencing, volleyball, swimming, rowing, squash, dry ski-ing available. *Other:* 60 take part in local community schemes. Other activities include a computer club, music (all the time), mathematics and technology clubs; charities' events strongly supported.

Careers In 1990, 82% leavers went on to degree courses; 6% to art/drama/music colleges; 7% to non-degree courses (eg upgrading A-levels for medicine); 4% straight into careers (eg acting, police training). Of those going on to degree courses, 11% went to Oxbridge; 64% to other universities; 24% to poly/colleges. 4% those going on to higher education went to courses in practical art; 1% in drama/acting; 1% in music; 65% in humanities/social sciences; 9% in medicine; and 21% in science/engineering.

Uniform School uniform worn except the sixth.

Houses/prefects No competitive houses. Prefects and head girl – elected by staff and girls. School Council.

Religion No compulsory worship.

Social Some joint functions with King's College Wimbledon and Tiffins. Trips, skiing and exchanges with France, Germany and Italy. Pupils allowed to bring own car/bike to school. Meals self service. No tobacco/alcohol allowed.

Discipline No corporal punishment. Pupils failing to produce homework once might expect a warning or to go on report.

Alumni association run by Mrs Sweetingham, c/o the School.

q

· *Queen Anne's (Caversham)* ·

Queen Anne's School
6 Henley Road
Caversham
Reading
Berkshire RG4 0DX
Tel 0734 471582

- Pupils 375
- Boys None
- Girls 11–18
  (Day/Board/Weekly)
- Upper sixth 61

- Termly fees
  £1695 (Day)
  £2712 (Board/
  Weekly)
- GSA
  Enquiries/application to
  the Headmistress

What it's like

Founded in 1894 and named after Queen Anne since she, in 1706, had granted a Charter to the Greycoat Hospital (founded in 1698 to provide education for the children of Westminster). Part of the original endowment went to the new school, which retains links with Westminster and the Greycoat Hospital. It has a most agreeable site near the village of Caversham (a few minutes' journey from Reading) and combines handsome buildings of some antiquity with modern additions. The school is well equipped with excellent facilities, including four libraries. It is based on firm Christian principles and the chapel has a central place in daily life. A sound general education is provided. High academic standards are expected and attained. A large staff permits a very favourable staff:pupil ratio of about 1:8. There is some emphasis on team games and the creative use of leisure time. Lower sixth-formers have their own leisure centre (with a kitchen) where they may entertain friends and guests. Upper sixth-formers have considerable freedom (they are expected to do a lot in the running of the school) and their houses are organised on student lines. Music is very well catered for and all pupils are taught to read music. Drama is quite strong, with several productions per year. A good deal of time is given to sports and games of which there is a wide range (including rowing and golf; plus the martial art judo). A large number of clubs and societies are available. Social and cultural events with other schools (including boys' schools) are a feature. A lot of community service work is taken on in the district, especially in connection with the elderly. The school supports a number of charities. There is some participation in the Duke of Edinburgh's Award Scheme.

School profile

Pupils Total age range 11–18, 375 girls (most boarding). Main entry ages 11, 12 and 13. *Transfer from maintained schools:* 25% main intake, plus 10% to sixth.
Entrance Common entrance exam used.

Scholarships (including music) plus bursaries.
Staff Headmistress Miss A M Scott, in post for 14 years.
Academic work GCSE and A-levels.

14 GCSE subjects offered; 17 at A-level (including A-level general studies). In 1989, 63 pupils in upper fifth, 61 in upper sixth. *GCSE:* in 1989, 80% upper fifth gained at least grade C in 8+ subjects; 20% in 5–7 subjects. *A-levels:* 10% upper sixth passed in 4+ subjects; 80% in 3; 10% in 2 subjects. 30% took science A-levels; 40% arts/humanities; 30% both. *Computing facilities:* Computer room with 16 terminals; computers in most departments. *Special provision:* Cambridge English for Foreign Students for a few highly intelligent overseas girls. No provision for dyslexia or handicaps.

· *Queen Elizabeth's (Blackburn)* ·

Queen Elizabeth's
Grammar School
Blackburn
Lancashire BB2 6DF
Tel 0254 59911/59955

- Pupils 1200
- Boys 8–18 (Day)
- Girls 16–18 (Day)
- Upper sixth 170

- Termly fees
  £1014 (Day)
- HMC, SHA
Enquiries/application to
the Head Master

What it's like

The original foundation was 1509; refounded in 1567 under royal charter by Elizabeth I. In 1882 it moved to its present site. The solid, well-designed and well-equipped buildings make a compact campus of about 16 acres in the north-west outskirts of Blackburn. Its junior school is nearby. There have been very considerable developments over the years, including a new wing in 1987 and a sports hall and pool in 1990. A distinguished school, it has high standards of teaching and impressive academic results (very many pupils go on to degree courses each year, many to Oxbridge). Christian in emphasis, the school is interdenominational in practice. There are close links with the cathedral. Very strong in music and art. Also much strength in sports and games. Active commitment to community services and a good record in the Duke of Edinburgh's Award Scheme.

School profile

Pupils Total age range 8–18; 1200 day pupils (1120 boys, 80 girls). Senior department 11–18, 1058 pupils (978 boys, 80 girls). Main entry ages 8, 9, 10 and 11 (boys); into sixth (boys and girls). Fair number are children of former pupils. *Transfer from maintained schools:* 90% senior intake, plus 85% to sixth.
Entrance Common entrance and own exam used. Oversubscribed. No special skills or religious requirements. Parents not expected to buy text books; maximum extras £400. 273 assisted places. 20–25 scholarships/bursaries, £1000–£100.
Parents 15+% are doctors, lawyers etc.
Staff Head Master P F Johnston. 88 full time staff. 9 part time. Annual turnover 3%. Average age 40.
Academic work GCSE and A-levels.

24 subjects offered (including A-level general studies). In 1990, 190 pupils in upper fifth, 170 in upper sixth. *GCSE:* in 1990, 70% upper fifth gained at least grade C in 8+ subjects; 28% in 5–7; and 2% in 1–4 subjects. *A-levels:* 70% upper sixth passed in 4+ subjects; 30% in 3 subjects. 67% took science A-levels; 30% arts/humanities; 3% both. *Computing facilities:* 22 networked Nimbus.
European Community *Languages:* French offered: to GCSE; A-level. German offered: to GCSE; A-level. Italian offered: non-examined subject. Spanish offered: to GCSE. 50–75% take GCSE in more than 1 EC language. *Exchanges:* Regular exchanges for pupils aged 11–16 to France, Germany, Greece and Italy.

Senior pupils' non-academic activities *Music:* 80 learn a musical instrument, 8 to Grade 6 or above, 3 accepted for Music School; 60 in school orchestra, 140 in choir. *Art:* 60 take art as non-examined subject; 20 take GCSE; 10 A-level; 4 accepted for Art School. *Sport:* Swimming, soccer, rugby, squash, cricket available. All take non-compulsory sport. 4 represent county/country (soccer, netball). *Other:* 20 have bronze Duke of Edinburgh's Award, 12 have silver and 4 have gold. Many sixth formers work for national charities. Other activities include a computer club, drama, debating.

Careers In 1990, 94% leavers went on to degree courses; 3% to art/drama/music colleges; 1% to non-degree courses; 2% straight into careers (eg armed forces). Of those going on to degree courses, 15% went to Oxbridge, 60% to other universities; 25% to poly/colleges. 1% those going on to higher education went to courses in practical art; 2% in drama/acting; 5% in music; 35% in humanities/social sciences; 20% in medicine; and 30% in science/engineering.

Uniform School uniform worn throughout.

Houses/prefects Competitive houses. Prefects, head boy/girl, head of house and house prefects – appointed by the Head and school.

Religion Religious worship certainly encouraged.

Social Pupils allowed to bring own car/bike to school. Meals self service. School shop. No tobacco/alcohol allowed.

Discipline No corporal punishment. Pupils failing to produce homework once might expect detention.

Former pupils Russell Harty; Bishop Peter Hall (Bishop of Woolwich); The late Vic Whitsey (Bishop of Chester); Sir Kenneth Durham (former Chairman of Unilever); Professor K Miller (Head of Engineering, Sheffield University).

· Queen Elizabeth (Wakefield) ·

Queen Elizabeth
Grammar School
Northgate
Wakefield
West Yorkshire
WF1 3QY
Tel 0924 373943

- Pupils 972
- Boys 7–18
 (Day)
- Girls None
- Upper sixth 88

- Termly fees
 £1007 (Day)
- HMC
Enquiries/application to
the Admissions
Secretary

What it's like

Founded in 1591 by royal charter, it is single-site and close to the city centre. The main building (an example of early Gothic revival) has been in use since 1854. Many extensions in the last 30 years have provided first-rate modern facilities. The junior school is in the main grounds. It has a wide catchment area and the pupils are of a wide social background. High standards of work and conduct are expected and academic results are good (very many go on to degree courses, including many to Oxbridge). Increasingly strong in music (there are traditional links with the cathedral and the school provides many of the choristers), drama and art. Very strong tradition of excellence in games and sports (many county representatives) and an impressive range of activities. Plentiful collaboration with Wakefield Girls' High School.

School profile

Pupils Total age range 7–18; 972 boys, 948 day, 24 boarding (being phased out). Senior department 11–18, 733 boys. Main entry ages 7, 9, 11, 12, 13 and into sixth. Approx 10% are children of former pupils. Own junior school provides more than 20% of intake to senior school. *Transfer from maintained schools:* 50% senior intake.

Entrance Common entrance and own exam used. Oversubscribed. No special skills or religious requirements. Parents not expected to buy text books; all extras optional including music tuition, £73 per term. 154 assisted places. 6 scholarships/bursaries per year (25–50% tuition fees), 11 sixth form scholarships (including music).

Parents 15+% are doctors, lawyers, etc; 15+% in industry or commerce. 60+% live within 30 miles.

Staff Headmaster R P Mardling, in post for 5 years. 58 full time staff, 2 part time. Annual turnover 5%. Average age mid-thirties.

Academic work GCSE and A-levels. 17 GCSE subjects offered; 19 at A-level (all take A-level general studies). In 1990, 99 pupils in upper fifth, 95 in upper sixth (now 88). *GCSE:* in 1990, 83 upper fifth gained at least grade C in 8+ subjects; 10 in 5–7; and 5 in 1–4 subjects. *A-levels:* 79 upper sixth passed in 4+ subjects; 6 in 3; 8 in 2; and 3 in 1 subject. 50 took science A-levels; 27 arts/humanities; 19 both. *Computing facilities:* Network of 14 BBC master compact computers with disk drive and printer facilities. 8 IBM compatible computers with hard disks and printer facilities. Domesday equipment. Computerised library database.

European Community *Languages:* French offered: to age 14; GCSE; AS-level; A-level. German offered: to age 14; GCSE; A-level. Italian offered: to GCSE. Spanish offered: to GCSE. 25–50% take GCSE in more than 1 EC language.

Senior pupils' non-academic activities *Music:* 332 currently play a musical instrument. Large joint school orchestra, wind band and choir. Senior swing band, wind band, orchestra and choirs. *Drama and dance:* 30 in school productions. 1 pa accepted for Drama/Dance School. *Art:* 25–35 take GCSE; 18 A-level. 5–8 per year accepted for Art School, 3 for art at university. 25–40 belong to photographic club. *Sport:* Rugby, cricket, cross-country, hockey, athletics, tennis, basketball, badminton, table tennis, volleyball, swimming, gymnastics, squash and weight training available. 300–400 take non-compulsory sport. 22 represent county (rugby, hockey, cricket, athletics). *Other:* 15 take part in local community schemes. 60 have bronze/silver/gold Duke of Edinburgh's Award. 6 take part in voluntary hospital work. Other activities include a computer club, chess, angling, bridge, fell-walking, golf; classical, geography, and history societies; orienteering, sailing, debating, shooting etc.

Careers In 1990, 80% leavers went on to degree courses; 8% to non-degree courses (eg art foundation course, HND engineering/business); 4% straight into careers (eg retail management, local government, banking); 8% other. Of those going on to degree courses, 13% went to Oxbridge, 65% to other universities; 21% to poly/colleges. 2% those going on to higher education went to courses in practical art; 2% in drama/acting; 2% in music; 56% in humanities/social sciences; 11% in medicine; and 28% in science/engineering.

Uniform School uniform worn throughout.

Houses/prefects No competitive houses. Prefects and head boy – appointed by Headmaster and staff. School Council.

Religion Compulsory school assembly (non-denominational).

Social Theatrical productions with Wakefield High. Organised trips abroad. Pupils allowed to bring own car/bike/motorbike to school. Meals self service. School shops selling tuck and games kit. No tobacco/alcohol allowed.

Discipline No corporal punishment. Pupils failing to produce homework once might expect either a verbal warning or 'Bad Record' (a note in the pupil's school diary); suspension/expulsion would be considered for those caught smoking cannabis on the premises.

Alumni association is run by Mr M Brereton, Flat 3, First Floor, 3 St John's Square, Wakefield.

Former pupils Mike Harrison (Captain, England Rugby Union); Prof Sir Hans Kornberg (Master of Christ College, Cambridge); Kenneth Leighton; Peter Dews (playwright/theatrical producer); Ronald Eyre; Lord Marshall; Lord Wolfenden; Rt Rev David Hope (Bishop-elect of London); Rt Rev Robert Hardy (Bishop of Lincoln).

· Queen Elizabeth's Hospital ·

Queen Elizabeth's
Hospital
Berkeley Place
Clifton
Bristol BS8 1JX
Tel 0272 291856

- Pupils 490
- Boys 11–18
  (Day/Board)
- Girls None
- Upper sixth 60

- Termly fees
  £998 (Day)
  £1752 (Board)
- HMC
  Enquiries/application to
  the Headmaster

What it's like

Founded in 1590, a Blue Coat school along the lines of Christ's Hospital, London. It has occupied its present site since 1847. Urban, it is near the university and city centre. Its buildings are imposing and very well equipped, including a new theatre. A selective entry school for bright boys, its academic standards are high. Generous endowment permits support of many pupils. Socially, it is comprehensive while being academically selective. Christian worship daily. Very strong music department, good drama and art. Impressive academic results: very many pupils go on to degree courses each year. Strong on games, and plentiful activities. Emphasis on outdoor pursuits. Some commitment to local community schemes and the Duke of Edinburgh's Award Scheme. It has close links with the City of Bristol and enjoys vigorous local support. Full use is made of the cultural amenities of the city.

School profile

Pupils Age range 11–18; 490 boys, 400 day, 90 boarding. Main entry ages 11, 13 and into sixth. Approx 5–10% are children of former pupils. *Transfer from maintained schools:* 70% main intakes, plus 80% to sixth.

Entrance Bristol area entrance exam used. Oversubscribed. No special skills or religious requirements. Parents not expected to buy text books; extras include music tuition, £60, and lunch 90p per day. 25 pa assisted places. 6 scholarships/bursaries pa, £2200-£500 pa, based on entrance exam; others related to family income.

Parents 60+% live within 30 miles; up to 5% live overseas.

Staff Head R Gliddon, in post for 5 years. 35 full time staff, 8 part time.

Annual turnover 10%. Average age 35.

Academic work GCSE and A-levels. 18 GCSE subjects offered; 14 at A-level (no A-level general studies). In 1990, 76 pupils in upper fifth, 60 in upper sixth. *GCSE:* in 1990, 79% upper fifth gained at least grade C in 8+ subjects; 21% in 5–7 subjects. *A-levels:* 7% upper sixth passed in 4+ subjects; 69% in 3; 20% in 2; and 3% in 1 subject. 40% took science A-levels; 45% arts/humanities; 15% both. *Computing facilities:* BBC micros, AppleMac and IBM compatible; network of latter. Two computer rooms as well as various department facilities. *Special provision:* As necessary for public examinations.

European Community *Languages:* French offered: to age 14; GCSE; A-level. German offered: to age 14; GCSE;

A-level. Spanish offered: to GCSE. 25–50% take GCSE in more than 1 EC language. *Exchanges:* Regular exchanges for pupils aged 11–18 to France and Germany. *Other:* French and Spanish assistants teach in school. Last year, 2 German, 1 Italian pupil. Visits to Europe by second year (to Brittany), fourth year history (Belgium and Northern France) and classics pupils (Italy). Sixth form involved in European conference.

Senior pupils' non-academic activities *Music:* 30 learn a musical instrument, 12 to Grade 6 or above; 2 Organ scholars; 1 plays in pop group beyond school; 15 in school orchestra, 25 in choir, 6 in pop group, 25 in wind band, 8 in brass group, 12 in woodwind group; 2 in National youth choir; 3 in County of Avon School Orchestra. *Drama and dance:* 35 in school productions; 14 in joint school plays. *Art:* 16 take GCSE, 4, A-level. 2 accepted for Art School. 12 belong to photographic club. *Sport:* Rugger, cricket, swimming, athletics, tennis, squash, badminton, fencing, judo, sailing, basketball, soccer, running, hiking available. 150 take non-compulsory sport; 26 hiking. 15 represent county/country (rugger, athletics, cricket). *Other:* 20 take part in local community schemes. 14 have bronze Duke of Edinburgh's Award, 4 have silver. Other activities include a computer club, chess club (Bristol league), debates (local competitions), quiz teams (local and national competitions), drama club, film society, YHA, ATC (40 boys).

Careers In 1990, 94% leavers went on to degree courses; 6% straight into careers (eg navy). Of those going on to degree courses, 5% went to Oxbridge, 55% to other universities; 40% to poly/colleges. 4% those going on to higher education went to courses in music; 40% in humanities/social sciences; and 56% in science/engineering.

Uniform School uniform worn, modified in sixth.

Houses/prefects Competitive houses. Prefects, head boy, head of house and house prefects – some elected, some appointed.

Religion Morning assembly, Sunday service for boarders.

Social Drama and music (choral and orchestral) with three local girls' schools; debates (Bristol Rotary Club event). Organised trip to France (French and history), Germany (German and rugger), winter ski trip. Meals formal. School tuckshop (at break). No tobacco/alcohol allowed.

Discipline No corporal punishment. Pupils failing to produce homework once might expect a reprimand or detention; those caught smoking cannabis could expect suspension or expulsion.

Boarding 25% have study bedroom (in pairs), 35% share (6); 40% are in dormitories of 5. Houses of 35 and 55, divided by age group. Resident qualified nurse, doctor visits. Central dining room. Senior pupils can provide and cook own food. 2 weekend exeats each term plus half-term. Visits to the local town allowed.

Alumni association is run by Mr R A Barrett, 33 West View Road, Keynsham, Bristol BS18 1BQ.

· *Queen Ethelburga's* ·

Queen Ethelburga's
College
Thorpe Underwood Hall
Ouseburn
York
YO5 9S2
Tel 0423 330711

- Pupils 205
- Boys 2$\frac{1}{2}$–11 only
- Girls 2$\frac{1}{2}$–18 (Day/ Board/Weekly)
- Upper sixth 21

- Termly fees £1280 (Day) £2135 (Board/ Weekly)
- Woodard

Enquiries/application to the Headmistress

What it's like

Founded in 1912 and named after the Anglo-Saxon queen who brought Christianity to the north in the 7th century. Queen Ethelburga's has all the advantages of being small; a happy, purposeful, family atmosphere prevails. There is considerable emphasis on Christian values, and religious practice in the Anglican tradition, plus a firm belief in the merits of a single-sex education. Academic standards are very creditable and the large staff permits a staff:pupil ratio of about 1:8. Results are good and a few girls go on to degree courses each year. The music, art and drama depts are very active. A good standard is attained in sports and games. The Parents' Association is particularly strong and the school has a high reputation locally. A commitment to local community schemes and an outstanding record in the Duke of Edinburgh's Award Scheme. It has moved to its present site, and admitted boys to the junior school for the first time, in 1991.

School profile

Pupils Total age range 4 1/2–18; 205 girls, 62 day, 143 boarding. Main entry ages, 5, 11 and into the sixth. Own junior department provides over 20% senior intake. *Transfer from maintained schools:* 20% intake at 11, plus 10% to sixth.

Entrance Common entrance and own exam used. No special skills or religious requirements. Parents not expected to buy text books. 8 scholarships (including music), clergy and sixth form bursaries; 50%–20% fees.

Staff Headmistress Mrs J M Town, 3 years in post. 21 full time staff, 13 part time. Annual turnover 10%. Average age 40.

Academic work GCSE, AS and A-levels. 12 subjects offered (including A-level general studies; community languages can be arranged). In 1989, 21 pupils in upper fifth, 21 in upper sixth. *GCSE:* in 1989, 60% upper fifth gained at least grade C in 8+ subjects; 25% in 5–7; and 15% in 1–4 subjects. *A-levels:* 15%

upper sixth passed in 4+ subjects; 20% in 3; 20% in 2; and 20% in 1 subject. 30% took science A-levels; 50% arts/ humanities; 20% both. *Computing facilities:* 10 BBC model B computers and 1 Amstrad 2086. 10 printers; plus 10 computers in new computer room. *Special provision:* Special Needs Unit. English as a foreign language.

Senior pupils' non-academic activities *Music:* 89 learn a musical instrument, 2 to Grade 6 or above; 40 in school choir, 6 in string ensemble, 10 wind, 10 recorder ensemble. *Drama and dance:* 20 in school productions. 3 take to Grade 6 or above. 6 take ballet. 6 entered eg public speaking competitions. *Art:* 86 take as non-examined subject; 22 GCSE; 8 A-level. 2 belong to eg photographic club. *Sport:* Lacrosse, netball, gymnastics, swimming, riding, tennis, squash, badminton, rounders, athletics, skiing (local dry ski slope) available. 100 take non-compulsory sport. 50 take exams. 7 represent county/district (lacrosse, netball). *Other:* 35 take part in local community schemes. 37 have bronze Duke of Edinburgh's Award, 13 have silver and 15 gold. Other activities include a computer club, golf, outdoor pursuits, car maintenance, canoeing, gliding, self-defence, sailing, play reading, hospital visiting, social work in homes and charity shops, cooking, jewellery making, brass rubbing.

Careers 1 full time and 1 part time careers adviser. Annual average accepted for *arts and humanities degree courses* at universities, 2; polytechnics/colleges, 3. *science and engineering degree courses* at universities, 2; medical schools, 1; polytechnics/colleges, 2. *other general training courses*, 5. Average going straight into careers in industry, 1; retail management, 2.

Uniform School uniform worn except the sixth.

Houses/prefects Competitive houses.

Prefects, head girl, head of house and house prefects. School Council.

Religion Religious worship encouraged.

Social Debates, dances, choir, literary studies outings, management courses organised with local schools. Annual visit to Switzerland, French trips and exchanges. Meals formal. School shop. No tobacco allowed; alcohol occasionally on controlled basis.

Discipline No corporal punishment. Pupils failing to produce homework once might expect reprimand; those caught smoking cigarettes on the premises might expect expulsion after warnings.

Boarding All seniors have own study bedroom. Houses, of approximately 50, plus sixth form house. Resident qualified nurse, visiting doctor. 2 weekend exeats each term. Visits to local town allowed: once a term at 14; weekly in sixth.

· Queen Margaret's (York) ·

Queen Margaret's School Escrick Park York YO4 6EU Tel 090 487 261	● Pupils 360 ● Boys None ● Girls 11–18 (Day/Board) ● Upper sixth 43	● Termly fees £1550 (Day) £2450 (Board) ● GSA Enquiries/application to the Headmaster

What it's like

Founded in 1901, moved to its present site in 1949. The main building is a huge and magnificent country house built in 1758 in 50 acres of splendid parkland. A C of E foundation, its pupils come from a wide social and geographic background ('global intake'). It has many of the advantages of a small school and enjoys a good staff:pupil ratio of 1:10. There is an almost full-time special needs department. A notable feature is the big parental involvement in many areas of school life (eg organisation, cultural, work experience etc). Very strong music, drama and art and a good range of sports, games and activities. Good record in the Duke of Edinburgh's Award Scheme.

School profile

Pupils Age range 11–18; 360 girls, 50 day, 310 boarding. Main entry ages 11–13 and into sixth. 5% are children of former pupils.

Entrance Common entrance. Oversubscribed. No special skills or religious requirements. 9 scholarships/bursaries, plus music scholarship, from half fees to £300.

Parents 15+% are doctors, lawyers, etc;

20+% in industry or commerce. 10+% live within 30 miles, up to 10% live overseas.

Staff Headmaster C S McGarrigle, in post for 8 years. 32 full time staff, 14 part time. Annual turnover 15%. Average age 40.

Academic work GCSE and A-levels. 21 subjects offered at A-level. Average size of fifth 60; upper sixth 40. *GCSE:* on average, 50 pupils pass 8+ subjects. *A-levels:* on average, upper sixth pupils pass 3 subjects. *Computing facilities:* A large resource centre; computers also in nine departments. *Special provision:* almost full time special needs department.

European Community *Languages:* French offered: to age 14; GCSE; AS-level; A-level. German offered: to age 14; GCSE; AS-level; A-level. Spanish offered: to age 14; GCSE; AS-level; A-level. 50–75% take GCSE in more than 1 EC language. *Exchanges:* Regular exchanges for pupils aged 14–18 to France. *Other:* Study of politics, includes EC.

Senior pupils' non-academic activities *Music:* 95 learn a musical instrument, 20 to Grade 6 or above; 25 in school orchestra, 30 in choir, 35 in school bands, 70 in choral society; 5 in National Childrens' Orchestra. *Drama and dance:* 120 in school productions. 2/3 entered dance festivals. 24 in senior theatre club including running junior theatre club. *Art:* Art, design, pottery, textiles, photography, history of art offered. *Sport:* Hockey, netball, lacrosse, golf, tennis, swimming, athletics, badminton, gymnastics, ski-ing, riding, orienteering, squash, martial arts and rounders available. 125 take extra tennis; 80 ride. 70 take exams. Lacrosse: 5 pupils represent county, 5 region, and 5 go into England trials. *Other:* 50 have bronze Duke of Edinburgh's Award, and 15 have gold. 10 work for national charities. Other activities include a computer club, cookery, needlework, outreach, chess, bridge,

fashion and design, driving lessons, and aerobics.

Careers In 1990, 75% leavers went on to degree courses; 10% to art/drama/music colleges; 15% to non-degree courses (eg agricultural, secretarial). Of those going on to degree courses, 7% went to Oxbridge, 80% to other universities; 13% to poly/colleges. 10% those going on to higher education went to courses in practical art; 2% in drama/acting; 75% in arts/humanities/social sciences; 8% in medicine; and 5% in science/engineering.

Uniform School uniform worn except sixth.

Houses/prefects Competitive houses. Prefects, head girl, heads of houses and house prefects – appointed by the Head. School Committee.

Religion Compulsory C of E worship.

Social Mission work locally, debates, social events, musical events (village invited). Organised trips abroad – skiing and to Kenya, Paris, Greece, Moscow. Pupils allowed to bring own bike/horse to school. Meals self service. School shop. No tobacco/alcohol allowed.

Discipline Pupils are required to produce homework and to keep rules; anyone caught smoking cannabis would be dismissed.

Boarding Upper sixth have own study bedroom, lower sixth share with others. Houses, of approximately 50, are divided by age. Resident qualified medical staff. Central dining room. Sixth form can provide and cook own food. 1–2 weekend and half-term exeats each term. Visits to local town allowed from 13 upwards.

Alumni association is run by Mrs Judith Cooke, Old House Farm, Stubbs Walden, Doncaster DN6 9BU.

Former pupils Winifred Holtby; Joan Hall (MP); Ann Jellicoe (writer); Dorothy Hutton (RA); Elizabeth Poston (musician).

· *Queen Mary* ·

Queen Mary School
Lytham St Annes
Lancashire
FY8 1DS
Tel 0253 723246

- Pupils 700
- Boys None
- Girls 6–18
- (Day)
- Upper sixth 64

- Termly fees
  £787 (Day)
- GSA
  Enquiries/application to
  the Head Mistress

What it's like

Its foundation derives from unusual circumstances: in 1719 a violent storm caused havoc in the area and local farmers made a national appeal for help. In the end, they decided to use the money collected, not to recoup their own losses, but to provide a school to benefit the community. Thus began the Lytham Charity which in 1930 established Queen Mary School as a grammar school for girls, a counterpart to the slightly older King Edward VII School for boys. The original neo-Georgian building remains the heart of the school to which there have been many additions on a 13-acre site which provides ample playing fields. It is now well equipped with modern facilities including a design and technology centre, two libraries and a sports hall. The predominantly female staff (there are quite a lot of part-time staff and visiting staff) permits a reasonably good staff:pupil ratio of about 1:14. Academic standards are high and results are good. Each year a number of girls go on to degree courses. There is no prefectorial system; all sixth-formers are expected to take some responsibility in the daily running of the school. Music in many forms is a major feature of the life. Drama is also well supported. There is a good deal of emphasis on physical education, games and sports. Games are played to a high standard and the school regularly supplies players to county and North of England teams. A large and varied programme of social services involves many senior and middle-school girls. There is also considerable participation in the Duke of Edinburgh's Award Scheme.

School profile

Pupils Total age range 6–18, 700 day girls. Senior department 11–18. Main entry ages 11 and into sixth. *Transfer from maintained schools:* 90% intake at 11, plus 100% into sixth.

Entrance Own entrance exam used. Assisted places. 1 scholarship and 6 bursaries pa.

Staff Head Mistress Miss M C Ritchie, in post for 10 years.

Academic work GCSE and A-levels. 20 subjects offered (including A-level general studies). In 1990, 99 pupils in upper fifth, 50 in upper sixth (now 64). *GCSE:* in 1990, 56 upper fifth gained at least grade C in 8+ subjects; 26 in 5–7; and 17 in 1–4 subjects. *A-levels:* 27 upper sixth passed in 4+ subjects; 13 in 3; 3 in

2; and 7 in 1 subject. 26% took science A-levels; 54% arts/humanities; 20% both. *Computing facilities:* 2 purpose-built rooms in technology block.

European Community *Languages:* French offered: to age 14; GCSE; A-level. German offered: to age 14; GCSE; A-level. 10–25% take GCSE in more than 1 EC language. *Exchanges:* Regular exchanges for pupils aged 11–16 to Germany.

Careers In 1990, 66% leavers went on to degree courses; 4% to art/drama/ music colleges; 14% to non-degree courses (eg additional A-levels, HND hotel and catering); 12% straight into careers (eg nursing, police, insurance, computing); 4% other. Of those going on to degree courses, 12% went to Oxbridge, 55% to other universities; 33% to poly/colleges. 3% those going on to higher education went to courses in music; 61% in humanities/social sciences; 15% in medicine; and 21% in science/engineering.

· Queen Victoria ·

Queen Victoria School
Dunblane
Perthshire
FK15 0JY
Tel 0786 822288

- Pupils 270
- Boys 10–18
- (Board)
- Girls None
- Higher year 27

- Termly fees £90
  (clothing charge)
- BSA
  Enquiries/application to
  the Headmaster

School profile

Pupils Total age range 10–18, 270 boarding boys. Main entry age 10. *Transfer from maintained schools:* 100% main intake.

Entrance All pupils must be the sons of servicemen or women who have served at least 4 years in the ranks in HM Forces – parents must either be Scottish or have served in a Scottish regiment. The school is largely financed by the Ministry of Defence.

Staff Headmaster J D Hankinson, in post for 11 years.

Academic work O/S-grades, Highers and CSYS. 18 subjects offered. In 1990, 33 pupils in O/S-grade year, 27 in Higher year, 6 in CSYS year. *O/S-grade:* in 1990, 6 gained at least grade 3 in 8+ subjects; 13 in 5–7; and 12 in 1–4 subjects. *Highers:* 3 passed in 5+ subjects; 2 in 4; 5 in 3; 8 in 2; and 9 in 1 subject. *CSYS:* 1 passed in 3 subjects; 1 in 2; and 3 in 1. *Computing facilities:* Computer classroom: BBC Master, Econet, Archimedes computers in all main subject departments. *Special provision:* Full-time special needs teacher.

European Community *Languages:* French offered: to age 14; S-grade; Higher. German offered: to age 14; S-grade; Higher; A-level. 10–25% take S-grade in more than 1 EC language.

Careers In 1990, 31% leavers went on to degree courses; 12% to art/drama/music colleges; 12% to non-degree courses; 34% straight into careers (eg army, navy, RAF, police, apprenticeships); 11% other. Of those going on to degree courses, 45% went to universities; 55% to poly/colleges. 3% those going on to higher education went to courses in practical art; 25% in humanities/social sciences; 3% in medicine; and 69% in science/engineering.

· *Queen's (Chester)* ·

The Queen's School
City Walls Road
Chester
CH1 2NN
Tel 0244 312078

- Pupils 578
- Boys 4–8 only (Day)
- Girls 4–18 (Day)
- Upper sixth 60

- Termly fees £852 (Day)
- GSA, SHA

Enquiries/application to the Secretary

What it's like

Founded in 1878, it has a pleasant urban site with gardens and playing fields on the west side of the city wall, near the Watergate. A combination of late Victorian and modern buildings. The school still uses the original assembly hall given by the Duke of Westminster in 1882 when Queen Victoria became the first patron. The junior and prep departments are housed in separate buildings in Liverpool Road. The school is interdenominational with strong Christian emphasis. A sound general education is provided and impressive results are obtained. Very many leavers go on to degree courses (including Oxbridge) and other further education each year. Considerable strength in music, drama and art. An adequate range of sports and games (high standards) and a fair range of extra-curricular activities.

School profile

Pupils Total age range 4–18; 578 day pupils (34 boys, 544 girls). Senior department 11–18, 430 girls. Main entry ages 4 (boys and girls), 8, 11 and into sixth (girls). *Transfer from maintained schools:* 38% senior intake, plus 90% to sixth.

Entrance Own entrance exam used. Oversubscribed. No religious requirements. Good all-round academic ability looked for. Parents not expected to buy text books. 17 assisted places pa. Bursaries available, dependent on need.

Parents All live within 30 miles.

Staff Head Mistress Miss D M Skilbeck, 1 year in post. 32 full time staff, 23 part time.

Academic work GCSE and A-levels (A-level general studies offered). In 1990, 60 pupils in upper fifth, 60 in upper sixth. *GCSE:* in 1990, 58 upper fifth gained at least grade C in 8+ subjects; 2 in 5–7 subjects. *A-levels:* 38 upper sixth passed in 4+ subjects; 23 in 3 subjects. 30% took science A-levels; 30% arts/humanities; 40% both. *Computing facilities:* Well-equipped room with BBC computers. *Special provision:* Some individual help.

European Community *Languages:* French offered: to age 14; GCSE; AS-level; A-level. German offered: to GCSE; A-level. Italian offered: to GCSE. Spanish offered: to GCSE. Over 75% take GCSE in more than 1 EC language. *Exchanges:* Regular exchanges for pupils aged 11–16 to France. *Other:* Native speakers as conversation assistants.

Senior pupils' non-academic activities *Music:* 2 orchestras, choir, wind, recorder and string groups. Strong interest in music, mainly for pleasure. *Drama:* Annual production with as large a cast as possible. *Art:* Sixth form take as non-examined subject; 15–20 take GCSE; 6–10 A-level. Several accepted for Art School. *Sport:* Hockey, lacrosse, tennis, swimming, rounders, athletics available. Many take part in non-compulsory sport. Some pupils represent county/country (hockey, lacrosse, tennis, athletics). *Other:* Some senior girls take part in local community schemes and enter voluntary schemes after leaving school. Other activities include a computer club, debating, Christian Union, netball and gym clubs. Duke of Edinburgh's Award scheme, public speaking.

Careers On average, 80–85% leavers go on to degree courses; of these, some 12%

597

go to Oxbridge, 88% to other universities or poly/colleges.

Uniform School uniform worn except the sixth.

Houses/prefects Competitive houses for games, music and drama. Head girl and deputies appointed by Head and staff (no prefects). School Committee.

Religion Short Christian assembly every morning.

Social Organised local events and joint functions with other schools from time to time. French and German exchanges; skiing trips abroad. Pupils allowed to bring own bike to school. Meals self service. Twice-weekly tuckshop. No tobacco/alcohol allowed.

Discipline No corporal punishment.

Alumni association run by Miss K M Wood, Four Winds, Stannage Lane, Churton, Chester.

· Queen's (London) ·

Queen's College,
London
43 Harley Street
London W1N 2BT
Tel 071 580 1533

- Pupils 397
- Boys None
- Girls 11–18
  (Day/Weekly)
- Upper sixth 70

- Termly fees
  £1500 (Day)
  £2500 (Weekly)
- GSA
  Enquiries/application to
  the College Registrar

What it's like

Founded in 1848, it was the pioneer college for the higher education of women and the first institution to provide both a sound academic education and proper qualifications for women. Queen Victoria herself was interested in its foundation and was its first patron; she contributed personally to funds. It has continued to be a pioneer institution. The main buildings date from 1762 and consist of three handsome Georgian houses with many additions and improvements over the years. There is a staff:pupil ratio of about 1:10. The teaching is good and exam results are consistently creditable. Very many of the sixth form proceed to degree courses each year, including Oxbridge, and great emphasis is placed on careers and advice. French, German, Italian and Spanish are offered to A-level (also Russian). Many girls take GCSE in more than one European language and there are regular exchanges with France. Music, drama and art are all strongly supported. There is a standard range of games and sports available (easy access to playing fields in the nearby Regent's Park).

School profile

Pupils Age range 11–18; 397 girls (386 day, 11 weekly boarders). Main entry ages 11, 14 and into sixth. 5% are children of former pupils. *Transfer from maintained schools:* 30% main intakes.

Entrance Own entrance exam used. No special skills or religious requirements. Parents expected to buy text books. 8 pa assisted places at 11.

Staff Principal: The Hon Lady Goodhart, first year in post. 35 full time staff, 16 part time.

Academic work GCSE and A-levels. 22 subjects offered (including Russian, German, Spanish, Italian and Classical Greek). In 1989, 51 pupils in upper fifth, 57 in upper sixth. *GCSE:* in 1989, 21 upper fifth gained at least grade C in 8+ subjects; 23 in 5–7; and 7 in 1–4 subjects. *A-levels:* 2 upper sixth passed in 4+ subjects; 36 in 3; 10 in 2; and 9 in 1 subject. 10% took science A-levels; 75% arts/humanities; 15% both. *Computing facilities:* New computer laboratory – 26 BBC network and 10 PCs.

European Community *Languages:* French offered: to age 14; GCSE; AS-level; A-level. German: GCSE; AS-level; A-level. Italian offered: to GCSE; AS-level; A-level. Spanish offered: to GCSE; AS-level; A-level. 26–50% take GCSE in more than 1 EC language. *Exchanges:* Regular exchanges for pupils aged 14–16 to France.

Senior pupils' non-academic activities *Music:* 70 learn a musical instrument, 28 to Grade 6 or above; 25 play in school orchestra, 33 in choir. *Drama and dance:* 60 in school productions; 10 in fringe theatre. 2 accepted for Drama/Dance Schools. *Art:* 15 take art as non-examined subject; 50 take GCSE; 22 A-level. 5 accepted for Art School. *Sport:* Netball, hockey, rounders, tennis, gymnastics, fencing, swimming available. 50 take non-compulsory sport. 2 pupils in English Fencing team. *Other:* Activities include a computer club, debating society, drama club, 2 choirs, 2 orchestras, maths club, writing club.

Careers In 1990, 83% leavers went on to degree courses; 10% to art/drama/music colleges; 7% straight into careers. Of those going on to degree courses, 17% went to Oxbridge; 56% to other universities; 24% to poly/colleges. 4% those going on to higher education went to courses in practical art; 2% in music; 88% in humanities/social sciences; and 12% in science/engineering.

Uniform School uniform not worn.

Houses/prefects No houses. Prefects, head girl – elected by staff, Principal and pupils.

Religion Anglican tradition with multi religions included. Separate Jewish prayers.

Social Regular trips abroad. Meals self service. School bookshop and art shop. No tobacco/alcohol allowed.

Alumni association is run by Mrs L Bernard, Old Queens Society, c/o the College.

· *Queen's (Taunton)* ·

Queen's College	● Pupils 437	● Termly fees
Taunton	● Boys 12–18	£1660 (Day)
Somerset	(Day/Board)	£2540 (Board)
TA1 4QS	● Girls 12–18	● HMC
Tel 0823 272559	(Day/Board)	Enquiries/application to
Fax 0823 388430	● Upper sixth 56	the Headmaster

What it's like

Founded in 1843, a Methodist foundation, it moved to its present premises in 1846. These are single-site and semi-rural in 30 acres on the southern outskirts of Taunton. Very pleasant buildings and fine playing fields. Junior school combined. Much development in the last 25–30 years. More extensions are currently under way. Facilities are good and the school is well positioned for field work, expeditions etc to Exmoor, Dartmoor and the Quantocks. An exceptionally strong music department; good drama and art. Many sixth formers go on to university degree courses. A good range of games, sports and activities. A distinguished record in the Duke of Edinburgh's Award Scheme. Vigorous local support.

School profile

Pupils Age range 12–18; 437 pupils, 241 day (112 boys, 129 girls), 196 boarding (156 boys, 40 girls). Main entry ages 12–13 and into sixth. Own junior school provides more than 20% of intake. *Transfer from maintained schools:* 40% main intakes, plus 60% to sixth.

Entrance Common entrance and own exam used. Oversubscribed for girls' boarding. Musical skills looked for; all denominations welcome. Parents not expected to buy text books. 14 assisted places pa. Various scholarships/bursaries, means-tested if over half fees.

Staff Head A P Hodgson, in post for 9 years. 43 full time staff, 14 part time. Annual turnover 5%.

Academic work GCSE and A-levels. 20 GCSE and A-level subjects offered; (no A-level general studies). In 1990, 85 pupils in upper fifth, 56 in upper sixth. *GCSE:* in 1990, 54 upper fifth gained at least grade C in 8+ subjects; 11 in 5–7; and 11 in 1–4 subjects. *A-levels:* 36 upper sixth passed in 3+ subjects; 12 in 2; and 8 in 1 subject. 45% took science A-levels; 35% arts/humanities; 20% both. *Computing facilities:* Extensive. *Special provision:* Specialist help for dyslexics.

European Community *Languages:* French offered: to age 14; GCSE; AS-level; A-level. Spanish offered: to age 14; GCSE; A-level. Over 75% take GCSE in more than 1 EC language. *Exchanges:* Regular exchanges for pupils aged 14–18 to France and Spain.

Senior pupils' non-academic activities *Music:* 230 learn a musical instrument, 1 accepted for Music School; 60 in school orchestra, 50 in school choir. *Drama and dance:* 50 take drama or dance. *Art:* All take as non-examined subject; 50 take GCSE; 3–4 A-level. 2 accepted for Art School. *Sport:* Rugby, hockey, netball, cricket, squash, badminton, swimming, athletics, tennis, fencing, trampolining and golf available. Many pupils represent county. *Other:* 60 have bronze Duke of Edinburgh's Award, 25 have silver and 20 gold. Other activities include woodwork, dressmaking, car maintenance, home economics; archive, history, geography and computer clubs.

Careers In 1990, 75% leavers went on to degree courses; 4% to art/drama/music colleges; 8% straight into careers (eg estate agency, farming); 13% other. Of those going on to degree courses, 5% went to Oxbridge, 70% to other universities; 25% to poly/colleges.

Uniform School uniform worn throughout.

Houses/prefects Competitive houses. Prefects, head boy/girl, head of house and house prefects – appointed by the Head.

Religion Part of a group of Methodist schools.

Social Organised trips abroad. Pupils allowed to bring own car/bike to school. Meals self service. School shop. No tobacco/alcohol allowed.

Discipline No corporal punishment. Pupils failing to produce homework once might expect to have to do it. Fines and suspension used, discipline for those caught smoking cigarettes on the premises would depend on the circumstances.

Boarding *Upper sixth* have own study bedroom, lower sixth share with 2; 50% are in dormitories of 6+. Single sex houses, of 45, same as competitive houses. Resident qualified nurse. Central dining room. Exeats each term. Visits to local town allowed for older pupils.

· *Queenswood* ·

Queenswood
Shepherds Way
Brookmans Park
Hatfield
Hertfordshire AL9 6NS
Tel 0707 52262
Fax 0707 49267

- Pupils 396
- Boys None
- Girls 11–18
  (Day/Board)
- Upper sixth 51

- Termly fees
  £1897 (Day)
  £2845 (Board)
- GSA, BSA
Enquiries/application to
the Admissions
Secretary

What it's like

Founded in 1894 at Clapham Park by two Methodist ministers, it moved to its present site in 1925. This site is in an exceptionally pleasant area of the Green Belt and comprises 420 acres of farmland, woodland and sports fields. There has been steady growth and expansion, not least during the 1980s and the school is now unusually well equipped for every need, both academic and extra-curricular. 22 new classrooms are fitted with broadband cabling thus enabling data and satellite TV channels to be accessed in each room. This brings potential for wide spread information technology in the school. Being within easy reach of London, its pupils make frequent visits to theatres, concerts and exhibitions. It is nationally known for its tennis centre. The school prides itself on its friendly atmosphere and general community spirit. It has a strong Christian foundation and the chapel plays a significant part in the life of the school. The staff:pupil ratio is about 1:9 and high academic standards can be achieved by good and average pupils. Exam results impressive. Very many of upper sixth go on to degree courses. All girls are expected to take A-levels. Music is very strong; there are two orchestras, a wind band, ensemble groups, three choirs and a choral society. There is also a great deal of emphasis on drama with high standards of performance. Tennis, hockey, athletics, badminton, swimming are the main sports; riding, golf, windsurfing, sailing, shooting are available for senior girls. Again high standards are attained and the school has provided numerous representatives at county level and some at national level in tennis and hockey. There are many clubs and societies for other extra-curricular activities. The school has a substantial commitment to local community schemes and has an impressive record in the Duke of Edinburgh's Award Scheme. It also runs its own exploration society.

School profile

Pupils Age range 11–18; 396 boarding girls; small number of day boarders from September 1991. Main entry ages 11, 12, 13 and into sixth. 6% are children of former pupils. *Transfer from maintained schools:* 3% main intake, plus 25% to sixth.

Entrance Common entrance exam used except under exceptional circumstances. Oversubscribed in sixth form. No special skills required except motivation to make good use of opportunities offered; no religious requirements. 8 scholarships pa (academic, music, tennis) at 11, 12, 13, 16, all means tested, 50% of fees or more.

Parents 15+% are doctors, lawyers etc. 15+% in industry. 10+% live within 30 miles; 27% live overseas, half of whom are foreign nationals.

Staff Head Mrs A M B Butler, in post for 10 years. 51 full time staff, 37 part time. Annual turnover 8%. Average age 37.

Academic work GCSE, AS and A-levels. 17 GCSE subjects offered; 13 at AS; 18 at A-level (including theatre studies, history of art; no A-level general studies). In 1990, 66 pupils in upper fifth, 51 in upper sixth. *GCSE:* in 1990, 56 upper fifth gained at least grade C in 8+ subjects; 19 in 5–7 subjects. *A-levels:* 2 upper sixth passed in 4+ subjects; 33 in 3 (including 5 with an additional AS-level); 15 in 2 subjects (including 5 with an additional AS-level). 5 took science A-levels; 38 arts/humanities; 13 both. 5 girls involved in Education for Engineering Scheme. *Computing facilities:* A network of BBC Masters; Archimedes for graphic design in art/technology department; desktop publishing; departmental computers. *Special provision:* Specialist help for intelligent dyslexic pupils only.

European Community *Languages:* French offered: to age 14; GCSE; AS-level; A-level. German offered: to age 14; GCSE; A-level. Spanish offered: to age 14; GCSE; AS-level; A-level. Over 75% take GCSE in more than 1 EC language. Pupils encouraged to take AS-level in French or Spanish, in addition to their normal A-levels. *Other:* Some Spanish and German pupils in school. Talk from MEP as part of lower sixth General Studies programme.

Senior pupils' non-academic activities *Music:* 214 learn a musical instrument, 35 to Grade 6 or above; 7 take GCSE; 5 AS/A-level; 2 accepted for Music College; 28 in school orchestra, 23 in wind band, 45 in choir, 74 in choral society, 15 in Queenswood Singers. 2 Pro Corda. *Drama and dance:* 238 in school productions (opportunity for all upper school to take part, front and backstage); 35 GCSE drama, 20 A-level theatre studies, 50 LAMDA acting medals. 6 take English and drama degrees. *Art:* 10 take art as non-examined subject; 15 belong to general art club. 30 take GCSE; 6 A-level art; 12 history of art A-level. 3 accepted for Art School; 3 history of art, 2 architecture at university. *Sport:* Tennis, hockey, swimming, badminton, lacrosse, netball, athletics, gymnastics, fencing, riding, trampolining, squash, golf, table tennis, rounders, self-defence, weights, shooting, windsurfing, sailing, health-related fitness available. 90% take part in non-compulsory sport. 20 take life saving and 5 trampolining exams. 20 pupils represent county (hockey, lacrosse, swimming, tennis, athletics). 3 at national level (tennis, hockey). *Other:* 23 working for bronze Duke of Edinburgh's Award, 23 silver, 20 gold. 90 are members of Exploration Society. 65 lower sixth in local community schemes plus Interact. 3–5 enter voluntary schemes after leaving school. Other activities include a computer club, driving lessons, chess club, Young Engineers club, Young Enterprise companies, junior and senior debating society, open ballet class, charity committee, drama workshops, orienteering club, sixth form weekly lectures, film society, cookery club, dressmaking, photography, Adventure Service Challenge Scheme and pottery club.

Careers In 1990, 88% leavers went on to degree courses; 6% to art/drama/music colleges; 3% to non-degree courses (eg HND business studies); 3% straight into careers (eg banking). Of those going on to degree courses, 10% went to Oxbridge, 60% to other universities; 30% to poly/colleges. 4% those going on to higher education went to courses in practical art; 4% in drama/acting; 2% in music; 66% in humanities/social sciences; 4% in medicine; and 20% in science/engineering.

Uniform School uniform worn except in upper sixth.

Houses/prefects Competitive houses. Prefects and head girl (upper sixth) appointed after wide consultation; head of house and house prefects (fifth years) selected within house. School Council, members chosen by girls.

Religion Both compulsory and voluntary worship exist. Majority of girls choose to be confirmed.

Social Debating (Haileybury and other schools), choral works (Oundle, Colfes), tennis, socials, discos, annual ball (various schools). Organised trips abroad for skiing, tennis, music (choral), language (French and Spanish), art, exploration society. Meals self service (2 formal meals pa). School shop and school bank. Wine with meals with adults present; no other alcohol or tobacco allowed.

Discipline No corporal punishment. Pupils failing to produce homework once

after being given an extension would be disciplined by their tutor; any girl caught smoking cannabis on the premises could expect to be expelled.

Boarding 60 have own study bedroom, 72 share with 1 or 2; 80 in dormitories of 4, 182 in dormitories of 6+. Houses, of approximately 40–58, divided broadly by age. 2 resident SRNs. Central dining room. Lower sixth pupils can provide and cook snacks (own kitchen); upper sixth given budget to cover all meals except lunch (own large kitchens). 4 exeats annually; extra for seniors if no school commitments. Visits to local town allowed for fourth year and above (usually Saturday); sixth allowed into London in groups.

Alumni association is run by Mrs Rosemary Cahill, Old Queenswoodian Association, Foxdown, Tile Barn, Woolton Hill, Newbury, Berkshire RG15 9UX.

_r_

· _Radley_ ·

Radley College
Abingdon
Oxfordshire
OX14 2HR
Tel 0235 520294

- Pupils 600
- Boys 13–18 (Board)
- Girls None
- Upper sixth 123

- Termly fees £3100 (Board)
- HMC
Enquiries/application to the Warden

What it's like

Founded in 1847 by the Rev William Sewell, Fellow of Exeter College, Oxford, to provide a public school education on the principles of the Church of England. Its agreeable and well-equipped buildings (boarding accommodation is comfortable) lie in a beautiful 700-acre estate 300 ft above sea level, 2.5 miles from Abingdon and 5 from Oxford. The environment is healthy. It is now one of the most successful of boarding schools for boys and has first-class facilities of all kinds. It retains strong links with Oxford and the Church of England. The chapel and religious education are an important part of the college's life. Two resident chaplains and the Warden are responsible for chapel services etc. A large and well-qualified staff (who work very hard) permits a staff:pupil ratio of 1:10. Academic standards are high and results excellent. Very many leavers go on to degree courses, many to Oxbridge. The music department is very strong (about 180 boys learn an instrument) and there is extensive activity in drama (annual school productions, shorter plays by dramatic societies, a production by the Gilbert and Sullivan society and house plays). There is a fine design centre in which work of high quality is produced. Sports facilities are exceptionally good and the college is well known for its achievements in rugby, cricket, hockey and rowing (there are boathouses on the Thames, a mile away). Numerous clubs and societies cater for virtually every extra-curricular need. There is also a golf course and the college runs its own beagle pack. The CCF is a large contingent: all boys join it when aged 14.5 and have to pass the proficiency exam before they leave the CCF. Considerable emphasis on outdoor pursuits and an impressive record in the Duke of Edinburgh's Award Scheme.

School profile

Pupils Age range 13–18; 600 boarding boys. Main entry ages 13, a few into sixth. Approx 20% are children of former pupils. _Transfer from maintained schools:_ None in main intakes, 1% to sixth.

Entrance Common entrance and own scholarship exam used. Oversubscribed. No special skills required; C of E preferred, other denominations accepted. Maximum extras £180 – theatre trips, account at school shop etc. 20 scholarships/exhibitions (7 for music), full fees to £300 pa.

Parents 15+% are doctors, lawyers etc;

15+% in industry or commerce. 10+% live within 30 miles; up to 10% live overseas.

Staff Warden R M Morgan, first year in post. 62 full time staff, 8 part time plus musicians. Annual turnover 6%. Average age 37.

Academic work GCSE and A-levels. 27 subjects offered (no A-level general studies). In 1990, 119 pupils in upper fifth, 123 in upper sixth. *GCSE:* in 1990, 116 upper fifth gained at least grade C in 7+ subjects; 6 in 4–6 subjects. *A-levels:* 113 upper sixth passed in 3+ subjects; 8 in 2 subjects. 32 took science A-levels; 51 arts/humanities; 38 both. *Computing facilities:* Computer department plus individual machines in departments and houses.

European Community *Languages:* French offered: to GCSE; AS-level; A-level. German offered: to GCSE; AS-level; A-level. Spanish offered: to GCSE; A-level. 25–50% take GCSE in more than 1 EC language.

Senior pupils' non-academic activities *Music:* 180 learn a musical instrument, 50 to Grade 6 or above, 1 or 2 accepted for Music School. *Drama and dance:* Large number in annual productions. *Art:* A small number take A-level. Potter in residence. *Sport:* Rugby (school game), rowing (own boathouse), hockey, cricket, tennis, diving, sub-aqua, windsurfing, gymnastics, athletics, squash, swimming, basketball, judo, karate, fencing, fives, rackets, sailing, golf available. All participate in some sport. Several pupils represent county in wide range of sports at relevant age levels. *Other:* Some take part in local community schemes. Many gain bronze, silver and gold awards in Duke of Edinburgh's Scheme. Other activities include a computer club, wide range of societies including antiques, beagling, bridge, canoeing, car, chess, classical, clay pigeon, cycling, debating, dramatic, film, history, karate, literary, magic circle, mountaineering, musical, natural history, philatelic, photographic, poetry, political, printing, scientific, Scottish dancing, trout fishing, CCF.

Careers On average, 90% leavers go on to degree courses; 10% to art/drama/music colleges, non-degree courses, or straight into careers. Of those going on to degree courses, 19% go to Oxbridge, 64% to other universities; 17% to poly/colleges. 77% those going on to higher education went to courses in arts/social sciences; 22% in medicine and science/engineering.

Uniform School uniform worn throughout.

Houses/prefects Competitive houses. Prefects, head boy, head of house and house prefects – appointed by the Head and housemasters. 'Chores' performed by junior boys. No fagging.

Religion Attendance compulsory at 4 short evening services a week plus one of a choice of Sunday services.

Social Debating, concerts etc with other schools. Annual ski-ing trip abroad. Pupils allowed to bring own bike to school. Meals self service. School shop. No tobacco/alcohol allowed.

Discipline No corporal punishment. Pupils failing to produce homework once might expect Saturday evening detention.

Boarding Most seniors have own study bedroom, a few are in dormitories of 6+ (in cubicles). 8 houses, of approximately 75, same as competitive houses. Resident qualified nurse. Central dining room. Pupils can provide and cook own food. Half-term plus 1 or 2 Saturday night exeats each term. Visits to local town allowed with written permission.

Alumni association run by A L Dowding, c/o the College.

· *Rannoch* ·

Rannoch School
Rannoch, by Pitlochry
Perthshire
PH17 2QQ
Tel 08822 332

- Pupils 295
- Boys 10–18
  (Day/Board)
- Girls 10–18
  (Day/Board)
- Upper sixth 40

- Termly fees
  £1490 (Day)
  £2520 (Board)
- SHMIS, Round
  Square
  Enquiries/application to
  the Headmaster

What it's like

Founded in 1959 by three masters from Gordonstoun, it has a marvellous site in 120 acres of grounds on the south shore of Loch Rannoch in a spectacular setting of highland scenery. The main building, formerly known as Dall, was built in 1855 by a chief of the Robertson clan. It is a towered and turreted mansion of Scottish 'baronial' lineage. Modern facilities, including converted farm buildings, provide excellent additional accommodation. A well-run and enterprising school, it has very strong links and contacts with the local highland community which gives vigorous support. Its 'international' spread of intake includes some 150 pupils from Scotland, 50-odd from England and about 80 from overseas (mostly the children of expatriates). It has high academic standards and impressive results. There is a staff:pupil ratio of about 1:12 and a large proportion of leavers for a school of this size go on to degree courses. Chapel services are compulsory and there is quite a lot of emphasis on religious education. Strong in music, drama and art, and considerable strength in games and sports. A big commitment to local community schemes. The fine range of clubs and societies caters for many needs. The environment is ideal for outdoor pursuits and a lot are available (including fishing, ski-ing, mountaineering, camping, sailing and canoeing). The school (not surprisingly) has a most remarkable record in the Duke of Edinburgh's Award Scheme (over 300 gold awards in 20 years).

School profile

Pupils Age range 10–18; 295 pupils, 8 day (5 boys, 3 girls), 287 boarding (242 boys, 45 girls). Main entry ages 10, 11, 12, 13+ and into sixth. Approx 10% are children of former pupils. *Transfer from maintained schools:* 60+% main intakes, plus 50% to sixth.

Entrance Common entrance and own exam used. Oversubscribed. Pleasant young people looked for; no religious requirements. Parents expected to pay a small charge per session for text books; minimal standard extras. 5 assisted places pa. Up to 10 scholarships/bursaries pa, up to three-quarters of fees.

Parents Parents drawn from a wide range of occupations. 150+ live in Scotland, 50+ in England and 80+ overseas.

Staff Headmaster M Barratt, in post for 7 years. 25 full time staff, 8 part time. Average age 30–40.

Academic work O-grades, S-grades, Highers and A-levels offered (including Higher and A-level geology; no A-level general studies). In 1990, 50 pupils in O/S-grade year, 40+ in Higher/A-level year. *O/S-grade:* in 1990, 60% pupils passed in 5–7 subjects; 40% in 1–4 subjects. *Highers:* 65% passed in 5+ or more subjects; 25% in 3; 20% in 2 subjects. *A-levels:* 100% passed in 3 subjects. (Some pupils take Highers, some A-levels.) There is an even spread of pupils taking science/engineering exams and arts/humanities exams. *Computing facilities:* 12 networked BBC Master series; sets in each of science and CDT departments. *Special provision:* Small remedial department for those with mild learning difficulties in English and mathematics.

European Community *Languages:* French offered: to age 14; GCSE; A-level. German offered: to age 14; GCSE; A-level. 10–25% take GCSE in more than 1 EC language. *Exchanges:* Regular exchanges for pupils aged 11–18 to Germany.

Senior pupils' non-academic activities *Music:* Nearly half the school learn a musical instrument; 40 in school orchestra, 50 in choir, 20 in piping and drumming. *Drama and dance:* Pupils participate in 2 productions each year. *Art:* 40 take as non-examined subject; 25 take O-grade; 10 Higher and A-level. 3 or 4 go to Art School each year. 20 belong to photographic club. *Sport:* Rugby, hockey, skiing, athletics, cross-country, basketball, football, cricket, tennis, sailing, swimming, orienteering and golf available. Sport is compulsory but a range of options. 15 take GCSE in PE. Pupils make regular appearances at county/country level (rugby, skiing and athletics). *Other:* 30 take part in local community schemes. 45 have bronze Duke of Edinburgh's Award, 45 have silver and 40 gold in 1990 (school has gained over 400 Gold Awards since 1968). Other activities include a computer club, hairdressing, archery, archaeology, auto-mechanics, bible-study, bridge, chess, clay pigeon shooting, cookery, debating, dressmaking, electronics, natural history, piping, Scottish country dancing. Also ambulance, fire and mountain services, loch patrol, building, meteorological and conservation services and many expeditions.

Careers In 1990, 40% leavers went on to degree courses; 30% to art/drama/music colleges; 20% to non-degree courses; 10% straight into careers (eg nursing, farming, armed services). Of those going on to degree courses, 5% went to Oxbridge, 55% to other universities; 40% to poly/colleges. 21% those going on to higher education went to courses in practical art; 7% in music; 14% in humanities/social sciences; 14% in medicine; and 43% in science/engineering.

Uniform School uniform worn throughout.

Houses/prefects Competitive houses. Prefects, head boy/girl, head of house and house prefects – appointed by the Head after consultation. Various school committees.

Religion Compulsory religious worship.

Social Very strong contact with local Highland community (large sum raised recently to save the village hall). Organised trips abroad and exchange systems. Pupils allowed to bring own bike to school. Meals self service. School shop. No tobacco/alcohol allowed.

Discipline No corporal punishment.

Boarding All sixth form have own study bedroom, many fifth formers share. Single sex houses, of approximately 50, same as competitive houses. Resident qualified medical staff. Central dining room. Pupils can provide and cook own food, within limits. Exeats permitted each term, number varies. Visits to the local town allowed.

Alumni association run by Mr Colin Mackay, 8 Merchiston Gardens, Edinburgh EH10 4DD. Telephone 031 337 4591.

· *Ratcliffe* ·

Ratcliffe College
Syston
Leicestershire LE7 8SG
Tel 0509 812221/
812522
Fax 0509 812791

- Pupils 451
- Boys 11–18
  (Day/Board/Weekly)
- Girls 11–18
  (Day/Board/Weekly)
- Upper sixth 58

- Termly fees
  £1470 (Day)
  £2220 (Board/
  Weekly)
- HMC
Enquiries/application to
the Headmaster

What it's like

Founded in 1847 by priests of the Institute of Charity, usually known as the Rosminians (after Antonio Rosmini), as a school for Catholic boys. It enjoys a fine site near the A46 with splendid grounds of a hundred acres of rural Leicestershire. The main buildings, designed by Pugin, form a compact block round a quadrangle with the handsome chapel occupying a central position. Recent years have seen the opening of a new chapel, science and music buildings and a fine sports centre. In 1977 girls were admitted to the sixth form and in 1984 a junior house for day boys and girls was inaugurated. As it is a Roman Catholic foundation most of the pupils are Catholics, but an increasing number of Christians of other persuasions have been accepted. A good deal of attention is given to religious instruction at all levels and Mass, daily prayers etc are an integral part of the school's life. The aim of the school is summed up by its motto Legis plenitudo charitas ('Charity is the fulfilment of the law'). Academically, morally, socially and spiritually it aims to provide the sort of formation and education which will equip pupils to succeed in their careers and to make the sort of contribution to society which is the ideal of the Christian life. A sound general education is provided and academic results are good. The staff:pupil ratio is a favourable 1:10. Many sixth form leavers go on to degree courses. Music, drama and art are all strongly supported. There is a music block and a concert hall. Concerts are frequent and professional musicians often perform at the college. The college has close links with Loughborough Drama Centre and has won a number of awards in local theatre festivals. The art department is very well equipped and produces work of high standards. The main games are rugby, hockey and cricket. Several court games are available and there is a flourishing boat club (fours). Not a few pupils have achieved success in sports and games at county and district levels. Between 25 and 30 clubs and societies cater for most extra-curricular activities. The CCF has a strong Army contingent. There are also a scout group and a voluntary service unit. Much emphasis is put on adventure training, Outward Bound courses, ski-ing and winter survival courses.

School profile

Pupils Age range 11–18; 451 pupils, 259 day (169 boys, 90 girls), 192 boarding (133 boys, 59 girls). Main entry ages 11, 13, 14 and into sixth. Own prep, Grace Dieu Manor. *Transfer from maintained schools:* 55% main intakes, plus 15% to sixth.

Entrance Own entrance exam and common entrance used. Assisted places, scholarships and bursaries.

Staff Headmaster Rev L G Hurdidge, in post for 7 years.

Academic work GCSE and A-levels. 16 GCSE subjects offered (no A-level general studies). In 1990, 87 pupils in upper fifth, 58 in upper sixth. *GCSE:* in 1990, 37 upper fifth gained at least grade C in 8+ subjects; 21 in 5–7; and 24 in 1–4

608

subjects. *A-levels:* 34 upper sixth passed in 3+ subjects; 10 in 2; and 7 in 1 subject. 24% took science A-levels; 66% arts/humanities; 10% both. *Computing facilities:* 16-station RML Nimbus network and approximately 30 BBC micros. *Special provision:* EFL tuition available.

European Community *Languages:* French offered: to age 14; GCSE; A-level. German offered: to age 14; GCSE; A-level. Spanish offered: to age 14; GCSE. 10–25% take GCSE in more than 1 EC language. *Exchanges:* Regular exchanges for pupils aged 14–18 to France. *Other:* Work experience to take place in France; reciprocal arrangement for French students in UK.

Careers In 1990, 72% leavers went on to degree courses; 14% to art colleges; 4% straight into careers (eg retailing trainee); 10% other. Of those going on to degree courses, 5% went to Oxbridge, 40% to other universities; 55% to poly/colleges. 14% those going on to higher education went to courses in practical art; 45% in humanities/social sciences; 4% in medicine; and 35% in science/engineering.

· *Read* ·

Read School
Drax
Selby
North Yorkshire
YO8 8NL
Tel 0757 618248

- Pupils 230
- Boys 8–18 (Day/Board/Weekly)
- Girls 16–18 (Day)
- Upper sixth 12

- Termly fees
  £840 (Day)
  £1700 (Board)
  £1590 (Weekly)
- ISAI, BSA
Enquiries/application to the Headmaster

What it's like

Founded in 1667, it has a very pleasant rural site in the village of Drax. Teaching is on two sites – main campus for 11+ and junior campus for 8–11. Boarding accommodation on three sites, all close together. Most of the buildings are early 19th century. There have been extensive modern developments in the last 30 years. Facilities are good. A small school, it is ideal for a wide range of ability, skills and interests. Strong music, drama and art departments. It gives a sound all-round education and girls are introduced to the sixth form this year. Good range of sport, games and activities including CCF. Some involvement in local community services and the Duke of Edinburgh's Award Scheme.

School profile

Pupils Total age range 8–18; 230 boys, 100 day, 130 boarding. Senior department 11–18, 190 boys. Main entry ages 8, 11, 13 and into sixth (boys); girls into sixth, as day girls, from 1991. Approx 5% are children of former pupils. *Transfer from maintained schools:* 5% senior intake, plus 5% to sixth.

Entrance Admission by interview. Not oversubscribed. No special skills or religious requirements. Parents not expected to buy text books; maximum compulsory extras, £5 plus trips etc. 8 scholarships/bursaries, up to half tuition fee.

Parents 15+% in the armed services. 30+% live within 30 miles; 10+% live overseas.

Staff Headmaster A J Saddler, in post for 6 years. 20 full time, 4 part time. Annual turnover 5%. Average age 35–40.

Academic work GCSE and A-levels. 15 subjects offered (including A-level general studies). In 1990, 40 pupils in upper fifth, 12 in upper sixth. *GCSE:* in

1990, 20% upper fifth gained at least grade C in 8+ subjects; 12% in 5–7; and 53% in 1–4 subjects. *A-levels:* 50% upper sixth passed in 3+ subjects; 20% in 2; and 30% in 1 subject. 40% took science A-levels; 50% arts/humanities; 10% both. *Computing facilities:* Nimbus 10-computer network plus several individual pc's. *Special provision:* Some extra English lessons provided.

European Community *Languages:* French offered: to age 14; GCSE; AS-level; A-level. German offered: to age 14; GCSE. 25–50% take GCSE in more than 1 EC language.

Senior pupils' non-academic activities *Music:* 50 learn a musical instrument, 6 to Grade 6 or above; 20 in school orchestra, 50 in choir. *Drama and dance:* 80 in school productions. *Art:* 50 take as non-examined subject; 25 take GCSE; 4 A-level. 2 accepted for Art School. 5 belong to photographic club. *Sport:* Rugby, soccer, hockey, cricket, tennis, swimming, cross-country, athletics, badminton and table tennis available. 80 take non-compulsory sport. 10 take exams. 8 represent county/country (rugby, cricket, athletics). *Other:* 15 take part in local community schemes. 10 have bronze Duke of Edinburgh's Award. 2 enter voluntary schemes after leaving school. Other activities include CCF, a computer club, chess, karate, YFC and fishing.

Careers In 1990, 50% leavers went on to degree courses; 10% to art/drama/music colleges; 10% to non-degree courses (eg agriculture); 20% straight into careers (eg army, farming); 10% other. Of those going on to degree courses, 80% went to universities; 20% to poly/colleges. 10% those going on to higher education went to courses in practical art; 40% in humanities/social sciences; 10% in medicine; and 40% in science/engineering.

Uniform School uniform worn except the sixth.

Houses/prefects Competitive houses. Prefects, head boy, head of house and house prefects – appointed by the Head.

Religion C of E worship.

Social Several local events organised; some trips abroad. Pupils allowed to bring own bike to school. Some meals formal, some self service. School shop. No tobacco/alcohol allowed.

Discipline No corporal punishment. Pupils failing to produce homework once might expect to repeat it.

Boarding 1% have own study bedroom, 20% share with 1 other; 60% are in dormitories of 6–10. Houses, of 100–10, are divided by age. Resident qualified medical staff. Central dining room. 36 hour exeats on request. Visits to local town allowed for boys 15+.

Alumni association run by its own officers, c/o Headmaster.

Former pupils John Sherwood (Olympic athlete); L V Appleyard (Ambassador).

· *Reading Blue Coat* ·

Reading Blue Coat School	• Pupils 550	• Termly fees
	• Boys 11–18	£1310 (Day)
Holme Park	(Day/Board/Weekly)	£2390 (Board)
Sonning	• Girls 16–18	£2320 (Weekly)
Berkshire RG4 0SU	(Day)	• SHMIS, BSA
Tel 0734 441005	• Upper sixth 59	Enquiries/application to
Fax 0734 442690		the Headmaster

What it's like
Founded in 1646 by Richard Aldworth, a merchant of London and Reading. Originally it was named 'Aldworth's Hospital'. In 1947 it moved to its present

premises at Holme Park. The main buildings comprise a magnificent brick-and-flint mansion in the Tudor collegiate style of architecture. It lies in a beautiful 45-acre wooded estate with a most agreeable frontage along the River Thames at Sonning Lock. A more pleasant environment it would be difficult to find. The school is well appointed and comfortable and there are good modern facilities, including recent laboratories, a purpose-built music school, libraries, sixth-form centre, art studios and workshops. The school has kept close links with the Church of England but the main concern is that pupils are taught and learn in an atmosphere where Christian values and standards are recognised and established within the community. There is some emphasis on prayer, worship and religious instruction. The staff:pupil ratio is about 1:11. A broad, sound and general education is provided and results are creditable. Many sixth formers go on to degree courses, some to Oxbridge. Music is very strong: there are a choral society, madrigal choir, orchestra, windband, brass group, recorder and chamber music ensembles. Art is also well supported. Facilities for games and sports (of which there is a standard range) are very good. The CCF is a large voluntary unit with Army, Navy and Air Force sections. A wide range of clubs and societies caters for most needs. Activities include archery, canoeing, clay-pigeon shooting, fencing and estate work. Considerable enterprise is shown in organising expeditions, excursions and tours overseas.

School profile

Pupils Age range 11–18, 550 pupils. Main entry ages 11, 13 (boys) and into sixth (boys and girls). *Transfer from maintained schools:* 50% main intakes, plus 25% to sixth.

Entrance Own entrance exam used. 6 scholarships, including music.

Staff Headmaster Reverend A C E Sanders, in post for 17 years.

Academic work GCSE and A-levels. 17 subjects offered (including AS general studies; not A-level). In 1990, 82 pupils in upper fifth, 59 in upper sixth. *GCSE:* in 1990, 74 upper fifth gained at least grade C in 6+ subjects. *A-levels:* 4 upper sixth passed in 4+ subjects; 36 in 3; 13 in 2; and 6 in 1 subject. 20 took science A-levels; 31 arts/humanities; 8 both. *Computing facilities:* Nimbus network with 30 stations. *Special provision:* Smaller class size in years 4 and 5.

European Community *Languages:* French offered: to age 14; GCSE; A-level. German offered: to age 14; GCSE; A-level. 10–25% take GCSE in more than 1 EC language. *Exchanges:* Regular exchanges for pupils aged 11–14 to France. *Other:* European Studies offered to pupils aged 11–14.

Careers In 1990, 85% leavers went on to degree courses; 5% to art/drama/music colleges; 5% to non-degree courses (eg HND business studies); 5% straight into careers (eg retail management). Of those going on to degree courses, 6% went to Oxbridge, 66% to other universities; 28% to poly/colleges. 6% those going on to higher education went to courses in practical art; 6% in music; 45% in humanities/social sciences; 3% in medicine; and 40% in science/engineering.

· *Red Maids'* ·

The Red Maids' School	● Pupils 479	● Termly fees
Westbury-on-Trym	● Boys None	£952 (Day)
Bristol	● Girls 11–18	£1904 (Board)
BS9 3AW	(Day/Board)	● GSA
Tel 0272 622641	● Upper sixth 59	Enquiries/application to
		the Headmistress

What it's like

Founded in 1634 through a bequest by John Whitson. It was originally a 'hospital for forty poor women children, daughters of Burgesses who were deceased or decayed'. The school owes its name to the fact that the inmates wore a costume of red cloth (still worn on ceremonial/traditional occasions). Today it occupies a fine 12-acre site in a north-west suburb of Bristol. It has handsome buildings, ancient and modern, set in beautiful gardens and grounds. Many modern additions provide comfortable accommodation and good up-to-date facilities. A sound general education is provided and the school enjoys a favourable staff:pupil ratio of about 1:11. Academic results are very good and very many girls go on to degree courses each year, including Oxbridge. Music, drama and art are strongly supported. An impressive range of sports and games is available and high standards are attained (not a few girls represent the school at county level each year). There is some commitment to local community services and some participation in the Duke of Edinburgh's Award Scheme.

School profile

Pupils Age range 11–18; 479 girls (366 day, 113 boarding). Main entry ages 11 and into sixth. *Transfer from maintained schools:* 75% main intake, plus a few to sixth.

Entrance Own entrance exam used. Oversubscribed. No special skills or religious requirements. Parents not expected to buy text books. 25 assisted places pa. 5 scholarships/bursaries pa, maximum £300.

Parents 15+% in the armed services; smaller percentage are doctors, lawyers or in industry.

Staff Headmistress Miss S Hampton, in post for 4 years. 35 full time staff, 16 part time. Annual turnover 6%. Average age late 30's.

Academic work GCSE, AS and A-levels. 19 subjects offered (including Russian, classical civilisation; AS-level general studies taken by all sixth form, not A-level). In 1990, 76 pupils in upper fifth, 54 in upper sixth (now 59). *GCSE:* in 1990, 73 upper fifth gained at least grade C in 8+ subjects; 3 in 5–7 subjects. *A-levels:* 5 upper sixth passed in 4+ subjects; 41 in 3; 6 in 2; and 1 in 1 subject. c50% took science A-levels; c25% arts/humanities; c25% both. *Computing facilities:* RM Nimbus network. *Special provision:* Extra English for overseas pupils, if necessary.

European Community *Languages:* French offered: to age 14; GCSE; A-level. German offered: to GCSE. Spanish offered: to age 14; GCSE; A-level. 50–75% take GCSE in more than 1 EC language. *Exchanges:* Regular exchanges for pupils aged 11–16 to France and Spain. *Other:* Spanish Erasmus student, at Bristol University Education department, attached to school part-time, 1 term.

Senior pupils' non-academic activities *Music:* Majority learn at least one musical instrument. GCSE and A-level music offered. Occasional pupil accepted for Music School. *Drama and dance:* Many in school productions. *Art:* 32 take GCSE; 7 A-level. 3 or 4 accepted for Art School. *Sport:* Hockey, tennis, cross-country, swimming, volleyball, fencing, squash, netball, athletics, gymnastics, dance available. Many pupils in sports teams and clubs. Up to 12 pa represent county (hockey, netball, tennis, athletics, cross-country). *Other:* 14 have bronze Duke of Edinburgh's Award. Some take part in local community schemes. Other activities include computer, bowling, chess and quiz clubs, Christian Union, golf, riding and learning to drive.

Careers In 1990, 80% leavers went on to degree courses; 12% to art/drama/music colleges; 8% straight into careers. Of those going on to degree courses, 10% went to Oxbridge, 65% to other universities; 25% to poly/colleges. 8% those going on to higher education went to courses in practical art; 20% in humanities/social sciences; 8% in medicine; and 35% in science/engineering.

Uniform School uniform worn, more flexible in sixth.

Houses/prefects Competitive houses; no prefects. Head girls (1 day, 1 boarder), head of house – elected by school. School Council.

Religion Compulsory worship.

Social Music/drama, joint Sunday service with brother school at least once a term. Organised trips to Greece, Italy, Russia, France (choir tour and watersports). Exchanges (France and Spain). Pupils allowed to bring own car/motorbike/bike to school. Meals formal at weekend lunchtimes, self service weekday lunchtimes. School tuck shop. Sixth form boarders may entertain friends in their common rooms during certain hours at weekends.

Discipline No corporal punishment.

Boarding All upper sixth have own study bedroom; lower sixth and fifth in single cubicles; rest in dormitories of 6+. Houses, of up to 36, divided by age. SRN on duty/call. Central dining room. *Upper sixth* can provide and cook own food. 2 exeats per term, and half-term. Visits to local town allowed, accompanied until aged 13.

Alumni association is run by Mrs B Wiltshire, c/o the School.

· *Redland High* ·

Redland High School	• Pupils 640	• Termly fees
Redland Court	• Boys None	£925 (Day)
Bristol	• Girls 4–18	• GSA
BS6 7EF	(Day)	Enquiries/application to
Tel 0272 245796	• Upper sixth 45–50	the Headmistress

What it's like

Founded in 1882 in Redland Grove as a small independent school. In 1885 it moved to its present site. The main building is a handsome 18th-century mansion in pleasant gardens. The playing fields are a few minutes' walk away. The junior school is opposite. Pupils come from all areas of Bristol and Avon and from all sections of the community. The sixth form plays a considerable part in the running of the school. The teaching is good and academic standards creditable. Many sixth formers go on to degree courses, including Oxbridge. Flourishing music, drama and art. A full range of sports and games and a good variety of extra-curricular activities. Some commitment to local community services and an impressive record in the Duke of Edinburgh's Award Scheme. Full use is made of Bristol's cultural amenities.

School profile

Pupils Total age range 4–18; 640 day girls. Senior department 11–18, 450 girls. Main entry ages 11 and into sixth.

Entrance Own entrance exam used. No special skills or religious requirements. Parents not expected to buy text books. 83 assisted places. Scholarships and bursaries at 11+ and in sixth, £1092 to £50.

Staff Headmistress Mrs Carol Lear, 2 years in post. 38 full time staff, 15 part time. Annual turnover 10%. Average age 35.

Academic work GCSE and A-levels (including A-level history of art). Average size of upper fifth 75; upper sixth 45–50. *A-levels:* on average, 1 pupil in upper sixth passes 4 subjects; 33, 3 subjects; 8, 2 subjects; 3 pass 1 subject. On average, 14 take science/engineering A-levels; 18 take arts/humanities; 14 a mixture. *Computing facilities:* Computer room with approx 8 computers.

European Community *Languages:* French offered: to age 14; GCSE; A-level. German offered: to age 14; GCSE; A-level. Spanish offered: to GCSE; A-level. 25–50% take GCSE in more than 1 EC language. *Exchanges:* Regular exchanges for pupils aged 14–16 to France and Germany. *Other:* In 1991, 8 sixth formers attended Paris conference on Europe 1992. Short visits to France and Germany, as well as exchanges.

Senior pupils' non-academic activities *Music:* 100 learn a musical instrument, 2 accepted for Music School; 26 in school orchestra, 16 in chamber orchestra, 12 in wind ensemble, 50 in choir, 20 in chamber groups; 7 in County Youth Orchestra, 2 in County Youth Wind Band. *Drama and dance:* 45 in school productions; occasional pupil accepted for Drama/Dance Schools or enters national competitions. *Art:* 6 take as non-examined subject; 76 take GCSE; 14 A-level; 12 history of art A-level. 4 accepted for Art School; 1 to study architecture; 1 landscape architecture; 4 history of art. *Sport:* Hockey, netball, tennis, new image rugby, athletics, cricket, swimming, badminton, cross country running, fencing available. 100+ play in school teams. 7 represent county (hockey, netball, tennis, cricket, orienteering). *Other:* 54 involved in bronze Duke of Edinburgh's Award, 10 involved in silver and 2 gold. Other activities include a computer club, Christian Union, conservation projects, community services and clubs for gymnastics, athletics, fencing, cricket, pottery, photography, art, geographical society, drama, outdoor activities, Young Enterprise, public speaking.

Careers In 1990, 80% leavers went on to degree courses; 7% to art/drama/music colleges; 5% to non-degree courses (eg nursing, HND business studies); 7% straight into careers (eg catering, retail management); 1% other. Of those going on to degree courses, 9% went to Oxbridge, 60% to other universities; 32% to poly/colleges. 7% those going on to higher education went to courses in practical art; 43% in humanities/social sciences; 5% in medicine; and 45% in science/engineering.

Uniform School uniform worn except the sixth.

Houses/prefects No competitive houses or prefects but sixth form executive committee; head girl – elected by staff and sixth. School Council.

Religion Daily school assembly.

Social Occasional joint meetings, musical performances and productions with other city schools. Exchanges with schools in Bordeaux and Marburg (Germany); ski-ing trips abroad; History of Art trip to Italy, Paris or Amsterdam; visits to Italy, Greece. Pupils allowed to bring own car/bike to school. No tobacco/alcohol allowed.

Discipline No corporal punishment.

Alumni association by Mrs Sally Read, c/o the School.

· Reed's ·

Reed's School
Sandy Lane
Cobham
Surrey
KT11 2ES
Tel 0932 63076

- Pupils 350
- Boys 11–18
  (Day/Board)
- Girls 16–18
  (Day/Board)
- Upper sixth 45

- Termly fees
  £1600 (Day)
  £2215 (Board)
- HMC
  Enquiries/application to
  the Headmaster's
  Secretary

What it's like

Founded in 1813 by Andrew Reed for the purpose of educating boys whose fathers had died. In 1958 the school expanded and all boys became eligible for entrance, but Foundation awards are still granted each year to boys who have lost the support of one or both of their parents. It has a very agreeable semi-rural site of about 50 acres of heath, woodland and playing fields near Esher. Between 1971 and 1990 there was a very large number (14) of developments and extensions as a result of which the school is now exceptionally well equipped. Junior and senior schools are combined on a compact campus where the original buildings blend in with the modern. It is proud of its charitable foundation and the Christian principles of the founder live on. Ecumenical in spirit and policy, it has some emphasis on worship in chapel and religious education is part of the curriculum. There is a favourable staff:pupil ratio of about 1:12. Exam results are creditable and many pupils go on to degree courses each year. Music and drama are strong; so is art. There is an adequate range of sports and games and all pupils have to take part in something. The school has a special scheme for gifted tennis players. The CCF contingent is large (RAF, Army and Naval sections) and all boys have to take part. Considerable emphasis on outdoor pursuits, practical skills and self-reliance. The Duke of Edinburgh's Award Scheme is well supported and there is some commitment to local community services.

School profile

Pupils Age range 11–18; 350 pupils, 170 day (168 boys, 2 girls), 180 boarders (178 boys, 2 girls). Main entry ages, 11, 12, 13 (boys); into sixth (boys and girls). 5% are children of former pupils. *Transfer from maintained schools:* 40% main intakes, plus 10% to sixth.
Entrance Common entrance and own exam used. Oversubscribed. No special skills required; pupils expected to be C of E. Parents not expected to buy text books; maximum extras £50. Assisted places. 10 scholarships pa, half fees–£100; bursaries.
Parents 15+% in industry. 30+% live within 30 miles; up to 10% live overseas.
Staff Headmaster D E Prince, in post for 8 years. 33 full time staff, 7 part time

(including 6 music). Annual turnover 8%. Average age 38.
Academic work GCSE and A-levels. 16 GCSE subjects offered; 15 at A-level (no A-level general studies). In 1990, 62 pupils in upper fifth, 45 in upper sixth. *GCSE:* in 1990, 35 upper fifth gained at least grade C in 8+ subjects; 19 in 5–7; and 12 in 1–4 subjects. *A-levels:* 2 upper sixth passed in 4+ subjects; 18 in 3; 12 in 2; and 9 in 1 subject. 20% took science A-levels; 55% arts/humanities; 25% both. *Computing facilities:* SJ-Econet Level 3 (being changed to Nimbus Ethernet) accessed by 12 Master 128/s and 4 BBC B's; 2 Apple-Macintosh SEs. *Special provision:* Part-time dyslexia specialist.

European Community *Languages:* French offered: to age 14; GCSE; AS-level; A-level. German offered: to age 14; GCSE; AS-level; A-level. Spanish offered: to GCSE; AS-level. 10–25% take GCSE in more than 1 EC language. *Exchanges:* Regular exchanges for pupils aged 14–18 to France and Germany. *Other:* Talks from MEPs.

Senior pupils' non-academic activities *Music:* 90 learn a musical instrument, 15 to Grade 6 or above; 2 accepted for Music School. 20 pupils play in school band, 30 in choir, 5 in school pop group. 1 in National Youth Orchestra, 4 in church choirs, 5 in other ensembles, 4 play in pop group outside school. *Drama and dance:* 20 in school productions; 20 in house plays. *Art:* 10 take as non-examined subject; 40 take GCSE; 13 A-level. 5 accepted for Art School. 15 belong to eg photographic club. *Sport:* Rugby, hockey, cricket, swimming, squash, tennis, athletics, badminton, sailing available. Some sport compulsory for all. 4 pupils represent county (hockey, rugby). *Other:* 16 have gold Duke of Edinburgh's Award. 14 in local community schemes. Other activities include driving lessons (sixth); printing club (prints school magazine, calendar etc).

Careers In 1990, 70% leavers went on to degree courses; 10% to art/drama/music colleges; 10% to non-degree courses (eg management, business administration); 5% straight into careers (eg services, police, city, management training); 5% other (eg Gap year). Of those going on to degree courses, 37% went to universities; 63% to poly/colleges. 10% those going on to higher education went to courses in practical art; 30% in humanities/social sciences; and 60% in science/engineering.

Uniform School uniform worn throughout.

Houses/prefects Competitive houses. Prefects, head boy, head of house and house prefects – appointed by the Head. School committee – no executive powers.

Religion Compulsory chapel.

Social Debates and outings with several local girls' schools. Organised trips abroad. Day pupils allowed to bring own car/motorbike/bike to school. Meals self service. School tuck shop. No tobacco/alcohol allowed.

Discipline No corporal punishment. Pupils failing to produce homework once might expect a comment in record book and to do it again; those caught smoking cannabis on the premises could expect expulsion.

Boarding Sixth form share study bedroom with 1, 2 or 3. 75% are in dormitories of 6–10. Single sex houses, of approx 45–50, same as competitive houses. Resident qualified nurse. Central dining room. Pupils can provide and cook own food – limited facilities. 2 fixed exeats each term, Saturday afternoon to Sunday evening/Monday morning. Visits to local town allowed once a week, strict control to age 13.

Former pupils John Alvey (Chairman of Alvey Committee); Brian Miles (Director, RNLI).

· *Reigate Grammar* ·

Reigate Grammar
School
Reigate Road
Reigate
Surrey RH2 0QS
Tel 0737 222231

- Pupils 870
- Boys 10–18
  (Day)
- Girls 16–18
  (Day)
- Upper sixth 131

- Termly fees
  £1200 (Day)
- HMC
  Enquiries/application to
  the Headmaster

What it's like

Founded in 1675 as a free school for ten poor boys and endowed through a bequest of Henry Smith, Alderman of the City of London. There were a number of extensions and developments in the 19th century and in the early part of the 20th. The most recent additions date from 1978 to 1983. The buildings are situated in pleasant surroundings to the east of Reigate town centre within easy reach of local public transport. There are 33 acres of playing fields two miles away. The school seeks to provide an education based on sound Christian principles and all pupils are expected to attend school services and religious education lessons unless exempted. The staff:pupil ratio is a favourable 1:12. A sound, general education is provided, academic standards are high and results are most creditable. From a very big sixth form, most go on to degree courses. Music and drama are very strongly supported and large numbers of pupils take part. There is much strength in sports and games. The school has a long record of success in district, county and national competitions and individual honours at county and national level are regularly achieved. A wide variety of clubs and societies is available. A flourishing CCF contingent includes Army, Navy and Air Force sections. There is also a sea scout group. The Duke of Edinburgh's Award Scheme has always been well supported and the school has won many gold awards. Social and community service is a major feature of this scheme at Reigate.

School profile

Pupils Age range 10–18, 870 day pupils. Main entry ages 10, 11, 13 (boys) and into the sixth (boys and girls). *Transfer from maintained schools:* 50% main intakes, plus 15% to sixth.

Entrance Common entrance and own exam used. 20 assisted places pa. Scholarships at 10, 11 and 13; bursaries.

Staff Headmaster J G Hamlin, in post for 9 years.

Academic work GCSE and A-levels. 18 subjects offered (no A-level general studies). In 1990, 117 pupils in fifth, 112 in upper sixth (now 131). *GCSE:* in 1990, 98 upper fifth gained at least grade C in 8+ subjects; 13 in 5–7; and 6 in 1–4 subjects. *A-levels:* 8 upper sixth passed in 4+ subjects; 92 in 3; 9 in 2; and 2 in 1 subject. 25% took science A-levels; 60% arts/humanities; 15% both. *Computing facilities:* BBC2 and Archimedes.

European Community *Languages:* French offered: to age 14; GCSE; A-level. German offered: to age 14; GCSE; A-level. Italian offered: non-examined subject. Spanish offered: to age 14; GCSE; A-level. 25–50% take GCSE in more than 1 EC language. *Exchanges:* Regular exchanges for pupils aged 11–18 to France, Germany and Spain.

Careers In 1990, 95% leavers went on to degree courses; 2% to art/drama/ music colleges; 3% to non-degree courses (eg art foundation course, HND theatre studies). Of those going on to degree courses, 7% went to Oxbridge, 73% to other universities; 20% to poly/colleges. 2% those going on to higher education went to courses in practical art; 58% in humanities/social sciences; 6% in medicine; and 34% in science/engineering.

· *Rendcomb* ·

Rendcomb College	• Pupils 270	• Termly fees
Cirencester	• Boys 11–18 (Board)	£2970 (Board)
Gloucestershire	• Girls 16–18 (Board)	• HMC
GL7 7HA	• Upper sixth 55	Enquiries/application to
Tel 028 583 213		the Headmaster

What it's like

Founded in 1920, it has very handsome buildings and is part of a tiny village in a superb 200-acre estate of Gloucestershire countryside. Generously endowed, it has excellent modern facilities and recent developments include new boarding houses, and new purpose-built modern language classrooms. A very friendly atmosphere, it has all the advantages of a small school and describes itself as 'unpretentious, business-like, hardworking and caring'. A good staff:pupil ratio of 1:10. Academic results are impressive for such a small school. Many go on to degree courses, including Oxbridge every year. French and German are offered to A-level and a high proportion of pupils takes GCSE in both. French is also offered as a non-examined language. There are regular exchanges with France and Germany. Very strong music, drama and art depts. Big commitment to local community schemes and an impressive record in the Duke of Edinburgh's Award Scheme.

School profile

Pupils Age range 11–18; 270 boarding (225 boys, 45 girls). Main entry ages 11 and 13 (boys); into sixth (boys and girls). Approx 5% are children of former pupils. *Transfer from maintained schools:* 40% main intake, plus 25% to sixth.
Entrance Common entrance and own exam used. Not oversubscribed. No special skills or religious requirements. Music tuition (£50 per term) extra to fees. Assisted places. Local authority boarding places; 12 academic, art, music and sport scholarships, full fees to £800. Bursaries for children of HM forces.
Parents 15+% in industry or commerce; 15% in armed services. 30+% live within 30 miles; up to 10% live overseas.
Staff Headmaster John Tolputt, in post for 4 years. 26 full time staff, 10 part time. Annual turnover 2%. Average age 35.
Academic work GCSE and A-levels offered (no A-level general studies). In 1989, 40 pupils in upper fifth, 55 in upper sixth. *GCSE:* on average, 62% upper fifth gain at least grade C in 8+ subjects; 28% in 5–7; and 10% in 1–4 subjects. *A-levels:* on average 8% upper sixth pass in 4+ subjects; 78% in 3; 9% in 2; and 5% in 1 subject. 33% take science A-levels; 33% arts/humanities; 33% both. *Computing facilities:* Computer room, network.
European Community *Languages:* French offered: to age 14; GCSE; A-level; non-examined. German offered: to age 14; GCSE; A-level. 50–75% take GCSE in more than 1 EC language. *Exchanges:* Regular exchanges for pupils aged 14–18 to France and Germany. *Other:* Regularly have German students in sixth form studying for 1–2 years. Satellite receiving equipment in languages department.
Senior pupils' non-academic activities *Music:* 120 learn a musical instru-

618

ment, 1 accepted for Music School; 50 in school orchestra, 42 in choir; 12 in pop groups. *Drama and dance:* 60 in school productions. 4 go on to work in theatre. *Art:* 60 take as non-examined subject; 10 take GCSE; 10 A-level. 4 accepted for Art School. *Sport:* Rugby, hockey, cricket, swimming, football, netball, running, athletics, squash and tennis available. 6 represent county/country (rugby, hockey, cricket). *Other:* 40 take part in local community schemes. 25 have bronze Duke of Edinburgh's Award, 10 have gold. Other activities include a computer club, bridge and film-making (winners of international awards).

Careers In 1990, 70% leavers went on to degree courses; 12% to art/drama/ music colleges; 10% to non-degree courses (eg agricultural, secretarial, HNDs); 5% straight into careers (eg farming, business, services); 3% other. Of those going on to degree courses, 10% went to Oxbridge, 55% to other universities; 35% to poly/colleges. 10% those going on to higher education went to courses in practical art; 3% in drama/ acting; 35% in humanities/social sciences; 10% in medicine; and 40% in science/engineering.

Uniform School uniform worn throughout (except by sixth form in free time).

Houses/prefects No competitive houses. Prefects, head boy and girl, head of house and house prefects – appointed by the Headmaster and staff. School Council.

Religion Compulsory assembly twice a week, church service on Sundays.

Social Numerous social events with other schools. Exchanges (France and Germany). Pupils allowed to bring own bike to school. Meals self service. Village shop in grounds. No pupils allowed tobacco; alcohol allowed in sixth form bar.

Discipline No corporal punishment. Pupils failing to produce homework once might expect to be kept back to do it; those caught smoking cannabis on the premises may expect expulsion.

Boarding Fifth and sixth forms have own study bedrooms, others share with up to 4. Single sex houses, of approximately 50. Resident qualified nurse and doctor. Central dining room. Pupils can provide and cook own food. Half-term and 2 long weekend exeats each term. Visits to local town allowed with permission.

Alumni association is run by Christopher Wood, c/o the College.

Former pupils David Vaisey (Bodleian Librarian); Richard Dunwoody (Grand National winning jockey).

· *Repton* ·

Repton School	● Pupils 572	● Termly fees
The Hall	● Boys 13–18	£2180 (Day)
Repton	(Day/Board)	£2940 (Board)
Derby	● Girls 13–18	● HMC
DE6 6FH	(Day/Board)	Enquiries to the
Tel 0283 702375	● Upper sixth 140	Headmaster
		Application to the
		Registrar

What it's like

Founded in 1557 as a boys school and having a decade of experience of girls in its sixth form, Repton has now decided to go fully co-educational and admit girls (13–18) from 1992. The school will be prepared to interview and test girls at 11+ if parents want an indication of whether their daughter is likely to meet its academic standards. The school is an integral part of the village of Repton (about 3000 inhabitants), and vice versa. The site was originally a Saxon settlement and has been occupied ever since. Over a thousand years of history is evident in the buildings and in extensive archaeological excavations. A civilised environment in which the architecture is very pleasing, as are the beautiful surroundings. It is a C of E foundation and quite a lot of emphasis is given to Anglican worship and practice. Facilities are extremely good. Academically, it is a high-powered school with very good teaching and consistently good results (very many leavers proceed to degree courses each year, including Oxbridge). Very strong music and art departments, and an outstanding record of dramatic presentations of many kinds. A very wide range of sport and games is on offer and standards are high (a lot of representatives at county level). Tennis is particularly strong (recognised by the LTA as one of the best schools). The CCF is strong and outdoor pursuits and adventure training have vigorous support. A big commitment to local community services in and around Repton and an impressive record in the Duke of Edinburgh's Award Scheme.

School profile

Pupils Age range 13–18; 572 pupils, 123 day (109 boys, 14 girls), 449 boarding (396 boys, 53 girls). Main entry ages 13+ (boys; girls from 1992); into sixth (boys and girls). Approx 10% are children of former pupils. Own prep school (Foremarke Hall) provides more than 20% of intake. *Transfer from maintained schools:* 3% main intake, plus 12% to sixth.

Entrance Common entrance exam used. Oversubscribed. Credit given for extra-curricular activities; most pupils are C of E but all denominations and religions welcomed. Parents not expected to buy text books; maximum extras, £50. 41 assisted places. 9 scholarships, 9 exhibitions pa, 50% to 20% fees; 4 music awards, up to 50% fees.

Staff Head G E Jones, in post for 4 years. 64 full time staff, 3 part time. Annual turnover 5%.

Academic work GCSE and A-levels. 18 GCSE subjects offered; 20 at A-level (including A-level general studies). In 1990, 93 pupils in upper fifth, 140 in upper sixth. *GCSE:* in 1990, 79 upper fifth gained at least grade C in 8+ subjects; 9 in 5–7 subjects. *A-levels:* 20 upper sixth passed in 4+ subjects; 88 in 3; 17 in 2; and 10 in 1 subject, excluding general studies. 30% took science A-levels; 30% arts/humanities; 40% both. *Computing facilities:* 18 BBCs; 8 BBC Masters; 10 Apple Macs; 3 Archimedes. *Special provision:* Special tutor for dyslexic pupils.

European Community *Languages:* French offered: to GCSE; A-level.

German offered: to GCSE; A-level. Italian and Spanish as non-examined subjects. 10–25% take GCSE in more than 1 EC language. *Other:* 6 German students in school. Challenge of Europe has been theme of sixth form conference, past 2 years.

Senior pupils' non-academic activities *Music:* 140 learn a musical instrument, 45 to Grade 6 or above, 10 awarded music scholarships. 3 to enter conservatoires; 80 in school orchestra, 60 in choir, 10 in pop group, 140 in choral society; 2 in National Youth Orchestra. *Drama and dance:* 80+ in school productions; 120 in house plays. *Art:* 40 take as non-examined subject; 25 take GCSE; 26 A-level; 6 take history of art. 7 accepted for Art School; 2 for architecture. 30 belong to photographic club. *Sport:* Football, cricket, Eton fives, hockey, lawn tennis (2 indoor courts), cross-country, athletics, shooting, fencing, golf, swimming, sailing, squash, rugby football, netball, badminton available. 150 take non-compulsory sport. 400 take compulsory sport. 38 represent county/country (hockey, soccer, tennis, cricket). *Other:* 90 take part in local community schemes. 30 have silver Duke of Edinburgh's Award, 10 have gold. Other activities include a computer club, art, astronomy, canoeing, chess, debating, wildfowl, mountaineering, photography, musical, woodwork, metalwork, dramatic and academic societies, driving lessons.

Careers In 1990, 80% leavers went on to degree courses; 4% to art/drama/

music colleges; 1% to non-degree courses; 1% straight into careers; 14% other (mostly Gap). Of those going on to degree courses, 8% went to Oxbridge, 72% to other universities; 20% to poly/colleges. 1% those going on to higher education went to courses in practical art; 1% in drama/acting; 1% in music; 70% in humanities/social sciences; 4% in medicine; and 24% in science/engineering.

Uniform School uniform worn except in the sixth.

Houses/prefects Competitive houses. Prefects, head boy/girl, head of house and house prefects – appointed by the Head and the Housemasters. No personal fagging, some communal services.

Religion Friday morning prayers, Sunday matins. Frequent voluntary services.

Social Modern languages exchanges can be arranged. Overseas trips have included cricket, hockey, ski-ing, music, athletics etc. Meals formal, by houses. School shop. No pupils allowed tobacco. Sixth form, over 17, allowed limited amount of alcohol three evenings/week.

Discipline No corporal punishment.

Pupils failing to produce homework once might expect extra work; those caught smoking cannabis on the premises would be required to leave the school.

Boarding 10% have own study bedroom, 19% share (2 or 3); 71% are in dormitories of 4+. Single sex houses, of approximately 55–60, same as competitive houses. Resident qualified nurse and doctor. No central dining room; each house has its own. Pupils can provide and cook own food. Half-term plus 1 weekend exeat each term and as many Sundays as required. Visits to the local town allowed, mostly for sixth formers.

Alumni association is run by J F M Walker, 14 High Street, Repton, Derby.

Former pupils Sir John Tooley (Royal Opera House); Robert Sangster (racehorse owner); Ian Grist MP; Sir John Stanley MP (Minister of State, Northern Ireland); Graeme Garden (TV); Roald Dahl (author); James Fenton (poet); Richard Heller (political journalist); Donald Carr and Richard Hutton (cricketers); Lord Ramsey (Archbishop of Canterbury); Sir J Grindrod (Archbishop of Australia).

· *Rickmansworth Masonic* ·

The Rickmansworth
Masonic School
Chorleywood Road
Rickmansworth
Hertfordshire WD3 4HF
Tel 0923 773168

- Pupils 660
- Boys None
- Girls 7–18
  (Day/Board)
- Upper sixth 50

- Termly fees
  £1194 (Day)
  £2083/£2053
  (Board/Weekly)
- GSA
Enquiries to the
Headmaster
Application to the
Admissions Secretary

What it's like

Founded in 1788, it moved from Central London in 1934 to an exceptionally fine purpose-built establishment of elegant and well-appointed buildings in 315 acres of superb grounds in the Chilterns. A very civilised environment. Extremely comfortable accommodation and first-rate facilities, including an unusually fine library. Chapel is central to the life of the school. The teaching is of a high standard with a staff:pupil ratio of 1:12. Good results and a number of pupils proceed to degree courses each year. Strong in music, drama and art. Much emphasis on debating and public speaking. A feature is the school drill: a display of callisthenics and movement. Good range of games, sport and activities. A fine record in the Duke of Edinburgh's Award Scheme.

School profile

Pupils Total age range 7–18; 660 girls, 328 day, 332 boarding. Senior department 11–18, 540 girls. Main entry ages 7, 11 and into sixth. Approx 2% are children of former pupils.

Entrance Common entrance and own exam used. Oversubscribed for day pupils. No special skills or religious requirements but school is Anglican. Parents not expected to buy text books; extras include standing charges £146 (day), £124 (boarders) plus music, drama, dancing, sport etc. 14 scholarships and unlimited bursaries for masonic families in need; scholarships £3430–£750.

Parents 15+% in industry or commerce. 30+% live within 30 miles; up to 10% live overseas.

Staff Headmaster D L Curtis, in post for 11 years. 54 full time staff, 13 part time. Annual turnover 5–10%. Average age 42.

Academic work GCSE, A-levels, RSA and Pitmans (A-level sociology and politics offered; design technology offered from 1991). On average, 81 pupils in upper fifth, 50 in upper sixth. *A-levels:* on average, 2 pupils in upper sixth pass in 4 subjects; 17 in 3; 15 in 2; and 7 in 1 subject. On average, 14 take science A-levels; 25 arts/humanities; 11 both. *Computing facilities:* 2 laboratories holding about 20 working computers. Individual computers in other departments. *Special provision:* for mildly dyslexic pupils.

Senior pupils' non-academic activities *Music:* 30 learn a musical instrument, 6–8 to Grade 6 or above; 1 accepted for Music School; 30 in school orchestra; 40 in choir; 15 in small choral group; 12 in instrumental groups. Junior Choir won competition to perform at Palladium in 'Joseph and his Amazing Technicolour Dreamcoat' with Jason Donovan. *Drama and dance:* 40 participate in sixth form musical/G & S; 20 in school plays; 40 take RSM speech and drama exams; 1 accepted for Drama/Dance School; 2 go on to work in theatre. *Art:* 20 take as non-examined subject; 30 take GCSE; 6 A-level; 3 accepted for Art School; 15 belong to photographic club; 12 to stage scenery group. *Sport:* Hockey, netball, badminton, squash, sailing, tennis, rounders, swimming, athletics, cross-country, trampolining available; riding can be arranged. 40 take non-compulsory sport. 6 take exams – mostly in life saving. 7 represent county/country (swimming, athletics and cross-country, tennis, hockey). *Other:* 4 take part in local community schemes. 20 have bronze Duke of Edinburgh's Award, 6 have silver and 2 have gold. 3 are Guides. 3 work for national charities beyond school. Other activities include a computer club, various cultural and academic societies, chess, bridge; driving lessons can be arranged; successful public speaking teams; Chapel, Sunday School; famous School Drill (150 years old).

Careers 1 full time adviser. Annual average accepted for *arts and humanities degree courses* at Oxbridge, 1; other universities, 12; polytechnics/colleges, 9. *science and engineering degree courses* at universities, 5; polytechnics/colleges, 5. *BEd*, 6. *other general training courses*, 13. Average going straight into careers in the armed services, 1; industry, 8; the City, 3; civil service, 6; music/drama, 2; other, 5.

Uniform School uniform worn, modified in sixth.

Houses/prefects Competitive houses. Prefects, head girl, head of house and house prefects – appointed by the Head with recommendations from staff and senior pupils.

Religion Attendance at religious worship compulsory on Sundays.

Social Joint debates, theatrical productions, musicals, games etc with other schools; also with the public at large. Organised trips abroad. Pupils allowed to bring own car to school. A few meals formal, most self service. School shop. No tobacco/alcohol allowed.

Discipline No corporal punishment.

Pupils failing to produce homework once might expect a warning; those caught smoking cannabis on the premises could expect expulsion.

Boarding 32% have own study bedroom, 8% share; 60% are in dormitories of 6+. Houses, of 40–48; separate houses for juniors and for sixth formers. 2 qualified sisters and 1 nursing assistant, doctor visits. Central dining room. Seniors can provide and cook own food. 2 weekend exeats each term, plus half-term. Visits to the local town allowed weekly for juniors; more often and unaccompanied for 16+.

Alumni association is run by Mrs Rosemary Turney, Hon Sec OMGA, c/o the School.

Former pupils Film and TV stars, newspapers (national editor), distinguished doctor. First female president of Cambridge Union.

· *Rishworth* ·

Rishworth School	● Pupils 632	● Termly fees
Rishworth	● Boys 4–18	£1350 (Day)
Sowerby Bridge	(Day/Board/Weekly)	£2550 (Board)
West Yorkshire	● Girls 4–18	£2220 (Weekly)
HX6 4QA	(Day/Board/Weekly)	● SHMIS
Tel 0422 822217	● Upper sixth 43	Enquiries/application to the Headmaster's Secretary

What it's like

Founded in 1724, it has occupied its present site since 1826. The buildings are handsome, solid, stone-built and lie in a beautiful valley (20 miles from Manchester and Leeds) with ample gardens and grounds. There have been a lot of modern additions, including a CDT centre, which provide good accommodation and up-to-date equipment. The environment is very healthy. The original school has become the chapel and there is some emphasis on worship and religious instruction. A good deal of attention is given to the principles and practice of Christianity. A broad general education is provided and the aim is to create a social and scholastic society in which boys and girls contribute as fully as possible to each other's education. Academic standards are highly creditable and results are good. Many sixth formers go on to degree courses each year. Strong music and drama depts. A good range of games and sports, and also extra-curricular activities. Considerable emphasis on outdoor pursuits for which the surroundings are ideal. The school has an outstanding record in the Duke of Edinburgh's Award Scheme.

School profile

Pupils Total age range 4–18; 632 pupils, 499 day (272 boys, 227 girls), 133 boarding (90 boys, 43 girls). (Boarding only for pupils aged 11–18.) Senior department 11–18. Main entry ages, 4, 7, 11 and into the sixth. 10% are children of former pupils. Own prep department provides 50% of senior intake. *Transfer from main-tained schools:* 40% senior intake, plus 70% to sixth.

Entrance Common entrance and own exam used. Oversubscribed. No special skills or religious requirements. Parents not expected to buy text books. 8 scholarships/bursaries, full to one-third fees; 10% reductions for children of C of

E priesthood or the armed services.

Parents 15+% in industry or commerce. 30+% live within 30 miles; 10+% live overseas.

Staff Headmaster A J Morsley, in post for 4 years. 52 full time staff, 4 part time. Annual turnover 4%. Average age 41.

Academic work GCSE and A-levels. 20 GCSE and A-level subjects offered (including Chinese, theatre studies, English language; A-level general studies for all sixth). In 1990, 89 pupils in upper fifth, 43 in upper sixth. *GCSE:* in 1990, 16 upper fifth gained at least grade C in 8+ subjects; 50 in 5–7; and 23 in 1–4 subjects. *A-levels:* 30 upper sixth passed in 4+ subjects; 6 in 3; 4 in 2; and 3 in 1 subject. 30% took science A-levels; 40% arts/humanities; 30% both. *Computing facilities:* 25 Nimbus, 10 Autocad, 10 BBC. *Special provision:* Dyslexic – some help from qualified staff. EFL tuition available.

European Community *Languages:* French offered: to age 14; GCSE; AS-level; A-level; Institute of Linguists. German: Institute of Linguists. Spanish offered: to age 14; GCSE; A-level. *Exchanges:* Regular exchanges for pupils aged 14–16 to Spain.

Senior pupils' non-academic activities *Music:* 120 learn a musical instrument, 7 to Grade 6 or above; 20 in school orchestra, 43 in choir, 2 go into music teaching. *Drama and dance:* 40 seniors in school productions. 3 take up to Grade 6 (ESB). 1 accepted for Drama/Dance School; 2 go on to work in theatre. *Art:* 5 take as non-examined subject; 35 GCSE; 6 A-level. 6 accepted for Art School. 4 belong to photographic club; others do pottery or textiles. *Sport:* Rugby, cricket, hockey, netball, gymnastics, swimming, soccer, cross-country, basketball, badminton, athletics, golf, tennis, squash, sailing, volleyball, fishing available. 120 take non-compulsory sport. 250 take AAA exams. 5 represent county/country (athletics,

squash). *Other:* 40–50 are taking bronze Duke of Edinburgh's Award, 20 have silver and 15 gold. Other activities include a computer club, driving lessons, CDT club.

Careers In 1990, 50% leavers went on to degree courses; 12% to art/drama/music colleges; 20% to non-degree courses; 18% straight into careers (eg banking, armed forces). Of those going on to degree courses, 5% went to Oxbridge, 55% to other universities; 40% to poly/colleges. 5% those going on to higher education went to courses in practical art; 40% in humanities/social sciences; 15% in medicine; and 40% in science/engineering.

Uniform School uniform worn throughout.

Houses/prefects Non-competitive houses. Prefects, head boy/girl, head of house and house prefects – appointed by Head.

Religion Religious worship encouraged; chapel attendance not compulsory in senior school.

Social Joint musical competition with local schools. 3 trips to France, 1 to Egypt, 1 to Spain, 2 ski-ing trips. Day pupils allowed to bring own car to school. Meals self service. School shop. No tobacco/alcohol allowed.

Discipline Pupils failing to produce homework once might expect detention; those caught smoking cannabis on the premises may expect expulsion (although this has not arisen).

Boarding 10% have own study bedroom, 60% share with 2 or 3; 30% in dormitories of 6+. Single sex houses, of 16–40, divided by age. 2 resident qualified nurses, 3 local doctors. Central dining room. Pupils can provide and cook some own food. 2 or 3 weekend exeats each term. Seniors allowed weekly visits to local town.

· RNIB New College ·

RNIB New College
(Worcester)
Whittington Road
Worcester
WR5 2JX
Tel 0905 763933

- Pupils 120
- Boys 10–18
  (Day/Board)
- Girls 10–18
  (Day/Board)
- Upper sixth 18

- Termly fees
  Normally payable
  by LEA
- HMC
  Enquiries/application to
  the Headmaster

What it's like

National and international specialist school for the blind or those with seriously defective sight. Gap students come from Poland and in addition to the examined languages in GCSE and A-level courses, language tuition in Italian, Spanish, Russian, Hindi and Arabic is offered to students in their last two years. Administered by the RNIB, fees are normally paid by the pupil's local education authority.

School profile

Pupils Age range 10–18; 120 boys and girls. Main entry ages 11 and into sixth. *Transfer from maintained schools:* 50% main intake, plus 50% to sixth.

Entrance Own assessment used. Most pupils' fees covered by their LEA.

Staff Head Rev B R Manthorp.

Academic work GCSE and A-levels. 20 subjects offered (including Japanese and occasionally A-level general studies; language tuition in last 2 years in Italian, Spanish, Russian, Hindi and Arabic). In 1990, 14 pupils in upper fifth, 18 in upper sixth. *Computing facilities:* 4 IT rooms and much more equipment in library/electronic classrooms etc. *Special provision:* All pupils are severely visually handicapped and may have other disabilities.

European Community *Languages:* French offered: to age 14; GCSE; A-level. German offered: to age 14; GCSE; A-level. 25–50% take GCSE in more than 1 EC language. Italian and Spanish offered in last 2 years. *Exchanges:* Regular exchanges for pupils aged 14–18 to France and Germany. *Other:* Plans for a German student to come to school.

Careers In 1990, 61% leavers went on to degree courses; 17% to non-degree courses; 11% straight into careers (eg telephoning, computing); 11% other. Of those going on to degree courses, 9% went to Oxbridge, 55% to other universities; 36% to poly/colleges. 73% those going on to higher education went to courses in humanities/social sciences; and 27% in science/engineering.

Social Gap students from Poland.

· *Robert Gordon's* ·

Robert Gordon's College Schoolhill Aberdeen AB9 1FR Tel 0224 646346	● Pupils 1167 ● Boys 5–17 (Day/Board) ● Girls 5–17 (Day/Board) ● Higher year 133	● Termly fees £913 (Day) £2013 (Board) ● HMC Enquiries/application to the Headmaster

What it's like

Founded in 1732 by Robert Gordon, a wealthy Aberdonian merchant in the Baltic ports, as a Hospital 'for Maintenance, Aliment, Entertainment, and Education of young boys'. In fact, the first occupants were the Hanoverian troops of the Duke of Cumberland, in 1746, on their way to Culloden. In 1750 the first boys were admitted. In 1881 the college was converted into a day school and in 1937 a boarding house was re-established. Robert Gordon's is urban on three sites; the senior and junior schools are on the original city centre site; the boarding house is a mile away, the playing fields $2^1/_2$ miles away. The main school buildings are magnificent and solid, in the 18th-century classical tradition, with elegant interiors. Extensive development has been possible over the years and the college is now very well equipped. In 1989 it entered on a five-year programme to introduce full co-education and there has been emphatic response to this enterprise. It is a non-denominational school. All pupils take a class in religious education and there are occasional religious services. The staff:pupil ratio is about 1:14. Academic standards are high and results consistently impressive. Very many leavers proceed to degree courses. Music is strong and treated as a practical subject in the curriculum. There are three choirs, senior and junior orchestras, a concert band and ensemble work. Regular large-scale musical productions. Art is also well supported, as is drama. Ballroom and country dancing have a sizeable following. A wide range of sports and games (including orienteering, angling and curling) is provided. Considerable emphasis on outdoor activities such as climbing, angling and ornithology. Thirty or more clubs and societies cater for most needs; debating, chess, charities and the CCF (voluntary, with Army section and pipe band) are particularly popular. Some community services and a high rate of success in the Duke of Edinburgh's Award Scheme.

School profile

Pupils Total age range 5–17; 1167 pupils, 1134 day (1007 boys, 127 girls), 33 boarding (30 boys, 3 girls). Senior department 11–17, 842 pupils (747 boys, 95 girls). Girls accepted since 1989, so ratio boys:girls changing rapidly. Main entry ages, 5, 9, 11 and into sixth. 10–15% are children of former pupils. 50% senior department from own junior. *Transfer from maintained schools:* 45% main intake, plus 38% to sixth.

Entrance Own entrance exam. Over-subscribed. No special skills or religious requirements. Parents expected to buy text books. Average extras £14. 15 assisted places pa. 35 scholarships/bursaries pa, full fees – £870.

Parents 15+% are doctors, lawyers etc, 15+% from industry/commerce, 15+% farming. 60+% live within 30 miles, 10% live overseas.

Staff Headmaster G A Allan, in post for 13 years. 75 full time staff, 8 part time. Annual turnover 3%. Average age 43.

Academic work O/S-grades, Highers. 20 subjects offered. In 1990, 147 pupils in fourth year (O-grade), 133 in fifth year (Higher). *O/S-grades:* in 1990, 125 fourth years gained at least grade C in 5–7 subjects; and 22 in 1–4 subjects. *Highers:* 83 fifth years passed in 4+ subjects; 23 in 3; 16 in 2; and 11 in 1 subject. 6% took arts/humanities Highers; 94% a mixture of science/engineering and arts/humanities. *Computing facilities:* 1 computer room and small word-processing unit. Computers in classrooms/laboratories as teaching aids. *Special provision:* 1 part-time teacher of learning support; 1 qualified EFL teacher.

European Community *Languages:* French offered: to age 14; S-grade; Higher. German offered: to S-grade; Higher. Italian offered: to S-grade; Higher. Up to 10% take S-grade in more than 1 EC language. *Exchanges:* Occasional EC pupils in school as part of private exchange scheme with individual families.

Senior pupils' non-academic activities *Music:* 30 learn a musical instrument, 12 up to Grade 6; 25 in school orchestra, 45 in school choir, 8 in pop group, 20 in pipe band; 4 in Grampian Region Schools Orchestra. *Drama and dance:* 14 in this session's major drama production. 100 take ballroom and country dancing. *Art:* 6 take art as non-examined subject; 32 take S-grade art; 28 Higher art; 8 belong to photographic club. *Sport:* Rugby, hockey, netball, volleyball, basketball, cross country, orienteering, ski-ing, curling, badminton, swimming, water polo, life-saving, table tennis, short tennis, weight-training, rock-climbing, cricket, tennis, athletics, golf available. 495 take non-compulsory sport. 270 take exams in swimming. 20 represent county/country (rugby, cricket, hockey (girls and boys), swimming, orienteering). *Other:* 10 take part in local community schemes. 43 working for bronze Duke of Edinburgh's Award, 38 silver and 41 gold; a few work for national charities. Over 30 clubs and societies – particularly prominent are debating, chess, charities, CCF.

Careers In 1990, 86% leavers went on to degree courses; 9% to non-degree courses; 5% straight into careers. Of those going on to degree courses, 2% went to Oxbridge; 75% to other universities; 23% to poly/colleges. 3% those going on to higher education went to courses in practical art; 28% in humanities/social sciences; 13% in medicine; 34% in science/engineering; and 18% in law and accountancy.

Uniform School uniform worn throughout.

Houses/prefects Competitive houses. Head boy/girl, prefects, house prefects, appointed by the head from nominations from staff and pupils.

Religion Attendance at religious worship compulsory (unless excused at parental request).

Social Debates, drama, music, dance with two local independent girls' schools. Debates with local maintained schools. Tours to Switzerland, Italy, Russia, Austria (ski-ing), France (Paris and St Malo), Belgium (concert band). Exchange with school in Graz (Austria). Pupils allowed to bring own bike. Meals self-service. School shop. No tobacco/alcohol allowed.

Discipline No corporal punishment. Pupils failing to produce homework once could expect warning from teacher and work to be handed in without fail the next day; those caught smoking cannabis on the premises could expect expulsion.

Boarding All share (with 1–5 others); accommodation arranged by sex and by age. 2 2-day exeats per term. Visits to the local town allowed at weekends only for age 12+.

Alumni association is run by Mr Philip G Dawson, James & George Collie, Advocates, 1 East Craibstone Street, Aberdeen.

· *Rodney* ·

Rodney School
Kirklington
Nr Newark
Nottinghamshire
NG22 8NB
Tel 0636 813281

- Pupils 252
- Boys 9–18
  (Day/Board/Weekly)
- Girls 9–18
  (Day/Board/Weekly)
- Upper sixth 10

- Termly fees
  £695 (Day)
  £1285 (Board/
  Weekly)
- ISAI
  Enquiries/application to
  the Principal

What it's like

Founded 1945. The main building is Kirklington Hall, a large country mansion with ample grounds on the edge of Sherwood Forest and close to the Dukeries. Good modern facilities. A sound education is provided and academic results are creditable. Quite strong in music and drama. An adequate range of sports, games and activities. County standard sports hall.

School profile

Pupils Total age range 9–18; 252 pupils, 114 day (63 boys, 51 girls), 138 boarding (80 boys, 58 girls). Senior department 11–18, 200 pupils (100 boys, 100 girls). Main entry ages 9, 11, 13 and into sixth. Approx 5% are children of former pupils. *Transfer from maintained schools:* 50% senior intakes, plus 5% to sixth.

Entrance Common entrance and own exam used. Oversubscribed. No special skills or religious requirements. Parents expected to buy text books. 2 sixth form scholarships/bursaries, £2000–£1500.

Parents 30+% live within 30 miles; up to 10% live overseas.

Staff Principal Miss J G Thomas, in post for 30 years. 18 full time staff, 12 part time. Annual turnover 1%. Average age 40.

Academic work GCSE and A-levels. 12 subjects offered (including A-level general studies). In 1989, 48 pupils in upper fifth, 10 in upper sixth. *GCSE:* in 1989, 30 upper fifth gained at least grade C in 8+ subjects; 10 in 5–7; and 2 in 1–4 subjects. *A-levels:* 4 upper sixth passed in 3 subjects; 3 in 2; and 2 in 1 subject. 7 took science A-levels; 2 arts/humanities. *Computing facilities:* 12 computers. *Special provision:* EFL.

Senior pupils' non-academic activities *Music:* 20 learn a musical instrument, 2 to Grade 6 or above, 1 accepted for Music School; 45 in school choir. *Drama and dance:* 70 in school productions; 90 take modern dance. 2 accepted for Drama/Dance Schools. *Art:* All take as non-examined subject; 20 take GCSE. 1 accepted for Art School. *Sport:* Rugby, hockey, squash, swimming, football, rounders, basketball. 15 take non-compulsory sport. 50 take exams in eg swimming. 2 represent county (rugby). *Other:* 5 have bronze Duke of Edinburgh's Award, some have silver. 60 work for national charities. Other activities include computer, rock and heather, canoeing clubs.

Careers 1 full time careers adviser. Some pupils go on to degree courses. Average accepted for general training courses, 4; average going straight into careers in armed services, 4; industry, 3; music/drama, 1.

Uniform School uniform worn, modified in the sixth.

Houses/prefects Competitive houses. Prefects, head boy/girl, head of house and house prefects – appointed by staff. Prefect Council.

Religion Religious worship encouraged.

Social Local amateur theatre group. Organised trips abroad. Concerts, theatre visits, ice skating, discos. Lunch self service. No tobacco/alcohol allowed.

Discipline Corporal punishment rare. Pupils failing to produce homework once might expect admonishment, thereafter detention.

Boarding 2 have own study bedroom, 100+ share. Resident qualified nurse.

Central dining room. Pupils allowed to provide and cook some of own food. 1 weekend exeat per fortnight. Visits to the local town allowed (accompanied).

Former pupils Dame Mary Bridges; Sir Kenneth McMillan.

· *Roedean* ·

Roedean School	● Pupils 470	● Termly fees
Brighton	● Boys None	£3195 (Board)
East Sussex BN2 5RQ	● Girls 11–18	● GSA
Tel 0273 603181	(Board)	Enquiries/application to
Fax 0273 676722	● Upper sixth 75	the Admissions
		Secretary

What it's like

Founded in 1885, it moved to its present site in 1898. It has a splendid position above the cliffs and overlooking the sea, between Brighton and Rottingdean. It is a purpose-built school with attractive and very well-equipped buildings on a large estate of which about 40 acres are given to playing fields and leisure activities. One of the most distinguished schools in Britain, it is well run and its very large and very well-qualified staff permits a staff:pupil ratio of 1:7. Few if any schools could match this. Academically high-powered, it gets excellent results each year. A very high proportion of sixth formers, for a school of this size, go on to degree courses, including Oxbridge. French and Spanish are offered to A-level, German to AS-level. A high proportion of girls takes GCSE in more than one European language. There are regular exchanges with France and Germany. Great emphasis is placed on careers advice and the teaching of leadership skills. Extremely strong in art, music and drama; virtually all pupils are involved in these activities. A wide range of games and sports is available and high standards are achieved. There is a big commitment to local community services. The school has an outstanding record in the Duke of Edinburgh's Award Scheme and the Young Enterprise Business Scheme.

School profile

Pupils Age range 11–18; 470 boarding girls. Main entry ages 11, 12, 13 and into sixth. Approx 5% are children of former pupils. *Transfer from maintained schools:* Very small (2 pupils in main intake, plus 1–2 to sixth).

Entrance Common entrance used; interviews for entry to sixth. Oversubscribed. Wide range of interests and skills looked for; no religious requirements. Parents not expected to buy text books; maximum extras £200. A number of scholarships/bursaries, mainly 50% fees.

Parents 15+% are doctors, lawyers etc; 15+% in industry or commerce. 30+% live within 30 miles; 10+% live overseas.

Staff Headmistress Mrs Ann R Longley, in post for 6 years. 56 full time staff, 22 part time. Annual turnover 12%. Average age 36.

Academic work GCSE and A-levels. 21 subjects offered (no A-level general studies). In 1990, 78 pupils in upper fifth, 69 in upper sixth (now 75). *GCSE:* in

629

1990, 76 upper fifth gained at least grade C in 5–7 subjects. *A/AS-levels:* 16 upper sixth passed in 4+ subjects; 31 in 3; 16 in 2; and 5 in 1 subject. 13 took science A/AS-levels; 23 arts/humanities; 33 both. *Computing facilities:* 3 computer rooms; 1 for computer studies and information technology (IBM based), 1 for computer assisted learning (BBC based) and one for CDT and for word processing. In addition, each department has at least 1 BBC. *Special provision:* Extra English for foreign pupils and for those with dyslexia.

European Community *Languages:* French offered: to age 14; GCSE; AS-level; A-level. German offered: to age 14; GCSE; AS-level. Spanish offered: to age 14; GCSE; AS-level; A-level. 50–75% take GCSE in more than 1 EC language. *Exchanges:* Regular exchanges for pupils aged 14–16 to France and Germany.

Senior pupils' non-academic activities *Music:* 398 learn a musical instrument, 62 to Grade 6 or above, 1 accepted for Music School (scholarship); 150 in school orchestras, 160 in choirs, 12 jazz band, 35 in chamber groups; 5 GCSE music, 6 'A' level, 2 A/S level. *Drama and dance:* 150 in school productions; 320, house drama; 15 LAMDA Gold medals, 1 LAMDA Diploma, 15 ESB Higher Cert. 150, verse speaking. 12 GCSE theatre arts; public speaking 6, Rotary 6, ESU 6. 25 entered competitions (Brighton Festival). 1 accepted to Drama/degree course; 120 take Dance (RAD). *Art:* 3 take as non-examined subject; 26 GCSE; 18 A-level. 5 accepted for Art School; 12 belong to photographic club; 19 take design & technology, 8 in engineering club. *Sport:* Lacrosse, netball, hockey, volleyball, squash, tennis, rounders, cricket, judo, swimming, fencing, badminton, athletics, riding available. 130 take non-compulsory sport. 8 take life-saving exams. 12 represent county/country (netball, lacrosse). *Other:* 72 take part in local community schemes. 10 have bronze Duke of Edinburgh's Award, 40 have silver and 30 gold. Other activities include a computer club, driving lessons (upper sixth), debating societies, drama club, Young Enterprise business companies.

Careers In 1990, 99% leavers went on to degree courses; 1% to non-degree courses (eg hotel and catering, physiotherapy). Of those going on to degree courses, 4% went to Oxbridge, 83% to other universities; 12% to poly/colleges. 71% those going on to higher education went to courses in arts/humanities/social sciences; 21% in medicine; and 8% in science/engineering.

Uniform School uniform worn except sixth form.

Houses/prefects Competitive houses. Head girl, prefects and head of house – appointed by Head, staff and sixth; house prefects – elected by school. Sixth Form Committee and School Council.

Religion Compulsory morning assembly and Sunday chapel except for practising members of other faiths; Roman Catholics attend own church and Jewish girls have tuition from local Rabbi.

Social Joint musical events, debates, quizzes, dances with local boys' schools. Sixth Form Society with Hurstpierpoint. Exchange with school in Spain; occasional organised trips to France; annual ski-ing holiday. Sixth form allowed to bring own bike to school. Meals self service. School bookshop, tuckshop and stationery store. No tobacco/alcohol allowed.

Discipline No corporal punishment. All rules, and penalties for breaking these, are clearly defined in the Student Handbook issued to each girl each year.

Boarding Sixth form have own study bedroom, upper fifth share bedroom with 2 and study with 2–3. Houses of approx 80 (1 for 11–12 year olds, 4 for 13–17, 1 upper sixth). Resident qualified sister, 2 visiting doctors. Central dining rooms. *Upper sixth* provide and cook own food some of the time. 2–3 Saturday night exeats termly plus half-term; more flexible in sixth. Visits to local town allowed – escorted for younger girls.

Alumni association run by Mrs M Woods, President, The Old Roedeanian Association, c/o the School.

Former pupils Lynda Chalker MP; Verity Lambert (actress and director); Sarah Miles (actress); Sally Oppenheimer MP; Dame Cecily Saunders (founder of hospice movement).

· Rosemead ·

Rosemead School
East Street
Littlehampton
West Sussex
BN17 6AJ
Tel 0903 716065

- Pupils 260
- Boys 4–13 only (Day)
- Girls 4–18 (Day/Board/Weekly)
- Upper sixth 19

- Termly fees
  £1445 (Day)
  £2495 (Board/Weekly)
- GSA
  Enquiries/application to the School Secretary

What it's like

Founded in 1919, it is single-site in Littlehampton, 10 minutes' walk from the sea, 5 miles from Arundel and 10 from Chichester. It comprises agreeable modern buildings and good up-to-date facilities in large gardens. The preparatory department is on the campus. It has most of the advantages of a small school and enjoys an excellent staff:pupil ratio of 1:7. Academic results are quite good and some sixth formers proceed to degree courses each year. The atmosphere is purposeful and friendly. Good range of games, sports and activities. Adequate music and drama.

School profile

Pupils Total age range 4–18; 260 pupils, 199 day (19 boys, 180 girls), 61 boarding girls. Senior department 10–18, 170 girls, no boys. Main entry ages 4 (boys and girls); 11, 13 and into sixth (girls). Approx 2% are children of former pupils. *Transfer from maintained schools:* 25% senior intake, plus 7% to sixth.

Entrance Common entrance and own exam used. Good command of English for overseas students required. Parents expected to buy text books only in sixth form. 3 scholarships plus bursaries, up to £1425.

Parents 15+% in industry or commerce. 65% live within 30 miles; 14% live overseas.

Staff Principal Mrs J Bevis, in post for 4 years. 28 full time staff, 10 part time. Annual turnover 8%. Average age 40.

Academic work GCSE and A-levels. 14 subjects offered (no A-level general studies). In 1990, 37 pupils in upper fifth, 19 in upper sixth. *GCSE:* in 1990, 30 upper fifth gained at least grade C in 8+ subjects; 7 in 5–7 subjects. *A-levels:* 1 upper sixth passed in 4+ subjects; 8 in 3; 8 in 2; and 2 in 1 subject. 4 took science A-levels; 9 arts/humanities; 6 both. *Computing facilities:* Computer room with 8 networked machines: 4 stand-alones; computers in library, geography room, science dept and business studies area. *Special provision:* Remedial English for the mildly dyslexic; EFL lessons for non-native speakers.

European Community *Languages:* French offered: to age 14; GCSE; A-level. German offered: to GCSE; A-level. 25–50% take GCSE in more than 1 EC language. *Other:* French, German and Spanish pupils in school (1 term–1 year). Extra private language coaching available at all levels. Younger pupils spend time at a study centre in Brittany.

Senior pupils' non-academic activities *Music:* 25 learn a musical instrument, 2 to Grade 6 or above; 15 in school orchestra, 35 in choir; 1 in National Children's Wind Orchestra. *Drama and dance:* 100 in school productions. 10 take Guildhall exams; 8, RAD senior grade and above. 2 accepted for Drama/Dance School. *Art:* 3 take as non-examined subject; 16 take GCSE; 12 A-level. 2 accepted for Art School. *Sport:* Lacrosse, netball, tennis, athletics, rounders, badminton, volleyball, swimming, riding, judo, ballet, squash, table tennis available. 50 take non-compulsory sport. Some represent county/country (lacrosse, tennis, netball). *Other:* 12 have bronze Duke of Edinburgh's Award. Other activities include a computer club, electronics, gym club, weight training, vehicle maintenance, folk club, chess.

Careers In 1990, 45% leavers went on to degree courses; 49% to art/drama/music colleges; 6% straight into careers. Of those going on to degree courses, 56% went to universities; 44% to poly/colleges. 31% those going on to higher education went to courses in practical art; 39% in humanities/social sciences; and 31% in science/engineering.

Uniform School uniform worn except in the sixth.

Houses/prefects Competitive houses. Head girl and prefects (chosen by Principal and staff); head of house by girls.

Religion Christians attend local churches.

Social Flourishing arts centre, public performances by visiting artists and master classes. School dances and reciprocal arrangements with nearby boys' boarding schools. Organised annual ski trip and trips to various parts of Europe; exchange visits to France. Pupils allowed to bring own bike to school. Meals canteen service. School thrift shop. No tobacco/alcohol allowed.

Discipline No corporal punishment. Pupils failing to produce prep once might expect to make up the work in their own time; those caught with drugs on the premises could expect expulsion.

Boarding 55% have own study bedroom, 20% share (4–6 approx); 25% are in dormitories of 6+. Houses, of 40–45, divided by age. Resident SRN and visiting school doctor. Central dining room. Sixth formers can provide and cook own food. Two weekend exeats each term. Visits to the local town allowed.

· *Rossall* ·

Rossall School	● Pupils 482	● Termly fees
Fleetwood	● Boys 11–18	£1635 (Day)
Lancashire	(Day/Board)	£2876 (Board)
FY7 8JW	● Girls 11–18	● HMC
Tel 0253 774204	(Day/Board)	Enquiries/application to
Fax 0253 772052	● Upper sixth 79	the Headmaster

What it's like

Founded in 1844 as a C of E foundation. Built as a school for the purpose of giving a sound education to the sons of clergy and lay people. It is well sited on the Lancashire coast between Blackpool and Fleetwood, semi–rural on an estate of 155 acres. The addition of new buildings and the refitting of the solid Victorian buildings has been a constant process (a larger chapel was erected in 1862) and much of the modern structure dates from 1955. Religious worship is encouraged and the chapel is used daily. A well-qualified teaching staff allows a staff:pupil ratio of about 1:10. Academic standards are high and good results are achieved. Many pupils go on to degree courses. Music is strong and drama is well supported. There is a good range of sports and games and a high level of attainment. Extra-curricular activities are plentiful. There is considerable emphasis on outdoor pursuits, self-reliance and practical skills. The CCF contingent is the most senior, having been formed in 1860 as the 65th Lancashire Volunteer Rifles. It has Army, RAF and Naval sections and all pupils are expected to join it after the first year. There is some commitment to local community services and the Duke of Edinburgh's Award Scheme.

School profile

Pupils Age range 11–18; 482 pupils, 94 day (55 boys, 39 girls), 388 boarders (107 boys, 281 girls). Main entry ages 11, 13 and into sixth. 15% are children of former pupils. Own prep provides 20% intake. *Transfer from maintained schools:* 14% main intakes, plus 15% to sixth.

Entrance Own exam used; common entrance occasionally. Oversubscribed at some levels. No special skills or religious requirements, though school is C of E foundation. 47 assisted places. 15+ scholarships pa, up to 100% fees; clerical and service bursaries.

Parents Some 25% live within 30 miles; 15% live overseas.

Staff Headmaster R D W Rhodes, in post for 4 years. 52 full time staff, 16 part time (including music). Annual turnover less than 10%.

Academic work GCSE, AS and A-levels. 17 subjects offered (including GCSE physical education and A-level general studies). In 1989, 83 pupils in upper fifth, 84 in upper sixth (now 79). *GCSE:* in 1989, 32 upper fifth gained at least grade C in 8+ subjects; 22 in 5–7; and 24 in 1–4 subjects. *A-levels:* 4 upper sixth passed in 4+ subjects; 42 in 3; 19 in 2; and 14 in 1 subject. 29% took science A-levels; 49% arts/humanities; 22% both. *Computing facilities:* Specialist IT department with 2 computer networks. Computer support in all major departments. *Special provision:* Support units for specific learning difficulties and overseas pupils.

European Community *Languages:* French offered: to age 14; GCSE; A-level. German offered: to age 14; GCSE; A-level. 10–25% take GCSE in more than 1 EC language. *Other:* Number of European pupils in school, for 1 term or more.

Senior pupils' non-academic activities *Music:* 210 learn one or more musical instruments; 40 pupils play in 2 school orchestras, 64 in choir, 70 in 2 bands.

Drama and dance: Two major productions each year. *Art:* 30 take as non-examined subject; 11 take GCSE; 6 A-level. *Sport:* Rugby, cricket, hockey, athletics, netball, squash, fives, cross-country, shooting, swimming available. *Other:* Pupils participate in bronze, silver and gold Duke of Edinburgh Awards, the Rossall Award and local community schemes. Range of other activities including a computer club, chess club, Christian Union, debating, sub-aqua, sailing, canoeing, fencing.

Careers In 1990, 74% leavers went on to degree courses; 2% to art/drama/music colleges; 14% to non-degree courses (eg land management, business studies, hospitality management); 8% straight into careers (eg armed forces, computing, retail management); 2% other. Of those going on to degree courses, 6% went to Oxbridge; 45% to other universities; 49% to poly/colleges. 2% those going on to higher education went to courses in practical art; 2% in music; 44% in humanities/social sciences; 20% in business studies; and 32% in science/engineering.

Uniform School uniform worn throughout.

Houses/prefects Competitive houses. School captain, house captains, monitors.

Religion Daily chapel compulsory, to provide school's multi-racial, multi-cultural community with a period of reflection.

Social Occasional (irregular) events with local schools. Regular sports tours abroad; no exchange systems. Meals cafeteria. Sixth form bar; no tobacco allowed.

Discipline No corporal punishment. Pupils failing to produce prep, complete work under supervision on half holidays; minor misdemeanors dealt with by school parade (tasks to be completed by 7.00 am). Any pupil in possession of cannabis must expect expulsion.

Boarding Sixth formers have own study bedroom; remainder in dormitories of 4–

10. Houses of 35–59, single sex except junior house (11–13). Resident qualified nurses. Central dining room. Pupils can provide and cook own snacks. Flexible policy to exeats. Visits to local town allowed, twice weekly.

Alumni association is run by Peter Bennett, General Secretary, Rossallian Club, c/o the School.

Former pupils Sir Thomas Beecham; Leslie Charteris; General Sir Thomas Hutton; Sir David Brown; Professor F R Smith.

· *Rougemont* ·

Rougemont School
Kingshill
Stow Hill
Newport
Gwent NP9 4EA
Tel 0633 253915/
211813

- Pupils 540
- Boys 3–18
  (Day)
- Girls 3–18
  (Day)
- Upper sixth 27

- Termly fees
  £1084 (Day)
- SHMIS
  Enquiries/application to
  the Admissions
  Secretary

What it's like

Founded in 1920, the main building was formerly the Archbishop of Wales' home. The school was established for 4–11 year olds to feed local grammar schools. The present school took shape after a parental buy-out in 1975 and a charitable trust was formed. The first sixth form opened in 1981. It is now an all-through 3–18 school, on two sites. High staff:pupil ratio of 1:10. Good academic results in GCSE and A-level. Very many sixth formers go on to degree courses each year. Adequate music, drama and art. Quite good sport and games (several county representatives). A most impressive record in the Duke of Edinburgh's Award Scheme.

School profile

Pupils Total age range 3–18; 540 day pupils (290 boys, 250 girls). Senior department 11–18, 336 pupils (195 boys, 141 girls). Main entry ages 3–4, 11 and into sixth. Approx 10% are children of former pupils. *Transfer from maintained schools:* 60% senior intake, plus 50% to sixth.

Entrance Common entrance and own exam used. Sometimes oversubscribed. No special skills or religious requirements. Parents only expected to buy specialist text books in sixth; no other extras. 9 scholarships/bursaries, maximum value full fees.

Parents 15+% are doctors, lawyers, etc.

Staff Headmaster Graham Sims, first year in post. 52 full time staff, 9 part time. Annual turnover 3%. Average age 43.

Academic work GCSE and A-levels.

16 GCSE subjects offered; 12 at A-level (no A-level general studies). On average, 43 pupils in upper fifth, 27 in upper sixth. *GCSE:* on average, 60% upper fifth gain at least grade C in 8+ subjects; 21% in 5–7; and 18% in 1–4 subjects. *A-levels:* on average, 67% upper sixth pass in 3 subjects; 17% in 2; and 9% in 1 subject. On average, 32% take science A-levels; 31% arts/humanities; 37% both. *Computing facilities:* Amstrad PCW 8256's; Amstrad CPC 464's; Campus 2000; computer club. *Special provision:* Individual tuition on withdrawal basis.

European Community *Languages:* French offered: to age 14; GCSE; AS-level; A-level. German offered: to age 14; GCSE; AS-level; A-level. Spanish to GCSE. Over 75% take GCSE in more than 1 EC language. *Exchanges:* Exchange with a German school in Coblenz recently established.

Senior pupils' non-academic activities *Music:* 15 learn a musical instrument, 3 to Grade 6 or above. 1 accepted for Music School; 3 play in pop group beyond school, 10 in school orchestra, 18 in choir, 1 in National Youth Orchestra, 3 in Gwent youth orchestra. *Drama and dance:* 25 in school productions; 1 candidate for Drama School. *Art:* 3 take as non-examined subject; 18 take GCSE; 3–5, A-level. 2–3 accepted for Art School. *Sport:* Rugby, cricket, basketball, squash, netball, rounders, tennis, indoor rifle range, athletics, swimming available. 20+ (sixth form) take non-compulsory sport. 2–3 take exams eg gymnastics, swimming. 11 pupils represent county (cricket, badminton, athletics, swimming). *Other:* 5–8 take part in local community schemes. 42 have bronze Duke of Edinburgh's Award, 35 have silver and 21 gold. 4–6 are Queen's Scouts. Other activities include a computer club and 11 activities grouped under Duke of Edinburgh's Award Scheme. Choirs, ensembles, chess, drama, ballet, elocution.

Careers In 1990, 91% leavers went on to degree courses; 3% to non-degree courses (eg secretarial); 3% straight into careers (eg transport); 3% other. Of those going on to degree courses, 48% went to universities; 52% to poly/colleges. 7% those going on to higher education went to courses in practical art; 3% in music; 41% in humanities/social sciences; 12% in medicine; and 38% in science/engineering.

Uniform School uniform worn throughout.

Houses/prefects Competitive houses. Prefects, head boy/girl, head of house and house prefects – appointed by the Headmaster, with staff consultation.

Religion Religious worship compulsory.

Social Three sets of debating competitions (Rotary, Business Women, English–Speaking Union). At least three organised trips abroad each year. Pupils allowed to bring own car/bike/motorbike to school. Meals self-service. School shop. No tobacco allowed; sixth form allowed alcohol at special supervised functions.

Discipline No corporal punishment. Pupils failing to produce homework once might expect disapproval; those caught smoking cannabis on the premises could expect expulsion.

Alumni association is run by Tim Webber, c/o the school.

· *Royal (Bath)* ·

The Royal School	● Pupils 403	● Termly fees
Lansdown	● Boys 3–7 only	£1957 (Day)
Bath	● Girls 3–18	£3066 (Board)
BA1 5SZ	(Day/Board)	● GSA
Tel 0225 313877	● Upper sixth 47	Enquiries/application to
Fax 0225 420338		the Headmistress

What it's like

Founded in 1864 to educate 'the Daughters of necessitous Officers of the Army at the lowest possible cost' and to help widows whose husbands had died in the Crimean War. Now, its pupils come from a wide range of backgrounds, but the daughters of servicemen still form the largest group in the school. It is urban and single-site in the very pleasant district of Lansdown, on the north side of the city. It prides itself on being a happy 'bonding' community which welcomes day pupils for all its activities. All pupils are expected to have serious career intentions and particular care is given to individual needs. It is a C of E foundation but ecumenical in spirit and policy. All girls attend chapel daily and boarders attend most Sundays. The National Curriculum is followed throughout the school. A broad general education is provided and results are creditable. A number of girls go on to degree courses each year including some to Oxbridge. Very strong in music and drama. A decent range of sports and games (very strong in lacrosse) and plentiful leisure activities. Growing commitment to local community services.

School profile

Pupils Total age range 3–18; 403 pupils, 173 day (17 boys, 156 girls), 230 boarding girls. Senior department, 11–18, 306 girls. Main entry ages 3 (boys and girls), 11, 13 and into sixth (girls). 5% are children of former pupils. *Transfer from maintained schools:* 10% senior intake, plus 5% to sixth.

Entrance Common entrance and own exam used. Not oversubscribed. All skills taken into account. No religious requirements but C of E foundation; broadly Christian with some other faiths. Parents not expected to buy text books; individual music, drama, sports coaching extra. 20 scholarships pa, $^1/_3$ to $^1/_6$ fees; exhibitions, $^1/_{12}$ fees.

Parents 15+% in the armed services; 15+% are doctors, lawyers, etc; 15+% are in industry. 10+% live within 30 miles; 10+% live overseas.

Staff Headmistress Dr Judith McClure, in post for 4 years.

Academic work GCSE, AS and A-levels. 21 subjects offered (including AS-level general studies). On average, 50 pupils in upper fifth, 47 in upper sixth. *GCSE:* on average, 30% fifth year gain at least grade C in 8+ subjects; 50% in 5–7; and 20% in 1–4 subjects. *A-levels:* on average, 5% upper sixth pass in 4+ subjects; 43% in 3; 25% in 2; and 15% in 1 subject. On average, 10 take science A-levels; 13 arts/humanities; 2 both. *Computing facilities:* Pupils have wide exposure to computing facilities; all departments have computers for use both during curriculum time and in pupils' free time. *Special provision:* Special needs department offers basic skills and EFL to small minority of students.

European Community *Languages:* French offered: to age 14; GCSE; AS-level; A-level. German offered: to age 14; GCSE; AS-level; A-level. Spanish offered: to age 14; GCSE; AS-level; A-level. 25–50% take GCSE in more than 1 EC language. *Exchanges:* Regular exchanges for pupils aged 11–18 to France, Germany, and Spain. *Other:* EC students in the sixth form. Resident foreign language assistants (French, German, Spanish). Foreign language teaching being expanded for non-specialists in the sixth form.

Senior pupils' non-academic activities *Music:* 200 learn a musical instrument, 30 to Grade 6 or above; 2 accepted for Music School or music at university. 25 pupils play in school orchestra, 30 in choir, others in chamber and recorder groups; 2 in Bath Society of Young Musicians; 60 in Mid-Somerset Festival, 90 in other choirs. *Drama and dance:* 150 in school productions; 3 in Bath Youth Theatre; 100 take grades in RAD, LAMDA. 100 enter Mid-Somerset Festival; 1 member of National Youth Theatre; 2 in ESU Shakespeare Competition. 2 go on to degree including drama. 15 take modern and tap, 17 ballet. *Art:* 15+ take GCSE; 5 A-level. 4 accepted for Art School. 25+ belong to eg photographic club, weekly art club. *Sport:* Lacrosse, tennis, hockey, netball, rounders, athletics, swimming, badminton, golf, volleyball, canoeing, horse riding, ski training, life saving training available. 100+ take part in non-compulsory sport. 30 take exams, eg swimming. 10 pupils in county lacrosse team; 2 in West of England team. *Other:* 20 working towards bronze Duke of Edinburgh's Award, 12 to silver, 3 to gold. 16 in local community schemes. Over 35 other activities including a computer club, self-defence, enterprise company, CDT, engineering society, Christian Union, dressmaking, winemaking, ropework, deaf sign language, fire service.

Careers In 1990, 48% leavers went on to degree courses; 4% to art/drama/music colleges; 48% to non-degree courses (eg agriculture, nursing, secretarial). Of those going on to degree courses, 15% went to Oxbridge, 50% to other universities; 35% to poly/colleges. 9% those going on to higher education went to courses in practical art; 9% in drama/acting; 9% in music; 43% in humanities/social sciences; 9% in medicine; and 22% in science/engineering.

Uniform School uniform, except in sixth.

Houses/prefects Competitive houses. Head girl, heads of houses and prefects appointed by Head; heads of boarding elected by school. School Council.

Religion Christian worship compulsory.

Social Young Engineers and Scientists, joint theatrical productions, open meetings, conferences and social events with other schools. Organised trips abroad and exchange systems. Pupils allowed to bring own car/bike to school. Meals self-service. School shop. No tobacco/alcohol allowed.

Discipline No corporal punishment. Pupils failing to produce homework once might expect a detention; those caught smoking cannabis on the premises (unprecedented) could expect serious consequences.

Boarding 15% have own study bedroom, 85% share (with 1, 2 or 3). Houses, of about 50, are laterally divided. Resident qualified nurse, visiting doctor. Central dining room. Pupils can provide and cook own food by arrangement. 2 weekend exeats termly plus half-term. Weekend visits to local town allowed, depending on age.

Alumni association is run by Mrs Unity Marriott, c/o the Royal School.

Former pupils Jean Nunn (Under Secretary, Cabinet Office; first woman to receive the Order of the Bath).

· Royal (Belfast) ·

The Royal Belfast Academical Institution
College Square
Belfast BT1 6DL
Tel 0232 240461

- Pupils 920
- Boys 11–19 (Day)
- Girls None
- Upper sixth 115

- Termly fees £60 (Day)
- HMC

Enquiries/admissions to the Principal

What it's like

Founded in 1810, the Institution was, until 1849, a university level institution as well as a school with faculties of arts and medicine. On the foundation of The Queen's College (now The Queen's University of Belfast) it became a school only. It is a voluntary grammar school (not an independent school) under the management of a board of governors constituted under a scheme authorised by the Privy Council of Ireland. It has an 8-acre site in the centre of the city where the first buildings were erected. These are fine buildings after the design of Sir John Soane. Many major additions have been made, most recently a new technology and design centre; is now equipped with excellent facilities. The playing fields are at Osborne Park, Bladon Park and Cranmore. The preparatory department (Inchmarlo) is near Osborne Park and Cranmore. Academic standards are high and results good; each year over two-thirds of the leavers go on to universities or to other places of higher or further education. Music and drama are strongly supported. The main sports and games are rugby, hockey, cricket, lawn tennis, rowing and athletics. Many pupils have participated in games and sports at national and international level. A large number of clubs and societies cater for most conceivable interests. There is a CCF contingent, a scout troup (with a venture scout section) and a community service group.

School profile

Pupils Age range 11–19, 920 day boys. Main entry age 11. Own junior school.

Entrance Entry through Transfer Procedure arranged by LEAs in Northern Ireland, together with Department of Education (NI). The overwhelming majority of pupils are 'non-fee-paying', ie they have been awarded a grant by LEAs on the basis of the 11+ Transfer Procedure. Foundation and leaving scholarships.

Staff Principal R M Ridley, first year in post.

Academic work GCSE, AS and A-levels. 18 GCSE subjects offered; 15 at A-level (AS-level general studies but no A-level). In 1990, 130 pupils in upper fifth, 115 in upper sixth. *GCSE:* in 1990, 76 upper fifth gained at least grade C in 8+ subjects; 30 in 5–7; and 24 in 1–4 subjects. *A-levels:* 11 upper sixth passed in 4+ subjects; 75 in 3; 20 in 2; and 8 in 1 subject. 45% took science A-levels; 20% arts/humanities; 35% both. *Computing facilities:* 2 suites of computer rooms (Amstrad, Nimbus) and facility for computer studies to A-level and IT Certificate of Competence.

European Community *Languages:* French offered: to age 14; GCSE; AS-level; A-level. German offered: to age 14; GCSE; A-level. Spanish offered: to age 14; GCSE; A-level. 10–25% take GCSE in more than 1 EC language. *Exchanges:* Regular exchanges for pupils aged 11–18 to France and Germany. *Other:* Trips to Europe arranged.

Careers In 1990, 75% leavers went on to degree courses; 5% to art/drama/music colleges; 5% to non-degree courses; 10% straight into careers; 5% other. Of those going on to degree courses, 13% went to Oxbridge; 45% to other universities; 20% to poly/colleges. 5% those going on to higher education went to courses in practical art; 5% in music; 40% in humanities/social sciences; 10% in medicine; and 40% in science/engineering.

· *Royal (Dungannon)* ·

The Royal School Dungannon Northland Row Dungannon County Tyrone Northern Ireland BT71 6AP Tel 08687 22710	● Pupils 650 ● Boys 4–19 (Day/Board/Weekly) ● Girls 4–19 (Day/Board/Weekly) ● Upper sixth 92	● Termly fees £710 (Day) £1460 (Board/ Weekly) ● SHMIS Enquiries/application to the Headmaster

What it's like

Founded in 1614, in 1986 it assimilated the Dungannon High School for Girls. Its ancient and modern buildings (the Old Building of the school is listed) lie on the edge of the town in a fine 40-acre estate in beautiful surroundings. The preparatory department is combined. The whole establishment is extremely well equipped with excellent facilities and is well known to be a centre of academic and sporting prowess; in fact, one of the most distinguished schools in Ireland. Results are good

638

and a large proportion of pupils proceed to university each year. Flourishing music, art and drama departments. A very good range of sport and games. Plentiful extra-curricular activities. Quite a good record in the Duke of Edinburgh's Award Scheme.

School profile

Pupils Total age range 4–19; 650 pupils, 608 day (284 boys, 324 girls), 42 boarding (30 boys, 12 girls). Senior department 11–19, 600 pupils (292 boys, 308 girls). Main entry ages 11 and into sixth. Approx 15% are children of former pupils. Dungannon Primary School and Howard Primary School, Dungannon both provide more than 20% of intake. *Transfer from maintained schools:* 95% senior intake, plus 2% to sixth.

Entrance Common entrance and own exam used. Not oversubscribed though good notice of boarding required. No special skills or religious requirements. Parents expected to pay a deposit of £15 for books; no other extras. 7 scholarships of £750–£200 pa; 3 bursaries of £150 pa.

Parents 25+% in industry or commerce; 15+% are doctors, lawyers, etc. 60+% live within 30 miles; up to 10% live overseas.

Staff Headmaster P D Hewitt, in post for 8 years. 40 full time staff, 6 part time. Annual turnover 1%. Average age 40.

Academic work GCSE and A-levels. 18 subjects offered (including Japanese for lower sixth; no A-level general studies). In 1990, 100 pupils in upper fifth, 92 in upper sixth. *GCSE:* in 1990, 46% upper fifth gained at least grade C in 8+ subjects; 34% in 5–7; and 20% in 1–4 subjects. *A-levels:* 6% upper sixth passed in 4+ subjects; 62% in 3; 17% in 2; and 10% in 1 subject. 42% took science A-levels; 6% arts/humanities; 50% both. *Computing facilities:* 6 BBCs, 2 15-station RM Nimbus laboratories. *Special provision:* Extra EFL tuition, 3 days a week after school.

European Community *Languages:* French offered: to age 14; GCSE; AS-level; A-level; non-examined subject. German offered: to age 14; GCSE; AS-level; A-level; non-examined subject. 25–50% take GCSE in more than 1 EC language. *Exchanges:* Regular exchanges for pupils aged 11–18 to France and Germany. *Other:* Regular visits to EC office in Belfast. Talks from MEPs available. Twinned with a German school in Bavaria.

Senior pupils' non-academic activities *Music:* 30% learn a musical instrument, 12 to Grade 6 or above, 1 accepted for Music School; 30 in school orchestra, 65 in senior choir; 30 in symphonic band; 5 in National Youth Orchestra. *Drama and dance:* 80 participate in school productions. *Art:* 5 take as non-examined subject; 50 take GCSE; 10 A-level. 3 accepted for Art School. 12 belong to photographic club. *Sport:* Rugby, hockey, cricket, athletics, golf, swimming, tennis, rambling, basketball, volleyball, cross-country, indoor soccer, table tennis, weights available. 70 take non–compulsory sport. 10 pupils represent county/country (rugby, shooting, athletics). *Other:* 5 have bronze Duke of Edinburgh's Award, 10 have silver and 4 have gold. 2 work for national charities beyond school. Other activities include a computer club, driving lessons, chess, Scripture Union, debating, photography, Blockbusters, public speaking, art, Trivial Pursuit.

Careers In 1990, 85% leavers went on to degree courses; 5% to art/drama/music colleges; 8% to non-degree courses (eg nursing, secretarial); 1–2% straight into careers (eg farm management, insurance); 1% other. Of those going on to degree courses, 12% went to Oxbridge; 71% to other universities; 18% to poly/colleges. 6% those going on to higher education went to courses in practical art; 2% in music; 44% in humanities/social sciences; 18% in medicine; and 30% in science/engineering.

Uniform School uniform worn throughout; boarders wear own clothes out-of-class.

Houses/prefects 4 competitive houses. Prefects, head boy/girl, head of house and house prefects – appointed by the Head after recommendations of house masters/

mistresses and sixth form.

Religion Compulsory morning assembly, Sunday morning service and Sunday evening for boarders. Exceptions made if parents request. Muslim, Hindu and Jewish preferences respected.

Social Debates, discos, sports meetings, quizzes, academic lectures. Annual European trip plus trips eg to Paris, skiing. Pupils allowed to bring own car/bike/motorbike to school. Some meals formal, some self-service. School shop. No tobacco/alcohol allowed.

Discipline No corporal punishment. Pupils failing to produce homework once might expect to have to repeat it; those caught smoking cannabis on the premises could expect expulsion (but drugs not a problem in Northern Ireland schools).

Boarding All boarders share a modern cubicle with one other. Dormitories divided by age and sex. Resident qualified nurse/doctor. Central dining room. Exeats, every 3–4 weekends. Visits to the local town allowed.

Alumni association is run by Very Rev Canon W R D McCreery, (OBA President), St Comgall's Rectory, 2 Raglan Road, Bangor, County Down. Miss V Leckey (OGA President), 14 Ranfurly Heights, Dungannon, County Tyrone, Northern Ireland.

· *Royal (Wolverhampton)* ·

Royal Wolverhampton
School
Penn Road
Wolverhampton
WV3 0EG
Tel 0902 341230

- Pupils 592
- Boys $2^1/_2$–18 (Day/Board/Weekly)
- Girls $2^1/_2$–18 (Day/Board/Weekly)
- Upper sixth 43

- Termly fees
  £1220 (Day)
  £2110 (Board)
  £1890 (Weekly)
- SHMIS, SHA
Enquiries/application to the Headmaster

What it's like

Founded in 1850 and co-ed virtually from the outset, it moved to its present site, a large wooded area a mile from the town centre, in 1854. The main buildings are an agreeable neo-Tudor design and there are fine gardens and ample playing fields. In recent years a major programme of modernisation and extension has been going on including a new technology block. Accommodation and facilities are good. The junior school is on the same site. Christian faith and values are central to the life of the school. Daily services are compulsory and religious education is for all. The teaching is of a high standard and results are good. Many leavers go on to degree courses each year. The staff:pupil ratio is about 1:11. Reasonably strong in music, drama and art. An impressive range of sports and games. Quite a lot of commitment to local community services, and a strong CCF.

School profile

Pupils Total age range $2^1/_2$–18; 592 pupils, 407 day (251 boys, 156 girls), 185 boarding (104 boys, 81 girls). Senior department 11–18, 320 pupils (180 boys, 140 girls). Main entry ages $2^1/_2$, 4, 11 and into sixth. Approx 15% are children of former pupils. *Transfer from maintained schools:* 20% main senior intake, plus 20% to sixth.

Entrance Own entrance exam used. Oversubscribed. No special skills or religious requirements although an Anglican school. Parents not expected to buy text books; maximum extras £25 per term.

Scholarships and bursaries, for music, sport, maths and sixth form.

Parents 15+% in armed services; 15+% in industry or commerce. 30+% live within 30 miles; 10+% live overseas.

Staff Headmaster Mr P Gorring, in post for 5 years. 30 full time staff in Senior School, 2 part time. Annual turnover under 5%. Average age 35.

Academic work GCSE and A-levels offered (including A-level general studies). In 1990, 55 pupils in upper fifth, 43 in upper sixth. *GCSE:* in 1990, 9% upper fifth gained at least grade C in 8+ subjects; 61% in 5–7; and 28% in 1–4 subjects. *A-levels:* 5% upper sixth passed in 4+ subjects; 75% in 3; 15% in 2; and 5% in 1 subject. 45% took science A-levels; 35% arts/humanities; 20% both. *Computing facilities:* Network system and several stand-alone pc's. *Special provision:* One member of staff helps a very small group of children.

European Community *Languages:* French offered: to age 14; GCSE; AS-level; A-level. German offered: to age 14; GCSE; AS-level; A-level. Up to 10% take GCSE in more than 1 EC language. *Exchanges:* Regular exchanges for pupils aged 11–18 to Germany. *Other:* Several bi-lingual pupils in school and 1 French boy.

Senior pupils' non-academic activities *Music:* 83 learn a musical instrument, 10 to Grade 6 or above, 1 accepted for Music School; 30 in school choir, 8 in school pop group. *Drama and dance:* 50 in school productions. 2 accepted for Drama/Dance School. *Art:* 15 take as non-examined subject; 16 take GCSE; 8 A-level. 3 accepted for Art School. *Sport:* Rugby, soccer, hockey, cricket, tennis, fencing, basketball, squash, volleyball, shooting, athletics, badminton, rounders available. 100 take non-compulsory sport. 10 take exams. 6 represent county (rugby, fencing, shooting, hockey, athletics). *Other:* 30 take part in local community schemes. Other activities include a computer club, driving lessons, chess, dance, self-defence, debating, public speaking, ice skating, ski-ing, CCF.

Careers In 1990, 75% leavers went on to degree courses; 20% to non-degree courses (eg physiotherapy); 5% straight into careers. Of those going on to degree courses, 3% went to Oxbridge; 50% to other universities; 47% to poly/colleges. 41% those going on to higher education went to courses in humanities/social sciences; 7% in medicine; and 52% in science/engineering.

Uniform School uniform worn throughout.

Houses/prefects Competitive houses. Prefects, head boy/girl, head of house and house prefects – appointed by Head after consultation.

Religion Compulsory daily service, Sunday service for boarders.

Social Debating competitions and games matches with other schools. 2 or more trips abroad annually. Some meals formal, some self-service. School shop. No tobacco/alcohol allowed.

Discipline No corporal punishment. Pupils failing to produce homework once might expect remonstration or reprimand; those caught smoking on the premises might expect suspension after warning, use of drugs will lead to expulsion.

Boarding 80% have own study bedroom, 20% share. Single sex houses, of approximately 35. Resident qualified nurse. Central dining room. Unlimited weekend exeats. Visits to local town allowed once a week.

Alumni association is run by P J Ward, President ORA, c/o the School.

Former pupils Eric Idle (Monty Python); Gilbert Harding (actor); Philip Oakes (author).

· *Royal Ballet* ·

The Royal Ballet
School
White Lodge
Richmond Park
Surrey TW10 5HR
Tel 081 748 6335

- Pupils 120
- Boys 11–18
  (Day/Board)
- Girls 11–18
  (Day/Board)
- Upper sixth Yes

- Termly fees
  £2374 (Day)
  £4082 (Board)
Enquiries/application to
the Ballet Secretary

What it's like

Started as the Academy of Choreographic Art in 1929 by Ninette de Valois. Under the auspices of Lilian Baylis, it became The Sadler's Wells Ballet School in 1931, and the Royal Ballet School at the granting of the Queen's 1956 charter. It provides most of the soloists and corps de ballet of the Royal Ballet and Sadler's Wells Royal Ballet. Tradition of teaching can be traced back to the Academie Royale de la Danse founded by Louis XIV in 1661. Although the majority of pupils are girls, there is an increasing number of boys. School puts on an annual performance at The Royal Opera House. Dance classes are built up from one a day until pupils study dance for 17 hours a week. Curriculum includes Classical Ballet, Character Dancing, English Folk Dancing, Scottish Social and Highland Dancing, Classical Greek and National Dancing, Dalcroze Eurythmics and Drama. Although nearly all pupils go on to become professional dancers, the school aims to provide an education that will be useful for fields outside dancing as well.

School profile

Pupils Age range 11–18; 120 pupils. (Boarding 11–16 only; most board). Main entry age, 11.

Entrance Audition and one year's trial. Potential talent and physical suitability looked for. Pupils eligible for aided pupils scheme.

Staff Director, Dame Merle Park. Academic Principal, Nigel Grant.

Academic work GCSE and A-levels. Most pupils take 7 GCSE. Some pupils take 1 or 2 A-levels. Dance offered to A-level. *Computing facilities:* BBC microcomputers/networks. *Special provision:* for EFL.

Careers Lower school pupils graduate to Upper School (Talgarth Road) at 16+. Many then join The Royal Ballet or Sadler's Wells Royal Ballet.

Social Meals self service. Shop selling dancewear and makeup.

Boarding Qualified nursing sister, termly orthopaedic examinations for Upper School. Student counsellor, physiotherapist attends daily.

Former pupils Lesley Collier; Anthony Dowell CBE; Dame Margot Fonteyn CBE; Dame Merle Park CBE; Lynne Seymour CBE; Wayne Sleep.

642

· *Royal Grammar (Guildford)* ·

The Royal Grammar
School
High Street
Guildford
Surrey GU1 3BB
Tel 0483 502424

- Pupils 800
- Boys 11–18
  (Day)
- Girls None
- Upper sixth 107

- Termly fees
  £1365 (Day)
- HMC
Enquiries/application to
the Headmaster's
Secretary

What it's like

Founded in 1509 by Robert Beckingham and established in 1552 by King Edward VI's Royal Charter, it is in the centre of Guildford, on both sides of the Upper High Street. The original buildings are handsome examples of Tudor architecture in the Oxbridge collegiate style and have been in continuous use for some 440 years. They include the remarkable 'Chained Library' (now the Headmaster's study), classrooms, the Mallison Library, the careers centre, the sixth-form common room and the prefects' room. A large new building, opened in 1965 on the other side of the High Street, contains a variety of modern facilities, including a great hall. Overall, the school is very well equipped, and 'the town and gown' relationship is thriving. Religious education is an integral part of the curriculum and RE periods are compulsory at all levels. Assemblies are Christian, and the school is closely linked with Holy Trinity Church nearby. Academic standards are high and compare favourably with those of the most distinguished schools in the country. With a large sixth form, a high proportion pass at least three A-levels and very many go on to degree courses, including many to Oxbridge. The staff:pupil ratio is about 1:12. Music and drama are strong. Many boys learn an instrument; there are an orchestra, several instrumental ensembles, a chamber choir and a choral society. At least one school play is presented each term (usually in conjunction with one of the local girls' schools). Rugby and cricket are the main games but a wide variety of sports and games is available. Sailing, rowing and golf are popular. An especially fine new sports ground near Shalford with 20 acres of fields has one of the best pavilions to be found anywhere. Recently, Guildford boys have won national and international honours in rugby, cricket, weight-lifting and rifle shooting. An impressive range of clubs and societies caters for most extra-curricular activities. The CCF contingent and a scout group flourish. Not a few pupils take successful part in the Duke of Edinburgh's Award Scheme (a lot of bronze and silver awards, and some gold) and many pupils contribute to local community services.

School profile

Pupils Age range 11–18; 800 day boys. Main entry ages 11, 13 and into sixth. Approx 5% are children of former pupils. *Transfer from maintained schools:* 60% main intake at 11 (not 13), plus 90% to sixth.

Entrance Common entrance and own entrance exam used. Oversubscribed. No special skills or religious requirements. Parents not expected to buy text books. 25 assisted places pa. 20 scholarships/ bursaries pa, full fees.

Staff Headmaster John Daniel, in post for 15 years. 68 full time staff, 9 part time. Annual turnover 10%. Average age 39.

Academic work GCSE and A-levels. 21 subjects offered (no A-level general studies). In 1990, 136 pupils in upper fifth, 107 in upper sixth. *GCSE:* in 1990, 127 upper fifth gained at least grade C in 8+ subjects; 9 in 5–7 subjects. *A-levels:* 14 upper sixth passed in 4+ subjects; 87 in 3; 4 in 2; and 1 in 1 subject. 43% took science A-levels; 26% arts/humanities; 31% both. *Computing facilities:* Nimbus science network. Many Apple/Macs.

European Community *Languages:* French offered: to age 14; GCSE; A-level; non-examined subject. German offered: to age 14; GCSE; A-level. Italian offered: non-examined subject. Spanish offered: non-examined subject. 10–25% take GCSE in more than 1 EC language. *Exchanges:* Regular exchanges for pupils aged 11–18 to France and Germany.

Senior pupils' non-academic activities *Music:* 84 learn a musical instrument, 37 to Grade 6 or above. 1 accepted for Music School. 38 in school orchestra, 40 in school choir. *Drama and dance:* 48 in school productions. *Art:* 12 take GCSE; 3 A-level. 1 accepted for Art School. *Sport:* Rugby, cricket, hockey, tennis, athletics, golf, shooting, swimming, sailing, softball, squash available. 110 pupils take non-compulsory sport. 10 represent county/country (rugby, tennis, athletics). *Other:* 10 take part in local community schemes. 28 have bronze Duke of Edinburgh's Award, 22 silver, 3 gold. 4 enter voluntary schemes after leaving school. Other activities include a computer club, chess, Christian Union, industry, historical, geographical, literary, martial arts, models, stamps and debating society.

Careers In 1990, 81% leavers went on to degree courses; 2% to art/drama/music colleges; 7% straight into careers; 10% other. Of those going on to degree courses, 26% went to Oxbridge; 68% to other universities; 6% to poly/colleges. 49% those going on to higher education went to courses in humanities/social sciences; 14% in medicine; and 37% in science/engineering.

Uniform School uniform worn throughout.

Houses/prefects Competitive houses. Prefects, head boy (appointed by the Headmaster); head of house (appointed by housemaster).

Religion Attendance at religious worship compulsory.

Social Music and drama with girls' schools. French and German exchanges; ski holidays. Pupils allowed to bring own car/bike/motorbike to school. Meals self-service. No tobacco/alcohol allowed.

Discipline No corporal punishment. Pupils failing to produce homework once might expect a detention. Those caught smoking cannabis on school premises would be expelled.

Alumni association is run by D H B Jones, c/o the school.

Former pupils R G D Willis (England cricket captain); Terry Jones (Monty Python).

· *Royal Grammar (Newcastle)* ·

Royal Grammar School	• Pupils 950	• Termly fees
Eskdale Terrace	• Boys 11–18	£850 (Day)
Newcastle upon Tyne	(Day)	• HMC
NE2 4DX	• Girls None	Enquiries/admissions to
Tel 091 281 5711	• Upper sixth 143	the Headmaster

What it's like

Founded and endowed early in the 16th century by Thomas Horsley. By virtue of Queen Elizabeth's charter in 1600 it became the 'Free Grammar School of Queen Elizabeth in Newcastle upon Tyne'. It is one of the most distinguished schools in the north of England, and indeed in the country. For 400 years plus it has enjoyed close links with the city and the region and its governing body consists largely of representatives from local authorities and universities. It is well sited in the centre of the city, near the civic and city centres, the university and polytechnic. Its pupils are drawn from a wide area. Most of the premises date from 1907. They were designed by Sir Edwin Cooper and described by Pevsner as 'friendly neo–Early Georgian'. Various extensions were made between the world wars. Since 1966 there have been several more, including a new junior school, music centre, sixth-form common room, a careers reference library and a computer centre. In 1984 the modernisation of the chemistry laboratories was completed and since then the swimming pool has been rebuilt to the finest modern specification. It is now an extremely well equipped school. The playing fields are on the main site and at Sutherland Park. Academic standards have always been high and results consistently good or excellent. Each year well over a hundred boys go on to degree courses, including many to Oxbridge. Music, drama, art and technical studies are very strong indeed. There are three school orchestras, plus lesser groups and several choirs. About a dozen concerts are given each year. Each year, too, there are five or six main productions in the theatre (one in a foreign language). A wide range (20 in all) of sports and games is available (including judo, rowing, orienteering and fencing). High standards are achieved and there have been many representatives at county, regional and national level. Numerous clubs and societies cater for most conceivable needs. Chess and debating are especially notable activities. There is a flourishing voluntary CCF and considerable emphasis on adventure training. The school has vigorous support in the city and locality.

School profile

Pupils Age range 11–18, 950 day boys. Main entry age 11. Own junior school. *Transfer from maintained schools:* 70% main intake, plus 70% to sixth.

Entrance Own entrance exam and common entrance used. 60 pa assisted places.

Staff Headmaster A S Cox, in post for 19 years.

Academic work GCSE, AS and A-levels. 19 GCSE subjects offered; 16 at AS-level, 19 at A-level; also Arabic (Schools Arabic Project – Certificate); several other languages as part of general studies options); no A-level general studies. In 1990, 132 pupils in upper fifth, 143 in upper sixth. *GCSE:* in 1990, 128 upper fifth gained at least grade C in 8+ subjects; 4 in 5–7 subjects. *A-levels:* 6 upper sixth passed in 4+ subjects; 117 in 3; 11 in 2; and 8 in 1 subject. 35% took science A-levels; 35% arts/humanities; 30% both. *Computing facilities:* 2 designated computing rooms; departmental equipment as required.

European Community *Languages:* French offered: to GCSE; AS-level; A-level. German offered: to GCSE; AS-level; A-level. Italian offered: non-examined subject. Spanish offered: non-examined subject. 25–50% take GCSE in more than 1 EC language. *Exchanges:* Regular exchanges for pupils aged 14–18 to France and Germany.

Careers In 1990, 80% leavers went on to degree courses; 1% to art/drama/music colleges; 4% straight into careers (eg banking); 15% other. Of those going on to degree courses, 18% went to Oxbridge; 63% to other universities; 18% to poly/colleges. 55% those going on to higher education went to courses in humanities/social sciences; 4% in medicine; and 41% in science/engineering.

· *Royal Grammar (Worcester)* ·

Royal Grammar School
Upper Tything
Worcester
WR1 1HP
Tel 0905 613391

- Pupils 900
- Boys 7–18
- (Day/Weekly)
- Girls None
- Upper sixth 100

- Termly fees
  £1092 (Day)
  £1923 (Weekly)
- HMC
  Enquiries/application to
  the Registrar

What it's like

Founded before 1291 (and thus one of the oldest schools in England) and given a charter by Elizabeth in 1561. Moved to its present site in 1868. Urban, single-site and near the city centre, it has fine buildings in spacious gardens. Playing fields are close by. The prep school is combined. Very good modern facilities already exist. A half-a-million pound project for more buildings is under way. In a friendly, civilised and well–disciplined environment, the pupils receive a thorough education. Results are good and many sixth form leavers go on to degree courses, including Oxbridge. Music and drama expanding; excellent computer facilities. There is a strong tradition of excellence in games, especially cricket. The CCF is vigorous and there is much emphasis on outdoor pursuits. Big commitment to local community schemes and an impressive record in the Duke of Edinburgh's Award Scheme. The school has a high reputation locally and is well supported. Full use is made of Worcester amenities, cultural and otherwise. The school has close links with local industry.

School profile

Pupils Total age range 7–18; 900 boys, 880 day, 20 weekly boarding. Senior department 11–18, 780 boys. Main entry ages 7–13 and into sixth. Approx 5% are children of former pupils. *Transfer from maintained schools:* 44% senior intake, plus 5% to sixth.

Entrance Own entrance exam used. Oversubscribed. School looks for potential contributors to its wide range of extra-curricular activities. Parents not expected to buy text books; individual music tuition and lunches are extra. Assisted places. Scholarships/bursaries.

Parents 15+% are doctors, lawyers, etc; 15+% in industry or commerce. 80+% live within 30 miles.

Staff Head T E Savage, in post for 12 years. 70 full time staff. Annual turnover 8%. Average age 35.

Academic work GCSE, AS and A-levels. 26 GCSE subjects offered; 16 at AS; 22 at A-level (including Russian and A-level general studies). In 1990, 102 pupils in fifth, 89 in upper sixth (now 100). *GCSE:* in 1990, 83% upper fifth gained at least grade C in 8+ subjects; 16% in 5–7 subjects. *A-levels:* 77% upper sixth passed in 3+ subjects; 16% in 2; and 6% in 1 subject. 26% took science A-levels; 54% arts/humanities; 20% both. *Computing facilities:* Two computing rooms. 60+ micros used within academic departments.

European Community *Languages:* French offered: to age 14; GCSE; AS-level; A-level. German offered: to age 14; GCSE; AS-level; A-level. 25–50% take GCSE in more than 1 EC language. *Exchanges:* Regular exchanges for pupils to France and Germany.

Senior pupils' non-academic activities *Music:* 130 learn a musical instrument, 20 to Grade 6 or above; 2 accepted for Music School; 70 in school orchestras, 170 in school choir; 2 in National Children's Wind Orchestra. *Drama and dance:* 90 in school productions. 10 now work in theatre. *Sport:* Rugby, soccer and cricket are major sports; athletics, badminton, basketball, cross-country, fencing, hockey, swimming, volleyball, rowing, sailing, canoeing, golf and table tennis available. Over 60 pupils represent county (rugby, cricket, soccer, swimming, athletics, badminton). *Other:* 149 take part in local community schemes. 50 take part in the Duke of Edinburgh's Award Scheme. Other activities include a computer club, driving lessons, CDT (school won BP Build-a-Car Competition 1988 and a number of other engineering awards recently); chess, radio controlled cars, railway, outward bound (Ten Tors), CCF (Army, Navy, RAF sections), electronics club.

Careers In 1990, 80% leavers went on to degree courses; 5% to art/drama/music colleges; 5% to non-degree courses (eg HND rural land management, hotel and catering management); 7% straight into careers (eg armed services, banking); 3% other. Of those going on to degree courses, 9% went to Oxbridge; 55% to other universities; 36% to poly/colleges. 5% those going on to higher education went to courses in practical art; 20% in humanities/social sciences; 2% in medicine; 25% in science/engineering; plus 48% to business, building, languages, law.

Uniform School uniform worn throughout.

Houses/prefects Competitive houses. Prefects, head boy, head of house and house prefects – appointed by the Head in consultation with the staff or by housemasters.

Religion Morning worship is non-denominational.

Social Frequent links with Alice Ottley especially for drama and music. German and French exchanges; cricket tour to Zimbabwe; rugby and drama to USA; music to Czechoslovakia; trips to USSR and Strasbourg; link with school in USA. Pupils allowed to bring own car/bike/motorbike to school. Meals self-service. School shop. No tobacco/alcohol allowed.

Discipline No corporal punishment.

Boarding Some have own study bedroom, or share with 2 or 3 others; one group of 6–8. 1 house. Central dining room. Pupils cannot provide and cook own food. Weekly boarding only. Visits to the local town allowed as required.

Former pupils Imran Khan.

· *Royal Hospital* ·

Royal Hospital School
Holbrook
Ipswich
Suffolk IP9 2RX
Tel 0473 328342

- Pupils 660
- Boys 11–18 (Board)
- Girls 11–18 (Board)
- Upper sixth 53

- Termly fees
  £1840 (Board)
- SHMIS
Enquiries/application to
the Headmaster

What it's like

Founded in 1712 at Greenwich as a boys' school, it moved in 1933 to its present exceptionally well-equipped new complex with 60 acres of beautiful grounds overlooking the River Stour at Holbrook, just south of Ipswich. It has recently gone co-educational, with the first girls' entry in 1991. The school enjoys first-rate facilities and accommodation in a civilised and healthy environment. Religious worship is compulsory. A large staff allows a staff:pupil ratio of about 1:10. Academic standards are high and results good. Many pupils go on to degree courses each year. Very strong indeed in music and drama. It has high standards also in sports and games (a lot of representatives at county and national level). Its naval tradition is continued in the large CCF contingent.

School profile

Pupils Age range 11–18; 660 boarding pupils (600 boys, 60 girls). Main entry ages 11, 12, 13 and into sixth (girls accepted since 1991). Approx 8% are children of former pupils. *Transfer from maintained schools:* 90% main intakes, none to sixth.

Entrance Common entrance or own exam used. Oversubscribed. No special skills or religious requirements. Parents not expected to buy text books; maximum extras, £40. Fees of children and grandchildren of seafarers are subsidised according to means test.

Parents 15+% in armed services. Up to 10% live within 30 miles; up to 10% live overseas.

Staff Headmaster M A B Kirk, in post for 7 years. 65 full time staff, 5 part time. Annual turnover 4%. Average age 38.

Academic work GCSE and A-levels. 18 subjects offered (including industrial studies, politics, electronics and A-level general studies). In 1990, 124 pupils in upper fifth, 53 in upper sixth. *GCSE:* in 1990, 30 upper fifth gained at least grade C in 8+ subjects; 64 in 5–7; and 30 in 1–4 subjects. *A-levels:* 10 upper sixth passed in 4+ subjects; 24 in 3; 13 in 2; and 6 in 1 subject. 22 took science A-levels; 20 arts/humanities; 11 both. *Computing facilities:* 30 BBC computers in 2 rooms; 7 departmental computers. *Special provision:* Local dyslexia centre available.

European Community *Languages:* French offered: to age 14; GCSE; A-level. German offered: to age 14; GCSE; A-level. Up to 10% take GCSE in more than 1 EC language. *Other:* EC pupils would be welcome (particularly Netherlands and France because of east coast position).

Senior pupils' non-academic activities *Music:* 120 learn a musical instrument, 10 to Grade 6 or above; 30 in school orchestra, 70 in choir. *Drama and dance:* 60 in school productions. *Art:* 5 take as non-examined subject; 20 GCSE; 4 A-level. 1 accepted for Art School. 10 belong to photographic club. *Sport:* Rugby, soccer, hockey, cricket, athletics, tennis, swimming, sailing, shooting, squash, cross-country available. 100 take non-compulsory sport. 20 take exams. 15 represent county/country (rugby, swimming, lifesaving, sailing). *Other:* 25 have bronze Duke of Edinburgh's Award, 15 have silver and 6 gold. Other activities include a computer club, driving lessons, chess, shooting.

Careers In 1990, 53% leavers went on to degree courses; 9% to art/drama/music colleges; 2% to non-degree courses (eg BTEC, HND, etc); 14% straight into careers (eg armed services, retail management); 22% other (gap year, reapplying, etc). Of those going on to degree courses, 5% went to Oxbridge; 65% to other universities; 30% to poly/colleges. 13% of those going on to higher education went to courses in practical art; 3% in drama/acting% 2% in music% 25% in humanities/social sciences; and 57% in science/engineering.

Uniform School uniform worn throughout.

Houses/prefects Competitive houses. Prefects, head boy, head of house and house prefects – appointed by Head. Sixth form committee.

Religion Compulsory attendance at religious worship; separate C of E and R C chapels.

Social Theatre, debates, dinner parties etc with girls' school. Organised trips abroad including ski-ing, adventure training, France (battlefields etc). Some pupils allowed to bring own bike to school. Some meals formal, some self-service. School shop. No tobacco/alcohol allowed.

Discipline No corporal punishment. Pupils failing to produce homework once might expect a warning; those caught smoking cannabis on the premises might expect expulsion.

Boarding 15% have own study bedroom, 75% are in dormitories of 6+. Houses, of approximately 60, same as competitive houses; separate house for upper sixth. Resident qualified nurse. Central dining room. Pupils can provide and cook own food in a limited way. 1 week's exeat at half-term. Sixth form allowed visits to local town.

Alumni association is run by P C Crick, c/o the School.

· *Royal Naval* ·

The Royal Naval
School
Farnham Lane
Haslemere
Surrey GU27 1HQ
Tel 0428 605415

- Pupils 290
- Boys None
- Girls 11–18
  (Day/Board/Weekly)
- Upper sixth 28

- Termly fees
  £1550 (Day)
  £2325 (Board/
  Weekly)
- GSA
  Enquiries/application to
  the Headmistress

What it's like

Founded in 1840 to provide for the daughters of marine and naval officers put on half pay at the end of the Napoleonic wars. Originally called the Royal Naval Female School. Nowadays two-thirds of its girls are from non–naval families. In 1942 it moved to its present site in Surrey where it occupies handsome buildings in 50 acres of pleasant wooded grounds. Excellent modern facilities which are being expanded. A sound education is provided and results are good. Many sixth form leavers go on to degree courses. Very strong indeed in music and drama (almost everyone is involved). Compulsory worship and prayers in the Anglican tradition. Big commitment to local community services and to adventure education. Good range of sports, games and extra-curricular activities. A fine record in the Duke of Edinburgh's Award Scheme.

School profile

Pupils Age range 11–18; 290 girls, 130 day, 160 boarding. Main entry ages 11, 13 and into sixth.

Entrance Common entrance and own entrance exam used. Not oversubscribed. No special skills required. C of E school but other religions accepted. Parents not generally expected to buy text books. 5 scholarships, $^1/_2$ fees–£300 pa.

Parents 15+% are doctors, lawyers, etc; 15+% in industry or commerce; 15+% in the armed services. 30+% live within 30 miles; up to 10% live overseas.

Staff Headmistress Dr J L Clough, in post for 3 years. 30 full time staff, 9 part time. Annual turnover 10%. Average age 39.

Academic work GCSE and A-levels. Average size of upper fifth 50, upper sixth 28. *GCSE:* on average, 30 pupils in upper fifth pass 8+ subjects; 15, 5–7 subjects; 5 pass 1–4 subjects. *A-levels:* on average 1 pupil in the upper sixth passes 4 subjects; 16, 3 subjects; 9, 2 subjects; 2 pass 1 subject. *Computing facilities:* BBC Micro and IBM network. *Special provision:* visit-

ing remedial teachers and extra coaching.

European Community *Languages:* French offered: to age 14; GCSE; A-level; non-examined subject. German offered: to age 14; GCSE; A-level. Spanish offered: to age 14; GCSE; A-level. 25–50% take GCSE in more than 1 EC language. *Exchanges:* Regular exchanges for pupils aged 11–18 to France and Germany. Choir exchange and work experience exchange with Germany. *Other:* 13–14 year olds visit Paris; 14–17 year olds 2 week study visit to France; 15–16 year olds visit Spain. German pupils in school for 1 term.

Senior pupils' non-academic activities *Music:* 140 learn a musical instrument, 40 to grade 5, some to grade 8; 38 in school orchestra, 80 in choir, 20 in wind band, 2 in Music Schools Saturday Junior School orchestras; 4 annual concerts. *Drama:* 90 in school productions; 150 in house drama, 150 in class drama. LAMDA and ESB exams, some to grade 8. *Art:* 29 take GCSE; 6 A-level. 2 accepted for Art School. *Sport:* Netball, lacrosse, tennis, swimming, badminton, squash, athletics, golf, rounders and volleyball available. 140 take non-compulsory sport. *Other:* 50 working for bronze Duke of Edinburgh's Award, 10 for silver, 10 for gold. Other activities include a computer club, electronics, cookery, debating, driving lessons, craft club and CREST (5 have bronze award, 1 silver).

Careers In 1990, 89% leavers went on to degree courses; 6% to non-degree courses (eg HND business school, air training); 3% straight into careers; 2% other. Of those going on to degree courses, 53% went to universities; 47% to poly/colleges. 6% those going on to higher education went to courses in drama/acting; 69% in humanities/social sciences; 2% in medicine; and 23% in science/engineering.

Uniform School uniform worn throughout.

Houses/prefects Competitive houses. Prefects, head girl, head of house and house prefects – elected by the school. School Council.

Religion Compulsory morning prayers, Sunday chapel (optional for non C of E pupils).

Social Dances, debates and social evenings with local schools. Regular school exchanges and ski-ing trips. Pupils allowed to bring own car/bike/motorbike to school. Meals self-service; salad bar. School shop. No tobacco/alcohol allowed.

Discipline No corporal punishment. Pupils failing to produce homework once might expect a talking to; those caught smoking cannabis on the premises might expect suspension or expulsion, depending on the circumstances.

Boarding Sixth formers have own or shared study bedroom. Houses, of 50+ divided by age. Resident SRN. Central dining room. Sixth formers can provide and cook own snacks. At least 2 weekend exeats each term. Visits to local town allowed on Saturdays and during free periods.

Alumni association is: Royal Naval School Society, c/o the School.

· *Royal Russell* ·

Royal Russell School
Coombe Lane
Croydon
Surrey CR9 5BX
Tel 081 657 4433
Fax 081 657 0207

- Pupils 690
- Boys 4–18
  (Day/Board/Weekly)
- Girls 4–18
  (Day/Board/Weekly)
- Upper sixth 50

- Termly fees
  £1305 (Day)
  £2485 (Board)
  £2390 (Weekly)
- SHMIS
  Enquiries/application to
  the Headmaster

What it's like

Founded in 1853, by a committee of textile workers to provide free education for the sons and daughters of 'necessitous' employees in the trade. Almost from the outset it was under the patronage of the royal family; since 1901 each succeeding monarch has been patron. In 1924 the school moved to its present site two miles south-east of Croydon where it stands in beautiful gardens in a delightful 100-acre, rural, wooded estate. Its elegant and well appointed buildings include a fine chapel and excellent modern facilities. It is basically a Church of England school, but pupils of all persuasions are welcome, and the approach to daily life is founded on Christian principles. There is some emphasis on religious education and worship. The staff:pupil ratio is approximately 1:12. A sound general education is provided and results appear to be creditable. Music is very strong. There is a large number of visiting teachers. Drama and art are also well supported. There are very good facilities for sports and games, of which there are the customary varieties, plus golf, judo and karate. A plentiful range of clubs and societies. The CCF has an Army and RAF unit open to boys and girls. Full use is made of the estate and a good deal of enterprise is shown in cultural visits, expeditions abroad etc. The school is unique in Britain in its involvement in the Model United Nations programmes. There is an annual four-day conference at the school and delegations are sent each year to the international conference in The Hague. Royal Russell has gained several honours for 'best delegations'.

School profile

Pupils Total age range 4–18, 690 pupils (day and boarding). Senior department 11–18, 400 pupils. Main entry age 11. *Transfer from maintained schools:* 10% main intake, plus 5% to sixth.

Entrance Own entrance exam used, report and interview. Scholarships/bursaries.

Staff Headmaster R D Balaam, in post for 10 years.

Academic work GCSE and A-levels. 22 GCSE subjects offered; 17 at A-level (no A-level general studies). In 1990, 80 pupils in upper fifth, 50 in upper sixth. *GCSE:* in 1990, 23 upper fifth gained at least grade C in 8+ subjects; 24 in 5–7; and 27 in 1–4 subjects. *A-levels:* 2 upper sixth passed in 4+ subjects; 19 in 3; 14 in 2; and 6 in 1 subject. 60% took science A-levels; 30% arts/humanities; 10% both. *Computing facilities:* 19 Atari 1040 machines; 40 BBCs, 6 RM Nimbus. *Special provision:* Extra English for foreign pupils; help with dyslexics.

European Community *Languages:* French offered: to age 14; GCSE; AS-level; A-level. German offered: to age 14; GCSE; AS-level; A-level. Italian offered: GCSE; A-level. Spanish offered: to GCSE; AS-level; A-level. 10–25% take GCSE in more than 1 EC language. *Exchanges:* Regular exchanges for pupils aged 11–18 to France and Germany. *Other:* Number of 'Euroboarders' in school for 1 term to 2 years, coupling academic education with improvement of their English.

Careers In 1990, 65% leavers went on to degree courses; $2^1/_2$% to art/drama/music colleges; $10^1/_2$% to non-degree courses (eg radiography, HND catering, resit A-levels); 15% straight into careers (eg banking, insurance, construction); 5% other. Of those going on to degree courses, 4% went to Oxbridge; 73% to other universities; 23% to poly/colleges. $3^1/_2$% those going on to higher education went to courses in practical art; 50% in humanities/social sciences; $3^1/_2$% in medicine; and 43% in science/engineering.

· *Rugby* ·

Rugby School
Rugby
Warwickshire
CV22 5EH
Tel 0788 543465

- Pupils 674
- Boys 12–18
  (Day/Board)
- Girls 13–18
  (Day/Board)
- Upper sixth 163

- Termly fees
  £1865 (Day)
  £3220 (Board)
- HMC
  Enquiries to
  Headmaster's
  Secretary
  Application to the
  Registrar

What it's like

Founded in 1567 by Lawrence Sheriff 'to serve chiefly the children of Rugby and Brownsover', it moved in 1750 to an old manor house on the site of the present School House. By the end of the 18th century it was established as a major public boarding school. Dr Arnold became Head in 1828 and added much to its fame. Substantial growth in the 19th century led to the addition of many of the buildings which give the school its distinctive character. Much more development has occurred in the 20th century, including a fully equipped theatre, extensive and comfortable boarding accommodation, science blocks, sports hall, 6-lane swimming pool, astro-turf pitch, a language lab, computer centres and a micro-electronics centre. It is now extremely well equipped. There are also fine gardens, 80 acres of playing fields, plus the amenities of Rugby town a few minutes away. A traditional school, but also warm, friendly and 'open to a degree that is quite undaunting'. It is a C of E foundation and a certain amount of worship and religious education are compulsory. A large and very well-qualified staff allows a staff:pupil ratio of about 1:8. Academically, it is one of the most high-powered schools and standards are very high. Results are consistently good and each year a very large number of pupils go on to degree courses, including many to Oxbridge. Very few schools have a better record. The science department is a leading one in Britain and originated much of the Nuffield science now used in schools. The music, drama and art departments are tremendously strong. About a third of the pupils have some involvement in music and virtually everyone is engaged in dramatic presentations at some time or another. Everybody takes a general course which includes philosophy and art as non-examined subjects. Rugby has long been renowned for its achievements in sports and games of which a great variety is available. There have been numerous representatives at county and international level. A very large number of clubs and societies cater for virtually every need. The Tawney Society is a most important academic society for visiting speakers on political, historical and cultural topics. There is a large voluntary CCF contingent involving about 300 boys and girls in Army, Navy and Air Force sections. The school has a considerable commitment to local community services and initiates a wide range of holiday courses of all kinds. It will become fully co-educational from September 1993 when girls will be accepted at 13+ as well as 16+.

School profile

Pupils Age range 12–18, 674 pupils. Senior department 13–18; 663 pupils, 96 day (76 boys, 20 girls), 567 boarding (484 boys, 83 girls). Main entry ages 13 and into sixth. Girls currently accepted in sixth only; will be accepted at 13 from 1993.

Approx 25% are children of former pupils. *Transfer from maintained schools:* into junior department, plus 10% to sixth. **Entrance** Common entrance used; interviews for 16+ intake. Oversubscribed. No special skills (but music and art scholarships); no religious requirements. Parents expected to buy text books; clothes and music lessons also extra. 16 scholarships and 42 foundationerships (day pupils).

Parents are largely professional; others in industry, finance, commerce or the services. 20+% live within 30 miles; up to 20% live overseas. Remainder widely spread over British Isles.

Staff Headmaster M B Mavor, 1 year in post. 86 full time staff, 14 part time. Annual turnover 5%. Average age 45.

Academic work GCSE and A-levels. 21 subjects offered (no A-level general studies). In 1990, 100 pupils in upper fifth, 163 in upper sixth. *GCSE:* in 1990, 89% upper fifth gained at least grade C in 8+ subjects. *A-levels:* 10% upper sixth passed in 4+ subjects; 91% in 3 subjects. 35% took science A-levels; 55% arts/humanities; 10% both. *Computing facilities:* Information Technology Centre. *Special provision:* Qualified teacher for dyslexia gives regular lessons; foreign pupils receive timetabled extra English lessons.

European Community *Languages:* French offered: to GCSE; A-level. German offered: to GCSE; A-level. Greek (modern) offered: to GCSE. Italian offered: non-examined subject. Spanish offered: to GCSE; A-level. 25–50% take GCSE in more than 1 EC language. *Exchanges:* Regular exchanges for pupils aged 16–18 to France, Germany and Spain. *Other:* Talks from MEPs and other distinguished European visitors. Biennial colloquium, 'Educating Europe' in 1990. Recent staff appointment of Director of European and International Liaison. Governing Body includes the British Ambassador to Paris (Sir Ewen Ferguson).

Senior pupils' non-academic activities *Music:* 150 learn a musical instrument, 80 to Grade 6 or above, 2 take ARCO exams; 80 in school orchestra, 40

in chamber choir, 25 in jazz and swing bands. *Drama and dance:* 550 in school and house productions. 6 accepted for Drama Schools, several working in theatre. *Art:* All take as non-examined subject at some stage; 15 A-level. 4 accepted for Art School. *Sport:* Rugby, hockey, cricket, athletics, swimming, squash, rackets, cross-country, rugby fives, tennis, fencing, shooting, Association football, badminton, golf, basketball, netball, volleyball, lacrosse, sailing etc available. Most take non-compulsory sport. 3 take coaching qualifications (hockey). 20+ represent county and 3 represent country (rugby, cricket, hockey, lacrosse, cross-country, fencing, athletics). *Other:* Many opt for social service which includes hospital visiting, helping disabled, visiting old people, teaching immigrant children, running play groups etc. 15 pa enter VSO. Other activities include computer club, chess, bridge, debating, natural history, hobbies, astronomy, voluntary CCF (300 pupils), driving lessons.

Careers In 1990, 87% leavers went on to degree courses; 2% to art/drama/music colleges; 2% to non-degree courses (eg agriculture); 3% straight into careers (eg City); 5% other. Of those going on to degree courses, 14% went to Oxbridge; 64% to other universities; 22% to poly/colleges. 1% those going on to higher education went to courses in practical art; 1% in drama/acting; 1% in music; 60% in humanities/social sciences/business studies; 10% in medicine; and 27% in science/engineering.

Uniform School uniform worn by boys; regulated dress for girls.

Houses/prefects Competitive houses. Prefects (The Levee) and head boy – appointed by Head; head of house, house prefects – appointed by house master. No school council but Levee takes some decisions.

Religion Compulsory 10-minute chapel 3 times/week; 4–5 'School' Sunday services each term; other Sundays choice between 'Forum' (ethical discussion) or Chapel Eucharist.

Social Musical co-operation including The Sinfonia orchestra with other local schools. 2 ski-ing trips abroad a year, 1

653

sports trip, natural history expeditions every other year (Galapagos, Borneo); annual exchanges (Vienna, Madrid, France). Pupils allowed to bring own bike to school (other vehicles rarely). All meals in house dining halls; lunch formal. Regular house dances. School shops. No tobacco; sixth form bar 2 nights/week (2 pint limit).

Discipline No corporal punishment. Pupils failing to produce homework might expect verbal reproof, $1\frac{1}{2}$hr detention for repeated offence; those caught in possession of drugs on the premises should expect immediate expulsion.

Boarding 10% have own study bedroom, 15% share with 1 other, 70% are in dormitories of 6+. Studies (shared between two) from entry; 50% have study to themselves. Houses, of approximately 60 (boys), 20–40 (girls), are main social unit. Resident qualified medical staff. Pupils can provide and cook own snacks. 3 termly exeats (1 week, 2 weekends), unlimited Sundays after Chapel/Forum. Visits to restricted area of local town allowed after lunch each day.

Alumni association is run by Mr I G Miller, The Knoll, Upper Stowe, near Weedon, Northamptonshire.

Former pupils Tom King MP; A N Wilson and Salman Rushdie (novelists); Marmaduke Hussey (Chairman of BBC Governors); David Croft (TV scriptwriter); Sir Ewen Fergusson (UK Ambassador, Paris); Robert Hardy (actor); Bishop Hugh Montefiore.

· *Runton and Sutherland* ·

Runton and Sutherland School
West Runton
Cromer
Norfolk NR27 9NF
Tel 026 375 661/2

- Pupils 240
- Boys 3–11 only
- Girls 3–18 (Day/Board/Weekly)
- Upper sixth 10

- Termly fees £925 (Day) £1870 (Board/ Weekly)
Enquiries/application to the Headmistress

What it's like

First founded in 1875, Sutherland House School merged with Runton Hill School, and moved into its buildings, in 1990. Runton and Sutherland School has a rural seaside site in north Norfolk, between Cromer and Sheringham. The four boarding houses are grouped at the centre. Numerous modern extensions, including new design and technology centre, modern sports hall and indoor swimming pool. The campus is compact. The school has been kept small as a matter of policy and a happy, family atmosphere prevails. It is C of E but multi-denominational. A sound education is given and results are good. The school has a tradition of music and drama, art and PE. A wide range of activities; a standard range of games and sports and strong on outdoor pursuits. A good record in the Duke of Edinburgh's Award Scheme.

School profile

Pupils Total age range 3–18; 240 pupils, 112 day (20 boys, 92 girls); 128 boarding girls. Main entry ages 3, 7, 11, 12, 13 and into sixth. Approx 3% are children of former pupils. *Transfer from maintained schools:* 5% main senior intakes.

Entrance Common entrance and own exam used. No special skills required; C of E but other denominations accepted. Parents not expected to buy text books; music tuition (£55 per term) extra, plus individual tuition in English or maths.

Scholarships (academic, music, art, drama and sports scholarships) to 50% fees. Bursaries for forces children.

Parents 30+% live within 30 miles; up to 10% live overseas.

Staff Headmistress Miss Anne C Ritchie, in post for 2 years. 17 full time staff, 6 part time. Annual turnover 5%. Average age 40.

Academic work GCSE and A-levels. 17 subjects offered (including theatre studies; no A-level general studies). On average, 38 pupils in fifth, 10 in upper sixth. *GCSE:* on average, 18 fifth gain at least grade C in 8+ subjects; 12 in 5–7; and 7 in 1–4 subjects. *A-levels:* on average, 4 upper sixth pass in 3 subjects; 4 in 2 subjects. On average 2% take science A-levels; 95% arts/humanities; 3% both. *Computing facilities:* 10 BBC micros. *Special provision:* Extra English lessons on a one-to-one basis.

European Community *Languages:* French offered: to age 14; GCSE; AS-level; A-level. German offered: to age 14; GCSE; AS-level; A-level. 25–50% take GCSE in more than 1 EC language. *Exchanges:* Regular exchanges for pupils aged 11–18 to France and Germany. *Other:* Fully integrated German and Spanish pupils in school, with extra English tuition.

Senior pupils' non-academic activities *Music:* 15 learn a musical instrument, 4 to Grade 6 or above; 5 in school orchestra; 24 in choir. *Drama and dance:* pupils take part in a range of productions including plays in Latin and French. 11 take drama as extra, 10 elocution and public speaking. *Art:* 3 take A-level. *Sport:* Tennis, rounders, basketball, hockey, badminton, netball, squash, golf, trampolining, gymnastics, swimming available. 6 represent county (hockey, netball). *Other:* 24 have bronze Duke of Edinburgh's Award, 18 have silver. Other activities include a computer club, driving lessons, chess, horticulture, ballet, jazz and dance clubs, art, mathematics, debating, public speaking and aerobic clubs all flourish.

Careers In 1990, 90% leavers went on to degree courses; 5% to art/drama/music colleges; 5% to non-degree courses (eg secretarial–linguist, tourism, caring). Of those going on to degree courses, 90% went to universities; 10% to poly/colleges. 5% those going on to higher education went to courses in practical art; 2% in drama/acting; 2% in music; 60% in humanities/social sciences; 2% in medicine; and 30% in science/engineering.

Uniform School uniform worn excepting in the sixth.

Houses/prefects Competitive houses. Prefects, head of School, head of house and house prefects – appointed by the Headmistress. School Council.

Religion Compulsory morning assembly, school and church services.

Social Cromer and North Norfolk Festival of Music and Drama, various discos and dances. Organised trips abroad and exchange systems. Meals: cafeteria service. No tobacco/alcohol allowed.

Discipline No corporal punishment. Those caught smoking cannabis on the premises would be expelled.

Boarding 12% have own study bedroom, none in dormitories of 6+. 4 houses, of 24–50, same as competitive houses with separate sixth form house. School doctor visits weekly. Central dining room. Pupils can prepare snacks. Two weekend exeats each term. Visits for seniors to Norwich by train to local restaurant at weekends and to local town allowed on Saturday afternoons – juniors only in groups.

Alumni association via Mrs C Shelton, Secretary, c/o the School.

· *Rydal* ·

Rydal School	• Pupils 358	• Termly fees
Lansdowne Road	• Boys 13–18	£1946 (Day)
Colwyn Bay	(Day/Board)	£2560 (Board)
Clwyd	• Girls 13–18	• HMC
LL29 7BT	(Day/Board)	Enquiries/application to
Tel 0492 530155	• Upper sixth 77	the Headmaster

What it's like

Founded in 1885, its agreeable and well-designed buildings occupy a fine site on the edge of Colwyn Bay and overlooking the Irish Sea. It has excellent facilities and accommodation. The preparatory school is combined. A Methodist school; religious services and religious education are an important part of the curriculum. The teaching is very good, academic standards are high and results are impressive. Many pupils go on to degree courses, including some to Oxbridge. French and German are offered to A-level and many pupils take GCSE in both. There are regular exchanges with France and Germany. Very strong indeed in drama, art and music. An excellent record in games and sports (a lot of county and international representatives). All games have a compulsory element. A wide range of activities, with some emphasis on outdoor pursuits (ideal because of the proximity of the sea and Snowdonia) and Duke of Edinburgh's Award. Some commitment to local community schemes.

School profile

Pupils Age range 13–18; 358 pupils, 112 day (78 boys, 34 girls), 246 boarding (161 boys, 85 girls). Main entry ages, 13 and into the sixth. 9% are children of former pupils. Rydal prep school provides over 50%. *Transfer from maintained schools:* 15% main intake, plus 75% to sixth.

Entrance Common entrance and own tests used. Oversubscribed. Welcomes musicians, sportsmen/women, artists; no religious requirements but school has a Methodist foundation. Parents expected to buy text books. 10 assisted places pa. 10 scholarships, 50% fees to 15%. Bursaries for clergy children (40–50%) and for service children (up to 20%).

Parents 15+% in industry or commerce. 10+% live overseas.

Staff Headmaster N W Thorne, first year in post. 33 full time staff, 9 part time. Annual turnover 2 or 3. Average age 38.

Academic work GCSE, AS and A-levels. 19 subjects offered (including AS level general studies, not A-level). In 1991, 74 pupils in upper fifth, 77 in upper sixth. *GCSE:* in 1990, 45 upper fifth gained at least grade C in 8+ subjects; 10 in 5–7; and 4 in 1–4 subjects. *A-levels:* on average, 4 upper sixth passed in 4+ subjects; 34 in 3; 22 in 2; and 9 in 1 subject. 26 took science A-levels; 42 arts/humanities; 8 both. *Computing facilities:* Nimbus network. *Special provision:* Some EFL teaching plus special help for dyslexics.

European Community *Languages:* French offered: to age 14; GCSE; AS-level; A-level. German offered: to age 14; GCSE; AS-level; A-level. 25–50% take GCSE in more than 1 EC language. *Exchanges:* Regular exchanges for pupils aged 14–16 to France and Germany. *Other:* Three German boys in school, a development of exchange with the Collegium Josephinum in Bonn.

Senior pupils' non-academic activities *Music:* 70 learn a musical instrument, 15–20 to Grade 6 or above, 1 accepted for Music School; 35 in school orchestra, 40–50 in choir, 10 in pop groups, 8 in wind ensemble, 8 in brass ensemble; 3 or 4 play in county youth orchestra. *Drama and dance:* 40–50 in school productions, more in house productions and behind the scenes. 1–2 pa accepted for Drama/Dance Schools. *Art:* 150 take as non-examined subject; 23 take GCSE; 6 A-level. 4 pa accepted for Art School. 12 belong to photographic club. *Sport:* Rugby, cricket, hockey (girls only), netball (girls only), squash, swimming, badminton, basketball, shooting, sailing, tennis, cross-country running, athletics, rounders (girls only) available. Compulsory games 3 times per week. 10 represent county (athletics, cross-country). *Other:* 20 take part in local community schemes. 12 have bronze Duke of Edinburgh's Award, 8 have silver. Other activities include a computer club, chess club (Sunday Times Schools Championships and Welsh Schools Championship), judo club, debating, historical, dramatic, geographical societies, etc.

Careers In 1990, 70% leavers went on to degree courses; 6% to art/drama/ music colleges; 14% to non-degree courses (eg HNDs in agriculture, engineering, auctioneering and valuation, business studies); 8% straight into careers (eg pilots, Royal Navy); 1% other. Of those going on to degree courses, 7% went to Oxbridge, 67% to other universities; 26% to poly/colleges. 4% those going on to higher education went to courses in practical art; 3% in drama/ acting; 1% in music; 49% in humanities/ social sciences; 4% in medicine; and 38% in science/engineering.

Uniform School uniform worn throughout.

Houses/prefects Competitive houses. Prefects, head boy/girl, head of house and house prefects – appointed by the Headmaster after consultation. School Council.

Religion Compulsory morning prayers and Sunday morning service.

Social Debates with Penrhos College and other local schools. Exchange visits with French and German schools. Ski-ing party abroad at Easter; climbing party in summer eg to Austrian Alps. Day pupils allowed to bring own car/motorbike to school. Meals self service. Several school shops (tuck, stationery, books, secondhand clothes). No tobacco/alcohol allowed.

Discipline No corporal punishment. Pupils failing to produce homework once would be expected to do it; those caught smoking cannabis could expect to be expelled.

Boarding 5% have own study bedroom, 85% share (2–4); 10% are in dormitories of 6+. Single sex houses, of approximately 33, same as competitive houses. 3 resident qualified nurses, local doctor. Central dining room. Sixth formers can provide and cook own food. 2 overnight exeats per term plus any Sunday. Visits to the local town allowed.

Alumni association run by M T Leach, Secretary of the Old Rydalian Club, c/o the School.

Former pupils Wilfred Wooller (sportsman); Professor Sir G R Elton (Historian); Professor Sir Michael Thompson (Vice Chancellor of Birmingham University); Professor Peter Butterworth (Pro-Vice-Chancellor, Surrey University).

· *Ryde* ·

Ryde School
Queen's Road
Ryde
Isle of Wight
PO33 3BE
Tel 0983 62229

- Pupils 621
- Boys 4–18
  (Day/Board/Weekly)
- Girls 4–18
  (Day)
- Upper sixth 46

- Termly fees
  £1074 (Day)
  £2145 (Board)
  £2042 (Weekly
- HMC, SHMIS
  Enquiries/application to
  the Headmaster

What it's like

Founded in 1921, it moved to its present site on the edge of the town in 1928. For the most part there are elegant buildings amidst fine gardens and playing fields on a site overlooking the Solent. The grounds cover about 17 acres and further sports fields have recently been acquired. There have been many additions to the buildings in recent years and the school is now very well equipped with new design centre and sports hall. Academic standards and results are good and many sixth form leavers go on to degree courses each year, including Oxbridge. Drama is very strong as are music and art. There is a good range of sports and games and a variety of extra–curricular activities.

School profile

Pupils Total age range 4–18; 621 pupils, 591 day (381 boys, 210 girls), 30 boarding. Senior department 11–18, 426 pupils (271 boys, 155 girls). Main entry ages 9, 11, 13 and into sixth. Approx 5% are children of former pupils. *Transfer from maintained schools:* 75% main senior intakes, plus 20% to sixth.
Entrance Common entrance sometimes used, otherwise by interview. Oversubscribed for some ages. No special skills or religious requirements. Parents not expected to buy text books; music tuition extra (£48 per term) and lunch for day pupils (£93 per term). 5 scholarships/bursaries pa, £1000–£500.
Parents 90+% live within 30 miles; up to 10% live overseas.
Staff Headmaster M D Featherstone, in post for 1 year. 43 full time staff, 6 part time. Annual turnover 8%. Average age 38.
Academic work GCSE, AS and A-levels offered. In 1990, 87 pupils in upper fifth, 46 in upper sixth. *GCSE:* in 1990, 44 upper fifth gained at least grade C in 8+ subjects; 32 in 5–7; and 7 in 1–4 subjects.

A-levels: 12 upper sixth passed in 4+ subjects; 16 in 3; 9 in 2; and 5 in 1 subject. 15 took science A-levels; 21 arts/humanities; 10 both. *Computing facilities:* BBCs, Archimedes.
European Community *Languages:* French offered: to age 14; GCSE; A-level. German offered: to age 14; GCSE; A-level. Spanish offered: to age 14; GCSE; A-level; non-examined subject. *Exchanges:* Regular exchanges for pupils aged 14–16 to France and Germany.
Careers In 1990, 67% leavers went on to degree courses; 3% to art/drama/music colleges; 10% to non-degree courses; 5% straight into careers; 15% other. Of those going on to degree courses, 14% went to Oxbridge; 62% to other universities; 24% to poly/colleges. 7% those going on to higher education went to courses in practical art; 3% in drama/acting; 7% in music; 56% in humanities/social sciences; 7% in medicine; and 20% in science/engineering.
Uniform School uniform worn throughout.
Houses/prefects Competitive houses.

Prefects, head boy/girl, head of house and house prefects – appointed by staff. Sixth Form Committee.

Religion Compulsory religious assembly.

Social Organised trips abroad. Sixth form pupils allowed to bring own car/bike to school. Meals formal. School shop. No tobacco/alcohol allowed.

Discipline No corporal punishment. A pupil failing to produce homework might expect detention; those caught smoking cannabis on the premises could expect expulsion.

Boarding Fifth and sixth formers have shared study bedrooms. 1 house of 25–30. Resident housemother. 2 weekend exeats per term. Visits to local town allowed.

Alumni association is run by J E Ball, The Coach House, Westridge Cross Dairy, Ryde, Isle of Wight.

Former pupils Philip Norman (journalist and author).

· Rye St Antony ·

Rye St Antony School	• Pupils 400	• Termly fees
Pullen's Lane	• Boys None	£1225 (Day)
Headington Hill	• Girls 7–18	£2180 (Board)
Oxford OX3 0BY	(Day/Board/Weekly)	£2086 (Weekly)
Tel 0865 62802	• Upper sixth 32	• GSA, SHA, CCSS
		Enquiries/application to
		the Headmistress

What it's like

Founded in 1930, the school moved to its present site on Headington Hill in 1939 and acquired further property in 1944. Since 1966 there has been a more or less continuous building programme which now provides good modern facilities of all kinds. Headington is an attractive residential part of Oxford, a mile or so from the city centre. The school, situated in 12 acres of grounds, with beautiful gardens, comprises four main boarding houses. Modern buildings harmonise with the Victorian houses. The beliefs and values of the Catholic faith are central to the life of the school and religious education is an integral part of the curriculum. A sound education is provided and results are impressive. The staff:pupil ratio is a favourable 1:10, and there is considerable emphasis on personal attention and tuition. Many leavers proceed to degree courses, including some to Oxbridge. French, Italian and Spanish are offered to A-level, German to GCSE. A number of girls take GCSE in more than one European language. There are regular exchanges to France and Spain. Music is strong; two-thirds of the girls learn an instrument. There are two choirs, an orchestra, a recorder group and smaller ensembles. Art is also strong throughout the school; a range of options is available in design, textiles and ceramics. Drama is vigorously supported and is treated as a curriculum subject. Games and sports facilities are adequate and a standard range of sport is available (plus fencing). Good standards are attained with occasional representation at county and regional level. A large number of girls are involved in local community services, parish work etc. The Duke of Edinburgh's Award Scheme is well supported (a high rate of success). Extensive use is made of Oxford's cultural amenities.

School profile

Pupils Total age range 7–18; 400 girls (240 day, 160 boarding). Senior department 11–18, 340 girls. Main entry ages, 7, 11, and into sixth. 10% are children of former pupils. *Transfer from maintained schools:* 40% main intake, 40% to sixth.

Entrance Common entrance (11+ only) and own exam used. Oversubscribed. No special skills required, preference given to Roman Catholics. Parents not expected to buy text books. Average extras £100 a term. Some scholarships/bursaries at Headmistress's discretion, one-third fees.

Parents 30+% live within 30 miles, less than 10% live overseas.

Staff Headmistress Miss A M Jones, 1 year in post. 37 full time staff, 33 part time. Annual turnover 2%. Average age 38.

Academic work GCSE and A-levels. 26 subjects offered (not including A-level general studies). In 1990, 43 pupils in upper fifth, 32 in upper sixth. *GCSE:* in 1990, 60% upper fifth gained at least grade C in 8+ subjects; 25% in 5–7; and 15% in 1–4 subjects. *A-levels:* 60% upper sixth passed in 3 subjects; 40% in 2 subjects. 10% took science A-levels; 60% arts/humanities; 30% both. *Computing facilities:* 10 BBC, 16 Archimedes, 2 Amstrad computers – in two rooms. *Special provision:* Individual or small group tuition available.

European Community *Languages:* French offered: to age 14; GCSE; A-level. German: to GCSE. Italian: to GCSE; A-level. Spanish: to GCSE; A-level. 10–25% take GCSE in more than 1 EC language. *Exchanges:* Regular exchanges for pupils aged 14–16 to France and Spain. *Other:* European studies offered to sixth form as part of general studies course. 1 year and 1 term places for EC pupils. Former headmistress has house in Normandy, regularly visited by groups of students.

Senior pupils' non-academic activities *Music:* 65% learn a musical instrument, 15% to Grade 5 and above; 40 in school orchestra, 35 in school choir. *Drama and dance:* Many in school productions. *Art:* 20% take GCSE art; 25% A-level art. Variable number accepted for Art School each year. *Sport:* Athletics, badminton, fencing, fitness-training, gymnastics, hockey, netball, rounders, squash, swimming, table-tennis, tennis available. Many take part in non-compulsory sport. Occasional representation for county (hockey, netball). *Other:* 50+ take part in local community schemes. 47 currently working for bronze Duke of Edinburgh's Award, 29 silver and 20 for gold. Some enter voluntary schemes after leaving school.

Careers In 1990, 90% leavers went on to degree courses; 6% to art/drama/music colleges; 4% to non-degree courses. Of those going on to degree courses, 5% went to Oxbridge; 55% to other universities; 40% to poly/colleges. 6% those going on to higher education went to courses in practical art; 74% in humanities/social sciences; and 20% in science/engineering.

Uniform School uniform worn, except in sixth.

Houses/prefects Competitive houses for sport. Head girl and prefects appointed by the head/elected by the school.

Religion All girls attend school masses and morning assembly.

Social Debates, ballroom dancing, social events with various local schools. Ski-ing in Alps (alternate years); visits to France; exchanges arranged. Meals formal. School tuck shop. No tobacco/alcohol allowed.

Discipline Considerable importance is attached to the acquisition of self-discipline and to recognition of the responsibilities of each individual within the school as a whole.

Boarding Most sixth form have own study bedrooms; age 13 upwards, share 1–4. Some girls aged 7–13 in dormitories of 6+. Houses, of 30–50. Two resident qualified nurses. Sixth form occasionally allowed to provide and cook own food. 3–4 weekend exeats each term. Visits to the local town allowed – frequency depends on age.

Alumni association is run by Mrs S Strouts, c/o the school.

S

· *Sacred Heart* ·

Sacred Heart School
Beechwood
Pembury Road
Tunbridge Wells
Kent TN2 3QD
Tel 0892 29193

- Pupils 262
- Boys None
- Girls 5–18
  (Day/Board/Weekly)
- Upper sixth 30

- Termly fees
  £1520 (Day)
  £2645 (Board/
  Weekly)
- GSA
  Enquiries/application to
  the Headmaster

What it's like

Founded in 1915, it is single-site on the outskirts of Tunbridge Wells in 22 acres of beautiful grounds. Handsome buildings and very good modern facilities. A friendly family school which has all the advantages of being small. It is a Roman Catholic foundation. A good broad general education is provided and a high proportion of leavers proceed to university. Strong art and drama departments. An excellent range of sport, games, societies and clubs. A good record in the Duke of Edinburgh's Award Scheme. Full use is made of the cultural amenities of the town.

School profile

Pupils Total age range 5–18; 262 girls, 134 day, 128 boarding. Senior department 11–18, 211 girls. Main entry ages 5, 11, 14 and into sixth. Approx 1% are children of former pupils. *Transfer from maintained schools:* 30% main senior intakes, none to sixth.

Entrance Common entrance exam used. Not oversubscribed. No special skills required; Roman Catholic foundation but any denomination welcome. Parents not expected to buy text books; other extras vary. 5 scholarships, value up to £1100 per term; bursaries available for girls already in school in financial need.

Parents 40+% live within 30 miles; 40+% live overseas.

Staff Headmaster Dr James A Fallon, in post for 12 years. 23 full time staff, 17 part time. Annual turnover 8%. Average age 42.

Academic work GCSE, AS and A-levels. 16 subjects offered at A-level (including law, psychology; no A-level general studies). In 1989, 37 pupils in upper fifth, 30 in upper sixth. *GCSE:* in 1989, 17 upper fifth gained at least grade C in 8+ subjects; 10 in 5–7; and 10 in 1–4 subjects. *A-levels:* 2 upper sixth passed in 4+ subjects; 16 in 3; 6 in 2; and 6 in 1 subject. 30% took science A-levels; 30% arts/humanities; 40% both. *Special provision:* Extra EFL classes for foreign students.

European Community *Languages:* French offered: to age 14; GCSE; A-level. German: GCSE; A-level. Spanish offered: to age 14; GCSE; A-level. 10–25% take GCSE in more than 1 EC language.

Other: Number of EC pupils in school – mainly Spanish, some French and German.

Senior pupils' non-academic activities *Music:* 30 learn a musical instrument, 20 to Grade 6 or above. 8 in school orchestra, 45 in choir; 1 in county youth orchestra; 2 students currently preparing for diploma examinations. *Drama and dance:* 10 in school productions. Some pupils taking ballet grades. Clubs for jazz dance and contemporary dance. *Art:* 6 take as non-examined subject; 24 GCSE, 6 A-level, 2 mature GCSE, 5 history of art. 2 accepted for art school. 10 belong to eg photographic club; 12 to pottery club. *Sport:* Hockey, swimming, basketball, volleyball, netball, gymnastics, badminton, cross-country, orienteering, tennis, cricket, rounders, squash, aerobics, rhythmic gymnastics, riding available. 52 take non-compulsory sport. *Other:* 16 take part in local community schemes. 24 have bronze Duke of Edinburgh's Award, 10 have silver. 10 work for national charities beyond school. Other activities include a computer club, chess, bridge, science, drama, public speaking and debating. Driving lessons can be arranged.

Careers 1 full time adviser. Annual average accepted for *arts and humanities degree courses* at universities, 14; polytechnics/colleges, 3. *science and engineering degree courses* at universities, 5; medical schools, 1. *BEd*, 2.

Uniform School uniform worn, modified in the sixth.

Houses/prefects Competitive houses. 2 head girls, heads of houses and prefects elected by school (Head has power of veto).

Religion Compulsory daily worship and Sunday mass.

Social Dances, debates with other schools, occasional joint theatrical productions. Annual ball for parents and seniors. Visits to Ascot on Ladies' Day. Frequent fixtures in all sports and activities. Organised trips and exchange systems with schools abroad. Pupils allowed to bring own car/bike to school. Meals self service. School shop. No tobacco allowed; wine only at formal functions.

Discipline No corporal punishment. Pupils failing to produce homework once might expect an order mark or warning; those caught smoking cannabis on the premises could expect expulsion.

Boarding 70 have own study bedroom, 30 share with 1 other; 12 are in dormitories of 6+. Qualified nurse on call. Central dining room. Exeats at parents'/guardians' discretion. Visits to local town allowed.

Former pupils Libby Purves; Julia Cumberlege.

· St Albans ·

St Albans School
Abbey Gateway
St Albans
Hertfordshire AL3 4HB
Tel 0727 55521

- Pupils 666
- Boys 11–18 (Day)
- Girls 16–18 (Day)
- Upper sixth 100

- Termly fees
  £1395 (Day)
- HMC
  Enquiries/application to
  the Headmaster

What it's like

Its origins date to the pre-Norman monastic school which, by 1300, occupied buildings near its present site and was controlled by the Abbot of St Albans. In c1570 Elizabeth I granted it a charter. Late in the 19th century it moved into the Abbey Gateway. It is urban and single-site and the playing fields are a mile away. Architecturally, it comprises a very interesting mixture of buildings dating from the late Middle Ages to the 1980s. Very well equipped with modern facilities, its main aim is to develop talent and responsibility and it retains close links with the Abbey. Academic standards are high and results are good. Very many pupils go on to degree courses, including many to Oxbridge. It has flourishing music, art and drama departments, a good range of sport and games and a thriving CCF. A good deal of use is made of its field study centre in South Wales. A big commitment to local community services, and an outstanding record in the Duke of Edinburgh's Award Scheme.

School profile

Pupils Age range 11–18; 666 day boys; 20 (rising to 40) girls in sixth form from 1991. Main entry ages 11, 13 (boys) and into sixth (boys and girls). Approx 3% are children of former pupils. *Transfer from maintained schools:* 80% intake at 11, 5% at 13, plus 50% to sixth.

Entrance Common entrance and own exam used. Oversubscribed. No special skills or religious requirements. Parents not expected to buy text books; maximum extras, £15. 150 assisted places. Up to 2 scholarships/bursaries per year.

Parents 15+% are from industry or commerce.

Staff Headmaster S C Wilkinson, in post for 7 years. 55 full time staff, 10 part time staff. Annual turnover 3%. Average age 38.

Academic work GCSE and A-levels offered (no A-level general studies). In 1990, 103 pupils in upper fifth, 100 in upper sixth. *GCSE:* in 1990, 77 upper fifth gained at least grade C in 8+ subjects; 21 in 5–7; and 4 in 1–4 subjects. *A-levels:* 13 upper sixth passed in 4+ subjects; 72 in 3; 13 in 2; and 3 in 1 subject. 35 took science A-levels; 44 arts/humanities; 21 both. *Computing facilities:* 2 computer rooms; 20 BBC Bs and Masters; 8 Archimedes; hard disk store networked to science and technology department computers; portable computers. *Special provision:* for mild dyslexia.

European Community *Languages:* French offered: to age 14; GCSE; A-level. German offered: to age 14; GCSE; A-level. Italian offered: non-examined subject. Spanish offered: to GCSE; non-examined subject. 10–25% take GCSE in more than 1 EC language. *Exchanges:* Regular exchanges for pupils aged 11–16 to France and Germany. *Other:* MEP visits to speak regularly.

Senior pupils' non-academic activities *Music:* 50 learn a musical instrument, 26 to Grade 6 or above, 1 accepted for Music School, 1 for university, 26 in school orchestras, 12 in choirs, 14 in pop group, 30 in ensembles, 1 in National Youth Orchestra, 6 in district youth orchestras. *Drama and dance:* 50 in school productions; 10 in St Alban's High productions; 20 in other productions; 28 take GCSE, 8 A-level. *Art:* 4 take as non-examined subject; 20 take GCSE; 12 A-level. 1 accepted for Art School. 6 belong to photographic club. *Sport:* Association and rugby football, hockey, cricket, tennis, cross-country, basketball, badminton, sailing, golf, squash, swimming and orienteering available. 110 take non-compulsory sport. 16 represent county/country (rugby, badminton, squash, cross-country). *Other:* 60 take part in local community schemes. 24 have silver Duke of Edinburgh's Award, 42 gold. Other activities include a computer club, driving lessons, chess and bridge clubs.

Careers In 1990, 86% leavers went on to degree courses; 3% to art/drama/music colleges; 3% straight into careers; 8% other. Of those going on to degree courses, 14% went to Oxbridge; 73% to other universities; 13% to poly/colleges. 2% those going on to higher education went to courses in practical art; 1% in drama/acting; 2% in music; 56% in humanities/social sciences; 5% in medicine; and 34% in science/engineering.

Uniform School uniform worn, except the sixth.

Houses/prefects No competitive houses. Prefects, head boy – appointed by the Head.

Religion Compulsory services, unless parents request otherwise.

Social Joint theatrical productions, oratorios, general studies, community service camp, fetes etc with other local schools. 2 or 3 skiing trips, mountaineering, exchanges to France, Germany and the USA. Pupils allowed to bring own car/bike/motorbike to school. Meals self service. School shop. No tobacco/alcohol allowed.

Discipline No corporal punishment. Pupils caught smoking cannabis on the premises could expect suspension at least.

Former pupils Professor C Renfrew (Master of Jesus College, Cambridge); Professor S Hawking.

· St Albans High ·

St Albans High School for Girls
3 Townsend Avenue
St Albans
Hertfordshire AL1 3SJ
Tel 0727 53800

- Pupils 523
- Boys None
- Girls 11–18 (Day)
- Upper sixth 60

- Termly fees £1125 (Day)
- GSA

What it's like

Founded in 1889 the school is situated on a pleasant urban site. The buildings are mainly purpose built with some modern additions. It is Christian by tradition and ethos and tries to put this into practice as a caring community, closely connected with St Albans Abbey; there are regular occasions of worship in the Anglican tradition. A broad academic education is provided and public examination results are good. Girls go on to a wide variety of careers, most via degree courses. Extra-curricular activities are plentiful and varied; music and drama are particularly strong. Facilities for PE and games include playing fields and a new sports hall. There is keen participation in the Duke of Edinburgh's Award Scheme. Parents are very much involved in the activities of the School.

School profile

Pupils Age range 11–18; 523 day girls. Main entry ages 11 and into sixth. Own prep school. *Transfer from maintained schools:* 45% main intake.

Entrance Own exam used. Oversubscribed. No special skills or religious requirements. Parents not expected to buy textbooks. 15 assisted places pa. Scholarships at 11 and 16; bursaries; special terms for daughters of clergy.

Parents 15+% doctors, lawyers, etc; 15+% in industry or commerce.

Staff Headmistress Miss E M Diggory, in post for 8 years. 38 full time staff, 20 part time.

Academic work GCSE and A-levels. 20 subjects offered (including Ancient Greek; no A-level general studies). In 1990, 74 pupils in upper fifth, 59 in upper sixth. *GCSE:* in 1990, 92% upper fifth gained at least grade C in 8+ subjects. *A-levels:* 90% upper sixth passed in 2 or more subjects. *Computing facilities:* 10 Apple Macs, 9 BBC micros, networked. *Special provision:* Some special provision in certain circumstances.

European Community *Languages:* French offered: to age 14; GCSE; AS-level; A-level. German offered: to age 14; GCSE; AS-level; A-level. Spanish offered: to age 14; GCSE. 25–50% take GCSE in more than 1 EC language. *Exchanges:* Regular exchanges for pupils aged 14–16 to France and Germany. Exchange trip planned to Reims for 13/14 year olds. *Other:* Talk from prospective Labour MEP (1989) to upper sixth.

Careers On average, 66% leavers went on to degree courses; 4% to art/drama/music colleges; 8% to non-degree courses; 2% straight into careers; 20% other. Of those going on to degree courses, 12% went to Oxbridge; 72% to other universities; 16% to poly/colleges.

8% those going on to higher education went to courses in practical art; 52% in humanities/social sciences; 3% in medicine; and 37% in science/engineering.

Uniform School uniform worn, except in sixth.

Houses/prefects Competitive houses. Head girl, prefects, head of house and house prefects, elected by the school. School Council.

Religion Attendance at religious worship compulsory, unless parents request otherwise.

Social Theatrical productions with St Albans, debating competitions with other schools. Exchanges with Dijon, Lüneberg and Vermont; visits to eg Russia, Florence. Sixth form allowed to bring car/bike/motorbike. Meals self-service. School shop. No tobacco/alcohol allowed.

Discipline No corporal punishment.

· St Ambrose ·

St Ambrose College
Wicker Lane
Hale Barns
Altrincham
Cheshire WA15 0HF
Tel 061 980 2711

- Pupils 785
- Boys 4–18 (Day)
- Girls None
- Upper sixth 80

- Termly fees £839 (Day)
- HMC

Enquiries/application to the Headmaster or Secretary

What it's like

Opened by the Christian Brothers in 1945. For 5 years the school was run in the Community residence. Between 1960 and 1962 the present school was started and there is now a modern purpose-built school in extensive parkland. It is a Roman Catholic foundation and most of the pupils are RCs. Pupils of other denominations are welcome. There is a good deal of emphasis on religious instruction and worship: Mass, prayers (public and private), retreats. A sound general education is provided and academic results are good. Many pupils go on to degree courses each year. There is some music, drama and art. A good range of sports and games and a fair variety of extra-curricular activities. The school has some commitment to local community services.

School profile

Pupils Total age range 4–18; 785 day boys. Senior department 11–18, 640 boys. Main entry ages 4, 7, 11 and into sixth. Approx 15% are children of former pupils. Own prep department provides more than 20% of intake. *Transfer from maintained schools:* 70% senior intake.

Entrance Own entrance exam used. Oversubscribed. No special skills; RC school but admits others. Parents not expected to buy text books. 88 assisted places. About 10 scholarships/bursaries pa.

Parents 15+% are doctors, lawyers, etc; 15+% in industry or commerce; 15+% are teachers.

Staff Headmaster Rev Bro T Coleman, in post for 6 years. 43 full time staff, 8 part time. Annual turnover 1–2%. Average age 30.

Academic work GCSE and A-levels. 14 subjects offered (including A-level general studies). In 1990, 82 pupils in upper fifth, 76 in upper sixth (now 80). *GCSE:* in 1990, 47 upper fifth gained at least grade C in 8+ subjects; 20 in 5–7; and 14 in 1–4 subjects. *A-levels:* 40 upper sixth passed in 4+ subjects; 14 in 3; 15 in

2; and 5 in 1 subject. 54% took science A-levels; 33% arts/humanities; 13% both. *Computing facilities:* well equipped laboratory.

European Community *Languages:* French offered: to age 14; GCSE; A-level. German offered: to age 14; GCSE; A-level. Italian offered: to GCSE; AS-level. 25–50% take GCSE in more than 1 EC language. *Exchanges:* Regular exchanges for pupils aged 14–16 to France and Germany.

Senior pupils' non-academic activities *Music:* 15 learn a musical instrument, 6 to Grade 6 or above. 15 in school orchestra, 30 in choir, 10 go on to play in pop group. *Drama and dance:* 30 in school productions. *Art:* 10 take GCSE; 6 A-level, 3 accepted for Art School. *Sport:* Rugby, cross-country, golf, squash, badminton, cricket, tennis, swimming available. 6 represent country (swimming, cross-country, athletics); many county representatives in all sports. *Other:* 15 take part in charity work. 6 enter voluntary schemes at home and abroad after leaving. Other activities include a computer club, debating, public speaking (competition level), theatre club, art, subito, hill walking, weight training.

Careers In 1990, 76% leavers went on to degree courses; 16% to non-degree courses or straight into careers (eg BBC, HND course, banking, surveying); 8% other. Of those going on to degree courses, 8% went to Oxbridge; 70% to other universities; 24% to poly/colleges. 1% those going on to higher education went to courses in drama/acting; 44% in humanities/social sciences; 16% in medicine; and 42% in science/engineering.

Uniform School uniform worn throughout.

Houses/prefects Competitive houses. Prefects, head boy – elected by school and staff.

Religion Worship encouraged; mass, prayers (private and assembly), retreats.

Social Drama, theatre and swimming gala with Loreto Convent School; local festivals. Organised visits to France, Germany, Austria. Pupils allowed to bring own car/bike/motorbike to school. Meals self-service. School shop. No alcohol; tobacco allowed in a restricted area.

Discipline No corporal punishment. Pupils failing to produce homework once might expect detention; those caught smoking cannabis on the premises might expect suspension, expulsion for importers.

· St Anne's (Windermere) ·

St Anne's School
Browhead
Windermere
Cumbria
LA23 1NW
Tel 05394 46164

- Pupils 418
- Boys 3–7 only (Day)
- Girls 3–18 (Day/Board)
- Upper sixth 40

- Termly fees
  £1730 (Day)
  £2530 (Board)
- GSA, SHMIS, Round Square
  Enquiries/application to the Headmaster

What it's like

Founded in 1863, it has a magnificent situation in the Lake District National Park, on a site of 80 acres with splendid views over Lake Windermere and the fells. Its pleasant and well equipped buildings are spread over two main sites. It is Christian in outlook but non–denominational. It attracts girls from all over the world and endeavours to provide a liberal and progressive education where activities such as sailing, canoeing, fell-walking, music, art, drama and voluntary service play an important part. It is a member of the Round Square Conference – a group of internationally based schools following the Kurt Hahn traditions – with whom links are forged and exchanges are made. The teaching is good and exam results are good. Many leavers proceed to degree courses each year. It is exceptionally strong in its music department and also strong in art and drama. Very good range of sports and games, societies and clubs. Much emphasis on outdoor pursuits and field studies, a very big commitment to local community schemes and an outstanding record in the Duke of Edinburgh's Award Scheme.

School profile

Pupils Total age range 3–18; 418 pupils, 138 day (18 boys, 120 girls), 280 boarding girls. Senior department 11–18, 302 girls. Main entry ages 3 (boys and girls); 11, 13 and into sixth (girls). Approx 5% are children of former pupils. *Transfer from maintained schools:* 30% senior intakes, plus 5% to sixth.

Entrance Own entrance exam used. No special skills or religious requirements. Parents not expected to buy text books; maximum extras £150–£200 for boarders, less for day girls. No assisted places. 13 scholarships available.

Parents 15+% are doctors, lawyers, farmers, etc; 15+% in industry or commerce. 10+% live within 30 miles; up to 10% live overseas.

Staff Headmaster M P Hawkins, in post for 5 years. 37 full time staff, 21 part time. Annual turnover 5%. Average age 30.

Academic work GCSE and A-level subjects offered (including theatre studies and A-level general studies). In 1991, 60 pupils in upper fifth, 40 in upper sixth. *GCSE:* in 1990, 36 upper fifth gained at least grade C in 8+ subjects; 21 in 5–7; and 3 in 1–4 subjects. *A-levels:* 27 upper sixth passed in 3+ subjects; 12 in 2; and 1 in 1 subject. 25% took science A-levels; 50% arts/humanities; 25% both. *Computing facilities:* 16 station RM Nimbus network. *Special provision:* English for foreign students.

European Community *Languages:* French offered: to age 14; GCSE; AS-level; A-level; Institute of Linguists. German offered: to age 14; GCSE; AS-level; A-level; Institute of Linguists. Italian offered: Institute of Linguists. Spanish offered: to age 14; GCSE; AS-level; A-level; Institute of Linguists. Over 75% take GCSE in more than 1 EC language. *Exchanges:* Regular exchanges for pupils aged 14–18 to France, Germany and Spain. Exchanges with European schools in Round Square Conference Group.

Senior pupils' non-academic activities *Music:* 192 learn a musical instrument; others have voice tuition and take grades and enter solo vocal competitions. There is an orchestra, string ensemble, concert band, flute choir, clarinet choir, chamber music ensembles; considerable scope for pianists to acquire accompanying skill. Senior choir recently sung at Carlisle Cathedral, Cartmel Priory; junior choir tour to Austria. Music plays an important part in the school week; informal lunch-time concerts, musical items for assembly and rehearsals keep the girls well motivated and respectful of each other's achievements. *Drama and dance:* 100 in school productions, 50 in other. 10 up to Grade 6 in ESB, RAD etc. 40 associated speech and drama, 5 entered competitions. *Art:* 50 take GCSE; 11 take A-level. 5 pa accepted for Art School. 50 belong to photographic/art/pottery club. *Sport:* Hockey, netball, swimming, tennis, cross-country, badminton, basketball, self-defence, gymnastics, dance – various, athletics and riding available. 120 take non–compulsory sport. 4 represent county (cross-country, netball, hurdling and sprinting). *Other:* 70 take part in local community schemes. 30 are taking bronze Duke of Edinburgh's Award, and 17 silver. Other activities include a computer club, driving lessons, bridge, debating, windsurfing, sailing (school is RYA centre), canoeing, sewing, knitting, railway modelling technology, basic wood modelling, origami, macrame, drawing and archery clubs.

Careers In 1990, 83% leavers went on to degree courses; 2% to non-degree courses (eg secretarial); 15% straight into careers. Of those going on to degree courses, 50% went to universities; 50% to poly/colleges. 20% those going on to higher education went to courses in practical art; 45% in humanities/social sciences; and 35% in science/engineering.

Uniform School uniform worn throughout.

Houses/prefects Competitive houses. No prefects. Head girl, deputies and heads of houses elected by the school. School Council.

Religion Morning and evening prayers. Sunday morning service.

Social Organised events with local independent schools. Exchanges with other Round Square schools and a French

school. Pupils allowed to bring own car/bike to school. Meals self-service. School shop. No tobacco/alcohol allowed.

Discipline No corporal punishment. Pupils failing to produce homework once can expect extra work; those involved with drugs can expect expulsion.

Boarding Sixth form have own study bedrooms, 60% share with others; 40% are in dormitories of 6+. 5 houses, of about 50. Resident qualified staff. Central dining room. Pupils can provide and cook own food in the senior house. 2 weekend exeats each term. Visits to local town allowed.

Alumni association is run by Mrs J Brown, 16 The Horseshoe, York.

Former pupils Dodie Smith (author).

· *St Anselm's* ·

St Anselm's College	● Pupils 650	● Termly fees
Manor Hill	● Boys 11–18	£774 (Day)
Birkenhead	(Day)	● HMC
Merseyside L43 1UQ	● Girls None	Enquiries/application to
Tel 051 652 1408	● Upper sixth 65	the Headmaster

What it's like

Founded in 1933 by the Congregation of Christian Brothers to serve the needs of Roman Catholic boys in the Wirral area. The vast majority of the boys are Roman Catholics but pupils of other denominations are taken. The college has vigorous local support. The school has large grounds near Birkenhead Park. The main school is built round a pleasant quadrangle and houses forms 1–5. Nearby is a sixth-form block, plus science and music blocks. There is a well-equipped audio-visual centre and a computer centre. Five minutes' walk from the main school, at Redcourt, is the preparatory department. St Anselm's is essentially a Roman Catholic school and boys of whatever religious persuasion are accepted on the understanding that they play a full part in religious activities which form an important part of school life. A good deal of attention to religious instruction is given at all levels. Prayers, Mass etc are an integral part of the life. There are occasional 'Retreats'. Academic standards are high and results are good. Many leavers go on to degree courses. The staff:pupil ratio is about 1:14. Music is especially strong. All boys are taught a musical instrument in their first three years and there is a flourishing choir and orchestra. There are first-class facilities for sports and games in which good standards are attained, particularly in cricket, cross-country and rugby. Games are compulsory for all except those medically exempted. There is a plentiful range of clubs and societies. Considerable emphasis is put on community and social services which are organised under the aegis of the

St Vincent de Paul Society. The school also runs a club for the mentally handi-capped which meets weekly and provides entertainment (outings, parties etc) for the mentally handicapped.

School profile

Pupils Age range 11–18, 650 day boys. Main entry age 11. Large proportion of intake from own prep. *Transfer from maintained schools:* 60% intake at 11, plus 60% to sixth.

Entrance Own entrance exam used, based on NFER tests. 30 assisted places plus 5 to sixth. 2 scholarships pa, 50% fees. Fees paid by LEA for some 40 pa RC pupils, resident in Wirral, who pass 11+ exam.

Staff Headmaster Rev Brother C J Sreenan.

Academic work GCSE, AS and A-levels. 21 GCSE subjects offered; 18 at A-level (including religious studies, British government and politics and A-level general studies). In 1990, 100 pupils in upper fifth, 65 in upper sixth. *GCSE:* in 1990, 46 upper fifth gained at least grade C in 8+ subjects; 34 in 5–7; and 20 in 1–4 subjects. *A-levels:* 4 upper sixth passed in 5+ subjects; 40 in 4+ subjects; 8 in 3; 8 in 2; and 4 in 1 subject. 50% took science A-levels; 50% arts/humanities. *Computing facilities:* Facilities for GCSE and AS level computer science. *Special provision:* Mildly visually handicapped.

European Community *Languages:* French offered: to GCSE; AS-level; A-level. German offered: to GCSE; AS-level; A-level. Spanish offered: to GCSE. 25–50% take GCSE in more than 1 EC language. *Exchanges:* Regular exchanges for pupils to France and Germany. *Other:* Work experience and shadowing in France and Germany.

Careers In 1990, 81% leavers went on to degree courses; 3% to art/drama/music colleges; 3% to non-degree courses; 14% other. Of those going on to degree courses, 3% went to Oxbridge; 64% to other universities; 33% to poly/colleges. 33% those going on to higher education went to courses in practical art; 67% in humanities/social sciences.

· *St Antony's-Leweston* ·

| St Antony's-Leweston School Sherborne Dorset DT9 6EN Tel 096 321 691 | • Pupils 392 • Boys None • Girls 11–18 (Day/Board) • Upper sixth 41 | • Termly fees £1575 (Day) £2480 (Board) • GSA, BSA Enquiries/application to the Headmistress |

What it's like

Founded in 1891, it derives from the pioneering work of the Congregation of the Sisters of Christian Instruction (founded in 1822) which created schools in many parts of the world. It is sited 3 miles south of Sherborne in a stretch of splendid Dorset countryside. The main building is a very elegant 19th century country house in beautiful gardens and parkland. A most civilised and healthy environment. Numerous modern extensions provide accommodation and good facilities, including labs, sports hall, arts centre, a health centre and a new design and technology centre. There is a brick-built church of unusual design. It is Roman Catholic, and a resident Dominican priest is the spiritual mentor. A happy, well run establishment where academic standards are high and results are good (many go on to degree courses). Four European languages are on offer – French, German, Italian and Spanish. Very strong indeed in music, drama and art. Also in sports and games (of which there is a wide range) and numerous other activities. Cultural collaboration with Sherborne Boys' school, Downside and Milton Abbey.

School profile

Pupils Age range 11–18; 392 girls, 88 day, 304 boarding. Main entry ages 11, 12, 13 and into sixth. Approx 5% are children of former pupils. St Antony's Convent Prep School provides some 30% of intake. *Transfer from maintained schools:* Varies (few).

Entrance Common entrance and own exam used. No special skills or religious requirements, although a Roman Catholic school. Parents not expected to buy text books; maximum £230 for 3 extras. No assisted places. Scholarships/bursaries, up to $^2/_3$ fees.

Parents 15+% in the armed services. 10+% live within 30 miles; 10+% live overseas. 4% are foreign students.

Staff Headmistress Mrs P Cartwright, in post for 8 years. 43 full time staff, 13 part time. Annual turnover 10%. Average age 40.

Academic work GCSE and A-levels. 22 GCSE and A-level subjects offered (no A-level general studies). In 1990, 68 pupils in upper fifth, 41 in upper sixth. *GCSE:* in 1990, 45 upper fifth gained at least grade C in 8+ subjects; 14 in 5–7; and 9 in 1–4 subjects. *A-levels:* 28 upper sixth passed in 3 subjects; 5 in 2; and 3 in 1 subject. 7 took science A-levels; 23 arts/humanities; 7 both. *Computing facilities:* Computers in design and technology centre; computer studies taught. *Special provision:* Extra English lessons; specialist teacher.

European Community *Languages:* French offered: to age 14; GCSE; A-level. German offered: to age 14; GCSE; A-level. Italian offered: to GCSE; A-level. Spanish offered: to age 14; GCSE; A-level. 25–50% take GCSE in more than 1 EC language. *Exchanges:* Regular exchanges for pupils aged 14–18 to France.

Senior pupils' non-academic activities *Music:* 67 learn a musical instrument, 27 to Grade 6 or above, 1 accepted for Music School; 10 in chamber orches-tra, 65 in school choral society, 14 in chamber music, 21 in chamber choir; 7 in Dorset Youth orchestra, 1 in Dorset band, 16 in Joint Sherborne Schools' Orchestra. *Speech and drama:* 83 in school productions, 127 in individual lessons, 18 pupils Guildhall Grade 7 upwards, 20 pupils LAMDA medal awards. 3 accepted to drama degree courses, 1 accepted for drama school, 12 accepted for theatre studies, 65 in Bath Mid-Somerset Festival, 43 in Taunton Festival, 6 auditioned for National Youth Theatre. *Art:* 55 take art and design GCSE, 31 history of art; 15 take art A-level; 1 accepted for university (graphics), 2 accepted at art school (textiles; foundation course); woodcarving, stonecarving, sculpture/pottery, photographic club, jewellery and silver smithing and craft club. *Sport:* Hockey, netball, gymnastics, dance, cross-country running, basketball, volleyball, badminton, indoor hockey, trampolining, fitness, aerobics, squash, swimming, tennis, athletics, fencing, rounders, riding, karate available. Sixth form also have golf, skiing, rugby, yoga. 250 take non-compulsory sport. 150 take exams in gym, swimming, athletics and karate. 45 represent county/country (netball, hockey, fencing and athletics). *Other:* Some sixth year girls take part in local community schemes. 33 taking bronze Duke of Edinburgh's Award. Other activities include a computer club, dance (classical ballet, modern stage and tap dancing as well as modern educational, ballroom and country dance), three cookery clubs, jewellery and silver smithing and craft club.

Careers In 1990, 80% leavers went on to degree courses; 3% to art/drama/music colleges; 17% to non-degree courses (eg nursing, photography). Of those going on to degree courses, 94% went to universities; 6% to poly/colleges. 3% those going on to higher education went to courses in practical art; 85% in humanities/social sciences; 3% in medicine; and 9% in science/engineering.

Uniform School uniform worn throughout.

Houses/prefects Competitive houses. Prefects, senior prefects, head girl, head of house and house secretary – elected by staff and prefects.

Religion Compulsory mass once a week. C of E girls encouraged to attend local church service on Sundays.

Social Joint Downside/Leweston concert held annually. Joint theatrical productions with Sherborne boys' school and Milton Abbey school. Some pupils take part in the 1st and 2nd Joint Sherborne Schools' orchestras. Annual trips abroad include a ski-ing trip, Italian history of art trip, Dieppe trip (weekend). Visits have also been arranged to Russia, Germany and the Himalayas. Pupils allowed to bring own car/bike/motorbike to school.

Meals self-service. School shop. No tobacco/alcohol allowed.

Discipline No corporal punishment. Pupils failing to produce homework once might expect a warning; those caught smoking cannabis on the premises might expect expulsion.

Boarding 51 (sixth form) have own study bedroom, 40 share with 1 other; 204 are in dormitories of 6+. 2 resident nurses, school doctor holds surgery twice a week. Central dining room. Pupils cannot provide and cook their own food. 2 long weekend exeats each term, short weekends (mid-day Sat–Sun) when required. Visits to the local town allowed.

Alumni association is run by Mrs Marielle Ahern.

Former pupils Sarah Payne; Erin Pizzey; Kristen Scott-Thomas; Colette Burke (nee Halligan).

· St Augustine's (London) ·

St Augustine's Priory
Hillcrest Road
London
W5 2JL
Tel 081-997 2022

- Pupils 412
- Boys None
- Girls 4–18
  (Day)
- Upper sixth 19

- Termly fees
  £755 (Day)
  Enquiries to Reverend
  Mother Prioress
  Applications to
  Secretary

What it's like

It has an urban site in a residential area, with extensive grounds and ample playing fields. An RC school run by nuns. Academic results appear satisfactory. French and Spanish are offered to A-level and many girls take GCSE in both. A number of pupils go on to degree courses. School offers music and drama and several extra-curricular activities. Good in art and hockey. No local community service or Duke of Edinburgh's Award Scheme.

School profile

Pupils Total age range 4–18; 412 day girls. Senior department 11–18, 250 girls. Main entry ages 4, 11 and into sixth. Approx 3% are children of former pupils. *Transfer from maintained schools:* 60% senior intake.

Entrance Own entrance exam used. Oversubscribed. No special skills looked for; school mainly RC but small number

of others accepted. Parents not expected to buy text books; maximum extras, £78.

Parents 15+% are doctors, lawyers etc; 15+% in industry or commerce.

Staff Headmistress Mother Mary Gabriel. 23 full time staff, 12 part time. Annual turnover 2%.

Academic work GCSE and A-levels. 15 subjects offered. In 1990, 33 pupils in upper fifth, 15 in upper sixth (now 19). *GCSE:* in 1990, 13 upper fifth gained at least grade C in 8+ subjects; 9 in 5–7; and 11 in 1–4 subjects. *A-levels:* 1 upper sixth passed in 4+ subjects; 5 in 3; 6 in 2; and 2 in 1 subject. 20% took science A-levels; 66% arts/humanities; 14% both. *Computing facilities:* GCSE computing recently started.

European Community *Languages:* French offered: to age 14; GCSE; A-level. Spanish offered: to age 14; GCSE; A-level. 25–50% take GCSE in more than 1 EC language. *Exchanges:* Some exchanges for pupils to France and Spain.

Senior pupils' non-academic activities *Music:* 35 learn a musical instrument, 3–4 to Grade 6 or above, 1 accepted for Music School. 30 in school choir. *Drama and dance:* Some pupils in school productions. *Art:* All take as non-examined subject; 20 GCSE; 4 A-level; 4 accepted for Art School. *Sport:* Hockey, tennis, netball, squash, rounders, swimming available. Some take non-compulsory sport; 6–7 represent county (hockey). Other activities include a computer club, debating, typing in sixth.

Careers In 1990, 60% leavers went on to degree courses; 13% to art/drama/music colleges; 27% to non-degree courses (eg FE college). Of those going on to degree courses, 47% went to universities; 53% to poly/colleges. 13% those going on to higher education went to courses in practical art; 54% in humanities/social sciences; 6% in medicine; and 27% in science/engineering.

Uniform School uniform worn throughout.

Houses/prefects Competitive houses. Prefects, head girl, head of house and house prefects – appointed by the Headmistress.

Religion Compulsory morning assembly and weekly mass.

Social Organised events with other schools; some trips abroad. Pupils who have passed cycling test allowed to bring own bike to school. Meals formal. School shop selling religious items. No tobacco/alcohol allowed.

Discipline No corporal punishment. Detention on Thursday evening. Suspension from school if smoking.

· *St Augustine's (Westgate-on-Sea)* ·

St Augustine's College 125 Canterbury Road Westgate-on-Sea Kent CT8 8NL Tel 0843 32441	● Pupils 111 ● Boys 13–18 (Day/Board) ● Girls None ● Upper sixth 15	● Termly fees £1725 (Day) £2600 (Board) Enquiries to the Secretary Application to the Headmaster

What it's like

Founded in 1865 at Ramsgate by Benedictine monks from Subiaco, it later moved to Westgate a few miles from the Abbey of St Augustine. The junior school shares the same site. Attractive buildings and very good facilities. It is single site and semi-rural in delightful grounds, close to the Ursuline Convent School. Both boys' schools are dedicated to a Catholic education. Everyone is expected to follow a full course of Roman Catholic instruction and to aspire to the standards of conduct, courtesy and discipline inherent in the Benedictine tradition. It has all the advantages of a small school with a staff:pupil ratio of 1:8. Academic standards are high (for a school of this size a large proportion of sixth form go on to degree courses). Strong music, drama and art; very good range of sport, games and activities.

School profile

Pupils Age range 13–18; 111 boys, 33 day, 78 boarding. Main entry ages 13 and into sixth. Own prep (Abbey School, Westgate) provides more than 20% of intake. *Transfer from maintained schools:* 10% intake at 13.

Entrance Common entrance used. Not oversubscribed. No special skills required; Roman Catholics preferred, but all religions accepted. Parents expected to buy text books; maximum extras approx £100. No fixed number or value of scholarships/ bursaries, available on merit and according to special circumstances.

Parents 15+% in industry or commerce; 15+% in professions. 40+% live within 30 miles; 40+% live overseas.

Staff Headmaster Mr K C Doherty, in post 4 years. 15 full time staff, 3 part time. Annual turnover 6%. Average age 47.

Academic work GCSE and A-levels. 16 GCSE and A-level subjects offered (including A-level general studies). In 1990, 29 pupils in upper fifth, 15 in upper sixth. *GCSE:* in 1990, 4 upper fifth gained at least grade C in 8+ subjects; 9 in 5–7; and 14 in 1–4 subjects. *A-levels:* 3 upper sixth passed in 4+ subjects; 4 in 3; 2 in 2; and 3 in 1 subject. 35% took science A-levels; 35% arts/humanities; 30% both. *Computing facilities:* Computer laboratory. Nimbus Z network with full software support including database, word processing and desktop publishing. *Special provision:* EFL teaching provided (and examination entry).

European Community *Languages:* French offered: to age 14; GCSE; A-level. German offered: to age 14; GCSE; A-level. 10–25% take GCSE in more than 1 EC language. *Other:* 3 Spanish pupils 1990/91.

Senior pupils' non-academic activities *Music:* 21 learn a musical instrument, 12 in school choir. *Drama and dance:* 20 in school productions. *Art:* 15 take GCSE; 4 take A-level. 4 belong to photographic club. *Sport:* Cricket, tennis, athletics, golf, volleyball, basketball, swimming, hockey, badminton, association football, squash, cross-country running, rugby available. 30 take non-compulsory sport. *Other:* 6 take part in local community schemes. 4 taking bronze Duke of Edinburgh's Award. Other activities include a computer club, snooker, library service, hobbies, electronics, art, pottery, chess, debating, drama.

Careers In 1990, 43% sixth form leavers went on to degree courses; 7% to art/drama/music colleges; 21% to non-degree courses; 14% straight into careers; 21% other. Of those going on to degree courses, 50% went to universities; 50% to poly/colleges. 14% those going on to higher education went to courses in practical art; 43% in humanities/social sciences; and 43% in science/engineering.

Uniform School uniform worn throughout.

Houses/prefects Competitive houses. Prefects. Head boy and head of house and house prefects. Appointed by the head after consulting staff and senior boys. Headmaster's council.

Religion Mass on Sundays and Wednesdays. Daily evening prayer, grace at meals.

Social Dances, productions and charity concerts with the Ursuline Convent School; Thanet schools' sixth form debates. Annual ski trip with Ursuline Convent. Pupils allowed to bring own bike to school; day boys also motor vehicle. Meals formal. School book shop selling stationery supplies, small tuck shop. No tobacco/alcohol allowed.

Discipline No corporal punishment. Pupils failing to produce homework once might expect to do it in their spare time; those caught smoking cannabis on the premises should expect to be expelled. Normal smoking is fined – £5 for the first offence, £10 and £15 for the second and third.

Boarding 26% have own study bedroom, 67% share with others, 7% are in dormitories of 6+. Houses are a cross-section of the school. Resident SRN, school doctor visits weekly. Central dining room. Weekend exeats at discretion. Visits to local town allowed.

Alumni association is run by Rev Fr Augustine Coyle OSB, St Augustine's College.

Former pupils Alastair Stewart (ITN newscaster).

· St Bede's (Hailsham) ·

St Bede's School
The Dicker
Hailsham,
East Sussex
BN27 3QH
Tel 0323 843252

- Pupils 340
- Boys 12–19
  (Day/Board)
- Girls 12–19
  (Day/Board)
- Upper sixth 60

- Termly fees
  £1900 (Day)
  £3050 (Board)
- SHMIS
  Enquiries/application to
  the Headmaster

What it's like

Founded in 1978, it is set in the village of Upper Dicker in the countryside. The buildings and playing fields occupy four sites around this small village. The main building is 'The Dicker', a big country house with 20 acres (formerly the home of the egregious and notorious Horatio Bottomley). Nearby Camberlot Hall is one of three residences for boy boarders; in all the school covers some 65 acres. There has been steady expansion since foundation and in 13 years the school has increased in numbers from 22 to 340. During the last few years there has been a deliberate policy to increase the sixth form and enrolment to the lower sixth is very strong. In 1990 out of a total sixth of 130+, some 40 were in the upper sixth and 90 in the lower. Other developments are under way and its facilities are already very good. It enjoys a staff:pupil ratio of $1:7\frac{1}{2}$. The academic standards are high and many sixth formers go on to degree courses. European languages on offer are French, German, Italian and Spanish and there are regular exchanges with France, Germany and Spain. It is strong in music, drama and art, and has a very wide range of games (particularly strong in tennis), sports and activities. There are over 70 clubs and societies providing for almost every conceivable interest. Outdoor pursuits are very popular and the school has its own riding stables.

School profile

Pupils Age range 12–19; 340 pupils, 100 day (60 boys, 40 girls), 240 boarding (146 boys, 94 girls). Main entry ages 12, 13 and into sixth.

Entrance Common entrance and own exam used. Fully subscribed. No special skills or religious requirements. Parents not expected to buy text books; average extras £100 (boarding) £50 (day). No assisted places. Up to 12 scholarships/bursaries (academic, musical, artistic, sporting and for all-rounders), 75% to 20% of fees.

Parents 15+% are in industry or commerce. 10+% live within 30 miles; 30+% live overseas.

Staff Headmaster R A Perrin, in post for 12 years. 45 full time staff, 10 part time. Annual turnover 10%. Average age 38.

Academic work GCSE and A-levels. Chinese, Dutch, Arabic, photography, agricultural science, office skills and information technology are offered to GCSE or A-level. Average size of upper fifth 75; upper sixth 60. *GCSE:* on average, pupils pass 6+ subjects. *A-levels:* on average, pupils pass $2\frac{1}{2}$ subjects. *Computing facilities:* RML Nimbus network. *Special provi-*

674

sion: for EFL and specific learning difficulties.

European Community *Languages:* Dutch offered: to GCSE. French offered: to GCSE; AS-level; A-level. German offered: to GCSE; AS-level; A-level. Italian offered: GCSE; AS-level; A-level. Spanish offered: to GCSE; AS-level; A-level. 10–25% take GCSE in more than 1 EC language. *Exchanges:* Regular exchanges for pupils aged 14–18 to France, Germany, and Spain.

Senior pupils' non-academic activities *Music:* 160 learn a musical instrument, 20 to Grade 6 or above; 30 in school orchestra, 30 in school choir, 80 in choral society. *Drama and dance:* 3 major productions annually, 45 in school productions, 26 in other. 20 take GCSE, 15 A-level. *Art:* 27 take as non-examined subject; 90 take GCSE; 25 take A-level. Regular entrants to Art School. 60 in art club, 11 in photography club, 15 in ceramics club. 6 take GCSE photography. *Sport:* Soccer, rugby, squash, tennis, cricket, athletics, hockey, netball, rounders, swimming, fencing, badminton, archery, golf, cross-country, riding, dry ski-ing, sailing, windsurfing, judo, outdoor pursuits, shooting, volleyball, basketball, gymnastics, weight training, and table tennis available. 300 take non-compulsory sport (all sport is non-compulsory). 10 take GCSE exams. 18 represent county/country (tennis, swimming, ski-ing, rugby). *Other:* 30 take part in school community work schemes. Other activities include a computer club, 75 clubs and activities, including scientific, engineering, literary, art/craft, social activities in surrounding area, musical, etc.

Careers In 1990, 70% leavers went on to degree courses; 15% to art/drama/ music colleges; 10% to non-degree courses; 5% straight into careers. Of those going on to degree courses, 60% went to universities; 40% to poly/colleges. 10% those going on to higher education went to courses in practical art; 5% in drama/acting; 5% in music; 25% in humanities/social sciences; 5% in medicine; and 50% in science/engineering.

Uniform Uniformity of dress, except girls in sixth.

Houses/prefects Competitive houses. Prefects, head of school, head of house and house prefects – appointed by the Headmaster and housemasters.

Religion Multi-religious School Meetings on Sundays and mid-week; plus C of E, RC and Free Church services.

Social Sixth Form Industrial Conference every two years with five other local schools; musical and termly theatrical productions. Annual school ski-ing trip, French, German, and Spanish visits. Pupils allowed to bring own bike/horse to school. Meals self-service. No tobacco/alcohol allowed.

Discipline No corporal punishment. Pupils failing to produce homework once might expect work detention; detention and gating for misdemeanours; expulsion for any drug offence.

Boarding All sixth and upper fifth have study bedrooms, usually shared with 1 other; 35 in dormitories of 6+. Single sex houses (2 girls', 3 boys') 40–70, as competitive houses. School doctor visits every morning. Central dining room. 2 weekend exeats each term. Visits to local towns allowed.

Former pupils Clare Wood (Wightman Cup Player 1987 and Federation Cup 1989); Julie Salmon (Federation Cup player 1989).

· St Bees ·

St Bees School
The School House
St Bees
Cumbria
CA27 0DU
Tel 0946 822263

- Pupils 345
- Boys 11–18
  (Day/Board/Weekly)
- Girls 11–18
  (Day/Board/Weekly)
- Upper sixth 47

- Termly fees
  £1820 (Day)
  £2600 (Board)
  £2550 (Weekly)
- HMC
  Enquiries/application to
  the Headmaster

What it's like

Founded in 1583 by Edmund Grindal, Archbishop of Canterbury. Late in the 19th century it changed from being a day grammar to one mainly for boarders. It became fully co-educational in 1976. It has a particularly fine site of 150 acres in the pleasant valley of St Bees, and is unique among schools in having not only the sea and a magnificent beach within half a mile, but also easy access to the entire Lake District. A very healthy environment. There are fine gardens and ample playing fields and the buildings are handsome. The original school building (1587) is now the dining hall. The principal older buildings are made of St Bees sandstone. There have been substantial developments since 1954 and the school is now very well equipped. The purpose of the school is to develop the individual talents of each pupil while providing an education based on Christian principles. The school is small enough for every child to be known by all members of staff. Particular emphasis is placed on academic excellence and good personal relationships. Self-reliance, individuality and consideration for others are encouraged. The chapel is used frequently and worship in the Anglican tradition is compulsory. A large staff allows a staff:pupil ratio of about 1:8. Academic standards are high and results consistently good. Very many pupils proceed to degree courses each year. Considerable strength in music, drama (all juniors receive lessons in drama as part of the curriculum) and art. An excellent range of sports and games, including Eton fives and golf (the school has its own course). Plentiful extra-curricular activities are available. There is a large and flourishing CCF; many pupils take part in the Duke of Edinburgh's Award Scheme and considerable emphasis is placed on outdoor pursuits for which the environment is ideal.

School profile

Pupils Age range 11–18; 345 pupils, 179 day (102 boys, 77 girls), 166 boarding (91 boys, 75 girls). Main entry ages 11, 13 and into sixth. Approx 10% are children of former pupils. *Transfer from maintained schools:* 80% main intakes, plus 80% to sixth.

Entrance Common entrance and own exam used. Good all-round ability looked for; no religious requirements. Parents expected to buy text books; maximum extras £300, including music, excursions, clothing, GCSE, sundries. 84 assisted places. Scholarships/bursaries available.

Parents 15+% in industry or commerce. 30+% live within 30 miles; up to 10% live overseas.

Staff Headmaster P A Chamberlain, 3 years in post. 35 full time staff, 3 part time. Annual turnover 3%. Average age 40.

Academic work GCSE and A-levels. 21 GCSE and A-level subjects offered (including photography, A-level general studies). In 1991, 63 pupils in upper fifth, 47 in upper sixth. *GCSE:* in 1990, 87% upper fifth gained at least grade C in 5+ subjects; and 3% in 1–4 subjects. *A-levels:* 53% upper sixth passed in 4+ subjects;

676

24% in 3. 50% took science A-levels; 40% arts/humanities; 10% both. *Computing facilities:* Full facilities for computer studies and information technology. **European Community** *Languages:* French offered: to age 14; GCSE; AS-level; A-level. German offered: to age 14; GCSE; AS-level; A-level. 25–50% take GCSE in more than 1 EC language. *Exchanges:* Regular exchanges for pupils aged 14–18 to France and Germany. *Other:* EC students regularly on short stays in school for linguistic tuition and experience.

Senior pupils' non-academic activities *Sport:* Hockey, netball, tennis, squash, badminton, archery, gymnastics, rugby, cricket, rounders, basketball, canoeing, swimming, rock climbing, track and field, fives, golf available. *Other:* CCF, Duke of Edinburgh's Award Scheme. Other activities include a computer club, craft club, chess, drama, philately, environmental group, young farmers, debating, choir, orchestra, instrumental ensembles, photography, graphics and design.

Careers In 1990, 88% leavers went on to degree courses; 4% to art/drama/music colleges; 2% to non-degree courses; 5% straight into careers (eg company management training schemes); 1% other. Of those going on to degree courses, 3% went to Oxbridge; 55% to other universities; 40% to poly/colleges. 2% those going on to higher education went to courses in practical art; 2% in drama/acting; 2% in music; 45% in humanities/social sciences; 9% in medicine; and 40% in science/engineering.

Uniform School uniform worn throughout.

Houses/prefects Prefects, head boy/girl, head of house and house prefects – appointed by the Head.

Religion Religious worship compulsory.

Social Debates and lectures with other local schools. Trips abroad and exchanges with schools abroad. Pupils allowed to bring own bike to school. Meals formal. School shop. No tobacco allowed; alcohol only at supervised sixth form bar discos.

Discipline No corporal punishment. High standards of conduct are expected and enforced. The scale of punishments varies according to the nature of the offence; pupils may be suspended or expelled for breaches of major school rules.

Boarding Single sex houses, of approximately 60, divided by age. Resident qualified medical staff. Central dining room. Pupils can provide and cook own food. Termly exeats. Visits to local town allowed.

Former pupils Professor R A McCance; Air Chief Marshal Sir Augustus Walker; Rowan Atkinson.

· *St Benedict's* ·

St Benedict's School
54 Eaton Rise
London W5 2ES
Tel 081 997 9828

- Pupils 603
- Boys 11–18 (Day)
- Girls 16–18 (Day)
- Upper sixth 90

- Termly fees
  £1250 (Day)
- HMC
Enquiries/application to
the Headmaster

What it's like

Founded in 1902 by monks from Downside Abbey. The school is attached to the Benedictine Abbey and monastery created in Ealing and is governed by the Abbot and the Community. An urban site with some gardens. The buildings are mostly

20th century and provide good accommodation and facilities. The playing fields are a mile away; junior school on the same site. The education is Benedictine and inculcates the values and ethos of the order. The study of religion, Roman Catholic and ecumenical, is compulsory. The curriculum includes classics. Academic standards are high and results are impressive (many go on to degree courses each year). Exceptionally strong in music and art. A good record in sports and games. Plentiful clubs and societies. A substantial commitment to local community schemes and a creditable record in the Duke of Edinburgh's Award Scheme.

School profile

Pupils Age range 11–18; 603 day pupils (567 boys, 36 girls). Main entry ages 11 and 13 (boys); into sixth (boys and girls). Approx 8% are children of former pupils. Own junior school provides more than 20% of intake. *Transfer from maintained schools:* 45% main intakes, plus 8% to sixth.

Entrance Common entrance and own exam used. Oversubscribed. All round and academic skills required; pupils largely Roman Catholic. Maximum extras, £100. 80 assisted places. Discretionary scholarships/bursaries.

Parents 60+% live within 30 miles; up to 10% live overseas.

Staff Headmaster A J Dachs, in post for 5 years. 52 full time staff, 10 part time.

Academic work GCSE and A-levels. 17 subjects offered (general studies is taught but not examined). In 1990, 91 pupils in upper fifth, 90 in upper sixth. *GCSE:* in 1990, 76 upper fifth gained at least grade C in 8+ subjects; 12 in 5–7; and 4 in 1–4 subjects. *A-levels:* 1 upper sixth passed in 4+ subjects; 68 in 3; 12 in 2; and 3 in 1 subject. 20% took science A-levels; 60% arts/humanities; 20% both. *Computing facilities:* Research machines, Nimbus network. *Special provision:* Tailored to individual needs within school's capability.

European Community *Languages:* French offered: to age 14; GCSE; AS-level; A-level. German offered: to age 14; GCSE; AS-level; A-level. Spanish offered: to age 14; GCSE; AS-level; A-level. 25–50% take GCSE in more than 1 EC language. *Exchanges:* Regular exchanges for pupils aged 11–18 to France.

Senior pupils' non-academic activities *Music:* 240 learn a musical instrument, 7 to Grade 6 or above; 40 in school orchestra, 60 in school choir, 15 in jazz band. *Drama and dance:* 14 in school productions. Occasional pupil accepted for Drama/Dance Schools. *Art:* 235 take art as non-examined subject; 14 take GCSE; 16 take A-level. 1 accepted for Art School. 12 in general class. 28 belong to eg photographic club. *Sport:* Rugby, cricket, squash, golf, swimming, netball, tennis, table tennis, cross-country, and athletics available. 40–50 take non-compulsory sport. 1 represents England, 11 represent county (rugby, golf, skiing, ice-skating). *Other:* 40 take part in local community schemes. 40 have bronze Duke of Edinburgh's Award, 10 have silver and 1 has gold. 50–60 enter voluntary schemes after leaving school. Other activities include chess and mountaineering.

Careers In 1990, 70% leavers went on to degree courses; 3% to art/drama/music colleges; 2% to non-degree courses (eg apprenticeships); 5% straight into careers (eg merchant banking); 10% other. Of those going on to degree courses, 12% went to Oxbridge; 62% to other universities; 26% to poly/colleges. 3% those going on to higher education went to courses in practical art; 64% in humanities/social sciences; 8% in medicine; and 25% in science/engineering.

Uniform School uniform worn throughout.

Houses/prefects No competitive houses. Prefects and head boy/girl – appointed by the Head.

Religion Roman Catholic services.

Social Debating and other regional competitions. Ski trips, art visits, language trips, and exchanges. Pupils allowed to bring own car/bike/motorbike to school. Meals self-service. No tobacco/alcohol allowed.

Discipline No corporal punishment.

Pupils failing to produce homework once might expect to have to do it under supervision.
Alumni association is run by Mr E Shuldham, Hon Sec, Old Priorian Association, c/o the School.
Former pupils 1 Cabinet Minister.

· St Catherine's ·

St Catherine's School
Bramley
Guildford
Surrey GU5 0DF
Tel 0483 893363

- Pupils 460
- Boys None
- Girls 11–18
  (Day/Board)
- Upper sixth 51

- Termly fees
  £1450 (Day)
  £2375 (Board)
- GSA
Enquiries/application to
the Head

What it's like

Founded in 1885, it shares the same Royal Charter and Council as Cranleigh Boys' School though each has a separate governing body. It has a compact campus in the village of Bramley in the Surrey hills, three miles south of Guildford. The site comprises attractive grounds and gardens, plus excellent playing fields and sports/games facilities. The buildings are predominantly modern, red-brick and pleasant. A recent centenary building provides further facilities and accommodation for boarders. The sixth form is housed in separate, modern accommodation. It is a Church of England school with its own chapel. Religious knowledge is taught throughout the school to all girls, and there are regular services in chapel. Academic standards are high and results are good. Many sixth formers go on to degree courses. There is considerable emphasis on music, which is strong: three choirs, an orchestra, a wind band and a madrigal group. Drama and ballet also flourish. A standard range of sports and games is available and a number of clubs and societies cater for extra-curricular activities. The Duke of Edinburgh's Award Scheme is well supported and there are thriving social service groups.

School profile

Pupils Age range 11–18, 460 girls (284 day, 176 boarding). Main entry age 11. Own junior provides 50% intake. *Transfer from maintained schools:* 20% main intake.
Entrance Own entrance exam used. Scholarships and assisted places.
Staff Head J R Palmer, in post for 8 years.
Academic work GCSE and A-levels. 21 subjects offered (no A-level general studies). In 1990, 72 pupils in upper fifth, 51 in upper sixth. *GCSE:* in 1990, 70 upper fifth gained at least grade C in 8+ subjects; 4 in 5–7; and 1 in 1–4 subjects. *A-levels:* 42 upper sixth passed in 3 subjects; 7 in 2; and 2 in 1 subject. 12 took science A-levels; 19 arts/humanities; 18 both. *Computing facilities:* New computer room. 25 RM Nimbus machines on a network and several stand alone machines in some laboratories/classrooms.
European Community *Languages:* French offered: to age 14; GCSE; AS-level; A-level. German offered: to age 14; GCSE; A-level. Spanish offered: to age 14; GCSE; A-level. 10–25% take GCSE in more than 1 EC language. *Exchanges:* Regular exchanges for pupils aged 11–14 to France.
Careers In 1990, 80% leavers went on to degree courses; 16% to art/drama/music colleges; 4% to non-degree

courses. Of those going on to degree courses, 8% went to Oxbridge, 58% to other universities; 34% to poly/colleges. 4% those going on to higher education went to courses in practical art; 2% in drama/acting; 82% in humanities/social sciences; 2% in medicine; and 10% in science/engineering.

· *St Christopher (Letchworth)* ·

St Christopher School
Barrington Road
Letchworth
Hertfordshire SG6 3JZ
Tel 0462 679301
Fax 0462 481578

- Pupils 526
- Boys $2^1/_2$–18 (Day/ Board)
- Girls $2^1/_2$–18 (Day/ Board)
- Upper sixth 49

- Termly fees
  £1550 (Day)
  £2740 (Board)
  Enquiries/application to the Admissions Secretary

What it's like

Founded in 1915 in Ebenezer Howard's Garden City, the school was a pioneering concept in education that attracted progressive causes. For the first few years it was controlled by the Theosophical Educational Trust which practised ecumenicism long before such a movement became established. In the 1920s the school was developed to give expression to the child centred ideals of the World Education Fellowship becoming very much a 'family' school, under the guidance of Lyn and Eleanor Harris whose son continued their regime until 1980. This family, who are still involved with the school, have provided continuity of purpose and fostered what the Quakers call 'an answering to that of God in every child'. This is the central purpose of the school. There is a domestic village atmosphere with most of the buildings in the Garden City idiom and surrounded by attractive grounds. The school provides a complete education from infancy to adulthood. Children of one family, whatever their ages, can attend the same school. Forty members of the teaching staff have their own children at the school. The staff:pupil ratio is 1:10. There are also 26 part-time teachers, so the ratio is even more favourable. The school has long been noted for the value it places on the individual. It attracts children (and parents) with strongly independent attitudes, those who find pressures elsewhere restrictive and those who need special care and attention. The school does not believe in artificial competition in academic work; thus there are no subject or form orders and no prizes. The teaching is of a high standard and academic results are creditable. Many sixth formers proceed to degree courses each year, including Oxbridge. The school is strong in music, drama and art. There is a very wide range of sports, games and extra-curricular activities, with special emphasis on outdoor pursuits such as rock-climbing, orienteering, canoeing and hill-walking. There are major expeditions for all in each year group. The school has strong local support and its pupils are involved in a range of ventures among the local community, including the young, the old and the mentally ill. There are strong international links and regular exchanges with schools in France and Germany and visits by sixth formers to development projects in Rajastan.

School profile

Pupils Total age range $2^1/_2$–18; 526 pupils, 285 day (159 boys, 126 girls), 241 boarders (108 boys, 133 girls). Senior department 11–18, 359 pupils (188 boys, 171 girls). Main entry ages $2^1/_2$, 9, 11 and into sixth (boarding from age 7). 10% are children of former pupils. Own junior department provides 50% senior intake.

Transfer from maintained schools: 25% senior intake, plus 15% to sixth.

Entrance Own informal tests at an interview day. Oversubscribed. Selection based on the ability to respond to opportunities, not only academic but in the creative arts, in outdoor pursuits and to participate in the school's unusual system of self-government. No religious requirements (no communal worship at the school so attractive to parents who do not want this for their children). Parents expected to buy only examination set text books for literature.

Parents 15+% in the theatre, media, music etc; 15+% are doctors, lawyers etc; 15+% in industry; 15+% in education. 30+% live within 30 miles; 10+% live overseas.

Staff Head Colin Reid, in post for 9 years. 53 full time staff, 26 part time. Annual turnover 8%. Average age 37.

Academic work GCSE and A-levels. 22 subjects offered (including A-level: theatre studies, classical civilization, history of art; no general studies but several AS-levels). In 1990, 54 pupils in upper fifth, 41 in upper sixth (now 49). *GCSE:* in 1990, 16 upper fifth gained at least grade C in 8+ subjects; 19 in 5–7; and 19 in 1–4 subjects. *A-levels:* 6 upper sixth passed in 4+ subjects; 24 in 3; 8 in 2; and 2 in 1 subject. 25% took science A-levels; 60% arts/humanities; 15% both. *Computing facilities:* As a pilot school for the 'Education 2000' project, we have over 50 RM Nimbus machines on three networks with open access until 10pm. *Special provision:* for limited number of pupils of good general ability requiring dyslexic or EFL help (both categories greatly oversubscribed).

European Community *Languages:* French offered: to age 14; GCSE; AS-level; A-level. German offered: to age 14; GCSE; AS-level; A-level. Spanish offered: to age 14; GCSE; A-level. 25–50% take GCSE in more than 1 EC language. *Exchanges:* Regular exchanges for pupils aged 11–16 to France and Germany. *Other:* Some 12 EC pupils in school for 1–3 terms.

Senior pupils' non-academic activities *Music:* 60 learn a musical instrument, 10 to Grade 6 or above; 1–2

accepted for Music School. 30 play in school orchestra, 30 in choir, 6 pop groups; 1 in National Youth Orchestra. *Drama and dance:* 150 in school productions. 6 major productions pa and annual drama festival, giving scope to pupil playwrights and directors. 4 pa accepted for Drama/Dance Schools. *Art:* 25 take as non-examined subject; 25 take GCSE; 12 A-level. 4 pa accepted for Art School. 20 belong to eg photographic club. *Sport:* Wide range includes soccer and cricket for boys, lacrosse and netball for girls. Also squash, badminton, hockey, athletics. Strong emphasis on outdoor pursuits: all students introduced to rock climbing, orienteering, canoeing, hillwalking. Major expedition for all in each year group. 10 pa take exams in lifesaving. Occasional representation at county level in lacrosse, athletics, cricket. *Other:* Pupils are involved in a range of ventures with the young, the old and the mentally ill; also strongly encouraged to enter voluntary schemes after leaving school. Pupils extensively involved in routine tasks and responsibilities. Unusually wide age range gives much scope for older pupils to be involved helpfully with the little ones.

Careers In 1990, 55% leavers (from fifth and sixth forms) went on to degree courses; 15% to art/drama/music colleges; 20% to non-degree courses; 5% straight into careers; 5% other. Of those going on to degree courses, 8% went to Oxbridge, 52% to other universities; 40% to poly/colleges. 10% those going on to higher education went to courses in practical art; 10% in drama/acting; 5% in music; 45% in humanities/social sciences; 5% in medicine; and 25% in science/engineering.

Uniform School uniform not worn apart from games and PE.

Houses/prefects Competitive houses for games. Prefects ('major officials'), head boy and girl – all elected by single transferable vote. School Council in existence since 1920 with much importance attached to its debates and decisions.

Religion No communal worship. Significant period of silence in each assembly and staff meeting.

Social Occasional sixth form conferences with other schools. Strong links with a German school (3 exchanges a year and joint theatrical/expeditions, projects) and 2 French schools (3 exchanges a year). Pupils allowed to bring own bike to school. Meals self service. Diet is entirely wholefood vegetarian (no meat or fish allowed on campus). School shop. Alcohol allowed occasionally under staff supervision; no tobacco.

Discipline No corporal punishment. School strongly inclined towards nonviolent and pacifist solutions to conflict. For pupils failing to produce homework once there are extra work sessions twice a week after school so they may repeat the work or catch up; a decision to expel anyone caught smoking cannabis on the premises would depend on the circumstances.

Boarding Nearly all sixth form have own study bedroom, younger pupils in rooms (2–3 sharing). 8 houses, of 12–60, divided by age group, mixed sex. 2 resident qualified nurses. Central dining room for lunch; breakfast and supper in own houses. Fifth and sixth form allowed to provide and cook own food. 2 weekend exeats each term, plus half-term. Visits to local town allowed daily after school from age 11.

Alumni association is run by Philip Wilde, Willowdown, Smith's End, Barley, Royston, Herts.

Former pupils Paul Hamlyn, Ralph Halpern (entrepreneurs); Michael Winner (film producer); Neil Coles (golfer); Shaun Slovo, Jonathan Croall, Jenny Diski (authors); Gavin Campbell (actor).

· St Clare's ·

School of St Clare	• Pupils 240	• Termly fees
Polwithen	• Boys 3–11 only	£1087 (Day)
Penzance	• Girls 3–18	£2035 (Board)
Cornwall TR18 4JR	(Day/Board/Weekly)	£1899 (Weekly)
Tel 0736 63271	• Upper sixth 8	• GSA, Woodard
		Enquiries/application to
		the Headmaster

What it's like

Founded in 1889, it moved to its present premises in 1918 and passed into the hands of the Woodard Corporation in 1928. It has a fine site in a residential area on the edge of Penzance, overlooking Mount's Bay. The main building is a big converted country house in 10 acres. Numerous modern extensions and facilities include a music school, 4 craft workshops and comfortable boarding accommodation. Junior school combined. Chapel and daily services play an important part in the school's life. It is a small, happy school with a healthy environment. Students come to it from all over the UK and the world. A sound general education is given and a number of leavers go on to degree courses. Strong drama and music departments. A good range of games and activities. Emphasis on outdoor pursuits. A sound record in the Duke of Edinburgh's Award Scheme; takes part in Ten Tors.

School profile

Pupils Total age range 3–18; 240 pupils, 163 day (38 boys, 125 girls), 77 boarding (7 boys, 70 girls). Senior department 11–18, 133 girls. Main entry ages 3–11 (boys), 3–16 (girls). Approx 10% are children of former pupils. Own junior school provides more than 40% of intake. *Transfer from maintained schools:* 30% senior intake.

Entrance Own entrance exam used. Oversubscribed. No special skills or religious requirements. Parents not expected to buy text books; other extras vary, from nil. No assisted places. 4–5 academic, sixth form and music scholarships, some clergy bursaries and reduction for service families – up to 50% of fees.

Parents 15+% are farmers; 15+% in the armed services; 15+% in industry or commerce. 60+% live within 30 miles, up to 10% live overseas.

Staff Headmaster Ian Halford, in post for 5 years. 18 full time staff, 20 part time (including music). Average age 40.

Academic work GCSE and A-levels. 15 subjects offered (no A-level general studies). In 1990, 23 pupils in upper fifth, 8 in upper sixth. *GCSE:* in 1990, 9 upper fifth gained at least grade C in 8+ subjects; 6 in 5–7; and 8 in 1–4 subjects. *A-levels:* All upper sixth passed in 2 arts/ humanities subjects. *Computing facilities:* 11 computers. *Special provision:* Special English classes.

European Community *Languages:* French offered: to age 14; GCSE; A-level. German offered: to age 14; GCSE; A-level. Spanish offered: to age 14; GCSE. 10–25% take GCSE in more than 1 EC language. *Exchanges:* Regular exchanges for pupils aged 11–16 to France. *Other:* 2 French girls spent a year in school.

Senior pupils' non-academic activities *Music:* Many learn a musical instrument, 6 to Grade 6 or above, 22 in school orchestra; 130 in 3 school choirs; 4 in county youth orchestra. *Drama and dance:* Many in school productions (a musical each year). *Art:* 17 take GCSE; 3 A-level. *Sport:* Hockey, netball, football, gymnastics, volleyball, cross-country, trampolining, cricket, tennis, athletics, swimming, judo, sailing, horseriding available. Many take non-compulsory sport. 4 pupils have represented county. *Other:* Some take part in local community schemes. 15 have bronze Duke of Edinburgh's Award, 4 have silver, 1 has gold. Other activities include archery, chess, judo, modern dance, Army Cadet Force, drama, canoeing.

Careers On average, 80% leavers go on to degree courses; 20% other. Of those going on to degree courses, all go to poly/ colleges, to courses in humanities/social sciences.

Uniform School uniform worn except the sixth.

Houses/prefects Competitive houses. Prefects, head girl, head of house and house prefects – appointed by the head/ staff and houses. School Council.

Religion Daily worship in school chapel; Sunday church for boarders.

Social Musical activities at YMCA. Organised trips abroad including ski-ing. Pupils allowed to bring own bike to school. Meals formal. School shop. No tobacco/ alcohol allowed.

Discipline No corporal punishment. Pupils failing to produce homework once might expect detention; those caught smoking or drinking on the premises could expect suspension initially, expulsion for repeated offence.

Boarding Sixth form have own study bedrooms. 80% in dormitories of 2–4, 20% in dormitories of 6; not in houses. Matrons are medically trained, GP on call. Central dining room. 2 or 3 weekend exeats each term. Visits to local town allowed.

Alumni association run by Mrs A Thomas, Nansloe Manor, Helston, Cornwall.

Former pupils Dr Caroline Jackson (MEP); Dr Susan Standring (lecturer in anatomy, Univ of London).

· St Columba's (Kilmacolm) ·

St Columba's School	• Pupils 552	• Termly fees
Duchal Road	• Boys 3–18 (Day)	£936 (Day)
Kilmacolm	• Girls 3–18 (Day)	• SHA, HAS
Renfrewshire	• Higher year 45	Enquiries/application to
Tel 05058 72238		the Rector

What it's like

Founded in 1897, its site is in the small village of Kilmacolm. The primary and secondary buildings are about a quarter of a mile apart. The surrounding countryside is delightful. The main building was erected in 1897 and there have been many extensions since. Facilities and accommodation are now very good. It became fully co-educational in 1978. Some religious services are compulsory. A sound general education is provided and results are highly creditable. Many go on to degree courses each year. There is music, drama and art, and a range of games, sports and extra-curricular activities. The school has a promising record in the Duke of Edinburgh's Award Scheme.

School profile

Pupils Total age range 3–18; 552 day pupils (215 boys, 337 girls). Senior department 11–18, 305 pupils (110 boys, 195 girls). Main entry ages 3, 11 and into sixth. Own primary dept provides more than 80% of senior intake. *Transfer from maintained schools:* 15% senior intake, plus 5% to sixth.

Entrance Own entrance exam used. Oversubscribed. No special skills or religious requirements. Parents not expected to buy text books. 35 assisted places.

Parents 15+% are in industry or commerce.

Staff Rector Andrew H Livingstone, in post for 4 years. 43 full time staff, 7 part time. Annual turnover 2%. Average age 42.

Academic work S-grade and Highers, CSYS. 15 subjects offered (no A-level general studies). In 1990, 45 pupils in S-grade year, 34 in Higher year (now 45), 10 in CSYS year. *S-grade:* in 1990, 18 pupils passed in 8+ subjects; 24 in 5–7; and 3 in 1–4 subjects. *Highers:* 9 pupils passed in 5+ or more subjects; 6 in 4; 6 in 3; 7 in 2; 3 in 1 subject. *CSYS:* 4 pupils passed in 3 subjects; 3 in 2; and 2 in 1 subject. 67% took science CSYS; 33% arts/humanities. *Computing facilities:* Computer laboratory.

European Community *Languages:* French offered: to age 14; S-grade; Higher; CSYS. German offered: to age 14; S-grade; Higher; CSYS. Spanish offered: to Scotvec module. 10–25% take S-grade in more than 1 EC language.

Senior pupils' non-academic activities *Music:* 20 learn a musical instrument, 4 to Grade 6 or above; 20 in school orchestras, 50 in choirs. *Drama and dance:* 20 in school productions. 2 take Grade 6 in ESB, RAD etc. *Art:* 10 take S-grade; 7 Higher; 1 A-level. 1 accepted for Art School. *Sport:* Rugby, hockey, tennis, squash, swimming, badminton, cricket, athletics available. 40 take non-compulsory sport. *Other:* 20 have bronze Duke of Edinburgh's Award, 9 have silver. 20 participate in debating/public speaking competitions.

Careers In 1990, 75% leavers went on to degree courses; 6% to art/drama/music colleges; 6% to non-degree courses (eg secretarial); 5% straight into careers; 8% other. Of those going on to degree courses, 66% went to universities; 34% to poly/colleges. 4% those going on to higher education went to courses in practical art; 58% in humanities/social sciences; 12% in medicine; and 26% in science/engineering.

Uniform School uniform worn throughout.

Houses/prefects Competitive houses. Prefects, head boy/girl, head of house and house prefects – elected by fifth and sixth forms.

Religion Compulsory morning prayers 3 times a week.

Social School dances, Burns' Supper with neighbouring school. Organised trips to France, Germany and ski-ing; annual sixth form trip; rugby and hockey tours. Meals self service. School tuck shop. No tobacco/alcohol allowed.

Discipline No corporal punishment. Pupils failing to produce homework once might expect additional work; those caught smoking cannabis on the premises could expect to be excluded.

· *St David's (Ashford)* ·

St David's School
Church Road
Ashford
Middlesex TW15 3DZ
Tel 0784 252494

- Pupils 450
- Boys Joint sixth
- Girls 5–18
  (Day/Board/Weekly)
- Upper sixth 30

- Termly fees
  £1250 (Day)
  £2150 (Board)
  £2025 (Weekly)
- GSA
  Enquiries/application to
  the Headmistress

What it's like

Founded in 1716 by the Most Honourable and Loyal Society of Ancient Britons in order to provide an education for the children of Welsh parentage in London. In 1857 it moved to its present site in Ashford. The first patron was the Prince of Wales and the Society remains under royal patronage. It has a very agreeable site of 30 acres (with a lake) on the outskirts of Ashford. The site also accommodates the junior school. The main building, a very handsome one of stone in the collegiate tradition of architecture, stands in beautiful gardens. There is also a fine chapel and additional modern buildings which are well appointed and well equipped. A broad general education is provided and results appear to be creditable. Joint A-level teaching with Halliford Boys' School. Music is strong: half the school learn an instrument and there are two choirs. Drama is also well supported. A standard range of sports and games is available. Tennis is particularly popular. There is a notable commitment to the Duke of Edinburgh's Award Scheme and many pupils have been highly successful. A good deal of local community service work is done.

School profile

Pupils Total age range 5–18, 450 girls (day and boarding). Senior department 11–18; sixth form joint with Halliford Boys School. Main entry ages 5 and 11. *Transfer from maintained schools:* 30% main intake at 11, plus 20% to sixth.

Entrance Own assessment used. Bursaries, scholarships.

Staff Headmistress Mrs Judith G Osborne, in post for 5 years.

Academic work GCSE and A-levels plus vocational (RSA, C&G etc). 19 GCSE subjects offered; 18 at A-level (including theatre studies, classical civilisation; no A-level general studies). In 1990, 37 pupils in upper fifth, 12 girls in upper sixth (joint with Halliford Boys' School). *GCSE:* in 1990, 8 upper fifth gained at least grade C in 8+ subjects; 14 in 5–7; and 15 in 1–4 subjects. *A-levels:* 5 upper sixth passed in 3 subjects; 2 in 2; and 5 in 1 subject. 33% took science A-levels; 66% arts/humanities. *Computing facilities:* IT facility. *Special provision:* 2 (private) tutors for EFL and dyslexia.

European Community *Languages:* French offered: to age 14; GCSE; AS-level; A-level. German offered: to age 14; GCSE; AS-level; A-level. Spanish offered: to GCSE; AS-level; A-level. 50–75% take GCSE in more than 1 EC language. *Exchanges:* Regular exchanges for pupils aged 11–16 to France and Germany. *Other:* Annual short visit by Spanish girls and ad hoc arrangements for EL girls in sixth.

Careers In 1990, 75% leavers went on to degree courses; 5% to art/drama/music colleges; 10% to non-degree courses (eg secretarial, personnel); 5% straight into careers (eg civil service); 5% other. Of those going on to degree courses, 5% went to Oxbridge, 75% to other universities; 20% to poly/colleges. 5% those going on to higher education went to courses in practical art; 45% in humanities/social sciences; and 50% in science/engineering.

· St David's (Brecon) ·

St David's Convent
Brecon
Powys
LD3 7DN
Tel 0874 2080/4474

- Pupils 185
- Boys 3–11 only
- Girls 3–18
  (Day/Board/Weekly)
- Upper sixth 5

- Termly fees
  £586 (Day)
  £1258 (Board)
  £1224 (Weekly)
  Enquiries/application to
  Sister Finbarr Muckley

What it's like

In 1948 the Ursuline Order (founded in 1535 for the education of children) took over St David's from the Sisters of the Holy Ghost who had established a school in 1903. It is a single-site establishment in one of the most attractive of small Welsh country towns set in magnificent countryside near the Brecon Beacons. Accommodation and facilities are good. The school comprises a kindergarten and preparatory department for boys, and a senior department for girls only. Fees are remarkably low. It is a Roman Catholic school, but thoroughly ecumenical and takes pupils of all denominations. Great emphasis is given to religious training and religious instruction is provided at all levels. In the senior school classes are Roman Catholic and Protestant. A sound general education is given and high academic (and moral) standards are aimed for. Sixth form results are impressive; a high proportion for a small school go on to degree courses. Music, drama and art are well supported, and there is an adequate range of games, sports and extra-curricular activities. Local community schemes (especially for the aged) are very active.

School profile

Pupils Total age range 3–18; 185 pupils, 125 day (30 boys, 95 girls); 60 boarding girls. Main entry ages 3 (boys and girls), 11 and into sixth (girls). Some 10% are children of former pupils. *Transfer from maintained schools:* 90% senior intake, none to sixth.

Entrance Own entrance exam used. Not oversubscribed. School caters for children of mixed abilities. No religious requirements. Parents not expected to buy text books. 1 full, or several partial, scholarships/bursaries at 11+, maximum value day school fees.

Parents 15+% in the armed services; 15+% are doctors, lawyers etc; 15+% are farmers. 30+% live within 30 miles; 10+% live overseas.

Staff Head Sister Finbarr Muckley, in post for 8 years. 11 full time staff, 9 part time. Annual turnover very small. Average age 35–40.

Academic work GCSE and A-levels; Cambridge EFL examinations. 14 subjects offered (no A-level general studies). In 1990, 8 pupils in upper fifth, 5 in upper sixth. *GCSE:* in 1989, 3 upper fifth gained at least grade C in 8+ subjects; 8 in 5–7; and 4 in 1–4 subjects. *A-levels:* 1 upper sixth passed in 3 subjects; 3 in 2; and 1 in 1 subject. 4 took arts/humanities A-levels; 1 both arts and science. *Computing facilities:* Computer classes for all. *Special provision:* EFL specialist teacher.

European Community *Languages:* French offered: to age 14; GCSE; A-level. German offered: to age 14; GCSE. Italian offered: to age 14; GCSE. Up to 10% take GCSE in more than 1 EC language. *Exchanges:* Regular exchanges for pupils aged 11–16 to France.

Senior pupils' non-academic activities *Music:* 40 learn a musical instrument, 6 to Grade 6 or above; 1 accepted for Music School. 10 pupils play in school orchestra, 40 in choir. *Drama and dance:* 50 in school productions. *Art:* All up to third form take as non–examined subject; 20 take GCSE; 4 A-level. 3 accepted for Art School. *Sport:* Netball, hockey, rounders, tennis; cricket for boys. 25 take part in non-compulsory sport; 15 take exams, eg swimming. 1 pupil represents county (netball); county netball champions in most age groups. *Other:* 6 have bronze Duke of Edinburgh's Award. 20 in local community schemes. Other activities include a computer club, Red Cross, guides, rangers, riding, hospital visiting.

Careers In 1990, 50% leavers went on to degree courses; 25% to art/drama/music colleges; 25% to non-degree courses. Of those going on to degree courses, 50% went to universities; 50% to poly/colleges. 10% those going on to higher education went to courses in practical art; 10% in music; 45% in humanities/social sciences; and 35% in science/engineering.

Uniform School uniform worn throughout.

Houses/prefects Competitive houses. Head girl, head of house and house prefects.

Religion Christian worship compulsory.

Social Joint choir with local boys' public school. Organised trips abroad and exchange systems. Pupils allowed to bring own car/bike to school (but not encouraged). Lunch self service, other meals formal. No tobacco/alcohol allowed.

Discipline No corporal punishment. Pupils failing to produce homework once might expect a verbal reprimand; those caught smoking cannabis on the premises could expect to be reported to parents (never occurred).

Boarding Sixth form have own study bedroom, if wished. Resident qualified nurse. Central dining room. Exeats each Sunday afternoon; home at quarter terms. Visits to local town allowed by sixth formers; younger girls with permission and in company of an older girl.

Alumni association is run by Sister Finbarr Muckley, c/o the school.

· St Denis and Cranley ·

St Denis and Cranley
School for Girls
Ettrick Road
Edinburgh EH10 5BJ
Tel 031 229 1500

- Pupils 230
- Boys None
- Girls 3–18
  (Day/Board/Weekly)
- Higher year 34

- Termly fees
  £1055 (Day)
  £2120 (Board/
  Weekly)
- GSA
  Enquiries/application to
  the Headmistress

What it's like

The school is a result of an amalgamation in 1979. St Denis was founded in 1855. For the first few years it was known by the name of each headmistress until the appointment, in 1908, of Miss Bourdass, a member of the staff of La Maison d'Education de la Legion d'Honneur, a school founded by Napoleon in the Paris suburb of St Denis. Cranley was founded in 1871 as Brunstane School in the Edinburgh suburb of Joppa. The present school is sited in a pleasant, residential district of Edinburgh. All buildings are on one site forming, with four boarding houses, a compact campus with fine lawns, trees, gardens and playing fields. It is quiet and spacious and well equipped. As it is a very small school it enjoys a happy, friendly and family atmosphere. The staff:pupil ratio is 1:10. A sound general education is provided and results are good. Many pupils go on to degree courses each year (quite a high proportion for a small school). There is quite a big commitment to music, drama and art. There is a good range of sports and games and a plentiful variety of extra-curricular activities. Quite a substantial commitment to local community services and an impressive record in the Duke of Edinburgh's Award Scheme.

School profile

Pupils Total age range 3–18; 230 girls, 135 day, 95 boarding. Senior department 12–18, 160 girls. Main entry ages 5, 9, 12 and into sixth. Approx 4% are children of former pupils. *Transfer from maintained schools:* 60% senior intake, plus 80% to sixth.

Entrance Own entrance exam used. Not oversubscribed. No special skills or religious requirements but pupils expected to participate in morning assembly and RE classes. Parents not expected to buy text books; maximum extras £80 (lunch day girls), £150 (boarders, pocket money, expeditions etc), plus music tuition, riding, skiing etc. 15 assisted places. 5 scholarships pa including art, music and science, £525–£260 per term. Reductions for daughters of clergy and forces.

Parents 15+% in armed services; 15+% are doctors, lawyers etc; 15% in industry or commerce. 30+% live within 30 miles; 10+% live overseas.

Staff Headmistress Mrs Jennifer M Munro, in post for 6 years. 18 full time staff, 7 part time plus music staff. Annual turnover 2%. Average age 44.

Academic work S-grade, Highers, A-levels and CSYS. 17 subjects offered (no A-level general studies). In 1989, 30 pupils in O-grade year, 25 in Higher year, 15 in A-level/CSYS year. *O-grade:* in 1989, 27 pupils gained at least grade 3 in 5–7 subjects; 3 in 1–4 subjects. *Highers:* 8 pupils passed in 5+ subjects; 3 in 4, 10 in 3, 3 in 2, 1 in 1 subject. *A-levels:* 2 pupils passed in 3 subjects; 5 in 2; and 5 in 1 subject. 40% took science A-levels; 40% arts/humanities; 20% both. *Computing facilities:* 7 BBC computers. *Special provision:* Qualified learning support teacher and part time EFL help.

688

Senior pupils' non-academic activities *Music:* 30 learn a musical instrument, 4 to Grade 6 or above, 1 accepted for Music School. 15 in school orchestra, 20 in choir. *Drama and dance:* 20–30 in school productions, 3 up to Grade 6 ESB, RAD etc, 1 accepted for Drama School, 1 in Scottish Youth Theatre. *Art:* All take as non-examined subject; 16 S-grade; 8 Higher; 3 A-level; 3 accepted for Art School. 8 belong to photographic club, 12 in art and craft club. *Sport:* Hockey, tennis, squash, badminton, athletics, trampolining, basketball, volleyball, swimming available. 50 take non-compulsory sport; 10 life-saving exams. 1 pupil represents county/country (skiing, hockey, squash). *Other:* 10 take part in local community schemes. 12 have bronze Duke of Edinburgh's Award, 6 have silver and 3 gold. 5 Ranger guides. 2 enter voluntary schemes after leaving; 20 work for national charities. Other activities include a computer club, pre-driving class, driving lessons arranged, chess, Scripture Union, geographical society, local Guide companies and Brownie packs, school community services club.

Careers 2 part time careers advisers. Annual average accepted for *arts and humanities degree courses* at Oxbridge, 1; other universities, 4; polytechnics/colleges, 4. *science and engineering degree courses* at universities, 8; medical school, 1; polytechnics/colleges, 3. *other general training courses*, 8. Average going straight into careers in armed services, approx 1 every three years; the church, approx 1 every three years; music/drama, 1.

Traditional school careers are medicine, nursing and para-medicine.

Uniform School uniform worn; optional in sixth form.

Houses/prefects Competitive houses. Prefects, head girl and head of house – elected by peers, staff and Head. School Council.

Religion Compulsory morning assembly (Hindus, Muslims etc may opt out but in practice do not).

Social English Speaking Union debates, sporting fixtures, occasional joint production, combined careers talks, Geographical Association etc with other schools. Trips to Germany, France, Spain; visiting schools from USA, New Zealand, Austria. Meals formal. School shop twice-weekly. No tobacco/alcohol allowed.

Discipline No corporal punishment. Pupils failing to produce homework once would have a warning; expulsion could follow a serious offence but it could depend on the effect of the offence on others.

Boarding 4% have own study bedroom. Houses include a junior and a sixth form one. Day time nurse, usually one medically-trained house staff member. Central dining room. 3 weekend exeats plus mid-term. Visits to local town allowed.

Alumni association run by The Secretary, St Denis & Cranley Association, c/o the School.

Former pupils Hannah Gordon, actress.

· St Dominic's (Brewood) ·

St Dominic's School
32 Bargate Street
Brewood
Stafford ST19 9BA
Tel 0902 850248

- Pupils 504
- Boys None
- Girls 3–18 (Day)
- Upper sixth 22

- Termly fees £927 (Day)
Enquiries/application to Secretary

What it's like

Founded in 1920 by the English Dominican Sisters and administered by them until 1975 when a board of directors took over the organisation. In 1984 the board bought the school from the Dominican order. It has a 9-acre site in the very attractive village of Brewood and its buildings, accommodation and facilities (including sporting facilities) are very good. A sound general education is given. The Christian ethos underpins all school activities. Academic results are good, particularly in English, home economics, science and languages; many sixth form leavers go on to degree courses. Very strong indeed in music and drama. A fair range of sport, games and activities. Successful participation in the Duke of Edinburgh's Award Scheme, Young Enterprise and sports tournaments.

School profile

Pupils Total age range 3–18; 504 day girls. Senior department 11–18, 341 girls. Main entry ages 3, 11 and into sixth. Approx 4% are children of former pupils. *Transfer from maintained schools:* 28% senior intake, plus 4% to sixth.

Entrance Own entrance exam used. No special skills (apart from national curriculum requirements at 11). Parents not expected to buy text books. 10 scholarships/bursaries for sixth form, £450–£100 per term.

Parents 15+% in industry or commerce; 15+% are doctors, lawyers, etc.

Staff Head Mrs K Butwilowska. 30 full time staff, 7 part time. Annual turnover 8%. Average age 40.

Academic work GCSE and A-levels (including A-level general studies). In 1989, 57 pupils in upper fifth, 22 in upper sixth. *GCSE:* in 1989, 37 upper fifth gained at least grade C in 8+ subjects; 17 in 5–7; and 2 in 1–4 subjects. *A-levels:* 9 upper sixth passed in 4+ subjects; 2 in 3; 6 in 2; and 4 in 1 subject. 9 took science A-levels; 6 arts/humanities; 7 both. *Computing facilities:* Facilities for groups of 20 pupils. GCSE; AEB practical and City & Guilds exams taken yearly.

Senior pupils' non-academic activities *Music:* 80 learn a musical instrument, 6 to Grade 6 or above; 30 in school orchestra, 60 in school choir, 40 in folk group; 1 in National Youth Orchestra, 3 in local amateur orchestra. *Drama and dance:* 40 in school productions, 22 take GCSE drama, 120 in speech and drama class; 4 up to Grade 6 in ESB, RAD and Guildhall, 1 has ESB advanced certificate, 74 have private speech and drama study. 100 enter local festivals. 1 has gone on to holiday puppet theatre. *Art:* 26 take GCSE; 4 take A-level. *Sport:* Hockey, netball, gymnastics, table tennis, badminton available. 150 take non-compulsory sport. 20–30 take exams, eg gymnastics, swimming. 6–7 represent county (golf, tennis, swimming, horse riding). *Other:* 17 have bronze Duke of Edinburgh's Award and 6 have silver.

Careers 1 full time adviser. Annual average accepted for *arts and humanities degree courses* at Oxbridge, 4; other universities, 10; polytechnics/colleges, 6. *science and engineering degree courses* at universities, 5; medical schools, 3; polytechnics/colleges, 5. BEd, 2. *other general training courses*, 40. Average going straight into careers in industry, 30; civil service, 5; music/drama, 5.

Uniform School uniform worn throughout.

Houses/prefects Competitive houses. Prefects, head girl and head of house – elected by the school.

Religion Assembly compulsory. Optional Mass and prayer groups.

Social Trips to France and Austria. Sixth form pupils allowed to bring own car to school. Meals formal. Drinks machines. No tobacco/alcohol allowed.

Discipline No corporal punishment. Pupils failing to produce homework once might expect detention in order to complete work on time; unethical conduct merits expulsion – no one has ever smoked.

Alumni association is run by Mr J D Walters, c/o the School.

· St Dominic's (Stone) ·

St Dominic's Priory
School
21 Station Road
Stone
Staffordshire ST15 8EN
Tel 0785 814181

- Pupils 511
- Boys 4–7 only
  (Day)
- Girls 4–18
  (Day)
- Upper sixth 15

- Termly fees
  £695 (Day)
- ISAI, CCSS, CTF
  Enquiries/application to
  the Secretary

What it's like

Founded in 1934 and conducted by the English Dominican Sisters, a Roman Catholic religious order. It has an agreeable urban site with gardens and well-appointed buildings. There are two main buildings: the senior school and the Croft (juniors), plus the nearby Croftside (nursery). The moral and religious training of the pupils has a high priority. There is a good deal of emphasis on religious instruction, prayer and worship. All pupils take religious studies at GCSE level. Preference is given to RCs but other denominations are welcome. The staff:pupil ratio is 1:21. A sound general education is provided and results are creditable. Many sixth formers proceed to degree courses each year. There is some music, and drama productions in the third year. An adequate range of sports and games and some extra-curricular activities. Some commitment to local community services and a promising record in the Duke of Edinburgh's Award Scheme. Fees are astonishingly low.

School profile

Pupils Total age range 4–18; 511 day pupils (39 boys, 463 girls). Senior department 11–18, 292 girls. Main entry ages 4 (boys and girls); 11 and into sixth (girls). Approx 10% are children of former pupils. *Transfer from maintained schools:* 30% senior intake.

Entrance Own entrance exam used. Oversubscribed. No special skills; preference given to RCs. Parents expected to buy text books; other extras optional. Few bursaries, value according to need.

Parents 15+% are doctors, lawyers etc; 15+% in industry or commerce. 60+% live within 30 miles.

Staff Headmistress Sister Mary Henry, in post for 4 years. 24 full time staff, 23 part time. Annual turnover, 2%.

Academic work GCSE and A-levels. 19 subjects offered (including Italian, A-level general studies). In 1991, 53 pupils in upper fifth, 15 in upper sixth. *GCSE:* in 1990, 29 upper fifth gained at least grade C in 8+ subjects; 22 in 5–7; and 12 in 1–4

691

subjects. *A-levels:* 2 upper sixth passed in 4+ subjects; 8 in 3; 3 in 2 subjects. 2 took science A-levels; 6 arts/humanities; 5 both. *Computing facilities:* Nimbus RM network for senior use. BBC computers in various classrooms; meteasat receiver. *Special provision:* Visits to Dyslexia Institute (5 minutes walk).

European Community *Languages:* French offered: to age 14; GCSE; A-level. German offered: to GCSE. Italian: to age 14; GCSE; A-level. 10–25% take GCSE in more than 1 EC language. *Exchanges:* Regular exchanges for pupils aged 14–16 to Belgium, France and Germany.

Senior pupils' non-academic activities *Music:* 18 learn a musical instrument, 5 to Grade 6 or above, 1 accepted for Music School, 6 in school orchestra; 9, choir; 6, madrigal group. *Drama and dance:* Drama productions in 3rd year; Silver Award for speech and drama. *Art:* 30 take GCSE, some take A-level Textiles and go on to career in textiles, 10 accepted for Art School. *Sport:* Swimming, riding, netball, tennis, dancing, badminton, table tennis available (indoor tennis centre to LTA standards). 69 take non-compulsory sport. 4 represent county (tennis, netball). *Other:* 8 take part in local community schemes. 36 have bronze Duke of Edinburgh's Award and 4 gold. Other activities include a computer club, chess club, recorder group, drama club and debating society, Greek club.

Careers In 1990, 55% leavers went on to degree courses; 5% to art/drama/music colleges; 15% to non-degree courses (eg secretarial, finishing); 5% straight into careers (eg dental assistant, banking); 21% other (eg sixth form colleges, boarding schools). Of those going on to degree courses, 67% went to universities; 33% to poly/colleges. 10% those going on to higher education went to courses in practical art; 80% in humanities/social sciences; and 10% in medicine.

Uniform School uniform worn throughout.

Houses/prefects Competitive houses. Prefects, head girl, head of house and house prefects elected by staff.

Religion Compulsory morning assembly; occasional mass.

Social Organised ski-ing, French language and Italian trips abroad. Meals self service. No tobacco/alcohol allowed.

Discipline No corporal punishment. Pupils failing to produce homework once might expect extra work in lunch hour.

Alumni association run by Miss Caroline Handforth, Coppice Farmhouse, Longton Road, Stone, Staffordshire.

Former pupils Lord Stafford; Hilaire Belloc's daughters; Hilary Pepler's grandchildren.

· St Dunstan's (Catford) ·

St Dunstan's College
Stanstead Road
Catford
London SE6 4TY
Tel 081 690 1274

- Pupils 810
- Boys 7–18
  (Day)
- Girls None
- Upper sixth 69

- Termly fees
  £1150 (Day)
- HMC
Enquiries/application to
the Admissions
Secretary

What it's like

Founded in 1888, it is urban and single-site and has big playing fields on site. Many additions have been made to the original and striking Victorian building and a new building and improvement programme is currently under way; facilities are very good. Preparatory and junior school combined. The main emphasis in the school is on the need to develop the all-round qualities of a pupil in and out of the classroom.

There is much stress on individual pastoral care and close links between home and school. The academic standards are high and results are good. A big sixth form. Many leavers go on to degree courses each year. There is a very strong music department (musicians are especially welcome); quite strong drama and art. A good range of sport and games, with high standards (quite a lot of representatives at county level). A large, strong CCF contingent and a very substantial commitment to local community schemes.

School profile

Pupils Total age range 7–18; 810 day boys. Senior department 11–18, 640 boys. Main entry ages 7, 11 and into sixth. Approx 7% are children of former pupils.

Entrance Own entrance exam used, occasionally common entrance. Oversubscribed. Musicians and genuine all-rounders especially welcome. Parents not expected to buy text books; extras include subscriptions, music and some sports coaching. 185 assisted places. 12 scholarships/bursaries pa, full fees to one-sixth fees.

Parents 15+% in industry or commerce; 15+% are doctors, lawyers, etc.

Staff Headmaster B D Dance, in post for 18 years. 62 full time staff, 6 part time. Annual turnover 5–6%. Average age 40.

Academic work GCSE and A-levels. 16 subjects offered; (no A-level general studies). In 1990, 115 pupils in upper fifth, 73 in upper sixth (now 69). *GCSE:* in 1990, 51 upper fifth gained at least grade C in 8+ subjects; 34 in 5–7; and 29 in 1–4 subjects. *A-levels:* 4 upper sixth passed in 4+ subjects; 49 in 3; 13 in 2; and 6 in 1 subject. 21 took science A-levels; 37 arts/humanities; 16 both. *Computing facilities:* Newly-equipped IT centre, with 16 workstations; on-line facilities for all science, maths and geography departments (also for lower school and prep department). *Special provision:* Private tuition for dyslexic pupils with specialist, college recommended teachers.

European Community *Languages:* French offered: to age 14; GCSE; A-level. German offered: to GCSE; AS-level; A-level. Italian offered: non-examined subject. Spanish offered: to A-level. 50–75% take GCSE in more than 1 EC language. *Other:* Modern languages society. Regular lectures by EC nationals about their respective countries and about EC.

Senior pupils' non-academic activities *Music:* 100+ learn a musical instrument, 30 to Grade 6 or above; 1 accepted for Music College in the last 3 years; 2 organ, 1 choral scholarship to Cambridge. 60 in school orchestra, 20 in chamber groups, 80 in senior school choir, 30 in chamber choir, 60 in parents and staff choral society; 10 in Bromley Schools Orchestra and bands. *Drama and dance:* 30 in school productions, 15 in other productions. *Art:* 87 take GCSE; 9 take A-level; 6 accepted for Art School in last 3 years. *Sport:* Rugby football, cricket, swimming, water polo, athletics, basketball, rugby fives, golf, judo, sailing, tennis, shooting, squash available. Sport compulsory. Award schemes occasionally. ASA and BAGA. 12 pupils represent county (rugby, cricket, swimming, water polo). *Other:* 85 take part in local community schemes. 20 have silver Duke of Edinburgh's Award, 1 has gold. Other activities include a computer club, chess, bridge, Go, debating, science society, Christian Union, electronics workshop, radio, first aid (St John Ambulance), combined cadet force (army and navy) and community service groups.

Careers In 1990, 60% leavers went on to degree courses; 1% to art/drama/music colleges; 3% straight into careers (eg commerce, merchant navy); 35% other. Of those going on to degree courses, 13% went to Oxbridge, 47% to other universities; 40% to poly/colleges. 1% those going on to higher education went to courses in practical art; 58% in humanities/social sciences; 4% in medicine; and 36% in science/engineering.

Uniform School uniform worn throughout.

Houses/prefects Competitive houses. Prefects, head boy, head of house and house prefects – appointed by the Head after consultation with staff and prefects. Separate councils for middle school and sixth form.

Religion Religious worship compulsory, subject to parental right to withdraw.

Social Close links for music, drama, debating, films with Bromley High. Visits to USA, Australia, Canada, Rumania, Russia, France, Germany and Italy recently taken place. Pupils allowed to bring own bike/motorbike to school. Meals self service. School shop. No tobacco allowed; wine at sixth form tutorial and society dinners (formal).

Discipline No corporal punishment. Pupils failing to produce homework once might expect work to be repeated, usually under supervision; those caught smoking cannabis on the premises could expect severe warning, attempt to discover source of supply, parents informed and placed on probation (ie a repeated offence would lead to expulsion).

Alumni association is run by Mr C L Watts, 26 Church Avenue, Beckenham, Kent.

Former pupils Prof Andrade (Brains Trust); Dr Walter Hamilton (Master of Magdalene College, Cambridge); Dr David Jenkins (Bishop of Durham); Wing Commander Stanford Tuck DSO, DFC; Major Johnson VC; Hubert Gregg (broadcaster); Michael Grade (Channel 4).

· St Dunstan's (Plymouth) ·

St Dunstan's Abbey
North Road West
Plymouth
Devon PL1 5DH
Tel 0752 663998

- Pupils 349
- Boys 4–7 only
- Girls 4–18
- (Day/Weekly)
- Upper sixth 21

- Termly fees
  £995 (Day)
  £1615 (Weekly)
- GSA
  Enquiries/application to the Headmistress

What it's like

Founded in 1867, it is single-site in the centre of the town. Its fine Victorian buildings were designed by William Butterfield. There has been an extensive programme of restoration and many modern facilities have been created. Religious worship is encouraged. Academic standards are high and very many sixth formers go on to degree courses. A very strong art department; considerable strength in music and drama. Some commitment to local community schemes.

School profile

Pupils Total age range 4–18; 349 girls, 311 day, 38 boarding. Senior department 11–18, 246 girls. Main entry ages 4, 9, 11 and into sixth. Approx 8% are children of former pupils. *Transfer from maintained schools:* 35% senior intake, plus 5% to sixth.

Entrance Own entrance exam used. Oversubscribed in some areas. No special skills or religious requirements. Parents not expected to buy text books; music tuition extra (£50 per term). 7 scholarships, 100–30% fees.

Parents 15+% in industry or commerce; 15+% are doctors, lawyers, etc; 15+% in the armed services. 60+% live within 30 miles.

Staff Headmistress Miss H L Abley, in post for 20 years. 25 full time staff, 17 part time. Annual turnover 3%. Average age 40.

Academic work GCSE and A-levels (including Chinese; no A-level general studies). In 1989, 43 pupils in upper fifth, 21 in upper sixth. *GCSE:* in 1989, 32 upper fifth gained at least grade C in 8+

694

subjects; 11 in 5–7 subjects. *A-levels:* 17 upper sixth passed in 3 subjects; 2 in 2 subjects. 5 took science A-levels; 5 arts/ humanities; 11 both. *Computing facilities:* BBC computers. *Special provision:* Extra help available.

European Community *Languages:* French offered: to age 14; GCSE; A-level. German offered: to age 14; GCSE; A-level. 10–25% take GCSE in more than 1 EC language. *Exchanges:* Regular exchanges for pupils aged 11–14 to France and Germany.

Senior pupils' non-academic activities *Music:* 26% learn a musical instrument, 4 to Grade 6 or above, 20 in school orchestra, 50 in school choir. *Drama and dance:* 80% in school productions. *Art:* All pupils take art as non-examined subject until third year; 16 take GCSE; 5 take A-level; average of 3 accepted for Art School. *Sport:* Netball, hockey, gymnastics, tennis, athletics available; (badminton, volleyball, squash, swimming – local sports centre); plus sailing and windsurfing for sixth. 40 pupils per year take exams, eg gymnastics, swimming. 12 represent county/city (netball, hockey). *Other:* Some take part in local community schemes and voluntary schemes after leaving school. Other activities include a computer club, ski club and Ten Tors.

Careers In 1990, 85% leavers went on to degree courses; 7% to non-degree courses (eg nursing); 7% other. Of those going on to degree courses, 8% went to Oxbridge, 76% to other universities; 16% to poly/colleges. 7% those going on to higher education went to courses in practical art; 35% in humanities/social sciences; 14% in medicine; and 35% in science/engineering.

Uniform School uniform worn, different in sixth.

Houses/prefects Competitive houses. Prefects appointed by head and staff; head girl, head of house and house prefects – appointed by the head and elected by the school.

Religion Religious worship encouraged but not compulsory. One compulsory lesson a week up to sixth form.

Social No organised events with local schools. Some organised trips abroad. Meals formal. No tobacco/alcohol allowed.

Discipline No corporal punishment. Pupils failing to produce homework once might expect warning/de-merit mark; those caught smoking cannabis on the premises could expect expulsion.

Boarding 3 have own study bedroom, 11 share with up to 3 others; 20 are in dormitories of 6+. Central dining room. Visits to local town allowed (in sixth).

Former pupils Dawn French; Lady Judith Wilcox (Chairman National Consumer Council).

· St Edmund's (Canterbury) ·

St Edmund's School
St Thomas' Hill
Canterbury
Kent CT2 8HU
Tel 0227 454575
Fax 0227 471083

- Pupils 576
- Boys 4–18 (Day/Board/Weekly)
- Girls 4–18 (Day/Board/Weekly)
- Upper sixth 55

- Termly fees £1830 (Day) £2975 (Board/Weekly)
- HMC, CSA Enquiries/application to the Registrar

What it's like

Founded in 1749 (named after St Edmund, Archbishop of Canterbury 1234–40), on the same foundation as St Margaret's School for Girls at Bushey. It moved from London to its present site in 1855 where it lies on a spur of the Downs in 60 acres of fine grounds a mile from Canterbury, with a magnificent view of the city and its cathedral. It enjoys substantial and well-designed buildings (the main structure, in Kentish ragstone, dates from 1855) and there has been much expansion since 1975, including a school hall, house premises, a language laboratory, science laboratories, a music school, a superb sports hall, dormitories and a girls' boarding house. It is now very well equipped indeed. The junior department is housed in a self-contained wing of the main building. The original purpose of the school was to provide an education for the sons of deceased clergy of the Church of England and the Church of Wales. The Christian basis of the school continues to be of prime importance and the chapel plays a central role in the life of the school. There is considerable emphasis on religious education, prayer and worship (thirty Cathedral choristers are members of the junior school). The declared aim of St Edmund's is to provide the widest possible opportunities for the individual, to develop his or her talents to the utmost and to provide a high level of pastoral care within a framework of firm but understanding discipline. Academic standards are high and results most creditable. Music is very strong indeed and there are numerous ensembles. A large number of pupils learn an instrument. Sports and games are well catered for and include (besides a standard range) association football, golf – there is a pitch-and-putt course – shooting and windsurfing (the sea is five miles away). A wide variety of extra–curricular activities is provided. The strong CCF (Army section) is compulsory for one year and is run to a high standard. Week-end activities are particularly well organised. Considerable involvement with the British Association of Young Scientists and also Young Enterprise. Substantial commitment to local community services.

School profile

Pupils Total age range 4–18; 576 pupils (day and boarding; boarding for boys from age 7, girls from 11 only). Senior department 13–18. Main entry ages 4, 7, 11, 13 and into sixth. *Transfer from maintained schools:* 7% senior intake.

Entrance Common entrance and own exam used. Scholarships and bursaries; chorister scholarships for boys 7–9. Fee reductions for children of service/diplomatic personnel and deceased clergy.

Staff Head J V Tyson, in post for 13 years.

Academic work GCSE and A-levels. 20 GCSE subjects offered; 18 at A-level (including French for business studies; no A-level general studies). In 1990, 57 pupils in upper fifth, 55 in upper sixth. *GCSE:* in 1990, 21 upper fifth gained at least grade C in 8+ subjects; 18 in 5–7; and 17 in 1–4 subjects. *A-levels:* 2 upper sixth passed in 4+ subjects; 24 in 3; 17 in 2; and 7 in 1 subject. 24% took maths/science A-levels; 54% arts/humanities; 22% both. *Computing facilities:* Network of RM Nimbus microcomputers. *Special provision:* Skilled individual help.

European Community *Languages:* French offered: to age 14; GCSE; A-level. German offered: to age 14; GCSE; A-level. 10–25% take GCSE in more than 1 EC language. *Other:* Links with a Gymnasium in Germany (reciprocal visits by musicians and sports teams); others being forged with French and German schools. Annual sixth form business studies trip to Strasbourg. Currently 3 German pupils in sixth form.

Careers In 1990, 67% sixth form leavers went on to degree courses; 5% to art/drama/music colleges; 18% to non-degree courses (eg banking, secretarial, construction, insurance); 10% other. Of those going on to degree courses, 5% went to Oxbridge, 51% to other universities; 43% to poly/colleges. 69% those going on to higher education went to courses in arts and social sciences; and 31% in science/engineering.

· *St Edmund's (Ware)* ·

St Edmund's College
Old Hall Green
Nr Ware
Hertfordshire
SG11 1DS
Tel 0920 821504
Fax 0920 823011

- Pupils 636
- Boys 7–18
  (Day/Board/Weekly)
- Girls 7–18
  (Day/Board/Weekly)
- Upper sixth 50

- Termly fees
  £1455 (Day)
  £2264 (Board)
  £2099 (Weekly)
- HMC, SHA
  Enquiries/application to
  the Headmaster

What it's like

The origins of St Edmund's College lie in two separate foundations: the English College at Douai, in northern France, and a clandestine Catholic school started at Silkstead in Hampshire during the 1640's. By 1792 this school was located in Old Hall near Ware, Hertfordshire. When the English College at Douai was dissolved during the French Revolution some of its refugees came to the Old Hall. There on St Edmund's Day 1793, the decision was taken to amalgamate the two institutions into St Edmund's College. For nearly two hundred years St Edmund's continued the tradition of providing an education for priests and laity alike. In 1975 the seminary was moved and so the school was able to expand. This resulted in the appointment of a lay Headmaster in 1984 and two years later the advent of co-education. Although transformed by these developments, the college has remained faithful to its purpose of providing Catholic education. What that means in practice can best be summed up in the words of the College's Patron and President, Cardinal George Basil Hume, Archbishop of Westminster. The college should produce young men and women of 'courage, competence and compassion'.

St Edmunds has imposing buildings in big grounds on a fine open site near the town. St Hugh's prep school and a junior house are on the same campus so continuous education is available. Numerous facilities include comfortable accommodation for boarders. Its prime aim is to provide the setting and the guidance to enable pupils to develop a mature Roman Catholic faith and practice. Attendance at chapel is compulsory. Religious instruction is an important part of the curriculum. A sound general education is given and results are good. Many leavers go on to degree courses each year. The College has a fine musical, artistic and dramatic tradition. Considerable emphasis on sport and games (especially rugby and hockey) with representatives at county level. A strong commitment to local community services, the Duke of Edinburgh's Award Scheme and CCF.

School profile

Pupils Total age range 7–18; 636 pupils, 470 day (277 boys, 193 girls), 166 boarding (125 boys, 41 girls). Senior department 13–18; 352 pupils (242 boys, 110 girls). Main entry ages 7, 11, 13 and into sixth. Approx 10% are children of former pupils. *Transfer from maintained schools:* 45% senior intakes, plus 30% to sixth.

Entrance Common entrance and own exam used. Oversubscribed. School is predominantly Roman Catholic. Parents not expected to buy text books; no extras. 80 assisted places. 10 scholarships/bursaries, half to one-third of fees pa.

Parents 5+% in the armed services; 15+% are doctors, lawyers, etc; 15+% in industry or commerce. 70+% live within 30 miles; 10+% live overseas.

Staff Headmaster D J J McEwen, in post for 7 years. 57 full time staff, 2 part time. Annual turnover 2–3%. Average age 40.

Academic work GCSE, AS and A-levels. 18 subjects offered (including A-level general studies). In 1990, 76 pupils in upper fifth, 50 in upper sixth. *GCSE:* in 1990, 50% upper fifth gained at least grade C in 8+ subjects; 26% in 5–7; and 20% in 1–4 subjects. *A-levels:* 24 upper sixth passed in 4+ subjects; 10 in 3; 3 in 2; and 3 in 1 subject. 44% took science A-levels; 37% arts/humanities; 19% both. *Computing facilities:* 25 BBCs in computing room. Wide variety of others in departments. *Special provision:* Part-time teacher to help pupils with mild dyslexia.

European Community *Languages:* French offered: to age 14; GCSE; AS-level; A-level. German offered: to age 14; GCSE; A-level. Spanish offered: to age 14; GCSE; A-level. 25–50% take GCSE in more than 1 EC language. *Exchanges:* Regular exchanges for pupils aged 14–16 to France.

Senior pupils' non-academic activities *Music:* 57 learn a musical instrument, 9 to Grade 6 or above. 18 play in school orchestra, 32 in school choir; 3 play in Hertford Orchestra, 1 does diploma work. *Drama and dance:* 100 in school productions; 20 pupils take LAMDA speech and drama exams. *Art:* 25 take GCSE art; 8, A-level. 2 accepted for Art School. 10 belong to photographic club. *Sport:* Rugby, cricket, swimming, athletics, tennis, hockey, netball, squash available. 150+ take non-compulsory sport. RLSS awards taken. 23 represent county/country (rugby, athletics). *Other:* 14 take part in local community schemes. 18 have bronze Duke of Edinburgh's Award, 10 have silver and 6 gold. Some enter voluntary schemes after leaving school. Other activities include a computer club, driving, CCF, rifle range, horse riding, car club.

Careers In 1990, 73% leavers went on to degree courses; 2% to art/drama/music colleges; 21% to non-degree courses; 2% straight into careers; 2% other. Of those going on to degree courses, 2% went to Oxbridge, 51% to other universities; 47% to poly/colleges. 2% those going on to higher education went to courses in practical art; 2% in drama/acting; 72% in humanities/social sciences; 7% in medicine; and 17% in science/engineering.

Uniform School uniform worn throughout.

Houses/prefects Competitive houses. Prefects, head boy/girl, heads of houses and house prefects.

Religion Compulsory religious worship on Sundays and feast days; many opportunities for voluntary worship.

Social Socials, sixth form conferences, careers conventions with local schools. Organised trips to France and ski trip. Pupils allowed to bring own bike to school. Meals self service. School shop. Wine and beer served at socials; otherwise no alcohol or tobacco.

Discipline No corporal punishment. Pupils failing to produce homework expect detention.

Boarding 35% have own study bedroom, 65% share with one other. Single sex houses, of approximately 60, same as competitive houses. Resident qualified medical staff. Central dining room. 2 weekend exeats each term. Visits to local town allowed.

Former pupils Archbishop Derek Worlock of Liverpool; Bishop David Konstant of Leeds.

· *St Edward's (Cheltenham)* ·

St Edward's School
Ashley Road
Charlton Kings
Cheltenham
GL52 6NT
Tel 0242 526697

- Pupils 906
- Boys 2$\frac{1}{2}$–18 (Day)
- Girls 2$\frac{1}{2}$–18 (Day)
- Upper sixth 45

- Termly fees £1273 (Day)
- ISAI

Enquiries/application to the Admissions Secretary

What it's like

Formed in 1987 by an amalgamation of two independent Catholic schools – Charlton Park and Whitefriars. St Edward's comprises three large sites on the outskirts of town. These are occupied by the First School, consisting of a kindergarten unit and pupils up to 8 years of age; the Middle School, with pupils from 8 to 13 years of age; and the Senior School for pupils up to 18 years of age. All the sites are well-equipped and have plenty of space and playing fields. St Edward's is a Roman Catholic foundation but open to pupils of all denominations. The Christian faith is central to the school not simply as a taught subject but as a way of living. Academic standards and results are good although the school aims at being a family school taking pupils of a broad range of ability. Each year many go on to degree courses, including Oxbridge. The particular strengths of the school lie in the creative arts and in sport. Each part of the school produces each year a major drama production and musical concerts and the whole school combines in the summer to organise a one-week Arts Festival. In sports, high standards are achieved and the school regularly competes in national competitions with a good level of success. There is a considerable number of clubs and extra-curricular activities.

School profile

Pupils Total age range 2$\frac{1}{2}$–18; 906 day pupils (380 boys, 526 girls). Senior school 13–18; 445 pupils. Main entry ages, 4–11 and into the sixth. Own junior school provides over 90% of senior intake. *Transfer from maintained schools:* 5% to sixth.

Entrance Own exam used; common entrance accepted. Oversubscribed in some lower age groups. No special skills or religious requirements. Parents not expected to buy text books or pay for normal school outings; meals and transport extra. No assisted places yet. Scholarships (at 11 and 16); discretionary awards.

Staff Principal Dr Keith Wood, 1 year in post. 78 full time staff, 15 part time. Annual turnover 5%. Average age 40.

Academic work GCSE and A-levels. 22 subjects offered (including theatre studies and A-level general studies). In 1989, 145 pupils in upper fifth, 45 in upper sixth. *GCSE:* in 1989, 34% upper fifth gained at least grade C in 8+ subjects; 25% in 5–7; and 32% in 1–4 subjects. *A-levels:* 5% upper sixth passed in 4+ subjects; 73% in 3; 10% in 2; and 12% in 1 subject. 38% took science A-levels; 44% arts/humanities; 18% both. *Computing facilities:* 4 rooms equipped with computers (2 computer science, 1 word-processing, 1 business studies); plus a range of computers in subject departments. *Special provision:* Two trained special needs teachers.

Senior pupils' non-academic activities *Music:* 55 learn a musical instrument, 24 to Grade 6 or above, 1 accepted for Music School. 30 in school orchestra, 40 in choir, 15 in madrigal and 9 in flute groups, 4 in County Youth Orchestra. 3 go on to play in pop group; 20 to choirs and orchestras. *Drama and dance:* 20–100 in school productions. 12 take up to Grade 6 in ESB, RAD etc, 1 accepted for Drama

School. *Art:* 6 take as non-examined subject; 65 GCSE; 9 A-level, 2 accepted for Art School. 35 belong to photographic club. *Sport:* Hockey, rugby, netball, 5-a-side football, badminton, squash, table tennis, swimming, volleyball, tennis, cricket, athletics, rounders, gymnastics, aerobics available. 100 take non-compulsory sport (teams and clubs), 5–8 take exams. 20 represent county (rugby, cross-country, athletics, badminton, squash, swimming); 6, ATC division (cross-country, rugby). *Other:* Other activities include a computer club, clubs for chess, wildlife (with nature reserve), astronomy, debating society; Duke of Edinburgh's Award scheme to be restarted soon.

Careers 5 part time careers advisers. Annual average accepted for *arts and humanities degree courses* at Oxbridge, 2; other universities, 11; polytechnics/colleges, 6. *science and engineering degree courses* at Oxbridge, 2; other universities, 4; medical schools, 1; polytechnics/colleges, 2. *BEd*, 3. *other general training courses*, 11. Average going straight into careers in armed services, 1; industry, 7;

the City, 1; civil service, 1; other, 9.

Uniform School uniform worn throughout.

Houses/prefects Competitive houses (except in senior school). Prefects, head boy/girl and deputy year captains – voted by sixth form and staff, appointed by Principal. School Council.

Religion Daily assembly, Mass at beginning and end of term compulsory.

Social Joint concerts with Cheltenham College, Dean Close School. Trips abroad to France, Greece etc, also skiing; exchanges to France, Germany. Pupils allowed to bring own car/bike/motorbike to school. Some meals formal, some self service. School shop. No tobacco/alcohol allowed.

Discipline No corporal punishment. Pupils failing to produce homework once might expect to repeat it; those caught smoking cannabis on the premises might expect suspension or expulsion.

Alumni association run by Mr Ablett, c/o the School.

Former pupils Lucy Soutter (international squash player).

· St Edward's (Liverpool) ·

St Edward's College
North Drive
Sandfield Park
Liverpool
L12 1LF
Tel 051 228 3376

- Pupils 650
- Boys 11–18 (Day)
- Girls 11–18 (Day)
- Upper sixth 100

- Termly fees £935 (Day)
- HMC

Enquiries/application to the Headmaster's Secretary

What it's like

Founded in 1900 and conducted by the Christian Brothers it is sited in a fine 30-acre wooded park in a residential district of the City and caters for a wide area of Merseyside. First-rate modern facilities are available. About 98% of the pupils are Roman Catholics (those of other faiths are accepted). A full course of religious education according to Catholic doctrine is an integral part of the curriculum. Attendance at services is obligatory. Academic standards are high and the school has a distinguished scholastic record. Many pupils go on to degree courses, including Oxbridge. French and Spanish are offered up to A-level and a high proportion of pupils takes GCSE in both. In addition, German and Portuguese are offered at AS-level. There are regular exchanges with France and Spain. Strong in drama; immensely strong in music – to the extent that it is almost an 'industry'.

There are many well-known alumni in the musical world. Very high standards in sports and games (a large number of county representatives, especially track and field athletes). A substantial commitment to local community services and an impressive record in the Duke of Edinburgh's Award Scheme.

School profile

Pupils Age range 11–18; 650 day pupils (600 boys, 50 girls). Main entry ages 11 and into sixth (girls already admitted to sixth form; admitted at age 11 from 1991). Own prep school provides more than 20% of intake. Approx 40% are children of former pupils.

Entrance Own entrance exam used. Oversubscribed. No special skills or religious requirements but 98% of pupils are Roman Catholic. Parents not expected to buy text books; no other extras. 385 assisted places. 10 scholarships/bursaries, £1400–£500 pa.

Parents 15+% are manual workers; 15+% are doctors, lawyers etc; 15+% in industry or commerce.

Staff Headmaster Rev Brother B D Sassi. 44 full time staff, 20 part time. Annual turnover 1%. Average age 45.

Academic work GCSE and A-levels. Average size of upper fifth 90; upper sixth 100. *GCSE:* on average, 14 pupils in upper fifth pass 1–4 subjects; 33, 5–7 subjects; 40 pass 8+ subjects. *A-levels:* on average, 4 pupils in upper sixth pass 1 subject; 7, 2 subjects; 20, 3 subjects and 61 pass 4 subjects. On average, 53 take science/engineering, 38 take arts and humanities, 9 a mixture. *Computing facilities:* 30 BBC computers and 15 Nimbus. *Special provision:* for EFL, dyslexic and mildly visually handicapped.

European Community *Languages:* French offered: to age 14; GCSE; AS-level; A-level. German: AS-level. Portuguese: AS-level. Spanish offered: to age 14; GCSE; AS-level; A-level. 50–75% take GCSE in more than 1 EC language. *Exchanges:* Regular exchanges for pupils aged 14–18 to France and Spain.

Senior pupils' non-academic activities *Music:* 50 learn a musical instrument, 26 to Grade 6 or above, 3 pa accepted for Music School, 3 to play in pop group, 1–3 pa to music degree at university; 36 in school orchestra, 40 in school choir, 5 school pop group, 4 barber shop quartet, 10 other pop groups; 1 in National Youth Orchestra, 3 Merseyside Youth Orchestra, 3 cathedral choir, 6 local orchestras. *Drama and dance:* 35 in school productions; 70 in charity review. *Art:* 25 take GCSE; 11 A-level. 1 accepted for Art School; 2 for architecture. 5 belong to eg photographic club. *Sport:* Rugby, cross-country, cricket, athletics, swimming, tennis, basketball, hockey, badminton, weight-training, volleyball, climbing available. 240 take non-compulsory sport; 120, other. 30 take sport exams. 23 represent county/country (rugby, athletics). *Other:* 20 take part in local community schemes. 26 have bronze Duke of Edinburgh's Award, 8 have silver and 4 gold. Other activities include a computer club, debating, public speaking, bridge, chess, model railway, quiz team, electronics.

Careers 1 part time careers advisor. Average number of pupils accepted for *arts and humanities degree courses* at Oxbridge, 4; other universities, 20; polytechnics or CHE, 6. *science and engineering degree courses* at Oxbridge, 4; other universities, 30; medical schools, 6; polytechnics or CHE, 3. *BEd,* 2. *other general training courses,* 1. Average number of pupils going straight into careers in armed services, 1; the Church, 1; industry, 4; civil service, 4.

Uniform School uniform worn throughout.

Houses/prefects Competitive houses. Prefects, head boy and girl – appointed by the Head.

Religion Morning assembly/prayer compulsory. Daily eucharistic service is encouraged.

Social Debates, public speaking and sporting events with local schools. Frequent trips and exchanges abroad arranged by modern language departments. Pupils allowed to bring own car/bike to school. Meals self service. No tobacco/alcohol allowed.

Discipline No corporal punishment. Pupils failing to produce homework once

might be told to produce it next day; those caught smoking cannabis on the premises may expect suspension.

Former pupils Michael Williams (actor); Michael Slemen and Edward Rudd (England Rugby players) and numerous musicians.

· St Edward's (Oxford) ·

St Edward's School
Woodstock Road
Oxford
OX2 7NN
Tel 0865 515241

- Pupils 576
- Boys 13–18 (Day/Board)
- Girls 16–18 (Day/Board)
- Upper sixth 125

- Termly fees
  £2350 (Day)
  £3125 (Board)
- HMC
Enquiries/application to the Registrar (0865 311345)

What it's like

Founded in 1863 by the Reverend Thomas Chamberlain. The original buildings were in New Inn Hall Street, Oxford. In 1873 the school moved to Summertown, two miles north of the city, on the Woodstock Road. There it enjoys a site of about 100 acres. The agreeable original buildings are in the Victorian collegiate style. Since 1963 there has been a comprehensive programme of renovation and development and the school is now very well equipped. The staff:pupil ratio is a very favourable 1:9. Academic standards are high and results are good. Each year very many pupils proceed to degree courses including many to Oxbridge. Music is well supported (two orchestras, a concert band and choir). There is a very strong dramatic tradition. Each year there are numerous small-scale productions, plus two major ones. For many years there has been strength in sports and games which are very well provided for with fine playing fields and a superb sports hall. A large number of clubs and societies cater for a wide range of interest. The CCF includes Air Force and Naval sections and there is a good deal of emphasis on open-air adventure training. Ample use is made of the cultural facilities of Oxford.

School profile

Pupils Total age range 13–18, 576 pupils. Main entry ages 13 (boys) and into sixth (boys and girls). *Transfer from maintained schools:* 2% main intake, plus 2% to sixth.

Entrance Common entrance exam used. Scholarships and bursaries.

Staff Warden D Christie, in post for 2 years.

Academic work GCSE and A-levels. 21 GCSE subjects offered; 22 at A-level (no A-level general studies). In 1990, 104 pupils in upper fifth, 120 in upper sixth (now 125). *GCSE:* in 1990, 87 upper fifth gained at least grade C in 8+ subjects; 14 in 5–7; and 3 in 1–4 subjects. *A-levels:* 7 upper sixth passed in 4+ subjects; 94 in 3; 12 in 2; and 7 in 1 subject. 25 took science A-levels; 48 arts/humanities; 47 both. *Computing facilities:* 12 networked Apple Macintosh, 6 networked Nimbus; Apple Macintosh and BBC B stand-alones.

European Community *Languages:* French offered: to GCSE; AS-level; A-level. German offered: to GCSE; AS-level; A-level. Spanish offered: to GCSE; AS-level; A-level. 25–50% take GCSE in more than 1 EC language. *Exchanges:* Regular exchanges for pupils aged 14–18 to France, Germany and Spain. *Other:* Regular small intake of pupils from eg Belgium, France, Germany and Italy.

Careers In 1990, 90% leavers went on to degree courses; 5% to non-degree courses; 5% straight into careers. Of those going on to degree courses, 17% went to Oxbridge, 68% to other universities; 15% to poly/colleges. 2% those going on to higher education went to courses in practical art; 1% in drama/acting; 1% in music; 66% in humanities/social sciences; 1% in medicine; and 29% in science/engineering.

· *St Elphin's* ·

St Elphin's School	● Pupils 360	● Termly fees
Darley Dale	● Boys 3–7 only	£1395 (Day)
Matlock	● Girls 3–18	£2396 (Board)
Derbyshire DE4 2HA	(Day/Board/Weekly)	£2276 (Weekly)
Tel 0629 733263	● Upper sixth 30	● GSA, SHA
		Enquiries/application to the Headmaster

What it's like

Founded in 1844 for the daughters of Anglican clergy, it moved to its present premises in Derbyshire in 1904. It is named after an obscure 7th century Saint who perished in battle. Its main original buildings, handsome in local stone, stand in beautiful gardens and grounds. There have been a number of fairly recent additions, including a gymnasium, a science block, library and rooms for arts, crafts and home economics. A new Nursery/Infants/Junior School and Sixth Form Boarding House will be completed in 1991. All the existing boarding accommodation is undergoing refurbishment.

The School has its own Chapel and this is central to its life. Pupils are encouraged to develop their Christian faith and life as fully as possible through prayer, corporate worship and teaching. There is a very favourable staff: pupil ratio of 1:11. A sound general education is provided and results are creditable. Many girls go on to design courses or further education each year.

Music is strong. There are an orchestra, wind band, instrumental groups and five choirs. Many girls learn an instrument. Drama is popular; several plays are presented each year and girls achieve excellent results in LAMDA and Guildhall examination. There are good facilities for sports and games on site and a standard range is available.

A plentiful variety of clubs and societies caters for extra-curricular activities. There is keen participation in the Duke of Edinburgh's Awards Scheme, the Debating Society and a very active Social Services Society which works for the local community and for national causes. The Young Enterprise groups have achieved notable successes with presentations of their companies to the Derby Area Board.

School profile

Pupils Total age range 3–18, 360 girls (day and boarding). Senior department 11–18. Main entry age 11. *Transfer from maintained schools:* 40% main intake at 11, plus 10% to sixth.

Entrance Own entrance exam used. Scholarships, exhibitions and awards, including music scholarship (half fees and free tuition on 2 instruments).

Staff Headmaster Peter Pollard, in post for 12 years.

Academic work GCSE and A-levels.

21 subjects offered (including A-level general studies). In 1991, 40 pupils in upper fifth, 30 in upper sixth. *GCSE:* in 1990, 23 upper fifth gained at least grade C in 8+ subjects; 11 in 5–7; and 10 in 1–4 subjects. *A-levels:* 6 upper sixth passed in 4+ subjects; 4 in 3; 10 in 2; and 1 in 1 subject. 4 took science A-levels; 10 arts/humanities; 7 both. *Computing facilities:* A fully equipped computer room; plus computers in science, English, classics, mathematics, geography etc. *Special provision:* EFL teacher; close liaison with the Sheffield Dyslexia Institute.

European Community *Languages:* French offered: to age 14; GCSE; A-level. German offered: to age 14; GCSE; A-level. Greek (modern) offered: to GCSE. 25–50% take GCSE in more than 1 EC language. *Exchanges:* Regular exchanges for pupils aged 14–18 to France and Germany. *Other:* Girls from France, Germany and Italy often spend a term in the school.

Careers In 1990, 48% leavers went on to degree courses; 4% to art/drama/music colleges; 12% to non-degree courses (eg nursing, speech/occupational therapy); 24% straight into careers (eg retail management, youth and community work); 12% other. Of those going on to degree courses, 3% usually go to Oxbridge, 48% to other universities; 48% to poly/colleges. 8% those going on to higher education went to courses in practical art; 8% in music; 50% in humanities/social sciences/languages; and 33% in science/engineering.

· *St Felix* ·

St Felix School
Southwold
Suffolk
IP18 6SD
Tel 0502 722175

- Pupils 340
- Boys None
- Girls 11–18
  (Day/Board)
- Upper sixth 40

- Termly fees
  £1585 (Day)
  £2563 (Board/
  Weekly)
- GSA

What it's like

Founded in 1897 by Margaret Isabella Gardiner, it is one of the few schools of its period actually designed and built as a school. It stands in 75 acres of beautiful gardens, lawns and playing fields near the Suffolk coast and within walking distance of Southwold. Norwich, Ipswich and Aldeburgh are easily accessible. It is extremely well equipped and has a chapel, a fine library and a new chemistry/design and technology/IT block. The junior school, St George's, stands in its own grounds next to the main school. There are 4 main boarding houses and separate houses for the lower and upper sixth all of which provide comfortable accommodation. Non-denominational in its foundation it welcomes girls of every religious faith. There is some emphasis on religious instruction and worship. St Felix has a strong academic bias. A large staff allows a very favourable staff:pupil ratio of about 1:10. Standards are high and results are very creditable. Many of the upper sixth go on to degree courses. French, German and Spanish are offered to A-level (also Italian as a non-examined language). Music, drama and art & design play an important part in the school's life. All instruments are taught and there are orchestras, a choir and ensemble groups. Inter-house music and drama competitions are held regularly. A large and well-equipped art department produces work of high quality. Many sports and games are available, as well as riding and water sports. Girls regularly represent Suffolk and East Anglia in hockey, tennis and athletics. There is a good range of extra-curricular activities. The school has a commitment to local community services and the houses run their own social service projects.

School profile

Pupils Age range 11–18; 340 girls (70 day, 270 boarding). Main entry ages 11+, 12+ and into sixth but entry at 13+ and 14+ too. Own junior school. *Transfer from maintained schools:* 10% main intakes, plus 7% to sixth.

Entrance Common entrance exam used. Assisted places at 11 and 12. Scholarships, including music awards.

Staff Head from September 1991 Mrs Susan Campion MA (Cantab), presently Head of Woodford County High School, London Borough of Redbridge.

Academic work GCSE, AS and A-levels. 21 GCSE subjects offered; 18 at A-level (including GCSE and AS-level general studies, no A-level). In 1990, 44 pupils in upper fifth (very low: 1991 – 57; 1992 – 72), 34 in upper sixth. *GCSE:* in 1990, 18 upper fifth gained at least grade C in 8+ subjects; 20 in 5–7; and 6 in 1–4 subjects. *A-levels:* 3 upper sixth passed in 4+ subjects; 20 in 3; 4 in 2; and 4 in 1 subject. 10 took science A-levels; 10 arts/humanities; 11 both. *Computing facilities:* Total of 34 machines: 24 RM Nimbus machines in 2 computer rooms and research machines; additional facilities in CDT and science – effective network system. *Special provision:* for mild dyslexia – also help given with EFL lessons for foreign students.

European Community *Languages:* French offered: to age 14; GCSE; AS-level; A-level. German offered: to age 14; GCSE; AS-level; A-level. Italian: non-examined. Spanish offered: to age 14; GCSE; AS-level; A-level. 10–25% take GCSE in more than 1 EC language. *Exchanges:* Regular exchanges for pupils aged 11–14 to France. *Other:* German, and Spanish girls attend school for 1 term–1 year.

Careers In 1990, 70% leavers went on to degree courses; 20% to art/drama/music colleges; 10% to non-degree courses. Of those going on to degree courses, 5% went to Oxbridge; 55% to other universities; 40% to poly/colleges. 3% those going on to higher education went to courses in practical art; 65% in humanities/social sciences; 3% in medicine; 14% in science/engineering; and others to finance/accountancy. Usually includes some girls going to study drama and music.

· St George's (Ascot) ·

St George's School
Ascot
Berkshire SL5 7DZ
Tel 0344 20273
Fax 0344 874213

- Pupils 277
- Boys None
- Girls 11–18 (Day/Board)
- Upper sixth 35

- Termly fees
  £1650 (Day)
  £2950 (Board)
- GSA
Enquiries to the Admissions Secretary Application to the Headmistress

What it's like

Founded at the turn of the century it has a fine site close to Windsor Great Park and opposite the Ascot racecourse. The grounds comprise 30 acres of fields, woods, streams and heathland and the handsome brick buildings have an elevated position with good views. The school is well equipped and has good sports facilities. There is a recently completed general teaching block with art, design and technology facilities and there has been a total renewal of the computer system this year. St George's is Christian in outlook and has its own chapel hall. A sound general education is provided, academic standards are sound and five European languages are at present in the curriculum or available by special arrangement – Dutch, French, German, Italian and Spanish. Very many sixth form leavers go on to degree courses. Music, drama and art are an important part of the curriculum. There is a wide range of sports, games and extra-curricular activities.

School profile

Pupils Age range 11–18; 277 girls, 91 day, 186 boarding. Main entry ages 11, 12 and into sixth and at other times when there are vacancies. Approx 2% are children of former pupils. *Transfer from maintained schools:* 1% intakes.

Entrance Common entrance used. No compulsory extras; charges for extra games and music.

Parents Some live overseas.

Staff Headmistress Mrs A M Griggs, 3 years in post.

Academic work GCSE and A-levels. 16 GCSE subjects offered; 18 at A-level (no A-level general studies). In 1990, 44 pupils in upper fifth, 35 in upper sixth. *GCSE:* in 1990, 39 upper fifth gained at least grade C in 8+ subjects; 4 in 5–7 subjects. *A-levels:* 28 upper sixth passed in 3 subjects; 2 in 2; and 1 in 1 subject. 5 took science A-levels; 23 arts/humanities; 3 both. *Computing facilities:* One computer room with 13 Acorn A3000 computers. 13 BBC B's and Master computers in other departments. *Special provision:* Problems diagnosed, if necessary, and then progress monitored. No special provisions.

European Community *Languages:* Dutch offered: to GCSE. French offered: to age 14; GCSE; A-level. German offered: to GCSE (in sixth). Italian offered: to GCSE. Spanish offered: to GCSE; A-level. Up to 10% take GCSE in more than 1 EC language. (Dutch and Italian are by special arrangement between parents, pupils and staff.) *Exchanges:* Regular exchanges for pupils aged 14–16 to France and Spain.

Senior pupils' non-academic activities *Music:* Over half the school learns at least 1 musical instrument; 3 choirs, 1 orchestra, woodwind ensemble, jazz and recorder groups. *Drama and dance:* Annual dramatic production; inter-house drama, declamation and public speaking competitions. *Art:* 2 studios, pottery workshop and photographic darkroom. *Sport:* Athletics, fencing, lacrosse, rounders, squash, swimming, table tennis, tennis, trampolining available. *Other:* Duke of Edinburgh's Award Scheme. Other activities include archery, bird-watching, cookery, cycling, first-aid, golf, karate, lacemaking, pet-keeping, photography, riding, Young Enterprise.

Careers In 1990, 90% leavers went on to degree courses; 3% to art/drama/music colleges; 3% to non-degree courses (eg agriculture); 3% other. Of those going on to degree courses, 61% went to universities; 39% to poly/colleges. 64% those going on to higher education went to courses in practical art, drama/acting and music; 19% in humanities/social sciences; 16% in medicine and science/engineering.

Uniform School uniform worn except in sixth.

Houses/prefects Competitive houses. School Council.

Religion Compulsory morning assembly in chapel. One compulsory Sunday service for Christians; Roman Catholics attend Mass; other religions may participate in their practices.

Social Contact with local schools encouraged; annual ski-ing trip, occasional visits to Russia and Australia.

Boarding Resident qualified nurse; doctor visits twice-weekly.

· St George's (Edinburgh) ·

St George's School for
Girls
Garscube Terrace
Edinburgh EH12 6BG
Tel 031 332 4575

- Pupils 850
- Boys None
- Girls 5–18
  (Day/Board)
- Higher year 78

- Termli fees
  £1050 (Day)
  £2060 (Board)
- GSA
  Enquiries/application to
  the Headmistress

What it's like

Founded in 1888 by a committee of distinguished women who were inspired by the new ideals for women's education. It has an attractive 11 acre urban site with excellent facilities, including a purpose built art block, music centre and centenary sports hall and good boarding accommodation. The primary school is on the same site. Christian assemblies are compulsory for all. Academically a very distinguished school, it has high standards of teaching and consistently good results. Very many leavers go on to university each year, including Oxbridge and all parts of the UK. Offers both the Scottish Highers and a 2-year GCE A-level course. It is very strong indeed in music, drama and art, with many successes in these fields. An excellent record in games and sports (a large number of country representatives each season). It also has an astonishing record in the Duke of Edinburgh's Award.

School profile

Pupils Total age range 5–18; 850 girls. Senior department 11–18, 547 girls (459 day, 88 boarding). Main entry ages 5, 9, 10, 11 and into sixth. Approx 10% are children of former pupils. *Transfer from maintained schools:* 20% senior intake, plus 40% to sixth.

Entrance Own entrance exam used. Frequently oversubscribed. No special skills or religious requirements. Parents not expected to buy text books; extra charges include lunch for day girls (£1.30/day), music tuition (£91), fencing and curling (£27 and £14). 21 assisted places; sixth form scholarships.

Parents 15+% are doctors, lawyers etc; 15+% in industry or commerce. 60+% live within 30 miles, up to 10% live overseas.

Staff Headmistress Mrs Jean G Scott, in post for 4 years. 62 full time staff, 16 part time. Annual turnover 1–5%. Average age 41.

Academic work GCSE, S-grades, Highers, A-levels, CSYS, SCOTVEC and RSA. 17 subjects offered. In 1990, 90 pupils in GCSE/S-grade year, 78 in Higher and L6 A-level year; 53 in A-level/CSYS year. *GCSE/S-grade:* in 1990, 80 pupils passed in 8+ subjects; 8 in 5–7; and 2 in 1–4 subjects. *Highers:* 28 pupils passed in 5+ subjects; 20 in 4; 7 in 3; 3 in 2; 4 in 1 subject. *A-levels:* 5 pupils passed in 4+ subjects; 14 in 3; 6 in 2; and 15 in 1 subject. *CSYS:* 7 passed; some take extra Highers. 53% took science A-levels; 35% arts/humanities; 12% both. *Computing facilities:* Stand alone BBC B, BBC Masters and A3000s. Econet with A3000s serves senior computer room and many senior classrooms.

European Community *Languages:* French offered: to age 14; GCSE; Higher; A-level; CCIP. German offered: to age 14; GCSE; Higher; A-level. Italian offered: Scotvec module. Spanish offered: to GCSE; Higher; A-level; Scotvec module. 25–50% take GCSE in more than 1 EC language. *Exchanges:* Regular exchanges for pupils aged 14–16 to France, Germany and Spain. *Other:* Post GCSE, pupils can take CCIP (Credit Commercial d'Institute de Paris) in business and secretarial French, scientific and

707

technological French or hotel and tourist French.

Senior pupils' non-academic activities *Music:* 400+ instrumental/vocal lessons each week. Numerous girls perform to Grade 8 standard and beyond, with several playing concertos both in and out of school. Entries to both Music Colleges and university music departments. Many take part in school orchestras, choirs, vocal groups, concert bands and chamber groups. Out of school a number play in the Edinburgh Youth Orchestra, National Children's Orchestra and National Youth Orchestra of Scotland. *Drama and dance:* 100 in school productions. Many enter Edinburgh competitive festival. Active drama clubs at all levels. *Art:* 60 take as non-examined subject; 45 GCSE; 22 Higher; 2 A-level. 2 accepted for Art School; 1 for university Fine Art course. 30 belong to art/photographic club. *Sport:* Aerobics, badminton, basketball, athletics, curling, fencing, hockey, lacrosse, netball, rounders, squash, tennis, table tennis, air rifle shooting, swimming, ski-ing, volleyball available. Well over 100 take non-compulsory sport. 20 per season represent country/district (lacrosse, hockey, fencing, tennis, squash, athletics, ski-ing). *Other:* 50 are currently working for bronze Duke of Edinburgh's Award, 43 for silver and 60 for gold. Other activities include a computer club, literary and debating society, history and drama clubs, wind bands and madrigal groups.

Careers In 1990, 76% leavers went on to degree courses; 5% to art/drama/music/dance colleges; 4% to non-degree courses (eg business studies, consumer studies, secretarial); 14% other. Of those going on to degree courses, 14% went to Oxbridge, 73% to other universities; 13% to poly/colleges. 3% those going on to higher education went to courses in practical art; 2% in drama/acting/dance; 2% in music; 64% in humanities/social sciences; 9% in medicine/veterinary science/physiotherapy; and 20% in science/engineering.

Uniform School uniform worn except the sixth.

Houses/prefects Competitive houses. Prefects, head girl, heads of houses – elected by the sixth form and staff.

Religion Compulsory Christian assembly each morning.

Social Balls, Scottish reel evenings, Burns' suppers, musical and dramatic productions with other local independent schools. Ski-ing trips, visits to Greece and Russia, exchanges with France and Germany and with Germantown Friends' School (Philadelphia). Pupils allowed to bring own car/bike to school. Meals formal in boarding houses, self service in school. No tobacco/alcohol allowed.

Discipline No corporal punishment. Pupils failing to produce homework once might expect reprimand; those caught smoking cannabis on the premises might expect expulsion.

Boarding 15% have own study bedroom, 10% share with another, 75% are in dormitories of 6+. Houses, of approximately 50, divided by age. At least 3 termly exeats. Weekends by arrangement with Housemistress. Visits to local town allowed.

Alumni association Secretary: Miss Fiona Gregson, 80 Comely Bank Avenue, Edinburgh EH4 1HE.

· *St George's (Weybridge)* ·

St George's College	● Pupils 550	● Termly fees
Woburn Park	● Boys 12–18	£1640 (Day)
Weybridge	(Day)	● HMC, SHMIS, SHA
Surrey	● Girls 16–18	Enquiries/application to
KT15 2QS	(Day)	the Headmaster's
Tel 0932 854811	● Upper sixth Yes	Secretary

What it's like

Founded in 1869 it moved to its present site in 1884 at Woburn Park where there are 100 acres of fine grounds, gardens and playing fields. Many extensions and developments have taken place over the years and the school is now very well equipped. It draws pupils from St Maur's Convent into a joint sixth form. It is run by the Josephite Fathers who are Roman Catholic. The religious life of the school is an integral part of its existence and religious instruction and regular worship are compulsory. There is a good range of sports and games (high standards are achieved); main sports are rugby, hockey, cricket, rowing and tennis. A good range of extra-curricular activities includes a substantial commitment to local community services through the St Vincent de Paul Society and the Duke of Edinburgh Award.

School profile

Pupils Age range 12–18; 550 pupils, (450 boys, 100 girls). Main entry ages 12, 13 (boys) and into sixth (boys and girls). Approx 15% are children of former pupils. Woburn Hill School provides 60+% of intake. *Transfer from maintained schools:* 10% main intakes, plus 5% to sixth.

Entrance Common entrance and own exam used. Not oversubscribed. No special skills; Catholic school but other Christian denominations welcome. Parents not expected to buy text books; other extras vary. 35 assisted places. 6 scholarships pa available; bursaries at discretion of school, depending on parental circumstances.

Staff Headmaster Rev J W Munton, in post for 4 years. 48 full time staff, 5 part time. Annual turnover 10%. Average age 40.

Academic work Information not available from school.

European Community *Languages:* French offered: to age 14; GCSE; AS-level; A-level. German offered: to AS-level; A-level. Italian offered: to GCSE; AS-level; A-level. Spanish offered: to age 14; GCSE; AS-level; A-level. 10–25% take GCSE in more than 1 EC language. A-level pupils visit relevant countries.

Senior pupils' non-academic activities *Music:* School choir, orchestra, other instrumental groups. *Drama and dance:* Annual play, drama groups. *Art:* Art and ceramics offered at GCSE and A-level. *Sport:* Rugby, hockey, cricket, tennis, rowing, athletics, squash, sailing, golf, badminton, basketball, volleyball, netball available. *Other:* Other activities include Duke of Edinburgh's Award Scheme, debating, the Armadillo (learned society), Byzantian (Arts) society, photography, model making, chess, bridge, play-reading, Amnesty International, Young Enterprise, community service.

Careers On average, 55% leavers go on to degree courses; 10% to art/drama/music colleges; 5% to non-degree courses (eg secretarial, business and finance); 5% straight into careers (eg armed services, British Airways); 25% other (retaking, reapplying). Of those going on to degree courses, 10% go to Oxbridge, 60% to other universities; 30% to poly/colleges. 15% those going on to higher education

709

go to courses in practical art; 55% in humanities/social sciences; 10% in medicine; and 20% in science/engineering.

Uniform School uniform worn.

Religion All follow some religious studies throughout the school. Religious assemblies occasionally; Mass or major feasts; various voluntary and compulsory services.

Social Organised trips to London museums, galleries and theatres; sports team tours (UK and Europe); annual skiing trip, history of art and geography expeditions to Europe, history department tours and choir tour.

Alumni association Old Georgians Association run by Father Francis Owen, CJ, Secretary, c/o the School.

· *St Gerard's* ·

St Gerard's School
Trust
Ffriddoedd Road
Bangor
Gwynedd LL57 2EL
Tel 0248 351656

- Pupils 316
- Boys 3–18 (Day)
- Girls 3–18 (Day)
- Upper sixth 12

- Termly fees £630 (Day)
- ISAI

Enquiries/application to the Head

What it's like

Founded in 1915, it was in the care of the Sisters of Mercy until transferred to lay management in 1990. A lay Head was appointed in January 1991. Single-site and semi-rural, it has pleasant buildings in wooded grounds. A Roman Catholic foundation, it is ecumenical and its ethos is firmly based on Christian principles. An increasing number of full-time members of staff and many part-time teachers. Fees are low and a good general education is given. Public examination results are consistently well above any school within a 20 mile radius. The majority of Upper 6th pupils go on to degree courses. French, German and Welsh are offered to A-level.

School profile

Pupils Total age range 3–18; 316 day pupils (118 boys, 198 girls). Senior department 11–18, 167 pupils (53 boys, 114 girls). Main entry ages 3, 7, 11, 13 and into sixth. Approx 5% are children of former pupils. *Transfer from maintained schools:* 3% senior intakes, plus 10% to sixth.

Entrance Own entrance exam used. Oversubscribed at some ages. No special skills or religious requirements. Parents not expected to buy text books; other extras £60 per term per subject. Means tested bursaries for Catholic pupils.

Parents Farmers, hoteliers, medical and other professionals.

Staff Head Miss Anne Parkinson, in post

for 1 year. 15 full time staff, 20 part time. Average age 41.

Academic work GCSE, AS and A-levels. 19 subjects offered (no A-level general studies). In 1990, 30 pupils in upper fifth, 12 in upper sixth. *GCSE:* in 1990, 72% upper fifth gained at least grade C in 8+ subjects. *A-levels:* In 1989, of an upper sixth of 7, 2 passed in 4+ subjects; 3 in 3; 1 in 2; and 1 in 1 subject. 5 took science A-levels; 1 arts/humanities; 1 both. *Computing facilities:* Fully equipped technology room with 11 computers and back up equipment, eg printers. *Special provision:* EFL can be offered; children with learning problems are assessed. Language therapist arranged for dyslexics.

European Community *Languages:* French offered: to age 14; GCSE; A-level. German offered: to age 14; GCSE; A-level. Welsh offered: to age 14; GCSE; A-level. *Exchanges:* Regular exchanges for pupils aged 11–16 to France.

Senior pupils' non-academic activities *Music:* 30 learn a musical instrument, 6 to Grade 6 or above; 10 in school orchestra, 20 in choir. Also wind band, string group. *Drama and dance:* School productions. Some take ESB, RAD etc. *Sport:* Hockey, netball, rounders, tennis, volleyball, basketball, cricket available. 20 take non-compulsory sport. 5–10 take exams eg gymnastics, swimming. 3 in heats for senior Gwynedd team. *Other:* Activities include a computer club, theatre visits (London and Manchester).

Careers In 1990, 65% sixth form leavers went on to degree courses; 23% to non-degree courses (eg pre-degree courses); 11% other (year out before degree). Of those going on to degree courses, 10% went to Oxbridge, 73% to other universities; 17% to poly/colleges. 54% those going on to higher education went to courses in humanities/social sciences; and 46% in science/engineering.

Uniform School uniform worn, modified in the sixth.

Houses/prefects Competitive houses. Prefects, head boy/girl, head of house and house prefects – elected by the sixth form.

Religion Compulsory assembly (parents are given right of withdrawal).

Social Games fixtures and occasional joint ski-ing holidays with other schools. French exchange (forms 2, 3 and 4). Journeys to Italy and Russia recently. Pupils allowed to bring own car/bike to school. Meals: packed lunches. School shop. No tobacco/alcohol allowed.

Discipline No corporal punishment. Pupils failing to produce homework once might expect a warning; subsequent action would involve detention and informing parents. School would be concerned to discover why a pupil was smoking and enter into a counselling relationship to help change behaviour; a pupil who continued to transgress school rules would be asked to leave.

· *St Helen's* ·

St Helen's School
Eastbury Road
Northwood
Middlesex HA6 3AS
Tel 09274 28511

- Pupils 923
- Boys None
- Girls 4–18
  (Day/Board/Weekly)
- Upper sixth 71

Termly fees
£1145 (Day)
£2160 (Board)
£2080 (Weekly)
- GSA, BSA
Enquiries to the
Headmistress
Application to the
Registrar

What it's like

Founded in 1899, it has a pleasant semi-rural site of some 21 acres of gardens and playing fields 18 miles north-west of London. A part of the Merchant Taylor's Educational Trust of St John Baptist and St Helen. It comprises a preparatory department, a junior school and a senior school housed in well-equipped buildings. There have been extensive developments and improvements in the last 10 years. Religious teaching is in accordance with the principles of the Church of England. It has a sound academic record with consistently good results. Very many sixth formers go on to degree courses each year, including many to Oxbridge. Strong music and drama and good art and design facilities. A very good range of sports and games in which high standards are attained, particularly in lacrosse and swimming. A plentiful range of extra-curricular activities and a promising record in the Duke of Edinburgh's Award Scheme. Regular use is made of London's cultural amenities.

School profile

Pupils Total age range 4–18; 923 girls, 828 day, 95 boarding. Senior department 11–18, 484 girls. Main entry ages 4, 11, 12 and into sixth. *Transfer from maintained schools:* 50% senior intakes, plus 2–3% to sixth.

Entrance Part of North London Consortium (entry at 11); Common entrance (at 12) and own exam (13 and 16). Oversubscribed. All talents considered; no religious requirements. Parents expected to buy sixth form text books; maximum extras, £50 per term. Assisted places, 5 scholarships.

Parents 4% in armed services; 15+% in industry or commerce. 60+% live within 30 miles; up to 15% live overseas.

Staff Headmistress Dr Y A Burne, in post for 4 years. 68 full time staff, 21 part time. Annual turnover 6%. Average age 35–40.

Academic work GCSE and A-levels. 25 subjects offered (general studies AS level taken by all sixth). In 1990, 83 pupils in upper fifth, 71 in upper sixth. *GCSE:* in 1990, 73 upper fifth gained at least grade C in 8+ subjects; 8 in 5–7; and 2 in 1–4 subjects. *A-levels:* 2 upper sixth passed in 4+ subjects; 60 in 3; 8 in 2 subjects. 15 took science A-levels; 26 arts/humanities; 29 both. *Computing facilities:* Econet network (SJ hard disk) with master 128s and ETs (16 in total), research machines, Nimbus network (12 stations VX with 120 Mb hard disc). *Special provision:* extra English lessons given on 1–1 basis for dyslexia and EFL.

European Community *Languages:* French offered: to age 14; GCSE; AS-level; A-level. German offered: to age 14; GCSE; AS-level; A-level. Italian offered: GCSE. Spanish offered: to age 14; GCSE; AS-level; A-level. 25–50% take GCSE in more than 1 EC language. *Exchanges:* Regular exchanges for pupils aged 11–18 to France, Germany and Spain. *Other:* European Youth Parliament.

Work experience with European links.

Senior pupils' non-academic activities *Music:* 294 learn a musical instrument, 48 studied to Grade 6 or above, 1 accepted for Music School, 1 for studio recording; 30 in school orchestra, 52 in choir; 3 in Harrow Youth Orchestra. *Drama and dance:* 40–60 in school productions; 80 in house productions; 15 with other schools. 17 take Associated Board (Speech and Drama) exams. 1–2 accepted for Drama/Dance Schools; 1 occasionally to work in theatre. *Art:* 33 take GCSE; 8 A-level. 7 accepted for Art School, 2 BTEC. 20 belong to photographic club. *Sport:* Netball, lacrosse, badminton, golf, judo, trampolining, gymnastics, fencing, volleyball, squash, modern dance, rounders, swimming, life saving, tennis available. Approx 250 take part in extra non-compulsory sport. 30 take RLSS bronze medallion and high awards; team entered annually for Ten Tors expedition. 15 represent county (lacrosse, tennis). *Other:* 139 working for bronze Duke of Edinburgh's Award, 31 silver and 4 gold. Other activities include a computer club, French circle, one week's course for PHAB (Physically Handicapped and Able Bodied) organised by sixth form, debating, Christian affairs discussion group, outward bound, industry links.

Careers In 1990, 92% leavers went on to degree courses; 3% to art/drama/music colleges; 2% to non-degree courses (eg secretarial); 3% straight into careers (eg banking, city). Of those going on to degree courses, 8% went to Oxbridge, 74% to other universities; 18% to poly/colleges. 3% those going on to higher education went to courses in practical art; 54% in humanities/social sciences; 11% in medicine; and 32% in science/engineering.

Uniform School uniform worn except the sixth.

Houses/prefects Competitive houses.

Prefects, head girl, head of house and house prefects – head girl and deputies appointed by Headmistress, prefects elected.

Religion Christian-based foundation although girls of many other denominations. Compulsory morning assembly, weekend services for boarders, other chapel services voluntary. Girls prepared for Confirmation.

Social Debates, theatrical and choral productions, local conferences with other schools. Trips abroad: languages eg Germany, France; educational eg Greece, Russia, Turkey; sporting eg lacrosse; skiing. Pupils allowed to bring own car/bike to school. Meals self service. No tobacco allowed, wine for special functions.

Discipline Pupils are encouraged to behave well; punishment includes detentions or some form of service to school which would be generally useful. Serious offences can lead to suspension or expulsion.

Boarding Full and weekly. Upper sixth have own study bedroom, lower sixth share; below lower fifth in dormitories of up to 7. Houses, of approx 30, same as competitive houses. Sanatorium with resident qualified nurse. Central dining room. Sixth form can provide and cook snacks. Half-term and 2 weekend exeats per term; more for sixth. Visits to local town allowed.

Alumni association run by Miss M R Seldon, 26 Grove Lane, Camberwell, London SE5.

Former pupils Patricia Hodge (actress); Commandant D M Blundell, CB, WRNS; Julia Allan (sculptress); Josephine Buchan (TV).

· S Hilary's (Alderley Edge) ·

S Hilary's School
Alderley Edge
Cheshire SK9 7AG
Tel 0625 583532

- Pupils 337
- Boys None
- Girls 4–18 (Day)
- Upper sixth 18

- Termly fees
  £1015 (Day)
- GSA, Woodard
Enquiries/application to
the Head Mistress

What it's like

Founded in 1876, a Woodard school, it is semi-rural and single-site in a pleasant residential area on the lower slopes of Alderley Edge, 15 miles south of Manchester. Junior and senior school share the campus and have well-designed and well-equipped buildings. Large playing fields are close by. A C of E foundation, but other denominations are accepted. Religious worship is compulsory. The school emphasises the importance of girls' education and the expectation that women can expect to fulfil several roles in their professional and family lives. It aims to develop a girl's abilities to the full, giving maximum opportunity for higher education and other avenues of professional training. There is a good staff:pupil ratio of 1:13. Academic attainments are high and many leavers go on to degree courses. Very strong in music and drama; quite a lot of emphasis on public speaking. Adequate games, sports and activities. Some participation in local community services.

School profile

Pupils Total age range 4–18; 337 day girls. Senior department 11–18, 210 girls. Main entry ages 4, 11 and into sixth. Approx 1% are children of former pupils. Own junior provides more than 20% of senior intake. *Transfer from maintained schools:* 10% senior intakes, plus 1% to sixth.

Entrance Own entrance exam used. C of E school but other denominations are accepted. Parents not expected to buy additional text books (initial book fee on entry); £93.00 lunch extra. Scholarships/bursaries.

Staff Head Mistress Mrs J Tracey, in post for 5 years. 26 full time staff, 11 part time.

Academic work GCSE and A-levels. Average size of upper fifth 36; upper sixth 18. *GCSE:* on average over 50% upper fifth gained at least grade C in 9 subjects. *A-levels:* on average, 6 take science A-levels; 7 take arts; 5 a mixture. *Computing facilities:* Computer suite and use of computers in subject areas.

European Community *Languages:* French offered: to age 14; GCSE; AS-level; A-level. German offered: to age 14; GCSE; A-level. 10–25% take GCSE in more than 1 EC language. *Exchanges:* Regular exchanges for pupils aged 14–16 to France.

Senior pupils' non-academic activities *Music:* 70 learn a musical instrument and take Associated Board exams. 20 in school orchestra, 80 in choir. *Drama and dance:* 80 seniors and 70 juniors in school productions. Guildhall exams may be taken. *Sport:* Hockey, netball, squash, tennis, rounders, swimming, volleyball, badminton, basketball available. Other activities include public speaking; involvement in charity concerts (speech and music); various clubs.

Careers In 1990, 70% leavers went on to degree courses; 12% to art/drama/music colleges; 12% to non-degree courses (eg nursing, secretarial, bilingual secretarial); 4% straight into careers (eg banking). Of those going on to degree courses, 40% went to universities; 60% to poly/colleges. 13% those going on to higher education went to courses in practical art; 6% in drama/acting; 45% in humanities/social sciences; 12% in medicine; and 20% in science/engineering.

Uniform School uniform worn.

Houses/prefects Competitive houses. Prefects, head girl and head of house – appointed by the Head. School Forum.

Religion Religious worship compulsory.

Social Organised ski trips abroad and French trips. Pupils allowed to bring own car to school. Meals formal. School tuck-shop and second-hand uniform shop.

Discipline No corporal punishment. Firm disciplinary procedures enforced.

· St Hilary's (Sevenoaks) ·

St Hilary's School
Bradbourne Park Road
Sevenoaks
Kent TN13 3LD
Tel 0732 453815

- Pupils 300
- Boys None
- Girls 3–18
  (Day)
- Upper sixth 10

- Termly fees
  £1275 (Day)
- GSA
  Enquiries/application to
  the Headmistress

What it's like

Founded in 1942, single-site and purpose-built in 4 acres of pleasant wooded grounds in a residential urban area, within easy walking distance of the station. Junior school combined. Religious worship is encouraged and religious instruction is an important part of the curriculum. With a staff:pupil ratio of 1:12, academic standards are kept high and results are good. Many sixth formers go on to degree courses each year. The PA is particularly strong and parental involvement is much encouraged. Strong in music, drama and art; adequate range of sports, games and activities. Considerable participation in voluntary community service and the Duke of Edinburgh's Award Scheme.

School profile

Pupils Total age range 3–18; 300 day girls. Senior department 11–18, 200 girls. Main entry ages 3, 5, 7, 11 and into sixth. Approx 10% are children of former pupils. *Transfer from maintained schools:* 30% senior intake.

Entrance Own entrance exam used. Sometimes oversubscribed. No special skills or religious requirements. Parents not expected to buy text books; other extras vary. 12 scholarships and 9 bursaries pa.

Parents 25+% in industry or commerce; 15+% are doctors, lawyers, etc. Up to 2% live overseas.

Staff Headmistress Mrs P Miles, in post for 14 years. 19 full time staff, 23 part time. Annual turnover 7.5%. Average age 44.

Academic work GCSE and A-levels. 16 subjects offered (no A-level general studies). In 1990, 28 pupils in upper fifth, 10 in upper sixth. *GCSE:* on average, 8 upper fifth pass at least grade C in 8+ subjects; 18 in 5–7; and 2 in 1–4 subjects. *A-levels:* on average 3 upper sixth pass in 3 subjects; 5 in 2; and 2 in 1 subject. On average 3 take science A-levels; 3 arts/humanities; 4 both. *Computing facilities:* Network system. *Special provision:* Dyslexia specialist in school two days/week.

European Community *Languages:* French offered: to age 14; GCSE; A-level. German offered: to age 14; GCSE; A-level. 25–50% take GCSE in more than 1 EC language. *Exchanges:* Regular exchanges for pupils aged 11–18 to France and Germany.

Senior pupils' non-academic activities *Music:* 100 learn a musical instrument, 12 to Grade 6 or above. 1 accepted for Music School. 40 in school orchestras, 60 in choirs, others in chamber group, string group, clarinet choir, wind bands, guitar group and local youth orchestras. *Drama and dance:* 80 in school productions; 2 drama clubs (weekly), 2 music/drama workshops (each term). *Art:* 16 take GCSE; 4 A-level. 2 accepted for Art School. *Sport:* Tennis, athletics, netball, hockey, cross-country running available. 45 take non-compulsory sport; 10 take exams eg swimming. 2 represent county/country (tennis, cross-country). *Other:* 50 seniors take part in local community scheme VSU. 18 have bronze Duke of Edinburgh's Award, 10 have silver. 4 enter voluntary schemes after leaving school. Other activities include computer, art, pottery, gym, 'Watch' (junior branch of the KTNC) clubs.

Careers In 1990, 90% leavers went on to degree courses; 10% straight into careers (eg leisure centre organisation). Of those going on to degree courses, 44% went to universities; 56% to poly/colleges. 11% those going on to higher education went to courses in practical art; 11% in music; 78% in humanities/social sciences.

Uniform School uniform worn, modified in the sixth.

Houses/prefects Competitive houses. Prefects, head girl, head of house and house prefects – appointed by the Head after consultation with the rest of the school. School Council.

Religion Daily assembly compulsory, worship encouraged.

Social Participation in local voluntary services unit. Organised trips abroad and exchange systems. Pupils allowed to bring own car/bike to school. Meals formal. No tobacco/alcohol allowed.

Discipline No corporal punishment. Pupils failing to produce homework once might expect a warning and parents informed; those caught smoking on the premises could expect severe warning or expulsion.

Alumni association Friends of St Hilary's School, run by Miss M J Strudwick, 10 Sandilands, Chipstead, Sevenoaks, Kent TN13 2SP.

· *St Hilda's (Whitby)* ·

St Hilda's School
Sneaton Castle
Whitby
North Yorkshire
Tel 0947 600051

- Pupils 235
- Boys 2^1/$_2$–18
  (Day/Board/Weekly)
- Girls 2^1/$_2$–18
  (Day/Board/Weekly)
- Upper sixth 14

- Termly fees
  £1040 (Day)
  £1890 (Board)
  £1850 (Weekly)
- ISAI
  Enquiries/application to
  the Headmistress

What it's like

Founded as a girls' school in 1915 by Sisters of the Anglican Order of the Holy Paraclete (order and school were twin foundations), it is now fully co-educational. After various moves the lower and upper schools now occupy separate sites about 1.5 miles apart. The lower school is at Carr Hall, a handsome stone manor house in 30 acres of fine gardens and grounds in the Esk valley. The upper school occupies Sneaton Castle, also a handsome stone mansion (dating from 1815). Excellent modern facilities are available. The headmistress is a Sister of the Order and about 5 other sisters have various roles within the school. Religious education and worship are in the Anglican tradition. A notable feature of the school is its pastoral care. (Boys have been admitted throughout the school since 1988.) It caters for a wide range of children including those with emotional difficulties due to broken homes. A good general education is provided and academic standards are high. A number of leavers go on to degree courses. Music, drama and art are quite important parts of the curriculum. A fair range of sports, games and activities. Some commitment to local community schemes and a promising record in the Duke of Edinburgh's Award Scheme.

School profile

Pupils Total age range 2^1/$_2$–18; 235 pupils, 135 day (45 boys, 90 girls), 100 boarding (5 boys, 95 girls). Senior department 13–18, 104 pupils (6 boys, 98 girls). Main entry ages 2^1/$_2$–11, 13 and into sixth. Approx 2% are children of former pupils. *Transfer from maintained schools:* 20% main intakes at 11 and 13, plus 30% to sixth.

Entrance Own entrance exam used. All special gifts are welcome; pupils preferably Christian but other faiths accepted. Parents expected to buy some text books; extra charges for extra-curricular commitments. 15 scholarships/bursaries available, £1200–£300 pa.

Parents 15+% in the armed services; 15+% in industry or commerce. 50+% live within 30 miles; 10+% live overseas.

Staff Headmistress Sister Janet Elizabeth. 19 full time staff, 14 part time.

Annual turnover 2%. Average age about 40.

Academic work GCSE and A-levels. 22 GCSE subjects offered; 18 at A-level (including A-level general studies). In 1991, 28 pupils in upper fifth, 14 in upper sixth. *GCSE:* in 1990, 14 upper fifth gained at least grade C in 8+ subjects; 6 in 5–7; and 3 in 1–4 subjects. *A-levels:* 1 upper sixth passed in 4+ subjects; 4 in 3; 3 in 2; and 3 in 1 subject. 30% took science A-levels; 5% arts/humanities; 65% both. *Computing facilities:* Computer lab. *Special provision:* Special dyslexia tuition. EFL.

European Community *Languages:* French offered: to age 14; GCSE; AS-level; A-level. German offered: to age 14; GCSE; AS-level; A-level. 25–50% take GCSE in more than 1 EC language. *Exchanges:* Regular exchanges for pupils

716

aged 11–16 to Germany. *Other:* German pupils regularly (French and Spanish occasionally) attend school for one term with the sixth form.

Senior pupils' non-academic activities *Music:* 60 learn a musical instrument, 10 to Grade 6 or above; 6 in school orchestra, 50 in school choir, 6 in pop group. *Drama and dance:* 50 in school productions. Up to gold LAMDA elocution and elementary ballet. *Art:* 15 take GCSE; 2 take A-level. 2 accepted for Art School and degree course at university. 8 belong to photographic club. *Sport:* Football, cricket, hockey, netball, tennis, rounders, squash, table tennis, badminton, athletics, swimming available. 20 take non-compulsory sport. 11 GCSE PE. 5 have represented county; 1 represented country. *Other:* 10 take part in local community schemes. 20 have bronze Duke of Edinburgh's Award, 10 have silver and 3 gold. 2 enter voluntary schemes after leaving; 2 work for national charities. Other activities include a computer club, driving lessons, karate, debates, disco dancing.

Careers In 1990, 46% leavers went on to degree courses; 15% to art/drama/music colleges; 23% to non-degree courses; 15% straight into careers (eg catering, armed services). Of those going on to degree courses, 83% went to universities; 17% to poly/colleges. 10% those going on to higher education went to courses in practical art; 10% in music; 30% in humanities/social sciences; and 50% in science engineering.

Uniform School uniform worn except the sixth.

Houses/prefects Competitive houses. All lower sixth are prefects; head girl and head of house elected. School Council.

Religion Compulsory daily prayers, Eucharist on Sundays and major holy days.

Social Debates and socials with local schools. Occasional trips abroad; exchange with St Hilda's (Perth, Australia). Sixth form allowed to bring own bike to school. Meals formal. School shop. No tobacco allowed; alcohol at High Table on Sundays.

Discipline No corporal punishment. Pupils failing to produce homework once might expect reprimand or detention; those caught smoking cannabis on the premises can expect expulsion.

Boarding 15% have own study bedroom. All boarders over 13 in single house. Resident qualified nurse. Central dining room. Sixth form can provide and cook own food. 2 weekend exeats each term. Occasional visits to local town allowed (daily in sixth).

· St James's and the Abbey ·

St James's and the
Abbey
West Malvern
Worcestershire
WR14 4DF
Tel 0684 560851

- Pupils 180
- Boys None
- Girls 11–18
  (Day/Board)
- Upper sixth 25

- Termly fees
  £1720 (Day)
  £2580 (Board)
- GSA
  Enquiries/application to
  the Headmistress

What it's like

In 1979 the Abbey School, Malvern Wells, and St James's were amalgamated. The school stands on the western slopes of the Malvern Hills and is set in 40 acres of beautiful gardens and parkland. Its handsome buildings are well equipped. Recent developments include an impressive science block and extensions to the library. It is predominantly a Church of England school but is inter-denominational and ecumenical in spirit and practice; the whole life of the school is an attempt to express

Christian principles. A sound general education is provided with particular attention given to those who have learning difficulties. A large staff permits an outstandingly favourable staff:pupil ratio of about 1:5. Academic standards are good and results creditable. Many leavers go on to degree courses. The range of European languages and exchanges is impressive. European languages include French, German, Modern Greek, Italian and Spanish and in one upper fifth house, French is spoken most of the time. There are exchange arrangements with France, Germany, Italy and Spain and the school has a chateau in France. Music, drama and art are well supported. Facilities for sports and games are excellent. A standard range of games and sports is provided, plus judo and fencing. Levels of performance are quite high and school teams have won county and regional competitions. An adequate range of clubs and societies for extra-curricular activities.

School profile

Pupils Age range 11–18, 180 girls (day and boarding). Main entry age 11. *Transfer from maintained schools:* 1% main intake, plus 1% to sixth.

Entrance Common entrance or own exam used. Scholarships (including music and science) and bursaries.

Staff Headmistress Miss E M Mullenger, in post for 5 years.

Academic work GCSE and A-levels. 22 subjects offered (including Japanese, theatre studies and A-level general studies). In 1990, 25 pupils in upper fifth, 20 in upper sixth (now 25). *GCSE:* in 1990, 9 upper fifth gained at least grade C in 8+ subjects; 9 in 5–7; and 7 in 1–4 subjects. *A-levels:* 1 upper sixth passed in 4+ subjects; 6 in 3; 7 in 2; and 6 in 1 subject. 25% took science A-levels; 50% arts/humanities; 25% both. *Computing facilities:* Well equipped computer room with BBCs and Amstrads. *Special provision:* Provision for mildly dyslexic girls and EFL teaching.

European Community *Languages:* French offered: to age 14; GCSE; AS-level; A-level. German offered: to age 14; GCSE; AS-level; A-level. Greek (modern) offered: to age 14; GCSE; AS-level; A-level. Italian offered: to age 14; GCSE. Spanish offered: to age 14; GCSE; AS-level; A-level. 10–25% take GCSE in more than 1 EC language. *Exchanges:* Regular exchanges for pupils aged 11–16 to France, Germany, Italy and Spain. *Other:* Handful of EC pupils in school for various periods (prospectus also in German and Spanish). One upper fifth house where French spoken most of the time. Chateau in Normandy.

Careers In 1990, 60% leavers went on to degree courses; 27% to non-degree courses; 13% other. Of those going on to degree courses, 67% went to universities; 33% to poly/colleges. 11% those going on to higher education went to courses in drama/acting; 11% in music; 56% in humanities/social sciences; 11% in medicine; and 11% in science/engineering.

· St John's (Leatherhead) ·

St John's School	• Pupils 435	• Termly fees
Leatherhead	• Boys 13–18	£1800 (Day)
Surrey	(Day/Board/Weekly)	£2500 (Board/
KT22 8SP	• Girls 16–18	Weekly)
Tel 0372 372021	(Day/Board/Weekly)	• HMC
Fax 0372 386606	• Upper sixth 98	Enquiries/application to
		the Secretary

What it's like

Founded 1857, originally as a small boarding school for the sons of clergy, St John's moved to its present site in 1872. A very pleasant campus on the edge of the town, it comprises 50 acres of delightful grounds dominated by the handsome late Victorian buildings to which there have been many modern additions providing excellent facilities and accommodation. Although the school looks for all-rounders, the aim is for academic excellence. Results are good. Many sixth form leavers go on to degree courses; including many to Oxbridge. It is a C of E foundation with a lively chapel life that supports the strong pastoral framework of the house system; attendance at worship is both compulsory and encouraged. The music, drama and art departments are very active and many boys are involved in theatrical presentations each year. The school has a long-standing reputation for achievement in games and sports, and games are held 5 days a week. A very substantial commitment to local community schemes and an outstanding record in the Duke of Edinburgh's Award Scheme.

School profile

Pupils Age range 13–18; 435 boys (235 day, 200 boarding) plus 40 girls (day and boarding). Main entry ages, 13 (boys) and into the sixth (boys and girls). Some children of former pupils. *Transfer from maintained schools:* Very few in main intake, 1 or 2 to sixth.

Entrance Common entrance and own tests used. Oversubscribed for day places. School looks for all-rounders; C of E school – all other religions accepted. Parents expected to buy text books (often available secondhand). 6 assisted places pa. 10–15 scholarships/exhibitions (including for art and music), 50–25% of day fees; also academic and music awards at 16; foundationships for sons of clergy.

Parents 10+% are clergy. 60+% live within 30 miles; less than 10% live overseas.

Staff Head D E Brown, in post for 5 years. 42 full time staff; 4 part time staff plus 12 music. Average age 37–43.

Academic work GCSE and A-levels. 20 subjects offered (no A-level general studies). In 1990, 99 pupils in upper fifth, 98 in upper sixth. *GCSE:* in 1990, 95 upper fifth gained at least grade C in 7+ subjects. *A-levels:* 60 upper sixth passed in 2+ subjects. 15 took science A-levels; 44 arts/humanities; 14 both. *Computing facilities:* Nimbus network of NC186's with 13 stations and a number of BBCs in various departments. *Special provision:* Dyslexic classes.

European Community *Languages:* French offered: to GCSE; AS-level; A-level. German offered: to GCSE; AS-level; A-level. Spanish offered: to GCSE; AS-level; A-level. 25–50% take GCSE in more than 1 EC language. *Exchanges:* Regular exchanges for pupils aged 14–18 to France, Germany and Spain.

Senior pupils' non-academic activities *Music:* 93 learn a musical instrument, 18 to Grade 6 or above, a few play in pop groups; 38 in school orchestra, 50 in school choirs. *Drama and dance:* 100 in 5 or 6 school productions. Some accepted for Drama Schools. *Art:* Most pupils take in first year; 19 take GCSE; 6, A-level. 20 belong to photographic club; 22 to pottery. *Sport:* Rugby, soccer, cricket, netball, lacrosse, sailing, tennis, golf, hockey, swimming, fives, squash, athletics, karate, table tennis, fencing, shooting available. All pupils take swimming; games 5 days a week. 12 pupils represent county (rugby, cricket, athletics and lacrosse). *Other:* 50 take part in local community schemes. 40 participating in silver Duke of Edinburgh's Award, and 10 gold. Other activities include a computer club, CDT club, volleyball, basketball, riding, chess, ski-ing, CCF and shooting.

Careers In 1990, 58% leavers went on to degree courses; 5% to art/drama/music colleges; 10% to non-degree courses; 20% straight into careers; 7% other. Of those going on to degree courses, 8% went to Oxbridge, 62% to other universities; 30% to poly/colleges. 6% those going on to higher education went to courses in practical art; 56% in humanities/social sciences; 5% in medicine; and 33% in science/engineering.

Uniform School uniform worn throughout.

Houses/prefects Competitive houses. Prefects, head of school (appointed by Head); head of house and house prefects (by housemasters). Some small tasks sometimes performed for prefects by junior boys (voluntary and paid).

Religion Attendance at chapel compulsory; full involvement encouraged.

Social Sixth form club; debates, music, discussion groups, occasional dances, charity rock concerts and annual conference on industry with local girls' schools. Organised trips/exchanges to France, Germany, Spain and America; sports tour to Holland, Belgium and West Indies. Field trips to France and North Africa. *Upper sixth* allowed to bring own car to school; others, bikes. Meals, cafeteria style. School shop. No tobacco/alcohol allowed.

Discipline No corporal punishment. Pupils failing to produce homework, do it in detention. Anyone caught smoking cannabis would be expelled.

Boarding Very few have own study bedroom, senior pupils share, juniors in dormitories of 6+. Houses, of 50–55. Resident qualified nurse. Central dining room. Pupils can provide and cook their own food. Weekly exeats. Daily visits to local town allowed (juniors with permission, seniors on trust).

Alumni association run by J R Templeman, c/o the School.

Former pupils Richard Rogers; Anthony Hope; David Hatch; Guy Michelmore; Gavin Hewitt.

· St Joseph's (Ipswich) ·

St Joseph's College
Birkfield
Ipswich
Suffolk
IP2 9DR
Tel 0473 690281

- Pupils 719
- Boys 11–18
  (Day/Board)
- Girls 16–18
  (Day/Board)
- Upper sixth 85

- Termly fees
  £1040 (Day)
  £1865 (Board)
  Enquiries/application to
  the Headmaster

What it's like

Founded in 1937 in the outskirts of Ipswich at Oakhill (now the prep school), it moved to Birkfield Lodge, a delightful Regency country house in 55 acres of wooded parkland in 1944. A very pleasant environment. Many modern extensions.

Boarding accommodation and facilities, including a new CDT centre and science laboratories, are now excellent. A Roman Catholic school, it is owned by the De La Salle Brothers (all of the staff are lay) and the religious education is compulsory for all. Attendance at Mass and certain other services is also obligatory. Pastoral care is particularly good and the college has the reputation of being a very happy community. A sound education in the grammar tradition is given. Music and art are strong departments. A wide variety of games and sports (many representatives at county level) and extra-curricular activities. Considerable commitment to local community schemes and a promising record in the Duke of Edinburgh's Award Scheme.

School profile

Pupils Age range 11–18; 719 pupils: 519 day (473 boys, 46 girls), 200 boarding boys. Main entry ages 11 (boys) and into sixth (boys and girls). Approx 15% are children of former pupils. Own prep school provides more than 20% of intake. *Transfer from maintained schools:* 50% main intake, plus 60% to sixth.

Entrance Common entrance and own exam used. Oversubscribed. No special skills; school Roman Catholic but over 50% pupils are not. Parents expected to buy some sixth form text books; maximum extras, £100. 75 assisted places. 4 scholarships (age 11); Governors' bursaries available.

Parents 15+% are farmers; 15+% in the armed services; 15+% in industry or commerce. 30+% live within 30 miles; up to 10% live overseas.

Staff Headmaster David Hennessy, in post for 4 years. 47 full time staff, 2 part time. Annual turnover 10%. Average age 39.

Academic work GCSE and A-levels. On average, 114 pupils in upper fifth, 85 in upper sixth. *GCSE:* on average, 28 upper fifth gain at least grade C in 8+ subjects; 29 in 5–7; and 42 in 1–4 subjects. *A-levels:* on average, 6 upper sixth pass in 4+ subjects; 31 in 3; 15 in 2; and 9 in 1 subject. On average, 31 took science A-levels; 26 arts/humanities; 27 both. *Computing facilities:* Local area network extends campus wide; RM chain 64 net, RML Nimbus net, computers being developed as curricular tools for every subject area. *Special provision:* EFL; dyslexic pupils admitted into mainstream education.

Senior pupils' non-academic activities *Music:* 65 learn a musical instrument; 14 in school orchestra, 40 in school choir. *Art:* 90 take GCSE; 20, A-level. 4 accepted for Art School. 12 belong to photographic club; 30 to pottery and other art clubs. *Sport:* Athletics, badminton, basketball, cross country, golf, hockey, sailing, skiing, soccer, squash, swimming, table tennis, volleyball, windsurfing available. 80 take non-compulsory sport. 10 take exams (life-saving). 15 pupils represent county/country (rugby, cricket, badminton, athletics, squash). *Other:* 24 take part in local community schemes. 54 have bronze Duke of Edinburgh's Award, 2 have silver. Other activities include a computer club (100 members), debating, chess, public speaking, history. Frequent and varied outings for boarders.

Careers 2 part time careers advisers. Annual average accepted for *arts and humanities degree courses* at Oxbridge, 1; other universities, 9; polytechnics/colleges, 5. *science and engineering degree courses* at Oxbridge, 1; other universities, 12; medical schools, 2; polytechnics/colleges, 2. *BEd,* 2. *other general training courses,* 2. Average going straight into careers in armed services, 2; industry, 3; the City, 1.

Uniform School uniform worn throughout.

Houses/prefects Competitive houses. Prefects, head boy, head of house and house prefects appointed by the Head. Pupils have corporate responsibility for areas in common.

Religion Compulsory Sunday Mass for boarders (whole school on important occasions); weekly assembly; plus voluntary daily Mass, confessions, vigils and prayers.

Social Annual skiing trips abroad, French exchange, community service project in summer holidays in Togo and Kenya. Day pupils allowed to bring own car/bike/motorbike to school. Meals self service. Secondhand uniform shop. Sixth form boarders allowed tobacco/alcohol in designated room.

Discipline No corporal punishment. Pupils failing to produce homework once might expect a warning. Detention/litter duty are standard sanctions. Expulsion only in extreme cases.

Boarding Sixth formers have own study bedroom, 40% share with 2–5, 35% in dormitories of 6+. Houses, of 20–80, divided by age. Attendant qualified matron; weekly doctor's visit – local doctor on call. Central dining room. Pupils can provide and cook own food. Frequent weekend exeats. Visits to local town allowed.

Alumni association run by C Keeble, 26 Quilter Road, Felixstowe, Suffolk.

Former pupils Earl Nelson; Christopher Mullin, MP.

· St Joseph's (Lincoln) ·

St Joseph's School
Upper Lindum Street
Lincoln
LN2 5RW
Tel 0522 543764

- Pupils 320
- Boys 5–11 only
- Girls 5–18
  (Day/Board)
- Upper sixth 13
  (new)

- Termly fees
  £870 (Day)
  £1795 (Board)
- GSA
  Enquiries/application to
  the Headmistress

What it's like

Founded in 1905 by the Sisters of Providence, it has a compact urban site close to the cathedral precinct. Its handsome buildings, ancient and modern, are well equipped with modern facilities. St Joseph's combines a junior and infant school with the senior school. The heart of the school is the chapel which is regularly used for worship. The school meets daily for prayer and regular religious instruction is given. The Christian ethos is strengthened by close links with Catholic and Anglican local clergy and with the Sisters of Providence who withdrew from the school in 1983. A sound, general education is provided and exam results are creditable. Music, drama and art are well supported. There is an adequate range of sports, games and extra-curricular activities.

School profile

Pupils Total age range 5–18; 320 pupils, 245 day (35 boys, 200 girls), 75 boarding girls. Senior department 11–18, 200 girls. Main entry ages 5 (boys and girls), 11 and into sixth (girls). *Transfer from maintained schools:* 60% senior intake, plus 20% to sixth.

Entrance Own entrance exam used. Not oversubscribed. No special skills or religious requirements. Parents not expected to buy text books.

Parents 60+% live within 30 miles; up to 10% live overseas.

Staff Headmistress Mrs Anne Scott, in post for 8 years. 25 full time staff, 11 part time. Annual turnover approx 7%.

Academic work GCSE and A-levels. A-level general studies offered. In 1989, 38 pupils in fifth, 13 (new) in upper sixth. *GCSE:* in 1989, 50% fifth form pupils gained at least grade C in 8+ subjects; 10% in 5–7; and 40% in 1–4 subjects. *A-levels:* 50% upper sixth passed in 4+ subjects; 40% in 3; 10% in 2 subjects. 80% took arts/humanities A-levels; 20% both arts and science (new science courses starting 1990). *Computing facilities:* Fully equipped computer room plus computers in several teaching rooms. *Special provision:* EFL lessons.

Senior pupils' non-academic activities *Music:* Several learn a musical instrument. School orchestra and choir. *Drama and dance:* School productions, workshops etc; all pupils encouraged to act. *Art:* Includes textiles, design, painting. *Sport:* Hockey, tennis, squash, badminton, netball, table tennis available. County tennis champions. *Other:* Activities include a computer club, Guides, folk club, table tennis, theatre visits etc.

Uniform School uniform worn except in sixth.

Houses/prefects No competitive houses. Prefects, head girl – elected by the school. School Council.

Religion Roman Catholic and Anglican.

Social Joint sporting activities with other schools. Many organised trips abroad and exchange systems. Meals self service. No tobacco/alcohol allowed.

Discipline No corporal punishment. Pupils failing to produce homework once are rarely punished; those caught smoking cannabis on the premises could expect their parents to be sent for and suspension likely to ensue (has never happened).

Boarding All share study bedrooms, 50% in dormitories of 6+. No resident medical staff. Central dining room. Exeats each term. Visits to local town allowed by fifth and sixth form.

· St Joseph's (Stoke) ·

St Joseph's College	• Pupils 475	• Termly fees
London Road	• Boys 4–18	£870 (Day)
Trent Vale	(Day)	• ISAI
Stoke on Trent	• Girls 4–18	Enquiries/application to
ST4 5NT	(Day)	the Headmaster
Tel 0782 48008	• Upper sixth 10	

What it's like

Founded in 1931 by the Christian Brothers, a religious congregation established in Ireland in 1802. Girls admitted to Form 1 in 1990 as the school changes to becoming fully co-educational. It has pleasant, well-designed buildings and stands on elevated grounds comprising 10 acres. At Hanford are 15 acres of playing fields. It caters for a wide area of North Staffordshire and surrounding districts and has a long record of service to the local community. A Roman Catholic school, it is conducted by the Christian Brothers. All pupils follow the religious education programme. Academic standards and results are good. Many leavers go on to degree courses each year. French and Spanish are offered to A-level and a high proportion of pupils takes both at GCSE. There are regular exchanges with France and Spain. It has a tremendously strong music department. All learn an instrument and about 220 pupils are involved in choirs and orchestras. The art department is also very strong. A very good range of sports and games in which standards are high (quite a few representatives at county level). A big commitment to local community services, charities etc.

School profile

Pupils Total age range, 4–18. 475 day pupils (405 boys, 70 girls). Senior department 11–18, 284 pupils (272 boys; 12 girls). Co-educational since 1990. Main entry ages 11 and into sixth. Approx 5% are children of former pupils. Own prep dept provides more than 60% senior intake. *Transfer from maintained schools:* 40% senior intake.

Entrance Own entrance exam used. Not

oversubscribed. No special skills or religious requirements. Parents not expected to buy text books. Assisted places. 6 scholarships/bursaries, value £600.

Parents 15+% are doctors, lawyers etc; 15+% in industry or commerce.

Staff Headmaster Rev Br P K Loughran, in post for 1 year. 33 full time staff, 7 part time. Annual turnover 3%.

Academic work GCSE and A-levels. 14 subjects offered (including A-level general studies). In 1990, 44 pupils in upper fifth, 10 in upper sixth. *GCSE:* in 1990, 40% upper fifth gained at least grade C in 9 subjects; 33% in 6–8; and 24% in 2–4 subjects. *A-levels:* 60% upper sixth passed in 4+ subjects; 10% in 3; 10% in 2; and 10% in 1 subject. 20% took science A-levels; 40% arts/ humanities; 40% both.

European Community *Languages:* French offered: to age 14; GCSE; AS-level; A-level. Italian: GCSE. Spanish offered: to age 14; GCSE; AS-level; A-level. 50–75% take GCSE in more than 1 EC language. *Exchanges:* Regular exchanges for pupils aged 14–18 to France and Spain.

Senior pupils' non-academic activities *Music:* All pupils learn a musical instrument, 6 to Grade 6 or above; 100 in school orchestra; 120 in school choir; 20 in brass and wind groups. *Art:* 240 take as non-examined subject; 30 GCSE; 1 A-level; 1 accepted for Art School. *Sport:* Rugby, athletics, cross-country, cricket, squash, golf, volleyball, tennis available. 100 take non-compulsory sport. 20 represent county/country (rugby, cricket, athletics). *Other:* 30 take part in handicapped club. Other activities include a computer club.

Careers In 1990, 80% leavers went on to degree courses; 20% straight into careers (eg post office, catering). Of those going on to degree courses, 63% went to universities; 37% to poly/colleges. 12% those going on to higher education went to courses in practical art; 25% in humanities/social sciences; 38% in medicine; and 25% in science/engineering.

Uniform School uniform worn throughout.

Houses/prefects Competitive houses. Prefects and head boy – elected by staff and sixth formers.

Religion Religious worship not compulsory for non-Catholics.

Social No organised contact with other schools at present; some organised trips abroad. Sixth form allowed to bring own car/bike/motorbike to school. Meals self service. Smoking by sixth formers tolerated; no alcohol.

Discipline No corporal punishment. Pupils failing to produce homework once might expect a reprimand or detention; those caught smoking cannabis on the premises would be excluded or expelled (never arisen).

· St Lawrence ·

St Lawrence College	● Pupils 590	● Termly fees
Ramsgate	● Boys 5–18	£1790 (Day)
Kent	(Day/Board/Weekly)	£2670 (Board/
CT11 7AE	● Girls 5–18	Weekly)
Tel 0843 587666/	(Day/Board/Weekly)	● HMC
592680	● Upper sixth 56	Enquiries/application to the Head

What it's like
Founded in 1879, it has a fine site on an estate of 160 acres in Thanet, on the coast between Ramsgate and Broadstairs and facing over the Channel. The surroundings

are impressive, with chalk cliffs, sandy beaches, nature reserves and yachting marina. Ramsgate and Sandwich are both attractive towns. It has agreeably designed and well-equipped buildings with comfortable boarding accommodation. The junior school stands on the same estate. It is a Church of England school with an Evangelical commitment and the chapel is at the centre of the college's life. There is considerable emphasis on worship, prayer, religious services and religious instruction. Many Lawrentians have entered the Ministry and the college has always had strong links with missionary societies. The staff:pupil ratio is a very favourable 1:10, and there are large visiting and assistant staffs. Academic standards are high and results most creditable. Not a few pupils go on to degree courses. Music and drama are particularly strong and play an important part in school life. Three major concerts, choral and orchestral, as well as a number of invitation concerts are held each year. The National Youth Orchestra has for many years made use of the college facilities. St Lawrence is also well known for its annual Shakespeare play. There are 35 acres of playing fields and facilities for sports and games are unusually good. A wide variety of sports and games is available and they include golf, judo, fencing, sailing and shooting. Standards in sports and games are high and the college is especially well known for its hockey. A large number of clubs and societies cater for most needs. The Christian Union is strongly supported and social service schemes receive much impetus through the chapel. There is a flourishing CCF contingent and there has been much success in the Duke of Edinburgh's Award Scheme.

School profile

Pupils Total age range 5–18; 590 pupils, 403 boys, 187 girls. Senior department 11–18; 370 pupils, 253 boys, 117 girls. Main entry ages 11, 13 and into sixth. *Transfer from maintained schools:* 25% senior intakes, plus 5% to sixth.

Entrance Common entrance and own exam used. Assisted places. Scholarships and bursaries.

Staff Head J H Binfield, in post for 8 years.

Academic work GCSE and A-levels. 21 subjects offered, including information technology, design technology, Spanish, Russian, Latin, Greek, German. No A-level general studies but all sixth take information technology and a European language as part of general studies programme. In 1989, 58 pupils in upper fifth, 56 in upper sixth. *GCSE:* in 1989, 36 upper fifth gained at least grade C in 8+ subjects; 16 in 5–7; and 6 in 1–4 subjects. *A-levels:* 6 upper sixth passed in 4+ subjects; 33 in 3; 10 in 2; and 7 in 1 subject. 34% took science A-levels; 50% arts/humanities; 16% both (mostly science, plus economics or a language). *Computing facilities:* 26 Nimbus network plus second network, computers in other areas (science block, design technology centre, geography, music, careers etc). *Special provision:* Bright dyslexics accepted. Some additional EFL tuition available.

· *St Leonards* ·

St Leonards School
St Andrews
Fife
Scotland KY16 9QU
Tel 0334 72126
Fax 0334 76152

- Pupils 400
- Boys None
- Girls 8–18
- (Day/Board)
- Upper sixth 55

- Termly fees
  £1550 (Day)
  £2950 (Board)
- GSA
  Enquiries/application to
  the Headmistress

What it's like

Founded in 1877, it has a single (and historic) site on the edge of the old town which is the seat of Scotland's oldest university. It is a very fine campus with 30 acres of parkland and playing fields and is generally regarded as one of the leading schools for girls in Britain. It has excellent facilities and accommodation and its computer centre is reckoned to be the best in Scotland. Religious attendance is compulsory. A very large staff permits a staff:pupil ratio of 1:7. The teaching is of a high standard and academic results are consistently impressive. Very many leavers go on to degree courses each year. European languages include French, German, Italian and Spanish. There are regular exchanges with France, Germany and Spain and language courses for A-level students in France. It is very strong in music, drama and art and has had many successes in these fields. Also very strong in games and sports (there are many county and international representatives, especially in hockey and lacrosse). A splendid range of extra-curricular activities and an outstanding record in the Duke of Edinburgh's Award Scheme.

School profile

Pupils Total age range 8–18; 400 girls, 80 day, 320 boarding. Senior department 12–18, 350 girls. Main entry ages 11, 12, 13 and into sixth. Approx 5% are children of former pupils. *Transfer from maintained schools:* 19% intakes 11–13, plus 4% to sixth.

Entrance Common entrance and own entrance test used. No special skills or religious requirements. Parents expected to buy some text books in sixth form; house accounts average £20. 22 assisted places. 30 scholarships/bursaries available, £50–£3000 pa.

Parents 15+% in industry or commerce; 15+% are doctors, lawyers etc. 30+% live within 30 miles; 20+% live overseas.

Staff Headmistress Mrs Mary James, 2 years in post. 51 full time staff, 17 part time. Annual turnover 5–10%. Average age mid–late 30s.

Academic work GCSE, AO-level, Highers and A-levels. 17 subjects offered (no A-level general studies). In 1990, 79 pupils in GCSE year, 55 in A-level/ Higher year. *GCSE:* in 1990, 69 upper fifth gained at least grade C in 8+ subjects; 9 in 5–7; and 1 in 4 subjects. *Highers:* 11 passed in 5+ or more subjects; 8 in 4; 3 in 3; 4 in 2 subjects. *A-levels:* 2 passed in 4 subjects; 40 in 3; 6 in 2 subjects. 9 took science A-levels; 18 arts/ humanities; 19 both. *Computing facilities:* 2 computing labs (Nimbus network), laser printer. *Special provision:* Tutoring for dyslexic pupils.

European Community *Languages:* French offered: to age 14; GCSE; A-level. German offered: to age 14; GCSE; A-level. Italian offered: to GCSE. Spanish offered: to GCSE; A-level. 10–25% take GCSE in more than 1 EC language. *Exchanges:* Regular exchanges for pupils aged 14–16 to France, Germany and Spain. *Other:* Language courses in France for A-level students. Spanish girls, different levels, in school.

Senior pupils' non-academic activities *Music:* 100 learn a musical instrument, approx 25 to Grade 6 or above; 10 take GCSE. 2 accepted for Music School. 53 in school orchestra, 60 in senior choir, 10 in jazz band, 20 in senior wind band, 28 in senior vocal groups, some pupils in Scottish Independent Schools Orchestra, 94 passed practical exams, 22 passed theory. *Drama and dance:* 25 seniors in school productions; 250 in inter-house drama festival; 48 take drama and speech training; 10 take LAMDA Grade 6 and over (verse and prose), 49 senior acting; 10 accepted for Scottish Youth Theatre, 1 for National Youth Theatre. Sixth form visit Stratford annually. *Art and Design:* 10 take as non-examined subject; 28 take GCSE; 5–10, A-level; 5 Higher art and design. Up to 6 accepted for Art School; 1–3 to university – fine art. *Sport:* Lacrosse, hockey, tennis, athletics, swimming, squash, shooting, fencing, golf, badminton, volleyball, basketball, ballet, canoeing, gymnastics, dance, judo, ski-ing available. 130 take non-compulsory sport; 1–2 fencing exams; 15–25 athletics; 6 life saving. Numerous pupils represent county and country (hockey, lacrosse, athletics). *Other:* 13 take part in local community schemes. 51 have bronze Duke of Edinburgh's Award, 30 have silver and 14 gold. Other activities include a computer club, chess club, history and arts society, geographical society, modern languages society, senior scientific society; political and philosophical society; driving lessons available.

Careers In 1990, 83% leavers went on to degree courses; 10% to non-degree courses (eg secretarial, business studies, nursing); 7% other. Of those going on to degree courses, 4% went to Oxbridge, 72% to other universities; 24% to poly/colleges. 4% those going on to higher education went to courses in practical art; 1% in drama/acting; 1% in music; 29% in humanities/social sciences; 1% in medicine; and 14% in science/engineering.

Uniform School uniform worn until upper sixth.

Houses/prefects Competitive houses. No prefects. Head girl and heads of houses – appointed by the Head and Housemistress. Vice heads (2) elected by pupils. School Council.

Religion Girls must attend a local church on Sundays. 2 or 3 school services are arranged each term.

Social Occasional links with local schools in music, debates – more usual to join up with public schools not too far away for debates, music, classics discussions etc. Many organised trips (recently to Nepal, Tanzania, Egypt, Italy, Spain and Greece) plus annual ski-ing trip and eg. choir trip to Austria (1991). Senior pupils allowed to bring own bike to school. Meals formal, self service on Saturday and Sunday evenings. No school shop, very near to local ones. No tobacco/alcohol allowed.

Discipline No corporal punishment. Pupils failing to produce homework once might be expected to produce it and perhaps do some additional work; those caught smoking cannabis on the premises would be expelled immediately.

Boarding *Upper sixth* have own study bedroom, lower sixth will in 1991; occasionally pupils share; 50% are in dormitories of 6+. Houses, of 30–48; separate upper sixth house. 2 resident SRNs, doctor visits every day. Central dining room. *Upper sixth* can provide and cook own food at weekends. Half-term and 2 weekend exeats each term. Visits to local town allowed.

Alumni association run by Miss B Bushnell, c/o the School.

· *St Leonards-Mayfield* ·

St Leonards-Mayfield
School
The Old Palace
Mayfield
East Sussex TN20 6PH
Tel 0435 873055
Fax 0435 872627

- Pupils 540
  Boys None
  Girls 11–18
  (Day/Board/Weekly)
- Upper sixth 87

- Termly fees
  £1700 (Day)
  £2550 (Board)
  £2525 (Weekly)
- GSA, CCSS
  Enquiries/application to
  the Headmistress

What it's like

Started in 1863 when the Duchess of Leeds presented to the foundress of the Society of the Holy Child Jesus the property which comprised the ruins (and the surrounding land) of the 'Old Palace' of the medieval archbishops of Canterbury. These and the synod hall were restored and the school opened in 1872. Besides the original buildings there are extensive modern facilities and accommodation in delightful grounds and gardens. A Roman Catholic foundation (boarders must be Catholic), the doctrines and practice of the church (attendance at Mass etc) are an important part of the curriculum. A high staff:pupil ratio of 1:10. Good academic standards prevail and many in sixth form go on to degree courses, including Oxbridge, each year. European languages include French, German, Italian and Spanish and individual exchanges are arranged into France, Germany, Italy and Spain. Drama and art departments are well supported and music is particularly strong. A wide range of sports, games and activities is available. The Duke of Edinburgh's Award Scheme is popular. Pupils are encouraged to participate in local community schemes.

School profile

Pupils Age range 11–18; 540 girls (165 day, 375 boarding). Main entry ages 11, 13 and into sixth. *Transfer from maintained schools:* 33% main intakes, plus 20% to sixth.

Entrance Common entrance and own scholarship exams used. Usually oversubscribed. Special gifts welcomed; boarders must be Roman Catholic. Parents are expected to buy a few text books. Means-tested scholarships and bursaries, up to full fees.

Parents 35% live within 30 miles; 30% live overseas.

Staff Headmistress Sister Jean Sinclair, in post for 9 years. 53 full time staff, 12 part time. Annual turnover varies.

Academic work GCSE and A-levels. 26 subjects offered (no A-level general studies). In 1990, 95 pupils in upper fifth, 75 in upper sixth (now 87). *GCSE:* in 1990, 78 upper fifth gained at least grade C in 8+ subjects; 12 in 5–7; and 5 in 4 subjects. *A- and AS-levels:* 4 upper sixth passed in 4 A-level subjects; 55 in 3 (including 8 passing an additional AS-level); 6 in 2; 8 in 1 (including 1 passing an additional AS-level); 1 in 1 AS-level. 9 took science A-levels; 43 arts/humanities; 23 both. *Computing facilities:* 2 RM Nimbus networks, one in general use, one in science and geography departments. *Special provision:* Specialist help for dyslexia, as recommended as far as possible. EFL: prepared for Cambridge First Certificate and Certificate in Proficiency.

European Community *Languages:* French offered: to age 14; GCSE; AS-level; A-level; Institute of Linguists. German offered: to age 14; GCSE; AS-level; A-level; Institute of Linguists. Italian offered: to age 14; GCSE; A-level; Institute of Linguists. Spanish offered: to age 14; GCSE; AS-level; A-level;

Institute of Linguists. 25–50% take GCSE in more than 1 EC language. *Exchanges:* Regular individual exchanges for pupils aged 11–18 to France, Germany, Italy and Spain.

Non-academic activities (whole school) *Music:* 300+ learn a musical instrument, 50 to Grade 6 or above; on average 1 accepted for Music School, 2 take degree courses; 40+ play in school orchestra, 200 in choir. *Drama and dance:* 80+ in two major school productions a year; c20 take exams in ESB, RAD etc. Some accepted for Drama/Dance Schools, 3 on to related degree courses. *Art:* c40 take GCSE art, c10 ceramics; some A-level art and ceramics. 4 pa accepted for Art School. *Sport:* Hockey, netball, tennis, swimming, volleyball, athletics, squash, judo, self-defence, fencing, aerobics, sailing, cross-country, riding, badminton, table tennis, ballet, modern dance available. Large numbers take part in non-compulsory sport. 20+ pupils represent county (hockey, netball, tennis, gymnastics). *Other:* Pupils enter Duke of Edinburgh's Award Scheme (bronze, silver and gold). c20 visit old and handicapped (own scheme). Several enter voluntary schemes or work for national charities after leaving school. Other activities include a computer group (voluntary) which helps produce programs to help dyslexics and adult literacy programmes. A number learn to drive, use video camera, debating, Young Enterprise, Neighbourhood Engineers, bridge; other activities depend on the enthusiasm of current pupils.

Careers In 1990, 86% leavers went on to degree courses; 3% to art/drama/music colleges; 11% to non-degree courses (eg secretarial, nursing, Montessori). Of those going on to degree courses, 9% went to Oxbridge, 68% to other universities; 23% to poly/colleges.

3% those going on to higher education went to courses in practical art; 2% in music; 67% in humanities/social sciences; 6% in medicine; and 22% in science/engineering.

Uniform School uniform worn except in upper sixth.

Houses/prefects Competitive houses. Prefects and head girl elected by main school and staff, approved by Head; house prefects approved by housemistress. School Council.

Religion Girls are expected to fulfil requirements of Roman Catholic church; voluntary forms of prayer encouraged.

Social Debates, socials, joint musical competitive performances with other schools. Trips abroad, ski-ing (annual), to Greece (biennial for classicists), Russia (for those studying Russian), individual exchanges to France, Germany, Spain, Italy. Sixth form allowed to bring own car/bike to school with good reason. Meals self service. Second-hand uniform sale arranged, book stall, vending machine. Alcohol allowed in controlled situations (eg at meal with tutor); no tobacco.

Discipline No corporal punishment. Pupils failing to produce homework once might expect to discuss reason for failure and to produce it; those caught smoking cannabis on the premises could expect immediate suspension, probably without return.

Boarding All upper sixth have own study bedroom, lower sixth and fifth share in pairs; remainder in small dormitories or ones partitioned into cubicles. Houses divided broadly by age. Resident nurse; accessible local practice. Pupils can provide and cook food to limited extent at weekends. 3 or 4 optional Sat/Sun exeats termly plus half-term. Visits to local town allowed on Saturdays (lower sixth up); all ages to local village.

· St Margaret's (Aberdeen) ·

St Margaret's School
for Girls
17 Albyn Place
Aberdeen AB9 1RH
Tel 0224 584466

- Pupils 400
- Boys 3–5 only
  (Day)
- Girls 3–18 (Day)
- Higher year 30

- Termly fees
  £836 (Day)
- GSA, HAS
Enquiries/application to
the Headmistress

What it's like

Founded in 1846 and the oldest all-through girls' school in Scotland, it is situated in Albyn Place, one of the city's finest conservation areas. Its facilities are first rate. The school aims to provide an all-round modern education with a sound academic basis. A variety of sports is available.

School profile

Pupils Total age range 3–18; 400 day pupils (7 boys, 393 girls). Senior department 12–18, 212 girls. Main entry ages 3 (boys and girls), 11, 12 (girls). *Transfer from maintained schools:* 50% intakes at 11 and 12, plus 1% to sixth.

Entrance Own test and interview. No special skills or religious requirements. Parents expected to buy text books; maximum extras, £65. 19 assisted places available. 1 internal scholarship for sixth year, £400.

Parents 15+% are doctors, lawyers etc; 15+% in industry or commerce.

Staff Headmistress Miss L M Ogilvie, 2 years in post. 32 full time staff, 14 part time. Annual turnover 1%.

Academic work O-grades/S-grades, Highers (plus 1 subject each at GCSE and A-level). 15 subjects offered. On average, 41 pupils in O/S-grade year, 29 in Higher, 14 in A-level/CSYS year. *O/S-grade:* in 1990, 15 passed 8 subjects; 13 in 5–7; and 6 in 1–4 subjects. *Highers:* 7 passed in 5+ subjects, 9 in 4, 18 in 3, 8 in 2, 3 in 1 subject. *Computing facilities:* 12 machines in new computer room; computers also in prep and junior departments, and some subject departments. *Special provision:* Dyslexic testing available and exam provision made; magnifiers provided for visually handicapped.

European Community *Languages:* French offered: to age 14; S-grade; Higher; CSYS. German offered: to age 14; S-grade; Higher; CSYS. 25–50% take S-grade in more than 1 EC language. *Exchanges:* Regular exchanges for pupils aged 14–16 to France. *Other:* French and German language assistants.

Senior pupils' non-academic activities *Music:* Orchestral groups, choirs. *Sport:* Athletics, badminton, basketball, cross country, dance, gymnastics, hockey, netball, squash, swimming, tennis, volleyball available. *Other activities* include computer club, Young Engineers' Club, drama society, debating society, Scripture Union and Duke of Edinburgh's Award Scheme.

Careers In 1990, 58% leavers went on to degree courses; 3% to art/drama/music colleges; 30% to non-degree courses (eg business studies, hospitality management, spatial design, travel and tourism); 3% straight into careers (eg ski-racing); 6% other. Of those going on to degree courses, 73% went to universities; 27% to poly/colleges. 70% those going on to higher education went to courses in humanities/social sciences; 5% in medicine; and 25% in science/engineering.

· St Margaret's (Edinburgh) ·

St Margaret's School
Edinburgh Ltd
East Suffolk Road
Edinburgh
EH16 5PJ
Tel 031 668 1986

- Pupils 830
- Boys 3–7 only (Day)
- Girls 3–18 (Day/Board)
- Higher year 100

- Termly fees £1060 (Day) £2130 (Board/ Weekly)
- GSA Enquiries/application to the Headmistress

What it's like

Founded in 1890, it is urban with the school houses around the site within a quarter of a mile of each other. There are pleasant buildings and grounds. The nursery and preparatory departments are combined. Very good facilities and comfortable boarding accommodation are provided. A certain amount of religious worship is compulsory. Many sixth formers go on to degree courses. French, German, Italian and Spanish are offered at S-level and many girls take S-level in more than one European language. (Italian is offered at Highers in addition to languages taught at S-level.) There are regular exchanges with France and Germany. The music, drama and art departments are very strong indeed. The school also has a very high reputation in sports and games (15–20 representatives at county level). The record in the Duke of Edinburgh's Award Scheme is outstanding.

School profile

Pupils Total age range 3–18; 830 pupils, 755 day (20 boys, 735 girls), 75 boarding girls. Senior department 12–18, 530 girls. Main entry ages 3, 5 (boys and girls), 12 and into the sixth (girls). 5% are children of former pupils. Own prep department provides over 40%. *Transfer from maintained schools:* 25% senior intake, plus 2% to sixth.

Entrance Own entrance exam used. Sometimes oversubscribed. No special skills or religious requirements. Parents not expected to buy text books. 54 assisted places. 5 scholarships/bursaries available, full day fees to half day fees.

Parents 15+% are in industry or commerce; 15+% are doctors, lawyers etc; 15+% are academics, lecturers etc. 60+% live within 30 miles; up to 10% live overseas.

Staff Headmistress Mrs M J Cameron, in post for 7 years. 60 full time staff, 20 part time. Annual turnover 2%. Average age 45.

Academic work S-grade, Highers, A-levels, CSYS and RSA. 24 subjects offered (including A-level general studies). In 1990, 98 in S-grade year, 92 in Higher (now 100), 74 in A-level/CSYS year. *S-grade:* in 1990, 59 pupils passed in 8+ subjects; 26 in 5–7; and 13 in 1–4 subjects. *Highers:* 30 passed in 5+ subjects, 13 in 4, 24 in 3, 9 in 2, 10 in 1 subject. *A-levels and CSYS:* 5 passed in 3 subjects; 5 in 2; and 29 in 1 subject. Many took Highers as well as, or instead of, A-levels and CSYS. 32% took science A-levels/CSYS; 67% arts/humanities. *Computing facilities:* 12 computers in each of 2 labs, plus computers in many classrooms. *Special provision:* Remedial; exam dispensations for dyslexics; EFL lessons.

European Community *Languages:* French offered: to age 14; S-grade; Higher; A-level. German offered: to age 14; S-grade; Higher; A-level. Italian: S-grade; Higher. Spanish offered: to age 14; S-grade; Higher; A-level. 25–50% take S-grade in more than 1 EC language. *Exchanges:* Regular exchanges for pupils aged 14–16 to France and Germany. *Other:* Regularly have French exchange pupils (2–3 weeks) and Spanish pupils for a year (occasionally French or German).

Senior pupils' non-academic activities *Music:* 230 learn a musical instrument, 15 to Grade 6 or above, 1 accepted for Music School; 50 in school orchestra, 35 in choir; 1 in National Youth Orchestra, 3 in county orchestra. *Drama and dance:* 100 in school productions. 1 accepted for Drama/Dance School. 1 goes on to work in theatre. *Art:* 20 take as non-examined subject; 40 take O-grade; 10 A-level/CSYS. 2 accepted for Art School. 50 belong to photographic club. *Sport:* Hockey, lacrosse, badminton, squash, swimming, tennis, athletics, dance-gymnastics available. 95% take non-compulsory sport; 60 take ski-ing. Pupils represent county (hockey, swimming, lacrosse, fencing, tennis). *Other:* 40+ take part in local community schemes. 45 have bronze Duke of Edinburgh's Award, 25 have silver and 25 gold. 2 enter voluntary schemes after leaving school. Other activities include a computer club, country dancing, self-defence, ski-ing. Boarders: riding, driving lessons.

Careers In 1990, 64% leavers went on to degree courses; 6% to art/drama/music colleges; 25% to non-degree courses (eg secretarial, cookery); 4% straight into careers (eg nursing); 1% other. Of those going on to degree courses, 67% went to universities; 33% to poly/colleges. 23% those going on to higher education went to courses in humanities/social sciences; 8% in medicine and para-medical; and 9% in science/engineering, plus others to eg business studies, agriculture.

Uniform School uniform worn except in the sixth.

Houses/prefects Competitive houses. No prefects. Head girl and head of house – elected by the school. School Council.

Religion Compulsory assembly and church on Sunday for boarders under 16.

Social Reel club, debates, productions with other local schools. Organised exchanges with France and Germany, trips of various kinds every year. Pupils allowed to bring own car/bike/motorbike to school. Meals self service. School shop. No tobacco/alcohol allowed.

Discipline No corporal punishment. Pupils failing to produce homework once might expect a reprimand; those caught smoking cannabis on the premises could expect suspension and their parents informed.

Boarding 1% have own study bedroom, 33% share (with 1); 25% are in dormitories of 6+. Houses, of 25 and 60 are divided by age group. Central dining room. Various exeats each term, up to every weekend for seniors. Visits to the local town allowed.

Alumni association run by Mrs Christine Seaton, c/o 110 Mayfield Road, Edinburgh 9.

· St Martha's (Hadley Wood) ·

St Martha's Convent	● Pupils 325	● Termly fees
Camlet Way	● Boys None	£690 (Day)
Hadley	● Girls 11–18	Enquiries/application to
Barnet	(Day)	the Headmistress
Hertfordshire	● Upper sixth 15	
Tel 081 449 6889		

What it's like

Founded in 1947, it lies opposite Hadley Wood just outside Barnet. The main building is Mount House, a very handsome 18th century country house with beautiful gardens and grounds. This has been adapted and is well equipped. It is run by the Sisters of St Martha, a Roman Catholic order which originated in the 17th century in the Dordogne. There is a certain amount of emphasis on religious instruction, prayer and worship. The academic standards are reasonable and results quite good. A few girls go on to degree courses each year. Some music and art but, apparently, minimal drama. A few sports and games but no extra-curricular activities and no community services or Duke of Edinburgh's Award Scheme.

School profile

Pupils Total age range 11–18; 325 day girls. Main entry ages 11 and into the sixth. Own junior school provides over 20%. 5% are children of former pupils.

Entrance Own entrance exam used. No special skills, Catholic school accepting other faiths. Parents expected to buy text books. No scholarships/bursaries but some Catholics accepted at part fees.

Parents 15+% in industry or commerce. 60+% live within 30 miles.

Staff Head Sister M Cecile Archer, in post for 11 years. 19 full time staff, 6 part time. Annual turnover 1–2%. Average age 35–40.

Academic work GCSE and A-levels. Average size of upper fifth 60; upper sixth 15. *GCSE:* on average, 13 pupils in upper fifth pass 1–4 subjects; 20, 5–7 subjects; 22 pass 8+ subjects. *A-levels:* on average, 2 pupils in upper sixth pass 1 subject; and 4 pass 2 subjects. On average, 6 take science/engineering A-levels; 6 take arts and humanities. *Computing facilities:* computer room.

European Community *Languages:* French offered: to age 14; GCSE; AS-level; A-level. German offered: to age 14; GCSE; AS-level; A-level. 10–25% take GCSE in more than 1 EC language. *Exchanges:* Regular exchanges for pupils aged 11–16 to France.

Senior pupils' non-academic activities *Music:* 40–50 learn a musical instrument, 15 in school orchestra, 30 in choir. *Art:* 23 take GCSE; 2 A-level. *Sport:* Netball, tennis, badminton, swimming, golf, squash available.

Careers On average, 60% leavers went on to degree courses; 30% to non-degree courses (eg secretarial, languages); 10% straight into careers (eg civil service, banking). Of those going on to degree courses, 50% went to universities; 50% to poly/colleges. 50% those going on to higher education went to courses in humanities/social sciences; and 50% in science/engineering.

Uniform School uniform worn except the sixth.

Houses/prefects No competitive houses. Prefects and head girl – appointed by the Head.

Religion Worship encouraged.

Social Some organised trips abroad. Sixth form allowed to bring own car to school. Meals self service. School shop. No tobacco/alcohol allowed.

Discipline No corporal punishment. Pupils failing to produce homework once might expect a warning; those caught smoking cannabis on the premises might expect suspension for a period.

· St Mary's (Ascot) ·

St Mary's School
St Mary's Road
Ascot
Berkshire SL5 9JF
Tel 0344 23721

- Pupils 330
- Boys None
- Girls 10–18
- (Day/Board)
- Upper sixth 45

- Termly fees
  £1788 (Day)
  £2980 (Board)
- GSA
  Enquiries/application to
  the Admissions
  Secretary

What it's like

Founded in 1885, it is semi-rural, single-site and purpose-built in 55 acres of very pleasant gardens and grounds. The buildings are well designed and accommodation comfortable. Very good modern facilities. It is owned and managed by the Institute of the Blessed Virgin Mary and several of the staff are Sisters of the Order. A Roman Catholic foundation. All pupils must be RCs. The doctrines and practices of the Church (attendance at Sunday Mass etc) are an essential part of the curriculum. Academically the standards are high and results are good. Each year very many sixth formers go on to degree courses, including Oxbridge. An impressive array of EC languages is offered – Dutch, French, German, Italian, Portuguese and Spanish. Strong in music, drama and art. A wide range of games, sports and activities. Commitment to local community schemes and a promising record in the Duke of Edinburgh's Award Scheme.

School profile

Pupils Age range 10–18; 330 girls, 10 day, 320 boarding. Main entry ages 10, 11 and into sixth. Approx 5% are children of former pupils. *Transfer from maintained schools:* Few.

Entrance Own entrance exam used. Oversubscribed. No special skills required but pupils should be Roman Catholic. Parents expected to buy text books in sixth form; maximum extras £150. Some discretionary bursaries.

Parents 15+% in industry or commerce. 30+% live within 30 miles; 10+% live overseas.

Staff Headmistress Sister Mark Orchard, in post for 8 years. 40 full time staff, 20 part time. Annual turnover 5%. Average age 42.

Academic work GCSE and A-levels. 16 subjects offered (including Russian and AS-level general studies). In 1991, 45 pupils in upper fifth, 45 in upper sixth. *GCSE:* in 1990, 94% upper fifth gained at least grade C in 7+ subjects. *A-levels:* 99% upper sixth passed in 3 subjects; 1%

in 2. 20% took science A-levels; 70% arts/humanities; 10% both. *Computing facilities:* 8 Archimedes computers; 4 BBC Masters.

European Community *Languages:* French offered: to age 14; GCSE; AS-level; A-level. German offered: to age 14; GCSE; AS-level; A-level. Italian offered: to age 14; GCSE; AS-level; A-level. Portuguese offered: to age 14; GCSE; AS-level; A-level. Spanish offered: to age 14; GCSE; AS-level; A-level. 25–50% take GCSE in more than 1 EC language. *Exchanges:* Scheme starting in 1992. *Other:* European co-ordinator on staff. Talks from MEP. Second in European Youth Parliament Competition.

Senior pupils' non-academic activities *Music:* 60% learn a musical instrument, 10 to Grade 6 or above, 1 accepted for Music School; 25 in school orchestra, 35 in chapel choir. Others in madrigal and junior choir. *Drama and dance:* 50 in school productions. 10 up to Grade 6 ESB etc. 2 accepted for Drama School. *Art:* 40

take as non-examined subject; 30 GCSE; 15 A-level. 2 accepted for Art and Architectural School. 20 take photography, 20 take pottery. *Sport:* Netball, hockey, tennis, rounders, athletics, water sports, gymnastics, swimming, badminton, keep fit, fencing, golf, squash (in Ascot town), trampolining, karate available. 40 take non-compulsory sport. *Other:* 45 take part in local community schemes. 25 have bronze Duke of Edinburgh's Award, 3 have silver and 2 gold. Several enter voluntary schemes in GAP year. Other activities include a computer club, bridge, debating, theatre, art appreciation, music appreciation, jazz dancing, wine tasting, driving.

Careers In 1990, 80% leavers went on to degree courses; 15% to art/drama/music colleges; 5% to non-degree courses (eg HND). Of those going on to degree courses, 10% went to Oxbridge, 82% to other universities; 8% to poly/colleges. 8% those going on to higher education went to courses in practical art; 3% in drama/acting; 83% in humanities/social sciences; and 6% in science/engineering.

Uniform School uniform worn, except the sixth.

Houses/prefects Competitive houses. Prefects, head girl, head of house and house prefects – mixture of appointment by Head and election by school.

Religion Compulsory worship in accordance with requirements of RC church.

Social Occasional debates, sports events, theatrical performances with other schools. Organised ski-ing trips abroad; A-level French/history of art trip to Paris. Senior pupils allowed to bring own bike to school. Meals self service. No tobacco/alcohol allowed.

Discipline No corporal punishment. Pupils failing to produce homework once might expect their tutor to be informed ('on report' on second occasion; detention on third). Those caught taking illicit drugs on the premises may expect immediate expulsion; those caught smoking are fined £20 for first offence, suspension for second.

Boarding 23% have own study bedroom, 57% share with 1 other; 20% are in dormitories of 6+. Houses, of 60, divided by age. Resident qualified nurse. Central dining room. 2 termly exeats. Visits to local town allowed.

Alumni association run by Sister Bridget Geoffrey-Smith, c/o the School.

Former pupils Sarah Hogg; Marina Warner.

· St Mary's (Calne) ·

St Mary's School
Calne
Wiltshire
SN11 0DF
Tel 0249 815899

- Pupils 312
- Boys None
- Girls 11–18
  (Day/Board)
- Upper sixth 37

- Termly fees
  £1620 (Day)
  £2725 (Board)
- GSA
  Enquiries/application to
  the Headmistress

What it's like

Founded in 1873 by Canon Duncan, the Vicar of Calne. It occupies an agreeable site of 25 acres on the outskirts of the small town at the edge of the Wiltshire Downs. All the school buildings are within the grounds which include attractive gardens. Since 1950 there has been a continuous development programme and the school is now very well equipped with modern facilities. An Anglican foundation, it puts some emphasis on worship and religious education (a chapel was built in 1972–3). By tradition it is a 'personal' school structured for the individual and it has

735

a friendly atmosphere. Quite a large staff allows a staff:pupil ratio of 1:10, or better, for there is a large number of peripatetic teachers. Exam results are impressive and for a school of this size a very large number of sixth formers go on to degree courses, including Oxbridge. The school is strong in pastoral care and has a large sixth form. Music is very vigorously supported (very many girls learn an instrument; many study two or more). Drama and art are major activities. A standard range of sports and games is available and there are plentiful extra-curricular activities. A large number of girls take part in local community schemes and the Duke of Edinburgh's Award Scheme has become increasingly important (a large number of awards).

School profile

Pupils Age range 11–18; 312 girls, 32 day, 280 boarding. Main entry ages 11, 12 and occasionally into sixth.

Entrance Common entrance exam used. Not oversubscribed. No special skills or religious requirements. Parents not expected to buy text books. 6 scholarships (academic, music; 2 sixth); some bursaries for current pupils.

Parents 15+% in industry. 10+% live within 30 miles; up to 10% live overseas.

Staff Headmistress Miss D H Burns, in post for 6 years. 36 full time staff, 31 part time. Annual turnover low, but variable. Average age 38.

Academic work GCSE and A-levels. 18 subjects offered (no A-level general studies). In 1990, 53 pupils in upper fifth, 37 in upper sixth. *GCSE:* in 1990, 51 upper fifth gained at least grade C in 8+ subjects; 1 in 5–7 subjects. *A-levels:* 1 upper sixth passed in 4+ subjects; 31 in 3; 6 in 2 subjects. 23% took science A-levels; 65% arts/humanities; 12% both. *Computing facilities:* 18 BBC Masters.

Senior pupils' non-academic activities *Music:* 249 learn a musical instrument, 11 to Grade 6 or above; 113 play in school orchestras or chamber groups, 116 in various choirs. *Drama:* up to 50 in public performances, all 1st/2nd year pupils in internal productions. *Art:* 16 take as non-examined subject; 22 take GCSE; 7 A-level; 10 history of art A-level. *Sport:* Lacrosse, hockey, netball, tennis, rounders, swimming, PE, dance, fencing available; also riding (at nearby stables). 30 take part in non-compulsory sport. 30 take exams BAGA awards. 3 pupils represent county (junior lacrosse). *Other:* 43 have bronze Duke of Edinburgh's Award, 19 silver and 4 gold. 53 in local community schemes. 7–10 enter voluntary schemes after leaving school. Other activities include a computer club, drama, art, video club, sports, acrobatics, volleyball, woodwork, cookery.

Careers 2 part time careers advisers. Annual average accepted for *degree courses* at Oxbridge, 4; other universities, 25; medical schools, 1–2; polytechnics/colleges, 6; *other general training courses*, 2–3. Average going straight into careers in the City, 1.

Uniform School uniform worn; dress code for sixth form.

Houses/prefects Competitive houses. No prefects. Head girl, head of house and house prefects – selected by staff and school. School Council.

Religion Morning assembly. Sunday chapel.

Social Oratorio with Marlborough Choral Society. Organised trips abroad to Russia and Normandy, exchange with Toulouse. Fifth form upwards allowed to bring own bike to school. Meals self service. Tuck shop. No tobacco/alcohol allowed.

Discipline No corporal punishment. Pupils failing to produce homework once might get a warning; those caught smoking cannabis on the premises could expect expulsion.

Boarding 50% have own study bedroom, 4% share; 15% are in dormitories of 6+. Houses, of approx 38–70, divided by age. Resident qualified nurse. Central dining room. *Upper sixth* can provide and cook own snacks, but main meals compulsory. 2 fixed weekend exeats each term plus others. Visits to local town allowed at lunchtimes, aged 11–18.

· St Mary's (Cambridge) ·

St Mary's School
Bateman Street
Cambridge
CB2 1LY
Tel 0223 353253

- Pupils 570
- Boys None
- Girls 11–18
- (Day/Weekly)
- Upper sixth 60

- Termly fees
  £891 (Day)
  £1595 (Weekly)
- GSA

Enquiries to the
Headmistress
Application to the
Admissions Secretary

What it's like

Founded in 1898, it is sited in the city centre, overlooking the university botanic garden, within easy walking distance of museums, theatres and colleges. Excellent facilities. Basically a Roman Catholic school, but inter-denominational. It is administered by the Religion of the Institute of The Blessed Virgin Mary. Mass and other services are attended by the majority of pupils. The religious education curriculum is based on Catholic doctrine and is followed by all pupils. Within the setting of a Christian community the school provides an education of the grammar school type. Academic standards are high. Very many leavers go on to degree courses, including Oxbridge each year. Talents for music, art, drama and sport are strongly encouraged. It is in fact extremely strong in drama, and very strong in music and art. Very much a local school working closely with parents. Well known in the area for its Christian teaching, pastoral care and happy and purposeful atmosphere. A wide variety of sports, games and extra-curricular activities. A very large commitment to local community schemes. Substantial participation in the Duke of Edinburgh's Award Scheme and an impressive record.

School profile

Pupils Age range 11–18; 570 girls, 490 day, 80 weekly boarding. Main entry ages 11 and into sixth. Approx 5% are children of former pupils. *Transfer from maintained schools:* 45% main intake, plus 45% to sixth.

Entrance Own entrance exam used. Oversubscribed. Special consideration given to candidates with talents in music and art. Roman Catholic school but other Christian denominations welcomed. Parents not expected to buy text books; no compulsory extras. 25 assisted places pa (including 5 for sixth).

Staff Headmistress Miss Michele Conway, 2 years in post. 42 full time staff, 10 part time plus music and drama staff. Average age 40.

Academic work GCSE, AS and A-levels. In 1990, 85 pupils in fifth year, 51 in upper sixth (now 60). *GCSE:* In 1990, 76 fifth years gained at least grade C in 8+ subjects; 9 in 5–7 subjects. *A-levels:* 1 upper sixth passed in 4+ subjects; 46 in 3; 1 in 2; and 3 in 1 subject. On average 10 take science A-levels; 36 arts/humanities; 20 both. *Computing facilities:* Large network of Archimedes and A3000's with laser, colour and dot-matrix printers. *Special provision:* Copes with mild dyslexia.

European Community *Languages:* French offered: to age 14; GCSE; AS-level; A-level. German offered: to age 14; GCSE; AS-level; A-level. Italian offered: to age 14; GCSE; AS-level; A-level. Spanish offered: to age 14; GCSE; AS-level; A-level. 25–50% take GCSE in more than 1 EC language. *Exchanges:* Regular exchanges for pupils aged 11–14 to France and Spain.

Non-academic activities *Music:* 275 learn a musical instrument, 15 to Grade 6 or above; 30 in school orchestra, 100 in choirs, 60 in various instrumental ensembles. *Drama and dance:* 50 in school productions, 200 in school drama competition, 30 in dance display. 20 to Grade 6 LAMDA, 10 in Cambridge Speech and Drama Festival. 2 accepted for Drama/Dance Schools. *Art:* 10 take art/ceramics as non-examined subject; 32 GCSE; 6 A-level. 3–4 accepted for Art School. 20 belong to eg photographic club. *Sport:* Athletics, badminton, canoeing, golf, gymnastics, hockey, judo, netball, rounders, squash, swimming, trampolining, tennis, table tennis, volleyball available. 140 take non–compulsory sport. 250 take exams in swimming, 10 in trampoline, 80 in gymnastics, 60 in athletics. 3 pupils represent country (tennis, swimming), 6 represent county, (tennis, cross country); school won East of England cup at tennis 1987. *Other:* 100 take part in local community schemes. 20 enter voluntary schemes after leaving; 2 work for national charities. 100 girls pa take part in the Duke of Edinburgh's Award Scheme. Other activities include a computer club, Young Enterprise (awards in 1987), debating, pottery, field work, dances.

Careers On average, 80% leavers went on to degree courses; 4% to art/drama/music colleges; 14% to non-degree courses (eg travel and tourism, further A-level courses); 2% straight into careers. Of those going on to degree courses, 14% went to Oxbridge, 68% to other universities; 18% to poly/colleges. 5% those going on to higher education went to courses in practical art; 2% in drama/acting; 2% in music; 59% in humanities/social sciences; 6% in medicine; and 26% in science/engineering.

Uniform School uniform worn except in sixth.

Houses/prefects No competitive houses. No prefects; duties shared by upper sixth. Head girl and group of deputies – elected by staff and sixth form. Sixth Form Council.

Religion All attend daily assembly and Christmas carol service. Mass and other services attended by majority of pupils. Roman Catholic RE curriculum followed by all pupils.

Social Combined Cambridge school choirs (major work in alternate years); debating, theatrical productions with other schools. Regular exchanges with school in Paris; Spanish, German, Italian exchanges; other excursions abroad. Pupils allowed to bring own bike to school. Meals self-service. School shop. No tobacco/alcohol allowed.

Discipline No corporal punishment. No penal code; pupils are expected to work hard and to respect the aims of the school. Parents would be consulted in serious cases, and decisions would depend on circumstances.

Boarding 45 have own study bedroom, 35 share (2–5 beds per room). Central dining room. All pupils return home at weekends. Visits to local town allowed, according to age.

Alumni association run by Mrs S de Backer, c/o the School.

· St Mary's (Colchester) ·

St Mary's School	• Pupils 590	• Termly fees
Lexden Road	• Boys None	£885 (Day)
Colchester	• Girls 4–17	• GSA
Essex CO3 3RB	(Day)	Enquiries/application to
Tel 0206 572544	• Upper sixth No	the Principal

What it's like

Founded in 1908, it is the only independent girls' school in the Colchester area offering secondary education. The senior school has an urban site; that of the lower school is semi-rural, 3 miles away on a 9-acre estate. Both have pleasant buildings and adequate facilities. A sound general education is provided. Most girls transfer at 16/17; no A-level courses. Strong music and art departments. A very good variety of sports, games and extra-curricular activities. Some commitment to local community schemes and the Duke of Edinburgh's Award Scheme.

School profile

Pupils Total age range 4–17; 590 day girls. Senior department 11–17, 300 girls. Main entry ages 4 and 11. Approx 50% of senior intake from own junior dept. Approx 10% are children of former pupils. *Transfer from maintained schools:* 28% senior intake.

Entrance Own entrance exam used. Oversubscribed. No special skills or religious requirements. Parents not expected to buy text books; extras include instrumental lessons (£55), field trips etc. No scholarships/bursaries.

Staff Principal Mrs G Mouser, in post for 10 years. 33 full time staff, 25 part time. Annual turnover 6%.

Academic work GCSE only. 21 subjects offered. In 1990, 62 pupils in upper fifth. *GCSE:* in 1990, 29 upper fifth gained at least grade C in 8+ subjects; 27 in 5–7; and 6 in 1–4 subjects. *Computing facilities:* Large specialist room, basic equipment. All pupils work towards CLAIT Certificate. *Special provision:* Outside coaching arranged for EFL; dyslexia coaching in school.

European Community *Languages:* French offered: to age 14; GCSE. German offered: to age 14; GCSE. Italian offered: to age 14; GCSE. Spanish offered: to GCSE. 25–50% take GCSE in more than 1 EC language. *Exchanges:* Regular exchanges for pupils aged 14–16 to France and Germany. *Other:* Spanish pupils in school for summer term.

Senior pupils' non-academic activities *Music:* 30+ learn a musical instrument, 6 to Grade 6 or above, 1 accepted for Music School; 20+ in school orchestra, 75 school choir; 2 county youth orchestra, 2 National Youth Orchestra. *Drama and dance:* 20–40 in school productions. 2 take ESB, RAD etc to Grade 6. 1 accepted for Drama/Dance school. *Art:* 20 take GCSE. *Sport:* Tennis, hockey, indoor hockey, netball, cross-country, athletics, gymnastics, badminton, squash, trampolining, weight training, basketball, volleyball, self-defence, golf, swimming, keep fit available. Sport compulsory. *Other:* 10 take part in local community schemes. 10 working for bronze Duke of Edinburgh's Award, 3 for silver.

Careers Most pupils leave at 16 for sixth form college.

Uniform School uniform worn throughout.

Houses/prefects Competitive houses. Prefects, head girl, head of house and house prefects elected by the school and staff.

Religion Daily assembly, Harvest Festival and carol services are compulsory.

Social Debates with Royal Grammar

School (boys) and local independent boys' school; occasional joint productions. Annual ski-ing holiday; biennial cruise; annual language courses in France; exchanges in France and Germany; exchanges to Italy starting. Pupils allowed to bring own car/bike to school. Meals formal. No tobacco/alcohol allowed.

Discipline No corporal punishment. Pupils failing to produce homework once might expect a stern reproach (detention and report system for frequent offenders); those caught smoking cigarettes on the premises can expect exclusion for 24 hours and letter home.

Alumni association run by Mrs J Woodland, c/o the School.

· St Mary's (Crosby) ·

St Mary's College
Crosby
Merseyside L23 3AB
Tel 051 924 3926

- Pupils 797
- Boys 4–18 (Day)
- Girls 4–18 (Day)
- Upper sixth 84

- Termly fees
  £942 (Day)
- HMC
  Enquiries/application to the Secretary

What it's like

Founded in 1919 by the Christian Brothers. Urban and single-site, except the playing fields which are on a separate site. The first school buildings were erected in 1923–4 and there has been regular expansion and development since. There is a preparatory department and a main school and facilities are now good. It is a Roman Catholic foundation and most pupils are RCs. However, other denominations are welcome. Considerable emphasis on religious education, prayer and worship which are all encouraged. A sound general education is provided and results are very good. Many pupils go on to degree courses, including Oxbridge. There is music and drama, and very considerable strength in art. A good range of sports and games in which high standards are achieved. An adequate range of extra-curricular activities. A voluntary CCF is flourishing.

School profile

Pupils Total age range 4–18 (became fully co-ed 1989); 797 day pupils (642 boys, 155 girls). Senior department 11–18, 575 pupils (497 boys, 78 girls). Main entry ages 4+, 11+, 13+ and into sixth. Approx 20% are children of former pupils. *Transfer from maintained schools:* 52% senior intake, plus 63% to sixth.

Entrance Own entrance exam used. Oversubscribed. No special skills required; RC school, other practising Christians admitted. Parents not expected to buy text books, nor pay for extras such as music lessons. 45 assisted places. 12 bursaries pa, £1800–£150.

Parents 15+% are doctors, lawyers etc; 15+% in industry or commerce.

Staff Head Rev Br P E Ryan, in post for 3 years. 42 full time staff, 11 part time. Annual turnover 5%. Average age 35.

Academic work GCSE and A-levels. A-level general studies offered. In 1989, 91 pupils in upper fifth, 84 in upper sixth. *GCSE:* in 1989, 37 upper fifth gained at least grade C in 8+ subjects; 37 in 5–7; and 16 in 1–4 subjects. *A-levels:* 38 upper sixth passed in 4+ subjects; 11 in 3; 22 in 2; and 3 in 1 subject. 35 took science A-levels; 39 arts/humanities; 10 both. *Computing facilities:* Mainly networked RM Nimbus, some BBCs linked to Prestel.

Senior pupils' non-academic activities *Music:* 2 learn a musical instrument to Grade 6 or above. 20 in school orchestra, 20 in choir, 2 in other orchestras. *Drama and dance:* 40 in school productions, 10 in other. 1 accepted for Drama School. *Art:* 150 take as non-examined subject; 30 GCSE; 10 A-level; 8 accepted for Art School. 20 belong to photographic club. *Sport:* Rugby, squash, cross-country, swimming, aerobics, weight training, athletics, cricket, golf available. 60 take non-compulsory sport, 5 take exams. 9 represent county/country (rugby, athletics). Other activities include a computer club and lively chess club.

Careers 1 full time careers adviser. Annual average accepted for *arts and humanities degree courses* at Oxbridge, 5; other universities, 10; polytechnics/colleges, 5. *science and engineering degree courses* at Oxbridge, 5; other universities, 20; medical schools, 8; polytechnics/colleges, 5. *BEd,* 3. Average going straight into careers in armed services, 4; the church, 1; industry, 4; civil service, 5; other, 10. Traditional school career is medicine.

Uniform School uniform worn throughout.

Houses/prefects Competitive houses. Prefects, head boy/girl – elected by the school. School Council.

Religion Worship encouraged.

Social Debating competitions. French/German/Spanish language exchanges, skiing and other trips abroad. Pupils allowed to bring own car/bike/motorbike to school. Meals self service. School shop selling uniform. No tobacco/alcohol allowed.

Discipline No corporal punishment. Pupils failing to produce homework once might expect to produce it as soon as possible; those caught smoking cannabis on the premises might expect parents to be called in.

Alumni association run by Mr J Summerfield, Chairman, St Mary's Old Boys' Association, Moor Lane, Crosby.

Former pupils John Birt (Deputy Director General, BBC); Kevin McNamara MP; Kevin Dunn (ITN correspondent); William Hanrahan (BBC).

· St Mary's (Gerrards Cross) ·

St Mary's School
Packhorse Road
Gerrards Cross
Buckinghamshire
SL9 8JQ
Tel 0753 883370

- Pupils 340
- Boys None
- Girls 3–18
  (Day)
- Upper sixth 18

- Termly fees
  £1180 (Day)
- GSA
  Enquiries/application to
  the Headmistress

What it's like

Founded in 1874 and originally run by the Anglican Sisters of the Community of St Mary the Virgin, Wantage, it began life in Paddington, London and moved to its present premises in 1937. The main building is a country house in ample gardens and grounds. There have been many modern extensions to provide good facilities. The junior and senior school are separate entities on the same site on the north edge of Gerrards Cross. Non-denominational but it adheres to Anglican practice and tradition. Academic standards are good. A number of sixth form go on to degree courses each year. Some emphasis on Europe. French, German, Italian and Spanish are on offer and many girls take two languages at GCSE. Regular exchanges into France and Germany and first and second years visit France. Good opportunities for drama, speech and music. Adequate range of games, sports and activities. A very impressive record in the Duke of Edinburgh's Award Scheme.

School profile

Pupils Total age range 3–18; 340 day girls. Senior department 11–18, 200 girls. Main entry ages 11 and into the sixth. Own junior school provides over 40% senior intake. *Transfer from maintained schools:* 60% senior intake, negligible intake into sixth.

Entrance Common entrance and own exam used. Oversubscribed. No special skills or religious requirements. 3 scholarships pa, £800–£200 per term plus 3 scholarships and 2 bursaries for sixth form.

Parents 15+% in industry or commerce.

Staff Headmistress Mrs J P G Smith, in post for 7 years. 22 full time staff, 22 part time. Annual turnover 1–2%.

Academic work GCSE and A-levels. 21 GCSE subjects offered; 17 at A-level (including theatre studies, no A-level general studies). On average, 25 pupils in upper fifth, 18 in upper sixth. *GCSE:* in 1990, 22% upper fifth gained at least grade C in 8+ subjects; 60% in 5–7; and 11% in 1–4 subjects. *A-levels:* 50% upper sixth passed in 3 subjects; 14% in 1 subject. 71% took arts/humanities A-levels; 14% both arts and sciences. *Computing facilities:* Computer room equipped with 7 stand-alone Nimbus PC186; 2 Nimbus PC186; 6 BBC B's and 1 BBC Master in selected classrooms. *Special provision:* Practical help (eg enlarged papers for visually handicapped) and some remedial teaching.

European Community *Languages:* French offered: to age 14; GCSE; A-level. German offered: to age 14; GCSE; A-level. Italian offered: to age 14; GCSE. Spanish offered: to age 14; GCSE; A-level. 50–75% take GCSE in more than 1 EC language. *Exchanges:* Regular exchanges to France and Germany. Individual exchanges to Italy. *Other:* First and second years visit France.

Senior pupils' non-academic activities *Music:* 80 learn a musical instrument, 3 to Grade 6 or above. 20 in school orchestra, 20 in senior recorder group, 38 senior school choir, 14 madrigal choir. Some win instrumental/choral awards at art festivals. *Drama and dance:* 70 in school productions, 110 take speech and drama, 20 in festival productions. 8 to Grade 6 ESB, RAD etc, 8 to New Era and LAMDA. 2 accepted for Drama/Dance Schools. 45 enter competitions; 10, National Youth Theatre auditions. *Art:* 28 take GCSE; 6 A-level. 1 accepted for Art School. *Sport:* Netball, rounders, hockey, athletics, tennis, swimming, gymnastics, trampolining, self-defence, squash, badminton, basketball, archery, volleyball, lacrosse, golf etc available. 40 take non-compulsory winter tennis; 20 in gym squad and trampolining club, 20 in badminton club. 3–4 take GCSE physical education. 8 represent county/country (tennis, swimming, gymnastics, show jumping). *Other:* Girls take gold and bronze Duke of Edinburgh's Award. Other clubs include a computer club, gardening, craft, country dancing, pet care, tap dancing, bridge and Young Enterprise group.

Careers In 1990, 40% leavers went on to degree courses; 8% to non-degree courses (eg nursing); 14% straight into careers (eg secretarial, BBC, finance); 35% other. Of those going on to degree courses, 40% went to universities; 60% to poly/colleges. 20% those going on to higher education went to courses in practical art; 10% in drama/acting; 40% in humanities/social sciences; and 30% in science/engineering.

Uniform School uniform worn except the sixth.

Houses/prefects Competitive houses. Prefects, head girl, head of house and house prefects – appointed by Head and staff and election by pupils.

Religion Compulsory non-denominational assembly.

Social Debates, sixth form ball, Young Enterprise with other local schools; organised trips abroad. Pupils allowed to bring own car to school. Meals self service. No tobacco/alcohol/make-up/jewellery allowed.

Discipline No corporal punishment. Pupils failing to produce homework once might expect detention; those caught smoking cigarettes on the premises would be liable to expulsion. Any involvement with drugs would be regarded in the most serious light.

Alumni association run by Mrs Sarah Simpson, c/o the School.

· St Mary's (Shaftesbury) ·

St Mary's School
Shaftesbury
Dorset
SP7 9LP
Tel 0747 54005

- Pupils 310
- Boys None
- Girls 10–18
  (Day/Board)
- Upper sixth 35

- Termly fees
  £1475 (Day)
  £2355 (Board)
- GSA, BSA
  Enquiries/application to
  the Headmistress

What it's like

Founded in 1945 by the Institute of the Blessed Virgin Mary in the tradition of its foundress Mary Ward (17th century) who said 'There is no such difference between men and women that women may not do great things, as we have seen by example of many saints who have done great things. And I hope in God it will be seen that women in time to come will do much.' The school has a handsome site of 50 acres about a mile outside the Saxon town of Shaftesbury. It has fine buildings and excellent facilities, including comfortable boarding accommodation. It aims to educate girls of all Christian denominations, but primarily Roman Catholics, in an environment which develops Christian values and prepares girls for any walk of life. Religious education is part of the core curriculum and there is considerable emphasis on worship and prayer. The staff:pupil ratio is about 1:10. Academic standards are creditable and results are good. Each year very many sixth formers go on to degree courses, including many to Oxbridge. Music is very strong indeed. Drama, ballet and modern dance are well supported. There is a fair range of clubs and societies and some participation in the Duke of Edinburgh's Award Scheme. A standard range of sports and games is available.

School profile

Pupils Total age range 10–18; 310 girls (100 day, 210 boarding). Senior department 11–18, 270 girls. Main entry ages 10, 11 and into sixth. Approx 5% are children of former pupils. *Transfer from maintained schools:* 50% main intake, plus 1–2 pa into sixth.

Entrance Common Entrance and own entrance exam used. Slightly oversubscribed. No special skills required. Parents expected to buy a few text books in sixth; maximum extras, £100 per term. 4 scholarships pa, 50% full fees.

Parents 15+% in the armed services.

10+% live within 30 miles; up to 10% live overseas.

Staff Headmistress Sister M Campion Livesey, in post for 6 years. 29 full time staff, 8 part time. Annual turnover 5%. Average age 40–45.

Academic work GCSE and A-levels. 16 GCSE subjects offered; 15 at A-level (AS-level general studies compulsory). In 1990, 46 pupils in upper fifth, 31 in upper sixth (now 35). *GCSE:* in 1990, 28 upper fifth gained at least grade C in 8+ subjects; 15 in 5–7; and 3 in 1–4 subjects. *A-levels:* 23 upper sixth passed in 3 subjects; 6 in 2; and 2 in 1 subject (excluding general studies). 13% took science A-levels; 74% arts/humanities; 13% both. *Computing facilities:* Computer room plus computers in maths, physics, chemistry, English depts. All pupils learn information technology.

European Community *Languages:* French offered: to age 14; GCSE; A-level. German offered: to GCSE. Italian offered: to GCSE; A-level. Spanish offered: to GCSE; A-level. 25–50% take GCSE in more than 1 EC language. *Exchanges:* Regular exchanges on an individual basis for pupils aged 14–18 to France and Spain. *Other:* Some 12 Spanish girls in school for 2 years or more (to GCSE and/or A-level); occasional French or German pupils for 1 term.

Senior pupils' non-academic activities *Music:* 50 learn a musical instrument, 15 to Grade 6 or above. 1 pa accepted for Music School. 35 in school choir, 30 play in small ensemble groups. *Drama and dance:* 53 in school productions; 1 pa accepted for Drama School. 29 to Grade 6 or above in LAMDA. *Art:* 40 take as non-examined subject, 17 take GCSE; 6 A-level. 1 accepted for Art School. 45 belong to photographic club. *Sport:* 60–70 pupils take non-compulsory sport. 12 take life-saving exams. 4 represent county (athletics, hockey) and 2 netball teams. *Other:* 6 take part in local community schemes. 5 have silver Duke of Edinburgh's Award, 5 gold. Other activities include a computer club, learning to drive, sixth form wine-tasting society, bridge, film, debating, literary and photographic societies; poly (general interest) society which has outside speakers. Junior drama and textiles clubs.

Careers In 1990, 81% leavers went on to degree courses; 6% to art/drama/music colleges; 12% to non-degree courses (eg secretarial, nursing, tourism, finance). Of those going on to degree courses, 12% went to Oxbridge, 54% to other universities; 34% to poly/colleges. 3% those going on to higher education went to courses in practical art; 3% in music; 78% in humanities/social sciences; 4% in medicine; and 12% in science/engineering.

Uniform School uniform worn, varied in sixth.

Houses/prefects Competitive houses. Prefects, head girl, head of house and house prefects – appointed by Head after consultation with staff and previous upper sixth.

Religion Attendance at religious worship compulsory.

Social Occasional debates and joint concerts. Trips abroad in 1991: ski-ing trip (3rd and 4th years); history of art trip to Florence (sixth); choir concert tour to Italy; senior pupils to Russia. Pupils allowed to bring own bike for Duke of Edinburgh scheme; upper sixth may bring own cars. Meals self-service. School tuck shop. No tobacco/alcohol allowed.

Discipline No corporal punishment. Pupils failing to produce homework once might expect to re-do it in own time, followed by re-do in weekly detention slot for this purpose. Those caught smoking cannabis on school premises could expect expulsion (has never happened).

Boarding All sixth form have own study bedroom, upper sixth in separate house; fifth form share in pairs, fourth 2–4. Pupils divided into houses, same as competitive, 40–45 boarders and 15–20 day girls. Sixth form can provide and cook own food to limited extent. Qualified nurse by day. Exeats, 2 weekend exeats termly (3 in sixth), Friday afternoon to Sunday evening. Visits to the local town range from 3rd year (2 Saturdays per term) to sixth (any Saturday and during week if free and with tutor's permission).

· St Mary's (Wantage) ·

St Mary's School
Wantage
Oxfordshire
OX12 8BZ
Tel 02357 3571/2

- Pupils 300
- Boys None
- Girls 11–18
  (Board)
- Upper sixth 32

- Termly fees
  £2575 (Board)
- GSA
  Enquiries/application to
  the Admissions
  Secretary

What it's like

Founded in 1872 by William Butler, the vicar of Wantage, and run until 1975 by the Sisters of the Anglican Community of St Mary the Virgin. On their withdrawal it became a charitable trust. It remains an Anglican foundation and most of the pupils are Anglicans. The well-appointed buildings are on a continuous site in the middle of the small, market town. The modern facilities are of a high standard. There is a large staff creating a ratio of 1:7 pupils, plus a large part-time staff. Academic standards are high and results good. Many upper sixth leavers go on to degree courses each year. Very strong in art, music and drama. A wide range of games, sports and activities. An impressive record in the Duke of Edinburgh's Award Scheme.

School profile

Pupils Age range 11–18; 300 boarding girls. Main entry ages 11+, 12+ and into sixth. Approx 8% are children of former pupils. *Transfer from maintained schools:* 2% intake.

Entrance Common entrance used. Oversubscribed. No special skills required; most pupils are Anglicans. Parents expected to buy some sixth form text books; average extras £120. 4 scholarships/bursaries, half to one-third fees.

Parents From a wide range of occupations. Up to 10% live within 30 miles; up to 10% live overseas.

Staff Head Revd Pat Johns, in post for 10 years. 40 full time staff, 32 part time. Annual turnover 5%. Average age mid-thirties.

Academic work GCSE and A-levels. 14 GCSE subjects offered; 19 at A-level (including history of art, theatre studies, classical civilisation). In 1990, 57 pupils in upper fifth, 32 in upper sixth. *GCSE:* in 1990, 36 upper fifth gained at least grade C in 8+ subjects; 18 in 5–7; and 3 in 1–4 subjects. *A-levels:* 15 upper sixth passed in 3 subjects; 12 in 2; and 3 in 1 subject. 7 took science A-levels; 14 arts/humanities; 9 both. *Computing facilities:* Network of 15 mixed 8-bit and 32-bit computers in one computing classroom; in addition being updated and expanded to minimum of one computer per department and study area. *Special provision:* Extra coaching available for mild dyslexia. EFL teaching available if necessary.

European Community *Languages:* French offered: to age 14; GCSE; AS-level; A-level. German offered: to age 14; GCSE; AS-level; A-level. Spanish offered: to GCSE; AS-level; A-level. 10–25% take GCSE in more than 1 EC language. *Exchanges:* Regular exchanges for pupils aged 14–16 to France and Germany. *Other:* Occasional pupils from France, Germany and Spain.

Senior pupils' non-academic activities *Music:* 100 learn a musical instrument, 25 to Grade 6 or above; 1 accepted for Music School; some do music as part of teacher training course. 22 in school orchestra, 40 in school choir; a few in local youth orchestras. *Drama and dance:* 40 in school productions, 14 in fourth year voluntary group; 30 take LAMDA exams.

2 accepted for Drama/Dance Schools; 5 have participated in Edinburgh Festival. *Art:* 3 take as non-examined subject; 27 GCSE, 7 A-level. 2–5 accepted for Art School. *Sport:* Lacrosse, netball, tennis (indoor and outdoor), rounders, gymnastics, swimming, basketball, volleyball, squash available. 200 take non-compulsory sport. 150, sports exams (BAGA, RLSS bronze medallion). 3 represent county/country at sport. *Other:* Sixth formers help at local primary/handicapped schools. 47 have bronze Duke of Edinburgh's Award, and 10, gold. Other activities include a computer club, science club, needlework, wind band; girls may make their own arrangements for driving lessons.

Careers On average, 60% leavers go on to degree courses; 6% to art/drama/music colleges; 34% to non-degree courses (eg agriculture, secretarial, fashion, stage, horsemanship, domestic science). Of those going on to degree courses, 1% go to Oxbridge, 75% to other universities; 24% to poly/colleges. 31% those going on to higher education go to courses in practical art; 1% in drama/acting; 1% in music; 36% in humanities/social sciences; 1% in medicine; and 30% in science/engineering.

Uniform School uniform worn except the sixth.

Houses/prefects Competitive houses (socials). Prefects and head girl – appointed by Head in consultation with staff and girls. School Council.

Religion Compulsory daily service and Sunday eucharist.

Social Organised dances, parties, singing, drama with local boys' public schools; some activities (eg careers convention) with local comprehensive. Annual exchange with Germany, sixth formers to Paris and Florence; ski-ing trips. Pupils over 15 allowed to bring own bike to school. Meals self service. School bookshop. No tobacco/alcohol allowed.

Discipline No corporal punishment. Those caught involved with drugs would be expelled as would persistent smokers.

Boarding 33% have own study bedroom, 5% share with 1 other, 20% are in dormitories of 6+. Houses, of approximately 50, divided by age group. Resident qualified nurse; doctor visits regularly. Central dining room. Sixth form can provide and cook their own snacks. 2 weekend exeats each term plus 2 days and half-term. Visits to local town allowed.

Alumni association Magazine edited by Mrs D Webb, c/o the School.

Former pupils Emma Nicholson MP; Lucinda Green (3-day eventer); Dame Ruth Railton (founder, National Youth Orchestra).

· St Mary's Music ·

St Mary's Music School
Old Coates House
Manor Place
Edinburgh
EH3 7EB
Tel 031 220 1664

- Pupils 45
- Boys 7–18 (Day/Board)
- Girls 7–18 (Day/Board)
- Upper sixth 9

- Termly fees Apply to School
- CSA

Enquiries/application to the Headmaster

What it's like

Founded in 1880 as the choir school of St Mary's Episcopal Cathedral, in 1972 it widened its scope to become a specialist music school. It continues its choral tradition, but the bulk of its pupils are now instrumentalists. Composition, singing, counterpoint, harmony and aural training are also taught. The pupils specialise in all branches of music. The academic side is also taken care of, and an all-round education is provided. The academic work takes place in Old Coates House, next to the cathedral, dating from 1614; the musical education at Palmerston Place, just opposite. Good facilities and accommodation. All pupils go on to music college or music degree courses.

School profile

Pupils Total age range 7–18; 45 pupils, 20 day, 25 boarding. Senior department 11–18, 29 pupils. Main entry ages 8–11 and into sixth.

Entrance Admission by audition. Oversubscribed. Good musical skills required, no religious requirements. Parents not expected to buy text books. 35 means tested aided places, 12 scholarships for choristers.

Parents 10+% live within 30 miles; up to 10% live overseas.

Staff Headmaster J P S Allison, in post for 11 years. 5 full time staff, 33 part time. Annual turnover 1–10%. Average age mid-30s.

Academic work O-grade, S-grade, Highers and A-levels. Average size of S4-form, 6; S6–form, 9. All take arts and humanities A-levels; most get 4–6 O-grades, 2–4 Highers and 1 A-level.

European Community *Languages:* French offered: to age 14; O/S-grade; Higher. German offered: to age 14; O/S-grade; Higher. Greek offered: to age 14. Italian offered: O/S-grade; Higher. Under 10% take O/S-grade in more than 1 EC language.

Senior pupils' non-academic activities *Music:* All pupils are musicians; all are accepted for Music Colleges. *Drama*

and dance: 2–6 in school productions. *Art:* 1 takes art as non-examined subject; 2 O-grade; 2–3 A-level. *Sport:* Badminton, fencing, swimming, hillwalking available. 10 take non-compulsory sport.

Careers In 1990, 44% leavers went on to degree courses; 56% to art/drama/music colleges. Of those going on to degree courses, 11% went to universities; 89% to poly/colleges. All go on to courses in music.

Uniform School uniform not worn.

Houses/prefects No competitive houses, prefects or head boy/girl.

Religion Compulsory religious worship.

Social Occasional activities (always musical) with other local schools. Occasional musical tours. Pupils allowed to bring own car/bike/motorbike to school. Meals self service. No tobacco/alcohol allowed.

Discipline No corporal punishment. Pupils failing to produce homework once would be asked why; those caught smoking cannabis on the premises should expect expulsion.

Boarding 1 has own study bedroom, others share (1 or 2 others). Central dining room. 3 exeats each term, 3–10 days. Visits to the local town allowed.

· *St Maur's* ·

St Maur's
Thames Street
Weybridge
Surrey KT13 8NL
Tel 0932 851411

Pupils 750
● Boys 4–7 only (Day)
● Girls 4–18 (Day)
● Upper sixth 57

● Termly fees £1600
Enquiries/application to the Headmistress

What it's like

Founded in 1898, it is semi-rural, single-site with spacious and pleasant grounds. The original building, now the convent, is an 18th-century country house. The main school building dates from 1897 and there have been many modern additions. About 50% of the pupils are Roman Catholics. Regular religious instruction and occasional attendance at Mass and other services form an integral part of the way of life. Academic standards are high. Four European languages are offered – French, German, Italian and Spanish; many take two at GCSE. Regular exchanges with France, Germany and Italy. Very many sixth form leavers go on to degree courses. The sixth form has been run for a quarter of a century now jointly with that of St George's College, Weybridge, a boys' school about a mile away. Tremendously strong in music. Vigorous drama and art departments. A good range of sports, games and activities. Some participation in local community schemes and the Duke of Edinburgh's Award Scheme.

School profile

Pupils Total age range 4–18; 750 day pupils (21 boys, 729 girls). Senior department 11–18, 450 girls. Main entry ages 4 and 5 (boys and girls), 11 and into sixth (girls). *Transfer from maintained schools:* 30% senior intakes.

Entrance Own entrance exam used. Oversubscribed. No special skills or religious requirements but about 50% are Roman Catholic. 15 assisted places. Scholarships and bursaries available including 1 for physically handicapped pupil.

Parents 15+% in industry or commerce; 15+% are doctors, lawyers etc.

Staff Headmistress Sister Helen Wynne. Annual turnover 5%. Average age 40.

Academic work GCSE and A-levels. 24 A-level subjects offered. In 1990, 75 pupils in fifth, 57 in upper sixth. *GCSE:* on average, 35 fifth pass at least grade C in 8+ subjects; 23 in 5–7 subjects. *A-levels:* on average 52 upper sixth pass in 3 subjects. Most pupils take A-levels in both science/engineering and art/humanities. *Computing facilities:* Nimbus networked system, 18 stations.

European Community *Languages:* French offered: to age 14; GCSE; AS-level; A-level. German offered: age 13–14; GCSE; AS-level; A-level. Italian offered: to GCSE; A-level. Spanish offered: age 13–14; GCSE; AS-level; A-level. 50–75% take GCSE in more than 1 EC language. *Exchanges:* Regular exchanges to France, Germany and Italy.

Senior pupils' non-academic activities *Music:* 170+ learn a musical instrument, 6+ to Grade 6 or above; 25–30 in school orchestra; 80–100 in choir. *Drama and dance:* Tuition for GCSE available.

Art: A-level art and ceramics available. *Sport:* Lacrosse, tennis, netball, swimming, gymnastics, athletics, private tennis coaching with a professional coach available all year. *Other:* Pupils take part in local community schemes and some in silver and gold Duke of Edinburgh's Award.

Careers In 1990, 85% sixth form leavers went on to degree courses; 15% to art/drama/music colleges. 40% fifth form go on to non-degree courses; others to sixth form colleges. Of those going on to degree courses, 2% went to Oxbridge, 80% to other universities; 18% to poly/colleges. 20% those going on to higher education went to courses in practical art; 15% in drama/acting; 5% in music; 20% in humanities/social sciences; 20% in medicine; and 20% in science/engineering.

Uniform School uniform worn throughout.

Houses/prefects Competitive houses. Prefects, head girl, head of house and house prefects – appointed by the Head after consultation with the school and staff.

Religion Compulsory assembly once a week. RE is compulsory part of the curriculum unless parents request otherwise.

Social Mixed sixth form with St George's College, Weybridge. Occasional social evenings. Several organised trips, mostly in sixth form. Pupils allowed to bring own car/bike to school. Meals self service. Beer and wine allowed under staff supervision for annual sixth form ball.

Discipline No corporal punishment. Pupils failing to produce homework once or constantly arriving late might expect to be admonished; those caught endangering their own or others' lives by eg smoking, physical violence, would be suspended or expelled following a parental interview (this has not arisen).

Alumni association is run by the Headmistress and the Sister Superior.

· *S Michaels (Petworth)* ·

S Michaels Burton Park
Petworth
West Sussex
GU28 0LS
Tel 0798 42517

- Pupils 180
- Boys None
- Girls 11–18
  (Day/Board/Weekly)
- Upper sixth 14

- Termly fees
  £1800 (Day)
  £2730 (Board/
  Weekly)
- GSA, Woodard
  Enquiries to the Lady
  Warden
  Application to Miss M
  House

What it's like

Founded in 1884, a Woodard school, the main building is a magnificent Georgian-style country house (1842) in splendid gardens on an estate of 150 acres at the foot of the South Downs, 3 miles from Petworth. In recent years there have been several additional buildings, and facilities and accommodation are first-rate. Girls who enter at 11 spend their first year in Wakefield House, a converted 18th-century farmhouse within the grounds, and Hastings House, a lodge house for weekly boarders. A C of E foundation, chapel is compulsory on weekdays; compulsory Sunday services for boarders. (There is a remarkably high staff:pupil ratio of 1:5.) Academic standards are high. A number of sixth formers go on to degree courses each year. Most pupils are involved in music and drama. Very good range of sports, games and activities. A particularly high standard in lacrosse (a lot of county representatives). An impressive record in the Duke of Edinburgh's Award Scheme.

School profile

Pupils Age range 11–18; 180 girls, 17 day, 163 boarding. Main entry ages 11+ and into sixth. Approx 5% are children of former pupils. *Transfer from maintained schools:* 5% intake.

Entrance Common entrance and own exam used. Not oversubscribed. No special skills required; C of E Foundation but pupils of other religions accepted provided they attend chapel. Parents not expected to buy text books; other extras vary. 2 academic and 2 music scholarships; plus a number of bursaries available to sixth form girls, daughters of service personnel and others on application.

Parents 15+% of parents in industry or commerce; 15+% are doctors, lawyers etc. 30+% live within 30 miles; 30+% live overseas.

Staff Lady Warden Miss V G Bolton, 2 years in post. 36 full time staff, 10 part time. Annual turnover 10%. Average age 40.

Academic work GCSE, AS and A-levels. 16 subjects offered (no A-level general studies). In 1990, 34 pupils in upper fifth, 14 in upper sixth. *GCSE:* in 1990, 15 upper fifth gained at least grade C in 8+ subjects; 10 in 5–7; and 9 in 1–4 subjects. *A-levels:* 7 upper sixth passed in 3 subjects; 2 in 2; 3 in 1. 90% took art/humanities A-levels; 10% both arts and sciences (usually more). *Computing facilities:* Computer department with 12 BBCs.

Special provision: Dyslexic specialist on staff and four qualified EFL staff.

European Community *Languages:* French offered: to age 14; GCSE; AS-level; A-level; Flaw (Foreign Languages At Work). German offered: to age 14; GCSE; A-level; Flaw. Spanish offered: to age 14; GCSE; A-level. 10–25% take GCSE in more than 1 EC language. *Exchanges:* Regular exchanges for pupils aged 11–14 to France. *Other:* 2–3 German students in school each year.

Senior pupils' non-academic activities *Music:* 50+ learn a musical instrument, 10 to Grade 6 or above. *Drama and dance:* 25 take Grade 6 in ESB, RAD etc. 1 or 2 a year accepted for Drama Schools. *Art:* 20 take GCSE; 4 A-level; 1 accepted for Art School. *Sport:* Lacrosse, netball, cross-country running, athletics, tennis, rounders, squash, badminton, swimming available; also, for fifth and sixth forms, golf, archery, yoga, windsurfing, real tennis. Most take non-compulsory sport. Nearly all take bronze life saving medal; few Award of Merit. 17 pupils represent county (lacrosse). *Other:* 35 have bronze Duke of Edinburgh's Award, 5–10 have silver. 3–4 GAP after leaving. Other activities include computer, pottery and jewellery clubs; sixth formers can learn to drive.

Careers In 1990, 60% leavers went on to degree courses; 5% to art/drama/music colleges; 33% to non-degree courses (eg agricultural, secretarial); 2% straight into careers (eg accountancy). Of those going on to degree courses, 60% went to universities; 40% to poly/colleges. 15% those going on to higher education went to courses in practical art; 10% in drama/acting; 60% in humanities/social sciences; and 5% in science/engineering.

Uniform School uniform worn; sixth on formal occasions only.

Houses/prefects Competitive houses. Prefects, elected; head girl, appointed by the Head; head of house and house prefects.

Religion Compulsory weekday chapel. Boarders attend Sunday service.

Social Many activities, sporting, musical etc with other Woodard schools. Organised trips to France to stay with French families; ski trips; exchanges with a German school. Pupils allowed to bring own bike to school from 14 upwards. Meals self service. School shop. No tobacco/alcohol allowed.

Discipline No corporal punishment. Pupils failing to produce homework once might expect to have to produce it within 24 hours (detention for second offence); those caught smoking illegal substances on the premises can expect expulsion.

Boarding Houses, of approximately 35, same as competitive houses. Resident qualified nurse. Central dining room. *Upper sixth* are provided with food and cook for themselves. 2 weekend exeats per term and half-term. Visits to the local town allowed.

Alumni association is run by Mrs Judy Simmonds, Tamarisk Cottage, Lake Lane, Barnham, West Sussex PO22 0AL.

· St Paul's (Boys) ·

St Paul's School
Lonsdale Road
Barnes
London SW13 9JT
Tel 081 748 9162
Fax 081 748 9557

- Pupils 750
- Boys 13–18
  (Day/Board/Weekly)
- Girls None
- Upper sixth 141

- Termly fees
  £1909 (Day)
  £3040 (Board/
  Weekly)
- HMC
  Enquiries to the High
  Master
  Applications to the
  Bursar

What it's like

Founded in 1509 by John Colet, Dean of St Paul's. A grammar school had previously existed for centuries in connection with the cathedral and Colet probably absorbed this in the new foundation. It moved from the cathedral site to Hammersmith in 1884 and then crossed the river to purpose-built premises in Barnes in 1968. Unfortunately, a promising site was wasted by the grimly practical Clasp system. The original buildings are serviceable but lacked distinction. A new technology building (1990) and art block (1991) greatly improved facilities and enhanced the environment. It is governed by the Mercers' Company, and has its own prep school, Colet Court (founded in 1881) on the same site. Religious instruction is in accordance with the C of E but attendance at services is voluntary. The academic reputation of the school remains formidable with the classics still prospering. A very high-powered teaching staff is strong in pastoral care (thanks to the well-established tutorial system) and produces outstanding results. Each year very many leavers go on to university, very many to Oxbridge. The school is tremendously strong in music, drama, technology and art and these departments work closely together and form an integral part of the academic and social life of the school. In music there are orchestras, choirs, jazz groups, instrumental ensembles and about 260 pupils learn an instrument. Several plays are produced each year and there are a number of minor workshop productions. The art department produces work of high quality. The school has a notable record in sports and games (there is a fine sports hall and separate gymnasium and fencing salle) and most pupils are involved in one or more of them. More than 30 extra-curricular activities are available.

School profile

Pupils Age range 13–18; 750 boys, 640 day, 110 boarding. Main entry ages 13+ and into sixth maximum of 8. Approx 10% are children of former pupils. Colet Court school provides 50% of intake. *Transfer from maintained schools:* 6% main intake, very few into sixth.

Entrance Common entrance and own scholarship exam used. Selection interviews at age 11/12. Oversubscribed. No special skills or religious requirements. Parents expected to buy some text books;

maximum extras, £100. 11 assisted places pa. 24 scholarships pa, 100–15% of fees plus bursaries.

Parents 60+% live within 30 miles.

Staff High Master Canon Peter Pilkington, in post for 5 years. 77 full time staff, 5 part time. Annual turnover 3–4%. Average age 35–38.

Academic work GCSE, AS and A-levels (no A-level general studies). In 1990, 160 pupils in upper fifth, 141 in upper sixth. *GCSE:* in 1990, 97% upper

751

fifth gained at least grade C in 8+ subjects; 3% in 5–7 subjects. *A-levels:* 11% upper sixth passed in 4+ subjects; 84% in 3; 4% in 2; and 1% in 1 subject. 38% took science A-levels; 50% arts/ humanities including maths; 12% both. *Computing facilities:* 60 Apple Macs, 16 RM Nimbus, 8 Archimedes, 10 BBC's.

European Community *Languages:* French offered: to age 14; GCSE; AS-level; A-level. German offered: to GCSE; AS-level; A-level. Italian offered: to GCSE; AS-level; A-level. Spanish offered: as non-examined subject. 50–75% take GCSE in more than 1 EC language. *Exchanges:* Regular exchanges for pupils aged 14–18 to France, Germany and Italy. *Other:* Special link with Collège Stanislas (Paris). Modern language assistants in French (2), German (1) and Italian (1). Lectures by eg Sir Leon Brittan on future of Europe. Satellite TV from Europe.

Senior pupils' non-academic activities *Music:* 250 learn a musical instrument in school, 50 outside, 50 to Grade 6 or above in school, 20 outside; 60 in school orchestra, 35 in choir, 5 in pop group, 15 in jazz groups, 40 in instrumental ensembles; 6 in youth orchestras; 10, junior orchestras of Music Colleges. *Drama and dance:* 50+ in school productions; 10–15, senior drama class. 10+ GCSE 2nd year (junior drama). 2 go on to work in theatre; 2 into National Youth Theatre. *Art:* 70 take as non-examined subject (studios open every lunchtime to interested pupils); 50 GCSE; 20 A-level; 5 take History of Art. 2 accepted for Art School. 20 belong to eg photographic club. *Sport:* Rugby, cricket, swimming, rowing, fencing, fives, athletics, tennis, sailing, judo, squash, basketball, badminton, golf, gymnastics available. 700 take non-compulsory sport. 1 pupil represents country in tennis. *Other:* 7–24 take part in local community schemes. Other activities include a computer club, aeromodelling, BAYS, backgammon, bridge, chess, Christian Union, debating, drama, electronics, European society, art appreciation, archaeological, history, classical, natural history and political societies, conjuring club.

Careers In 1990, 87% leavers went on to degree courses; 2% to art/drama/ music colleges; 1% straight into careers; 10% other. Of those going on to degree courses, 30% went to Oxbridge, 68% to other universities; 2% to poly/colleges. 1% those going on to higher education went to courses in practical art; 1% in drama/acting; 1% in music; 63% in humanities/social sciences; 4% in medicine; and 30% in science/engineering.

Houses/prefects Competitive houses. Prefects, head boy – appointed by Head.

Religion Voluntary worship.

Social Central atrium for social gathering. Debates, concerts and joint theatrical productions with St Paul's Girls and other schools. Organised trips abroad. Day pupils allowed to bring own bike/car/ motorbike to school. Meals self service. School shop (uniform and tuck). No tobacco/alcohol allowed.

Discipline No corporal punishment. Pupils failing to produce homework once might expect a warning; those caught smoking cannabis on the premises might expect expulsion.

Boarding One-third have own study bedroom, others share with up to 6. Houses of approx 60. Resident matrons. Central dining room. Pupils can provide and cook own food. Exeats every weekend. Visits to local town allowed 4.00–5.30 pm.

Alumni association run by M K Seigel, c/o the School.

Former pupils Kenneth Baker, MP; Clement Freud; Admiral Treacher; Sir Robin Renwick; Magnus Pyke; Dr Jonathan Miller; Lord McColl; W Galen Weston; Peter Shaffer (playwright); Eric Newby (travel writer); Max Beloff (writer); Sir Kenneth Dover; Professor R F Gombrich; Chris Barber (musician); John Simpson (BBC foreign correspondent); John Cavanagh (fashion designer); Sir Isaiah Berlin among many others.

· *St Paul's (Girls')* ·

St Paul's Girls' School	• Pupils 635	• Termly fees
Brook Green	• Boys None	£1512 (Day)
London	• Girls 11–18	• GSA
W6 7BS	(Day)	Enquiries/application to
Tel 071-603 2288	• Upper sixth 109	the High Mistress

What it's like

Like its counterpart for boys, it belongs to the Christian Foundation originally provided by Dean Colet in 1509. The trustees are the Worshipful Company of Mercers and there are very close ties between school and Mercers. Its handsome Edwardian buildings lie in a pleasant part of Hammersmith and are outstandingly well equipped by any standards with, among other things, comfortable common rooms, first-class art rooms and workshops, excellent libraries, a range of computers and a fine theatre in memory of Dame Celia Johnson. Games and sports facilities are all provided on site and include an Olympic-sized swimming pool. Religious instruction is in accordance with the principles of the Church of England. A very large and extremely well-qualified staff (there are well over 30 in the music department alone) allows a staff:pupil ratio of about 1:7. Academically it is formidably high-powered, equally strong in arts and sciences. Maths, physics, chemistry and Latin are compulsory; quite a few girls study Classics. There is no streaming; all forms are of mixed ability and interests. In maths, French and Latin pupils are in sets based on ability. Considerable importance is attached to girls establishing from the outset good habits of work and learning to read and think independently. Academic results are consistently outstanding. Almost all leavers go on to degree courses; a very high proportion to Oxbridge. French and German are offered at GCSE and A-level, Italian and Spanish at A-level only. Many girls take GCSE in both French and German. There are regular exchanges with France, Germany and Italy, and one-term exchanges are encouraged. Since the appointment of the school's first director of music, the late Gustav Holst, music has been an important activity. There is a specially built music wing with a concert hall and individual sound-proof teaching rooms. The Great Hall has an organ. There are 2 orchestras, a wind band and several choirs. A high proportion of girls learn one or more instruments. A great deal of dramatic work is done each year, including workshop productions. The standards are very high. They are equally high in a wide variety of sports and games and physical education. All girls are taught self-defence in one of the martial arts. Dancing, ballet and fencing are also taught to a high level. There are numerous extra-curricular activities and numerous clubs and societies with special emphasis on art, drama and music. Computing and BAYS (British Association of Young Scientists) flourish.

School profile

Staff High Mistress Mrs Helen Williams, 1 year in post.

Entry Own exam used. Foundation awards including for art, music and organ.

Computing facilities 26 BBC micros; Acorn Archimedes linked in a level 3 Econet network, together with an Amstrad used for word processing.

European Community *Languages:* French offered: to GCSE; A-level. German offered: to GCSE; A-level. Italian: A-level. Spanish: A-level. 25–

753

50% take GCSE in more than 1 EC language. Language tuition may be arranged in the holidays. *Exchanges:* Regular exchanges for pupils aged 11–18 to France, Germany and Italy. Longer (1 term) exchanges encouraged. *Other:* European Youth Parliament, UK representatives 1991. Usually 1 German student spends 1 term in lower sixth each year. 1 pupil from school spends 1 term in Europe.

Careers In 1990, 97% leavers went on to degree courses; 2% to art/drama/music colleges; 1% to non-degree courses (eg secretarial, cooking). Of those going on to degree courses, 36% went to Oxbridge, 62% to other universities; 2% to poly/colleges. 1% those going on to higher education went to courses in practical art; 2% in music; 77% in humanities/social sciences; 10% in medicine; and 10% in science/engineering.

· *St Peter's (York)* ·

St Peter's School
York
YO3 6AB
Tel 0904 623213

- Pupils 467
- Boys 13–18 (Day/Board)
- Girls 13–18 (Day/Board)
- Upper sixth 90

- Termly fees £1467 (Day) £2521 (Board)
- HMC Enquiries/application to the Head Master

What it's like
Founded in 627 and thus one of the oldest schools in Europe. Alcuin was a pupil and headmaster. Its first head was a saint (Paulinus). The present head (as he points out himself) has not yet been canonised. Guy Fawkes was an old boy. It is urban, single-site by the Ouse and is exceptionally well equipped in fine buildings dating from the 1830s to the present day. The prep school, St Olave's, is on the same site (very many pupils are drawn from it). Religious worship is compulsory thrice weekly. The teaching is good and academic standards are high. Very many leavers proceed to degree courses each year, including many to Oxbridge. Strong in the drama and art departments; tremendously strong music department. Wide variety of sports and games (good standards attained) and a big range of activities. There is a vigorous CCF contingent. Emphasis on outdoor pursuits. Considerable commitment to local community schemes and a creditable record in the Duke of Edinburgh's Award Scheme.

School profile
Pupils Age range 13–18; 467 pupils, 313 day (227 boys, 86 girls), 154 boarding (108 boys, 46 girls). Main entry ages 13 and into sixth. Approx 10% are children of former pupils. Own junior school (St Olave's) provides more than 70% of intake. *Transfer from maintained schools:* 15% main intake, plus 30% to sixth.
Entrance Common entrance and own exam used. Oversubscribed. No special skills or religious requirements but all attend chapel (C of E). Parents not expected to buy text books. 120 assisted places. 6–8 scholarships/bursaries, up to half tuition fees.
Parents 15+% in industry or commerce. 60+% live within 30 miles; up to 10% overseas.
Staff Head Master R N Pittman, in post for 6 years. 43 full time staff. Annual turnover 6%. Average age 35.
Academic work GCSE and A-levels. 18 GCSE subjects offered; 20 at A-level (including A-level general studies for all).

754

In 1990, 91 pupils in fifth, 90 in upper sixth. *GCSE:* in 1990, 75 fifth gained at least grade C in 8+ subjects; 12 in 5–7; and 8 in 1–4 subjects. *A-levels:* 80 upper sixth passed in 4+ subjects; 10 in 3; 2 in 2; and 2 in 1 subject. 41% took science A-levels; 40% arts/humanities; 19% both. *Computing facilities:* 20 machines in computer department. *Special provision:* Extra English provision for a very few pupils.

European Community *Languages:* French offered: to age 14; GCSE; AS-level; A-level. German offered: to age 14; GCSE; A-level. A-level. 10–25% take GCSE in more than 1 EC language. *Exchanges:* Regular exchanges for pupils aged 11–16 to France and Germany. *Other:* Various school parties to Europe. EC pupils welcomed for 1 term or more.

Senior pupils' non-academic activities *Music:* 150 learn a musical instrument, 50 to Grade 6 or above; 60 in school orchestra, 80 in choir, 20 in pop group, 40 in band, 40 in ensembles. *Drama and dance:* 50 in school productions; 70 in house plays. *Art:* 30 take as non-examined subject; 20 GCSE; 10 A-level; 2 accepted for Art School. 20 belong to eg photographic club. *Sport:* Rugby, cricket, tennis, rowing, swimming, badminton, squash, netball, basketball, indoor soccer, cross-country, athletics, hockey, aerobics available. 10 represent county/country (hockey, rugby, athletics, tennis etc). *Other:* 80 take part in local community schemes. 10 have bronze Duke of Edinburgh's Award, 10 have silver and 5 gold. Other activities include a computer club, chess, debating, science, choral society.

Careers In 1990, 81% leavers went on to degree courses; 4% to art/drama/ music colleges; 5% to non-degree courses; 6% straight into careers; 4% other. Of those going on to degree courses, 12% went to Oxbridge, 75% to other universities; 13% to poly/colleges. 3% those going on to higher education went to courses in practical art; 1% in drama/acting; 2% in music; 52% in humanities/social sciences; 4% in medicine; and 38% in science/engineering.

Uniform School uniform worn except in sixth.

Houses/prefects Competitive houses. Prefects, head boy/girl, head of house and house prefects – appointed by the Head and staff.

Religion Compulsory (3 services in the week).

Social Many holiday expeditions to eg Sahara, Norway, Iceland, USSR, Snowdonia, Loire Valley, First World War battlefields, Italy. Pupils allowed to bring own car to school. Meals self service. School shop. No tobacco/alcohol allowed.

Discipline No corporal punishment. Pupils failing to produce homework once might expect a rebuke and to do it; those caught smoking cannabis on the premises would be expelled.

Boarding Sixth form in own study bedrooms or share with up to 3 others. Single sex houses, of approximately 50, mixed ages. Resident SRN. Central dining room. Pupils can provide and cook own food. 28 hour exeats, each weekend. Strictly regulated visits to the local town allowed.

Alumni association is run by Mr R D Harding, Hall Cottage, Foremarke, Repton, Derbyshire DE6 6ES.

Former pupils Parkinson (of Parkinson's Law); Norman Yardley (England cricket captain); Guy Fawkes.

· St Teresa's ·

St Teresa's Convent
School
Effingham Hill
Dorking
Surrey RH5 6ST
Tel 0372 452037/
454896

- Pupils 345
- Boys None
- Girls 11–18
  (Day/Board/Weekly)
- Upper sixth 25

- Termly fees
  £1345 (Day)
  £2415 (Board/
  Weekly)
- GSA, SHA, CCSS
  Enquiries to the
  Headmaster
  Application to the
  Admissions Secretary

What it's like

St Teresa's was founded by the Religious of Christian Instruction in 1928 on what was originally part of a manor site recorded in the Domesday Book. The main house, dating from 1799, is the centre of the school, now greatly extended to provide modern facilities. The junior school, Grove House, from which very many pupils are drawn, is at Grove House, Effingham, about $1\frac{1}{2}$ miles away. St Teresa's is situated amid beautiful, rural surroundings, 22 miles from London, in 45 acres of grounds amongst the Surrey hills. (Both schools are ten minutes from the M25 and within half an hour of Heathrow and Gatwick). Its prime aim is to provide a broad education based on Christian principles in a happy, caring atmosphere. A Roman Catholic foundation, it welcomes other denominations. Small classes and a very favourable staff:pupil ratio of 1:7. A broad curriculum provides an all-round education. St Teresa's welcomes girls from other schools into its sixth form. 20 A-level subjects are offered and modern information technology develops secretarial and computer skills. Very many sixth formers go on to degree courses. Pupils are involved in a wide range of extra-curricular activities – music, drama, arts and crafts, debating and many others. The school has its own open-air heated swimming pool, hard tennis courts, an all-weather hockey pitch and a multi-purpose sports hall. Girls have represented Surrey (hockey) and the school participates in the Duke of Edinburgh's Award Scheme, has own Girl Guides, travel, foreign exchanges and visits are important.

School profile

Pupils Age range 11–18; 345 girls (200 day, 145 boarding). Main entry ages 11, 12, 13 and into sixth. Own junior school, Grove House, provides 80% intake. *Transfer from maintained schools:* 4% main intake.

Entrance Own entrance exam used. Oversubscribed. No special skills or religious requirements. Parents not expected to buy textbooks. A number of scholarships/bursaries at 11 and 16, full or proportion of day fees.

Parents Significant proportion drawn from armed services, Church, theatre, media, music, doctors, lawyers, industry, farming and Government posts at home and abroad. 70% live within 30 miles; 13% live overseas.

Staff Headmaster Leslie Allan, in post for 4 years. 33 full time staff, 9 part time, 18 peripatetic. Annual turnover 15%. Average age 42.

Academic work GCSE and A-levels. 20 GCSE and A-level subjects offered. On average, 60 pupils in upper fifth, 25 in upper sixth. *GCSE:* in 1990, 24 upper fifth gained at least grade C in 8+ subjects; 27 in 5–7; and 6 in 1–4 subjects. *A-levels:* On average 2 upper sixth passes in 4+ subjects; 10 in 3; 9 in 2; and 8 in 1 subject. On average 6 take science A-levels; 14 arts/humanities; 10 both. *Computing facilities:* Computer lab with 18 Nimbus computers, plus computers in other areas including second computer lab. *Special provision:* Lessons in EFL by specialist teacher; small groups or individual teaching.

European Community *Languages:* French offered: to age 14; GCSE; AS-level; A-level. German offered: to age 14; GCSE; AS-level; A-level. Spanish offered: to age 14; GCSE; AS-level; A-level. Over 75% take GCSE in more than 1 EC language. *Exchanges:* Regular exchanges for pupils aged 14–18 to France. *Other:* French and Spanish boarders.

Non-academic activities (whole school) *Music:* 140 learn a musical instrument, 10 to Grade 6 or above; 40 pupils play in school orchestra, 70 in choirs, 2 string groups, 2 woodwind groups, 1 recorder group. *Drama and dance:* 200 in school productions; 60 take dance/drama lessons. *Art:* 19 take GCSE; 8 A-level. 4 accepted for Art School. 10 belong to eg photographic club. *Sport:* Hockey, netball, tennis, rounders, basketball, volleyball, athletics, cross-country, badminton, riding, football, swimming, gymnastics, trampolining available. 200 take part in non-compulsory sport; 20 take swimming exams, 25 judo. 4 pupils represent county (hockey). *Other:* 40 have bronze Duke of Edinburgh's Award, 4 silver, 1 gold. 10–15 visit geriatrics and 8–10 help with Riding for the Disabled. Other activities include Girl Guides, a computer club, driving lessons, riding, debating society.

Careers In 1990, 96% leavers went on to degree courses; 2% to art/drama/music colleges; 2% to non-degree courses. Of those going on to degree courses, 90% went to universities; 10% to poly/colleges. 20% those going on to higher education went to courses in practical art; 3% in drama/acting; 2% in music; 5% in humanities/social sciences; 10% in medicine; and 60% in science/engineering.

Uniform School uniform worn except in sixth, who wear it for special occasions.

Houses/prefects Competitive houses. Prefects, head girl, head of house and house prefects – elected by school, ratified by Head and staff. School Council.

Religion All girls attend assemblies and chapel.

Social Debates, theatre trips, modern languages events and social events with local boys' independent schools. Organised trips abroad and exchange systems. Meals self service. School shop. No tobacco/alcohol allowed.

Discipline Clearly understood grade system of discipline 2–5. Grades decided at weekly staff meeting. Pupils failing to produce homework once would be given the lowest (grade 2) or warning; those caught with drugs or alcohol on the premises would be expelled immediately.

Boarding Fifth and sixth have own study bedrooms; others share or in dormitories. Houses divided by age group. Resident qualified nurse. Central dining room. Pupils can provide and cook own food on special occasions. Half term plus 2 weekend exeats each term. Visits to local town allowed once a week, 11–16; sixth form by arrangement.

Alumni association St Teresa's Old Girls' Association (STOGA) – information from Sister Catherine at the school.

Former pupils Lynne Reid-Banks (author); Faye Maschler (restaurateur and food critic); Jennifer Michelmore (actress).

· *Scarborough* ·

Scarborough College
Filey Road
Scarborough
North Yorkshire
YO11 3BA
Tel 0723 360620

- Pupils 440
- Boys 11–18
  (Day/Board)
- Girls 11–18
  (Day/Board)
- Upper sixth 40

- Termly fees
  £1288 (Day)
  £2393 (Board)
- SHMIS
  Enquiries/application to
  the Headmaster's
  Secretary

What it's like

Founded in 1876, it has a splendid site south of Scarborough on the eastern slopes of Oliver's Mount, overlooking Scarborough Castle and the South Bay. The main Victorian building is a fine example of its kind. In the last 25 years there have been many developments and facilities are good. It is a Christian and interdenominational establishment with high academic standards and good results. The music, drama and art departments are well supported. A good record in games and sports (quite a lot of county representatives). Many extra-curricular activities cater for most needs. A flourishing CCF and some emphasis on outdoor pursuits. Some involvement in the Duke of Edinburgh's Award Scheme.

School profile

Pupils Age range 11–18; 440 pupils, 317 day (188 boys, 129 girls); 123 boarding (69 boys, 54 girls). Main entry ages, 11, 13, and into the sixth. Own junior school provides 50% of intake. 10% are children of former pupils. *Transfer from maintained schools:* 10% intake.

Entrance Common entrance and own exam used. Sometimes oversubscribed. Pupils with high potential in music and art encouraged; college is Christian and interdenominational. Parents not expected to buy text books. Assisted places. 15 scholarships/bursaries pa, £2175–£816.

Parents 15+% in industry or commerce. 60+% live within 30 miles; 15% live overseas.

Staff Headmaster Dr D S Hempsall, in post for 5 years. 36 full time staff, 6 part time. Annual turnover 7%. Average age 38.

Academic work GCSE and A-levels. 17 subjects offered (including A-level psychology and general studies). In 1989, 82 pupils in upper fifth, 40 in upper sixth. *GCSE:* in 1989, 75 upper fifth gained at least grade C in 8+ subjects; 6 in 5–7; and 1 in 1–4 subjects. *A-levels:* 21 upper sixth

passed in 4+ subjects; 16 in 3; 4 in 2 subjects. 40% took science A-levels; 40% arts/humanities; 20% both. *Computing facilities:* Computer centre; computers in departments. *Special provision:* Specialist tuition for dyslexia.

Senior pupils' non-academic activities *Music:* 50 learn a musical instrument, 22 to Grade 6 or above; 2 accepted for Music School; 30 in school orchestra, 20 in choir, 10 in school pop group, 14 in sixth form choir; 1 in National Youth Orchestra. All participate in annual music competition; 15 go on to play in pop group. *Drama and dance:* 25 in school productions; 10 in drama club. 2 enter competitions. 3 go on to work in theatre. *Art:* 4 take as non-examined subject; 28 take GCSE; 9 A-level. 2 accepted for Art School. 3 belong to photographic club, 18 to art society. *Sport:* Main girls' games: hockey, netball, rounders; main boys' games: rugby, hockey, cricket; also tennis, table tennis, cross-country, badminton, gymnastics, squash, riding, swimming, golf available. 50+ take non-compulsory sport. 8 represent county/country (rugby, hockey, badminton). *Other:* 10 have silver

Duke of Edinburgh's Award, 1 has gold. 2 work for national charities. Other activities include a computer and microelectronics club, public speaking, theatre visits, Christian Union, Young Farmers, model railway, psychology society, science, art, child care, electronics, video, guitar, engineering, shooting, CCF, craft, photography, chess etc.

Careers 2 part time advisers. Annual average accepted for *arts and humanities degree courses* at Oxbridge, 1; other universities, 8; polytechnics/colleges, 5. *science and engineering degree courses* at universities, 6; medical schools, 1; polytechnics/colleges, 2. *BEd*, 1. *other general training courses*, 22. Average going straight into careers in armed services, 3; industry, 4; other, into farming and tourism related industries.

Uniform School uniform worn except in the sixth.

Houses/prefects Competitive houses. Prefects, head boy/girl – appointed by Headmaster following recommendations made by housemasters/mistresses. Head of house and house prefects appointed by Housemaster/mistress.

Religion Assemblies compulsory; additional voluntary services; bible study sessions; Christian Union.

Social Debates, industrial conferences, departmental lectures with local schools. Exchanges to France and Germany; other trips abroad, skiing, junior languages, CCF. Pupils allowed to bring own car/bike/motorbike to school. Meals self service. School shop. No tobacco allowed; alcohol when approved by house staff.

Discipline No corporal punishment. Pupils failing to produce homework without satisfactory reason might expect detention; those caught smoking cannabis on the premises could expect expulsion.

Boarding 20% have own study bedroom, 32% share; 23% are in dormitories of 6+. Houses, of 30–40, same as competitive houses; single sex apart from Junior House. Resident qualified nurse. Central dining room. Pupils can provide and cook own food. Exeats at discretion of house staff. Visits to the local town allowed.

Alumni association run by J M Precious, Secretary to the OSA, c/o the College.

Former pupils Ian Carmichael (actor); Brian Reading.

· *Scarisbrick Hall* ·

Scarisbrick Hall School
Scarisbrick
Ormskirk
Lancashire L40 9RQ
Tel 0704 880200

- Pupils 490
- Boys 3–18 (Day)
- Girls 3–18 (Day)
- Upper sixth 19

- Termly fees
  £665 (Day)
Enquiries/application to
the Headmaster

What it's like

Founded in 1964, it lies 3 miles from Ormskirk in a superb private estate of 440 acres comprising gardens, woodland, pastures and a lake. The main building is Scarisbrick Hall itself: a vast country mansion of 150 apartments designed by Pugin. Ornate, ostentatious and derivative, it is a good example of residential Gothic renaissance (as such, it is officially listed and protected). New buildings include a chapel, classroom blocks and a gym. There is strong emphasis on evangelical faith and practice. A surprisingly small number of full-time staff. Academically it appears to be well run and many sixth form leavers proceed to degree courses each year. Some music, art and drama. Fees are low.

School profile

Pupils Total age range 3–18; 490 day pupils (240 boys, 250 girls). Senior department 11–18, 280 pupils (140 boys, 140 girls). Main entry ages 3, 4, 7, 11 and into sixth. Few are children of former pupils (school not old enough to have many).

Entrance Common entrance but mainly own exam used. Sometimes oversubscribed. No special skills or religious requirements. Parents not expected to buy text books; music tuition (£60) extra. Some scholarships (based on results in entrance exam, 11+ or GCSE) value 75%–25% of fees.

Parents 15+% in industry or commerce.

Staff Headmaster D M Raynor, in post for 13 years. 26 full time staff, 10 part time. Annual turnover 5%. Average age 46.

Academic work GCSE and A-levels. 15 subjects offered (including A-level general studies). In 1990, 58 pupils in upper fifth, 19 in upper sixth. *GCSE:* in 1990, 41 upper fifth gained at least grade C in 8+ subjects; 7 in 5–7; and 8 in 1–4 subjects. *A-levels:* 12 upper sixth passed in 4+ subjects; 4 in 3; 1 in 2; and 2 in 1 subject. 5 took science A-levels; 7 arts/humanities; 7 both. *Computing facilities:* 16 computers, 16 VDU's, 4 printers, 8 single disk drives, 1 dual, 1 double-sided disk drive, 2 TVs, 2 videos, 1 Prestel system.

European Community *Languages:* French offered: to age 14; GCSE; A-level. German offered: to age 14; GCSE; A-level. 25–50% take GCSE in more than 1 EC language. *Exchanges:* Regular exchanges for pupils aged 11–16 to Germany.

Senior pupils' non-academic activities *Music:* 50 learn a musical instrument, 8 to Grade 6 or above, 1 accepted for Music School; 90 in school orchestra;

4 in Sefton or Lancashire schools' orchestra. *Drama and dance:* 3 up to Grade 6 in ESB, RAD etc. *Art:* 10 take GCSE; 2 A-level. *Sport:* Soccer, rugby union, cricket, basketball, athletics, tennis, netball, cross-country, badminton, swimming available. 54 take exams in eg gymnastics, swimming. 1 represents country (hockey); 2 represent county (tennis). *Other:* 6 have bronze Duke of Edinburgh's Award, 5 have silver (taken out of school). 5 work for national charities. Other activities include driving lessons, science society, charity fund-raising events, Christian Fellowship, orchestra, chess club.

Careers In 1990 79% leavers went on to degree courses; 5% to non-degree courses (eg tourism, hotel management); 16% straight into careers (eg banking, armed services). Of those going on to degree courses, 67% went to universities; 33% to poly/colleges. 60% those going on to higher education went to courses in humanities/social sciences; 7% in medicine; and 33% in science/engineering.

Uniform School uniform worn throughout.

Houses/prefects Competitive houses. Prefects, head boy and girl, head of house and house prefects – appointed by staff.

Religion Compulsory school assembly (Christian non-denominational).

Social Trips abroad: ski-ing in the Alps, exchange with German school, visits to France. No bicycles allowed. School shop selling stationery and uniform. No tobacco/alcohol allowed.

Discipline Corporal punishment (boys only) for serious misbehaviour. Pupils failing to produce homework once might expect reprimand/warning/work to be done at lunchtime; those caught smoking cannabis on the premises might expect expulsion.

· *Seaford* ·

Seaford College
Petworth
West Sussex
GU28 0NB
Tel 07986 392

- Pupils 400
- Boys 11–18 (Board)
- Girls None
- Upper sixth 60

- Termly fees £2530
- SHMIS
Enquiries/application to
the Registrar

What it's like

Founded in 1884, it moved to West Sussex in 1946 and has a fine site in 320 acres of splendid wooded parkland below the Downs. Very civilised buildings (including 35 different houses for members of staff) and excellent modern facilities including a new CDT/Art block (1990) and a junior house (11+) opened in 1991. A staff:pupil ratio of 1:10. A very good general education is provided and a number of leavers proceed to degree courses each year. Religious worship and practice is compulsory in the school chapel which dates to pre-Norman times. The declared aims of the school are to promote all that is best in the ethos and atmosphere in an English independent school while infusing a modern and progressive spirit into all its activities. It aims to produce a civilised young man who will make the best possible use of his abilities. Good music, drama and art departments. Wide range of sport, games and extra-curricular activities.

School profile

Pupils Age range 11–19; 400 boys; day boys 11–13; boarding 13–19. Main entry ages 11, 13 and into sixth. Approx 3% are children of former pupils.

Entrance Common entrance and own exam used. Oversubscribed. Skills in music and sport an advantage; most pupils are C of E but not essential. Parents expected to buy text books in sixth; compulsory extras £10. No assisted places at present. About 20 scholarships/bursaries pa (academic, art, choral, music, games, sixth form and forces), 10% to full fees.

Parents 15+% in industry or commerce. 30+% live within 30 miles; up to 10% live overseas.

Staff Headmaster R C Hannaford, 1 year in post. 43 full time staff, 15 part time. Annual turnover 4%. Average age 35.

Academic work GCSE, A-levels, BTEC National Diploma (business and finance). In 1990, 80 pupils in upper fifth, 60 in upper sixth. 30% upper sixth took science/engineering A-levels, 30% arts/humanities, 40% both. *Computing facilities:* 18 BBCs in junior lab, 5 Nimbus in senior lab. *Special provision:* Some help for dyslexics.

European Community *Languages:* French offered: to GCSE; A-level. German offered: to GCSE; A-level. Spanish offered: to GCSE; A-level.

Senior pupils' non-academic activities (sixth form) *Music:* 25 have instrumental or vocal music lessons, 7 belong to concert band and jazz bands and 5 to madrigal choir. Music prefect and house music prefects organise the inter-house music competition and take an active part in running the department's events. *Drama and dance:* 50 in school productions, 25 in drama workshop. *Art:* 14 take as non-examined subject; 48 take GCSE; 17 take A-level. 4 accepted for Art School. 25 belong to eg photographic club. *Sport:* Rugby, hockey, cross-country, cricket, athletics, squash, shooting, tennis, badminton, basketball, archery, canoeing, fencing, karate, swimming, trampolining available. 200 take non-compulsory sport. 25 take exams in life saving, 10 karate, 3 divisional hockey. 5 represent county (hockey, rugby). *Other:* 15 take part in local community schemes. Other activities include a computer club, gun club, driving lessons, bridge, dungeons and dragons, chess, electronics, fly fishing, life saving, modern languages society, nautical, parascending, philatelic, model aircraft, creative writing.

Careers In 1990, 40% leavers went on to degree courses; 10% to art/drama/music colleges; 10% to non-degree courses; 20% straight into careers (eg business, management); 20% other (eg resits). Of those going on to degree courses, 50% went to universities; 50% to poly/colleges. 10% those going on to higher education went to courses in practical art; 5% in drama/acting; 5% in music; 30% in humanities/social sciences; 10% in medicine; and 40% in science/engineering.

Uniform School uniform worn, modified in sixth.

Houses/prefects Competitive houses. Prefects and head boy appointed by Headmaster; head of house and house prefects by housemasters. Junior boys do chores for the community.

Religion Religious worship compulsory.

Social Tennis, lacrosse and debates with local girls' school; social visits to sixth form club. Organised trips abroad. Pupils allowed to bring own bike to school (prefects can sometimes bring cars). Meals self service. School shop. Beer and wine allowed in sixth form club; no tobacco.

Discipline Corporal punishment would be administered only after consultation with parents (none used in last 5 years). Pupils failing to produce homework might expect a reprimand. Further failure would result in detention. Those caught smoking could expect a fine which would be sent to a cancer charity.

Boarding 160 have own study bedroom, 100 share; 180 are in dormitories of 6+. Houses, of 78–90, same as competitive houses. Resident qualified nurses. Central dining room. Some basic cooking facilities in boarding houses. 2 or 3 weekend exeats each term, and half-term. Visits to local town allowed.

Alumni association run by D Heden, c/o the College.

· *Sedbergh* ·

Sedbergh School	● Pupils 498	● Termly fees
Sedbergh	● Boys 11–18	£2065 (Day)
Cumbria	(Day/Board)	£2950 (Board)
LA10 5HG	● Girls None	Enquiries/application to
Tel 05396 20535	● Upper sixth 90	the Headmaster's
	● HMC	Secretary/Registrar

What it's like

Founded in 1525, it is next to a small market town with the boarding houses scattered over a big rural site in a setting of the Cumbrian hills which is superb by any standards. Excellent modern facilities and comfortable accommodation. Religious services are essentially Anglican and all attend regular worship in chapel. A first-rate education is provided and results are consistently good. Very many leavers go on to degree courses, including many to Oxbridge. There is a tremendously strong music department (250 boys learn an instrument); also very strong in drama and art. It has an outstanding record in sports and games (especially rugby and cricket) with many county representatives. All boys are involved in compulsory sport each day. Plentiful activities and much emphasis on outdoor pursuits (eg fell walking, climbing, fishing and caving) for which the environment is ideal. Frequent expeditions into the Lake District. The CCF is strong. A big commitment to local community schemes (numerous charity events) and a remarkable record in the Duke of Edinburgh's Award Scheme.

School profile

Pupils Age range 11–18; 498 boys, 8 day, 490 boarding. Main entry ages 11, 13 and into sixth. Approx 15% are children of former pupils.

Entrance Common entrance and own scholarship entrance exam used. Oversubscribed. Good all-rounders looked for at entry; specialist scholarships available in music and art. No religious requirements. Parents expected to buy text books; maximum extras £150 including instrumental tuition. 26 assisted places. 75 scholarships and 46 bursaries, up to full fees.

Parents Up to 10% live within 30 miles; up to 10% live overseas.

Staff Headmaster Dr R G Baxter, in post for 9 years. 46 full time staff, 17 part time. Annual turnover 8.5%. Average age 40.

Academic work GCSE and A-levels. Average size of fifth 90; upper sixth 90. *GCSE:* on average, 17 pupils in the fifth pass 5–7 subjects; 73 pass 8+ subjects. *A-levels:* on average, 14 pupils in upper sixth pass 2 subjects; 66, 3 subjects and 10 pass 4 subjects. On average, 45 take science/engineering A-levels; 35 take arts and humanities; 9 a mixture. Design – CDT (Technology) and CDT (Design and Realisation) are offered to GCSE/A-level. *Computing facilities:* Nimbus-AX network in lab plus computers in physics, chemistry, economics, design, languages, careers, bookshop, and all boarding houses.

European Community *Languages:* French offered: to age 14; GCSE; AS-level; A-level. German offered: to age 14; GCSE; A-level. Over-75% take GCSE in more than 1 EC language. *Exchanges:* Regular exchanges for pupils of all ages to France, sixth form to Germany.

Senior school pupils' (13+) non-academic activities *Music:* 250 learn a musical instrument, 30 to Grade 6 or above, 1 accepted for Music School; 70 in school orchestras (1st and 2nd), bands, jazz orchestra, 50 in chapel, 50 approx in choral society, 12 in school pop group, 15 in early music group, 100 in opera/musical; 1 in National Youth Orchestra. *Drama and dance:* 70–80 in school productions, 150 in house plays, etc. 3 accepted for Drama Schools recently. *Art:* Most take as non–examined subject, 40 take GCSE, 10 take A-level; 1 accepted for Art School. 20 belong to eg photographic club, 25 in art society. *Sport:* Rugby, football, cricket, swimming, water polo, tennis, fives, squash, athletics, cross-country, running, hockey, golf, basketball, badminton, table tennis, shooting, archery, yard soccer available. All boys take part in compulsory sport each day. Most do more. All fourth form do Royal Life Saving course. 15–20 pupils pa represent county (rugby, cricket, athletics, fives, hockey, shooting). *Other:* 50 take part in local community schemes. 65 taking bronze Duke of Edinburgh's Award, 30 taking silver and 15 gold. 30 take part in holiday for NSPCC at school. 150 take part in many other charity events. Other activities include a computer club, CCF (army and navy). All boys canoe, sail, rock climb, abseil, cave, orienteer. Societies: natural history, junior and senior debating, chess, bridge, campanology, clay pigeon shooting, etc. Driving lessons arranged.

Careers In 1990, 82% leavers went on to degree courses; 5% to art/drama/music colleges; 5% to non-degree courses; 7% straight into careers (eg armed forces, banking, business); 1% other. Of those going on to degree courses, 13% went to Oxbridge; 62% to other universities; 25% to poly/colleges. 6% those going on to higher education went to courses in practical art; 2% in drama/acting; 3% in music; 59% in humanities/social sciences; 5% in medicine; and 25% in science/engineering.

Uniform School uniform worn throughout.

Houses/prefects Competitive houses. Prefects, head boy and head of house and house prefects – appointed by the headmaster or housemaster.

Religion Religious worship compulsory.

Chapel every Sunday, assembly each day. House prayers in evening.

Social Organised local events with girls schools for all age groups: activities (sailing, climbing etc), debates, theatre, music, dances, roller skating, dinners, English/history lectures. Many organised trips, recently include expedition to Arctic, Sahara, Iceland, ski-ing in France and Italy. Cricket: Holland and West Indies. Rugby: Canada and Portugal. Chapel choir to Belgium and Germany. Exchanges with schools in Germany (sixth form) and France (all age groups, 3 weeks). Some pupils allowed to bring own bike to school. Meals formal, in houses. School shops selling games equipment, books, tuck. No tobacco allowed. There is an upper sixth bar.

Discipline No corporal punishment. Pupils failing to produce homework once might expect a repeat on special paper – signed before and after by housemaster; those caught smoking cannabis on the premises could expect expulsion.

Boarding All sixth form (180) have own study bedroom, a few fifth formers share; only third form are in dormitories of 6+. Houses, of approximately 65, same as competitive houses. Resident qualified nurse and full-time school doctor. Most pupils can provide and cook own food. One half-term exeat per term. Visits to the local town allowed daily.

Alumni association is run by The Secretary, The Old Sedberghian Club, Malim Lodge, Sedbergh School, Sedbergh, Cumbria LA10 5RY.

· *Sevenoaks* ·

Sevenoaks School	● Pupils 910	● Termly fees
Sevenoaks	● Boys 11–18	£1758 (Day)
Kent	(Day/Board)	£2895 (Board)
TN13 1HU	● Girls 11–18	● HMC
Tel 0732 455133	(Day/Board)	Enquiries/application to
	● Upper sixth 200	the Registrar

What it's like

Founded in 1418 by Sir William Sevenoke, Mayor of London and friend of Henry V by way of thank offering for his share in the victory at Agincourt. It is one of the three oldest lay foundations in England. The first building of note was designed by the Earl of Burlington in 1718 (now in use as one of the boarding houses). In the 20th century numerous additions have been made and the school has a compact and attractive campus (100 acres adjoining Knole Park) on the edge of town, with excellent modern facilities. These include international houses for sixth form boys and girls, first-rate computerised library and science, electronics and computing centre; a purpose-built theatre and music centre with sophisticated equipment stand near a sports hall and a complex of three covered tennis courts. The school has its own chaplain and religious education centre. Religious studies is taught throughout the school and 'The Church in the School' holds services in the local parish church. Sevenoaks is high-powered academically (the staff:pupil ratio is about 1:10) and gets consistently good results. Each year very many pupils go on to degree courses, including many to Oxbridge. The school is one of the very few that offers courses leading to the International Baccalaureate (IB), and 10% of parents live overseas. French, German and Spanish are offered for GCSE, the IB and A-level; Dutch and Italian for the IB only. An exceptionally high proportion of pupils takes GCSE in more than one European language. There are regular exchanges with France, Germany and Spain. The music, drama and art depts are all tremendously strong and active. Each year there is the Sevenoaks Summer Festival, a major local artistic event organised by the school and run for the benefit of the whole community of the town. Sport and games are an important part of the curriculum. There is a wide variety of these and high standards are attained (a large number of representatives at county and national level each year – rugby and tennis are particular strengths). An equally wide range of extra-curricular activities (about 30). The CCF is a large and flourishing contingent. Sevenoaks was one of the pioneers of school-based community services in Britain. There is now a federal unit comprising 17 local schools with 600 volunteers. About 250 of these are from Sevenoaks. The school also has a remarkable record in the Duke of Edinburgh's Award Scheme.

School profile

Pupils Age range 11–18; 910 pupils (550 boys, 360 girls), 580 day and 330 boarders. Main entry ages 11, 13 and into sixth. *Transfer from maintained schools:* 30% main intakes, plus 18% to sixth.

Entrance Common entrance and own exam used at 13. Own exam at 11; interview at sixth form level. Oversubscribed. All special skills and all faiths welcomed. Parents have an option on the purchase of text books. 5 assisted places pa. 50 scholarships/bursaries, full fees to £250.

Parents 50+% in industry or commerce. 65% live within 30 miles; 10+% live overseas.

Staff Head Richard Barker, in post for 10 years. 90 full time staff, 40 part time. Annual turnover 5–10%. Average age under 40.

Academic work GCSE, A-levels, International Baccalaureate. 20 subjects offered (including general studies and wide range of languages at A-level). In 1989, 142 pupils in upper fifth, 186 in upper sixth (now 200). *GCSE:* in 1989, 121 upper fifth gained at least grade C in 8+ subjects; 18 in 5–7; and 3 in 1–4 subjects. *A-levels:* 13 upper sixth passed in 4+ subjects; 153 in 3; 18 in 2; and 2 in 1 subject. 28% took science A-levels; 30% arts/humanities; 42% both. 35% sixth form take IB instead of A-levels. *Computing facilities:* Computing department with some 40 computers on two networks and PDP 11/34A miniframe computer. New facilities include IBM compatible hardware/software allowing students to investigate uses related to industry as well as software specific to educational needs. Other departments use the facilities, many having own computers and some having links to the computing department which allow them to access the large database stored here. Courses range from information technology GCSE to programming for beginners; desktop publishing to information systems; business studies and computing to electronic painting. The computing facilities are available for use by the 280 (Computing Society) members 12 hours a day, every day and during the holidays. *Special provision:* Some special provisions made.

European Community *Languages:* Dutch offered to IB. French offered: to age 14; GCSE; IB; A-level. German offered: to age 14; GCSE; IB; A-level. Italian offered to: IB. Spanish offered: to age 14; GCSE; IB; A-level. Over 75% take GCSE in more than 1 EC language. *Exchanges:* Regular exchanges for pupils aged 11–18 to France, Germany and Spain. *Other:* 35% of sixth form study IB (International Baccalaureat) instead of A-levels; of these, some 80 are from overseas, predominantly EC. Participated in European Youth Parliament at Fonteinbleau. Regular tours, eg sport, drama. Regular talks from MEPs, embassy officials, etc.

Senior pupils' non-academic activities *Music:* 320 learn a musical instrument, 2 accepted for Music School. 50 in school orchestra; 60 in choir; 74 in bands; 25 in string ensembles; 22 in chamber group; 3 in Kent Youth Orchestra; average 3 pupils a year in National Youth Orchestra. *Drama and dance:* 150 involved each year in school productions; 18 take GCSE; 110 take drama/dance classes.

Art: 100 take as non-examined subject; 30 GCSE; 19 A-level/IB. 6 accepted for Art School. 35 belong to photographic club. *Sport:* rugby, soccer, tennis, hockey, shooting, netball, basketball, aerobics, athletics, fencing, gymnastics, weight lifting, cricket, swimming, badminton, squash, riding, cross-country running, sailing, rowing available. Some sport compulsory; considerable participation in non-compulsory sport. 3 represent country (rugby); 20 represent county (rugby, hockey, cross-country). *Other:* Extensive participation in voluntary/community work; flourishing CCF contingent and Duke of Edinburgh's Award. Other activities include clubs for aquarium, astronomy, bridge, chemistry, chess, Christian Fellowship, classics, computer, contacto, debating, electronics, film, geography, history, languages, life class, maths, natural history, needle club, philosophy, pottery, shooting, SSPNS, technology, war games.

Careers In 1990, 75% leavers went on to degree courses; 3% to art/drama/music colleges; $^1/_2$% to non-degree courses (eg secretarial); $3^1/_2$% straight into careers (eg army, navy, broking, banking, tennis coaching, family business); 18% other. Of those going on to degree courses, 18% went to Oxbridge, 72% to other universities; 10% to poly/colleges. 5% those going on to higher education went to courses in practical art; 2% in drama/acting; 1% in music; 65% in humanities/social sciences; 5% in medicine; and 22% in science/engineering.

Uniform School uniform worn throughout.

Houses/prefects Houses/pastoral groups in Upper, Middle and Junior Divisions. Prefects, head boy/girl, head of house and house prefects – appointed by Head. School Council.

Religion Compulsory assemblies, some with religious content. Services largely voluntary including communion services. Annual confirmation 25–35 pupils.

Social Occasional ventures with other schools eg Young Enterprise Scheme. Exchanges with variety of schools in UK, France, Germany and Spain. Pupils allowed to bring own car/bike/motorbike to school. Meals self service. School shops for tuck, stationery, second-hand clothes. No tobacco/alcohol allowed.

Discipline No corporal punishment. Pupils failing to produce homework once might expect verbal reprimand; very strict drug punishment.

Boarding 20% have own study bedroom, 70% share, 5% are in dormitories of 6+. Single sex houses, of approximately 50. Central dining room. Pupils can provide and cook own food. Half-term and 2 weekend exeats termly. Visits to local town allowed.

Alumni association run by Dr R Hackett, School House, Sevenoaks School.

· *Shaftesbury* ·

Shaftesbury	• Pupils 50	• Termly fees
Independent School	• Boys 5–18	£890 (Day)
Godstone Road	(Day)	Enquiries/application to
Purley	• Girls 5–18	the Headmaster
Surrey	(Day)	
Tel 081 668 8080	• Upper sixth 2	

What it's like

Founded in 1976, a one-acre site with playground on the edge of the green belt. Playing fields one and a half miles away. Good solid buildings, formerly those of Purley Grammar School. A lot of money has been put into improving facilities, which are good. A Christian foundation but non–denominational. At the moment it has only 50 pupils, and the intention is to keep the number below 150. An average class of 10 pupils. After only 15 years it is already a flourishing establishment, and with impressive results. Much emphasis on personal care and attention. Strong music and drama (most pupils are involved). An impressive range of sports and games. Some local community service work.

School profile

Pupils Total age range 5–18; 50 day pupils (32 boys, 18 girls). Senior department 11–18, 30 pupils (20 boys, 10 girls). Main entry ages 5, 10, 11, and 13; entry at all ages possible. *Transfer from maintained schools:* 75% senior intake.

Entrance Own entrance exam used. Academic skills and other skills taken into account; no religious requirements. Parents not expected to buy text books; no compulsory extras, £3 per term insurance is voluntary. 5 scholarships/bursaries, up to 75% fees.

Parents 15+% in industry or commerce.

Staff Headmaster P A B Gowlland, in post for 15 years. 5 full time staff, 10 part time. Annual turnover 10–20%.

Academic work GCSE and A-levels. 15 subjects offered (no A-level general studies). In 1989, 11 pupils in upper fifth, 2 in upper sixth. *GCSE:* in 1990, 63% upper fifth gained at least grade C in 7+ subjects; *A-levels:* 100% upper sixth passed in 2 subjects. Most took science A-levels. *Computing facilities:* 6 computers, printer. *Special provision:* Small class size (average 10) means individual help can be given.

European Community *Languages:* French offered: to age 14; GCSE; A-level. *Exchanges:* Regular exchanges for pupils aged 14–16 to France.

Senior pupils' non-academic activities *Music:* 5 learn a musical instrument, 12 in school choir which combines with other choirs for major works (Creation, Messiah, Mozart Requiem, etc). *Drama and dance:* Most participate in school productions, local and national drama festivals – many awards won. *Art:* 5 take GCSE; 1 A-level. 1 accepted for Art

School in recent years. *Sport:* Football, cricket, badminton, athletics, squash, table tennis, swimming, netball, volleyball, rounders, cross-country available. 6 take non-compulsory sport. Former winners of Surrey Schools U15 cup (badminton). Independent Schools Association National Finals – usually have some representatives. *Other:* Some take part in local community schemes. Other activities include a computer club, Christian Union, very strong drama club. 6 times host school for Independent Schools Association National Drama Festival.

Careers On average, 50% leavers went on to degree courses; 25% to non-degree courses (eg secretarial, catering); 25% straight into careers (eg armed services, banking, tax). Of those going on to degree courses, 25% went to Oxbridge; 75% to other universities. 25% those going on to higher education went to courses in humanities/social sciences; 25% in medicine; and 50% in science/engineering.

Uniform School uniform worn throughout.

Houses/prefects No competitive houses. Sixth form act as prefects.

Religion Everyone attends assembly.

Social Joint choral works with ISAI schools. Day trip to France every year. Pupils allowed to bring own car/bike/motorbike to school. No tobacco/alcohol allowed.

Discipline Corporal punishment only by Head. Pupils failing to produce homework once might expect to produce it by next day; those caught smoking cannabis on the premises could expect suspension.

Alumni association is run by Headmaster.

· *Shebbear* ·

Shebbear College
Shebbear
Beaworthy
North Devon EX21 5HJ
Tel 040 928 228

- Pupils 350
- Boys 7–18
  (Day/Board)
- Girls 16–18
  (Day)
- Upper sixth 25

- Termly fees
  £1195 (Day)
  £2218 (Board)
- SHMIS
  Enquiries/application to
  the Headmaster

What it's like

Founded in 1841 by the Bible Christians, it is now under a Methodist Board of Management and works in partnership with its sister school, Edgehill College, Bideford. It has an estate of 100 acres in fine unspoilt countryside, with Dartmoor National Park to the south and the Atlantic to the west. The buildings are very pleasant and well equipped and there have been many first-rate extensions over the last 20 years. The essential quality of the school is its blend of family atmosphere with traditional discipline and Christian ethos. It has all the advantages of a small school and a large staff permits a staff:pupil ratio of 1:10. It caters for those who need plenty of care and attention as well as for the bright. The standard of teaching is high and results are good. The art, music and drama departments are all strong and there is a good deal of collaboration with Edgehill College in music and other social activities. A range of sports and games (the facilities for these are exceptionally good) and a wide range of extra-curricular activities (with emphasis on outdoor pursuits for which the environment is ideal). The college has an outstanding record in the Duke of Edinburgh's Award Scheme.

School profile

Pupils Total age range 7–18; 350 pupils, 170 day (168 boys, 2 girls) 180 boarding. Senior department 11–18, 290 pupils. Main entry ages (boys) 7, 11, 13, occasionally into the sixth; girls into the sixth. A few are children of former pupils. Own junior school provides about 30% senior intake. *Transfer from maintained schools:* 70% senior intake, plus 50% to sixth.

Entrance Common entrance and own exam used. Oversubscribed for day boys at 11. No special skills or religious requirements. Parents not expected to buy text books. Scholarships for academic/artistic ability, bursaries for boarding, up to 50% of fees.

Parents 15+% in armed services. 30+% live within 30 miles; up to 10% live overseas.

Staff Headmaster R J Buley, in post for 8 years. 32 full time staff, 4 part time. Annual turnover 6%. Average age 40.

Academic work GCSE, A-levels, RSA Business Studies. 18 GCSE subjects offered; 15 at A-level (A-level general studies introduced 1990). In 1989, 57 pupils in upper fifth, 25 in upper sixth. *GCSE:* in 1989, 33% upper fifth gained at least grade C in 8+ subjects; 33% in 5–7; and 27% in 1–4 subjects. *A-levels:* 12% upper sixth passed in 4+ subjects; 32% in 3; 24% in 2; and 16% in 1 subject. 50% took science A-levels; 35% arts/humanities; 15% both. *Computing facilities:* Computer centre with Prestel; BBC and Amstrad computers; plus facilities in various departments. *Special provision:* for EFL.

Senior pupils' non-academic activities *Music:* 60 learn a musical instrument, 14 to Grade 6 or above. 16 in school orchestra, 40 in choir, 8 in barbershop, 1 in County Youth Orchestra. *Drama and dance:* 70 in school musical, 12–20 in straight drama. *Art:* All lower sixth and years 1–3 take art as non-examined subject; 25 take GCSE; 2–4 A-level; 2 accepted for Art School. 12 in photographic club, 12 pottery club. *Sport:* Rugby, cricket, squash, badminton, tennis, judo, fencing, swimming, cross-country, athletics, basketball, table tennis, football available. Most take non-compulsory sport, 6 rugby and 6 cricket teams. 5 represent county (rugby, cricket). *Other:* 108 have Duke of Edinburgh's Awards. Other activities include a computer club, outdoor expeditions, model railways, stamp collecting etc.

Careers Senior member of staff advises.

Uniform School uniform worn throughout.

Houses/prefects Competitive houses. Prefects, head boy (school captain), head of house and house prefects; Head appoints school captain; house masters appoint house captains and prefects. Sixth form committee.

Religion Compulsory daily morning chapel; all boarders attend Sunday evening.

Social Socials, debates, quizzes, cookery and life skills classes with Edgehill College (sister school). Organised trips abroad. Pupils allowed to bring own car/bike/motorbike to school. Meals self service. School shop. No tobacco/alcohol allowed.

Discipline No corporal punishment. Pupils failing to produce homework once might expect reprimand or 2 sides of written work.

Boarding Sixth form have study bedrooms, some share. Houses, of 35–45, divided by age within division of competitive houses. Resident qualified medical staff. Central dining room. Weekend exeats as arranged. Sixth form visits to local town allowed at weekends.

Alumni association run by Mr A Andrews, Ranelagh, Boughton Hall Avenue, Send, Woking, Surrey GU23 7DE.

· *Sheffield High* ·

Sheffield High School
10 Rutland Park
Sheffield
S10 2PE
Tel 0742 660324

- Pupils 676
- Boys None
- Girls 4–18
  (Day)
- Upper sixth 50

- Termly fees
  £1052 (Day)
- GSA, GPDST
Enquiries/application to
the Headmistress

What it's like

Founded in 1878, it moved to its present premises in 1884 and occupies a single site in spacious grounds in the pleasant suburb of Broomhill. Junior school combined at Melbourne House. Many additions have been made to the original Victorian buildings and facilities are first-rate. It provides a sound general education and results are impressive. Many sixth form leavers go on to degree courses each year. French and German are offered to A-level, Spanish to GCSE. A high proportion of girls takes GCSE in more than one European language. There are regular exchanges with France and Germany. A good range of sports, games and activities. Adequate music, drama and art. A promising record in the Duke of Edinburgh's Award Scheme and substantial commitment to local community services.

School profile

Pupils Total age range 4–18; 676 day girls. Senior department 11–18, 505 girls. Main entry ages 4, 11 and into sixth.

Approx 40% are children of former pupils.

Entrance Own entrance exam used.

Oversubscribed. No special skills or religious requirements. Parents not expected to buy text books; music tuition extra. 21 assisted places. Scholarships and bursaries in senior department.

Staff Headmistress Mrs M A Houston, 1 year in post. 38 full time staff, 13 part time. Annual turnover 2%. Average age 41.

Academic work GCSE and A-levels. Russian, Greek, Geology offered to GCSE/A-level. Average size of upper fifth 82; upper sixth 50. *GCSE:* on average, 61 upper fifth gained at least grade C in 8+ subjects; 14 in 5–7; 7 in 1–4 subjects. *A-levels:* on average, 6 upper sixth pass in 4+ subjects; 35 in 3; 5 in 2; 2 in 1 subject. On average, 17 take science/engineering A-levels; 34 take arts and humanities; 14 a mixture. *Computing facilities:* Nimbus, Amstrad. Fitted computer room.

European Community *Languages:* French offered: to age 14; GCSE; AS-level; A-level. German offered: to age 14; GCSE; AS-level; A-level. Spanish: GCSE. 50–75% take GCSE in more than 1 EC language. *Exchanges:* Regular exchanges for pupils aged 11–18 to France and Germany.

Senior pupils' non-academic activities (sixth form) *Music:* 20 learn a musical instrument, 6 to Grade 6 or above, 1 accepted for Music School, 1 plays in pop group; 12 in school orchestra, 10 in school choir; 6 in Sheffield Youth Orchestra, 4 in Sheffield Girls' Choir. *Drama and dance:* 20 in school productions. 2 to Grade 6 in ESB, RAD, etc; 1 entered competitions, 40 in debating classes; 1 accepted for Drama School. *Art:* 2 take GCSE, 5 take A-level. 3 accepted for Art School. *Sport:* Hockey, netball, tennis, rounders, volleyball, athletics, badminton, table tennis available. 19 take non-compulsory sport. 3 take exams, eg gymnastics, swimming. 6 represent county (hockey, netball, athletics, badminton).

Other: 30 take part in local community schemes. 8 have bronze Duke of Edinburgh's Award, 4 have silver and 3 gold. Other activities include a computer club. Sixth form go out for wide range of activities eg golf, squash, ice skating. Clubs: drama, debating, Christian Union, choir, orchestra, recorder group, outdoor pursuits.

Careers In 1990, 90% leavers went on to degree courses; 8% to art/drama/music colleges; 2% straight into careers. Of those going on to degree courses, 3% went to Oxbridge, 77% to other universities; 20% to poly/colleges. 10% those going on to higher education went to courses in practical art; 3% in music; 49% in humanities/social sciences; 10% in medicine; and 28% in science/engineering.

Uniform School uniform worn except in the sixth.

Houses/prefects Competitive houses. Prefects, head girl and head of house – elected by sixth form and staff. School Council.

Religion Compulsory religious assembly on four mornings out of five. Pupil involvement.

Social Games fixtures with local schools, debating with schools, joint music and drama with local boys' independent school. Ski-ing trips, exchanges and visits to France, Germany and Russia. Educational cruises. Pupils allowed to bring own car/bike/motorbike to school. Meals self service. School tuck shop. No tobacco/alcohol allowed.

Discipline No corporal punishment. Pupils failing to produce homework once might expect detention; those caught smoking cannabis on the premises could expect expulsion.

Alumni association Details from school.

Former pupils Margaret Drabble (journalist and writer); Sally Oppenheimer; A S Byatt.

· *Sherborne (Boys)* ·

Sherborne School	• Pupils 651	• Termly fees
Sherborne	• Boys 13–18	£2450 (Day)
Dorset	(Day/Board)	£3200 (Board)
DT9 3AP	• Girls None	• HMC
Tel 0935 812646	• Upper sixth 130	Enquiries/application to
		the Registrar

What it's like

Its origins date back to the 8th century when some kind of school at Sherborne was begun by St Aldhelm. It was linked with the Benedictine Abbey, whose first Abbot was probably Thomas Copeland, in 1437. The school was refounded by Edward VI in 1550. The school stands on land which formerly belonged to the monastery, and the library, chapel and study block were once Abbey buildings. The Abbey itself is very fine and the whole school forms an architectural complex which is delightful and lies in the centre of one of the most attractive country towns in England. Some of the houses are dispersed in the town but all are within 5 minutes' walk of the main school buildings. There is, inevitably, a close 'town and gown' relationship. There have been numerous modern extensions and facilities are excellent (including outstandingly good libraries). It is a happy school with a strong pastoral care/tutorial system built round a traditional boarding house structure. Emphasis on religious practice in the Anglican tradition is considerable. Sunday services and twice weekly chapel are compulsory. There is a wide range of voluntary communion and other services. Theology is taught throughout the school to a high level. Academic standards are very high and results are impressive. Very many leavers go on to degree courses each year, including many to Oxbridge. A staff:pupil ratio of 1:9. There is a very strong tradition in music (about half the school is involved) and a wide variety of dramatic activity. A wide range of sports and games is available and standards are high (a lot of representatives at county and national level). An unusually big range of extra-curricular activities. The CCF is large (200 or more boys). Boys also help with the running of a 25-acre nature reserve near the town. There is a field centre on Exmoor. A substantial commitment to local community services.

School profile

Pupils Age range 13–18; 651 boys, 21 day, 630 boarding. Main entry ages 13 and a few into sixth. Approx 10% are children of former pupils.

Entrance Common entrance and own exam used. Oversubscribed. No special skills or religious requirements. Few extras. 17 scholarships/bursaries pa, three-quarters to one-fifth fees.

Parents 15+% in the armed services; 15+% are doctors, lawyers etc. 30+% live within 30 miles; up to 10% live overseas.

Staff Head P H Lapping, in post for 2 years. 76 full time staff, 18 part time (mainly music). Annual turnover 5%. Average age 39.

Academic work GCSE and A-levels. (No A-level general studies). In 1990, 133 pupils in upper fifth, 121 in upper sixth (now 130). *GCSE:* in 1990, 120 upper fifth gained at least grade C in 8+ subjects; 13 in 5–7 subjects. *A-levels:* 9 upper sixth passed in 4+ subjects; 87 in 3; 16 in 2; and 9 in 1 subject. 31% took science A-levels; 31% arts/humanities; 38% both. *Computing facilities:* 24 Acorn Archimedes for classwork and individual use. 12 computers in technical activity centre for computer-aided design.

European Community *Languages:* French offered: to GCSE; AS-level; A-level. German offered: to GCSE; A-level. Spanish offered: to GCSE; A-level. 25–50% take GCSE in more than 1 EC language. *Exchanges:* Regular exchanges for lower sixth language pupils to France, Germany, or Spain for half term. *Other:* European Studies offered as part of General Studies to pupils aged 16–18.

Senior pupils' non-academic activities *Music:* Recently 3 choral and 2 organ scholarship awards, 3 National Youth Orchestra entries, 7 Dorset Youth Orchestra entries; 75–80 in joint orchestras, 50 in chapel choir, 45 in concert band, 17 in swing band, 9 in each of 2 jazz bands, 80 in joint musical productions, 100 in choral society, 45 in each of the house concerts. *Drama:* 250 involved in all aspects of school and house drama productions. 3 accepted by National Youth Theatre. 2 to read drama at university. *Art:* 16 take GCSE; 13 A-level. 30 belong to eg photographic club. *Sport:* Rugby, cricket, hockey, soccer, squash, fives, athletics, basketball, cross-country, fencing, golf, swimming, tennis, sailing, shooting available. Virtually 100% take non–compulsory sport. 2–3 pupils pa reach national level, 12 county level (rugby, hockey, cricket). *Other:* 15% take part in local community schemes. 20 work for national charities. Other activities include CCF, driving lessons and wide range of societies covering all academic fields, Christian forum, film, bridge, horticulture, typing, sub-aqua, ornithology, instrument making, chess.

Careers In 1990, 80% leavers went on to degree courses; 4% to art/drama/music colleges; 2% to non-degree courses; 3% straight into careers; 11% other. Of those going on to degree courses, 9% went to Oxbridge; 79% to other universities; 12% to poly/colleges. 8% those going on to higher education

went to courses in practical art; 1% in drama/acting; 1% in music; 63% in humanities/social sciences; 4% in medicine; and 23% in science/engineering.

Uniform School uniform worn, modified in sixth.

Houses/prefects Nine competitive houses. Prefects, head boy, head of house and house prefects – appointed by Head.

Religion Compulsory Sunday service and chapel twice-weekly. Wide range of voluntary communion and other services.

Social Regular concerts, debates, dances, sixth form general studies with Sherborne Girls' School and St Antony's-Leweston. Pupils allowed to bring own bike to school. Meals self service. School shop sells uniform and sports kit. No tobacco/alcohol allowed.

Discipline No corporal punishment. Pupils failing to produce homework once might expect repetition of similar exercise; failing that, they would do a Saturday evening detention. Those caught smoking cannabis on the premises could expect expulsion.

Boarding 25% have own study bedroom, 50% share; 25% are in dormitories of 6+. Houses, of approximately 70. Resident qualified sanatorium sister; local medical practitioner. Central dining room. Pupils can provide and cook light snacks and coffee/tea in houses. 2 weekend exeats termly. Visits to local town allowed.

Alumni association run by M R G Earls-Davis Esq, Hon Sec Old Shirburnian Society, c/o the School.

Former pupils David Sheppard (Bishop of Liverpool); Christopher Chataway MP; Jeremy Irons; Nigel Dempster; Generals Sir Steuart Pringle and Julian Thompson (both Royal Marines); Lt Gen. Sir John Wilsey (GOC N. Ireland); Brigadier Patrick Cordingley (7 Armoured Division in the Gulf); Michael McCrum (Vice Chancellor, Cambridge); Jonathan Powell (Director, BBC1); John Le Carré; Richard Eyre (Director of National Theatre).

· *Sherborne (Girls)* ·

Sherborne School for
Girls
Sherborne
Dorset
DT9 3QN
Tel 0935 812245

- Pupils 465
- Boys None
- Girls 12–18
  (Day/Board)
- Upper sixth 76

- Termly fees
  £1840 (Day)
  £2760 (Board)
- GSA
- BSA
Enquiries/application to
the Headmistress

What it's like

Founded in 1899, single-site in 40 acres on a hill overlooking open country and on the edge of the very delightful town of Sherborne. Pleasant buildings and first-class accommodation. A C of E foundation, some of its services are compulsory. A distinguished and civilised establishment where academic standards and attainments are high. An exceptionally good staff:pupil ratio of 1:7.5. Very many leavers go on to Degree courses, including Oxbridge. A tremendously strong music department; good drama and art. First-rate games facilities and a high standard in sports and games (a very large number of representatives at county level). Wide range of societies, clubs etc catering for most needs. Big commitment to local community schemes and an impressive record in the Duke of Edinburgh's Award Scheme. There is frequent co-operation with Sherborne's boys' school.

School profile

Pupils Total age range 12–18; 465 girls, 5 day, 460 boarding. Main entry ages 12+, 13+ and into sixth. Approx 7% are children of former pupils.

Entrance Common entrance and scholarship exams used. Oversubscribed. No special skills or religious requirements but school is C of E. Parents not expected to buy text books; average extras £170 per term. 11 scholarships/exhibitions, £1840–£690 pa.

Parents 15+% in the armed services; 15+% are doctors, lawyers, etc. 10+% live within 30 miles; up to 10% live overseas.

Staff Headmistress Miss J M Taylor, in post for 5 years. 48 full time staff, 27 part time. Annual turnover 5%. Average age 42.5.

Academic work GCSE and A-levels. 23 subjects offered, including Italian, Russian, history of art and social biology to A-level. Average size of upper fifth 85; upper sixth 78. *GCSE:* on average, 82 upper fifth gained at least grade C in 8+ subjects; 3, 5–7 subjects. *A-levels:* 6 upper sixth pass in 4 subjects; 64 in 3; 4 in 2; and 1 in 1 subject. On average, 13 take science/engineering A-levels; 56 take arts/humanities; 6 a mixture. *Computing facilities:* 12 Archimedes, 1 British Research machine; 1 Apple and Spread Sheets; number of BBC micros. *Special provision:* for mild dyslexia.

European Community *Languages:* French offered: to GCSE; A-level; non-examined subject. German offered: to GCSE; A-level. Italian offered: to GCSE; A-level. Spanish offered: to GCSE; A-level. Over 75% take GCSE in more than 1 EC language. *Exchanges:* Regular exchanges for pupils to age 16 to France and Germany. *Other:* French Language at Work and conversation French in sixth form. Some EC pupils studying in school.

Senior pupils' non-academic activities *Music:* 350 learn a musical instrument, 100 to Grade 6 or above, 2 accepted for Music School, 2 go on to university to study music. 40 in school orchestra, 65 in school choir, 15 in musical society (oratoria), 24 in madrigal society, 40 in opera/

773

musical, 15 in chamber orchestras; 1 in National Youth Orchestra, 3 in county orchestras, 50 study chamber music, 2–4 take A-level music, 12 take GCSE. *Drama:* 80 in school productions (50 on stage, 30 backstage); 40 in junior drama society, 107 taking Guildhall exams, 1 National Youth Theatre member; 146 take speech and drama. *Art:* 25–30 take GCSE; 16 take A-level. *Sport:* Athletics, hockey, lacrosse, swimming, fencing, tennis, squash, volleyball, gymnastics, badminton, judo, basketball available. 29 represent county (fencing, cross-country, lacrosse, hockey, swimming, athletics, tennis). *Other:* 40 are working on bronze Duke of Edinburgh's Award, 25–30 on silver, 2 on gold. Other activities include a computer club, learning to drive, ride, canoe, sail. Lively societies: drama, debating, gym.

Careers In 1990, 80% leavers went on to degree courses; 5% to art/drama/music colleges; 5% to non-degree courses (eg secretarial); 2% straight into careers (eg administrative trainee scheme); 8% other (eg temporary work, travelling, etc). Of those going on to degree courses 8% went to Oxbridge; 78% to other universities; 15% to poly/colleges. 10% those going on to higher education went to courses in practical art; 2% in drama/acting; 1% in music; 73% in humanities/social sciences; 8% in medicine; and 6% in science/engineering.

Uniform School uniform worn except in the sixth.

Houses/prefects Competitive houses. Head girl and vice heads appointed by Head; head of house and house prefects appointed by house mistresses. Elected upper sixth committee for administration.

Religion Religious worship compulsory.

Social Joint orchestra, joint drama, languages club, youth social services with local schools. Trips abroad and exchange systems with schools abroad. Pupils allowed to bring own bike to school. Meals formal; self service in upper sixth house. No tobacco/alcohol allowed.

Discipline No corporal punishment. Pupils failing to produce homework once might expect to do it in own time; those caught smoking cannabis on the premises could expect expulsion.

Boarding Upper sixth have own study bedrooms; majority of remainder in cubicles in dormitories of 6–10. 8 houses, of 45–53, all ages plus upper sixth house. Resident qualified nurse and visiting doctor. 1 night exeat per term and half-term. Visits to local town allowed.

Alumni association run by Mrs S Stockley, The Hayes, Huntsworth, Bridgwater, Somerset TA7 0AH.

Former pupils Dame Diana Reader Harris DBE; Maria Aitken.

· *Sherrardswood* ·

Sherrardswood School	● Pupils 296	● Termly fees
Welwyn Garden City	● Boys 4–18	£1125 (Day)
Hertfordshire	(Day/Board/Weekly)	£2120 (Board/
AL8 7JN	● Girls 4–18	Weekly)
Tel 0707 322281	(Day/Board/Weekly)	● ISAI
	● Upper sixth 13	Enquiries/application to the Headmaster

What it's like

Founded in 1928. The main building is a fine 18th-century house in 25 acres of delightful parkland shared by the junior school and the boarders. The Senior

School is near the centre of Welwyn Garden City. Accommodation is comfortable and modern facilities plentiful. A sound general education is provided. French and German are offered to A-level and many pupils take GCSE in more than one European language. From a small sixth form, some go on to degree courses, including Oxbridge. Music, art and drama are on the curriculum. A good range of sport, games and activities.

School profile

Pupils Total age range 4–18; 296 pupils, 242 day (118 boys, 124 girls), 54 boarding (30 boys, 24 girls). Senior department 11–18, 144 pupils (71 boys, 73 girls). Main entry ages 4, 11 and into sixth. *Transfer from maintained schools:* 10% senior intakes.

Entrance Parents expected to buy text books for sixth formers. 2 scholarships/bursaries pa, up to one-third fees.

Staff Headmaster T M Ham, in post for 7 years. 21 full time staff, 5 part time.

Academic work GCSE and A-levels. 15 subjects offered; (no A-level general studies). In 1991, 25 pupils in upper fifth, 13 in upper sixth. *GCSE:* in 1990, 60% upper fifth gained at least grade C in 8+ subjects. *A-levels:* 40% upper sixth passed in 3 subjects. 30% took science A-levels; 60% arts/humanities; 10% both. *Computing facilities:* BBC Masters and BBC B's. *Special provision:* No provision for dyslex-ics. Small amount of EFL.

European Community *Languages:* French offered: to age 14; GCSE; AS-level; A-level. German offered: to age 14; GCSE; AS-level; A-level. 25–50% take GCSE in more than 1 EC language.

Careers In 1990, 40% sixth form leavers went on to degree courses; 10% to art/drama/music colleges; 50% straight into careers. Of those going on to degree courses, 30% went to Oxbridge, 35% to other universities; 35% to poly/colleges.

Uniform School uniform worn except in the sixth.

Houses/prefects Competitive houses. Prefects, head boy/girl, head of house and house prefects – appointed by the Head. School Council.

Social Pupils allowed to bring own car/bicycle/motorbike to school.

Discipline No corporal punishment.

· *Shiplake* ·

Shiplake College
Henley-on-Thames
Oxfordshire
RG9 4BW
Tel 0734 402455

- Pupils 335
- Boys 13–18
  (Day/Board)
- Girls None
- Upper sixth 50

- Termly fees
  £1885 (Day)
  £2870 (Board)
- SHMIS
  Enquiries/application to
  the Headmaster

What it's like

Founded in 1959, it has a very attractive site on the north bank of the Thames, 2.5 miles upstream from Henley. It is based on the site of the historic Shiplake Court. First-rate facilities and comfortable accommodation have been created. In worship it follows C of E practice; church services (the village church is next to the college) are compulsory. Academic standards are high and about 10% of pupils proceed to degree courses. Strong in music, drama, art, debating and public speaking. Very good record in sports (especially rowing and rugby), with a lot of representatives at national and county level. Five representatives in rowing at international level.

Compulsory sport/games four afternoons a week and compulsory CCF for 3 years. Emphasis on outdoor pursuits and adventure training (expeditions to Himalayas, Norway and the Alps). About 30 minor extra-curricular activities available. Considerable participation in local community schemes and an impressive record in the Duke of Edinburgh's Award Scheme.

School profile

Pupils Age range 13–18; 335 boys, 65 day, 270 boarding. Main entry ages 13 and into sixth. *Transfer from maintained schools:* 5% intakes (such pupils welcomed).

Entrance Common entrance and own exam used. Oversubscribed (school tries to redirect boys not regarded as suitable before common entrance). C of E school but other denominations and religions welcomed. Parents not expected to buy text books; maximum extras, £250. 5 day-boy scholarships and 2 bursaries for sons of schoolmasters one-third to half fees.

Parents 15+% in industry or commerce. 30+% live within 30 miles, up to 10% live overseas.

Staff Headmaster N V Bevan, 3 years in post. 38 full time staff, 4 part time. Annual turnover 5%. Average age 36.

Academic work GCSE and A-levels. 20 subjects offered (no A-level general studies). In 1990, 83 pupils in fifth, 40 in upper sixth (now 50). *GCSE:* in 1990, 39 fifth gained at least grade C in 5+ subjects; 58 in 1–4 subjects. *A-levels:* 5 upper sixth passed in 3+ subjects; 6 in 2; and 8 in 1 subject. 25% took science A-levels; 60% arts/humanities; 15% both. *Computing facilities:* 25 Amstrads, 2 Macintosh, Unix network. *Special provision:* 16 dyslexic pupils accepted each year. Remedial section within English department.

European Community *Languages:* French offered: to age 14; GCSE; AS-level; A-level. German offered: to GCSE; non-examined subject. Spanish offered: to GCSE; AS-level; A-level. Up to 10% take GCSE in more than 1 EC language. *Exchanges:* Regular exchanges for pupils aged 14–16 to France. *Other:* EC pupils welcomed for 1 term/year, helped by 'overseas' tutor.

Senior pupils' non-academic activities *Music:* 40 learn a musical instrument, 4 to Grade 6 or above, 1 accepted for Music School; 18 in school orchestra, 22 in choir, all in school choral society.

Drama and dance: 150 in school productions, compulsory drama workshops in first year. Occasional pupil accepted for Drama School. *Art:* 10 take as non-examined subject; 19 take GCSE art, 12 ceramics; 10 take A-level art, 2 ceramics. 3 accepted for Art School. *Sport:* Rugby, hockey, cricket, rowing, tennis, squash, sailing, shooting, badminton, basketball, cross-country, athletics, swimming available. Sport is compulsory on 4 afternoons a week; 50% take non-compulsory sport. 8 represent county (rugby), 5 represent country (World Junior Rowing Championships; Under 18 England rugby team). *Other:* 76 take part in local community schemes. 26 have silver Duke of Edinburgh's Award, and 8 gold. CCF is compulsory for 3 years. Other activities include a computer club, chess, woodwork, metalwork, pottery, electronics, natural history, ferreting.

Careers In 1990, 10% leavers went on to degree courses; 6% to art/drama/music colleges; 50% to non-degree courses (eg HND business studies, agricultural college, A-level retake); 4% straight into careers (eg technical theatre, armed forces, family business); 30% other. Of those going on to degree courses, 10% went to Oxbridge; 20% to other universities; 70% to poly/colleges. 13% those going on to higher education went to courses in practical art; 2% in drama/acting; 70% in humanities/social sciences; and 15% in science/engineering.

Uniform School uniform worn throughout.

Houses/prefects Competitive houses. Prefects, head boy, head of house and house prefects – appointed by housemasters and Head.

Religion Regular chapel services.

Social Conferences, composite crews for national/international regattas, drama etc with local schools. Annual expedition to

Himalayas, art trip to Paris, French department trip to Paris, ski-ing trip to Alps. 40% pupils go on trip or expedition in holidays. Meals self service. School shop. No tobacco allowed; beer allowed in Junior Common Room for boys over 17 with parents' permission.

Discipline No corporal punishment. Pupils failing to produce homework once might expect to repeat it; those caught smoking cannabis on the premises can expect expulsion. Failure to live up to acceptable standards results in withdrawal of privileges.

Boarding 20% have own study bedroom, 30% share with 1 or 2; 10% are in dormitories of 6+. Houses, of 65–70, same as competitive houses. Resident qualified nurse. Central dining room. 2 weekend and half-term exeats each term. Occasional visits to local town allowed, weekly for seniors.

Alumni association run by H E Wells-Furby Esq, c/o the College.

· *Shrewsbury* ·

The Schools	● Pupils 670	● Termly fees
Shrewsbury	● Boys 13–18	£2145 (Day)
Shropshire	(Day/Board)	£3040 (Board)
SY3 7BA	● Girls None	● HMC
Tel 0743 344537	● Upper sixth 135	Enquiries/application to the Headmaster

What it's like

Founded in 1552 by charter of Edward VI, it occupies a splendid site of 105 acres on a loop of the Severn on a high bluff overlooking the old town of Shrewsbury. Its buildings, ancient and modern, are very fine indeed and include a Jacobean library. This is one of the very few important scholarly libraries in a public school and possesses valuable medieval manuscripts and the entire collection of books owned by the school in Stuart times. It is a local and national school with 8 boarding houses and 2 day-boy houses. The school house has about 100 boys, the others about 60. A sixth form annexe caters for a few senior boys where the bar and common room function as a club. New buildings include a dining hall which seats 700, a magnificent science block, a new gym, a computer room and the purpose-built Ashton theatre. Religious worship is in the Anglican tradition and all boys are expected to attend one mid-week service and one Sunday service. A large staff allows a staff:pupil ratio of 1:9. Academic standards are high. Many leavers go on to degree courses. There is a very strong tradition in music. Tuition in every orchestral instrument is available. There are 2 orchestras, a wind band, jazz band, chapel choir, concert choir and madrigal choir. Concerts are frequent and there is regular contact with local musical groups. The art school and workshops are very well equipped and many activities are catered for. Frequent dramatic productions are presented by the school and by individual houses. Facilities for sports and games are first rate and high standards are achieved. Many societies and clubs provide for most extra-curricular needs. Clubs include printing, electronics and canoe-building. Open-air activities such as hill-walking and mountaineering are encouraged. There is a flourishing CCF contingent.

School profile

Pupils Age range 13–18; 670 boys (125 day, 545 boarding). Main entry ages 13 and into sixth.

Entrance Common entrance and own exam used. Scholarships (including music and sixth).

Staff Headmaster F E Maidment, in post for 3 years.

· *Shrewsbury High* ·

Shrewsbury High School	● Pupils 620	● GSA
32 Town Walls	● Boys None	● GPDST
Shrewsbury	● Girls 4–18 (Day)	
Shropshire SY1 1TN	● Upper sixth 30	Enquiries/application to
Tel 0743 62872	● Termly fees £908 (Day)	the Headmistress

What it's like

Founded in 1885, it transferred to its present site in 1897. Over the years it has expanded steadily and various buildings have been bought. Its pleasant grounds slope down to the Severn. A sound general education is given and academic results are good. Many sixth formers go on to degree courses each year, including Oxbridge. A fair range of sports, games and extra-curricular activities including art, drama and music. School's own junior department is about a mile away.

School profile

Pupils Total age range 4–18; 620 day girls. Senior department 11–18, 410 girls. Main entry ages 4, 7, 9, 11 and into sixth. Several are children of former pupils. Own junior department provides more than 60% of senior intake. *Transfer from maintained schools:* 22% senior intake, plus 50% small sixth intake.

Entrance Own entrance exam used. No special skills or religious requirements. Parents not expected to buy text books. 14 assisted places pa. Some scholarships/ bursaries available.

Parents 15+% are doctors, lawyers etc; 15+% farmers.

Staff Headmistress Miss S Gardner, 1 year in post. 33 full time staff, 18 part time.

Academic work GCSE and A-levels. 19 GCSE subjects offered (including A-level general studies). In 1990, 59 pupils in upper fifth, 30 in upper sixth. *GCSE:* in 1990, 54 upper fifth gained at least grade C in 8+ subjects; 5 in 5–7 subjects. *A-levels:* 15 upper sixth passed in 4+ sub-

jects; 10 in 3; 3 in 2; 2 in 1 subject. 20% took science A-levels; 56% arts/ humanities; 23% both. *Computing facilities:* 8-480Z Chain network (being upgraded); 5 BBC Masters; 3 BBC Bs; 1 Archimedes and colour printer; 4 printers.

European Community *Languages:* French offered: to age 14; GCSE; A-level. German offered: to GCSE; A-level. Italian offered: to GCSE. Spanish offered: as a non-examined subject. 25–50% take GCSE in more than 1 EC language. *Exchanges:* Regular exchanges for pupils aged 14–16 to France and Germany. *Other:* Local MEP visits school occasionally.

Senior pupils' non-academic activities A number of pupils participate in music, drama, art and sport; details not available. Hockey, netball, tennis, athletics, swimming, badminton, rowing are available as well as chess, debating, technology, electronics and several computer clubs.

Careers In 1990, 77% leavers went on

to degree courses; 3% to art/drama/ music colleges; 7% to non-degree courses (eg bilingual secretarial, HND computer studies); 3% straight into careers (eg finance); 10% other. Of those going on to degree courses, 7% went to Oxbridge; 50% to other universities; 20% to poly/ colleges. 4% those going on to higher education went to courses in practical art; 4% in music; 56% in humanities/social sciences; 12% in medicine, dentistry, nursing; 20% in science/engineering; 4% education.

Uniform School uniform worn except in the sixth.

Houses/prefects Competitive houses. No prefects; head girl – elected by staff and school. School Council.

Religion Regular non-denominational morning assembly.

Social Drama, music, debating, dances with local schools; organised trips abroad, eg skiing. Pupils allowed to bring own car/bike to school. Meals self service. No tobacco/alcohol allowed.

Discipline No corporal punishment. Minor misdemeanors dealt with according to the circumstances. No regular detentions necessary; emphasis on positive self-discipline.

· *Sibford* ·

Sibford School
Sibford Ferris
Banbury
Oxfordshire OX15 5QL
Tel 0295 78441
Fax 0295 788444

- Pupils 350
- Boys 7–18 (Day/Board/Weekly)
- Girls 7–18 (Day/Board/Weekly)
- Upper sixth 10

- Termly fees £1332 (Day) £2617 (Board/ Weekly) £527 (Specific Learning Difficulties supplement) Enquiries/application to the Admissions Secretary

What it's like

Founded in 1842, it has a single-site campus in a small village a few miles from Banbury. Very pleasant rural surroundings. The oldest building is a 17th-century manor house. There has been steady expansion over the years to provide very good up-to-date facilities. Its Quaker background is of great importance and the philosophy and principles of Quakerism are central to the school life. The intake is cosmopolitan. Non-academic students are particularly cared for. There are some non-examination courses and it is strong on vocational education. The Certificate of Pre-Vocational Education and BTEC 1st Certificate is available in the sixth form for those who are not academic but have plentiful talent and skills. There is a good special needs department including a well-established Sp.LD unit. A sound general training is given and the staff:pupil ratio is 1:8. French and German are offered to GCSE and some pupils take GCSE in more than one European language. French is also offered for FLAW. A range of sports, games and activities. Some participation in local community services, the Duke of Edinburgh's Award Scheme and work experience is undertaken by every sixth former.

School profile

Pupils Total age range 7–18. Senior department 11–18, 330 pupils, 95 day (63 boys, 32 girls), 235 boarding (150 boys, 85 girls). Main entry ages 7–11, 13 and into the sixth. Approx 3% are children of former pupils. *Transfer from maintained* *schools:* 50% senior intake, plus 10% to sixth.

Entrance Oversubscribed in some areas. Creative skills particularly valued; no religious requirements. Parents not expected to buy text books. Scholarships/bursaries available to Quaker children on the basis of need.

Parents 30+% live within 30 miles; 25% live overseas.

Staff Headmaster John Dunston, 1 year in post. 38 full time staff, 6 part time plus visiting music staff. Annual turnover 5%. Average age 38–40.

Academic work GCSE and A-levels, BTEC 1st Certificate, CPVE and the Cambridge Certificates. No A-level general studies. In 1990, 65 pupils in upper fifth, 10 in upper sixth. It is not school's policy to publish examination information. *Special provision:* highly sophisticated and long established (15 years) Specific Learning Difficulties unit; also EFL department.

European Community *Languages:* French offered: to age 14; GCSE; AS-level; A-level; Flaw (Foreign Languages at Work). German: GCSE. 10–25% take GCSE in more than 1 EC language.

Senior pupils' non-academic activities *Music:* 96 learn a musical instrument, senior and junior choir, music theatre group, mixed ensembles of all sizes and styles. *Drama and dance:* 80–100 in school productions; 45 take GCSE/A-level drama. 4–5 accepted for Drama Schools; 40 enter competitions; 2 go on to work in theatre. *Art:* 20 take as non-examined subject; 48 take GCSE; 9 A-level. 15 belong to eg photographic club;

3–4 accepted for Art School. *Sport:* Rugby, soccer, cricket (boys); hockey, netball, squash, tennis (girls); plus volleyball, swimming, athletics, basketball, badminton available. 230 take non-compulsory sport. *Other:* 5 take part in local community schemes. 20 have bronze Duke of Edinburgh's Award, 6 have silver.

Careers On average, 5% leavers went on to degree courses; 5% to art/drama/music colleges; 75% to non-degree courses; 15% straight into careers (eg retail management, caring, training schemes).

Uniform School uniform worn except in sixth.

Houses/prefects Houses are non-competitive. Head boy/girl, head of house and house prefects – appointed by the Head or house staff.

Religion Religious worship encouraged.

Social No organised events with other schools. Organised trips abroad. Pupils allowed to bring bike to school. Some meals formal, some self service. School shop.

Discipline No corporal punishment.

Boarding All sixth formers share a study bedroom; 12% in dormitories of 6+. Houses, of approximately 40, some single sex, some mixed; separate mixed sixth form house. Resident qualified nurse. Central dining room. Pupils can provide and cook supplementary food. Weekly boarding available. Visits to the local town allowed weekly from fourth form upwards.

Alumni association run by Ian Weatherhead, c/o the School.

Former pupils Paul Eddington; Sir John Berg.

· *Sidcot* ·

Sidcot School
Winscombe
Avon
BS25 1PD
Tel 093 484 3102

- Pupils 301
- Boys 9–18
  (Day/Board/Weekly)
- Girls 9–18
  (Day/Board/Weekly)
- Upper sixth 25

- Termly fees
  £1375 (Day)
  £2375 (Board/
  Weekly)
- SHMIS
  Enquiries/application to
  the Headmaster

What it's like

Founded in 1808, one of the oldest co-educational schools in the country, it has a very pleasant rural site of 110 acres in the Mendips, 8 miles from Weston-super-Mare. Its buildings are an agreeable mixture of the old and modern, but the facilities are up-to-date. A Quaker school, the principles and philosophy of Quakerism are adhered to. A sound general education is given and a number of sixth form proceed to degree courses each year. Very strong indeed in the music, drama and art departments. A good range of sport and games and plentiful emphasis on outdoor pursuits.

School profile

Pupils Total age range 9–18; 301 pupils, 141 day (89 boys, 52 girls), 160 boarding (85 boys, 75 girls). Senior department 11–18; 233 pupils (143 boys, 90 girls). Main entry ages 9, 11, 13 and into the sixth. *Transfer from maintained schools:* 70% senior intake, plus 50% to sixth.

Entrance Common entrance and own exam used. Usually oversubscribed. Average intellectual ability or above looked for; no religious requirements. Parents not expected to buy text books. 30 scholarships/bursaries and special scheme aids children from Quaker families, £300–£1000.

Parents 30+% live within 30 miles; 10+% live overseas.

Staff Headmaster Christopher Greenfield, in post for 5 years.

Academic work GCSE and A-levels. 20 subjects offered (including theatre studies, sociology, economics and A-level general studies). In 1990, 41 pupils in upper fifth, 17 in upper sixth (now 25). *GCSE:* in 1990, 8 upper fifth gained at least grade C in 8+ subjects; 15 in 5–7; and 18 in 1–4 subjects. *A-levels:* 3 upper sixth passed in 3 subjects; 7 in 2; and 6 in 1 subject. 4 took science A-levels; 9 arts/humanities; 4 both. *Computing facilities:* Computer centre (4 BBC's, 10 Amstrads); 10 BBC's in other departments. *Special provision:* Supplementary educational programme; EFL programme.

European Community *Languages:* French offered: to age 14; GCSE; AS-level; A-level. German offered: to age 14; GCSE; AS-level; A-level. Spanish offered: to GCSE; AS-level; A-level. 10–25% take GCSE in more than 1 EC language. *Exchanges:* Regular exchanges for pupils aged 11–16 to France and Germany. *Other:* European Studies offered to pupils aged 11–14. International club. Visits to Eruope. Close links with MEP. Approx 10 EC pupils; EFL programme and tutor for overseas pupils.

Senior pupils' non-academic activities *Music:* 80 learn a musical instrument, 5 to Grade 6 or above, 9 in school orchestra, 30 in school choir, 4 in school pop group, 5 in string ensemble, wind band and swing band; 1 in Winscombe orchestra. *Drama and dance:* 80 in school productions. 1 accepted for Drama School. *Art:* 6 take as non–examined subject, 15 take GCSE, 4 take A-level. 2

accepted for Art School, 1 for architecture. 10 belong eg to photographic club, 10 in set building, lighting, dance decorations etc. *Sport:* Usual sports available plus basketball, squash, table tennis, pool. All pupils take non-compulsory sport. 20 take swimming exams. 4 represent county (rugby, soccer, athletics, hockey, cricket, cross-country). *Other:* 6 have silver Duke of Edinburgh's Award. Other activities include a computer club and 60 clubs and societies.

Careers In 1990, 50% upper sixth leavers went on to degree courses; 5% to art/drama/music colleges; 25% to non-degree courses (eg HND business studies, nursing, higher education abroad; 5% straight into careers (eg administrative training); 15% other (eg Gap year). Of those going on to degree courses, 10% went to Oxbridge; 65% to other universities; 25% to poly/colleges. 5% those going on to higher education went to courses in practical art; 5% in music; 25% in humanities/social sciences; and 65% in science/engineering.

Uniform School uniform worn except in the sixth.

Houses/prefects Competitive houses.

All sixth form and some upper fifth have prefectorial duties. Head boy/girl, head of house and house prefects – appointed by the Head. School Council.

Religion Boarders expected to attend Quaker Meeting for worship about once a month but most religions represented in the school.

Social Biennial joint concerts with other schools. Two or three visits abroad each year. Senior pupils allowed to bring own car/bike to school. Most meals self service. School shop. No tobacco/alcohol allowed.

Discipline No corporal punishment. Punishments escalate from gating to suspension to expulsion; expulsion expected for any involvement with drugs.

Boarding Houses, of 30–40, divided by age group; single sex except for junior house. Qualified nurses. Central dining room. Exeats any weekend, mid-day Saturday to Sunday evening. Visits to local town allowed for pupils over 14, Saturday afternoons.

Alumni association is run by Michael van Blankenstein, 22 Park Road, High Barnet, Hertfordshire EN5 5SQ.

· *Silcoates* ·

Silcoates School
Wrenthorpe
Wakefield
West Yorkshire
WF2 0PD
Tel 0924 291614
Fax 0924 368690

- Pupils 570
- Boys 7–18
  (Day/Board/
  Weekly)
- Girls 16–18
  (Day/Board/
  Weekly)
- Upper sixth 76

- Termly fees
  £1392 (Day)
  £2491 (Board/
  Weekly)
- HMC, SHMIS
  Enquiries to the
  Headmaster
  Application to
  Admissions Secretary

What it's like

Founded in 1820 for the sons of ministers and missionaries in the Congregational Church, it is single site and semi-urban, 2 miles west of Wakefield. There are 55 acres of magnificent gardens and playing fields and many modern well-equipped buildings. Facilities are first-rate. The school has an inter-denominational approach to Christianity but retains links with the United Reformed Church. A well-run school it has high academic standards and consistently good results. A number of sixth formers go on to degree courses, including Oxbridge, each year. Reasonable strength in music, drama and art. A wide range of sports and games (standards are high and there have been a large number of representatives at county and national level). Equally good range of extra-curricular activities and a fine record in the Duke of Edinburgh's Award Scheme.

School profile

Pupils Total age range 7–18; 570 pupils, 483 day (465 boys, 18 girls), 88 boarding (78 boys, 10 girls). Senior department 11–18, 420 pupils (372 boys, 28 girls). Main entry ages 7, 11 (boys) and into sixth (boys and girls). *Transfer from maintained schools:* 46% senior intake, plus 4% to sixth.

Entrance Common entrance and own exam used. Not oversubscribed. No special skills or religious requirements. Parents not expected to buy text books; instrumental tuition extra, £58 per term. Bursaries for up to half fees for good GCSE results.

Parents 15+% in industry or commerce. 30+% live within 30 miles; up to 10% live overseas.

Staff Headmaster J C Baggaley, in post for 13 years. 42 full time staff, 2 part time. Annual turnover 4%. Average age 36.

Academic work GCSE and A-levels. 16 subjects offered (including A-level general studies). In 1990, 56 pupils in upper fifth, 59 in upper sixth (now 76). *GCSE:* in 1990, 37% upper fifth gained at least grade C in 8+ subjects; 38% in 5–7; and 25% in 1–4 subjects. *A-levels:* 26% upper sixth passed in 4+ subjects; 41% in 3; 20% in 2; and 13% in 1 subject. 37% took science A-levels; 44% arts/ humanities; 19% both. *Computing facilities:* 16 Nimbus networked; 3 Amstrad PC 1512; 4 BBC computers. *Special provision:* Teacher from Dyslexic Centre visits school.

European Community *Languages:* French offered: to age 14; GCSE; A-level. German offered: to age 14; GCSE; A-level. 10–25% take GCSE in more than 1 EC language. *Exchanges:* Regular exchanges for pupils aged 14–18 to France and Germany. *Other:* Pupils from EC welcomed for short periods.

Senior pupils' non-academic activities *Music:* 110 learn a musical instrument, 15 to Grade 6 or above; 30 in wind band, 50 in choir, 6 in jazz group. *Drama and dance:* 10–30 in school productions. *Art:* 30 GCSE; 20 A-level art and design. 25 belong to photographic club. *Sport:* Rugby, cricket, golf, swimming, table tennis, tennis, squash, hockey, badminton, cross-country, athletics, basketball available. 85% take non-compulsory sport. 1 represents country (rugby); 22 represent county (rugby, table tennis, cross-country, athletics, cricket, squash, swimming). *Other:* 10 take part in local community schemes. 30 have bronze Duke of Edinburgh's Award, 20 have silver and 10 gold. Other activities include a computer club, chess, bridge, canoeing, debating, motor and film clubs, public speaking, sixth form society.

Careers In 1990, 64% leavers went on to degree courses; 9% to art/drama/ music colleges; 4% to non-degree courses (eg business studies, rural estate management); 13% straight into careers (eg banking, diplomatic corps, armed services); 10% other. Of those going on to degree courses, 6% went to Oxbridge; 65% to other universities; 29% to poly/colleges. 58% those going on to higher education went to courses in humanities/social sciences; 1% in medicine; and 24% in science/engineering.

Uniform School uniform worn throughout.

Houses/prefects Competitive houses. Prefects, head boy, head of house and house prefects – appointed by Headmaster after consultation with staff.

Religion Compulsory daily morning assembly in chapel; Sunday evening chapel compulsory for boarders, encouraged for day boys; weekly holy communion.

Social Debates with local comprehensive school. French, German, cycling, skiing trips; Yorkshire/Westphalia German schools exchange. Day pupils allowed to bring own car to school, boarders own bike. Meals self service. School shop. No tobacco/alcohol allowed.

Discipline No corporal punishment. Pupils failing to produce homework once might expect verbal warning; those caught drunk on the premises might expect suspension following discussion with staff and parents.

Boarding 6 have own study bedroom, 25% share with 2 others; 11 dormitories of 6+. Single sex houses. Resident qualified nurse. Central dining room. Weekend exeats at request of parents or guardian. Visits to local town allowed at weekends.

Alumni association run by George Holmes, Kilby Lodge, St John's, Wakefield WF1 2RB.

· *Sir William Perkins's* ·

Sir William Perkins's
School
Guildford Road
Chertsey
Surrey KT16 9BN
Tel 0932 562161/
560264

- Pupils 495
- Boys None
- Girls 11–18
  (Day)
- Upper sixth 53

- Termly fees
  £955 (Day)
- GSA
Enquiries/application to
the Headmistress

What it's like

Founded in 1725 by Sir William, in Chertsey, it moved to its present site (also in Chertsey) in 1828. This comprises 16 acres of attractive gardens and playing fields. It has handsome buildings which are very well equipped. Religious education is non-denominational. A sound general education is provided and results are good. The staff:pupil ratio is about 1:13. Many sixth formers go on to degree courses, a high proportion to Oxbridge. French, German and Spanish are offered at GCSE and a high proportion of girls takes GCSE in more than one European language. Music is very strong: many girls play an instrument and the school has an orchestra, wind ensemble, recorder groups and four choirs. Drama is also strong and there is a variety of productions each year. A range of games and sports is available and there are numerous clubs and societies. Girls are encouraged to contribute to community services in local hospitals and day centres. Each form adopts a charity and works for its support.

School profile

Pupils Age range 11–18, 495 day girls. Main entry age 11. *Transfer from maintained schools:* 50% main intake, plus 15% to sixth.

Entrance Own entrance exam used. Assisted places. Scholarships/bursaries.

Staff Headmistress Mrs A Darlow, in post for 9 years.

Academic work GCSE, AS- and A-levels. 14 GCSE subjects offered; 16 at A-level; several AS-levels, including general studies. In 1990, 82 pupils in upper fifth, 53 in upper sixth. *GCSE:* in 1990, 56 upper fifth gained at least grade C in 8+ subjects; 19 in 5–7 subjects. *A-levels:* 3 upper sixth passed in 4+ subjects; 33 in 3; 12 in 2; and 1 in 1 subject. 9 took science A-levels; 17 arts/humanities; 23 both. *Computing facilities:* 14 Archimedes in computer room and machines in other specialist rooms. *Special provision:* Extra tuition for eg EFL, organised out of school hours.

European Community *Languages:* French offered: to age 14; GCSE; AS-level; A-level. German offered: to age 14;

GCSE; AS-level; A-level. Spanish offered: to GCSE; AS-level. 50–75% take GCSE in more than 1 EC language. *Exchanges:* Regular exchanges for pupils aged 11–16 to France, Germany and Spain. *Other:* BP Spanish work experience exchange for sixth form.

Careers In 1990, 84% leavers went on to degree courses; 2% to art/drama/music colleges; 4% to non-degree courses (eg secretarial, lab technician); 2% straight into careers; 8% other (retaking A-levels). Of those going on to degree courses, 20% went to Oxbridge; 58% to other universities; 22% to poly/colleges. 58% those going on to higher education went to courses in humanities/social sciences; 5% in medicine; and 37% in science/engineering.

· *South Hampstead High* ·

South Hampstead High School
3 Maresfield Gardens
London NW3 5SS
Tel 071–435 2899

- Pupils 690
- Boys None
- Girls 5–18 (Day)
- Upper sixth 61

- Termly fees £1228 (Day)
- GSA, GPDST
Enquiries/application to the Secretary

What it's like

Founded in 1876, urban, single-site, it has occupied its present premises since 1882. The core is the original Victorian building. Well-equipped new buildings include a theatre and sports hall and a separate sixth form house. The junior school is nearby. It is a selective and highly academic school and standards are high. Most leavers go on to degree courses each year, including many to Oxbridge. Very strong in music (200 girls learn an instrument) and fairly strong in drama and art. Very good range of games and sports. Numerous activities, clubs and societies. It has flourishing local connections and a substantial commitment to local community schemes. A fine record in the Duke of Edinburgh's Award Scheme.

School profile

Pupils Total age range 5–18; 690 day girls. Senior department 11–18, 530 girls. Main entry ages 5, 11+ and into sixth. Approx 4% are children of former pupils. *Transfer from maintained schools:* 45% senior intake.

Entrance Own entrance exam used. Oversubscribed. No special skills or religious requirements. Parents not expected to buy text books; only music tuition extra. 18 assisted places pa. 1–3 scholarships/bursaries pa (25–50% fees).

Parents 15+% are doctors, lawyers, etc; 15+% in industry or commerce; 15+% in the theatre, music, media etc.

Staff Headmistress Mrs D A Burgess, in post for 15 years. 40 full time staff, 19 part time.

Academic work GCSE and A-levels. 14 GCSE subjects offered; 20 at A-level (general studies taught but not examined). In 1990, 76 pupils in upper fifth, 61 in upper sixth. *GCSE:* in 1990, 61 upper fifth gained at least grade C in 8+ subjects; 14 in 5–7 subjects. *A-levels:* 5 upper sixth passed in 4+ subjects; 52 in 3; 3 in 2; and 1 in 1 subject. 16% took science A-levels; 45% arts/humanities; 37% both. *Computing facilities:* RML Nimbus; networked 10 machines; BBC Acorn B; 8 free-standing in separate departments; 10 BBC Acorn B on Technology Bus, visits once a week.

European Community *Languages:* French offered: to age 14; GCSE; AS-level; A-level. German offered: to age 14;

GCSE; A-level. Italian offered: to GCSE. Spanish offered: to age 14; GCSE; A-level. 25–50% take GCSE in more than 1 EC language. *Exchanges:* Regular exchanges for pupils aged 14–16 to France. *Other:* Talks from MEPs and other speakers with European-wide interests as part of sixth form world affairs course. Possibility of work experience in Europe.

Senior pupils' non-academic activities *Music:* 200 learn a musical instrument, 5 to Grade 6 or above, 1–2 accepted for Music School; 60 in school orchestras, 60 in school choir, plus ensembles and chamber music; 1 in National Youth Orchestra, 8–10 in junior departments of music colleges. *Drama and dance:* regular school productions and dance workshops. 1–2 accepted for Drama/Dance Schools; occasional pupil in films and national theatre. *Art:* 16 take as non-examined subject including textiles, screenprinting, photography; 68 take GCSE; 20 history of art; 24 take A-level. 3–6 accepted for Art School. *Sport:* Hockey, netball, tennis, badminton, squash, basketball, trampolining, swimming, rounders, volleyball, gymnastics and dance available. 200 take non-compulsory sport. 2 represent county (tennis) 1 in national training squad (tennis). *Other:* 55+ take part in local community schemes. 45 are working for bronze Duke of Edinburgh's Award, 6 for silver. Numerous clubs (ornithology, science, craft) and societies (debating, political and economic). General studies programme (includes dressmaking, information technology, photography, screenprinting, Italian etc).

Careers In 1990, 90% leavers went on to degree courses; 4% to art/drama/ music colleges (usually more); 4% to non-degree courses (eg advertising, physiotherapy); 2% other. Of those going on to degree courses, 20% went to Oxbridge; 70% to other universities; 10% to poly/colleges. 2% those going on to higher education went to courses in music; 62% in humanities/social sciences; 14% in medicine; and 22% in science/engineering.

Uniform School uniform worn except the sixth.

Houses/prefects No competitive houses. No prefects but head girl. School Council.

Religion Everyone attends a non-denominational assembly.

Social Joint choral concert annually with boys' public school; joint drama productions; shared societies/speakers/debates. Trips to Russia and France, skiing, adventure holiday. Pupils allowed to bring own car/bike/motorbike to school. Meals self service. No tobacco/alcohol allowed.

Discipline No corporal punishment. Pupils failing to produce homework once might expect reprimand; those caught smoking cannabis on the premises might expect expulsion. (The policy of the Council is to suspend the pupil and inform the police.)

Former pupils Rabbi Julia Neuberger; Fay Weldon (author); Miriam Karlin and Angela Lansbury (actresses); Nina Milkina, Sarah Francis and Joanna Macgregor (musicians); The Baroness Birk (politician); Harriet Mena Hill (painter); Professors Jennifer Temkin and Tessa Goldsmith and many other academics.

· *Southbank International* ·

Southbank – The
American International
School
36/38 Kensington Park
Road
London W11 3BU
Tel 071 229 8230
Fax 071 229 3784

- Pupils 196
- Boys 10–18
  (Day)
- Girls 10–18
  (Day)
- Upper sixth 30

- Termly fees
  £2200 (Day)
- ISAI, ECIS
  Enquiries/application to
  the Registrar

What it's like

Founded in 1979, located in a handsome Victorian building in Kensington close to Notting Hill Gate underground station. It is an official centre for the International Baccalaureate. All the main European languages are offered for the IB – Danish, Dutch, French, German, Modern Greek, Italian, Portuguese and Spanish – an altogether exceptionally great variety. Only Danish, French, German and Spanish are offered at GCSE but an exceptionally high proportion of pupils takes GCSE in more than one European language. The teaching is of high standard and results are good. A very high proportion of sixth formers, for a school this size, go on to degree courses, many to read economics. EFL teaching available. Good drama and art. Fair range of games, clubs and societies. Full use is made of the capital's cultural amenities. It is a day school only.

School profile

Pupils Age range 10–18; 196 day pupils (106 boys, 90 girls). Main entry ages 10 and into sixth. *Transfer from maintained schools:* 66% main intake, plus 75% to sixth.

Entrance Oversubscribed. No special skills or religious requirements. 24 scholarships/bursaries, £2800 to £500.

Parents 15+% are doctors, lawyers etc; 15+% in industry or commerce.

Staff Head Milton E Toubkin, in post for 11 years. 22 full time staff, 18 part time. Annual turnover 5%.

Academic work GCSE, International Baccalaureate. 12 subjects offered plus many different languages eg Dutch, Farsi, Greek, Hebrew, Japanese, Scandinavian. In 1990, 45 pupils in upper fifth, 30 in upper sixth. *GCSE:* in 1990, 10 upper fifth gained at least grade C in 5–7 subjects; 23 in 1–4 subjects. (GCSEs sat *en passant* for International Baccalaureate.). *International Baccalaureate:* 13 upper sixth passed in 6 subjects. Two scored 42 points. IB is taken in six subjects; all in-clude arts, science, language and maths. *Computing facilities:* 10 Apple Macintosh computers. *Special provision:* ESL teaching.

European Community *Languages:* Danish offered: to age 14; GCSE; IB. Dutch: IB. French offered: to age 14; GCSE; IB. German offered: to age 14; GCSE; IB. Greek (modern): IB. Italian: IB. Portuguese: IB. Spanish: GCSE; A-level; IB. Over 75% take GCSE in more than 1 EC language.

Senior pupils' non-academic activities *Music:* 12 learn a musical instrument, 3 in school pop groups. *Drama and dance:* 30 in school productions. 1 accepted for Drama/Dance Schools. *Art:* 16 take as a non-examined subject; 8 take GCSE; 8 International Baccalaureate. 3 accepted for Art School. *Sport:* Soccer, basketball, badminton, swimming, tennis, jujitsu available. 42 take non-compulsory sport. 3 represent county (gymnastics, horse riding, tennis). *Other:* 10 take part in local community schemes. Other activities include a computer club, a Year book, arts forum, Model United Nations and a band.

Careers In 1990, 95% leavers went on to degree courses; 5% to art/drama/music colleges. Of those going on to degree courses, 98% went to universities; 2% to poly/colleges. 46% those going on to higher education went to courses in humanities/social sciences and 48% in economics; 4% in medicine; and 2% in science/engineering.

Uniform School uniform not worn.

Houses/prefects No competitive houses, prefects or head boy/girl. School Council.

Religion No compulsory religious worship.

Social Major events include International Dinner and the School Prom. Organised trips abroad. Pupils allowed to bring own car/bike/motorbike to school. Meals self service. School shop. No alcohol/tobacco allowed.

Discipline No corporal punishment. Pupils failing to produce homework once might expect reprimand and warning; those involved with drugs would be referred to school's Drugs Committee and counselling before re-admission.

Alumni association is run by Miss Mary Langford, c/o the School.

· Stamford ·

Stamford School
St St Paul's Street
Stamford
Lincolnshire
PE9 2BS
Tel 0780 62171

- Pupils 951
- Boys 8–18 (Day/Board)
- Girls None
- Upper sixth 94

- Termly fees £980 (Day) £1960 (Board)
- HMC

Enquiries/application to the Headmaster

What it's like

Founded in 1532 by William Radcliffe, it has been in continuous existence since. In the 19th century both it and the High School were endowed by the Governors of Browne's Hospital. Both schools adopted William Browne's crest: a stork sitting on a woolsack, with the motto 'Christ me spede'; both have the same board of governors. They are run separately but work in close conjunction, sharing many cultural, social and educational activities. Over the centuries both have played a major part in the life of this town and the neighbourhood. Their daily life is interwoven with that of the town and there is a close 'town and gown' relationship. Stamford School's buildings lie to the north-east of the town in some 34 acres of agreeable grounds and playing fields. The buildings include the site of the Hall occupied by the secessionists from Brasenose Hall, Oxford, in 1344. The oldest building is the chapel, originally part of the 12th-century St Paul's Church. Much of the school was rebuilt in 1875; since then there has been a continuous programme of modernisation and extension. It is now very much up-to-date and enjoys excellent facilities for living and working. An Anglican foundation, it follows the liturgy of the Church of England but welcomes boys of other faiths. A large staff permits a staff:pupil ratio of about 1:13. Academic standards are high and results good. Many boys go on to degree courses each year, including Oxbridge. Music is very strong indeed (about 250 learn an instrument; choirs and orchestras are vigorously supported). Drama is also strong. A standard range of sports and games is provided and there are many successful teams (a large number of representatives at county level; some at national level). The CCF contingent is unusually big (Army,

RAF and Naval sections) and the majority of senior boys join it for at least two years. Local community services are a popular alternative (one group produces a weekly newspaper for the blind). Many clubs and societies cater for most needs. There has been a traditional commitment to the Duke of Edinburgh's Award Scheme in which the school has an outstanding record of success. Each year a large number of overseas trips is organised, plus sporting tours all over the country. There have been both rugby and cricket tours to Australia recently.

School profile

Pupils Total age range 8–18; 951 boys (698 day, 253 boarding). Senior department 13–18, 692 boys. Main entry ages 8, 11, 13 and into sixth. 5% are children of former pupils. *Transfer from maintained schools:* 50% intake at 13 and to sixth.

Entrance Common entrance and own exam used. Oversubscribed. No special skills or religious requirements. Parents not expected to buy text books. 67 assisted places. Approx 12 scholarships/bursaries pa, full fees – £100.

Parents 15+% in the armed services; 15+% in industry. 60+% live within 30 miles; up to 10% live overseas.

Staff Headmaster G J Timm, in post for 12 years. 70 full time staff, 28 part time. Annual turnover 5%. Average age 37.

Academic work GCSE, AS and A-levels. 26 GCSE subjects offered; 2 at AS-level; 20 at A-level (including Greek and Russian to GCSE/A-level; no A-level general studies). In 1990, 122 pupils in fifth, 94 in upper sixth. *GCSE:* in 1990, 71% fifth gained at least grade C in 8+ subjects; 24% in 5–7; and 5% in 1–4 subjects. *A-levels:* On average 3% upper sixth pass in 4+ subjects; 62% in 3; 19% in 2; and 10% in 1 subject. 14 take science A-levels; 87 arts/humanities; 15 both. *Computing facilities:* 2 Econet networks with 60 BBC's, Masters and Archimedes computers. *Special provision:* One teacher gives individual lessons to dyslexic pupils.

European Community *Languages:* French offered: to age 14; GCSE; A-level. German offered: to age 14; GCSE; A-level. Spanish offered: to GCSE. 50–75% take GCSE in more than 1 EC language. *Exchanges:* Regular exchanges for pupils aged 16–18 to France and Germany. *Other:* Holiday use of boarding and other facilities by some 50 Greek children.

Senior pupils' non-academic activities *Music:* 250 learn a musical instrument, 25 to Grade 6 or above; 3 accepted for Music School. 120 play in school orchestra, 120 in choir; 25 play in pop group beyond school. *Drama and dance:* 120 in school productions; group setting up own production for performance to local primary school children. 2–3 accepted for English with Drama degree courses. *Art:* 12 take as non–examined subject; 38 take GCSE; 16 A-level. 5–7 accepted for Art School. *Sport:* Rugby, hockey, golf, soccer, cricket, tennis, squash, fencing, athletics, cross country, badminton, basketball available. 150 take non–compulsory sport. 30+ pupils represent county (hockey, cricket, rugby, athletics, cross-country). *Other:* 110 have bronze Duke of Edinburgh's Award, 60 silver, 48 gold. 37 in local community schemes. 2–5 enter voluntary schemes after leaving school. Other activities include computer clubs, chess, science society, business society, CCF, bands, Young Enterprise.

Careers In 1990, 54% leavers went on to degree courses; 2% to art/drama/music colleges; 8% to non-degree courses (eg civil engineering, geography, agriculture, hotel/catering); 6% straight into careers (eg banking, retailing, armed services, industry). Of those going on to degree courses, 8% went to Oxbridge; 63% to other universities; 27% to poly/colleges. 2% those going on to higher education went to courses in practical art; 3% in drama/acting; 56% in humanities/social sciences; 3% in medicine; and 48% in science/engineering.

Uniform School uniform worn throughout.

Houses/prefects Competitive houses. Prefects, head boy, head of house and house prefects. School prefects appointed by Head, house prefects by House-masters.

Religion Christian worship compulsory.

Social Plays, musical events, choir, certain sixth form studies with sister school. Various organised trips abroad (fieldwork, ski-ing etc); teacher exchange with Camberwell Grammar School, Australia; pupil exchange with St Albans School, Washington, DC. Pupils allowed to bring own car/motorbike/bike to school. Meals self service except in junior boarding houses. School shop. No tobacco/alcohol allowed.

Discipline No corporal punishment. Pupils failing to produce homework once might expect to be admonished and kept in if persistent; those caught smoking cannabis on the premises would be suspended, while all factors considered – expulsion likely.

Boarding 7% have own study bedroom, 35% share; 58% in dormitories of 6+. Houses, of 36–83, divided by age group (8–12; 13–18). Resident qualified nurse. Central dining room for senior boarders. Pupils can provide and cook coffee, tea and toast. Exeats for seniors most weekends; juniors, two weekends per term. Seniors allowed to local town daily with permission; juniors, rationed.

Alumni association is run by H A Staveley, Chairman, 5 Reeves Lane, Wing, Oakham, Leicestershire LE15 8SD.

Former pupils M J K Smith (cricketer); John Terraine (historian); Robert Clift (Olympic Gold Medallist, hockey); Simon Hodgkinson (rugby); Mark James (golfer); the Bishop of Worcester.

· *Stamford High* ·

Stamford High School
St Martin's
Stamford
Lincolnshire PE9 2LJ
Tel 0780 62330

- Pupils 1016
- Boys 4–8 only
- Girls 4–18
  (Day/Board/Weekly)
- Upper sixth 91

- Termly fees
  £980 (Day)
  £1764 (Board)
  £1740 (Weekly)
- GSA, BSA
  Enquiries/application to
  the Headmistress

What it's like

Founded in 1877, it belongs to the Stamford Endowed Schools which also includes Stamford School. Both have the same board of governors. They are run separately but work in close conjunction, sharing many cultural, social and educational activities. Over the centuries both have played a major part in the life of the town and the neighbourhood. Their daily life is interwoven with that of the town and there is a close 'town and gown' relationship. Stamford High School has a fine site in the centre of town, which is a place of considerable beauty and much architectural interest. Facilities are very good and boarding accommodation comfortable. The school is non-denominational but there is some emphasis on religious education and there are daily prayers for all pupils. Sunday services are compulsory for boarders. A well-qualified staff of 76, plus part-timers, permits a staff:pupil ratio of about 1:12. Academic standards are high and results consistently creditable. Many girls go on to degree courses each year, including Oxbridge. French, German and Spanish are offered to A-level and a high proportion of girls takes more than one European language at GCSE. There are regular exchanges with France, Germany and Spain. The school's academic aim is to avoid early specialisation and to encourage the best of traditional and modern methods of learning. Music and drama are strongly supported. Some 300 girls learn a musical instrument. There are several dramatic productions each year. Sports and games are well catered for and include, besides the standard range, Tae kwon do, fencing and Olympic gymnastics. There is a wide variety of clubs and societies. Girls are encouraged to take part in community and social services. The Duke of Edinburgh's Award Scheme is exceptionally popular and the school has a phenomenal record of success in the number of bronze, silver and gold medals awarded.

School profile

Pupils Total age range 4–18; 1016 pupils, 868 day (44 boys, 824 girls), 148 boarding girls. Senior department 11–18, 742 girls. Main entry ages 4 (boys and girls); 8, 11 and into sixth (girls). Approx 5% are children of former pupils. *Transfer from maintained schools:* 50% of main intake at 11, plus 10% into sixth.

Entrance Own entrance exam used. Oversubscribed. Musical and sporting ability welcomed; no religious requirements. Parents not expected to buy text books; no compulsory extras. 15 assisted places pa. 6 scholarships/bursaries pa, full tuition—£300.

Parents 15+% in industry or commerce; 15+% in the armed services, 15+% are doctors, lawyers, etc. 60+% live within 30 miles; up to 10% live overseas.

Staff Headmistress Gladys K Bland, in post for 13 years. 75 full time staff, 14 part time. Annual turnover 5%. Average age 38.

Academic work GCSE, AS and A-levels. 18 GCSE subjects offered; 21 at A-level (no A-level general studies). In 1990, 118 pupils in upper fifth, 91 in upper sixth. *GCSE:* in 1990, 92 upper fifth gained at least grade C in 8+ subjects; 19 in 5–7; and 3 in 1–4 subjects. *A-levels:* 3 upper sixth passed in 4 subjects; 53 in 3; 16 in 2; and 7 in 1 subject. 14 took science A-levels; 52 arts/humanities; 17 both. *Computing facilities:* Main computer centre, linked to computers in CDT centre; plus computers in arts and science departments. *Special provision:* Testing and special tuition arranged for dyslexic pupils.

European Community *Languages:* French offered: to age 14; GCSE; AS-level; A-level. German offered: to age 14; GCSE; A-level. Spanish offered: to age 14; GCSE; A-level. 50–75% take GCSE in more than 1 EC language. *Exchanges:* Regular exchanges for pupils aged 11–18 to France, Germany and Spain.

Senior pupils' non-academic activities *Music:* 380 learn a musical instrument, 60 to Grade 6 or above. 1–2 pa accepted for Music School. 86 in school orchestras, 120 in school choirs, 30 in orchestras outside school. *Drama and dance:* 60 in school productions; 180 take exams in ESB, RAD etc. 2 or 3 accepted for Drama Schools. *Art:* 78 take as non-examined subject, 56 take GCSE; 14 A-level. 5 accepted for Art School; 4 take history of art courses. 14 take GCSE photography. *Sport:* Hockey, netball, tennis, athletics, volleyball, badminton, basketball, swimming, Olympic gymnastics, golf, cross-country, rounders, ten-pin bowling, fencing available. 298 pupils take non-compulsory sport. 30 take exams. Average of 5 represent county. *Other:* 164 have bronze Duke of Edinburgh's Award, 64 silver, 68 gold. Other activities include a computer club, Tae Kwon Do club, Christian Union, chess club, public speaking, geography, young naturalists, science clubs, theatre, design and technology, board games, football club.

Careers In 1990, 75% leavers went on to degree courses; 4% to art/drama/music colleges; 7% to non-degree courses (eg nursing, HND international office management); 14% straight into careers (eg retail management, hotel management). Of those going on to degree courses, 10% went to Oxbridge; 55% to other universities; 35% to poly/colleges. 5% those going on to higher education went to courses in practical art; 1% in drama/acting; 5% in music; 64% in humanities/social sciences; 5% in medicine; and 20% in science/engineering.

Uniform School uniform worn throughout.

Houses/prefects No competitive houses. Prefects, head girl, head of house and house prefects – elected by the sixth, except in boarding houses. School Council.

Religion Religious worship compulsory, though exemption allowed on grounds of conscience.

Social Joint activities with Stamford School include film, Brazenose Society, historical lectures, science society, joint musical and dramatic performances and dances. Trips abroad include ski trips, GCSE visits to Switzerland, USSR, Eastern Europe, history of art tours in France and Italy; linked school in Bonn, exchange visits to France and Spain. Pupils allowed to bring own car/bike/ motorbike to school. Meals self-service. School shop. No tobacco/alcohol allowed.

Discipline No corporal punishment. Pupils failing to produce homework once might expect to be admonished and asked to produce it; those caught smoking cannabis on the school premises could expect expulsion.

Boarding 1% have own study bedroom, 27% share – mainly 2; 72% in dormitories of 6+. Houses, divided by age, 49–60. A housemistress is SRN. Sixth form pupils can provide and cook own food. 2 weekend exeats termly plus unlimited day exeats. Visits to the local town: special shopping expeditions by juniors, ranging to daily visits for upper fifth and sixth.

Alumni association is run by Mrs A Marshall.

· *Stanbridge Earls* ·

Stanbridge Earls	• Pupils 174	• Termly fees
Romsey	• Boys 11–18	£2200 (Day)
Hampshire	(Day/Board/Weekly)	£2950 (Board/
SO51 0ZS	• Girls 11–18	Weekly)
Tel 0794 516777	(Day/Board/Weekly)	Enquiries/application to
	• Upper sixth 15	the Headmaster

What it's like

Founded in 1952, it is largely housed in a beautiful building of medieval origins and Tudor appearance and is of considerable architectural and historical interest. King Alfred is thought to have lived on the site and King Ethelwolf to have been buried there in the 9th century. The 13th century chapel is at the heart of the building. Made of stone and flint, it is the oldest part. The mansion lies in 50 acres of splendid landscaped grounds and gardens, with woodland and a chain of small lakes. The neighbouring countryside is largely farmland, with the New Forest 3 miles away. There is considerable emphasis on religious education and worship in the Anglican tradition. It has all the advantages of being a small school, and its most particular feature is its big remedial department staffed by a dozen teachers (some full-time, some part-time). The school tends to specialise in pupils who for various reasons have 'under achieved'. There is much emphasis on personal attention and the large staff (plus a lot of part-timers) permits a staff:pupil ratio of about 1:5. Much is achieved academically and though the sixth form is small, several pupils go on to degree courses each year. Art and drama are particular strengths. There is an excellent range of sports and games (including fishing and riding) and a plentiful variety of extra-curricular activities.

School profile

Pupils Total age range 11–18; 174 pupils, 18 day (14 boys, 4 girls); 156 boarding (141 boys, 15 girls). Main entry ages, 11, 13 and into the sixth. *Transfer from maintained schools:* 10% main intakes, plus 2% to sixth.

Entrance Common entrance sometimes used. Oversubscribed. No special skills or religious requirements although C of E predominates. Parents not expected to buy text books. 10 scholarships, 33% fees.

Parents 15+% in armed services; 15+% in industry or commerce; 15+% in farming. Up to 10% live within 30 miles; 10+% live overseas.

Staff Headmaster Howard Moxon, in post for 7 years. 30 full time staff, 16 part time. Annual turnover 4%. Average age 33.

Academic work GCSE and A-levels. 20 subjects offered (including photography, motor vehicle engineering; no A-level general studies). In 1990, 42 pupils in upper fifth, 15 in upper sixth. *GCSE:* in 1990, 10% upper fifth gained at least grade C in 8+ subjects; 30% in 5–7; and 60% in 1–4 subjects. *A-levels:* 20% upper sixth passed in 3 subjects; 20% in 2; and 50% in 1 subject. 40% took science A-levels; 40% arts/humanities; 20% both. *Computing facilities:* Own room – Archimedes BBC computers – networked linked. *Special provision:* Special Unit with 12 specialist trained staff.

European Community *Languages:* French offered: to age 14; GCSE; A-level. Italian offered: to age 14; GCSE. 10–25% take GCSE in more than 1 EC language. *Exchanges:* Regular exchanges to Germany. *Other:* French department visit to France at least once a year. 3 German pupils pa (1/term) join fourth year for all subjects.

Senior pupils' non-academic activities *Music:* 20 learn a musical instrument, 1 to Grade 6 or above. 3 in county youth orchestra, 10 in school music groups. *Drama and dance:* 30 in school productions. 1 accepted for Drama

School, 1 goes on to work in theatre, 3 in youth theatre. *Art:* 30 take GCSE; 4 A-level; 5 accepted for Art School, 5 for photography. 21 belong to photographic club. *Sport:* Swimming, squash, tennis, rugby, hockey, cricket, badminton, netball, basketball, athletics, gymnastics, judo, sailing, riding, fishing, canoeing available. 80 take non-compulsory sport, 12 take exams. 3 represent county/country (cross-country, rugby, cricket).

Other activities include a computer club, driving lessons, chess, draughts, motor vehicle maintenance; Duke of Edinburgh's Award Scheme.

Careers In 1990, 10% leavers went on to degree courses; 15% to non-degree courses; 38% straight into careers; 37% other. Of those going on to degree courses, 20% went to universities; 80% to poly/colleges. 60% those going on to higher education went to courses in practical art; 20% in humanities/social sciences; and 20% in science/engineering.

Uniform School uniform worn except the sixth.

Houses/prefects Competitive houses. Prefects, head boy/girl, head of house and house prefects – appointed by the Head after discussion with housemasters. School Council.

Religion Compulsory worship.

Social Debates and speaking competitions with other local schools; some trips abroad. Pupils allowed to bring own bike to school. Meals self service. School shop. No tobacco allowed; alcohol (no spirits) at limited times in staff/sixth form bar.

Discipline No corporal punishment. Pupils failing to produce homework once might expect reprimand and discussion; those caught smoking cannabis on the premises would expect expulsion.

Boarding 5% have own study bedroom, 28% share, 36% are in dormitories of 6+. Single sex houses. Resident qualified nurse. Central dining room. Pupils can provide and cook own food. 3 termly exeats (up to a week). Visits to local town allowed.

Alumni association run by Secretary to the Wyvern Society, c/o the School.

Former pupils Paul Cox (artist); Marc Sinden (actor); Michael Blodgett (sculptor); Christopher Neame (actor/producer); Charles Balchin (TV producer).

· Stonar ·

Stonar
Cottles Park
Atworth
Melksham
Wiltshire SN12 8NT
Tel 0225 702309

- Pupils 500
- Boys None
- Girls 5–18
  (Day/Board/Weekly)
- Upper sixth 50

- Termly fees
  £1315 (Day)
  £2375 (Board/
  Weekly)
- GSA
  Enquiries/application to
  the Registrar

What it's like

Founded in 1921 at Sandwich, it moved to its present site in 1939. The main building is a very handsome listed 19th century country house set in 40 acres of splendid parkland. Facilities are very good and boarding accommodation is comfortable. Religious worship is compulsory in the Anglican tradition but all denominations are welcome. A large staff allows a staff:pupil ratio of 1:9 (and there is quite a large part-time staff). A good general education is provided and results are impressive. Many girls go on to degree courses each year. There is a big commitment to music, drama and art. A fine range of sports and games is available and there is an excellent variety of extra-curricular activities (including riding: the school has its own stables and a number of horses and ponies). A promising record in the Duke of Edinburgh's Award Scheme.

School profile

Pupils Total age range 5–18; 500 girls, (220 day, 280 boarding). Senior department 11–18, 402 girls. Main entry ages 5, 11, 13 and into sixth. Less than 5% are children of former pupils. *Transfer from maintained schools:* 20% senior intake, plus 10% to sixth.

Entrance Own entrance exam used. Not oversubscribed. No special skills or religious requirements. Parents not expected to buy text books; maximum extras £80. 4 scholarships plus bursaries for music, riding, art, sport.

Parents 15+% in industry or commerce. 30+% live within 30 miles; 10+% live overseas.

Staff Head Mrs Susan Hopkinson, in post for 6 years. 51 full time staff, 22 part time. Annual turnover 3%. Average age 36.

Academic work GCSE, AS and A-levels. 20 GCSE subjects offered; 26 at A-level (no A-level general studies). In 1990, 51 pupils in upper fifth, 50 in upper sixth. *GCSE:* in 1990, 35% upper fifth gained at least grade C in 8+ subjects; 48% in 5–7; and 17% in 1–4 subjects. *A-levels:* 55% upper sixth passed in 3 subjects; 35% in 2; and 10% in 1 subject. 10% took science A-levels; 50% arts/humanities; 40% both. *Computing facilities:* Archimedes network; labs, library, music school fully equipped. *Special provision:* Help with dyslexia. Specialist teacher for EFL.

European Community *Languages:* French offered: to age 14; GCSE; AS-level; A-level. German offered: to age 14; GCSE; AS-level; A-level. Italian offered: to age 14; GCSE; AS-level; A-level.

Spanish offered: to age 14; GCSE; AS-level; A-level. 10–25% take GCSE in more than 1 EC language.

Senior pupils' non-academic activities *Music:* 230 learn a musical instrument, 10 to Grade 6 or above, 1 accepted for Music School; 19 in school orchestra, 50 in choir, 14 in wind band. *Drama and dance:* 50 in school productions, 2 take to Grade 6 in ESB, RAD etc. 3 accepted for Drama School. *Art:* 33 take GCSE; 12 A-level; 6 A-level photography; 14 A-level history of art; 4 accepted for Art School; 20 belong to photographic club; 35 to art club. *Sport:* Hockey, netball, cross-country, squash, volleyball, gymnastics, trampolining, canoeing, cricket, badminton, tennis, rounders, athletics, swimming, riding available. 150 take non-compulsory sport. All girls take life-saving exams; 30, GCSE PE. 19 represent county/country (hockey, swimming, cross-country, athletics). *Other:* Some take part in local community schemes. 20 have bronze Duke of Edinburgh's Award, 1 has silver and 6 gold. Other activities include a computer club, driving lessons, indoor riding to BHSAI, chess club, debating society, typing; 50 take Emergency Aid Certificate.

Careers On average, 50% leavers go on to degree courses; 4% to art/drama/music colleges; 15% to non-degree courses (eg nursing, mining, BTEC courses); 20% straight into careers. Of those going on to degree courses, 3% go to Oxbridge; 33% to other universities; 15% to poly/colleges. 10% those going on to higher education go to courses in practical art; 1% in drama/acting; 3% in music; 15% in humanities/social sciences; 6% in medicine; and 6% in science/engineering.

Uniform School uniform worn except in the sixth.

Houses/prefects Competitive houses. Prefects, head girl, head of house and house prefects – appointed by the Head. School Council.

Religion Attendance at religious worship compulsory.

Social Organised local events and trips abroad. Pupils allowed to bring own bike/horse to school. Meals self service. School shop. No tobacco/alcohol allowed.

Discipline No corporal punishment. Pupils failing to produce homework once might expect a warning; those caught smoking cannabis on the premises would expect expulsion.

Boarding Sixth have study bedrooms, rest share with 2–6. Houses, of approximately 38. Resident qualified nurse. Central dining room. 2 weekend exeats and a week at half-term. Visits to local town allowed.

Alumni association run by Mrs D Watts, 7 Salter Road, Sandbanks, Poole, Dorset.

Former pupils Katharine Schlesinger (actress).

· Stonyhurst ·

Stonyhurst College
Stonyhurst
Lancashire
BB6 9PZ
Tel 025 486 345

- Pupils 432
- Boys 13–18 (Day/Board)
- Girls 16–18 (Day)
- Upper sixth 85

- Termly fees £1489 (Day) £2792 (Board)
- HMC
Enquiries/application to the Headmaster

What it's like

Founded in 1593 at St Omers, it moved to Bruges in 1762 and to Liege in 1773. Forced to leave the continent at the outbreak of the French Revolution, it established itself at the Hall of Stonyhurst in 1794. It has very fine buildings in a beautiful setting in the Ribble Valley on the slopes of Longridge Fells. Its two prep schools are St Mary's Hall (at Stonyhurst) and St John's at Windsor. Extremely well equipped with modern facilities, the college is run by the Society of Jesus (a number of whose priests are on the teaching staff) and describes itself as 'a community of boys, parents, Jesuits, lay staff, old boys and friends'. It undertakes to provide instruction in Catholic doctrine and to educate boys in the principles and practice of their faith. Its large staff permits a ratio of 1:8 pupils. Excellent teaching is provided and academic standards and results are high. There are very many university entrants per year, especially for a school of this size, and almost all sixth form go on to degree courses. Very strong indeed in music (200 boys learn an instrument, 150 participate in orchestras) and drama. Wide range of games, sports and activities. Excellent standards in games with a number of county and national representatives. Considerable emphasis on outdoor pursuits for which the environment is ideal. A big cadet corps contingent. Very substantial commitment to local community schemes and charities and a good record in the Duke of Edinburgh's Award Scheme.

School profile

Pupils Age range 13–18; 432 pupils, 35 day (32 boys, 3 girls), 397 boarding (boys). Main entry ages 13+ (boys) and into sixth (boys and girls). St Mary's Hall, Stonyhurst and St John's Beaumont, Windsor provide more than 20% of intake.

Entrance Common entrance and own exam used. Not oversubscribed. Special skills taken into account. Pupils should be Roman Catholic although Christians of other denominations are considered. Parents are not expected to buy text books; other extras variable. 26 assisted places. 10–12 academic and music scholarships, up to $\frac{1}{2}$ fees; college bursaries.

Parents 15+% in industry or commerce; 14+% are doctors, lawyers, etc. 10+% live within 30 miles; 15+% live overseas.

Staff Headmaster Dr Giles Mercer, in post for 6 years. 52 full time staff, 8 part time. Annual turnover 3.

Academic work GCSE and A-levels. 21 GCSE subjects offered; 20 at A-level (including astronomy and A-level general studies). In 1990, 90 pupils in upper fifth, 85 in upper sixth. *GCSE:* in 1990, 66 upper fifth gained at least grade C in 8+ subjects; 15 in 5–7; and 9 in 1–4 subjects. *A-levels:* 6 upper sixth passed in 4+ subjects; 61 in 3; 14 in 2; and 3 in 1 subject. 23% took science A-levels; 31% arts/humanities; 46% both. *Computing facilities:* 16 station computer network in design and technology. *Special provision:* Subsidiary classes outside the timetable, either alone or in small groups.

European Community *Languages:* French offered: to age 14; GCSE; A-level; Institute of Linguists. German offered: to GCSE; A-level. Spanish offered: to GCSE; A-level. 25–50% take GCSE in more than 1 EC language. *Exchanges:* Regular exchanges for pupils aged 16–18 to France and Germany. *Other:* Visit and talk by local MEP. 39 EC pupils at school.

Senior pupils' non-academic activities *Music:* Approx 50% learn a musical instrument; 150 in school orchestras, 80 in choir, 20 in dance band; 2 in National Youth Orchestra; orchestra tours. *Drama:* Most pupils in school productions during the year. *Art:* 18 take GCSE; 5 A-level. 4 accepted for architecture. 6 belong to eg photographic club; 5 to typography and printing. *Sport:* Rugby, cricket, swimming, cross-country, badminton, squash, tennis, golf (9 hole school golf course), fishing, shooting, indoor games (basketball etc) available. Two-thirds take non-compulsory sport. 20 take exams eg gymnastics, swimming. 12 represent county (rugby, cricket, athletics). *Other:* 29 take part in local community schemes. 17 have bronze Duke of Edinburgh's Award, 9 have silver and 3 gold. Other activities include a computer club, driving lessons, good chess club, flourishing astronomy society (school observatory), debating, political, literary and scientific societies, video film unit.

Careers In 1990, 85% leavers went on to degree courses; 3% to art/drama/music colleges; 1% to non-degree courses (eg HND business German); 3% straight into careers (eg Hong Kong police, army); 8% other. Of those going on to degree courses, 6% went to Oxbridge; 67% to other universities; 15% to poly/colleges. 4% those going on to higher education went to courses in practical art; 45% in drama/acting; 22% in humanities/social sciences; 21% in medicine; and 8% in science/engineering.

Uniform School uniform worn throughout ('home clothes' for part of weekend).

Houses/prefects Competitive houses for sports only. Prefects and head boy – appointed by the Headmaster.

Religion Compulsory weekly Mass, year group Mass weekly, Sunday evening service. Morning and evening prayers.

Social Exchanges with schools in Reims and Toulouse. Pupils allowed to bring own bike to school (from second year). Meals formal and self service. School shop. No tobacco/alcohol allowed.

Discipline Pupils failing to produce homework once might expect some loss of free time; those caught smoking cannabis on the premises could expect expulsion (though this has not been a problem).

Boarding 117 have own study bedroom; own cubicle for years 1 and 2. Houses divided by age group. Resident qualified full and part time nursing staff. Central dining room. Exeats only for special family occasions. Visits to the local town allowed, with permission for older boys.

Alumni association: The Stonyhurst Association, c/o the College.

Former pupils Lord Devlin; General Vernon Walters (US Ambassador to UN); Arthur Conan Doyle; Charles Laughton; Paul Johnson.

· Stover ·

Stover School	● Pupils 275	● Termly fees
Newton Abbot	● Boys None	£1005 (Day)
Devon	● Girls 11–18	£2000 (Board)
TQ12 6QG	(Day/Board/Weekly)	£1950 (Weekly)
Tel 0626 54505	● Upper sixth 15	● GSA
		Enquiries to the School Secretary/Application to the Headteacher

What it's like

Founded in 1932, it lies in 64 acres of grounds, part of the original Stover Park. There are beautiful landscaped gardens and fine playing fields with splendid views across Dartmoor. The main building is a superb 18th century Palladian mansion (1777), formerly the home of the Duke of Somerset. Since foundation there have been several additions and developments. A relaxed and friendly atmosphere prevails and there is a policy of trying to suit the needs of the individual. Worship is in the Anglican tradition. A sound general education is provided. A standard range of games and sports is available, and there is a large variety of extra-curricular activities. Considerable emphasis on outdoor pursuits for which the environment is ideal, and an impressive record in the Duke of Edinburgh's Award Scheme.

School profile

Pupils Age range 11–18; 275 girls, 110 day, 165 boarding. Main entry ages 11 and into sixth. *Transfer from maintained schools:* 50% main intake, plus occasional pupil to sixth.

Entrance Own entrance exam used. Oversubscribed. No special skills or religious requirements but strong Anglican links. Parents not expected to buy text books. 4 scholarships/bursaries pa, 50–10% of fees.

Parents 10+% live within 30 miles; 5+% live overseas.

Staff Headmistress Mrs W E Lunel, in post for 6 years. 15 full time staff, 14 part time. Average age 35.

Academic work GCSE and A-levels, Pitman Commercial subjects, City and Guilds practical. Average size of upper fifth 45; upper sixth 15. *Computing facilities:* Nimbus network.

European Community *Languages:* French offered: to age 14; GCSE; A-level. German offered: to age 14; GCSE; A-level. 25–50% take GCSE in more than 1 EC language. *Exchanges:* Regular exchanges for pupils aged 14–16 to France and Germany.

Senior pupils' non-academic activities *Music:* Approx 65% girls learn a musical instrument; some play for Devon schools' orchestra and other musical groups; all musicians participate in group music. *Drama and dance:* school productions. *Sport:* Lacrosse, cross-country, swimming, tennis, netball, rounders, athletics available. 70% take non-compulsory sport eg riding, hill-walking. Many take exams. *Other:* Wide variety of other activities including computer club.

Careers In 1990 out of 12 leavers, 7 went on to degree courses; 2 to non-degree courses (eg HND food and consumer studies, beauty therapy); 2 straight into careers (eg lab technician, riding instructor); 1 Gap year. Of those going on to degree courses, 1 went to Oxbridge; 2 to other universities; 4 to poly/colleges. Of those going on to higher education 6 went to courses in humanities/social sciences; 1 in medicine.

Uniform School uniform worn except in the sixth.

Houses/prefects Competitive houses. Prefects, head girl, head of house and house prefects – appointed by the Head after consultation with staff and prefects.

Religion Morning service compulsory.

Social Young Enterprise scheme with other local schools; some organised trips abroad. Pupils allowed to bring own car/bike/motorbike to school. Meals self service. School shop.

Discipline No corporal punishment. Removal of privileges is the normal sanction. Pupils failing to produce homework expect prep detention.

Boarding Head girl has own study bedroom, sixth form share; remainder in dormitories of 6+. Houses, of approximately 50, are divided by age. Resident qualified nurse. Central dining room. Sixth form can provide and cook own food. 2 weekend exeats and half-term. Visits to local town allowed.

Alumni association run by Mrs M Kearney, c/o the School.

· *Stowe* ·

Stowe School
Buckingham
MK18 5EH
Tel 0280 813164

- Pupils 580
- Boys 13–18
  (Day/Board)
- Girls 16–18
  (Day/Board)
- Upper sixth 132

- Termly fees
  £2282 (Day)
  £3262 (Board)
- HMC, SHA, Allied
  Enquiries/application to
  the Headmaster

What it's like

Founded in 1923, it lies in a magnificent park of 750 acres landscaped by Vanbrugh, Bridgman, Kent and Brown. The main building – the original Stowe House – was the seat of the Temple Family and the Dukes of Buckingham and Chandos. It is a huge and elegant country house finished in 1770 to designs by Adam. Modern facilities of every conceivable kind are outstanding. All pupils are expected to attend religious services in the Anglican tradition with special arrangements for RCs on Sundays. Academic standards are high and many sixth formers go on to degree courses each year. Pupils are expected to work hard and maintain a high standard of good manners. It is a well run school with a strong emphasis on personal help. Tremendously strong in music, drama and art. Wide variety of sports and games (high standards are achieved). A large number of clubs and societies (33) cater for most needs. Substantial commitment to local community schemes and the Duke of Edinburgh's Award Scheme.

School profile

Pupils Age range 13–18; 580 pupils, 40 day (30 boys, 10 girls), 540 boarding (470 boys, 70 girls). Main entry ages 13 (boys) and into sixth (boys and girls). 14% are children of former pupils. *Transfer from maintained schools:* 3% main intakes.

Entrance Common entrance used; own exam where CE is inappropriate. Any special skill is of interest; no religious requirements but pupils must attend religious services. Parents expected to buy text books; other extras variable. 3 assisted places (sixth form only). 14 scholarships, exhibitions and bursaries available (academic, music and art) up to full fees.

Parents 15+% in industry or commerce; 15+% are doctors, lawyers etc. 10+% live within 30 miles; 10+% live overseas.

Staff Headmaster J G L Nichols, 2 years in post. Annual turnover of staff 5–10%.

Academic work GCSE and A-levels. 17 GCSE subjects offered; 16 at A-level (including AS-level general studies but not A-level). In 1990, 108 pupils in upper fifth, 132 in upper sixth. *GCSE:* in 1990, 47% upper fifth gained at least grade C in 8+ subjects; 33% in 5–7; and 20% in 1–4 subjects. *A-levels:* 2% upper sixth passed in 4+ subjects; 75% in 3; 20% in 2; and 5% in 1 subject. 15% took science A-levels; 70% arts/humanities; 15% both. *Computing facilities:* 16 IBM PC compatibles in computer room and desk-top publishing studio; IBM compatible PCs in design & biology departments; BBCs or equivalent in each maths classroom and most other departments. *Special provision:* Regular part-time support for those with special learning difficulties.

European Community *Languages:* French offered: to GCSE; AS-level; A-level. German offered: to GCSE; A-level. Spanish offered: to GCSE; A-level. 25–50% take GCSE in more than 1 EC language. *Exchanges:* Regular exchanges for pupils aged 16–18 to France and Germany, occasionally to Spain. *Other:* Always have EC pupils in school; French, German and Spanish nationals as assistant teachers. Plan to introduce subsidiary Italian and Eurolingua Society in sixth form.

Senior pupils' non-academic activities *Sport:* Rugby football, hockey, cricket, tennis, athletics, squash, swimming, golf, badminton, fives, cross-country running, sailing, canoeing, shooting, fencing, archery, beagling, lacrosse, netball, riding available.

Careers In 1990, 65% leavers went on to degree courses; 5% to art/drama/music colleges; 5% to non-degree courses; 5% straight into careers (eg city insurance, commodity markets etc); 20% other. Of those going on to degree courses, 7% went to Oxbridge; 70% to other universities; 23% to poly/colleges. Approx. 5% those going on to higher education went to courses in practical art; 1% in drama/acting; 3% in music; 77% in humanities/social sciences; 4% in medicine; and 10% in science/engineering.

Uniform School uniform not worn, but dress regulations exist.

Houses/prefects Prefects, head boy/girl, head of house and house prefects – appointed by the Headmaster.

Religion Compulsory attendance at religious worship.

Social Industrial Conference (with Royal Latin School), public speaking with other schools. Organised trips abroad – to Nepal most years and eg South America and skiing parties to Europe. Pupils allowed to bring own bicycle to school. Meals self service. School shop. No tobacco allowed; beer/cider bar for top year with strict control.

Discipline No corporal punishment. Pupils failing to produce satisfactory homework once should expect to do it again properly with further sanctions; those known to be smoking cannabis or drinking spirits on the premises should expect expulsion.

Boarding All sixth form have own study bedroom. Houses, of 55–60, full age range in each. Resident qualified nurse and daily visits by doctor. Two central dining rooms. Pupils can provide and cook their own food. Exeats at half-term and up to two other weekends each term. Visits to the local town allowed.

Alumni association is run locally by Mr C J G Atkinson, c/o the School.

Former pupils Leonard Cheshire VC; Lord Quinton; Sir Nigel Broackes; Robert Kee; General Sir Frank Kitson; David Scott Cowper; Richard Branson; David Wynne; David Shepherd; David Fanshawe; Howard Goodall; Sir Nicholas Henderson; Lord Sainsbury; Lord McAlpine; Laurence Whistler.

· Stowford ·

Stowford College
95 Brighton Road
Sutton
Surrey SM2 5SR
Tel 081-661 9444

- Pupils 100
- Boys 7–18 (Day)
- Girls 7–18 (Day)
- Upper sixth 10

- Termly fees
  £978 (Day)
  Enquiries/application to
  the Principal

What it's like

Founded in 1975, it is one of the smaller independent schools. It particularly suits those pupils who dislike large impersonal schools. Single-site, in an agreeable urban residential area with good public transport links. It is a handsome building with well-equipped laboratories and art room. The staff:pupil ratio is favourable – 1:12. About 60% of students come from the maintained sector. Rules and regulations are kept to a minimum, no uniform above 14 years of age. The school prides itself on insistence on hard work and homework in a friendly and informal atmosphere.

School profile

Pupils Age range 7–18; 100 day pupils (60 boys, 40 girls). Main entry ages 7–14 and into sixth. *Transfer from maintained schools:* 60% main intakes, plus 50% to sixth.

Entrance Entrance by interview. Commitment to hard work and effort demanded; no religious requirements. Parents not expected to buy text books; field courses extra (£30 per term). Scholarships from £500–£270 per term.

Parents 15+% are doctors, lawyers etc; 15+% in industry or commerce. Up to 10% live overseas.

Staff Head A J Hennessy, in post for 15 years. 8 full time staff, 5 part time. Annual turnover, 15%. Average age, 30.

Academic work GCSE and A-levels (no A-level general studies offered). In 1990, 32 pupils in upper fifth, 5 in upper sixth. *GCSE:* in 1990, 4 upper fifth gained at least grade C in 8+ subjects; 5 in 5–7; and 21 in 1–4 subjects. *A-levels:* 1 upper sixth passed in 3 subjects; 3 in 2; and 1 in 1 subject. 60% took science A-levels; 20% arts/humanities; 20% both. *Computing facilities:* 6 BBC computers including model B's and Masters. *Special provision:* Appropriate provisions available for all students with difficulties, eg EFL, dyslexia, mild visual handicap.

European Community *Languages:* French offered: to age 14; GCSE. *Other:* Visits to France. Ex-pupil now studying in France.

Senior pupils' non-academic activities *Art:* 4 take as non-examined subject; 10, GCSE; 1, A-level; 1 accepted for Art School. *Sport:* Basketball, squash, badminton, football, netball, rounders, swimming, tennis available. 4 take non-compulsory sport. Other activities include chess club, biology club, Christian Union and junior camping club.

Careers In 1990, 25% leavers went on to degree courses; 10% to art/drama/music colleges; 40% to non-degree courses (eg chiropractice, video, nursery nursing); 20% straight into careers; 5% other. Of those going on to degree courses, 33% went to universities; 34% to poly/colleges. 10% those going on to higher education went to courses in practical art; 30% in humanities/social sciences; 10% in medicine; and 50% in science/engineering.

Uniform No uniform aged 14+.

Houses/prefects No competitive houses. Prefects, head boy/girl. School Council.

Religion No compulsory worship.

Social French day trips. Pupils allowed to bring own car/bike/motorbike to school. School tuck shop. No alcohol.

Discipline Pupils failing to produce homework once might expect lunchtime detention. A pupil smoking cannabis might expect to be asked to leave Stowford.

Alumni association run by C J Grace, c/o the School.

· Stratford House ·

Stratford House School
8/10 Southborough
Road
Bickley
Kent BR1 2EB
Tel 081 467 3580

- Pupils 410
- Boys None
- Girls 4–18
  (Day)
- Upper sixth 20

- Termly fees
  £1150 (Day)
- GSA
Enquiries/application to
the Headmistress

What it's like

Founded in 1912, it lies beside a station in a pleasant outer London suburb with all its buildings on one site. There are agreeable gardens. The original buildings are mid-Victorian but these have been added to and the school now has modern labs, good classrooms, a new sixth form centre and its own playing fields nearby. It specialises in academic children who lack confidence and need a small caring community in order to flourish. The teaching is good and standards and results are creditable. Many pupils go on to degree courses each year. Music is strong, there is a lot of drama, and art. A very good range of sports and games and a lot of clubs and societies for extra-curricular activities. There is a commitment in the sixth form to local community services.

School profile

Pupils Total age range 4–18; 410 day girls. Senior department 11–18, 250 girls. Main entry ages 4, 11 and into sixth. Approx 5–10% are children of former pupils. *Transfer from maintained schools:* 30% main intake, plus 10% to sixth.

Entrance Own entrance exam used. Oversubscribed. Musical skill an advantage; no religious requirements. Parents not expected to buy text books; maximum extras, £10. Scholarships 6 pa, up to one-third of fees; bursaries where needed.

Parents 15+% in theatre, media, music etc; 15+% are doctors, lawyers etc; 15+% in industry or commerce.

Staff Headmistress Mrs A Williamson, in post for 15 years. 23 full time staff, 24 part time. Annual turnover 5%. Average age 42.

Academic work GCSE and A-levels. 22 subjects offered (including photography and A-level general studies). In 1990, 40 pupils in upper fifth, 20 in upper sixth. *GCSE:* in 1990, 45% upper fifth gained at least grade C in 8+ subjects; 38% in 5–7; and 17% in 1–4 subjects. *A-levels:* 10% upper sixth passed in 4+ subjects; 80% in 3; 10% in 2 subjects. 50% took science A-levels; 30% arts/humanities; 20% both. *Computing facilities:* All first years and sixth formers have compulsory IT course. GCSE computer studies is popular.

European Community *Languages:* French offered: to age 14; GCSE; AS-level; A-level; non-examined subject. German offered: to age 14; GCSE; AS-level; A-level; non-examined subject. Spanish offered; to age 14; GCSE; A-level. 50–75% take GCSE in more than 1 EC language. *Exchanges:* Regular exchanges for pupils aged 11–16 to France, Germany, and Spain. *Other:* Regular contact with MEP. 'Foreign languages at work' course for sixth form.

Senior pupils' non-academic activities *Music:* 30% learn a musical instrument. School orchestra, 2 choirs, 2 wind bands, string group, recorder group and guitars. *Drama and dance:* All in house productions. 10–20% in school productions. 5% accepted for Drama/Dance School, 5% work in theatre. *Art:* 18 take GCSE; 4 A-level art, 2 take history of art and 2 technical graphics. 3 accepted for Art School. *Sport:* Netball, lacrosse, gymnastics, tennis, swimming, athletics, volleyball, badminton, table tennis, trampolining, fencing, squash, horse riding, golf available. Pupils represent county/country (lacrosse, fencing, athletics). *Other:* Half sixth form take part in local community schemes. Other activities: some 20 clubs, including a computer club, numerous drama clubs and small music groups.

Careers In 1990, 80% leavers went on to degree courses; 5% to art/drama/music colleges; 3% to non-degree courses (eg beauty culture, engineering, legal secretary); 7% straight into careers (eg banking, civil service, BBC). Of those going on to degree courses, 6% went to Oxbridge; 78% to other universities; 12% to poly/colleges. 10% those going on to higher education went to courses in practical art; 5% in drama/acting; 8% in music; 33% in humanities/social sciences; 15% in medicine; and 25% in science/engineering.

Uniform School uniform worn throughout, modified in sixth.

Houses/prefects Competitive houses. Prefects, head girl, head, secretary and treasurer of house – elected by school and staff.

Religion Morning assembly compulsory; exceptions rare.

Social Debates and lectures at other schools; concerts and theatrical productions with Colfes. Ski-ing trip and educational cruises abroad. Pupils allowed to bring own car/bike to school. Meals self service. School shop. No tobacco/alcohol allowed.

Discipline No corporal punishment. Pupils failing to produce homework once will get a black mark (detention for 3 black marks); those caught smoking cannabis on the premises will be expelled.

Alumni association run by Miss Jill Atkinson, c/o the School.

Former pupils Audrey Coleman (formerly hostage in Iran); Pamela Hutchison (British Ambassador during the Falklands campaign).

· *Strathallan* ·

Strathallan School
Forgandenny
Perth
PH2 9EG
Tel 0738 812546

- Pupils 493
- Boys 10–18 (Board)
- Girls 10–18 (Day/Board)
- Upper sixth 75

- Termly fees
  £1790 (Day)
  £2550 (Board)
- HMC
  Enquiries/application to the Headmaster

What it's like

Founded in 1912 at Bridge of Allan, it moved to its present site at Forgandenny in 1920. The nucleus of the school is a huge and splendid 19th-century country house, on the edge of the village, in a superb estate of 160 acres. Spread round the original house are many modern additions. Facilities are first-rate. Religious practice follows the Church of Scotland, but the school is interdenominational. A high standard of teaching is provided (the staff:pupil ratio is 1:10) and results are very good. Each year many pupils go on to degree courses, including to Oxbridge. French, German, Italian and Spanish are offered to A-level and many pupils take GCSE in more than one European language. The music, drama and art departments are very strong. A good range of games, sports and activities. The CCF is well supported. Considerable emphasis on outdoor pursuits for which the environment is ideal. A promising record in the Duke of Edinburgh's Award Scheme.

School profile

Pupils Total age range 10–18; 493 pupils, 13 day (all girls), 480 boarding (380 boys, 100 girls). Senior department 13–18, 400 pupils (300 boys, 100 girls). Main entry ages 10, 11, 12, 13 and into sixth. Approx 10% are children of former pupils. *Transfer from maintained schools:* 20% main intakes over 11, plus 33% to sixth.

Entrance Common entrance and own exam used. Sometimes oversubscribed. No special skills required. Interdenominational. Parents not expected to buy text books; maximum extras £150. 32 assisted places. 30 scholarships/bursaries, 20–80% of fees.

Parents Up to 10% live within 30 miles; 10+% live overseas.

Staff Headmaster C D Pighills, in post for 15 years. 47 full time staff, 12 part time. Annual turnover 3%. Average age 38.

Academic work GCSE, S-grade, Scottish Highers and A-levels. 16+ subjects offered, no A-level general studies. Average number of pupils in GCSE year, 90; average number in A-level year, approx 75. *Computing facilities:* Special department and other machines in virtually all departments. *Special provision:* for remedial English.

European Community *Languages:* French offered: to age 14; GCSE; AS-level; A-level. German offered: to age 14; GCSE; AS-level; A-level. Italian offered: to age 14; GCSE; AS-level; A-level. Spanish offered: to age 14; GCSE; AS-level; A-level. 25–50% take GCSE in more than 1 EC language.

Senior pupils' non-academic activities *Music:* Junior and senior orchestras, wind band, chapel choir; 1 pupil plays in Scottish Youth Orchestra; 2 accepted for university music degree. *Drama and dance:* Many in school productions. Occasionally a pupil is accepted to Scottish School of Drama. *Art:* 40 take as non-examined subject; 12 take GCSE; 11 A-level. 1–2 accepted for Art School. 12 belong to photographic club. *Sport:* Cricket, rugby, hockey, athletics, swimming, basketball, squash, badminton, sailing, canoeing available. All school take non-compulsory sport. Pupils represent county/country at various sports; eg 1 in Olympic ski-squad. *Other:* 45+ have bronze Duke of Edinburgh's Award. Some enter voluntary schemes after leaving school. Other activities include a computer club, chess, cooking, sewing (girls), design/technology/electronics, debating, play reading, fishing, clay pigeon shooting, driving lessons.

Careers In 1990, 60% leavers went on to degree courses; 20% to art/drama/music colleges; 10% to non-degree courses; 10% other. Of those going on to degree courses, 10% went to Oxbridge; 50% to other universities; 40% to poly/colleges.

Uniform Dress regulations throughout.

Houses/prefects Competitive houses. Prefects, head boy/girl, head of house and house prefects – appointed by the Head after consultation.

Religion Attendance at religious worship compulsory.

Social Theatre excursions, debates, musical events with other local schools. Organised language trips to Paris; sporting trips to Canada, France, South America; ski-ing in Austria. Meals self service. School shop. No tobacco/alcohol allowed.

Discipline No corporal punishment. Pupils failing to produce homework once might expect to have to do it – usually on Sunday afternoon.

Boarding Boys from second year in senior school (from 1991) and all girls have own study bedroom. Single sex houses, of approximately 60, same as competitive houses. Resident qualified nursing sister. Central dining room. Seniors allowed to provide and cook own food. Half-term and 1 Saturday night exeat each term. Visits to the local town allowed for upper sixth only.

· *Streatham High* ·

Streatham Hill & Clapham High School Wavertree Road London SW2 3SR Tel 081 674 6912	● Pupils 530 ● Boys None ● Girls 5–18 (Day) ● Upper sixth 40	● Termly fees £1024 (Day) ● GPDST Enquiries/application to the Headmistress

What it's like ›

Opened in 1887 as Brixton Hill High School, it moved after 7 years to new purpose-built premises on Streatham Hill. In 1938 it amalgamated with Clapham

High School. It has agreeable buildings in very pleasant gardens and grounds. The good facilities include a splendid library, fine labs, art studios and a CDT centre. Interdenominational; worship is encouraged. A sound, well-balanced, general education is provided. Academic results are good and the school has a high reputation in the locality. Each year 25–30 girls go on to university. There is a substantial commitment to music, drama and art. Sports and games are very well provided for (including Olympic gymnastics). There is a plentiful variety of extra-curricular activities.

School profile

Pupils Total age range 5–18; 530 day girls. Senior department 11–18, 385 girls. Main entry ages 5, 11 and into the sixth. Own junior department provides over 70%. Very few are children of former pupils.

Entrance Own entrance exam used. Heavily oversubscribed. Musical skill looked for; no religious requirements. Parents not expected to buy text books. 153 assisted places. 18 scholarships, £684–£100 per term; also bursaries.

Parents 15+% in theatre, media, music etc; 15+% are doctors, lawyers etc; 15+% in industry or commerce.

Staff Headmistress Miss G M Ellis, in post for 12 years. 35 full time staff, 6 part time. Annual turnover 5%. Average age 34.

Academic work GCSE and A-levels. Average size of upper fifth 50; upper sixth 30 (now 40). *GCSE:* on average, 43 pupils in upper fifth pass 8+ subjects. *A-levels:* on average, 1 pupil in upper sixth passes 4 subjects; 25, 3 subjects and 4 pass 2 subjects. On average, 25% take science/engineering A-levels; 25% take arts and humanities; 50% a mixture. *Computing facilities:* 2 fully equipped rooms in main school (networked), 6 extra machines in science, geography and CDT department.

European Community *Languages:* French offered: to age 14; GCSE; AS-level; A-level. German offered: to age 14; GCSE; A-level. Italian offered: to A-level. Spanish offered: to age 14; GCSE; A-level. More than 75% take GCSE in more than 1 EC language. *Exchanges:* Regular exchanges for pupils aged 11–18 to France, Germany, and Spain. *Other:* Regular visits from MEPs. Regular conversation lessons. Work experience abroad being planned.

Senior pupils' non-academic activities *Music:* 50% learn a musical instrument, 25% to Grade 6 or above, 1–2 accepted for Music School. 10% in school orchestra, 10% in choir. *Drama and dance:* 30% in school productions. 4% go on to work in theatre. *Art:* 5% take as non-examined subject; 45% GCSE; 10% A-level; 2 accepted for Art School. 2% belong to photographic club. *Sport:* Netball, swimming, skating, tennis, squash, basketball, rounders, weights, bowls, Olympic gymnastics, aerobics, sports acrobatics available. 50% take non-compulsory sport, 20% take exams. 2 pa represent county (netball). *Other:* 5% take part in local community schemes. Other activities include a computer club, chess, debating, science society, electronics, Christian Union, cultural society, dance club, public speaking (all girls).

Careers In 1990, 80% leavers went on to degree courses; 5% to art/drama/music colleges; 10% to non-degree courses (eg London College of Printing); 3% straight into careers (eg retail management); 2% other. Of those going on to degree courses, 5% went to Oxbridge; 60% to other universities; 15% to poly/colleges. 5% those going on to higher education went to courses in practical art; 60% in humanities/social sciences; 15% in medicine; and 20% in science/engineering.

Uniform School uniform worn except in the sixth.

Houses/prefects Competitive houses. No prefects; head girl – elected by staff and senior girls. School Council.

Religion Worship encouraged.

Social Frequent visits to France, Austria, Italy, Greece. Pupils allowed to bring own bike to school. Meals self service. No tobacco/alcohol allowed.

Discipline No corporal punishment.

Pupils failing to produce homework once might expect detention after school; those caught smoking cannabis on the premises might expect expulsion.

Former pupils June Whitfield (actress); Norman Hartnell (fashion designer); Henry Willis (organ builder).

· Sunderland Church High ·

Sunderland Church
High School
Mowbray Road
Sunderland
Tel 091 5674984

- Pupils 410
- Boys 16–18 (Day)
- Girls 3–18 (Day)
- Upper sixth 35

- Termly fees
  £1006 (Day)
- GSA
  Enquiries/application to
  the Headmistress

What it's like

Founded in 1884 by the Church Schools Company, it has an agreeable urban campus with pleasant grounds. The preparatory and nursery departments are on another site close by. The main school is housed in the original building and has been extensively modernised over the years. It is now well equipped for secondary teaching. The Centenary Building nearby was recently completed to provide new classrooms, laboratories and a music centre. The senior school has playing fields at the prep department five minutes' walk away. Being a Church school it lays stress on the creation of a Christian atmosphere but is ecumenical in spirit and policy. The staff:pupil ratio is about 1:12. A sound general education is provided and results are creditable. Very many leavers go on to degree courses each year. Music, drama and art are well supported. There is a decent range of games and sports and a fair variety of extra-curricular activities is available including the Duke of Edinburgh's Award Scheme.

School profile

Pupils Total age range 3–18; 410 pupils. Senior department 11–18; 223 pupils (17 boys, 220 girls). Main entry ages 11 (girls); into sixth (boys and girls). 2% are children of former pupils. *Transfer from maintained schools:* 24% senior intake, plus 4% to sixth.

Entrance Own entrance exam used. Not oversubscribed. No special skills or religious requirements. Parents not expected to buy text books; music lessons extra, £45 per term. 2 scholarships at 11+ and in sixth form at discretion and pupil need, 1 term's fees, plus music scholarship.

Parents 15+% are doctors, lawyers etc; 15+% are teachers; 15+% in industry.

Staff Headmistress Mrs M Thrush, in post for 10 years. 28 full time staff, 9 part time. Annual turnover 5%. Average age 40.

Academic work GCSE and A-levels. 18 GCSE and A-level subjects offered (including Latin and A-level general studies). In 1990, 29 pupils in upper fifth, 22 in upper sixth (now 35). *GCSE:* in 1990, 16 upper fifth gained at least grade C in 8+ subjects; 7 in 5–7 subjects. *A-levels:* 7 upper sixth passed in 4+ subjects; 6 in 3; 6 in 2; and 3 in 1 subject. 11 took science A-levels; 9 arts/humanities; 2 both. *Computing facilities:* Nimbus, Acorn and BBC (being updated). *Special provision:* Extra tuition to improve English (have had no pupils with severe dyslexic or visual problems).

European Community *Languages:* French offered: to age 14; GCSE; AS-level; A-level. German offered: to age 14; GCSE; AS-level; A-level. 25–50% take GCSE in more than 1 EC language.

Exchanges: Regular exchanges for pupils aged 14–16 to France and Germany.

Senior pupils' non-academic activities *Music:* 100+ learn a musical instrument, 14 to Grade 6 or above. 40 play in school orchestras, 70 in choirs, 8 in other orchestras or music courses. *Drama and dance:* 40 in school productions; 12 in local drama clubs. *Art:* 6 take GCSE; 2 A-level. *Sport:* 50 take part in non-compulsory sport. 4 pupils represent county (tennis, golf, athletics); 3 represent the town (hockey, cross country, gymnastics); 1 represents country (junior show jumping). *Other:* 15 have bronze Duke of Edinburgh's Award, 1 silver and 1 gold. Other activities include a computer club, Christian Union, art, cookery, craft and karate clubs, drama, choirs, orchestra, wind group.

Careers In 1990, 93% leavers went on to degree courses; 7% to non-degree courses (eg HND estate management, personal assistant). Of those going on to degree courses, 4% went to Oxbridge; 59% to other universities; 37% to poly/colleges. 34% those going on to higher education went to courses in humanities/social sciences; 4% in medicine; and 62% in science/engineering.

Uniform School uniform worn except in sixth.

Houses/prefects Competitive houses. Prefects, head boy/girl, head of house and house prefects – appointed by Head, taking views of peer group into account.

Religion Attendance at religious worship compulsory.

Social Debates with local prep school. Organised trips abroad and exchange systems. Pupils allowed to bring own car to school. Meals self service. No tobacco/alcohol allowed.

Discipline No corporal punishment. Pupils failing to produce homework once receive a verbal reprimand; a detention on the second occasion. Those caught smoking cannabis on the premises would be asked to leave.

Alumni association is run by Mrs Alice Renney, Moulsford, Sea Lane, Sunderland.

Former pupils Kate Adie; Jane Grigson.

· *Surbiton High* ·

Surbiton High School	● Pupils 678	● Termly fees
Surbiton Crescent	● Boys 5–11 only	£1130 (Day)
Kingston upon Thames	(Day)	● GSA, CSCL
Surrey KT1 2JT	● Girls 5–18 (Day)	Enquiries/application to
Tel 081 546 5245	● Upper sixth 30	the Headmistress

What it's like

Founded in 1884, owned by the Church Schools Company, it stands in a quiet part of Surbiton in pleasant grounds. The buildings are well designed and facilities are good. The junior and senior girls' departments are in the same road; boys' department 2 minutes away. Basically it is a C of E establishment but all faiths are welcome. A friendly school where individuals are valued and encouraged to develop their talents. Academic results very creditable and most sixth formers proceed to degree courses each year, including Oxbridge. Strong music, drama and art departments. A fair range of games, sports and activities. A promising record in the Duke of Edinburgh's Award Scheme.

School profile

Pupils Total age range 5–18; 678 day pupils (96 boys, 582 girls). Senior department 11–18, 459 girls. Main entry ages 5, 8 (boys), 5, 10, 11 and into sixth (girls). Approx 3% are children of former pupils. *Transfer from maintained schools:* 30% senior intake.

Entrance Own entrance exam used. Oversubscribed. No special skills or religious requirements. Variable extras. Assisted places at 11+. Sixth form bursaries available, half fees. Reduced fees for clergy children.

Staff Headmistress Mrs R A Thynne, in post for 12 years. 46 full time staff, 15 part time.

Academic work GCSE and A-levels. 24 subjects offered (no A-level general studies). In 1990, 60 pupils in upper fifth, 30 in upper sixth. *GCSE:* in 1990, 89% upper fifth gained at least grade C in 8+ subjects; 11% in 5–7 subjects. *A-levels:* 91% upper sixth passed in 3+ subjects; 30% took science A-levels; 40% arts/humanities; 30% both. *Computing facilities:* Specialist computer room with additional computers throughout the school. Specialist desk-top publishing facilities including laser and colour printers. All sixth form take computer awareness course.

European Community *Languages:* French offered: to age 14; GCSE; AS-level; A-level; Institute of Linguists. German offered: to age 14; GCSE; AS-level; A-level; as non-examined subject. Spanish offered: GCSE; AS-level; A-level. 25–50% take GCSE in more than 1 EC language. *Exchanges:* Regular exchanges for pupils aged 14–18 to France and Germany. *Other:* European Studies offered to pupils aged 14–18. Talks from MEPs etc 14–16 from 1991.

Senior pupils' non-academic activities (GCSE and above) *Music:* 41% learn a musical instrument; 10 in school orchestra, 40 in choirs, 20 in chamber groups. *Drama and dance:* 60 in school productions. 20 take LAMDA examinations. 2 accepted for drama degrees. *Art:* 13 take A-level; 6 take history of art. 5 accepted for Art School. *Sport:* Gymnastics, judo, trampolining, dance, hockey, netball, tennis, athletics, rounders, swimming, badminton, squash, skating, ski-ing, weight training available. 26 take non-compulsory sport. 4 represent county (hockey, netball, tennis, squash). *Other:* 7+ have bronze Duke of Edinburgh's Award, 15+ have silver. Other activities include a computer club, photography and ceramics; sixth form Young Enterprise.

Careers In 1990, 77% leavers went on to degree courses; 10% to art/drama/music colleges; 13% other. Of those going on to degree courses, 17% went to Oxbridge; 74% to other universities; 9% to poly/colleges. 12% those going on to higher education went to courses in practical art; 4% in music; 61% in humanities/social sciences; 8% in medicine; and 15% in science/engineering.

Uniform School uniform worn except in sixth.

Houses/prefects No competitive houses. No prefects but permanent sixth form committee. Head girl – appointed by Head after discussion with staff and pupils. School Council.

Religion Compulsory attendance at daily assembly, pupils often taking participatory role in leading prayers.

Social Observer Mace Debating Competition with other schools; sixth form theatre club; inter-sixth form public speaking competition. Organised visits to Russia, France, Belgium; regular skiing holidays; French and German exchanges. Pupils allowed to bring own car/bike to school. Meals self service. Cafeteria for seniors. No tobacco/alcohol allowed.

Discipline Pupils failing to produce homework once might expect a reprimand; those caught smoking cannabis on the premises could expect expulsion.

· Sutton High ·

Sutton High School
55 Cheam Road
Sutton
Surrey SM1 2AX
Tel 081 642 0594

- Pupils 820
- Boys None
- Girls 4–18
  (Day)
- Upper sixth 73

- Termly fees
  £1024 (Day)
- GPDST
  Enquiries/application to
  the Headmistress

What it's like

Founded in 1884, it is one of 25 schools administered by the GPDST and uses its original building, though there have been many alterations and additions. The school now occupies what were formerly family houses in Cheam Road and Grove Road and has much purpose-built accommodation. The junior school is in three houses in Grove Road. Overall it is a pleasant campus with some games facilities on site. A sound general education is provided and results are good. Very many girls go on to degree courses each year, including many to Oxbridge. There is a considerable commitment to music and much strength in drama (the school has an open-air theatre built by parents and pupils). An excellent range of games and sports (high standards are achieved) and plentiful extra-curricular activities. A lot of girls contribute to local social services and the school has an impressive record in the Duke of Edinburgh's Award Scheme.

School profile

Pupils Total age range 4–18; 820 day girls. Senior department 11–18, 565 girls. Main entry ages 4, 7, 11 and into sixth. *Transfer from maintained schools:* 45% senior intakes.

Entrance Own entrance exam used. Oversubscribed. Good academic ability looked for; no religious requirements. Parents not expected to buy text books. 17 assisted places pa. 6 scholarships, 100–5% of fees; bursaries in cases of financial need.

Staff Headmistress Miss A E Cavendish, in post for 10 years. 33 full time staff, 16 part time. Annual turnover approx 5%.

Academic work GCSE and A-levels. 21 subjects offered (no A-level general studies). On average, 91 pupils in upper fifth, 62 in upper sixth. *GCSE:* on average, 73 upper fifth gained at least grade C in 8+ subjects; 17 in 5–7; and 1 in 1–4 subjects. *A-levels:* 2 upper sixth passed in 4+ subjects; 48 in 3; 10 in 2; and 1 in 1 subject. 19 took science A-levels; 18 arts/humanities; 25 both. *Computing facilities:* Well-equipped computer laboratory.

European Community *Languages:* French offered: to age 14; GCSE; AS-level; A-level. German offered: to age 14; GCSE; A-level. Spanish offered: as a non-examined subject. 25–50% take GCSE in more than 1 EC language. *Exchanges:* Regular exchanges for pupils aged 14–18 to France and Germany.

Senior pupils' non-academic activities *Music:* 210 learn a musical instrument, 58 to Grade 6 or above, 1–2 accepted for Music School, 1 to play in pop group; 55 in school orchestra, 35 in choir, 1 in National Children's Orchestra, 4 Stoneleigh Youth Orchestra, 3 Junior College Orchestra. *Drama and dance:* 100–150 in 2 annual school productions; 150, sixth form revue; 150–200, senior drama competition; 100–115 in middle school drama competition. 84 take ABRSM, Speech and Drama; 45 Poetry Vanguard. 5 participate in festivals. 1 accepted for Drama/Dance School. *Art:* 40 take as non-examined subject; 30 GCSE; 10 A-level; 1 accepted for Art School. *Sport:* Hockey, netball, tennis, rounders, swimming, athletics, badminton, volleyball, basketball, squash, gymnastics, indoor hockey, keep fit available. 180 in school teams; 13, PE options. 13 represent county (tennis, netball, hockey, badminton). *Other:* 140 have bronze Duke of Edinburgh's Award, 12 have silver and 6 gold. 80 do work experience after GCSE. 2 enter voluntary schemes after leaving. Other activities include computer clubs, Christian Union, wildlife club, chess, debating.

Careers On average, 80% leavers went on to degree courses; 3% to art/drama/music colleges; 10% to non-degree courses; 5% straight into careers; 2% other. Of those going on to degree courses, 15% went to Oxbridge; 60% to other universities; 25% to poly/colleges. 4% those going on to higher education went to courses in practical art; 4% in drama/acting; 4% in music; 55% in humanities/social sciences; 11% in medi-

cine; and 22% in science/engineering.

Uniform School uniform worn except in the sixth.

Houses/prefects No competitive houses. 2 head girls and 4–5 deputies – elected by staff and seniors. School Council.

Religion Attendance at daily assembly expected unless parents request otherwise.

Social Inter-sixth society with local schools, occasional joint productions with Sutton Manor School. Organised trips abroad. Pupils allowed to bring own car/bike/motorbike to school. Meals self service. No tobacco/alcohol allowed.

Discipline No corporal punishment. Pupils failing to produce homework once might expect a kindly reproof; those caught smoking cannabis on the premises should expect automatic suspension.

· *Sutton Valence* ·

Sutton Valence School
Sutton Valence
Maidstone
Kent
ME17 3HL
Tel 0622 842281

- Pupils 415
- Boys 11–18 (Day/Board/Weekly)
- Girls 11–18 (Day/Board/Weekly)
- Upper sixth 60

- Termly fees £1766 (Day) £2756 (Board/Weekly)
- HMC, SHA

Enquiries/application to the Admissions Secretary

What it's like

Founded in 1576, most of its buildings are in the village and the school houses are scattered about the village. The overall site comprises about 100 acres on the slopes of a high ridge overlooking the Weald. There is excellent accommodation, delightful gardens and big playing fields. Modern teaching facilities are first-rate. The school has a reputation for close pastoral care, and the staff:pupil ratio of 1:10 helps to produce high academic standards and good results (about 40 go on to higher education per year). Flourishing music and art depts; *very* strong in drama. An impressive range of games and sports in which high standards are achieved (20 plus representatives at county level). A very large number of clubs and societies provide for most conceivable needs. Big commitment to local community schemes.

810

School profile

Pupils Age range 11–18; 415 pupils, 224 day (134 boys, 90 girls), 191 full or weekly boarding (143 boys, 48 girls). Main entry ages 11, 13 and into sixth. Approx 8% are children of former pupils. *Transfer from maintained schools:* 90% at 11, 7% at 13, plus 5% to sixth.

Entrance Common entrance and own exam used. Girls' places oversubscribed. All-rounders looked for; Anglican foundation but others accepted. Parents expected to buy text books; maximum extras, £200. 15 assisted places pa. Scholarships for academic, music and art, up to 67% fees pa; bursaries according to need.

Parents 15+% in industry or commerce. 60+% live within 30 miles; up to 10% live overseas.

Staff Headmaster M R Haywood, in post for 11 years. 37 full time staff, 4 part time. Annual turnover 2–3. Average age 36.

Academic work GCSE and A-levels. 19 subjects offered (including GCSE Russian; A-level general studies compulsory for all sixth form). In 1990, 65 pupils in fifth, 60 in upper sixth. *GCSE:* in 1990, 35 upper fifth gained at least grade C in 8+ subjects; 25 in 5–7; and 5 in 1–4 subjects. *A-levels:* 7 upper sixth passed in 4+ subjects; 40 in 3; 10 in 2; and 3 in 1 subject. 30 took science A-levels; 24 arts/humanities; 6 both. *Computing facilities:* 12 Nimbus, 10 BBC B's, 4 BBC Masters, 1 RM 380Z, 1 RM 480Z. *Special provision:* Sympathy for mild dyslexics; EFL classes for non-English speakers.

European Community *Languages:* French offered: to age 14; GCSE; AS-level; A-level. German offered: to age 14; GCSE; AS-level; A-level. Spanish offered: to GCSE. 25–50% take GCSE in more than 1 EC language. *Exchanges:* Regular exchanges for pupils aged 14–16 to France. *Other:* European Studies offered to pupils aged 16–18. More exchanges and work experience being developed. Music tours of France and Benelux countries. French and German pupils in sixth form.

Senior pupils' non-academic activities *Music:* 180 learn a musical instrument, 20 to Grade 6 or above; 35 in school orchestra; 90 in choirs; 20 in senior woodwind; 8 in jazz band; 40 in wind band; 6 accepted for music scholarships. *Drama and dance:* 150 in school productions; 100 in house drama. *Art:* 40 take as non-examined subject; 34 take GCSE; 15 A-level; 10 belong to eg photographic club; 9 stage crew etc; 3 accepted for Art School. *Sport:* Cricket, rugby, hockey, fives, cross-country, swimming, athletics, squash, tennis, judo, fencing, golf, sailing, climbing, netball, badminton available. Some take exams in sailing, 1; life saving, 15; judo, 15. 21 pupils represent county (hockey, netball, rugby, cricket, golf, fencing, athletics, judo). *Other:* 70 take part in local community schemes. 66 have bronze Duke of Edinburgh's Award, 25 silver and 10 gold. Other activities include 32 various clubs and societies including computer club, CCF, debating, driving, drama, community service etc.

Careers In 1990, 75% leavers went on to degree courses; 15% to art/drama/music colleges; 5% to non-degree courses (eg agriculture, language/legal secretarial); 5% straight into careers (eg trainee management, banking, insurance). Of those going on to degree courses, 7% went to Oxbridge; 73% to other universities; 20% to poly/colleges. 5% those going on to higher education went to courses in practical art; 2% in drama/acting; 2% in music; 25% in humanities/social sciences; 4% in medicine; and 47% in science/engineering.

Uniform School uniform worn throughout.

Houses/prefects Non-competitive houses. Prefects, head boy/girl, head of house and house prefects – appointed by the Headmaster.

Religion Daily Chapel, Sunday service (boarders).

Social Debates, dances, industry conferences, choral activities with local schools. Organised exchanges to Beauvais. Day pupils allowed to bring own car/bike/motorbike to school. Meals self service. School shop. No tobacco/alcohol allowed.

Discipline No corporal punishment. Pupils failing to produce homework once would expect to do extra work; those caught smoking cannabis on the premises could expect expulsion.

Boarding 33% have own study bedroom, 66% are in dormitories of 6+. Single sex houses, of approx 60. Resident qualified nurse. Central dining room. Weekly boarding an option. Visits to the local town allowed, at housemaster's discretion.

Alumni association is run by Mr C R G Shaw, c/o the School.

Former pupils Sir Charles Groves; Compton Rennie; Sir Rustam Feroze; Peter Fairley; Terence Cuneo; Marc Benson.

· *Sydenham High* ·

Sydenham High School	● Pupils 675	● Termly fees
19 Westwood Hill	● Boys None	£1027 (Day)
Sydenham	● Girls 5–18	● GSA, GPDST
London SE26 6BL	(Day)	Enquiries/application to
Tel 081 778 8737	● Upper sixth 40	the Headmistress

What it's like

Founded in 1887, it has two urban sites in the London suburb of Sydenham; the junior house is about 200 yards away from the senior school. The present buildings, set in five acres of grounds, were occupied in 1935. There has been considerable expansion and development in recent years and the school is now well equipped. A sound general education is provided and exam results are very creditable. Each year some girls go on to degree courses. There is notable strength in music, drama and art. A good range of standard sports and games is provided and there are plentiful extra-curricular activities. Some commitment to local social services.

School profile

Pupils Total age range 5–18, 675 day girls. Senior department 11–18, 450 girls. Main entry ages 5, 7, 11, 13 and into sixth. *Transfer from maintained schools:* 40% main intakes at 11 and 13, plus 100% to sixth.

Entrance Assisted places and scholarships/bursaries.

Staff Headmistress Mrs Geraldine Baker, in post for 3 years.

Academic work GCSE, AS and A-levels. 20 subjects offered (plus general studies, but not examined). In 1989, 61 pupils in upper fifth, 42 in upper sixth. *GCSE:* in 1989, 29 upper fifth gained at least grade C in 8+ subjects; 21 in 5–7; and 10 in 1–4 subjects. *A-levels:* 1 upper sixth passed in 4+ subjects; 28 in 3; 10 in 2; and 3 in 1 subject. 50% took science A-levels; 50% arts/humanities. *Computing facilities:* Research machine network, plus individual departmental computers. *Special provision:* Pupils with eg dyslexia or need for EFL tuition are referred to specialists for help.

· *Sylvia Young* ·

Sylvia Young Theatre
School
Rossmore Road
London NW1 6NJ
Tel 071 402 0673

- Pupils 140
- Boys 7–16 (Day)
- Girls 7–16 (Day)
- Upper sixth No

- Termly fees
  £805 (Day)
- ISAI
Enquiries/application to
the Headteacher

What it's like

Founded in 1981, it has agreeable premises on a single site in north London. The school is committed to providing a balanced theatrical and academic curriculum to ensure that students have a wide range of career and higher education options open to them. Besides the basic academic subjects they are taught speech, singing, tap, jazz, ballet and drama. Most pupils go on to drama or acting courses or straight into the theatre and film industries. It is a happy school with an enthusiastic staff. The pupils are highly motivated and are encouraged to express themselves and contribute on all levels. There is close communication between parents and staff and a flourishing PTA. Pastoral care is taken very seriously. Form tutors liaise closely with parents. Spare time is spent in rehearsals for school shows and charity events.

School profile

Pupils Total age range 7–16; 140 day pupils (boys and girls). Main entry ages 7 and 11.

Entrance Audition, interview, written assessment used. Oversubscribed. Potential in performing arts looked for; no religious requirements. Parents not expected to buy text books; maximum extras £25. LEA grants available.

Staff Head Maggie Melville, in post for 6 years. 2 full time staff, 16 part time. Age range 20s–50s.

Academic work *GCSE:* on average, 10 pupils in fifth pass 1–4 subjects; 4, 5–7 subjects. *Computing facilities:* BBC 'B' micro. *Special provision:* A visiting tutor from the Learning Centre.

European Community *Languages:* French offered: to age 14; GCSE.

Senior pupils' non-academic activities *Drama and dance:* Some pupils in cabaret groups and charity shows. Some pupils gain ISTD tap; LAMDA acting, verse and prose; RAD ballet. Some pupils accepted for Drama/Dance Schools, enter competitions, go on to work in theatre or musicals. *Art:* GCSE taken. All extra time is spent in rehearsals for school shows and charity events.

Careers In 1990, 50% leavers went on to courses in drama/acting; 25% straight into careers in films or theatre; 25% other.

Uniform School uniform worn.

Houses/prefects School Council.

Religion Religious worship not compulsory.

Social Day trips to France. Many educational outings organised. Meals self service or packed lunch. School shop. No tobacco/alcohol allowed.

Discipline No corporal punishment. Pupils failing to produce homework once might expect to complete it by the next day or do a detention; those caught smoking on the premises could expect their parents to be called in and to be asked to leave.

Former pupils Tisha Dean (East-Enders); Frances Ruffelle (Tony Award winner 1987 – Les Miserables); Rachel Robertson.

_t_

· _Talbot Heath_ ·

Talbot Heath
Rothesay Road
Bournemouth
BH4 9NJ
Tel 0202 761881

- Pupils 598
- Boys None
- Girls 8–18 (Day/Board)
- Upper sixth 53

- Termly fees
  £1325 (Day)
  £2316 (Board)
  £2254 (Weekly)
- GSA, SHA
  Enquiries/application to the Headmistress

What it's like

Founded in 1886 it moved to its present site in 1935. The premises are purpose-built on a single site in woodlands 1.5 miles from the town centre and 2 miles from the coast. It has very good facilities and comfortable accommodation. A liberal education on a religious basis is provided. Academic standards are high and results good. Many leavers go on to degree courses each year. There are flourishing art and drama departments and a tremendously strong music department (150–200 girls learn an instrument). A very good range of sports and games (a lot of county representatives) and a fair variety of extra-curricular activities. Some commitment to local community schemes.

School profile

Pupils Total age range 8–18; 598 girls, 528 day, 70 boarding. Senior department 11–18, 504 girls. Main entry ages 8, 11 and into sixth. Approx 1–2% are children of former pupils. Own junior school provides over 20% of intake. _Transfer from maintained schools:_ 50% senior intake, plus 20% to sixth.

Entrance Own entrance exam used. Oversubscribed. Academic and personal potential looked for. Parents not expected to buy text books. 140 assisted places. 11–12 scholarships/bursaries pa, full day fees to £200 pa.

Parents 30+% live within 30 miles; 10+% live overseas.

Staff Headmistress Miss C E Austin-Smith, in post for 15 years. 40 full time staff, 21 part time plus visiting staff for extra subjects. Annual turnover 5%. Average age 42.

Academic work GCSE and A-levels. 19–20 subjects offered (including Russian and Italian; no A-level general studies). In 1989, 89 pupils in upper fifth, 53 in upper sixth. _GCSE:_ in 1989, 71 upper fifth gained at least grade C in 8+ subjects; 17 in 5–7; and 1 in 1–4 subjects. _A-levels:_ 2 upper sixth passed in 4+ subjects; 35 in 3; 12 in 2; and 1 in 1 subject. 16 took science A-levels; 21 arts/humanities; 16 both. _Computing facilities:_ 16 computers in main computer lab, plus in departments and Junior School. Taught to all 11+, 12+ girls; GCSE computer studies offered. Computer club facilities available throughout. _Special provision:_ Special help with dyslexia, individual support with

814

spelling etc. Individual EFL lessons for girls from abroad. No provision for visual handicap.

Senior pupils' non-academic activities *Music:* 150–200 learn a musical instrument, 50 to Grade 6 or above, 1 or 2 pa accepted for Music School; 60–70 in school orchestras, 120 in school choirs, 20 handbell ringers; 2 or 3 have had auditions with National Youth Orchestra; 20–30 play in Wessex, Bournemouth and Dorset youth orchestras. *Drama and dance:* 20–30 in school productions. 2 to Grade 6 in ESB, RAD. Occasional pupil accepted for Drama/Dance School or working in theatre. Girls audition for National Youth Theatre as well as for local theatres. *Art:* 35 take GCSE; 7 A-level. 1 accepted for Art School; 1 for architecture. 20 belong to photographic club, 10 to other. *Sport:* Hockey, netball, tennis, rounders, cricket, athletics, table tennis, swimming, gymnastics, sports acrobatics, modern educational dance, keep fit, badminton, volleyball available; also for seniors, golf, archery, riding, sailing, self defence, yoga and trampolining. 190 take non-compulsory sport. 1 represents country (tennis); 9 represent county (hockey, swimming, tennis); others recently represented county at fencing, cricket, netball. *Other:* 15 take part in local community schemes. 1 Queen's Guide. Other activities include a computer club, chess, dance, gymnastics and electronics clubs; science, geography, art, screen printing, conservation, history, and public speaking societies. Newly started Duke of Edinburgh's Award Scheme.

Careers 3 part time careers advisers. Annual average accepted for *arts and humanities degree courses* at Oxbridge, 2; other universities, 10; polytechnics/colleges, 3. *science and engineering degree courses* at Oxbridge, 2; other universities, 8; medical schools, 3; polytechnics/colleges, 3. *BEd,* 6. *other general training courses,* 6. Average going straight into careers in armed services, 1; civil service, 1; music/drama, 1. Traditional school careers are medicine, nursing.

Uniform School uniform worn, mufti in the sixth.

Houses/prefects No competitive houses. Prefects – all sixth formers share duties and responsibilities. 2 head girls, head of house and house prefects – democratic nomination and election, final confirmation by Headmistress.

Religion Only Jewish and Moslem girls excused morning assembly.

Social Some dramatic activity, debates and dances with local boys' grammar school. Regular annual exchanges in Normandy, visits to Paris, Italy, USA, Israel; regular skiing holidays (often France/Italy). Pupils allowed to bring own car/bike/motorbike to school. Meals formal. Uniform exchange shop. No tobacco/alcohol allowed.

Discipline No corporal punishment. Pupils failing to produce homework once might expect rebuke and insistence on production of work the following day; those caught smoking cannabis on the premises would expect expulsion.

Boarding 7% have own study bedroom, 25% in single study cubicles, 25% double study bedrooms, 43% are in dormitories. Houses, of approximately 45. Resident qualified nurse. No central dining room. Sixth formers can provide and cook some own food, 2 weekend exeats each term plus half term. Visits to local town allowed by seniors (15+).

Alumni association run by the Headmistress.

Former pupils Lady Faithfull; Judge Daffodil Cosgrave; Dilys Powell.

· *Taunton* ·

Taunton School
Taunton
Somerset
TA2 6AD
Tel 0823 284596

- Pupils 1082
- Boys 3–18
  (Day/Board)
- Girls 3–18
  (Day/Board)
- Upper sixth 106

- Termly fees
  £1882 (Day)
  £2933 (Board)
- HMC, GSA
  Enquiries/application to
  the Admissions'
  Secretary

What it's like

Founded in 1847, it lies on the edge of the county town in spacious grounds, with open country to the north. The main buildings are mid-Victorian Gothic. The town itself is an interesting and attractive place, surrounded by splendid countryside, and very handy for Bristol, Bath, Exeter and Wells. There are 2 single-sex prep schools: Taunton Junior Boys' School and Taunton Junior Girls' School, close by. Continuous education from 3–18 is available. Modern extensions provide excellent accommodation and facilities, including fine libraries. It is a C of E school and some worship is compulsory. A very large staff of 136 full-timers (plus 39 part–timers) permit a staff:pupil ratio of 1:8. The teaching is good and academic standards and results are first-rate. Many leavers go on to degree courses each year. The music and drama departments are very strong indeed. The school has considerable strength in games and sports, with many representatives at county, regional and international level. A wide variety of activities caters for most needs. A substantial commitment to local community schemes and an outstanding record in the Duke of Edinburgh's Award Scheme (45 bronze, 40 silver, 40 gold).

School profile

Pupils Total age range 3–18; 1082 pupils, 666 day (351 boys, 315 girls), 416 boarding (258 boys, 158 girls). Senior school 13–18; 602 pupils (340 boys, 262 girls). Main entry ages 3, 7, 11, 13 and into the sixth. 10% are children of former pupils. Own junior school provides over 70% senior intake. *Transfer from maintained schools:* 15% senior intakes, plus 12% to sixth.

Entrance Common entrance used. No special skills or religious requirements. Parents expected to buy text books. 11 assisted places pa. 107 scholarships/bursaries, £1408–£60.

Parents 15+% in industry or commerce. 40+% live within 30 miles; up to 10% live overseas.

Staff Headmaster B B Sutton, in post 3 years. 136 full time staff, 39 part time. Annual turnover 5%. Average age 45.

Academic work GCSE and A-levels.

23 subjects offered (no A-level general studies). In 1990, 137 pupils in upper fifth, 113 in upper sixth. *GCSE:* in 1990, 79 upper fifth gained at least grade C in 8+ subjects; 27 in 5–7; and 27 in 1–4 subjects. *A-levels:* 7 upper sixth passed in 4+ subjects; 49 in 3; 33 in 2; and 16 in 1 subject. 50 took science A-levels; 59 arts/humanities; 4 both. *Computing facilities:* Computer literacy taught as part of foundation course in third year. Computers used widely as a teaching tool from kindergarten upwards. *Special provision:* Mildly dyslexic children given special assistance. EFL coaching available.

European Community *Languages:* French offered: to age 14; GCSE; AS-level; A-level. German offered: to age 14; GCSE; AS-level; A-level. Spanish offered: to age 14; GCSE; AS-level; A-level. 10–25% take GCSE in more than 1 EC language. *Exchanges:* Regular exchanges for pupils aged 11–14 to France and Germany.

Senior pupils' non-academic activities *Music:* 165 learn a musical instrument, 35 to Grade 6 or above, 1 accepted for music at university; 45 in school orchestra, 85 in choir, 18 in chamber music group; 3 in National Children's Orchestra, occasional pupil in National Youth Orchestra; 1 choral scholar. *Drama and dance:* 150 in school productions; 6 in other. 10 take Guildhall speech and drama exams. 1 accepted for Drama/Dance School. *Art:* 28 take GCSE; 10 A-level; 4 history of art. 4 accepted for Art School; 4 for BTEC course. *Sport:* Rugby, cricket, hockey, athletics, cross-country, tennis, squash, badminton, fencing, judo, canoeing, netball (girls) available. 300 take non-compulsory sport. 35 represent county/region/country (rugby, hockey, cricket, netball, athletics). *Other:* 30 take part in local community schemes. 45 have bronze Duke of Edinburgh's Award, 45 have silver and 30 gold. 5 enter voluntary schemes after leaving; 2 work for national charities. Other activities include a computer club, debating, chess, scientific society, bridge, bell ringing, driving lessons, etc.

Careers In 1990, 80% leavers went on to degree courses; 3% to art/drama/music colleges; 4% to non-degree courses (eg agricultural, secretarial); 2% straight into careers; 10% other (including resits). Of those going on to degree courses, 5% went to Oxbridge; 43% to other universities; 32% to poly/colleges. 3% those going on to higher education went to courses in practical art; 45% in humanities/social sciences; 8% in medicine; and 38% in science/engineering.

Uniform School uniform worn throughout.

Houses/prefects Pastoral non-competitive houses. Prefects, head boy and girl, head of house and house prefects – appointed by the Head after consultation with staff and heads of school.

Religion 3 compulsory chapel services per week, 1 on Sundays for boarders; communion voluntary.

Social Occasional musical events with other schools. Exchanges with France and Germany. Pupils allowed to bring own car/bike/motorbike to school. Meals self service. School shop. No tobacco/alcohol allowed.

Discipline No corporal punishment. Pupils failing to produce homework once might expect to be given another chance to do so; those caught smoking cannabis on the premises might be suspended or expelled for breaking school rules.

Boarding 20% have own study bedroom, 18% share with 1 other; 5% are in dormitories of 6+. Single sex houses, up to 50, divided for pastoral reasons. Resident qualified nurses. Central dining room. Pupils can provide and cook own snacks. 2 weekend exeats each term plus half-term. Unlimited visits to local town with permission, over 13.

Alumni association run by M J O Willacy, Secretary, Old Tauntonian Association, c/o the School.

Former pupils Admiral of the Fleet Lord Hill Norton; Sue Brown (1st woman Cox in Varsity Boat Race); John Jameson (Warwicks and England cricketer); Barbara Jefford (Shakespearian actress); R A Gerrard (England Rugby); Wing Cdr J R D Braham; Major F G Blaker, VC.

· Teesside High ·

Teesside High School
The Avenue
Eaglescliffe
Stockton-on-Tees
Cleveland TS16 9AT
Tel 0642 782095

- Pupils 550
- Boys None
- Girls 4–18 (Day)
- Upper sixth 35

- Termly fees £1038 (Day)
- GSA

Enquiries/application to the Headmistress

What it's like

Founded in 1970, through the amalgamation of the Queen Victoria High School and the Cleveland School, it is situated in 19 acres of particularly beautiful wooded grounds on the banks of the River Tees, thus having the benefit of a rural setting while being near a residential centre. It is a purpose-built school with excellent modern facilities including, recently, a school hall, sixth-form block, classrooms, conference rooms and common rooms. The full-time staff:pupil ratio is about 1:15, but there are a large number of part-time staff. Academic standards are good and results are creditable. Very many leavers go on to degree courses, including Oxbridge. Music, drama and art are all well supported and plentiful use is made of the cultural facilities of Newcastle, Durham and York. The school is well provided with playing fields and standards in games and sports are quite high (not a few representatives at county and regional level). A fair range of clubs and societies. The Duke of Edinburgh's Award Scheme is popular and there is a good deal of emphasis on open-air activities such as sailing, canoeing, potholing, mountaineering and camping. Social and community service work is highly organised.

School profile

Pupils Total age range 4–18; 550 day girls. Senior department 11–18, 361 girls. Main entry ages 5, 7, 11 and into sixth. Small percentage are children of former pupils. *Transfer from maintained schools:* One-third main intake at 11, plus small percentage into sixth.

Entrance Own entrance exam used. Oversubscribed in some areas. Academic ability looked for; no religious requirements. Parents not expected to buy text books. Discount fees available in sixth, variable value.

Parents 15+% parents are in industry or commerce, 15+% are doctors, lawyers, etc.

Staff Headmistress Mrs J Coles, in post for 9 years. 35 full time staff, 24 part time. Annual turnover, low. Average age 40's.

Academic work GCSE and A-levels. 26 subjects offered (including Greek and A-level general studies). In 1990, 61 pupils in upper fifth, 35 in upper sixth.

GCSE: in 1990, 66% upper fifth gained at least grade C in 8+ subjects; 29% in 5–7; and 5% in 1–4 subjects. *A-levels:* 10 upper sixth passed in 4+ subjects; 3 in 3; 4 in 2; and 2 in 1 subject. 3 took science A-levels; 12 arts/humanities; 4 both. *Computing facilities:* 19 computers and 8 printers. *Special provision:* Dyslexic, mildly visually and physically handicapped pupils accepted; private EFL coaching arranged.

European Community *Languages:* French offered: to age 14; GCSE; AS-level; A-level. German offered: to age 14; GCSE; AS-level; A-level. Spanish offered: to GCSE; AS-level; A-level. 50–75% take GCSE in more than 1 EC language. *Other:* MEP gives talks to sixth form. Regular visits by pupils aged 11–14 to France (working holidays with specific language assignments).

Senior pupils' non-academic activities *Music:* 120 learn a musical instrument in school, 15 to Grade 6 or above. 1

accepted to read music at university. 32 in school orchestra, 74 in school choirs, 8 in ensembles, 50 play recorders, 1 in National Youth Orchestra, 1 in National Youth Choir, 1 plays in jazz orchestra outside school, 10 in county groups. *Drama and dance:* 220 in school productions; 1 goes to work in theatre. *Art:* 14 take GCSE; 4 A-level. 1 accepted for art foundation course, 1 to architecture school. *Sport:* Hockey, tennis, netball, rounders, swimming, volleyball, golf, athletics, badminton, gymnastics available. Some take tests in swimming and gymnastics. Pupils represent county (athletics, tennis, gymnastics, swimming, hockey). *Other:* 54 have bronze Duke of Edinburgh's Award, 10 silver, 4 gold. Other activities include chess, debate, gymnastics, yoga, drama workshop, public speaking, classics, natural history, aerobics.

Careers On average, 90% leavers went on to degree courses; 5% to art/drama/music colleges; 2% to non-degree courses (eg HND business studies, secretarial); 2% straight into careers (eg banking, gas board). Of those going on to degree courses, 11% went to Oxbridge; 50% to other universities; 35% to poly/colleges. 5% those going on to higher education went to courses in practical art; 65% in humanities/social sciences; 15% in medicine; and 10% in science/engineering.

Uniform School uniform worn, except in sixth.

Houses/prefects Competitive houses. Prefects, head girl, head of house and house prefects – elected by the school.

Religion Religious worship compulsory except for strict orthodox.

Social Debates, concerts, disco with local independent schools; community work. Trips abroad include French, German, classics visits, ski visit, individual exchanges. Pupils allowed to bring own car/bike to school. Meals self-service. No tobacco/alcohol allowed.

Discipline No corporal punishment. Pupils failing to produce homework once might expect an order mark and be seen by staff; those caught smoking cannabis on the premises would be expelled.

Alumni association is run by Mrs J Willis, c/o The School.

· *Tettenhall* ·

Tettenhall College
Wolverhampton
West Midlands
WV6 8QX
Tel 0902 751119

- Pupils 460
- Boys 7–19
  (Day/Board)
- Girls 7–19
  (Day/Board)
- Upper sixth 40

- Termly fees
  £1410 (Day)
  £2290 (Board)
- HMC, SHMIS

Enquiries/application to the Headmaster

What it's like

Founded in 1863 by a group of Wolverhampton businessmen to provide a school for the sons of Non-conformists, it is now an inter-denominational school which became co-educational in 1982. It has a most agreeable site in the old village of Tettenhall in 33 acres of attractive grounds three miles from Wolverhampton. The original building contains the boys' boarding houses, the dining hall, chapel and big school; the girls' boarding houses are new. Nearby is 'The Towers' which houses the lower school form rooms, the music department and a 19th-century theatre. Playing fields are on site. All pupils attend RE and the chapel services which are non-sectarian. Tettenhall has many of the advantages of a small school and enjoys a favourable staff:pupil ratio of about 1:9. Many leavers go on to degree courses. A broad general education is provided and results are good. Music and drama are well supported. A standard range of sports and games is available and there are numerous clubs and societies for extra-curricular activities. A social services group is very active and pupils participate in the Duke of Edinburgh's Award Scheme.

School profile

Pupils Total age range 7–19, 460 pupils. Senior department 13–19, 280 pupils. Main entry age 7, 11 and 13. Own prep school. *Transfer from maintained schools:* 90% main intakes.

Entrance Common entrance or test places interviews used. 7–9 scholarships (including 2 music) plus other awards for art, drama or sport.

Staff Headmaster W J Dale, in post for 23 years.

Academic work GCSE and A-levels. 18 GCSE subjects offered; 16 at A-level (including general studies). In 1989, 56 pupils in upper fifth, 33 in upper sixth. *GCSE:* in 1989, 17 upper fifth gained at least grade C in 8+ subjects; 15 in 5–7; and 24 in 1–4 subjects. *A-levels:* 7 upper sixth passed in 4+ subjects; 8 in 3; 4 in 2; and 4 in 1 subject. 34% took science A-levels; 57% arts/humanities; 8% both. *Computing facilities:* Extensive. *Special provision:* EFL department.

European Community *Languages:* French offered: to age 14; GCSE; A-level. German offered: to age 14; GCSE; A-level. Italian offered: to A-level. Spanish offered: to A-level. 10–25% take GCSE in more than 1 EC language. *Exchanges:* No exchanges for pupils yet. *Other:* EC pupils encouraged to spend a term or more in school; strong EFL department.

Careers In 1990, 90% sixth form leavers went on to degree courses; 6% to non-degree courses (eg HND business studies); 4% straight into careers (eg banking). Of those going on to degree courses, 58% went to universities; 42% to poly/colleges. 49% those going on to higher education went to courses in humanities/social sciences; 3% in medicine; and 48% in science/engineering.

· *Tonbridge* ·

Tonbridge School
Tonbridge
Kent
TN9 1JP
Tel 0732 365555

- Pupils 650
- Boys 13–18
  (Day/Board)
- Girls None
- Upper sixth 135

- Termly fees
  £2150 (Day)
  £3050 (Board)
- HMC
  Enquiries/application to
  the Headmaster

What it's like

Founded in 1553 by Sir Andrew Judde, it expanded considerably during the 19th century to become one of the major public schools. It retains close links with the Worshipful Company of Skinners. The fine campus lies on the northern edge of the town. There are a lot of handsome Victorian buildings to which there have been numerous additions in recent years to provide first-class facilities and accommodation. Beautiful playing fields lie next to the school. A C of E foundation, there are some compulsory services and some emphasis on Anglican tradition and practice. A high standard of teaching, and academic results are extremely good. Almost all pupils go on to university each year and about a quarter of these go to Oxbridge. The music dept is tremendously strong. Art and drama are pretty strong. The school has long had a wide reputation for excellence in sports and games. There is a wide variety of these and a lot of Tonbridge boys have achieved county and international recognition. The CCF has a big contingent and there are numerous clubs and societies which cater for most needs. Very substantial commitment to local community schemes and a fine record in the Duke of Edinburgh's Award Scheme.

School profile

Pupils Total age range 13–18; 650 boys, 210 day, 440 boarding. Main entry ages 13+; very few into sixth. Approx 10% are children of former pupils.

Entrance Common entrance and own scholarship exam used. Oversubscribed. No special skills or religious requirements (C of E foundation, but other faiths welcomed). Parents expected to buy most text books. 3 assisted places at 16+. 25 scholarships for academic, music and art, full fees to one-sixth remission; foundation bursaries for individuals in need of assistance.

Parents 15+% are doctors, lawyers, etc; 15+% in industry or commerce. 30+% live within 30 miles; 10+% live overseas.

Staff Headmaster J M Hammond, first year in post. 69 full time staff, 5 part time. Annual turnover 5%. Average age 39.

Academic work GCSE and A-levels. Russian and electronics offered to GCSE and A-level. Average size of upper fifth 135; upper sixth 135. *GCSE:* on average, 120 pupils in upper fifth pass 8+ subjects; 13, 5–7 subjects; 2 pass 1–4 subjects. *A-levels:* on average, 25 pupils in the upper sixth pass 4 subjects; 95, 3 subjects; 10, 2 subjects; 5 pass 1 subject. On average, 47 take science/engineering A-levels; 53 take arts and humanities; 35 take a mixture. *Computing facilities:* Several 30 Mbyte Winchester file servers serving 3 independent but interconnected Econet networks with c100 computers; Archimedes, IBMs and BBCs, all the usual word-processing, spread sheet, desktop publishing and CAD packages support most departments, plus extensive applications software. *Special provision:* for mildly dyslexic pupils with above average IQs.

European Community *Languages:* French offered: to GCSE; A-level. German offered: to GCSE; A-level. Italian offered: as a non-examined subject. Spanish offered: to GCSE; A-level. Over 75% take GCSE in more than 1 EC language. *Exchanges:* Regular exchanges for pupils aged 14–18 to France, Germany, and Spain.

Senior pupils' non-academic activities *Music:* Over 200 learn musical instruments, about 100 to Grade 6 or above, 2 accepted for Music School, 2 accepted for university music degree; school orchestra, over 100 play in wind bands, about 60 play in chamber music groups; 100 in full choir, 6 in pop group; 2 in Kent Youth Orchestra; usually 1 in National Youth Orchestra. *Drama and dance:* 40 in school productions, 30 in house plays. *Art:* 35 take as non-examined subject; 28 take GCSE; 24 A-level. 1 or 2 accepted for Art School; 1 for History of Art; 2 or 3 for architecture; 1 for landscape architecture; 1 for design consultancy. Extensive facilities open to all at any time. *Sport:* Cricket, rugby, hockey, athletics, cross-country, tennis, badminton, squash, fives, rackets, fencing, judo, golf, rowing, sailing, shooting, swimming, climbing, canoeing, sub-aqua, riding available. 180 take non-compulsory sport (200 take it seriously in top school teams). 30 take exams. 12 represent county/country in cricket. *Other:* 85 take part in local community schemes. 20 participate in silver Duke of Edinburgh's Award and 40 are trying for gold. 2 enter voluntary schemes after leaving school. Other activities include a computer club, aero and radio modelling, bridge, chess, choral, Christian Fellowship, computing, debating, film, general knowledge, junior dramatic, medical group, natural history, opera, radio, plus numerous cultural societies, particularly for Upper School.

Careers On average, 93% leavers went on to degree courses; 2% to art/drama/ music colleges; 2% to non-degree courses (eg foundation accountancy, agriculture); 3% straight into careers (eg insurance, armed services). Of those going on to degree courses, 19% went to Oxbridge; 64% to other universities; 12% to poly/ colleges. Under 1% those going on to higher education went to courses in practical art; under 1% in drama/acting; under 1% in music; 61% in humanities/ social sciences; 6% in medicine; and 31% in science/engineering.

Uniform School uniform worn throughout.

Houses/prefects Competitive houses. Prefects and head boy (appointed by Headmaster); head of house and house prefects (appointed by house masters).

Religion Compulsory chapel, Sundays and 4 mornings per week.

Social Major choral performances, combined band concerts. Young Enterprise, weekly lectures by distinguished speakers, girls from local schools for drama productions and dances; industry courses.

French school exchange arrangement, plus smaller groups with German, Austrian and Spanish schools. Holiday exchanges, organised trips to Greece, Russia, France etc, plus orchestral/choral tours to USA/Germany etc. Pupils allowed to bring own bike to school. Meals formal in houses. School shop. No tobacco/alcohol allowed.

Discipline No corporal punishment. Pupils failing to produce homework once might expect to do it, plus some extra, in own time; those involved with drugs on or off the premises may expect expulsion.

Boarding 40% have own study bedroom, 3% share with 1 other; 20% are in dormitories of 6+. About 60 in each house. Sanatorium sister and assistance. Pupils can provide and cook own food. 2 24-hour exeats plus half-term each term. Visits to local town allowed.

Former pupils Colin Cowdrey; Frederick Forsyth; Sir Patrick Mayhew; Richard Ellison; Bill Bruford; Maurice Denham; Benjamin Whitrow; David Tomlinson; Christopher Cowdrey; Vikram Seth.

· *Tormead* ·

Tormead School	● Pupils 545	● Termly fees
Cranley Road	● Boys None	£1145 (Day)
Guildford	● Girls 5–18 (Day)	● GSA
Surrey GU1 2JD	● Upper sixth 36	Enquiries/application to
Tel 0483 575101		the Headmistress

What it's like

Founded in 1905. There is emphasis on Christian tradition with daily religious services. All boarders attend Christ Church on Sundays. It is academically strong. The majority of girls stay on for A-levels and many of the upper sixth go on to degree courses. Drama and music are well supported. A standard range of sports and games is available, plus a fair variety of clubs and societies. The school takes part in the Duke of Edinburgh's Award Scheme and has a lively community service organisation.

School profile

Pupils Total age range 5–18, 545 day girls. Main entry age 5. *Transfer from maintained schools:* 10% main intake at 11+, plus occasional pupil to sixth.

Entrance Own entrance exam used. Scholarships, bursaries and assisted places at 11+.

Staff New Headmistress in 1992, not yet appointed.

Academic work GCSE and A-levels. 19 subjects offered (no A-level general studies). In 1989, 58 pupils in upper fifth, 36 in upper sixth. *GCSE:* in 1989, 78% upper fifth gained at least grade C in 8+ subjects; 22% in 5–7 subjects. *A-levels:* 11% upper sixth passed in 4+ subjects;

67% in 3; 22% in 2 subjects. 33% took science A-levels; 38% arts/humanities; 29% both. *Computing facilities:* Fully equipped computer room, plus computers in all laboratories, libraries and some classrooms. *Special provision:* Special lessons can be arranged (little demand).

European Community *Languages:* French offered: to age 14; GCSE; A-level. German offered: to age 14; GCSE; A-level. Spanish offered: to age 14; GCSE; A-level. 10–25% take GCSE in more than 1 EC language. *Exchanges:* Regular exchanges for pupils aged 11–14 to France.

· Trinity (Croydon) ·

Trinity School of John Whitgift
Shirley Park
Croydon
Surrey CR9 7AT
Tel 081 656 9541
Fax 081 655 0522

- Pupils 825
- Boys 10–18 (Day)
- Girls None
- Upper sixth 98

- Termly fees £1254 (Day)
- HMC

Enquiries/application to the Headmaster

What it's like

Founded in 1596 by Archbishop John Whitgift, it moved from central Croydon to its present site in 1965. This comprises a brand-new complex of buildings and playing fields in an open suburban area of 27 acres. Other playing fields nearby. It has excellent facilities and comfortable accommodation. The standard of teaching is high and so are the academic levels attained. Very many leavers proceed to degree courses each year; many at Oxbridge. Religious worship is broadly conceived and religious education continues up to the end of the fifth year. There is a very strong musical tradition and the choirs frequently take part in national events. Considerable strength also in drama. Numerous productions in 2 well-equipped theatres. A very good record in sports and games and considerable emphasis on outdoor pursuits. A wide variety of clubs and societies cater for most needs. There is an active CCF contingent and a very active community service unit. A notable record in the Duke of Edinburgh's Award Scheme.

School profile

Pupils Total age range 10–18; 825 day boys. Senior department 11–18, 775 boys. Main entry ages 10, 11, 13 and into sixth. Approx 5% are children of former pupils.

Transfer from maintained schools: 70% main intakes.

Entrance Own entrance exam used. Oversubscribed. No special skills or religious requirements. Parents not expected to buy text books. 150 assisted places. Scholarships: half to quarter fees. Bursaries – according to parental income.

Parents 15+% in industry or commerce.

Staff Headmaster R J Wilson, in post for 18 years. 64 full time staff, 6 part time. Annual turnover 6. Average age 37.

Academic work GCSE and A-levels. 18 GCSE subjects offered; 20 at A-level (general studies taught but not examined). In 1989, 127 pupils in upper fifth, 98 in upper sixth. *GCSE:* in 1990, 105 upper fifth gained at least grade C in 8+ subjects; 17 in 5–7; and 5 in 1–4 subjects. *A- and AS-levels:* 27 upper sixth passed in 4+ subjects; 45 in 3; 20 in 2; and 5 in 1 subject. 31 took science A-levels; 30 arts/humanities; 31 both. *Computing facilities:* 30 booth lab, plus research lab. *Special provision:* Extra tuition for dyslexic pupils.

European Community *Languages:* French offered: to age 14; GCSE; A-level. German offered: to age 14; GCSE; A-level. Italian offered: as non-examined subject. Spanish offered: to age 14; GCSE; A-level. 25–50% take GCSE in more than 1 EC language. *Exchanges:* Regular exchanges for pupils aged 11–16 to France and Germany.

Senior pupils' non-academic activities *Music:* 200+ learn a musical instrument, 60 to Grade 6 or above. Many orchestras and choirs (Trinity Boys Choir has regular professional engagements). Many go on to professional musical activities. *Drama and dance:* 50 in school productions. *Art and Design:* 51 take GCSE; 16 A/AS-level. 2 accepted for Art School. *Sport:* Rugby, hockey, cricket, swimming, water polo, squash, badminton, athletics, cross-country, volleyball and sub-aqua available. Lots take non-compulsory sport. Many represent county/country. *Other:* 40 take part in local community schemes. 30 have bronze Duke of Edinburgh's Award, 20 have silver and 10 have gold. Many other activities include a computer club.

Careers In 1990, 80% leavers went on to degree courses; 5% to art/drama/music colleges; 5% straight into careers; 10% other. Of those going on to degree courses, 15% went to Oxbridge; 60% to other universities; 25% to poly/colleges. 40% those going on to higher education went to courses in humanities/social sciences; 10% in medicine; and 50% in science/engineering.

Uniform School uniform worn except in the sixth.

Houses/prefects Competitive houses. Prefects and head boy – appointed by the Head and the school. Sixth form School Council.

Religion Worship encouraged.

Social Sixth form society, dramatic and musical productions with local girls' schools. Lots of organised trips abroad. Pupils allowed to bring own car/bike/motorbike to school. Meals self-service. School shop selling tuck. No pupils allowed tobacco/alcohol.

Discipline No corporal punishment. Pupils failing to produce homework once might expect no punishment; those caught smoking cannabis on the premises might expect expulsion.

Alumni association is run by The Secretary, Lime Meadow Avenue, Sanderstead, Croydon.

· *Truro High* ·

Truro High School
Falmouth Road
Truro
Cornwall
TR1 2HU
Tel 0872 72830

- Pupils 408
- Boys 3–7 only (Day)
- Girls 3–18 (Day/Board)
- Upper sixth 32

- Termly fees
  £1090 (Day)
  £1990 (Board)
  £1957 (Weekly)
- GSA
  Enquiries/application to the Headmistress

What it's like

Founded in 1880 by Archbishop Benson, the first Bishop of Truro. A single-site school, with a fine view over the city and cathedral. The handsome and well-equipped buildings lie in most attractive gardens and grounds. It enjoys a healthy and delightful environment with the bonus of the nearby Cornish countryside. The school prides itself on a happy, positive atmosphere and expertise in the special needs of girls. Regular prayers and services (including some in the cathedral) are held. The president of the governing body is the Bishop of Truro. A wide academic curriculum is available. The staff:pupil ratio is a favourable one of about 1:12. A well-qualified staff provides a sound, general education with consistently good results in GCSE and A-level. Many sixth-formers go on to degree courses. French, German, Italian and Spanish are offered to A-level and Italian and Spanish are also offered to the sixth form at GCSE. A high proportion of girls takes more than one European language at GCSE level, and there are regular exchanges with France, Germany and Italy. There are many musical activities involving choirs and orchestra and musical standards are high. Drama is also well supported. There is a wide range of games and sports (including archery and fencing) and numerous clubs and societies for extra-curricular activities. These include judo and self-defence. Plentiful excursions, expeditions and cultural trips. The school also participates in the Duke of Edinburgh's Award Scheme with success. There is an annual activities week for the whole school.

School profile

Pupils Total age range 3–18; 408 pupils, 348 day (8 boys, 340 girls), 74 boarding girls. Senior department 11–18, 350 girls. Main entry ages 3 (boys); up to 11 and into sixth (girls). 10% are children of former pupils. *Transfer from maintained schools:* 50% main intake, plus 8% to sixth.
Entrance Own entrance exam used. Not oversubscribed. Ability to follow curriculum required; no special religious requirements. Parents not expected to buy text books. No compulsory extras. 15 assisted places. 7 scholarships/bursaries (including 1 music scholarship), half fees.
Parents 30+% live within 30 miles, 10% live overseas.

Staff Head Mrs J F Marshall, in post for 8 years. 32 full time staff, 16 part time. Annual turnover 5%. Average age 42.
Academic work GCSE, AS and A-levels, RSA. 22 subjects offered (including Italian, Spanish and drama; not A-level general studies). In 1990, 65 pupils in upper fifth, 32 in upper sixth. *GCSE:* in 1990, 57% upper fifth gained at least grade C in 8+ subjects; 28% in 5–7; and 5% in 1–4 subjects. *A-levels:* 6% upper sixth passed in 4+ subjects; 70% in 3; 23% in 2 subjects. 12% took science A-levels; 64% arts/humanities; 24% both. *Computing facilities:* Fully-equipped computer room and range of classroom com-

puters in senior school. *Special provision:* Extra tuition arranged (charged to parents).

European Community *Languages:* French offered: GCSE; AS-level; A-level. German: GCSE; AS-level; A-level. Italian (in sixth form): GCSE; AS-level; A-level and as non-examined subject. Spanish (in sixth form): to GCSE, AS-level; A-level and as non-examined subject. 50–75% take GCSE in more than 1 EC language. *Exchanges:* Regular exchanges for pupils aged 11–18 to France, Germany and Italy. *Other:* EC pupils welcomed in school. Strong languages programme throughout.

Senior pupils' non-academic activities *Music:* approx 80 learn a musical instrument, 8 up to Grade 8; 2–3 pa accepted for Music School; 2–3 pa to teacher training specialising in music. Finalist – Young Musician of the Year. 10 in school orchestra, 15 in school choir, other various musical ensembles. 1–2 in National Youth Orchestra; 4 in County Youth Orchestra. *Drama and dance:* Large number throughout school in school productions; approx 80 up to LAMDA Gold medal; 1–2 pa accepted for Drama/Dance School; 1–2 pa to degree with drama specialisation. *Art:* 12 take art as non-examined subject; 26 take GCSE art; 6 A-level art; 2–3 pa accepted for Art School. 20 belong to photographic club; art/pottery club for whole school. *Sport:* Hockey, netball, swimming, tennis, athletics, badminton, volleyball, basketball, table tennis, rounders available. 20 take non-compulsory sport. 10 represent county (hockey, tennis, athletics, swimming, badminton, golf). *Other:* Some take part in local community schemes. 22 have bronze Duke of Edinburgh's Award, 7 silver and 3 gold. Some enter voluntary schemes after leaving school or work for national charities. Other activities include drama, art, linguists, mathematics, photography, computer clubs; Christian Union, tennis coaching, 1st year club, debating society, wildlife club, judo, self-defence.

Careers In 1990, 73% sixth form leavers went on to degree courses; 15% to non-degree courses (eg business studies, occupational therapy); 10% straight into careers (eg army, banking); 2% other. Of those going on to degree courses, 16% went to Oxbridge; 50% to other universities; 44% to poly/colleges. 10% those going on to higher education on average go to courses in practical art; 10% in drama/acting; 10% in music; 30% in humanities/social sciences; 10% in medicine; and 30% in science/engineering.

Uniform School uniform worn, except in sixth.

Houses/prefects No competitive houses. All sixth form have responsibilities; some specific school officers. Head girl, heads of boarding houses, appointed by the head, staff and sixth form. School Council.

Religion Attendance at religious worship compulsory.

Social Social events, local music festivals, some trips abroad with other schools. Study and recreational visits to France, Germany, Italy, Switzerland and Austria. Pupils allowed to bring own car/bike/motorbike. Meals self-service. School shop. No tobacco/alcohol allowed.

Discipline No corporal punishment. Pupils failing to produce homework once could expect reprimand and extra work; those caught smoking cannabis on the premises could expect expulsion.

Boarding All upper sixth have own study bedrooms; lower sixth and fifth forms in rooms of 2 or 3. Houses of 20–30, divided by age. Resident qualified nurse. Sixth form pupils can provide and cook own food. Exeats by arrangement with parents. Daytime visits to the local town allowed from 2nd year senior (frequency increases with age: from once/week to daily for sixth).

Alumni association is run by Mrs M Dustow, Secretary, Trobus Farm, Ladock, Truro.

· *Tudor Hall* ·

Tudor Hall School
Wykham Park
Banbury
Oxfordshire
OX16 9UR
Tel 0295 263434

- Pupils 250
- Boys None
- Girls 11–18
  (Day/Board)
- Upper sixth 34

- Termly fees
  £1690 (Day)
  £2650 (Board)
- GSA
  Enquiries/application to
  the Headmistress

What it's like

Founded in 1850 at Forest Hill, it moved to Chislehurst in 1908, was evacuated during the Second World War to Burnt Norton, and ultimately became settled at Wykham Park, one and a half miles from Banbury. There it is housed in a 17th-century manor house, and also in a fine 18th-century house next door. The rooms are handsome and well furnished. Boarding accommodation and general facilities are excellent. Outside are comparably beautiful gardens and parkland. Some attention is given to religious education in the Anglican tradition, and on Sundays there is worship in one of the local parish churches. A large and well-qualified staff permits an unusually favourable staff:pupil ratio of about 1:7.5. Academic standards are good and results creditable. Many leavers go on to degree courses. Facilities for music are especially good (a music school was opened by Sir Geraint Evans in 1986). There is much emphasis on music and the school has an orchestra, a choir and a choral society. Drama is well supported. Facilities for sports and games are first class, and include a sports hall. Apart from the standard range of sports and games, fencing and riding are available. There is an impressive range of clubs and societies. The Duke of Edinburgh's Award Scheme is popular and quite a few girls are involved in local social and community services.

School profile

Pupils Age range 11–18, 250 girls (day and boarding). Main entry age 11. *Transfer from maintained schools:* 2% main intake, plus 1% to sixth.

Entrance Common entrance exam used.

Staff Headmistress Miss N Godfrey, in post for 7 years.

Academic work GCSE, AS and A-levels. 20 subjects offered (including AS level general studies; not A-level). In 1990, 39 pupils in upper fifth, 34 in upper sixth. *GCSE:* in 1990, 20 upper fifth gained at least grade C in 8+ subjects; 18 in 5–7 subjects. *A-levels:* 29 upper sixth passed in 3 subjects; 5 in 2 subjects.

Computing facilities: Nimbus and BBC for Cambridge Information Technology Certificate.

European Community *Languages:* French offered: to age 14; GCSE; A-level. German offered: to GCSE; A-level. Italian offered: to Institute of Linguists. Spanish offered: to GCSE; A-level. 50–75% take GCSE in more than 1 EC language.

Careers In 1990, 50% leavers went on to degree courses; 10% to art/drama/music colleges. 10% those going on to higher education went to courses in practical art.

u

· *University College School* ·

University College
School
Frognal
Hampstead
London NW3 6XH
Tel 071 435 2215

- Pupils 800
- Boys 7–18 (Day)
- Girls None
- Upper sixth 102

- Termly fees
  £1690 (Day)
- HMC

Enquiries/application to
the Headmaster

What it's like

Founded in Gower Street in 1830 as part of University College London. A junior school was opened in Hampstead in 1891 and the main school moved to purpose-built accommodation in Hampstead in 1907. The school is set in pleasant grounds in a very agreeable residential area, 5 minutes' walk from Hampstead Heath; 27 acres of school's own playing fields are within walking distance. There have been extensive additions to the original handsome buildings and facilities are first-rate. The main aims of the school's philosophy and policy are the pursuit of academic excellence, a respect for and encouragement of independent thought and individual judgement, a broad curriculum and the lack of any religious barriers. A large staff permits a staff:pupil ratio of about 1:10 and academic attainments are high. Very many sixth formers go on to degree courses each year, including many to Oxbridge. The school is very strong in music and drama and provides an excellent range of activities. It also has a distinguished record in games.

School profile

Pupils Total age range 7–18; 800 day boys. Senior department 13–18, 520 boys. Main entry ages 7+, 9+, 11+, 13+ and into sixth. Approx 5% are children of former pupils. *Transfer from maintained schools:* 100% intake at 11, 10% at 13, plus 60% to sixth.

Entrance Common entrance and own exam used. Oversubscribed. No religious requirements. Academic competence and an ability to contribute to the wider life of the school looked for. Parents are charged separately for text books. 10 assisted places pa for 11 year olds and 5 for sixth form. No set number of scholarships; grants and bursaries available up to full fees.

Parents Most are professional people (doctors, lawyers, etc).

Staff Headmaster G D Slaughter, in post for 8 years. 50 full time staff, 10 part time (music). Annual turnover 4%. Average age mid thirties.

Academic work GCSE and A-levels. 14 GCSE subjects offered; 17 at A-level (including Russian; no A-level general studies). In 1990, 108 pupils in upper fifth, 102 in upper sixth. *GCSE:* in 1990, 86 upper fifth gained at least grade C in 8+ subjects; 11 in 5–7; and 5 in 1–4 subjects. *A-levels:* 5 upper sixth passed in 4+ subjects; 87 in 3; 5 in 2 subjects. 28 took science A-levels; 52 arts/humanities; 17 both. *Computing facilities:* Two computer rooms.

European Community *Languages:* French offered: to age 14; GCSE; A-level. German offered: to age 14; GCSE; A-level. Spanish offered: as non-examined subject. 25–50% take GCSE in more than 1 EC language. *Exchanges:* Regular exchanges for pupils aged 14–18 to France, Germany, and Netherlands.

Senior pupils' non-academic activities *Music:* 60 in school orchestra, wind band, numerous small ensembles, pop groups. About 300 in choral society, involving parents, staff and children. *Drama and dance:* 28 boys take GCSE drama; one major school production per term. *Art:* 10 take as non-examined subject; 20 take GCSE; 4 A-level. 2 accepted for Art School. *Sport:* Rugby, sailing, football, hockey, cricket, athletics, tennis, golf, swimming, badminton, fencing, karate, basketball, fives and squash available. The vast majority play in 5-a-side football tournaments, table tennis, swimming etc. *Other:* 25 take part in local community schemes. Other activities include a computer club, a wide range of societies including chess, backgammon, politics and economics, science, geography, history, classical; driving lessons, war games, Christian Union, Jewish Society, bridge, live-action role playing society, tiddly-winks, photography etc.

Careers In 1990, 90% leavers went on to degree courses; 2% to art/drama/music colleges; 4% to non-degree courses (eg A-level repeats); 3% straight into careers. Of those going on to degree courses, 16% went to Oxbridge; 66% to other universities; 8% to poly/colleges. 4% those going on to higher education went to courses in practical art; 2% in drama/acting; 2% in music; 66% in humanities/social sciences; 6% in medicine; and 20% in science/engineering.

Uniform School uniform worn except the sixth.

Houses/prefects Competitive houses ('demes'). Prefects (monitors), head boy – appointed by the Head. No head of house or house prefects.

Religion No compulsory worship.

Social Plays, choral society etc in close co-operation with South Hampstead High School. Organised trips abroad including sporting exchange with the Lycee Marcelin Berthelot (Paris) and drama exchange with College Pierre Mendes (Normandy). Pupils allowed to bring own car/bike/motorbike to school. Meals self service. School tuck shop. No tobacco/alcohol allowed.

Discipline No corporal punishment. Pupils failing to produce homework once might expect a warning; those caught in possession of drugs on the premises must anticipate expulsion.

Former pupils Chris Bonnington; Roger Bannister; Stephen Spender; Julian Lloyd-Webber.

· *Upper Chine* ·

Upper Chine School
Church Road
Shanklin
Isle of Wight
PO37 6QU
Tel 0983 862208

- Pupils 216
- Boys 3–9 only (Day)
- Girls 3–18 (Day/Board/Weekly)
- Upper sixth 13

- Termly fees
  £1180 (Day)
  £2220 (Board)
  £1980 (Weekly)
- GSA
  Enquiries/application to the Headmistress

What it's like

Founded in 1799 Upper Chine moved to Shanklin in 1914. Set in 30 acres of very beautiful gardens close to the sea, the school is situated on the outskirts of Shanklin Old Village. In both junior and senior school a large, well qualified staff permits a ratio of 1:8 pupils. A happy friendly atmosphere prevails and there are all the advantages of a small school. Academic standards are good and almost all upper sixth form leavers go on to further education, the majority to degree courses. Virtually everyone is engaged in music and drama and the school is fortunate in having its own purpose built theatre. Sports and games feature strongly and there is a wide variety of activities both in and out of school. There is a commitment to the local community and numerous formal and informal activities including the Duke of Edinburgh's Award Scheme.

School profile

Pupils Total age range 3–18; 216 pupils, 81 day (9 boys, 72 girls), 135 boarding girls. Senior department 11–18, 160 girls. Main entry ages 3–6 (boys and girls), 10, 11, 12 and into sixth (girls). Approx 2% are children of former pupils. *Transfer from maintained schools:* 2% senior intake.

Entrance Common entrance and own exam used. Not oversubscribed. No special skills or religious requirements, but most are C of E. Average extras, £60 per term. Various scholarships/bursaries, up to £2000 pa.

Parents 15+% in the armed services. 60+% live within 30 miles; up to 10% live overseas.

Staff Headmistress Dr Helen Harvey, one year in post. 27 full time staff, 9 part time. Annual turnover 5–10%. Average age 40–45.

Academic work GCSE and A-levels. 17 subjects offered (including AS-level but not A-level general studies). In 1990, 34 pupils in upper fifth, 13 in upper sixth. *GCSE:* in 1990, 10 upper fifth gained at least grade C in 8+ subjects; 18 in 5–7; and 8 in 1–4 subjects. *A-levels:* 1 upper sixth passed in 4+ subjects; 7 in 3; 3 in 2; and 3 in 1 subject. 20% took science A-levels; 50% arts/humanities; 30% both. *Computing facilities:* Computer labs in senior and prep school. *Special provision:* Specialist teacher available.

European Community *Languages:* French offered: to age 14; GCSE; AS-level; A-level; non-examined subject. German offered: to age 14; GCSE; AS-level; A-level. Spanish offered: to age 14; GCSE; AS-level; A-level. 25–50% take GCSE in more than 1 EC language. *Other:* EC pupils (France, Germany, Netherlands, Spain) for summer or for several terms – extra English teaching provided for them.

Senior pupils' non-academic activities *Music:* 100+ learn a musical instrument, 6 to Grade 6 or above; 35 in school orchestra, 55 in choir, all in biennial house competitions. *Drama and dance:* 75 in school productions, all in biennial house drama competitions. 10 take Grade 6 in ESB, RAD etc. 1 accepted for Drama/

Dance Schools, 1 works in the theatre. *Art:* 5–10 take as non-examined subject; 15–20 take GCSE; 3 A-level. 1 accepted for Art School. *Sport:* Hockey, netball, badminton, squash, rounders, tennis, table tennis, swimming, sailing, windsurfing and judo available. 2–4 represent county/country (hockey, netball). *Other:* Many take part in local community schemes. 36 have bronze Duke of Edinburgh's Award, 6 have silver and 2 gold. Other activities include a computer club, public speaking, driving lessons, karate, golf, orienteering.

Careers In 1990, 50% leavers went on to degree courses; 12% to art/drama/music colleges; 6% to non-degree courses (eg bilingual secretarial); 32% other. Of those going on to degree courses, 13% went to Oxbridge; 62% to other universities; 25% to poly/colleges. 9% those going on to higher education went to courses in practical art; 64% in humanities/social sciences; and 27% in science/engineering.

Uniform School uniform worn except in sixth.

Houses/prefects Competitive houses. Head girl, prefects and house captains – elected by the Head, staff and sixth form. School Council.

Religion Morning assembly and compulsory Sunday service. Provision for RC girls to attend mass locally.

Social Debates, informal talks, matches etc with other local schools. Trips to France, Germany, Austria and Italy. Pupils with licences allowed to bring own motorbike to school. Formal lunch and breakfast, self service supper. School shop. No tobacco/alcohol allowed.

Discipline No corporal punishment. Emphasis on developing self-discipline through the strict enforcement of clearly defined rules set out in the school hand book. Rules are not excessive and were discussed with the girls but failure to stick to them is viewed seriously. Pupils are always expected to produce homework. Possession of cannabis or similar substances would lead to immediate expulsion.

Boarding All sixth formers have own study bedroom. Houses, of 14–28, divided by age. Resident qualified nurse. Central dining room. Sixth form can provide and cook own food. One 2-night exeat each term (more in sixth). Visits to local town allowed.

Alumni association is run by Mrs Margaret Ward-Booth, c/o School.

· *Uppingham* ·

Uppingham School
Uppingham
Rutland
LE15 9QE
Tel 0572 822216

- Pupils 680
- Boys 13–18 (Board)
- Girls 16–18 (Board)
- Upper sixth 146

- Termly fees
  £3250 (Board)
- HMC
Enquiries/application to
the Headmaster

What it's like

Founded in 1584 by Robert Johnson, it lies in the centre of the small and attractive market town of Uppingham. The town itself is a conservation area and many of the school buildings are listed. The buildings and playing fields (of which there are 56 acres) spread right across the town, providing a close 'town and gown' relationship. The original 16th century school room is now the art school. There are many well-designed modern buildings and not a few from the period of the great 19th century headmaster, Edward Thring, who provided a variety of musical, sporting and practical activities then virtually unknown in comparable schools. It is a C of E foundation and worship in the Anglican tradition is compulsory. A large staff allows a staff:pupil ratio of 1:9. The standards of teaching are high and academic results are good. Many leavers go on to degree courses, including Oxbridge. The school's music is very strong. Among the many excellent modern facilities is a theatre where many dramatic presentations are staged. The school has long had a high reputation for its achievements in sports and games, and there is a very active CCF. A wide range of extra-curricular activities is available. The community service unit is one of the largest in the country.

School profile

Pupils Age range 13–18; 680 boarding pupils (600 boys, 80 girls). Main entry ages 13 (boys) and into sixth (boys and girls). Approx 15% are children of former pupils. *Transfer from maintained schools:* 5% main intake, plus 20% to sixth.

Entrance Common entrance used. Not heavily oversubscribed. No special skills required; C of E foundation, others accepted. Parents expected to buy some sixth form text books; other extras variable. At least 12 scholarships/bursaries pa, one-half to one-tenth fees.

Parents 20+% are doctors, lawyers, etc; 25+% in industry or commerce; 30+% in agriculture and related activities. 10+% live within 30 miles; up to 10% live overseas.

Staff Headmaster Dr S C Winkley, first year in post. 75 full time staff. Annual turnover 5%. Average age 37.

Academic work GCSE and A-levels. 18 GCSE subjects offered; 20 at A-level (including design and music; no A-level general studies). In 1990;, 123 pupils in upper fifth, 146 in upper sixth. *GCSE:* in 1990, 96 upper fifth gained at least grade C in 8+ subjects; 24 in 5–7; and 3 in 1–4 subjects. *A-levels:* 5 upper sixth passed in 4+ subjects; 89 in 3; 39 in 2; and 12 in 1 subject. 35% took science A-levels; 45% arts/humanities; 20% both. *Computing facilities:* Large computer centre, 15 BBC Acorns, Econet network; computers in most departments. *Special provision:* Limited assistance available.

European Community *Languages:* French offered: to age 14; GCSE; AS-level; A-level. German offered: to age 14; GCSE; AS-level; A-level. Italian offered: as a non-examined subject. Spanish offered: to age 14; GCSE; A-level. 25–50% take GCSE in more than 1 EC language. *Exchanges:* Regular exchanges for pupils aged 14–18 to France and Germany. *Other:* Occasional German pupils in sixth form.

Senior pupils' non-academic activities *Music:* 50+% learn a musical instrument, 30% to Grade 6 or above; 100 in school orchestras, 40 in choir, 200+ in concert choir. Number of Oxbridge organ and choral awards (5 in 1990). *Drama and dance:* 120 in last major production. *Art:* 20 take GCSE; 10 A-level. Some accepted for foundation courses. *Sport:* Rugby, hockey, cross country, athletics, cricket, tennis, shooting, squash, Eton fives, swimming, golf, cycling, water polo, life saving, sailing, wind surfing, canoeing, sub aqua, badminton, volleyball, basketball, gymnastics, fencing, rock climbing available. *Other:* Some pupils take part in local community schemes. Computer centre open most hours of the day; CCF, debating etc.

Careers In 1990, 75% leavers went on to degree courses; 5% to art/drama/music colleges; 10% to non-degree courses (eg HND agriculture, physiotherapy); 2% straight into careers (eg army); 8% other. Of those going on to degree courses, 15% went to Oxbridge; 60% to other universities; 25% to poly/colleges. 8% those going on to higher education went to courses in practical art; 2% in music; 52% in humanities/social sciences; 8% in medicine; and 30% in science/engineering.

Uniform School uniform worn throughout.

Houses/prefects Residential houses. Prefects, head boy/girl, head of house and house prefects – appointed by Headmaster or housemaster.

Religion Attendance at chapel compulsory.

Social French and German exchanges.

Meals formal, in houses. School shop. No tobacco allowed, occasional bar for upper sixth.

Discipline No corporal punishment. Firm line taken on major offences.

Boarding Single sex houses, of approximately 50, mixed ages. Resident qualified nurse. Limited exeats. Visits to local town allowed.

Alumni association is run by W M Bussey, c/o the School.

V

· Victoria (Belfast) ·

Victoria College
Cranmore Park
Belfast
BT9 6JA
Tel 0232 661506

- Pupils 762
- Boys None
- Girls 4–18 (Day/ Board/Weekly)
- Upper sixth 113

- Termly fees
  £1950 (Day)
  £2700 (Board/ Weekly)
  Enquiries/application to the Headmistress

What it's like

Founded in 1859 by Mrs Margaret Byers, it is one of the longest established girls' schools in the British Isles. Since 1972 it has occupied its present site at Cranmore Park in beautiful grounds in a secluded and quiet residential area in south Belfast, a very pleasant environment. The school operates on two campuses 4 minutes' walk apart. The purpose-built buildings are modern and compact and very well equipped. Drumglass House, an elegant Georgian building, is the boarding establishment. There are excellent sports and games facilities in the grounds. A non-denominational school, it works a selective system and academic standards are high. Results are impressive and many sixth formers go on to degree coursees each year in Great Britain and Northern Ireland. Strong in music, less strong in drama. A very good range of sports and games (a large number of county and national representatives) and an equally good range of extra-curricular activities. There is a big commitment to local community services. The college has a phenomenal record in the Duke of Edinburgh's Award Scheme: probably without equal in any British boys' or girls' school.

School profile

Pupils Total age range 4–18; 762 girls, 722 day, 40 boarding. Senior department 11–18; 618 girls. Main entry ages, 4, 11 and into the sixth. 30% are children of former pupils. *Transfer from maintained schools:* 95% senior intakes.

Entrance Oversubscribed. No special skills or religious requirements. Parents not expected to buy text books. 2 scholarships for boarders, up to £300. Non-fee-paying status for pupils who satisfy residential qualification and pass selection tests.

Parents 15+% are doctors, lawyers etc;

15+% in industry or commerce. 60+% live within 30 miles; up to 10% live overseas.

Staff Headmistress Dr C J Higginson. 49 full time staff, 14 part time. Annual turnover 4%. Average age 37.

Academic work GCSE, AS and A-levels. 24 subjects offered (including Italian, Greek, Latin, A-level politics and computer science; general studies taught to all sixth but not examined). In 1989, 92 pupils in upper fifth, 113 in upper sixth. *GCSE:* in 1989, 59% upper fifth gained at least grade C in 8+ subjects; 31% in 5–7;

and 10% in 1–4 subjects. *A-levels:* 4 upper sixth passed in 4+ subjects; 60 in 3; 39 in 2; and 6 in 1 subject. 33% took science A-levels; 33% arts/humanities; 34% both. *Computing facilities:* Nimbus network (12 computer stations), Apple Mac (all in Senior Resource Centre); 9 BBC Masters in Senior School; 7 BBC in Junior School; 4 in Prep dept. Extensive new technology facilities currently being provided, which include computer rooms. *Special provision:* Private help available after school.

Senior pupils' non-academic activities *Music:* 120 learn a musical instrument, 30 to Grade 6 or above, 20 accepted for Music School. 30 in school orchestra, 60 in choir. One major musical production each year. *Drama and dance:* 50 in Junior drama group. Timetabled drama classes for Forms 1 and 2. *Art:* 13 A-level candidates; 6 accepted for Art School and degree courses in history/appreciation of art, conservation, architecture. *Sport:* Hockey, tennis, athletics, netball, fencing, cricket, table tennis, gymnastics, trampolining, swimming and life-saving, squash, badminton, dance, keep fit available. 240 take non-compulsory sport; 30 take exams. 11 represent county/country (hockey, tennis, fencing, squash, athletics, table tennis). *Other:* 60 take part in local community schemes. 85 have bronze Duke of Edinburgh's Award, 60 have silver and 60 gold. Other activities include computer club, social services group, peace and reconciliation movement, Guides, traffic education, driving lessons.

Careers 3 part time advisers (staff), 1 local officer. Annual average accepted for *arts and humanities degree courses* at Oxbridge, 5; other universities, 27; polytechnics/colleges, 6. *science and engineering degree courses* at Oxbridge, 2; other universities, 27. *BEd*, 3. *other general training courses*, 4. Average going straight into careers in armed services, 2; industry, 1; other, 5. Medicine, law and sciences are most popular careers.

Uniform School uniform worn throughout.

Houses/prefects Competitive houses. No prefects. Head girl and head of house – elected by sixth form, confirmed by staff. School Council.

Religion Compulsory non-denominational assembly unless parents request otherwise.

Social Sport, debates, conferences, quizzes, lectures, concerts, plays with other schools. Regular organised trips abroad (France, Germany, Spain, Italy). Meals formal in boarding house, self service in school dining hall. Tuckshops on each campus. No tobacco/alcohol allowed.

Discipline No corporal punishment. Pupils failing to produce homework once might expect a warning and to produce work next day; anyone guilty of conduct harmful to herself or to others would receive warning of dangers and counselling, contact would be made with parents.

Boarding 40% have own cubicle, 30% are in dormitories of 6+. 1 boarding house. Resident qualified medical staff. Central dining room. Pupils can provide and cook own food in small groups. Some weekly boarders. Visits to local town allowed when local conditions permit including theatre and cultural events; seniors indirectly supervised at weekends; juniors supervised.

Alumni association run by Hon Secretary, 1 Malone View Avenue, Belfast 9.

Former pupils Helen Waddese; local TV personalities; BBC producers.

· *Victoria (Jersey)* ·

Victoria College
St Helier
Jersey
Channel Islands
Tel 0534 37591

- Pupils 866
- Boys 7–19 (Day/ Board/Weekly)
- Girls None
- Upper sixth 62

- Termly fees
  £477 (Day)
  £2304 (Board)
  £1975 (Weekly)
- HMC
  Enquiries/application to the Headmaster

What it's like

Founded in 1852 it has an impressive site on a spur overlooking the town of St Helier with fine views over the bay to the south. There are parkland, gardens and playing fields. The original Victorian buildings (including the Great Hall) are still used, and there have been numerous modern additions. The prep school (in new buildings) was opened in 1966 and this is sited at the south end of the college lawn. A well-run school it has high academic standards and gets good results. Many sixth formers go on to degree courses each year. Strong in drama and art. A wide variety of sports and games is available and high standards are achieved (quite a lot of representatives at county and national level). The college has a flourishing CCF and a large number of pupils take part in a wide range of activities. A good record in the Duke of Edinburgh's Award Scheme.

School profile

Pupils Total age range 7–19; 866 boys, 836 day, 30 boarding. Senior department 11–19, 577 boys. Main entry ages 7, 11, 13 and into sixth. Approx 25% are children of former pupils. Own prep department provides more than 60% of intake. *Transfer from maintained schools:* 30% senior intakes, plus 5% to sixth.

Entrance Common entrance and own exam used. Not oversubscribed. No special skills or religious requirements. Parents not expected to buy text books; maximum extras, £50 pa. 4 scholarships/bursaries pa for local residents only, up to full day fees.

Parents 15+% are doctors, lawyers etc; 15+% in industry or commerce; 15+% in finance. 60+% live within 30 miles; up to 10% live overseas.

Staff Headmaster M H Devenport, in post for 23 years. 43 full time staff, 5 part time. Annual turnover 7%. Average age 41.

Academic work GCSE and A-levels. 20 subjects offered (including theatre arts and A-level general studies). In 1990, 95 pupils in upper fifth, 62 in upper sixth. *GCSE:* in 1989, 57% upper fifth gained at least grade C in 8+ subjects; 25% in 5–7; and 16% in 1–4 subjects. *A-levels:* 33% upper sixth passed in 4+ subjects; 44% in 3; 9% in 2; and 10% in 1 subject. 33% took science A-levels; 54% arts/humanities; 13% both. *Computing facilities:* 12 computers in lab. Machines in most departments (new computer centre soon). *Special provision:* Special coaching is offered for those for whom English is a foreign language and an extra charge is made.

European Community *Languages:* French offered: to age 14; GCSE; A-level. German offered: to age 14; GCSE; A-level. Spanish offered: to age 14; GCSE; A-level. 25–50% take GCSE in more than 1 EC language. *Exchanges:* Regular exchanges for pupils aged 11–18 to France and Germany.

Senior pupils' non-academic activities *Music:* 30 learn a musical instrument, 12 to Grade 6 or above; 22 in school orchestra, 15 choir, 12 brass ensemble, 5 string quintet; 11 in Jersey Youth Orchestra, 10 Jersey Youth Wind Band; 5 go on to play in pop group. *Drama and dance:* 30 in school productions; 80 in house plays. *Art:* 12 take as non-examined subject; 20 take GCSE; 8 A-level. 3 accepted for Art School. 10 belong to eg photographic club. *Sport:* Soccer, rugby, squash, shooting, athletics, cross-country, hockey, sailing, cricket, swimming, golf, tennis, basketball, fives, fencing, karate, archery, badminton available. 175 take non-compulsory sport. 12 represent county/country (rugby, squash, hockey, cricket, shooting). *Other:* 50 take part in local community schemes. 30 have silver Duke of Edinburgh's Award. Some work for national charities after leaving. Other activities include computer club, chess, CCF, marine biology.

Careers In 1990, 53% leavers went on to degree courses; 4% to art/drama/music colleges; 6% to non-degree courses; 25% straight into careers (eg banking, armed services, agriculture); 12% other. Of those going on to degree courses, 11% went to Oxbridge; 60% to other universities; 29% to poly/colleges. 6% those going on to higher education went to courses in practical art; 53% in humanities/social sciences; 2% in medicine; and 39% in science/engineering.

Uniform School uniform worn throughout.

Houses/prefects Competitive houses. Prefects, head boy, head of house and house prefects – appointed by senior staff with pupils' advice. School Council.

Religion Daily Christian assembly; parents may request withdrawal.

Social Debating contests with local schools; Jersey Youth Orchestra and Theatre, local Eisteddfod; annual dramatic production with Girls' College. Regular French exchanges. Pupils allowed to bring own car/bike/motorbike to school. Meals formal for boarders, self service for day pupils. School shops sell tuck, second-hand uniform. No tobacco/alcohol allowed.

Discipline No corporal punishment. Pupils failing to produce homework once might expect extra work; those caught smoking cannabis on the premises might expect suspension or expulsion.

Boarding One-third have own study bedroom, remainder in dormitories of less than 6. Houses divided by age. Resident qualified matron, doctor on call. Central dining room. Seniors can provide and cook own snacks. Exeats any weekend. Visits to local town allowed for 15+.

Alumni association run by Dr Jonathan Osmont, Florence House, 39 Cleveland Road, St Helier, Jersey CI.

Former pupils Kenneth More; Air Vice Marshal Alcock; Ambassadors Sir Martin Le Quesne and Sir Arthur De La Mare; Sir William Haley (former Editor, The Times); Sir Peter Crill (Bailiff of Jersey); Dr A E Mourant FRS.

· *Wadhurst* ·

Wadhurst College
Wadhurst
East Sussex
TN5 6JA
Tel 089 288 3193

- Pupils 220
- Boys 11–18
  (Dance only)
- Girls 9–18 (Day/
  Board/Weekly)
- Upper sixth 13

- Termly fees
  £1570 (Day)
  £2495 (Board)
  £2445 (Weekly)
- GSA
Enquiries/application to
the Headmaster

What it's like

Wadhurst College incorporates the Legat Ballet School, which enhances its vocational curriculum. A major building programme has been completed; there is a new sports hall, ballet studios, sixth form centre, dormitories and common rooms.

School profile

Pupils Total age range 9–18; 220 pupils; 9 boys (ballet only), 211 girls. Main entry ages 9, 11, 12, 13 and into sixth. *Transfer from maintained schools:* 30% main senior intake, plus 10% to sixth.

Entrance Common entrance and own exam used or ballet audition. Scholarships (including for music and science) and bursaries (daughters of the clergy or missionaries).

Staff Head R W R Purdom, 1 year in post.

Academic work GCSE and A-levels. 23 subjects offered (including A-level general studies, Russian, Chinese and Japanese). In 1990, 50 pupils in upper fifth, 13 in upper sixth. *GCSE:* In 1990, average pupil passed 3.8 subjects grade C or above. *A-levels:* In 1989 average pupil passed 1.8 subjects. 25% took science A-levels; 25% arts/humanities; 50% both. *Computing facilities:* Computer room and computers in departments. *Special provision:* Special needs teacher.

European Community *Languages:* French offered: to age 14; GCSE; AS-level; A-level. German offered: to age 14; GCSE; AS-level; A-level. Spanish offered: to GCSE. 10–25% take GCSE in more than 1 EC language. *Exchanges:* Regular exchanges for pupils aged 14–16 to France.

Careers In 1990, 50% leavers went on to degree courses; 20% to art/drama/music colleges; 10% to non-degree courses (eg secretarial); 20% other. Of those going on to degree courses, 8% went to Oxbridge; 60% to other universities; 32% to poly/colleges. 25% those going on to higher education went to courses in practical art; 20% in drama/acting; 8% in music; 30% in humanities/social sciences; 8% in nursing; and 9% in science/engineering.

· *Wakefield High* ·

Wakefield Girls' High
School
Wentworth Street
Wakefield
West Yorkshire
WF1 2QS
Tel 0924 372490

- Pupils 760
- Boys None
- Girls 11–18
  (Day)
- Upper sixth 88

- Termly fees £995
- GSA

Enquiries/application to
the Headmistress

What it's like

Founded in 1878, the school occupies an extensive and agreeable site near the centre of Wakefield. The Georgian house in which it began has been adapted and extended over the years and excellent facilities now include a recent science and technology centre, a sixth-form centre, gymnasia, large libraries and an assembly hall which takes the whole school. A few minutes walk away are six acres of well-equipped playing fields. The junior school is nearby and enjoys fine grounds and buildings. Girls follow a broad curriculum which keeps a wide range of options open until A-level; co-operation with brother school, the Queen Elizabeth Grammar School for boys at sixth form level has increased pupil choice and protected minority subjects. Academic standards are high and results are very creditable. Most leavers go on to higher education, including a few to Oxbridge. The staff:pupil ratio is a favourable 1:11. Considerable strength in music and drama in which there are joint activities with the Queen Elizabeth Grammar School. A standard range of sports and games (including golf and orienteering) and a plentiful variety of clubs and societies. The community service unit is very active.

School profile

Pupils Age range 11–18; 760 day girls. Main entry ages 11 and into sixth. Own junior school. *Transfer from maintained schools:* 60% main senior intake, plus 45% to sixth.

Entrance Own exam used. Assisted places. Bursaries.

Staff Headmistress Mrs P A Langham, in post for 3 years.

Academic work GCSE and A-levels. A-level general studies offered. In 1990, 123 pupils in upper fifth, 88 in upper sixth. *GCSE:* in 1990, 99 upper fifth gained at least grade C in 8+ subjects; 17 in 5–7; and 17 in 1–4 subjects. *A-levels:* 52 upper sixth passed in 4+ subjects; 22 in 3; 9 in 2; and 5 in 1 subject. *Computing facilities:* Wide range. Computing taught in first three years to all pupils.

European Community *Languages:* French offered: to age 14; GCSE; AS-level; A-level; Institute of Linguists. German offered: to GCSE; A-level; Institute of Linguists. Spanish offered: to GCSE. Up to 10% take GCSE in more than 1 EC language. *Exchanges:* Regular exchanges for pupils aged 14–16 to France and Germany.

Careers In 1990, 94% leavers went on to degree courses; 3% straight into careers; 3% other. Of those going on to degree courses, 6% went to Oxbridge; 46% to other universities; 45% to poly/colleges. 1% those going on to higher education went to courses in practical art; 1% in drama/acting; 59% in humanities/social sciences; 4% in medicine; and 36% in science/engineering.

· *Walthamstow Hall* ·

Walthamstow Hall	● Pupils 530	● Termly fees
Hollybush Lane	● Boys None	£1380 (Day)
Sevenoaks	● Girls 5–18 (Day/	£2545 (Board/
Kent	Board/Weekly)	Weekly)
TN13 3UL	● Upper sixth 52	● GSA
Tel 0732 451334		Enquiries to the
		Registrar
		Application to the
		Headmistress

What it's like

Founded in 1838 for the daughters of missionaries and sited in the village of Walthamstow. Shortly afterwards, its brother school, Eltham College, was founded for the missionaries' sons. In 1882 the school moved to Sevenoaks where it has a most agreeable site on the outskirts of the town. The original Victorian house, in delightful grounds and gardens, is the heart of the school. Many modern buildings provide good all-round facilities including a new theatre/music/drama centre. The school is interdenominational. Formerly a Direct Grant school, it is still academically selective and offers a broad grammar school education. Academic results are highly creditable and each year many girls go on to degree courses, including to Oxbridge. The staff-pupil ratio is favourable, with 21 part-time teachers and 35 full-time. Music, drama and art are well supported. There is a good range of sports and games and several county representatives; plus a fair variety of extra-curricular activities. Local community service flourishes and the school has an impressive record in the Duke of Edinburgh's Award Scheme.

School profile

Pupils Total age range 5–18; 530 girls (450 day, 80 boarding). Senior department 11–18, 400 girls. Main entry ages 5, 7, 11 and into sixth. 2% are children of former pupils. *Transfer from maintained schools:* 20% senior intake, plus 33% to sixth.

Entrance Own entrance exam used. Oversubscribed. No special skills or religious requirements but a Christian foundation. Parents not expected to buy textbooks. 75 assisted places. 5 scholarships (including one music), £750–£480; c35 bursaries per year.

Parents 15+% are doctors, lawyers etc; 15+% in industry. 60+% live within 30 miles; 10+% live overseas.

Staff Headmistress Mrs J S Lang, in post for 7 years. 35 full time staff, 21 part time. Annual turnover 4%.

Academic work GCSE, AS and A-levels. 18 GCSE subjects offered; 20 at A-level (no A-level general studies). On average, 62 pupils in upper fifth, 52 in upper sixth. *GCSE:* on average, 46 upper fifth gain at least grade C in 8+ subjects; 13 in 5–7; and 4 in 1–4 subjects. *A-levels:* on average 3 upper sixth pass in 4+ subjects; 31 in 3; 12 in 2; and 5 in 1 subject. 17 take science A-levels; 20 arts/humanities; 14 both. *Computing facilities:* RML Nimbus network. *Special provision:* Extra help from willing staff; occasional paid EFL tuition arranged.

European Community *Languages:* French offered: to age 14; GCSE; A-level. German offered: to age 14; GCSE; AS-level; A-level. 25–50% take GCSE in more than 1 EC language. *Exchanges:* Regular exchanges for pupils aged 11–18 to France and Germany. *Other:* French and German pupils welcome (2 weeks to 2 years), for whom EFL arranged.

Senior pupils' non-academic activities *Music:* 30 learn a musical instrument, 13 to Grade 6 or above; 2 accepted for Music School, 1 to teach music; 20 play in school orchestra, 10 in choir; 6 in Kent Youth Orchestra. *Drama:* 45 in school productions; 10 take grades in ESB, RAD. 1 accepted for Drama School. *Art:* 20 take as non-examined subject; 20 GCSE; 7 A-level. 2 accepted for Art School. 10 belong to eg photographic club. *Sport:* Lacrosse, netball, tennis, judo, sailing, squash, badminton, gym, golf, volleyball, swimming available. Free choice of sports in sixth form, willing participation of 95%. 8 pupils represent county (lacrosse, netball). *Other:* 20 have bronze Duke of Edinburgh's Award, 10 silver, 2 gold. 50 in local community schemes. Other activities include an informal computer club during lunch-hours, driving, photography, voluntary service, keep fit, self-defence.

Careers In 1990, 70% leavers went on to degree courses; 1% to art/drama/music colleges; 3% to non-degree courses (eg secretarial); 1% straight into careers (eg engineering apprentice); 11% other (eg Gap year). Of those going on to degree courses, 17% went to Oxbridge; 60% to other universities; 22% to poly/colleges. 11% those going on to higher education went to courses in practical art; 3% in music; 38% in humanities/social sciences; 11% in medicine; and 36% in science/engineering.

Uniform School uniform worn except in sixth.

Houses/prefects Competitive houses. Prefects, head girl, head of house and house prefects – elected by school. School Council.

Religion Prayers each morning, and evening for boarders. Sunday evening service; local churches for Sunday morning.

Social Voluntary service unit involves all local schools. Some music/drama exchanges. Organised trips abroad to France and Germany; also skiing trips. Pupils allowed to bring own car/motorbike/bike to school on request. Meals formal. Secondhand uniform shop. No tobacco/alcohol allowed.

Discipline No corporal punishment. Pupils failing to produce homework once would be admonished; those caught smoking cannabis on the premises could expect expulsion.

Boarding 80% seniors have own study bedroom, 20% in double. Juniors share 2,3,4-bed rooms. Houses, of approx 35–60, divided by age. SRN cover 24 hours. Central dining room. Sixth-formers can provide and cook snacks. 2 weekend exeats each term. Visits to local town allowed; 8–13 weekly, escorted; 14+ in groups, on request.

Alumni association is run by Mrs Carole Hills, c/o the School.

· *Warminster* ·

Warminster School
Warminster
Wiltshire
BA12 8PJ
Tel 0985 213038/
213358

- Pupils 500
- Boys 5–18
  (Day/Board)
- Girls 5–18
  (Day/Board)
- Upper sixth 40

- Termly fees
  £1290 (Day)
  £2145 (Board/
  Weekly)
- SHMIS
  Enquiries/application to
  The Master

What it's like

Formed in 1973 by the amalgamation of the Lord Weymouth School (founded in 1707) and the school of St Monica (founded in 1874). Its handsome and well-equipped buildings lie in beautiful gardens and grounds on a semi-rural site on the edge of the very attractive old town and facing open country. The school has long-established and close links with the town and the locality where it enjoys strong support. The junior school is combined on a neighbouring site. Thus continuous education is available from age 5. Warminster is a small friendly school whose declared aim is to develop the potential and recognise the value of all pupils. A large staff allows a staff:pupil ratio of 1:10. Standards are high and results good. Many leavers go on to degree courses and practical art courses each year. More than half the school is involved in music and about 85 pupils learn an instrument. A similar number are engaged in dramatic activities and there is an unusually strong design dept. A high reputation in sport and games (a large number of representatives at county level). A big CCF contingent, a wide variety of extra-curricular activities, a substantial commitment to local community schemes and a well-established Duke of Edinburgh's Award Scheme.

School profile

Pupils Total age range 5–18; 500 pupils, 210 day (129 boys, 81 girls), 290 boarding (155 boys, 135 girls). Senior department 12–18, 326 pupils (192 boys, 134 girls). Main entry ages 11, 13 and into sixth. Approx 10% are children of former pupils. Own junior school provides more than 60% of senior intake. *Transfer from maintained schools:* 30% senior intakes, plus 55% to sixth.

Entrance Common entrance and own exam used. Oversubscribed. No special skills or religious requirements. Parents not expected to buy text books; other extras maximum £60. 20 scholarships/bursaries for sixth formers, £1500 to £200 per term.

Parents 20+% in armed services; 15+% in industry or commerce. 20+% live within 30 miles; 10+% live overseas.

Staff Headmaster T D Holgate, one year

in post. 46 full time staff, 4 part time. Annual turnover 8%. Average age 34.

Academic work GCSE and A-levels. 18 subjects offered (including business studies, environmental science, politics; no A-level but AS-level general studies). In 1990, 68 pupils in upper fifth, 40 in upper sixth. *GCSE:* in 1990, 11 upper fifth gained at least grade C in 8+ subjects; 24 in 5–7; and 23 in 1–4 subjects. *A-levels:* 10 upper sixth passed in 3 subjects; 10 in 2; and 10 in 1 subject. 40% took science A-levels; 35% arts/humanities; 25% both. *Computing facilities:* Computer centre and CAL for most departments. *Special provision:* Dyslexia unit with qualified staff.

European Community *Languages:* French offered: to age 14; GCSE; A-level. German offered: to age 14; GCSE; A-level. Spanish offered: to GCSE; A-level. 10–25% take GCSE in more than 1 EC language. *Exchanges:* No regular exchanges but visits for pupils aged 11–18 to France and Germany. *Other:* European Studies offered to pupils aged 11–16. 1 pupil each from Germany and Spain in school.

Senior pupils' non-academic activities *Music:* 168 learn a musical instrument, 15 to Grade 6 or above; 40 in school orchestra, 10 in pop group. *Drama and dance:* 180 in school productions. 10 to Grade 6 in ESB, RAD etc. 1 accepted for Drama/Dance Schools, 2 go on to work in the theatre. *Art:* 280 take as non-examined subject; 36 take GCSE; 10 A-level. 5 accepted for Art School. 20 belong to photographic club. *Sport:* Football, cricket, hockey, netball, athletics, cross-country, basketball, squash, volleyball, fives, golf, riding available. 250 take non-compulsory sport. 25 represent county/country (hockey, football, athletics, cross-country, basketball, squash). *Other:* 20 take part in local community schemes. 25 have bronze Duke of Edinburgh's Award, a number have silver and gold, 120+ in CCF. 5 enter voluntary schemes after leaving school. Other activities include a computer club, driving lessons, over 40 different clubs and societies.

Careers In 1990, 50% leavers went on to degree courses; 30% to art/drama/music colleges; 18% to non-degree courses (eg art foundation); 2% straight into careers (eg building, navy). Of those going on to degree courses, 30% went to universities; 70% to poly/colleges. 30% those going on to higher education went to courses in practical art; 2% in drama/acting; 30% in humanities/social sciences; and 48% in science/engineering.

Uniform School uniform worn except the sixth.

Houses/prefects Competitive houses. Prefects, head boy and girl, head of house and house prefects – appointed by the Head or house staff. School Council.

Religion Daily assembly and Sunday morning chapel.

Social Drama, debates, social service, mini-Enterprise. Annual exchanges with schools in France, Germany and Spain, ski-ing. Some meals formal, some self service. School shop. No tobacco/alcohol allowed.

Discipline No corporal punishment. Pupils failing to produce homework once might expect detention; those caught smoking cannabis on the premises might expect expulsion.

Boarding Sixth and fifth forms have own study bedroom, 5% are in dormitories of 6+. Single sex houses, of 35–60, divided by age. Resident qualified medical staff. Central dining room. Pupils can provide and cook own food. Exeats at half-term and any weekend. Visits to local town allowed.

Alumni association is run by Mr J Boatman, 12 Malthouse Court, The Butts, Frome, Somerset.

Former pupils F Jaeger, C J Benjamin, E J Baddeley; F Bartholomew (actors); Ian Macdonald (racing driver); Thomas Arnold (headmaster); David Backhouse (sculptor); Lord Christopher Thynne; Major-General C E N Lomax; Major-General C H Foulkes; Admiral P H Hall-Thompson; E J Davies (world long jump record holder); Grosvenor Thomas (painter).

· *Warwick* ·

Warwick School	• Pupils 983	• Termly fees
Myton Road	• Boys 7–19 (Day/	£1070 (Day)
Warwick	Board/Weekly)	£2320 (Board)
CV34 6PP	• Girls None	£2170 (Weekly)
Tel 0926 492484	• Upper sixth 106	• HMC
		Enquiries/application to
		the Headmaster

What it's like

Founded in c914 in the reign of Edward the Confessor (the putative patron), it occupied its present site, on the banks of the Avon south of the town, in 1879. The main building is an arresting example of the rococo Tudor style and other buildings have developed round it in an E-shaped pattern. There are several impressive Victorian buildings and a variety of much more recent ones. Large playing fields lie alongside. Over the past decade large sums have been invested in developing and improving the boarding and academic facilities. Major expenditure on the development continues. A C of E foundation, in which attendance at chapel is compulsory with considerable emphasis on religious education. There are longstanding and very close associations between the school and the town and there is vigorous local support. Academic standards and achievements are of a high order: very many leavers go on to degree courses each year, including Oxbridge. The music, drama and art departments are very strong. The school boasts a remarkable number of clubs and societies (50 in all) which cater for almost every conceivable need. There is an excellent range of sports and games (about 800 pupils are involved in these) and high standards are attained (20 or more representatives at county level). Another notable feature is the substantial commitment to local community schemes.

School profile

Pupils Total age range 7–19; 983 boys, 926 day, 57 boarding. Senior department 11–19, 801 boys. Main entry ages 7+, 11+, 13+ and into sixth. Approx 5% are children of former pupils. *Transfer from maintained schools:* 46% senior intakes, plus 50% to sixth (4% total sixth form).

Entrance Own entrance exam used. Oversubscribed. No special skills or religious requirements. Parents not expected to buy text books; extras include lunch, instrumental tuition. 170 assisted places. 100 scholarships, bursaries for tuition or boarding fees.

Parents 15+% in industry or commerce. 60+% live within 30 miles; up to 10% live overseas.

Staff Headmaster P J Cheshire, in post 4 years. 61 full time staff, 5 part time. Annual turnover 5%. Average age 40.

Academic work GCSE and A-levels. 21 subjects offered (including A-level general studies; GCSE Russian in sixth form). In 1990, 122 pupils in upper fifth, 106 in upper sixth. *GCSE:* in 1990, 67% upper fifth gained at least grade C in 8+ subjects; 29% in 5–7; and 4% in 1–4 subjects. *A-levels:* 75% upper sixth passed in 4+ subjects; 20% in 3; 2% in 2; and 1% in 1 subject; many boys take AS-levels in addition. 26% took science A-levels; 46% arts/humanities; 28% both. *Computing facilities:* 30 BBC microMcomputers; 10 Archimedes; GCSE and AS-level.

European Community *Languages:* French offered: to age 14; GCSE; AS-level; A-level. German offered: to age 14; GCSE; A-level. Spanish offered: to age 14; GCSE. 25–50% take GCSE in more than 1 EC language. *Exchanges:* Regular exchanges to France and Germany.

Senior pupils' non-academic activities *Music:* 275 learn a musical instrument, 45 to Grade 6 or above, 1 accepted for University Music Course; 75 in choir, 90 in 2 school orchestras, wind band and junior wind band, 5+ in pop group, 10 in madrigal group; 10 in local orchestra; 18 in orchestra, choir, madrigal group beyond school. *Drama and dance:* 100 in school productions; 10 in others. *Art and Design:* 30 take as non-examined subject; 50 take GCSE; 19 A-level. 4 accepted for Art foundation course, 1 for art history. Art club available for all boys; art appreciation in general studies programme as option for all sixth form. *Sport:* Rugby, hockey, cricket, football, tennis, cross-country, squash, badminton, basketball, fencing, judo, aikido, archery, shooting, canoeing, athletics available. 20 represent county (rugby, cricket, hockey, swimming, tennis). *Other:* 130 take part in local community schemes. 200 in CCF. Other activities include 50 different societies eg chess, a computer club, debating, music, drama, photographic, media studies, bee-keeping, horticulture.

Careers In 1990, 84% leavers went on to degree courses; 2% to art/drama/music colleges; 1% to non-degree courses (eg HND manufacturing management); 3% straight into careers (eg army); 10% other. Of those going on to degree courses, 16% went to Oxbridge; 63% to other universities; 21% to poly/colleges. 3% those going on to higher education went to courses in practical art; 1% in drama/acting; 1% in music; 49% in humanities/social sciences; 4% in medicine; and 41% in science/engineering.

Uniform School uniform worn, modified in the sixth.

Houses/prefects 6 competitive houses. Prefects and boarding house prefects – elected; head boy appointed. School Council.

Religion Compulsory Chapel.

Social Joint concert with King's High; also joint plays and society meetings. Organised trips to Canada, USA, Germany, France. Pupils allowed to bring own car/bike/motorbike to school. Meals self service. School shop. No tobacco/alcohol allowed.

Discipline No corporal punishment. Pupils failing to produce homework could expect detention; those caught smoking cannabis on the premises could expect expulsion.

Boarding Prefects and upper sixth have own study bedroom, most of the rest share with one other; youngest in rooms of 2–6. Houses, of 20–52 divided by age. Central dining room. Sixth formers may prepare light snacks in own kitchen. Half term and 2 weekend exeats each term. Visits to the local town allowed daily from the age of 13.

Alumni association is run by Mr P H E Bailey, Secretary, Old Warwickian Association, 24 Park Road, Leamington Spa, Warwickshire.

· *Welbeck* ·

Welbeck College	● Pupils 150	● Termly fees
Worksop	● Boys 16–19	means-tested up to
Nottinghamshire	(Board)	£650 (Board)
S80 3LN	● Girls None	● BSA
Tel 0909 476326	● Upper sixth 65	Enquiries/application to
		the Principal

What it's like

Founded in 1953 to prepare young men for future professional service in the Army's technical corps. It enjoys a superb site and magnificent amenities in a large park in the Dukeries. The fine main building was formerly the home of the Dukes of Portland. All boys entering Welbeck have a common aim: to gain a commission in the technical corps of the Army. Two years study at Welbeck for A-levels is followed by one year at the RMA Sandhurst. It offers excellent career opportunities and enables an officer to qualify, while serving, for membership of almost any of the professional bodies in the engineering field. It is a highly organised and highly motivated establishment. A large staff permits a staff:pupil ratio of about 1:8. Consistently good results are achieved and each year many students proceed to degree courses, very many reading for their degrees 'in-service'. Music and drama are strong, and an unusually wide variety of sports and games is available. Standards in these are high. There is much emphasis on physical fitness and outdoor pursuits. As might be expected, the CCF is obligatory, but Welbeck is not run as a military unit and in most respects is like any other boarding sixth-form college.

School profile

Pupils Age range 16–19; 150 boarding boys. Entry at 16. *Transfer from maintained sector:* 90%.

Entrance Own entrance exam used. Oversubscribed. Leadership skills and ability in mathematics and physics looked for. No religious requirements. Parents not expected to buy text books.

Parents 10+% in the armed services. Up to 10% live overseas.

Staff Principal J K Jones, first year in post. 19 full time staff, 2 part time. Annual turnover 10%.

Academic work A-levels. 8 subjects offered (including general studies). In 1989, 78 in upper sixth. In 1989, 45 upper sixth passed in 4+ subjects; 18 in 3; 8 in 2; and 5 in 1 subject. 90% took science/engineering A-levels; 10% with some arts/humanities. *Computing facilities:* Extensive Apricot computing and word processing facility, great deal of useful software. Currently 39 machines plus further 12.

Senior students' non-academic activities *Music:* 2 learn a musical instrument; 15 play in school orchestra, 25 in choir, 4 in school pop group. *Drama and dance:* 60 in school productions. *Art:* 12 take as non-examined subject; 10 belong to eg photographic club. *Sport:* Rugby, hockey, cross-country, cricket, athletics, tennis, swimming, sailing, shooting, badminton, basketball, volleyball, fencing, judo, karate, climbing, soccer, table tennis, snooker, golf, squash, gymnastics, canoeing available. 150 take part in non-compulsory sport. 2 students represent county (rugby, judo). *Other:* 12 have gold Duke of Edinburgh's Award. Other activities include a computer club, chess club, CCF, offshore sailing, film appreciation, bell ringing, war games, popular music society and learning to drive.

Careers 1 full time careers adviser. Annual average accepted for *science and engineering degree courses* at Oxbridge, 4; other universities, 44. Average going straight into careers in the armed services, 65; other, 7. Most students go into the technical corps of the Army and read degree 'in-service'.

Uniform Uniform worn.

Houses/prefects Competitive houses. Housemasters appoint house prefects and heads of houses, from whom Principal chooses Head of College.

Religion Compulsory worship.

Social Good social contacts with 3 girls' schools. Organised skiing trip to Germany; rugby tour to France; offshore sailing. Lunch formal, other meals self service. School shop. No tobacco/alcohol allowed.

Discipline No corporal punishment. Students failing to produce homework once might expect to be told to do it by another deadline or be put in detention; those caught smoking would be gated, those with drugs expelled.

Boarding 1 out of 150 has own study bedroom, 80% are in dormitories of 6+. Houses, of approx 75, same as for competitive purposes. Resident qualified nurse. Central dining room. Half-term exeats only. Visits to local town allowed by arrangement with Housemaster.

Alumni association is run by the Bursar, c/o the College.

· *Wellingborough* ·

The School
Wellingborough
Northamptonshire
NN8 2BX
Tel 0933 222427

- Pupils 730
- Boys 8–18 (Day/ Board/Weekly)
- Girls 8–18 (Day/ Board/Weekly)
- Upper sixth 71

- Termly fees £1410 (Day) £2320 (Board/ Weekly)
- HMC Enquiries/application to the Headmaster

What it's like

Founded in 1595, it has occupied its present site since 1881. This is an attractive, compact campus (on the south side of the town) with pleasant buildings, lovely gardens and ample playing fields (about 50 acres in all). There have been many developments in the last 20 years and the school has first-rate facilities. A pre-preparatory school opened on the same campus in 1990, providing the possibility of continuous education from 4–18. Chapel services and teaching are in accordance with the principles of the Church of England. A well-run school, it provides a sound general education with good academic results. Many sixth formers go on to degree courses each year, including many to Oxbridge. French and German are offered to A-level; French also for the Institute of Linguists. There are regular exchanges with France and Germany. Music, drama, art and design technology (new centre open September 1990) are regarded as particularly important disciplines and activities; music is especially strong. An excellent range of sports and games in which high standards are achieved (a lot of representatives at county and national level). There is also a good variety of extra-curricular activities. Some commitment to local community services and a promising record in the Duke of Edinburgh's Award Scheme.

School profile

Pupils Total age range 8–18; 730 pupils, 640 day (419 boys, 221 girls) 90 boarding (49 boys, 41 girls). Senior department 13–18; 450 pupils (290 boys, 160 girls). Main entry ages, 13 and into the sixth. 8% are children of former pupils. Own junior school provides 65% senior intake. *Transfer from maintained schools:* 25% intakes over 11, plus 85% to sixth.

Entrance Common entrance and own tests used. All skills welcomed; Christian environment (C of E chapel services). Parents expected to buy sixth form text books. 60 assisted places. 12 scholarships (including sport), one-sixth to half fees; at 13+ 3 Foundation Scholarships (full fees) each year at 11+. Some bursaries.

Parents 15+% are doctors, lawyers etc; 15+% in industry or commerce. 60+% live within 30 miles; up to 10% live overseas.

Staff Headmaster G Garrett, in post for 18 years. 41 full time staff, 8 part time. Annual turnover 10%. Average age 40.

Academic work GCSE, AS and A-levels. 18 subjects offered (including A-level general studies). In 1990, 98 pupils in upper fifth, 71 in upper sixth. *GCSE:* in 1990, 60 upper fifth gained at least grade C in 8+ subjects; 20 in 5–7; and 18 in 1–4 subjects. *A-levels:* 23 upper sixth passed in 4+ subjects; 31 in 3; 13 in 2; and 4 in 1 subject. 20 took science A-levels; 25 arts/humanities; 26 both. *Computing facilities:* Network with 2 rooms, file server, 12 BBC Masters and 12 BBC B machines; 10 Archimedes computers networked in the Design Centre; word processors in some houses. *Special provision:* Extra help given to dyslexic pupils if needed (follow normal timetable). EFL arranged if needed.

European Community *Languages:* French offered: to age 14; GCSE; A-level; Institute of Linguists. German: GCSE; A-level. Spanish: non-examined (sometimes). 10–25% take GCSE in more than 1 EC language. *Exchanges:* Regular exchanges for pupils aged 14–16 to France and Germany. *Other:* European Studies offered to pupils aged 11–14. Some EC contacts result in boarding pupils in school for 1 term–1 year.

Senior pupils' non-academic activities *Music:* 90 learn a musical instrument, 35 to Grade 6 or above, occasional acceptance for Music School, pop group or university; 35 in school orchestra, 10 in choir, 35 in wind band; 1 in National Youth Wind Band, 12 in county bands and orchestras. *Drama and dance:* Annual play/musical, house drama festival, public-speaking competition. *Art:* 10–12 take as non-examined subject; 20 take GCSE art/ceramics; 9 take A-level. 2–3 accepted for Art School. *Design/Technology:* 30 take GCSE Design. *Sport:* Football, cross-country, hockey (girls), netball, tennis, rounders, rugby, cricket, swimming, shooting, badminton, athletics (track and field), basketball, volleyball, fencing, weight training, riding, golf (own 9-hole course) available. 280 take non-compulsory sport. 21 represent county (girls' hockey, badminton, athletics, jogging, cricket, tennis, cross-country, athletics, table tennis); 1 recent pupil represented country (table tennis). *Other:* 80 currently involved in Duke of Edinburgh's Award Scheme, 16 have bronze, 5 have silver and 1 gold. Other activities include computer club, driving lessons (in town), debating, chess.

Careers In 1990, 55% leavers went on to degree courses; 3% to art/drama/music colleges; 25% to non-degree courses (eg BTEC, pre-nursing); 10% straight into careers (eg services, banking, family business); 7% to other schools. Of those going on to degree courses, 8% went to Oxbridge, 69% to other universities; 23% to poly/colleges. 3% those going on to higher education went to courses in practical art; 3% in music; 65% in humanities/social sciences; 5% in medicine; and 24% in science/engineering.

Uniform School uniform worn throughout.

Houses/prefects Competitive houses (3 boarding, 6 day). Prefects, head boy/girl, head of house and house prefects – appointed by Head after consultation.

Religion Compulsory morning chapel service (C of E).

Social Sporting and cultural competitions with local schools. French exchange (Marseille). French visits (guardian scheme), exchange through Dragons International, German exchange (Anna-Schmidt Schule, Frankfurt), annual skiing party; trekking (Himalayas); music/dance tour to Germany. Lunch formal, others self service. School shop. No tobacco allowed; beer/cider only in licensed sixth form club.

Discipline No corporal punishment. Pupils failing to produce homework once might expect to do it for next morning, detention for repeated offence; those caught smoking cigarettes on the premises can expect parents to be contacted and possible expulsion, depending on circumstances.

Boarding *Upper sixth* have own study bedroom, 50% share with 1 other, 40% share in 3s or 4s. 3 single sex boarding houses, of approximately 30 boys, 20 girls, same as competitive houses. Qualified nurse resident when required; doctor visits 3 times/week. Central dining room. Pupils can provide and cook own food in limited facilities. 2 termly exeats, Saturday afternoon to Sunday evening. Visits to local town allowed from 13 (after lunch or before 6.15).

Alumni association run by Mr R W S Burrell, c/o the School.

Former pupils David Wilson-Johnson (baritone); Ray Whitney MP; General Sir Peter Hudson; Richard Coles (Communards pop singer).

· *Wellington (Ayr)* ·

Wellington School
Carleton Turrets
Craigweil Road
Ayr
KA7 2XH
Tel 0292 269321

- Pupils 500
- Boys None
- Girls 3–18
- (Day/Board)
- Higher year 60

- Termly fees
  £1080 (Day)
  £2150 (Board)
- GSA
  Enquiries/application to
  the Headmistress

What it's like

Founded in 1836 to educate 'young ladies of quality' in French, history, music, art and embroidery. By 1900 it had a considerable reputation and had grown. In 1923 it moved to its present site Carleton Turrets, a split site, semi-rural, with all buildings within a few minutes' walk of each other. Ayr itself is a very attractive town, with two theatres and several museums, close to the sea. The school includes a junior department and a kindergarten. Good sporting facilities on site. A well-run school, most pupils go on to higher and further education each year. Strong in music and drama. There is a vigorous sporting tradition with a large number of representatives at national and county level (especially hockey). There is also a strong careers department and a work shadowing scheme for 17 year olds. A wide range of extracurricular activities is available. An impressive record in the Duke of Edinburgh's Award Scheme (60 girls).

School profile

Pupils Total age range 3–18; 500 girls, 423 day, 77 boarding. Senior department 12–18, 325 girls. Main entry ages 3, 10, 12 and into sixth. Approx 25% are children of former pupils. Own junior school, Sleaford House, provides more than 20% of intake.

Entrance Own entrance exam. Usually oversubscribed. Ability in English, maths, music and sport looked for; no religious requirements. Parents expected to buy some text books (most covered by small hire charge). 12% of pupils on assisted places. Bursaries for senior boarders and day pupils, value variable.

Parents 15+% in armed services; 15+% are doctors, lawyers etc; 15+% in industry or commerce; 15+% are teachers. 60+% live within 30 miles; 10+% live overseas.

Staff Head Mrs D A Gardner, 2 years in post. 47 full time staff, 17 part time. Annual turnover 4–5%. Average age 35.

Academic work O-grades, S-grades, Highers, CSYS (GCSE and A-levels in special cases). Spanish, Latin, Greek, computing, Russian offered at Higher and CSYS levels. Average size of O/S-grade year, 60; Higher year, 60; CSYS year 35. *O/S-grades:* on average, 2 pupils pass 8+ subjects; 40, 5–7 subjects; 18 pass 1–4 subjects. *Highers:* on average, 10 pass in 5+ subjects; 20 in 4; 11 in 3; 7 in 2; 6 in 1 subject. *Computing facilities:* 12 stand alone systems in computer room, 7 in departments; pupils may use machines under supervision at lunchtimes. *Special provision:* can be made for dyslexia and EFL.

European Community *Languages:* French offered: to age 14; O/S-grade; Higher; CSYS. German offered: to age 14; O/S-grade; Higher; CSYS. Italian offered: as non-examined subject. Spanish offered: to age 14; O/S-grade; Higher; CSYS. 25–50% take O/S-grade in more than 1 EC language. *Exchanges:* Regular exchanges for pupils aged 14–16 to France and Germany.

Senior pupils' non-academic activities *Music:* 43 learn a musical instrument, 10 to Grade 6 or above. 40 in school orchestra, 85 in choir; string quartet; 16 in recorder and madrigal groups. 1 in National Youth Orchestra, 3 in other orchestras. *Drama and dance:* 90 in school productions. 30 take LAMDA Grade 6 or above; 50 take individual speech and drama (elocution). *Art:* clubs after school, as well as courses. *Sport:* Hockey, netball, athletics, tennis, swimming, badminton, golf, gymnastics, squash, self-defence, riding, short tennis, skating, ski-ing avail-

able. 3 pupils represent county at sport, 2 represent country (hockey). *Other:* 50 have bronze Duke of Edinburgh's Award, 6 have silver and 2 gold. Other activities include chess, Girls' Venture Corps, debating, first aid, Scripture Union.

Careers In 1990, 79% leavers went on to degree courses; 5% to art/drama/music colleges; 13% to non-degree courses (eg Orthoptics diploma, chiropody, HND computing); 1% straight into careers (eg banking); 2% other schools. Of those going on to degree courses, 2% went to Oxbridge; 68% to other universities; 30% to poly/colleges. 5% those going on to higher education went to courses in practical art; 1% in music; 67% in humanities/social sciences; 5% in medicine; and 11% in science/engineering.

Uniform School uniform worn throughout.

Houses/prefects Competitive houses. Prefects, head girl, head of house and house prefects – appointed by Head with staff advice. School Council.

Religion Daily assembly (Jews excepted); boarders attend Sunday church of their choice (most attend Church of Scotland).

Social Debates, ESU, dances, trivial pursuit challenges, sport, music and drama festivals with other schools. Bi-annual French and German school exchange, trips to Germany, Russia, skiing. Pupils allowed to bring own car/bike/motorbike to school. Meals self service. School shop. No tobacco/alcohol allowed.

Boarding Houses, of 30–50, divided by age. Central dining room. Sixth form buy and cook own food at weekends. Half term and 2 exeats each term (but houses remain open), plus 2 other weekends for sixth form. Visits to local town allowed Saturday morning; accompanied under 16, more freedom for older pupils.

Alumni association run by Mrs F Grier, c/o The School.

Former pupils Dr Elizabeth Hewat (theologian and historian); Miss Elizabeth Kyle (author); Miss Kirsty Wark (presenter, BBC TV).

· *Wellington (Somerset)* ·

Wellington School
Wellington
Somerset
TA21 8NT
Tel 0823 664511

- Pupils 810
- Boys 10–18
  (Day/Board)
- Girls 10–18
  (Day/Board)
- Upper sixth 72

- Termly fees
  £1045 (Day)
  £1945 (Board)
- BSA
  Enquiries/application to
  the Headmaster

What it's like

The school first came into existence on its present site, as a private school, in 1837 and was refounded in 1879 with yet further reorganisation in 1908. Lying on the southern side of Wellington, at the foot of the Blackdown Hills, it has pleasant well-equipped buildings in gardens with about 24 acres of playing fields. Academic standards are high and results good with many sixth form leavers going on to degree courses each year. Music and art are strong. Drama involves large numbers of pupils in a great deal of activity. A wide range of sports and games exist and high standards are achieved (a large number of representatives at county and national level). Considerable commitment to local community schemes. A flourishing CCF and much emphasis on Outward Bound activities. A good record in the Duke of Edinburgh's Award Scheme.

School profile

Pupils Total age range 10–18; 810 pupils, 589 day (315 boys, 274 girls), 221 boarding (136 boys, 85 girls). Senior department 11–18, 766 pupils (431 boys, 335 girls). Main entry ages 11+ and into sixth. Approx 20% are children of former pupils. *Transfer from maintained schools:* 70% senior intakes, plus 5% to sixth.

Entrance Common entrance and own exam used. No special skills or religious requirements. Parents not expected to buy text books; maximum extras £150. 40 assisted places (5 at sixth form). Some scholarships.

Parents 15+% come from armed services; 15+% are in industry or commerce. 30+% live within 30 miles; up to 10% live overseas.

Staff Headmaster A J Rogers, first year in post. 55 full time staff, 5 part time. Annual turnover 4–5%. Average age 40.

Academic work GCSE and A-levels. 17 subjects offered (no A-level general studies). In 1990, 116 pupils in upper fifth, 72 in upper sixth. *GCSE:* in 1990, 60% upper fifth gained at least grade C in 8+ subjects; 27% in 5–7; and 13% in 1–4

subjects. *A-levels:* 13% upper sixth passed in 4+ subjects; 67% in 3; 13% in 2; and 7% in 1 subject. 27% took science A-levels; 33% arts/humanities; 40% both. *Computing facilities:* Computer centre housing a fleet of Archimedes with open access to all pupils. Departmental computers (Archimedes) for CDT, science, art, geography and economics depts. *Special provision:* Extra English tuition is provided by qualified EFL visiting teachers for overseas students.

European Community *Languages:* French offered: to age 14; GCSE; A-level. German offered: to age 14; GCSE; A-level. 50–75% take GCSE in more than 1 EC language. French and German for Business Studies offered in lower sixth. *Exchanges:* Regular exchanges for pupils aged 11–18 to France and Germany. *Other:* French and German pupils, some for term, some for year, some for A-level course.

Senior pupils' non-academic activities *Music:* over 130 learn a musical instrument, 24 to Grade 6 or above, 2 go on to play in pop group, 2 go on to further music courses. 35 in school orchestras, 60 in choirs, 20+ in ensembles (brass, recorder, woodwind), 2 in county youth orchestra. *Drama and dance:* 40 in school productions, 250+ in house play festival. 10 take to Grade 6 ESB, 5 Poetry Society exams, 20–30 in theatre workshops. *Art:* 2 take as non-examined subject, 66 take GCSE, 17 A-level. 6 accepted for Art School, 1 for university. 12 belong to photographic and 15 to art club. *Sport:* Rugby, hockey, cricket, athletics, cross-country, netball, rounders, swimming, badminton, squash, tennis available. Most take non-compulsory sport; some take life-saving exams. 30+ represent county/country (rugby, hockey, athletics, cross-country, netball). *Other:* 40 take part in local community schemes. 25 have bronze Duke of Edinburgh's Award, 15 have silver and 1 gold. 3 work for national charities. Other activities include computer club (open during free periods), corps of drums, dynamic chess club, others for film, stage crew, building, ju-jitsu, bridge club, fun-running and young farmers; CCF, adventure training, first aid, ecological conservation, horticulture, swimming club, badminton, cookery, photography, model railway, CDT, textiles, art and inventors. Horse riding (National Schools' Hickstead runners up).

Careers In 1990, 86% leavers went on to degree courses; 6% to art/drama/music colleges; 2% to non-degree courses (eg HND child care, leisure studies); 6% straight into careers (eg catering, estate agency, RAF, nursing, farming, banking). Of those going on to degree courses, 4% went to Oxbridge; 64% to other universities; 32% to poly/colleges. 7% those going on to higher education went to courses in practical art; 1% in music;

60% in humanities/social sciences; 6% in medicine; and 26% in science/engineering.

Uniform School uniform worn throughout.

Houses/prefects Competitive houses. No prefects; school captains/vice captains appointed by Headmaster; house captains by housemasters.

Religion Daily chapel services; C of E worship encouraged; RI for all unless parents wish otherwise.

Social Public speaking competition with other schools. Exchanges with Lillebonne, France (town twinning) and Immenstadt, Bavaria. Day pupils allowed to bring own car/bike/motorbike to school; boarders, bike only. Meals self service. School tuckshop. No tobacco/alcohol allowed.

Discipline Pupils failing to produce homework once are expected to produce it within 24 hours; those caught smoking cannabis on the premises might expect immediate suspension, subsequent expulsion.

Boarding Single sex houses, of approx 50, same as competitive houses. Resident qualified nurse, doctor on call. Central dining room. Pupils can provide and cook own food. Exeats of 24 hours at discretion of house staff. Visits to local town allowed after school.

Former pupils David Suchet (actor); Jeffrey Archer (author); Keith Floyd (gourmet/broadcaster); Brigadier Shelford Bidwell (military historian); Michael Green (ITN correspondent); Prof Ellis Baker (pharmacologist); Judges John Baker and David Williams; Kenneth Steele (former Chief Constable, Avon & Somerset); Frank Gillard (veteran broadcaster/war correspondent).

· *Wellington (Wirral)* ·

Wellington School
Wellington Road
Bebington
Wirral
L63 7NG
Tel 051 645 2332

- Pupils 270
- Boys 11–19 (Day)
- Girls 11–19 (Day)
- Upper sixth 25

- Termly fees £835 (Day)
- ISAI

Enquiries to the Headmaster

Application to the Secretary

What it's like

Founded in 1953 by its former headmaster, it has an urban site in the Wirral. Pleasant buildings and about 4 acres of grounds and 15 acres of playing fields. It aims to provide a liberal education in the arts and sciences for boys and girls of average or above average ability, and to educate them in a Christian environment. There is a staff:pupil ratio of 1:12. Results are creditable and a number of pupils go on to degree courses each year. Music and art strong. An adequate range of sports and games. No community services.

School profile

Pupils Total age range 11–19; 270 day pupils (203 boys, 67 girls). Main entry ages 11, 13 and into sixth. Approx 10% are children of former pupils.

Entrance Common entrance and own entrance exam used. Not oversubscribed. No special skills or religious requirements. Parents expected to buy text books; maximum extras £75. 5 scholarships/bursaries, £635 to ⅓ fees.

Parents 15+% are doctors, lawyers etc; 15+% in industry or commerce; 15+% are lecturers and accountants.

Staff Head T Capper, in post for 1 year. 15 full time staff, 6 part time. Annual turnover 10%. Average age 37.

Academic work GCSE and A-levels. Average size of fifth 42; upper sixth 14, now increased to 25. *GCSE:* on average, 3 pupils in fifth pass 8+ subjects; 38, 5–7 subjects; 4 pass 1–4 subjects. *A-levels:* (while upper sixth 14) on average, 2 pupils in the upper sixth pass 4 subjects; 8, 3 subjects; 3, 2 subjects and 1 passes 1 subject. On average, 7 take science/engineering A-levels; 4 take arts and humanities; 3 a mixture. Computer department.

European Community *Languages:* French offered: to age 14; GCSE; A-level. Spanish offered: as a non-examined subject. Under 10% take GCSE in more than 1 EC language. *Exchanges:* Regular exchanges for pupils aged 11–18 to France.

Senior pupils' non-academic activities *Art:* 30 take GCSE; 3 A-level. 2 accepted for Art School. *Sport:* Rugby, soccer, netball, basketball, cricket, swimming, athletics (track and field), squash, golf, table tennis available. *Other:* Duke of Edinburgh's Awards. Other activities include rifle, chess, film, drama, needlework clubs, debating and railway societies.

Careers In 1990, 38% leavers went on to degree courses (84% sixth form leavers); 4% to art/drama/music colleges; 4% to non-degree courses (eg agriculture); 28% straight into careers (eg industry, the City, civil service). Of those going on to degree courses, 3% went to Oxbridge; 47% to other universities; 50% to poly/colleges. 6% those going on to higher education went to courses in practical art; 38% in humanities/social sciences; 6% in medicine; and 50% in science/engineering.

Uniform School uniform worn except in the sixth.

Houses/prefects Competitive houses.

853

Prefects, head boy/girl – appointed by Head.

Religion Worship encouraged.

Social Inter-school debates. Some organised trips abroad. Pupils allowed to bring own car/bike/motorbike to school. Meals self service. School shop. No tobacco/alcohol allowed.

Discipline Corporal punishment not allowed. Caution system operates for eg pupils failing to produce homework. Pupils may be suspended for up to 1 week for serious misconduct/work; expelled for very serious offences.

Alumni association run by Mr Jeremy Stephens, 75 Church Road, Bebington, Wirral.

· *Wellington College* ·

Wellington College	• Pupils 832	• Termly fees
Crowthorne	• Boys 13–18	£2275 (Day)
Berkshire	(Day/Board)	£3125 (Board)
RG11 7PU	• Girls 16–18	• HMC
Tel 0344 772261	(Day/Board)	Enquiries/application to
	• Upper sixth 173	the Registrar

What it's like

Founded in 1853, by public subscription in memory of the Duke, granted a royal charter in that year. The Monarch is the Visitor and appointments of governors and changes in statutes are approved by Buckingham Palace. By 1872 it had become a major public school. Its original grand and imposing buildings were designed by Shaw who, with remarkable foresight, provided each pupil with a bed-sitting room. Its chapel was designed by Gilbert Scott. Many additional buildings now provide excellent accommodation and facilities. The college lies in an estate of over 400 acres and has fine gardens and superb playing fields. The prep school (Eagle House) has its own grounds nearby. The spiritual and religious life of the college is of considerable importance and pupils are encouraged to commit themselves fully as Christians. High standards of teaching prevail and academic results are first rate. Many leavers go on to degree courses each year, including many to Oxbridge. French, German and Spanish are offered to A-level and there are regular exchange arrangements (France and Germany) which are being extended. The music department is immensely strong (there are orchestras, choirs, bands, and over 350 pupils learn an instrument) and the college is very strong, too, in drama and art. Wellington has a high reputation in games and sports of which a wide variety is provided. There are many clubs, societies and extra-curricular activities. The CCF has a large contingent and the college maintains its traditional links with the army (many Wellingtonians have been distinguished soldiers). There is a commitment to local community schemes, involving some 150–200 pupils, a higher proportion than many schools.

School profile

Pupils Age range 13–18; 832 pupils, 130 day (122 boys, 8 girls), 702 boarding (660 boys, 42 girls). Main entry ages 13+ (boys) and into sixth (boys and girls). Approx 30% are children of former pupils. Eagle House Prep School provides significant proportion of intake. *Transfer from maintained schools:* Very few at 13, slightly more to sixth.

Entrance Common entrance and own scholarship exam used; competitive exam and interview for sixth form girls. Oversubscribed. No special skills or religious requirements. Parents expected to buy text books; extras charged vary. 34 assisted places. 14+ scholarships, up to half fees; bursaries also available.

Parents 10+% in the armed services; 40+% in industry or commerce. 50+% live within 30 miles; up to 15% live overseas.

Staff Head C J Driver, in post 1 year. 86 full time staff, 4 part time. Annual turnover 4%. Average age 41.

Academic work GCSE, AS and A-levels. 21 GCSE subjects offered; 25 at A-level (including Arabic; A-level general studies – if there is demand). In 1990, 153 pupils in upper fifth, 181 in upper sixth. *GCSE:* in 1990, 135 upper fifth gained at least grade C in 8+ subjects; 18 in 5–7 subjects. *A-levels:* 46 upper sixth passed in 4+ subjects; 106 in 3; 16 in 2; and 11 in 1 subject. 45 took science A-levels; 80 arts/humanities; 36 both. *Computing facilities:* Excellent. New block with Nimbus. *Special provision:* Some arrangements for badly dyslexic.

European Community *Languages:* French offered: to age 14; GCSE; AS-level; A-level. German offered: to age 14; GCSE; A-level. Spanish offered: to age 14; GCSE; A-level. Over 75% take GCSE in more than 1 EC language. *Exchanges:* Regular exchanges for pupils aged 14–18 to France and Germany.

Senior pupils' non-academic activities *Music:* 376 learn musical instruments, 50 to Grade 6 or above, small number accepted for Music Scholarships; 50 in school orchestra, 65 in choir, 100 in bands. *Drama and dance:* 30+ in school productions. 6 take AEB A-level/GCSE. 2–4 accepted for Drama/Dance schools, 2–4 go on to work in theatre. 12 take lighting course; 12, sound course; 18, general studies; 26 in theatre club. *Art:* 44 take as non-examined subject; 45 take GCSE; 25 A-level art; 12, history of art. 3 accepted for Art School, 4 for architec-

tural courses. 15 belong to photographic club. *Sport:* Rugby, cricket, hockey, athletics, archery, basketball, fencing, cross-country running, fives, golf, karate, rackets, sailing, shooting, ski-ing, soccer, squash, sub-aqua, swimming, tennis available. Vast majority of pupils take non-compulsory sport. 3 represent county/country in hockey and honours in cricket and rugby. *Other:* 150–200 take part in local community schemes. Other activities include a computer club, driving lessons, astronomy, bridge, chess, debating, natural history, opera, pottery, printing, Christian Forum, travel/expeditions.

Careers In 1989, 85% leavers went on to degree courses; $1^1/_2$% to art/drama/music colleges; 3% to non-degree courses (eg agriculture, pilot training, hotel management HND); $7^1/_2$% straight into careers (eg army, Lloyds, family business); 3% other. Of those going on to degree courses, 10% went to Oxbridge; 71% to other universities; 19% to poly/colleges. Under 2% those going on to higher education went to courses in practical art; under 1% in drama/acting; under 1% in music; 65% in humanities/social sciences; 4% in medicine; and 28% in science/engineering. (70% leavers take Gap year.)

Uniform Dress regulations modified in sixth.

Houses/prefects The pastoral organisation is based in houses. Prefects, head boy and girl, head of house and house prefects – appointed by Headmaster and housemasters.

Religion Some compulsory services and some voluntary.

Social Local events include choral/orchestral events, debates and occasional dances. French and German exchanges, chamber choir to France/Germany, modern languages department to eg Bordeaux, Paris. Pupils allowed to bring own bike to school. Meals self service. School shop. No tobacco allowed but a junior common room for the sixth form.

Discipline No corporal punishment. Pupils failing to produce homework might expect extra school; detentions used for serious disciplinary offences.

Boarding Most have own study bedroom after 1st year. Houses, of approximately 55 for boys, 1 for the 50 girls. Resident Sister; school doctor visits daily. Central dining room. Half term plus 2 weekend exeats in the long terms, 1 in the Lent term. Visits to local town allowed with housemaster's permission.

Former pupils Too numerous to mention.

· *Wells Cathedral* ·

Wells Cathedral School
Wells
Somerset
BA5 2ST
Tel 0749 72117

- Pupils 585
- Boys 11–18
  (Day/Board)
- Girls 11–18
  (Day/Board)
- Upper sixth 66

- Termly fees
  £1235 (Day)
  £2184 (Board)
- HMC, SHMIS
  Enquiries/application to
  the Head Master

What it's like

Founded in the 12th century, the school has one of the finest sites in Europe, on the edge of Wells and a little to the north of the cathedral. It occupies all but one of the medieval and 18th-century buildings of 'the Liberty'. By virtue of its outstanding historical and architectural interest the cathedral, the bishop's palace, the Vicar's Close and 'the Liberty' are an important conservation area. The site includes a number of lovely walled gardens and an area of parkland used for playing fields. The school is well equipped with modern facilities and accommodation, including well-equipped laboratories, libraries and a big music school. A large staff permits a staff:pupil ratio of about 1:11, plus over 40 part-timers most of whom are peripatetic music teachers. Academic standards are high and results good. Many sixth form leavers go on to degree courses each year, including to Oxbridge. One of the school's great strengths is music; it is one of the five music schools attracting government finance for some of its pupils. Many pupils are involved in choirs, orchestras and bands. A large number learn an instrument. As it is an ancient church school there are close links with the cathedral. Worship in the Anglican tradition is both compulsory and encouraged. The drama department is also strong. There is a broad range of games and sports available and a large and varied number of extra-curricular activities. The CCF has an active contingent and there is a sizeable community service group. A promising record in the Duke of Edinburgh's Award Scheme. Outdoor pursuits form an integral part of the school curriculum.

School profile

Pupils Age range 11–18; 585 pupils, 290 day (145 boys, 145 girls), 295 boarders (148 boys, 147 girls). Main entry ages 11 and into sixth. Less than 1% are children of former pupils. Own junior school provides 80% intake at age 11. *Transfer from maintained schools:* 20% main intake, plus 10% to sixth.

Entrance Common entrance and own exam used. Oversubscribed. No special skills or religious requirements. Maximum extras £70 plus lunch for day pupils. Aided pupils (for music specialist). 75 assisted places. A number of scholarships/bursaries per year £700–£100.

Parents 21% in the armed services. 50+% live within 30 miles; 11+% live overseas.

Staff Head Master J S Baxter, in post for 5 years. 57 full time staff, 5 part time. Annual turnover 7%. Average age 38.

Academic work GCSE and A-levels.

21 GCSE and A-level subjects offered (no A-level general studies). In 1990, 99 pupils in upper fifth, 66 in upper sixth. *GCSE:* in 1990, 45 upper fifth gained at least grade C in 8+ subjects; 40 in 5–7; and 14 in 1–4 subjects. *A-levels:* 9 upper sixth passed in 4+ subjects; 37 in 3; 12 in 2; and 6 in 1 subject. 17 took science A-levels; 25 arts/humanities; 24 both. *Computing facilities:* Dual role computer centre for teaching and access by pupils. *Special provision:* EFL and pupils who are dyslexic or mildly visually handicapped.

European Community *Languages:* French offered: to age 14; GCSE; A-level. German offered: to GCSE; AS-level; A-level. Spanish offered: to GCSE; A-level. 25–50% take GCSE in more than 1 EC language. French Language at Work course in lower sixth. *Exchanges:* Regular exchanges for pupils aged 14–18 to France and Germany. *Other:* Some EC pupils in sixth form; use of satellite dish.

Senior pupils' non-academic activities *Music:* Approximately half the school learn a musical instrument, over 100 to Grade 6 or above; some accepted for Music Colleges, others to university music courses; most pupils of Grade 6+ play in a school orchestras, many in 3 choirs, 45 in concert band, 35 in symphony band, 18 in big band, 10 brass ensembles involving 54 pupils; there are 27 string chamber and ensembles, 50 in woodwind chamber groups, 8 in National Children's Orchestra. *Drama and dance:* 5 major productions annually; senior and middle school productions involve 150 pupils; sixth form production directed by students; 2 house drama competitions annually involving 200 pupils. 13 take GCSE drama and theatre arts; A-level theatre studies starting. *Art:* 31 take GCSE; 12, A-level. *Sport:* Athletics, badminton, basketball, canoeing, caving, cricket, cross-country, gymnastics, golf, hockey, horse riding, netball, rounders, rugby, sailing, soccer, squash, swimming, table tennis, tennis, volleyball available. 12 pupils represent county (hockey, cricket, rugby, netball, basketball). *Other:* 15 do bronze Duke of Edinburgh's Award. 35 in community service group. Currently 32 activities available 1 afternoon a week; wide range of subjects from chess to car maintenance and pupils choose and can interchange, mostly on a termly basis.

Careers In 1990, 70% leavers went on to degree courses; 8% to art/drama/ music colleges; 10% straight into careers (eg banking, retail management); 12% other. Of those going on to degree courses, 18% went to Oxbridge; 69% to other universities; 14% to poly/colleges. 1% those going on to higher education went to courses in practical art; 16% in music; 55% in humanities/social sciences; 3% in medicine; and 25% in science/engineering.

Uniform School uniform worn throughout.

Houses/prefects Competitive houses. Prefects, head boy/girl, head of house and house prefects – appointed and elected by staff and school.

Religion Compulsory worship.

Social Debates, prefects' conferences, sport, sixth form society. Organised trips abroad and exchange systems. Day pupils allowed to bring own car/bike to school. Meals self service. School shop. No tobacco/alcohol allowed.

Discipline No corporal punishment. Pupils failing to produce homework once might expect to do it again; those caught smoking cannabis on the premises could expect expulsion.

Boarding 1% have own study bedroom, 70% share (with 1 or 2); 5% are in dormitories of 6+. Single sex houses, of 27–54, divided by age group (middle and senior). Resident qualified nurse. Central dining room. Pupils can provide and cook snacks. 2 exeats each term of $1\frac{1}{2}$ days. Visits to local town allowed with permission at 16+.

Alumni association is run by E Dennison, Chairman – Old Wellensians, 13 Bowfell Close, Taunton, Somerset TA1 4JP.

Former pupils Brian Beazer; Malcolm Nash; Danny Nightingale.

· *Wentworth Milton Mount* ·

Wentworth Milton
Mount
College Road
Boscombe
Bournemouth
Dorset BH5 2DY
Tel 0202 423266

- Pupils 320
- Boys None
- Girls 11–18 (Day/
  Board/Weekly)
- Upper sixth 25

- Termly fees
  £1340 (Day)
  £2155 (Board/
  Weekly)
- GSA
  Enquiries/application to
  the Headmistress

What it's like

The school is the joint foundation of Wentworth School, Bournemouth, and Milton Mount College, Crawley. The former was established in 1889 as a Christian, inter-denominational school, and the latter in 1871 for the education of the daughters of Congregational ministers. In 1962 the schools amalgamated. The traditional connection with Milton Mount College is kept up through bursaries to daughters of members of the United Reformed Church (Congregational/Presbyterian). The school has handsome buildings on the top of Southborne Cliffs on the shores of Bournemouth Bay. The main and central buildings were formerly one of Lord Portman's mansions. Since 1970 there have been several impressive additions, including a sixth-form complex, study bedrooms, a music school, an art school and a huge sports hall. Facilities are of a high standard. The education includes training based on the Christian faith; all girls attend prayers on weekdays and church services on Sunday. Academic standards are good. Ample playing fields in the adjacent grounds allow a full range of sports and games. Clubs and societies cater for many extra-curricular activities.

School profile

Pupils Age range 11–18, 320 girls (day and boarding). Main entry age 11. *Transfer from maintained schools:* 15% main intake.
Entrance Common entrance and own exam used. Scholarships and bursaries available (including for daughters of ministers and lay members of URC).
Staff Headmistress Miss Sandra Coe, 1 year in post.
Academic work GCSE and A-levels. 22 subjects offered (no A-level general studies). In 1990, 66 pupils in upper fifth, 25 in upper sixth. *GCSE:* in 1990, 31 upper fifth gained at least grade C in 8+ subjects; 22 in 5–7; and 13 in 1–4 subjects. *A-levels:* 14 upper sixth passed in 3+ subjects; 4 in 2; and 6 in 1 subject. 5 took science A-levels; 14 arts/humanities; 5 both. *Computing facilities:* Technology suite with network of IBM compatibles plus BBC B's for class use. *Special provision:* Individual tuition may be provided for dyslexics and those for whom English is not native tongue.
European Community *Languages:* French offered: to age 14; GCSE; A-level. German offered: to age 14; GCSE; A-level. Spanish offered: to GCSE. 25–50% take GCSE in more than 1 EC language. *Exchanges:* Regular exchanges for pupils aged 11–16 to France and Germany. *Other:* Talks from MEPs; attendance at lectures on European unity.
Careers In 1990, 50% leavers went on to degree courses; 8% to art/drama/music colleges; 19% to non-degree courses; 4% other. Of those going on to degree courses, 31% went to universities; 80% to poly/colleges. 8% those going on to higher education went to courses in practical art; 19% in humanities/social sciences; $11\frac{1}{2}$% in medicine; and 15% in science/engineering.

· *West Buckland* ·

West Buckland School
Barnstaple
Devon
EX32 0SX
Tel 05986 281

- Pupils 570
- Boys 7–18 (Day/ Board/Weekly)
- Girls 7–18 (Day/ Board/Weekly)
- Upper sixth 40

- Termly fees £1179 (Day) £2171 (Board/ Weekly)
- HMC

Enquiries/application to the Head Master's Secretary

What it's like

Founded in 1858, it lies on the south-west edge of Exmoor, 10 miles from Barnstaple, on a 90-acre site. The school is contained in handsome 19th-century buildings with many modern additions, the most recent being the girls' junior house. It is an Anglican foundation and Christian teaching and principles underlie much of its life. It has developed a strong sense of community and there is much emphasis on everyone participating in the life of the school. The need for success is also emphasised. A sound general education is provided and results are good. A number of sixth form leavers go on to higher education each year. There are very active music, drama and art departments. A lot of emphasis on sports and games (standards are high; numerous county and some international representatives). The CCF contingent is flourishing and outdoor pursuits are popular. A most impressive record in the Duke of Edinburgh's Award Scheme.

School profile

Pupils Total age range 7–18; 570 pupils, 392 day (220 boys, 172 girls), 178 boarding (123 boys, 55 girls). Senior department 11–18, 479 pupils (292 boys, 187 girls). Main entry ages 7, 11, 13 and into sixth. Approx 10% are children of former pupils. *Transfer from maintained schools:* 50% senior intakes, plus 75% to sixth.

Entrance Common entrance and own exam used. Oversubscribed. No special skills or religious requirements. Parents not expected to buy text books; lunches extra (£60 per term). 14 assisted places pa. 6 scholarships/bursaries pa, £1050–£220 per term.

Parents Parents come from a broad mix of occupations. 70+% live within 30 miles; up to 10% live overseas.

Staff Head Michael Downward, in post for 12 years. 47 full time staff, 10 part time. Annual turnover 5%. Average age 39.

Academic work GCSE and A-levels. Approximately 16 subjects offered (including A-level general studies). On average, 75 pupils in upper fifth, 38 in upper sixth. *GCSE:* on average, 29 upper fifth gained at least grade C in 8+ subjects; 25 in 5–7; and 19 in 1–4 subjects. *A-levels:* on average, 18 upper sixth passed in 4+ subjects; 8 in 3; 8 in 2; and 3 in 1 subject. On average, 37% take science A-levels; 40% arts/humanities; 23% both. *Computing facilities:* BBC Econet. 12 in central lab; 11 elsewhere; all major departments connected, plus Apple Macintosh. *Special provision:* 2 specialist EFL staff.

European Community *Languages:* French offered: to age 14; GCSE; A-level; and as non-examined subject. German offered: to age 14; GCSE; A-level; and as non-examined subject. Spanish offered: to age 14; GCSE; Institute of Linguists; and as non-examined subject. 10–25% take GCSE in more than 1 EC language. *Exchanges:* Regular exchanges for pupils aged 11–16 to France and Germany. *Other:* EC pupils attend for periods ranging from 3 weeks to 1 year.

Senior pupils' non-academic activities *Music:* 87 learn a musical instrument, 19 to Grade 6 or above. 31 in school orchestra, 45 in choir, 13 in madrigal group. *Drama and dance:* 25 in school productions; 1 accepted for Drama/Dance School. *Art:* 14 take as non-examined subject; 22 take GCSE; 5, A-level. 1 accepted for Art School. 8 belong to photographic club; 4 to others. *Sport:* Rugby, netball, cross-country, hockey, basketball, fencing, squash, cricket, tennis, athletics, rounders, swimming and others available. 130 take non-compulsory sport. 18 take exams. 16 represent county/country (rugby, cricket, athletics). *Other:* 39 have bronze Duke of Edinburgh's Award, 21 have silver and 5 gold. 2 enter voluntary schemes after leaving school; 1 works for national charities. Other activities include a computer club, archery, bell ringing, chess, Christian Union, debating, shooting and others.

Careers On average, 55% leavers went on to degree courses; 15% to art/drama/music colleges; 15% to non-degree courses; 15% straight into careers. Of those going on to degree courses, 13% went to Oxbridge; 67% to other universities; 20% to poly/colleges, $7^1/_2$% those going on to higher education went to courses in practical art; 5% in music; 35% in humanities/social sciences; $7^1/_2$% in medicine; and 45% in science/engineering.

Uniform School uniform worn, alternative suit for sixth form.

Houses/prefects Competitive houses. Prefects, head boy and girl, head of house and house prefects – appointed.

Religion Morning assembly and Sunday service compulsory; lively voluntary Christian Union in lunch hour.

Social No regular events organised with local schools. Annual ski training and mountain expeditions. Annual exchanges with schools in France/Germany. Upper sixth allowed to bring own car/bike/motorbike to school. Meals self-service. School shops selling tuck, basic equipment and second-hand. Sixth form pupils allowed tobacco/alcohol in restricted location.

Discipline No corporal punishment. Pupils failing to produce homework once might expect to have to complete it; those caught smoking cannabis on the premises could expect to be withdrawn.

Boarding Upper sixth have own study bedroom; 15% share (3 to a room); 75% in dormitories of 6+. Single sex houses, of 90+ (including day pupils), same as competitive houses. Resident qualified nurse. Central dining room. Exeats to suit individual needs. Visits to local town (10 miles away) allowed weekly at 13+; special bus runs on Saturdays.

Former pupils R F Delderfield (playwright and novelist); Brian Aldiss (science fiction writer); John Ashworth (Director LSE).

· *West Heath* ·

West Heath School
Ashgrove Road
Sevenoaks
Kent
TN13 1SR
Tel 0732 452541

- Pupils 170
- Boys None
- Girls 11–18
- (Day/Board)
- Upper sixth 25

- Termly fees
  £1930 (Day)
  £2750 (Board)
- GSA, SHA, ISA,
  BSA
Enquiries/application to
the School Secretary

What it's like

Founded in 1865, it has pleasant, well-designed buildings and excellent facilities and accommodation (there is an indoor sports hall, indoor swimming pool and dance studios). It is situated in a rural site of 32 acres of woodland and grassland on the edge of town. A sound general education is provided. French and German are offered to A-level; German, Italian and Spanish to GCSE. A number of sixth formers go on to degree courses each year. Very strong indeed in music (virtually everyone is involved) and good in art. Adequate sport, games and activities. A promising record in the Duke of Edinburgh's Award Scheme.

School profile

Pupils Age range 11–18; 170 girls, 20 day, 150 boarding. Main entry ages 11, 12, 13 and occasionally into sixth. Approx 40% are children of former pupils. *Transfer from maintained schools:* 1% main intake.

Entrance Common entrance exam used. No special skills or religious requirements but school is wholly Christian. Parents expected to buy text books; extras variable.

Parents 10+% live within 30 miles.

Staff Principal Mrs D Cohn-Sherbok, 3 years in post. 17 full time staff, 28 part time. Annual turnover 5%. Average age 40.

Academic work GCSE and A-levels. 16 subjects offered (no A-level general studies). In 1990, 35 pupils in upper fifth, 25 in upper sixth. *Computing facilities:* Computer room equipped with BBC, Master 128 and Archimedes.

European Community *Languages:* Dutch offered: to age 14; GCSE. French offered: to age 14; GCSE; A-level. German offered: to age 14; GCSE; A-level. Italian offered: to GCSE. Spanish offered: to GCSE. 10–25% take GCSE in more than 1 EC language.

Senior pupils' non-academic activi- ties *Music:* 70 learn a musical instrument, 20 to Grade 6 or above. 20 in string orchestra, 20 in wind band, 60 in 2 choirs. *Drama and dance:* Everyone participates in school productions (4 annually). *Art:* 20 take GCSE; 5, A-level including textiles and ceramics. *Sport:* Lacrosse, tennis, badminton, squash, sailing, gymnastics, trampolining, self-defence, netball, swimming available. 5 represent county at various sports. *Other:* 20 have bronze or silver Duke of Edinburgh's Award. Other activities include debating, photography, computing, public speaking, speech and drama, Young Enterprise.

Careers In 1990, 70% leavers went on to degree courses; 30% to non-degree courses (eg nursing, secretarial). Of those going on to degree courses, 70% went to universities; 30% to poly/colleges. 10% those going on to higher education went to courses in practical art; 80% in humanities/social sciences; and 10% in science/engineering.

Uniform School uniform worn for morning classes and games, except in the sixth.

Houses/prefects No competitive houses. Prefects, head girl and house prefects – elected by the school.

Religion Compulsory attendance at services.

Social Debates and conferences with local schools. Organised ski and cultural trips abroad. Senior pupils allowed to bring own bike to school. Meals formal. School shop. No tobacco/alcohol allowed.

Discipline No corporal punishment. Those caught smoking or drinking alcohol on the premises could expect expulsion after a warning and a fine.

Boarding Fifth and lower sixth have own study bedroom, upper sixth are in bungalows in the grounds; others in dormitories of 6+. Central dining rooms. Sixth form can provide and cook own suppers. Half term and 2 weekend exeats each term. Visits to the local town allowed for seniors.

· *Westbourne* ·

The Westbourne School for Girls Ltd 1 Winton Drive Glasgow G12 0PY Tel 041 339 6006/9107	• Pupils 280 • Boys None • Girls 2½–18 (Day) • Higher year 35	• Termly fees £1062 (Day) • HAS, SCIS Enquiries/application to the Headmaster

What it's like

Founded in 1877, it has a pleasant site in the west end of the city and 3 miles from its centre. It comprises two main buildings and combines junior and senior schools. A full range of up-to-date facilities is available. A well-run, purposeful school with a large staff enabling a staff:pupil ratio of about 1:10. Academic standards are high and results good. Very many of the girls go on to degree courses each year. There is considerable strength in music, art and drama. A fine range of games and sports is provided and good standards are attained (not a few county representatives). Also a good variety of extra-curricular activities. The school's record in the Duke of Edinburgh's Award Scheme is impressive.

School profile

Pupils Total age range 2½–18; 280 day girls. Senior department 11–18, 180 girls. Main entry ages 2½, 5, 12, 13 and into sixth. Approx. 20% are children of former pupils. *Transfer from maintained schools:* 80% senior intakes, none to sixth.

Entrance Own entrance exam used. No special skills or religious requirements. Parents expected to buy text books. 60 assisted places. 6 scholarships/bursaries available, £450–£300.

Parents 15+% in industry or commerce; 15+% are doctors, lawyers, etc.

Staff Headmaster Mr J N Cross, in post 3 years. 26 full time staff, 5 part time. Annual turnover 2%. Average age 40.

Academic work O-grades, S-grades, Highers, CSYS and A-levels. 17 subjects offered. In 1990 size of O/S-grade year, 31; Higher year, 35; CSYS year, 31. *O/S-grades:* in 1990, 8 pupils passed in 8+ subjects; 10 in 5–7 subjects; 16 in 1–4 subjects. *Highers:* In 1989, 8 passed in 5+ subjects; 12 in 4; 10 in 3; 16 in 2; 9 in 1 subject. *Computing facilities:* Fully equipped computing centre and computers in many subject rooms.

European Community *Languages:* French offered: to age 14; S-grade; Higher; CSYS. German offered: to age 14; S-grade; Higher; CSYS. 25–50% take GCSE in more than 1 EC language.

Senior pupils' non-academic activities *Music:* 50 learn a musical instrument, 10 to Grade 6 or above. 3 accepted for Music School. 6 in guitar group and 15 in ensembles after leaving school; 28 in school orchestra, 25 in choir, 6 in Glasgow Youth Choir, 6 in Scottish National Orchestra Junior Chorus, 3 in Scottish Opera, 1 runner-up in choir girl of the year 1987. *Drama and dance:* 60 in school productions; 35 in opera; 12 stage and dance movement; 2 accepted for Drama/Dance Schools; 1 goes on to work in theatre. *Art:* 6 take as non-examined subject; 18, O-grade; 12, Higher. 4 accepted for Art School; 6 for architecture. 10 belong to photographic club. *Sport:* Hockey, tennis, athletics, swimming, squash, badminton, volleyball, netball, basketball, gymnastics, Scottish country dancing, ethnic dancing, ski-ing, skating available. 75 take non-compulsory sport; 50 take exams eg gymnastics, swimming. 8 represent county/country (athletics, hockey, tennis, golf, squash, swimming). *Other:* 41 take part in local community schemes. 18 have bronze Duke of Edinburgh's Award and 18 gold; 8 enter voluntary schemes after leaving school; 15 work for national charities. Other activities include a computer club, chess club, literary and debating society, public speaking, Scripture Union.

Careers In 1990, 60% leavers went on to degree courses; 5% to art/drama/music colleges; 5% to non-degree courses; 10% straight into careers; 20% other. Of those going on to degree courses, 45% went to universities; 45% to poly/colleges. 75% those going on to higher education went to courses in humanities/social sciences; 5% in medicine; and 10% in science/engineering.

Uniform School uniform worn throughout.

Houses/prefects Competitive houses. Prefects, head girl, head of house and house prefects – voted by the Head, staff and school. School Council.

Religion Attendance at religious worship compulsory.

Social Inter-school debates, quiz competitions, drama and musical productions and dances. Organised annual ski trips; trips to France, Germany and Soviet Union. Pupils allowed to bring own car/bike to school. Meals self service. School shop. No tobacco/alcohol allowed.

Discipline No corporal punishment. Pupils failing to produce homework once might expect to have to produce the work the following day; those caught smoking cannabis on the premises could expect parents to be sent for and Chairman of Board of Governors consulted.

Alumni association run by The Secretary, Old Girls' Club, c/o the School.

Former pupils Vivien Heilbron, Lorna Heilbron, Joyce Deans (drama and TV); Fiona Kennedy (TV singer); Dr Ruth Jarrett (Aids Researcher, Glasgow University); Dr Myra Nimmo (Commonwealth athlete); Kirsten Borland (town planner).

· *Westfield* ·

Westfield School	● Pupils 360	● Termly fees
Oakfield House	● Boys None	£986 (Day)
Oakfield Road	● Girls 3–18	● GSA
Gosforth	(Day)	Enquiries/application to
Newcastle upon Tyne	● Upper sixth 17	the Headmistress's
NE3 4HS		Secretary
Tel 091 285 1948		

What it's like

Founded in 1959, it is suburban with the senior school on a 5-acre site and the junior on a separate one, one-quarter of a mile away. It is owned by the Northbrian

Educational Trust. Agreeable buildings and good modern facilities. A sound basic education is given and results are creditable. Each year about half the pupils from U6 go on to degree courses. French and German are offered to A-level and also for FLAW; Spanish also for GCSE. There are regular exchanges with France and Germany. Flourishing music, art and drama departments. A good standard in sports and games (quite a lot of county representatives) and an impressive range of activities. A very promising record in the Duke of Edinburgh's Award Scheme.

School profile

Pupils Total age range 3–18; 360 day girls. Senior department 11–18, 210 girls. Entry at any age from 3–14 and into sixth. Approx 10% are children of former pupils. *Transfer from maintained schools:* 30+% senior intake.

Entrance Own entrance exam used. Some years oversubscribed. No special skills or religious requirements. Parents not expected to buy text books. Up to 10 scholarships/bursaries pa, 90–25% of fees.

Parents 15+% in industry or commerce; 15+% are doctors, lawyers, etc.

Staff Headmistress Mrs Marion Farndale, 1 year in post. 32 full time staff, 5 part time. Annual turnover 8%. Average age 38.

Academic work GCSE and A-levels, RSA. 20 subjects offered (including GCSE general studies, not A-level; business studies course in sixth form). On average, 36 pupils in upper fifth, 17 in upper sixth. *GCSE:* on average, 16 upper fifth gain at least grade C in 8+ subjects; 13 in 5–7; and 4 in 1–4 subjects. *A-levels:* on average, 10 upper sixth pass in 3 subjects; 3 in 2; and 4 in 1 subject. On average, 7 take science A-levels; 10 arts/ humanities. *Computing facilities:* BBC/ Commodore; computer lab plus machines in some classrooms. *Special provision:* 'Withdrawal' English specialist; visiting teacher from Dyslexia Unit (charged extra).

European Community *Languages:* French offered: to age 14; GCSE; AS-level; A-level; Flaw (Foreign Languages at Work). German offered: to age 14; GCSE; AS-level; A-level; Flaw. Spanish: GCSE. Under 10% take GCSE in more than 1 EC language. *Exchanges:* Regular exchanges for pupils aged 14–16 to France and Germany.

Senior pupils' non-academic activities *Music:* 52 learn a musical instrument; 20 in school orchestra, 40 in choir. *Drama and dance:* up to 80 in school productions, 100 in workshops etc. 8 take Guildhall Grade 7, 6 Grade 5; others participate in local amateur/operatic societies. *Sport:* Netball, hockey, swimming, tennis, trampolining, gymnastics, athletics, volleyball, rounders available. 40 take non-compulsory sport. 15 represent county/country at various sports. *Other:* 20 have bronze Duke of Edinburgh's Award, 5 have silver and 2 gold. Other activities include a computer club, tapestry, art, gardening, Bridge, fencing, life drawing, debating.

Careers In 1990, 55% leavers went on to degree courses; 10% to art/drama/ music colleges; 15% to non-degree courses (eg catering); 10% straight into careers (eg banking); 10% other. Of those going on to degree courses, 50% went to universities; 50% to poly/colleges. 5% those going on to higher education went to courses in practical art; 5% in drama/ acting; 80% in humanities/social sciences; and 10% in science/engineering.

Uniform School uniform worn except in the sixth.

Houses/prefects Competitive houses. Prefects, head girl, head of house – appointed jointly by the Head and school. School Council.

Religion Attendance at morning assembly compulsory, usually involves Christian worship.

Social Occasional social activities with various boys' schools. Organised trips to France, Germany, Russia from time to time. Regular and well attended ski-ing trips and tennis coaching holidays. Pupils allowed to bring own car/bike/motorbike to school. Meals self service. School shop.

No tobacco/alcohol allowed.
Discipline No corporal punishment. Detentions given for failure to do homework. Great emphasis is placed on a high standard of behaviour and a respect for others.
Alumni association run by Mrs Ann Robinson, c/o the School.

· *Westholme* ·

Westholme School
Meins Road
Blackburn
Lancashire BB2 6QU
Tel 0254 53447

- Pupils 1000
- Boys 4–8 only (Day)
- Girls 4–18 (Day)
- Upper sixth 60

- Termly fees £890 (Day)
- GSA

Enquiries/application to the Registrar

What it's like

Founded in 1923, the upper school is semi-rural and single-site. Its two prep departments are on two other sites. The well-designed and pleasant buildings stand in attractive gardens and grounds. Facilities are good for science, music, design and technology, drama and sport and there has been continual development over the last 30 years during which time there have been 15 major additions. Its liberal and sound education is based on Christian principles and practice. Standards are good academically and very many sixth formers go on to degree courses each year. French, German and Spanish are not only offered to A-level but also for the Institute of Linguists and as non-examined subjects. An exceptionally high proportion of pupils takes GCSE in more than one European language. There are regular exchanges with France, Germany and Spain. Strong in music, drama and art. A good record in the Duke of Edinburgh's Award Scheme.

School profile

Pupils Total age range 4–18; 1000 day pupils (100 boys, 900 girls). Senior department 11–18, 600 girls. Main entry ages 4 (boys and girls), 8, 11 and into sixth (girls). Approx 20% are children of former pupils. Own middle school provides 50% senior intake. *Transfer from maintained schools:* 50% senior intake plus 2% to sixth.
Entrance Own entrance exam used. Oversubscribed. No religious requirements. Parents not expected to buy text books; maximum extras £100. Assisted places. 100 scholarships/bursaries, £295–£90 per term.
Parents 15+% in industry or commerce; 15+% are doctors, lawyers, etc.
Staff Principal Mrs Lillian Croston, in post 3 years. 59 full time staff, 12 part time. Annual turnover 2%. Average age 40.
Academic work GCSE, AS, A-levels and S-levels. A-level general studies offered to all sixth form. In 1991, 100 pupils in upper fifth, 60 in upper sixth. *GCSE:* in 1990, 85% upper fifth gained at least grade C in 8+ subjects; 15% in 5–7 subjects. *A-levels:* Of an upper sixth of 45, 18 passed in 4+ subjects; 19 in 3; 7 in 2; and 1 in 1 subject. 9% took science A-levels; 64% arts/humanities; 27% both. *Computing facilities:* 1 computer room; 1 room used largely for word processing; several departments have their own computer. *Special provision:* Physically handicapped children can cope well with our ground floor site (all specialist facilities are at ground floor).

865

European Community *Languages:* French offered: to age 14; GCSE; AS-level; A-level; Institute of Linguists; and as a non-examined subject. German offered: to age 14; GCSE; AS-level; A-level; Institute of Linguists; and as a non-examined subject. Spanish offered: to age 14; GCSE; AS-level; A-level; Institute of Linguists; and as a non-examined subject. Over 75% take GCSE in more than 1 EC language. *Exchanges:* Regular exchanges for pupils aged 11–18 to France, Germany and Spain. *Other:* French (and occasionally German and Spanish) students in school regularly, either as sixth form pupils or teacher assistants holding conversation classes.

Senior pupils' non-academic activities *Music:* 70 learn a musical instrument, 40 to Grade 6 or above; 110 in school orchestra, 80 in choir; 50 participate in musical productions at school; 3 in Lancashire Schools' Symphony Orchestra. *Drama and dance:* 30 (including understudies) in school productions. 22 take ESB Certificate in spoken English for higher education. 2 accepted for Drama/Dance Schools. *Art:* 50 take GCSE; 10, A-level; 12, A-level history of art. 2 accepted for Art School. *Sport:* Badminton, tennis, hockey, volleyball, netball, rounders, swimming, athletics available. 40 take non-compulsory sport. 10 represent county (badminton, tennis, athletics). *Other:* 36 have bronze Duke of Edinburgh's Award, 20 have silver and 10 have gold. Other activities include public speaking societies, computer, film, cookery, health and pony clubs.

Careers In 1990, 91% leavers went on to degree courses; 4% to art/drama/music colleges; 1% to non-degree courses (eg agriculture); 2% straight into careers (eg management trainee schemes). Of those going on to degree courses, 2% went to Oxbridge, 78% to other universities; 20% to poly/colleges. 4% those going on to higher education went to courses in practical art; 2% in drama/acting; 2% in music; 54% in humanities/social sciences; 8% in medicine; and 30% in science/engineering.

Uniform School uniform worn; different in the sixth.

Houses/prefects Competitive houses. Prefects, head girl, head of house and house prefects – appointed by staff and pupils. School Council.

Religion Compulsory morning assembly.

Social Joint concerts and joint general studies lectures with local schools. Organised trips abroad and exchange systems. Pupils allowed to bring own car/bike/motorbike/horse to school. Meals self service. No tobacco/alcohol allowed.

Discipline No corporal punishment. Pupils failing to produce homework once might expect lunchtime detention; twilight detention for persistent offenders. Those caught smoking cannabis on the premises could expect expulsion after interview with parents.

Alumni association run by Mrs E Gibson, c/o the School.

· *Westminster* ·

Westminster School
17 Dean's Yard
London
SW1P 3PB
Tel 071 222 5516

- Pupils 607
- Boys 13–18
- (Day/Board)
- Girls 16–18
- (Day/Board)
- Upper sixth 147

- Termly fees
  £2130 (Day)
  £3200 (Board/
  Weekly)
- HMC
  Enquiries/application to
  the Registrar

What it's like

Founded by Elizabeth I in 1560. For some centuries before the Reformation, the Benedictine monks of Westminster Abbey had run a small school for boys, but when the monastery was dissolved in 1540 Henry VIII ensured that education was continued at Westminster by including provision for 40 scholars in the constitution of Westminster Abbey. This provision was confirmed by his daughter in 1560, establishing at the same time links between the school and Christ Church, Oxford and Trinity, Cambridge. As the school prospered, the scholars were soon outnumbered by the non-scholars or Town Boys as they were called. From the beginning of the 17th century the school became well known and it remains one of the most distinguished in the country. It has a unique site beside the Abbey and Parliament and is renowned for its respect for learning, its individuality and nonconformity, and in more recent times its system of weekly boarding. It is blessed with many fine buildings (some of great architectural merit) which are elegant and beautiful within as well as without. The buildings are enhanced by pleasant gardens. The main playing field is at Vincent Square. Recently 7–9 Dean Bradley Street was bought to create a massive new science building. The school is already one of the best equipped in Britain. It naturally has close links with the Abbey which is used regularly for worship. A large staff (plus a large part-time staff) allows a very favourable staff:pupil ratio. A very high-powered school academically, it achieves consistently excellent results and sends each year almost all its sixth form to university, nearly half to Oxbridge. The music, drama and art departments are well known for their excellence and there is a great deal of musical and dramatic activity. There is a wide range of sports and games (in which high standards are achieved) and a very wide variety of extra-curricular activities. Much use is made of the cultural facilities of London. Many distinguished speakers address clubs and societies. A flourishing Expeditions Society organises many events.

School profile

Pupils Age range 13–18; 607 pupils, 377 day (325 boys, 52 girls), 230 boarding (200 boys, 30 girls). Main entry ages 13+ (boys) and into sixth (boys and girls). Approx 5% are children of former pupils. Westminster Under School provides approx 40% of intake. *Transfer from maintained schools:* None in main intake, 10 to sixth.

Entrance Common entrance; own scholarship exam (The Challenge) and sixth form entrance exam used. Skills in sport, music, art useful; no religious requirements. Parents expected to buy text books; maximum extras, £200 per term. Up to 8 assisted places pa for pupils from Under School. 8 scholarships pa, half boarding fee; some sixth form bursaries.

Parents 15+% are doctors, lawyers etc. 60+% live within 30 miles; up to 10% live overseas.

Staff Head Master David Summerscale, in post 4 years. 62 full time staff, 30 part time. Annual turnover 4%. Average age 35.

Academic work GCSE, AS and A-levels. 18 subjects offered (no A-level general studies). In 1990, 99 pupils in upper fifth, 147 in upper sixth. *GCSE:* in 1990, 99 upper fifth gained at least grade C in 8+ subjects. *A-levels:* 38 upper sixth passed in 4+ subjects; 106 in 3; 3 in 2 subjects. 30% took science A-levels; 30% arts/humanities; 40% both. *Computing facilities:* Open access to BBC/Archimedes in computer room and laboratories.

European Community *Languages:* French offered: to GCSE; AS-level; A-level. German offered: to GCSE; AS-level; A-level. Greek offered: to GCSE; A-level. Spanish offered: to GCSE; AS-level; A-level. Over 75% take GCSE in more than 1 EC language. *Exchanges:* Regular exchanges for pupils aged 14–18 to Germany and Spain.

Senior pupils' non-academic activities *Music:* 180 learn a musical instrument, 18 to Grade 6 or above; 30 in school orchestra, 40 in choir, 4 in jazz group. *Drama and dance:* 85 in school productions. *Art:* 80 take as non-examined subject; 25 take GCSE; 12, A-level. 15 belong to photographic club; 30 take ceramics. *Sport:* Athletics, cricket, fencing, fives, football, martial arts, netball, shooting, squash, rowing, swimming, tennis etc available. A number of pupils represent county/country in a range of sports. *Other:* 20 take part in local community schemes. Other activities include debating, chess, computers, bookbinding.

Careers In 1990, 98% leavers went on to degree courses; 2% to art/drama/music colleges. Of those going on to degree courses, 50% went to Oxbridge; 50% to other universities. 2% those going on to higher education went to courses in practical art; 1% in music; 50% in humanities/social sciences; 10% in medicine; and 35% in science/engineering.

Uniform School uniform worn by boys throughout; girls have dress guide-lines.

Houses/prefects Competitive houses. Prefects (monitors), head boy (captain of school), heads of house and house prefects (monitors) – appointed by Head Master.

Religion Compulsory morning service in Westminster Abbey 3 times/week. Weekly assembly in School Hall.

Social Joint events with other schools organised occasionally. Annual German exchange, group visits to Spain, Russia, Greece. Sixth form allowed to bring own bike to school. Lunch formal, others self service. School shop. No tobacco/alcohol allowed.

Discipline No corporal punishment. Pupils failing to produce homework once might expect to produce it next lesson; threat of detention for future offence. Those caught smoking cannabis, whether on or off the premises, would expect expulsion.

Boarding 40% have own study bedroom, 40% share with 1 other, 20% are in dormitories of 6+. Single sex houses, of approx 70. Resident qualified nurse, visiting doctor. Central dining room for breakfast and supper. Virtually all are weekly boarders, going home Saturday lunchtime to Monday am. Visits to town allowed.

Alumni association run by S E Murray, c/o School.

Former pupils Peter Ustinov; Michael Flanders; Donald Swann; Lord M Havers; Nigel Lawson; Antony Howard; Dominic Harrod; Andrew Lloyd-Webber; Dan Topolski; Henry Tizard; Sir Andrew Huxley; Sir John Gielgud; Sir Adrian Boult etc.

· *Westonbirt* ·

Westonbirt School
Tetbury
Gloucestershire
GL8 8QG
Tel 066688 333

- Pupils 280
- Boys None
- Girls 11–19
- (Day/Board)
- Upper sixth 40

- Termly fees
  £1723 (Day)
  £2678 (Board)
- GSA, Allied

Enquiries to the Head
Applications to the
Registrar

What it's like

Founded in 1928 on the Cotswold estate of Sir George Holford. Westonbirt House is the main building: a magnificent Renaissance style mansion – in effect a rural palace – which lies in 500 acres of fine gardens and parkland. More beautiful surroundings it would be difficult to find. Over the years it has been adapted and new buildings have been added, most recently an art/technology block. The orangery has been converted into a theatre and concert hall. Facilities and accommodation are first class. The ethos tends towards a good all-round education which develops individual talents – whatever they may be. Religious services (held in the village church) are Anglican and are compulsory. Academic standards are creditable. Many sixth formers go on to degree courses each year. Very strong in music, art and drama. A good range of games, sports and activities. A promising record in the Duke of Edinburgh's Award Scheme and a thriving Young Enterprise Company.

School profile

Pupils Age range 11–19; 280 girls, 20 day, 260 boarding. Main entry age 11+; also 12+, 13+ and into sixth. *Transfer from maintained schools:* 2% main intakes, plus 1% to sixth.

Entrance Common entrance and own entrance papers used. Sometimes oversubscribed. Aptitude at music, drama, art, and sport helps; school is C of E and all are required to attend services. Parents not expected to buy text books; extras include music and sports coaching, excursions, public exam fees etc. 7 scholarships/bursaries, 50–10% of fees.

Parents 10+% live within 30 miles; 10+% live overseas.

Staff Head Mrs Gillian Hylson-Smith, in post since 1986. 35 full time staff, 7 part time. Annual turnover 5%. Average age 40.

Academic work GCSE and A-levels (including A-level theatre studies; AS-level business studies; no A-level general studies). In 1990, 36 pupils in upper fifth,

40 in upper sixth. *GCSE:* in 1990, 30 upper fifth gained at least grade C in 8+ subjects; 4 in 5–7; and 2 in 1–4 subjects. *A-levels:* on average, 2 upper sixth pass in 4+ subjects; 29 in 3; 5 in 2; and 5 in 1 subject. On average, 12 take science A-levels; 20 arts/humanities; 8 both. *Computing facilities:* Room with 9 computers plus computers in careers room, science labs, library and technology centre. *Special provision:* EFL coaching; individual coaching paid for separately.

European Community *Languages:* French offered: to age 14; GCSE; AS-level; A-level. Italian offered: as a non-examined subject. Spanish offered: to GCSE; AS-level; A-level. Up to 10% take GCSE in more than 1 EC language. *Exchanges:* Regular exchanges for pupils aged 11–16 to France and Spain.

Non-academic activities *Music:* 40 learn a musical instrument to Grade 6 or above; 57 in 2 school orchestras; 120 in choirs; 26 in chamber groups. *Drama and*

dance: 62 adult grades and gold (LAMDA); numerous entries to mid-Somerset festival; A-level theatre studies offered; first year, junior and senior productions each year. *Art:* 48 take GCSE; 9 take A-level art, 25 history of art; 10 take GCSE photography; 18 belong to photographic club. *Sport:* Lacrosse, netball, hockey, tennis, swimming, athletics, rounders, badminton, volley-ball, unihoc, basketball, squash, cross-country available. 25 take non-compulsory sport. 30 in trampoline club. 6 take exams in life saving, others take dance and gymnastics. 10 pupils represent county at lacrosse, cross-country and athletics. *Other:* 15 take part in local community schemes. 20 have bronze Duke of Edinburgh's Award, 6 have silver.

Careers In 1990, 41% leavers went on to degree courses; 12% to art/drama/music colleges; 41% to non-degree courses (eg secretarial, agriculture, nursing, tutorial); 6% other. Of those going on to degree courses, 7% went to Oxbridge, 64% to other universities; 29% to poly/colleges. 22% those going on to higher education went to courses in practical art; 5.5% in drama/acting; 5.5% in music; 50% in humanities/social sciences; and 17% in science/engineering.

Uniform School uniform worn except in the sixth.

Houses/prefects Competitive houses. All sixth form have prefectorial duties. Head girl, head of house and house prefects – appointed by the Head after consultation with staff and girls.

Religion Compulsory daily prayers and Sunday service.

Social Music and discos with Bristol boys' day schools and other independent schools. Organised French ski-ing trip, art history French trip. Meals formal, except supper. School shop. No tobacco/alcohol allowed.

Discipline No corporal punishment. Pupils failing to produce homework once might expect detention; those caught smoking cannabis on the premises could expect expulsion.

Boarding 26% have own study bedroom, 2% share with one; very few are in dormitories of 6+. Houses, of approximately 45, same as competitive houses. Resident qualified nurse and visiting doctor. Central dining room. Sixth form pupils can provide and cook own food. 3 exeats each term, 1 or 2 nights. Visits to the local town allowed about every fortnight.

Alumni association c/o The Registrar, Westonbirt.

· *Whitgift* ·

Whitgift School	● Pupils 910	● Termly fees
Haling Park	● Boys 10–18	£1140 (Day)
South Croydon	(Day)	● HMC
Surrey CR2 6YT	● Girls None	Enquiries/application to
Tel 081-688 9222	● Upper sixth 113	the Headmaster

What it's like

Founded in 1596 by John Whitgift, Archbishop of Canterbury. After steady decline in the 18th century it was reborn in North End, Croydon. In 1931 it moved to its present site in Haling Park: 45 acres of wooded parkland, formerly the estate of Lord Howard of Effingham. These are exceptionally beautiful surroundings for an urban day school. The buildings are well designed and well equipped (including a music school, swimming pool and a superb sports hall). Further new buildings comprise a centre linking design and technology with science and fine art, together with a new library and computer centre. One of the fundamental aims of the school is to balance an excellent academic record with a wide range of co-curricular activities. A friendly and happy school, it has an ecumenical approach to religious worship. Academically high-powered it achieves very good results and many sixth formers go on to degree courses including a very high proportion to Oxbridge. French and German are offered to A-level, Italian and Spanish at GCSE and other European languages are offered for the Institute of Linguists. A high proportion of boys takes GCSE in more than one European language. There are regular exchanges with Denmark, France, Germany and Italy. Very strong in music, drama and art. Very high standards, too, in sports and games of which there is a wide variety. A flourishing CCF and outdoor pursuits scheme. A plentiful range of extra-curricular activities, a substantial commitment to local community services and a good record in the Duke of Edinburgh's Award Scheme.

School profile

Pupils Total age range 10–18; 910 day boys. Senior department 13–18, 640 boys. Main entry ages 10, 11, 13 and into sixth. Approx 5% are children of former pupils. *Transfer from maintained schools:* 44% at ages 10, 11, plus 50% to sixth.

Entrance Common entrance and own exam used. Oversubscribed. No special skills or religious requirements. Parents not expected to buy text books. 91 assisted places. Whitgift Foundation provides large number of scholarships/bursaries.

Staff Headmaster C A Barnett, first year in post. Annual staff turnover 10%.

Academic work GCSE and A-levels. 20 GCSE subjects offered; 19 at A-level (including business studies and Greek; no A-level general studies). In 1990, 135 pupils in fifth, 113 in upper sixth. *GCSE:* in 1990, 89% Fifth gained at least grade C in 8+ subjects; 6% in 5–7; and 4% in 1–4 subjects. *A-levels:* 19% upper sixth passed in 4+ subjects; 57% in 3; 18% in 2; and 6% in 1 subject. 24% took science A-levels; 56% arts/humanities many with maths; 20% both. *Computing facilities:* Computer laboratory and workshop; word-processing annexe to library; wide use of computers in departments. *Special provision:* Individual difficulties handled as appropriate.

European Community *Languages:* French offered: to age 14; GCSE; AS-level; A-level. German offered: to age 14; GCSE; AS-level; A-level. Italian: GCSE. Spanish: GCSE. 50–75% take GCSE in more than 1 EC language. *Exchanges:* Regular exchanges for pupils aged 11–18 to Denmark, France, Germany and Italy. *Other:* European Youth Parliament. Sixth form study visits. Opportunity for senior pupils to spend up to 6 weeks in continental link schools.

Senior pupils' non-academic activities *Music:* Well supported; high standard of tuition in orchestral and other instruments, piano, organ by 3 full-time, and many visiting staff; many instrumental/choral groups; opera performed most years. *Drama:* Several productions a year; major play tours abroad; own studio workshop. *Art:* Pottery, sculpture, lithography, stage design and photography offered. *Sport:* Rugby, hockey, cricket, swimming, athletics, cross-country, fencing, squash, fives, basketball, badminton etc available. *Other:* Many take part in local community schemes. Other activities include computer, chess, debating, current affairs, clubs, CCF, adventure training.

Careers In 1990, 60% leavers went on to degree courses; 4% to art/drama/music colleges; 8% straight into careers (eg police, customs, banking); 28% other (improving A-level grades). Of those going on to degree courses, 38% went to Oxbridge, 52% to other universities; 10% to poly/colleges. 3% those going on to higher education went to courses in practical art; 3% in music; 62% in humanities/social sciences; 5% in medicine; and 27% in science/engineering.

Uniform School uniform worn to 16; dress code in sixth.

Houses/prefects Competitive houses.

Prefects, head boy, head of house and house prefects – appointed by Head or housemasters.

Religion Compulsory twice-weekly assembly for whole school; additional two for juniors.

Social Joint functions with local girls' schools; sailing and climbing journeys. School exchanges (France, Germany, Czechoslovakia, Denmark) and other foreign links, ski-ing trips. Pupils allowed to bring own car/bike/motorbike to school. Meals self service for seniors; formal for juniors. No tobacco/alcohol allowed.

Discipline No corporal punishment.

Former pupils Sir Reg Prentice; Martin Jarvis; Raman Subba Row; Ian Beer (former headmaster of Harrow); Sir Peter Bowness; Prof Sir Robert Boyd FRS (and 6 other FRS); Gp Capt John Cunningham; Roger Freeman MP; Sir David Hancock (perm sec DES); Lord Justice Mauer; Sir Bryan Roberts; Lord Wedderburn of Charlton; Sir Gordon Witteridge KCMG.

· *William Hulme's* ·

William Hulme's Grammar School Alexandra Park Manchester M16 8PR Tel 061 226 2054	● Pupils 791 ● Boys 11–18 (Day) ● Girls 11–18 (Day) ● Upper sixth 106	● Termly fees £1030 (Day) ● HMC Enquiries to the Headmaster Application to Bursar

What it's like

Founded by the Hulme Trust and opened in 1887, it has an urban site set in 16 acres of grounds 2.5 miles south of Manchester city centre. Steady expansion and development have taken place throughout the 20th century, with many additions in the last 25 years. It is now extremely well equipped. Non-denominational and now co-educational. It has high academic standards and good results. Many pupils go on to degree courses each year. French, German and Spanish are offered to A-level and Italian at A-level only. There are regular exchanges with France, Germany and Spain. There is an increasing amount of music and art, and drama is flourishing. A wide range of sports and games in which high standards are attained (regular representation at county and national level). Extra-curricular activities are numerous. A voluntary and flourishing CCF and some commitment to the Duke of Edinburgh's Award Scheme. Extensive use is made of the school's own field study centre in Wensleydale and also of the cultural amenities of Manchester.

School profile

Pupils Age range 11–18; 791 day pupils (655 boys, 136 girls; full co-education still developing). Main entry ages 11 and some into sixth.

Entrance Own 11+ exam used. Oversubscribed. Range of aptitudes looked for; no special religious requirements. Parents not expected to buy text books; £99 for meals is only basic extra charge. 35 assisted places pa. Scholarships/bursaries, value £2000–£1000.

Staff Headmaster P D Briggs, in post for 4 years. 58 full time staff, 9 part time. Annual turnover 1%. Average age 39.

Academic work GCSE and A-levels. 22 subjects offered (including A-level general studies). In 1990, 112 pupils in fifth, 106 in upper sixth. *GCSE:* in 1990,

74 upper fifth gained at least grade C in 8+ subjects; 27 in 5–7; and 15 in 1–4 subjects. *A-levels:* 31 upper sixth passed in 4+ subjects; 31 in 3; 17 in 2; and 7 in 1 subject. 54% took science A-levels; 32% arts/humanities; 14% both. *Computing facilities:* Computer lab (17 BBC's, 1 Archimedes); Design Centre (4 Archimedes); various BBC's and microprocessors in chemistry, history and physics departments.

European Community *Languages:* French offered: to age 14; GCSE; A-level. German: GCSE; A-level. Greek (modern): A-level. Spanish: GCSE; A-level. *Exchanges:* Regular exchanges for pupils aged 14–18 to France, Germany and Spain.

Senior pupils' non-academic activities *Music:* 42 learn a musical instrument. 28 in school orchestra, 63 in choir. *Drama and dance:* 50 in school productions, 80 in house plays. *Art:* 20 take as non-examined subject, 10 GCSE, 4 A-level. 1 accepted for Art School. *Sport:* Rugby, lacrosse, hockey, netball, cricket, tennis, swimming, badminton, squash available. All take part in some non-compulsory sport (badminton, weight training, squash, cross-country). 10 pupils represent county (rugby, lacrosse, cricket, squash), 3 represent country (speed skating, modern pentathlon, lacrosse). *Other:* 20 have bronze Duke of Edinburgh's Award and 10 silver. Other activities include many clubs and societies, also computer, Outward Bound, climbing, chess, video unit. Raises £10,000 a year for charity; frequent visits to Waverley Old People's Home.

Careers 1 full time, 1 part time adviser. Annual average accepted for *arts and humanities degree courses* at Oxbridge, 4; other universities, 16; polytechnics/colleges, 8. *science and engineering degree courses* at Oxbridge, 1; other universities, 27; medical schools, 6; polytechnics/colleges, 12. Average going straight into careers in armed services, 1; the City, 3.

Uniform School uniform worn, modified in sixth.

Houses/prefects Competitive houses. Prefects, head boy – appointed by Head; head of house and house prefects – appointed by housemaster. Committee (elected) runs sixth form.

Religion Daily non-denominational Christian assembly; weekly Jewish religious assembly.

Social Debates, discussions, lectures, dances, industrial and European Conferences. German and Russian exchanges; trips to France, Spain; sports tours to USA, Canada, West Indies. Pupils allowed to bring own car/bike/motorbike to school. Meals self service. School book and tuck shops. No tobacco/alcohol allowed.

Discipline No corporal punishment. Pupils failing to produce homework expect to do work next day and detention thereafter.

Alumni association Secretary: Mr P Marlton, 8 Stalmine Avenue, Heald Green, Cheshire SK8 3JG.

Former pupils Sir Robert Mark; Air Chief Marshal Sir Joseph Gilbert; Judge Michael Blackburn; John Lee MP; Michael Lord MP.

· *Wimbledon High* ·

Wimbledon High
School
Mansel Road
London SW19 4AB
Tel 081 946 1756

- Pupils 760
- Boys None
- Girls 5–18
  (Day)
- Upper sixth 56

- Termly fees
  £1024 (Day)
- GSA, GPDST
Enquiries/application to
the Head Mistress

What it's like

Founded in 1880 it has an agreeable urban site. The junior and senior departments are on one campus. The main playing fields are 10 minutes' walk away on the site of the original All England Lawn Tennis Club. The school has a reputation for excellent academic standards and a high regard for pastoral care. It draws its pupils from a wide area and a variety of backgrounds. Academic results are consistently good and each year many pupils go on to degree courses, including many to Oxbridge. Music, drama and art are all strongly supported. An adequate range of sports and games and extra-curricular activities. Some commitment to local community services and the Duke of Edinburgh's Award Scheme.

School profile

Pupils Total age range 5–18; 760 day girls. Senior department 11–18, 510 girls. Main entry ages 5+, 7+, 11+ and into sixth. *Transfer from maintained schools:* 50% senior intake plus 16% to sixth.

Entrance Own entrance exam used. Oversubscribed. No special skills or religious requirements. Parents not expected to buy text books; music tuition (£80) and lunches (£89) extra. 70 assisted places. Scholarships (1 pa plus sixth form), half fees; bursaries.

Parents 15+% are doctors, lawyers etc; 15% in industry or commerce.

Staff Head Mistress Mrs R A Smith, in post for 9 years. 46 full time staff, 36 part time (including 20 music). Annual turnover 10%. Average age 40.

Academic work GCSE, AS and A-levels. 20 subjects offered (including GCSE Latin and Greek; no A-level general studies). In 1990, 65 pupils in upper fifth, 56 in upper sixth. *GCSE:* in 1990, 52 upper fifth gained at least grade C in 8+ subjects; 8 in 5–7 subjects. *A-levels:* 3 upper sixth passed in 4+ subjects; 40 in 3; 8 in 2; and 3 in 1 subject. 27 took science A-levels; 16 arts/humanities; 16 both. *Computing facilities:* Network of 9 stations (RML Chain 64) and 5 BBC computers.

Special provision: Appropriate support for dyslexic and mildly visually handicapped pupils.

European Community *Languages:* French offered: to age 14; GCSE; AS-level; A-level. German offered: to age 14; GCSE; AS-level; A-level. Spanish offered: to GCSE. 50–75% take GCSE in more than 1 EC language. *Exchanges:* Regular exchanges for pupils aged 11–18 to France and Germany.

Senior pupils' non-academic activities *Music:* 160 learn a musical instrument, 80 to Grade 6 or above; 40 in school orchestra, 75 in choir, 20 in jazz band; 6 in National Youth Orchestra. *Drama and dance:* 50–60 in official school productions, 40 in informal productions; 12 take AS-level drama and theatre arts. 1 works in theatre, 2 in National Youth Theatre, 2 applying for drama courses. *Art:* 40 take as non-examined subject in sixth form; 61 take GCSE; 16 take A-level. 2 accepted for Art School. *Sport:* Hockey, netball, tennis, rounders, squash, badminton, volleyball, table tennis, athletics, swimming, gymnastics available. Teams for all major games at all levels. Several represent county/country (hockey). *Other:* 20 take part in local community schemes. 16 have bronze Duke of Edinburgh's Award; at least 1 enters voluntary schemes after leaving. Other activities include computer club, modern dance, design & technology.

Careers In 1990, 57% leavers went on to degree courses; 15% to art/drama/music colleges; 4% to non-degree courses (eg nursing, administrative procedures); 26% other. Of those going on to degree courses, 13% went to Oxbridge; 84% to other universities; 3% to poly/colleges. 12% those going on to higher education went to courses in practical art; 5% in drama/acting; 7% in music; 32% in humanities/social sciences; 2% in medicine; and 42% in science/engineering.

Uniform School uniform worn except in the sixth.

Houses/prefects No competitive houses. No prefects but sixth form committee elected by staff and pupils. Head girl chosen by Headmistress from committee.

Religion Daily non-denominational religious assembly.

Social Debating society, drama, choir and orchestra with King's (Wimbledon). French and German exchanges, ski-ing, sixth form art visits to Italy, hockey to Holland, choir to Canada. Sixth form allowed to drive to school but no parking available in grounds. Meals self service. No tobacco/alcohol allowed.

Discipline No corporal punishment. Pupils failing to produce homework once might expect verbal warning, possibly a note in homework diary; those caught smoking cannabis on the premises might expect immediate suspension, probably subsequent expulsion.

Alumni association run by Mrs Jean Appleby, 1 Ridgeway Place, London SW19 4EW.

· *Winchester* ·

Winchester College	● Pupils 660	● Termly fees
College Street	● Boys 13–18	£2700 (Day)
Winchester	(Day/Board)	£3600 (Board)
Hampshire	● Girls None	● HMC
SO23 9NA	● Upper sixth	Enquiries to Head-
Tel 0962 54328	130	master or Registrar
		Application to Registrar

What it's like

Founded in 1382 by William of Wykeham, Bishop of Winchester and Chancellor to Richard II. It lies at the edge of the city and close to the water meadows. It has the longest unbroken history of any school in the country and has been in continuous occupation of its original buildings for 600 years. Most of them are still used for the purpose for which they were designed, and they are virtually without rival among school buildings for their venerability and beauty. The Scholars still live in the 14th-century 'College' as it is known. The medieval buildings are open to visitors. Other buildings date from the 17th, 18th and 19th centuries, plus some recent structures. Accommodation and facilities are first rate. They include exceptionally good libraries, a theatre and a music school. Intellectually and academically, Winchester is one of the most distinguished schools in Britain and standards are very high. A large staff permits a staff:pupil ratio of 1:8. Between 110–120 pupils go on to university each year, and these include 40 plus to Oxbridge. French, German and Spanish are offered to A-level and many boys take GCSE in more than one European language. Italian is offered as a non-examined language. A tremendously strong music department involves a majority of the school; two-thirds of the pupils learn a musical instrument and there are several choirs and orchestras. There are numerous school and house dramatic productions involving 200 or more boys. The art department is also very strong. Thirty different sports and games are available (including Winchester football which is peculiar to the College). High standards prevail in sport and games and there have been many representatives at international and county level. A very large number of extra-curricular activities are available. The College also has an impressive commitment to local community schemes.

School profile

Pupils Age range 13–18; 660 boys, 25 day, 635 boarding. Main entry ages 13 and a few into sixth. Approx 17% are children of former pupils.

Entrance Own entrance exam used. Oversubscribed (registration from age 8). Academic ability and other interests looked for. No religious requirements. Music tuition, books etc extra charge. 5 assisted places pa. 15 scholarships pa, £4980–£7800 plus some 6 music awards, average value £3900.

Parents 15+% are in industry or commerce; 15+% are doctors, lawyers etc. 10+% live within 30 miles; up to 10% live overseas.

Staff Headmaster J P Sabben-Clare, in post for 3 years. 83 full time staff, 8 part time. Annual turnover 3%.

Academic work GCSE and A-levels. Average size of upper fifth 130; upper sixth 130. *GCSE:* on average, 125 pupils in upper fifth pass 8+ subjects. *A-levels:* on average, 40 pupils in upper sixth pass 4 subjects; 85, 3 subjects and 5 pass 2 subjects. On average, 40 take science/engineering A-levels; 40 take arts and humanities; 50 a mixture. *Computing facilities:* 16 BBC micros and Archimedes connected by a network system plus computers belonging to masters.

European Community *Languages:* French offered: to GCSE; A-level. German: GCSE; A-level. Italian: non-examined. Spanish: GCSE; A-level. 25–50% take GCSE in more than 1 EC language. *Exchanges:* Regular exchanges for pupils aged 14–16 to France and Germany.

Senior pupils' non-academic activities *Music:* Two-thirds of pupils learn a musical instrument, most to Grade 6 or above; 3–4 accepted for Music School plus instrumental/choral awards to Oxbridge; 100 in school orchestra, 150 in choir, 20 in pop group, string quartets, brass quintets, wind quintets, composition (10 pupils); 2 in National Youth Orchestra. *Drama and dance:* 200 participate in school and house productions. 1 accepted for Drama/Dance School. *Art:* 25 take art as non-examined subject; 24 take GCSE; 18, A-level. 2 accepted for Art School; 2 for architecture. 20 belong to eg photographic club; 100 to art society (for talks). *Sport:* Athletics, badminton, basketball, canoeing, cricket, fencing, fishing, fives, gymnastics, hockey, judo, karate, rackets, rowing, sailing, shooting, soccer, squash, steeplechase, sub-aqua, swimming, tennis, trampoline, volleyball, water polo, weight and circuit training, Winchester College football available. 300 take non-compulsory sport; 120 compulsory PE. 40 take exams in swimming. 4 pupils represent country at rowing; 28 represent county (judo, water polo, athletics). *Other:* 100 take part in local community schemes. 2 have gold Duke of Edinburgh's Award. 30 enter voluntary schemes after leaving school. Other activities include a computer club, archaeology, astronomy, bell-ringing, chess, classics, debating, drama, film, modern language play reading, music, natural history, philately, photography, printing, science. The Empson Society has lectures on literature, the Toynbee Society on historical and philosophical subjects.

Careers 4 part time advisers. Average number of pupils accepted for *arts and humanities degree courses* at Oxbridge, 36; other universities, 42; polytechnics or CHE, 1. *science and engineering degree courses* at Oxbridge, 15, other universities, 28 (of which 8 read medicine); polytechnics or CHE, 1. Average number of pupils going straight into careers in the armed services, 2; the City, 1; music/drama, 2; other, 10.

Uniform School uniform not worn, but dress regulations; scholars wear gowns.

Houses/prefects Competitive houses. Prefects, head boy, head of house and house prefects – chosen by Housemasters after consultation with prefects; approved by the Headmaster.

Religion Compulsory religious worship.

Social Debates, music, drama; mostly with St Swithun's School. Organised trips abroad eg ski-ing; art trips to Italy; exchange with a Paris Lycee. Pupils allowed to bring own bike to school. Meals formal. School shop. No tobacco/alcohol allowed.

Discipline No corporal punishment. Pupils failing to produce homework once might expect a reprimand from teacher and work to be produced; those caught smoking cannabis on the premises could expect rustication; expulsion if selling it.

Boarding 15% have own study bedroom, 80% are in dormitories of 6+. Houses of 55, same as competitive houses. Resident matron. No central dining room. 4-day weekend exeats in summer and Easter terms; 10 days exeat in winter term. Visits to the local town allowed.

Alumni association run by P S W K Maclure.

Former pupils Viscount Whitelaw; Sir Geoffrey Howe; Douglas Jay; Peter Jay; Lord Penney; Sir Jeremy Morse; George Younger; Field Marshal Lord Carver; Professor Freeman Dyson; Howard Angus; William Mann; Tim Brooke-Taylor; Brian Trubshaw; Richard Noble.

· *Withington* ·

Withington Girls'
School
Wellington Road
Fallowfield
Manchester M14 6BL
Tel 061 224 1077/8820

- Pupils 565
- Boys None
- Girls 7–18
  (Day)
- Upper sixth 62

- Termly fees
  £905 (Day)
- GSA
Enquiries/application to
the Headmistress

What it's like

Founded in 1890, it is urban single-site, housed in a pleasant late 19th-century building with large adjoining playing fields. There have been many additions over the years and modern facilities are excellent. Academic standards are high and results good. Very many sixth formers go on to degree courses, including many to Oxbridge. French and German are offered to A-level and Italian to GCSE. A very high proportion of girls takes GCSE in more than one European language. There are regular exchanges with France and Germany. Extremely strong music and drama departments and a fine range of activities. The school has a high reputation for its achievements in sport and games (there have been and are many representatives at county level). A promising record in the Duke of Edinburgh's Award Scheme. The school enjoys vigorous local support and has a strong commitment to local community services.

School profile

Pupils Total age range 7–18; 565 day girls. Senior department 11–18, 470 girls. Main entry ages 7–9, 11 and into sixth. Under 5% are children of former pupils. Own junior school provides more than 20% of intake. *Transfer from maintained schools:* 45–50% intake at 11, plus 80% to sixth.

Entrance Own entrance exam used. Oversubscribed. All round ability and excellent potential looked for; no religious requirements. Parents not expected to buy text books; lunches (£135 pa) extra. 70 assisted places. Bursaries available in cases of need, assessed individually.

Parents 15+% in industry or commerce; 15+% are doctors, lawyers etc.

Staff Headmistress Mrs Margaret Kenyon, in post for 6 years. 36 full time staff, 7 part time. Annual turnover, 5–7.5%. Average age, 40.

Academic work GCSE and A-levels. 18 subjects offered (including Greek and A-level general studies). On average, 69 pupils in upper fifth, 64 in upper sixth (now 62). *GCSE:* on average, 67 upper fifth gain at least grade C in 8+ subjects; 2 in 5–7 subjects. *A-levels:* on average, 24 upper sixth pass in 4+ subjects; 37 in 3; 2 in 2; and 1 in 1 subject. On average 35% take science A-levels; 30% arts/humanities; 35% both. *Computing facilities:* Nimbus network with 13 stations in specially designed computer room.

European Community *Languages:* French offered: to GCSE; AS-level; A-level. German offered: to GCSE; A-level. Italian: GCSE. 50–75% take GCSE in more than 1 EC language. *Exchanges:* Regular exchanges for pupils aged 11–18 to France and Germany. German sixth-former spent 1 term in school with reciprocal visit to her gymnasium by her hosting sixth-former.

Senior pupils' non-academic activities *Music:* 60+ learn a musical instrument, 30+ to Grade 6 or above; 2–3 accepted for Music School; 40+ in senior school orchestra, 50 in junior school orchestra, 75 in senior choir, 40 in wind band, some members of Northern Youth Orchestra, 20 in Stockport Youth Orchestras, 10 in Trafford Youth Orchestras. *Drama and dance:* 150+ in school productions, many help and perform in local and youth theatre; 2 take up to Grade 6 ESB, RAD; 4 IBTA, NATB elementary ballet awards. 2 accepted for Drama/Dance Schools (including university courses). 1 goes on to work in theatre approx every 5 years. *Art:* 15 take GCSE; 4, A-level; 2–3 accepted for Art School. *Sport:* Hockey, lacrosse, netball, badminton, table tennis, volleyball, tennis, cricket, rounders, aerobics, trampolining, self defence, basketball, badminton available. 150 take non-compulsory sport. 5 do county training. 10 pupils represent county (tennis, lacrosse, hockey). *Other:* 100+ take part in local community schemes. 40 working for bronze Duke of Edinburgh's Award, 9 have silver and 1 gold. 100+ work for national charities. Other activities include a computer club, active scientific society (many outside speakers), electronics, bridge, ski-ing, hiking, active modern language society, current affairs and debating societies.

Careers In 1990, $98^1/_2$% leavers went on to degree courses; $1^1/_2$% other. Of those going on to degree courses, 16% went to Oxbridge, 77% to other universities; 7% to poly/colleges. $1^1/_2$% those going on to higher education went to courses in practical art; $1^1/_2$% in drama/acting; 3% in music; 48% in humanities/social sciences; 16% in medicine; and 30% in science/engineering.

Uniform School uniform worn, modified in sixth.

Houses/prefects Competitive houses. All upper sixth form are prefects. Head girl, 2–3 deputies chosen by Headmistress after consulting sixth form and staff. House captains and vice captains elected by house.

Religion All encouraged to take part. Monday assembly compulsory; separate Jewish assembly once weekly.

Social Girls are invited to lectures at Manchester Grammar School and audition for plays there. Organised ski-ing trips, adventure holidays in the Lake District and abroad for 12–13 year-olds. French/German trips for GCSE candidates. Cultural visits abroad for sixth form. Pupils allowed to bring own car to school. Meals self service. No tobacco/alcohol allowed.

Discipline No corporal punishment. Pupils failing to produce homework once might expect a verbal reminder; those caught smoking cannabis on the premises would be expelled.

Alumni association run by Mrs Marjorie Rawsthorn, 20 Legh Road, Adlington, Macclesfield SK10 4NE.

Former pupils Judith and Sandra Chalmers.

· *Woldingham* ·

Woldingham School
Marden Park
Woldingham
Surrey CR3 7YA
Tel 0883 349431
Fax 0883 348653

- Pupils 450
- Boys None
- Girls 11–18
  (Day/Board)
- Upper sixth 64

- Termly fees
  £1600 (Day)
  £2645 (Board)
- GSA
  Enquiries/application to
  Admissions Secretary

What it's like

Founded in 1842 by the Society of the Sacred Heart. In 1946 it moved from Roehampton to Woldingham, Surrey. Today it is under lay management and is part of the international network of Sacred Heart Schools in the trusteeship of the Society and run according to its educational aims and philosophy. The estate at Marden Park was first developed by Sir Robert Clayton in the 17th century. The original mansion was destroyed by fire; the present 19th century senior school building is set in magnificent grounds and gardens. The junior house is a modern building with accommodation for some 160 girls. Much has been achieved in recent years. Developments include an assembly hall, 120 sixth form study-bedrooms, 3 art studios, an information technology/business studies suite, an indoor swimming pool and purpose-built science and technology centre (9 laboratories). It is a Roman Catholic school in the ecumenical tradition. Its primary purpose is to provide a sound education which will help girls to become mature and committed Christians who can make independent decisions in their careers and personal lives. All pupils take religious studies at GCSE level. Students are encouraged to participate in the Church's liturgical year. Girls are expected to play a full part in the running of the school and responsibilities and privileges are introduced at an early stage. A large staff allows a very favourable staff:pupil ratio of about 1:9. Academic standards are high and results good. Most sixth formers proceed to degree courses, including at Oxbridge. A very big commitment to drama, music and art. A good range of sports and games and extra-curricular activities. A promising record in the Duke of Edinburgh's Award Scheme and a strong debating society.

School profile

Pupils Age range 11–18; 450 girls, 90 day, 360 boarding. Main entry age 11. *Transfer from maintained schools:* 1% main intake.

Entrance Common entrance used.

Oversubscribed. No special skills required; RC and other Christian denominations preferred. Parents expected to buy text books. 1 academic sixth form scholarship.

Parents 35+% in industry or commerce. 10+% live within 30 miles; 20+% expatriates overseas.

Staff Headmistress Dr P Dineen, in post for 6 years. 62 full time staff, 2 part time. Annual turnover 12%. Average age 35.

Academic work GCSE and A-levels. 17 GCSE subjects offered; 18 at A-level (no A-level general studies). In 1990, 68 pupils in upper fifth, 64 in upper sixth. *GCSE:* in 1990, 50 upper fifth gained at least grade C in 8+ subjects; 12 in 5–7; and 2 in 1–4 subjects. *A-levels:* 44 upper sixth passed in 3 subjects; 13 in 2; and 7 in 1 subject. 19% took science A-levels; 70% arts/humanities; 11% both. *Computing facilities:* IT taught in all years via 20 station Nimbus AX network in IT room. Also Nimbus computers in library, science, maths, art and languages departments.

European Community *Languages:* French offered: to age 14; GCSE; AS-level; A-level. German offered: to age 14; GCSE; A-level. Spanish offered: to age 14; GCSE; AS-level; A-level. 25–50% take GCSE in more than 1 EC language. Goal is for all girls to take 2 modern languages to 16. *Exchanges:* Regular exchanges for pupils aged 14–18 to Belgium, France, Germany and Spain. Also staff exchanges. *Other:* European Studies offered to pupils aged 16–18. School is associated with other Sacred Heart schools in Europe, principals of which now hold regular meetings. Exhibits relating to EC always on view. Sixth form been addressed by local MEP.

Senior pupils' non-academic activities *Music:* 312 learn a musical instrument, 10 to Grade 6 or above. 98 in school orchestras, 220 in choirs, 50 in pop groups. *Drama and dance:* 200 in school productions. 3 to Grade 6 in ESB, RAD etc. *Art:* 30 take GCSE, 12 take A-level, 5 accepted for Art School, 50 belong to eg photographic club. *Sport:* Hockey, netball, rounders, tennis, track and field, gymnastics and dance, squash, swimming, badminton available. 12 represent county/country (tennis, athletics, hockey). *Other:* Duke of Edinburgh's Award, chess, driving lessons.

Careers In 1990, 80% leavers went on to degree courses; 5% to art/drama/music colleges; 5% to non-degree courses (eg secretarial); 10% other. Of those going on to degree courses, 8% went to Oxbridge; 50% to other universities; 42% to poly/colleges. 20% those going on to higher education went to courses in practical art; 10% in drama/acting; 50% in humanities/social sciences; 8% in medicine; and 12% in science/engineering.

Uniform School uniform worn throughout.

Houses/prefects Competitive houses. Prefects, head girl, head of house and house prefects – shortlisted by sixth, selected by senior staff.

Religion Compulsory Mass on Sunday.

Social Regular debates and dances with local schools. Visits to Russia (history), Italy (history of art), Austria (ski-ing and choir), France, Spain and Germany (languages). Third year upwards allowed to bring own bike to school. Meals self service. School shop. No tobacco/alcohol allowed.

Discipline No corporal punishment. Pupils failing to produce homework once might expect tutorial direction; those caught smoking on the premises might expect suspension; involvement in drug-taking would incur immediate expulsion.

Boarding 30% have own study bedroom, 17% share, 20% are in dormitories of 6+. Not divided into houses. 2 resident qualified nurses; 2 doctors, dentist and physiotherapist in attendance. 2 central dining rooms. Exeats each weekend from Saturday noon. Visits to local town allowed (14+) Saturday afternoons.

Alumni association run by Miss L Ferrar, 14 Abercorn Place, London NW8 9XP.

· *Wolverhampton Grammar* ·

Wolverhampton
Grammar School
Compton Road
Wolverhampton
WV3 9RB
Tel 0902 21326

- Pupils 630
- Boys 11–18
  (Day)
- Girls 16–18
  (Day)
- Upper sixth 90

- Termly fees
  £1131 (Day)
- HMC

Enquiries/application to
the Headmaster

What it's like

Founded in 1512 by Sir Stephen Jenyns, a member of the Merchant Taylors' Company and Lord Mayor of London in the year of Henry VIII's coronation, for the 'instruction of youth in good manners and learning'. The school was originally in the middle of Wolverhampton and in 1875 moved to its present fine 25-acre site on Compton Road, half a mile from the centre of Wolverhampton. The original buildings are handsome and there have been many modern additions to create first-rate facilities for a school which has a high reputation locally. Pupils come in from a wide catchment area, including Stourbridge, Kidderminster, Bridgnorth, Stafford, Telford, and Walsall. Girls have been admitted to the sixth form since 1984. The school is non-denominational but many of the staff and pupils are practising Christians. There is some emphasis on worship and practice in the Anglican tradition and religious education is part of the curriculum at all levels. A sound general education is provided by a well-qualified staff (staff:pupil ratio of about 1:12) and academic standards and results are consistently good. Many sixth formers go on to degree courses, including at Oxbridge. Music is very strong. There are choirs, orchestras, a concert band, a jazz band and a choral society (number 200). Public performances are frequent. There is a good deal of emphasis on drama. The art department is also strong and work of a high standard is produced. A wide range of sports and games is provided, and there are generally several representatives at county and regional level. A plentiful variety of clubs and societies exists for extra-curricular activities. A flourishing scout group involves a number of boys in outdoor pursuits, including Outward Bound and sailing courses. Some success has been achieved in the Duke of Edinburgh's Award Scheme. Full use is made of the cultural amenities at Stratford, Birmingham and Wolverhampton.

School profile

Pupils Age range 11–18; 630 day pupils (597 boys, 33 girls). Main entry ages 11, 13 (boys); into sixth (boys and girls). Small proportion are children of former pupils. *Transfer from maintained schools:* 80% main intakes, plus 60% to sixth.

Entrance Own entrance exam used at 11 and 13. Oversubscribed. No special skills or religious requirements. Parents not expected to buy text-books. 260 assisted places. Academic scholarships and music exhibition at 11 and 13.

Parents 15+% are doctors, lawyers etc; 15+% in industry.

Staff Headmaster Bernard Trafford, 1 year in post. 51 full time staff, 4 part time. Annual turnover 8%. Average age 35–40.

Academic work GCSE and A-levels. 17 subjects offered (including A-level general studies). In 1991, 95 pupils in upper fifth, 90 in upper sixth. *GCSE:* in 1990, 99% upper fifth gained at least grade C in 8+ subjects; 1% in 5–7 subjects. *A-levels:* 55% upper sixth passed in 4+ subjects; 23% in 3; 8% in 2; and 10% in 1 subject. 37% took science A-levels; 36% arts/humanities; 27% both. *Computing facilities:* A new Computer-aided

Learning Centre, and numerous departmental computers.

European Community *Languages:* French offered: to age 14 (all pupils); GCSE; A-level. German offered: to age 14 (all pupils); GCSE; A-level. 25–50% take GCSE in more than 1 EC language. Business French and German courses in sixth. *Exchanges:* Regular exchanges for pupils aged 14–16 to France and Germany. *Other:* Talks from MEP to sixth every 2 years.

Senior pupils' non-academic activities *Music:* 20 learn a musical instrument, all to Grade 6 or above. 20 play in school orchestra, 35 in choir, 6 in Wolverhampton Youth Orchestra. 2 play in pop group beyond school. *Drama and dance:* 20 in school productions; 10 in other. *Art:* 3 take as non-examined subject; 18 GCSE; 7 A-level. 6 belong to eg photographic club. *Sport:* Association football, rugby, hockey, Eton fives, cross-country, cricket, tennis, athletics, swimming, badminton, basketball, volleyball available. 200 take part in non-compulsory sport. 12 take exams eg GCSE in PE. 5 pupils represent county (cricket, soccer, rugby, hockey, Eton fives); 1 nationally (soccer). *Other:* 16 have bronze Duke of Edinburgh's Award, 16 gold. Other activities include a computer club, canoeing, chess, Scouts (and Venture Scouts).

Careers In 1990, 85% leavers went on to degree courses; 5% to art/drama/music colleges; 5% straight into careers (eg bank training scheme); 5% other. Of those going on to degree courses, 12.5% went to Oxbridge; 52.5% to other universities; 35% to poly/colleges. 4% those going on to higher education went to courses in practical art; 5% in music; 54% in humanities/social sciences; 10% in medicine; and 25% in science/engineering.

Uniform School uniform worn throughout.

Houses/prefects Competitive houses. Limited number of prefects, entire upper sixth perform duties; head boy/girl, house captains – elected by their contemporaries.

Religion Compulsory daily assemblies.

Social 4 trips abroad organised annually. Pupils allowed to bring own car/motorbike/bike to school. Meals self service. School tuck shop. No tobacco/alcohol allowed.

Discipline No corporal punishment. Pupils failing to produce homework once would receive punishment only in aggravating circumstances; those caught smoking cannabis on the premises could expect expulsion.

Alumni association is run by the Secretary, Old Wulfrunians Ltd, 253a Castlecroft Road, Wolverhampton WV3 8DN.

Former pupils Lord Normanbrook (Secretary to the War Cabinet); David Wright (HM Ambassador to South Korea).

· *Woodbridge* ·

Woodbridge School	● Pupils 545	● Termly fees
Woodbridge	● Boys 11–18	£1530 (Day)
Suffolk	(Day/Board)	£2510 (Board)
IP12 4JH	● Girls 11–18	● HMC
Tel 0394 385547	(Day/Board)	Enquiries/application to
	● Upper sixth 80	the Head

What it's like

Founded in 1577, it lapsed during the Civil Wars and was refounded in 1662. It occupied premises in Seckford Street and in 1864 moved to its present beautiful site overlooking the River Deben. For 300 years it was the boys' grammar school for the area and became co-ed in 1974. It possesses fine buildings (old and modern) on a delightful campus of gardens and playing fields covering some 45 acres and is 5 minutes' walk from the centre of the most interesting town of Woodbridge. There has been steady expansion and in recent years there have been added a sixth-form centre, a superb sports hall, a music school, an art block and a technology block. It is now very well-equipped. Woodbridge Abbey is the junior school nearby. A C of E school, it is ecumenical in spirit and practice, with some emphasis on worship and religious instruction. A sound general education is provided and academic standards are high. Many sixth formers go on to degree courses. There is considerable emphasis on pastoral care and constant contact with parents. The school has a good range of sports and games and standards in these are high (a good many representatives at county level). A wide variety of extra-curricular activities is available and the school has a promising record in the Duke of Edinburgh's Award Scheme.

School profile

Pupils Age range 11–18; 545 pupils, 300 boys, 245 girls (day and boarding). Main entry ages 11 and into sixth. Own junior school. *Transfer from maintained schools:* 40% main intake, plus 8% to sixth.

Entrance Common entrance and own exam used. 101 assisted places. 60 scholarships/bursaries.

Staff Head Dr David Younger, in post for 6 years.

Academic work GCSE and A-levels. No A-level general studies. On average, 80 pupils in upper fifth, 80 in upper sixth. *GCSE:* in 1989, 63 upper fifth gained at least grade C in 8+ subjects; 13 in 5–7; and 4 in 1–4 subjects. *A-levels:* 6 upper sixth passed in 4+ subjects; 53 in 3; 15 in 2; and 6 in 1 subject. 45% took science A-levels; 45% arts/humanities; 10% both. *Computing facilities:* Extensive.

· *Woodhouse Grove* ·

Woodhouse Grove
School
Apperley Bridge
Bradford
West Yorkshire
BD10 0NR
Tel 0532 502477
Fax 0532 505290

- Pupils 580
- Boys 11–19
  (Day/Board)
- Girls 11–19
  (Day/Board)
- Upper sixth 80

- Termly fees
  £1245 (Day)
  £2035 (Board)
- HMC
  Enquiries/application to
  the Headmaster

What it's like

Founded in 1812, the main school and Bronte House (the junior department) have fine buildings in spacious grounds in the Aire Valley near Leeds and Bradford. Excellent all-round facilities including a new business management school and comfortable boarding accommodation are provided. A Methodist foundation, it attempts to provide a caring community and each pupil is encouraged to develop individual talents to the full. Religious worship in the Methodist tradition is compulsory. Academic standards are high and results good. Many sixth formers go on to degree courses each year. French and German are offered to A-level and there are regular exchanges with France and Germany. French, German, Italian, Spanish (and Russian) are offered as non-examined languages, and, unusually, there are classes in all five languages for parents. It is very strong in music, especially instrumental music. Sporting facilities are first rate and the standards in sport and games are high (several county representatives). There is some commitment to local community services and it has a promising record in the Duke of Edinburgh's Award Scheme.

School profile

Pupils Age range 11–19; 580 pupils, 440 day (280 boys, 160 girls), 140 boarding (85 boys, 55 girls). Main entry ages 11 and into sixth. Approx 5% are children of former pupils. Own junior school, Bronte House, provides 50% of intake. *Transfer from maintained schools:* 33% main intake, plus 12% to sixth.

Entrance Common entrance and own exam used. Oversubscribed. Aptitude in instrumental music, sport looked for; no religious requirements but school is Methodist. Text books provided by the school; extras include excursions, extra tuition eg music. 130 assisted places. About 20 academic and music scholarships each year, up to £2500 pa.

Parents 15+% are in the armed services. 60+% live within 30 miles; 10+% live overseas.

Staff Headmaster D A Miller, in post for 18 years. 40 full time staff, 25 part time. Annual turnover 3%. Average age 43.

Academic work GCSE and A-levels. 20 subjects offered (including A-level general studies). In 1990, 90 pupils in upper fifth, 80 in upper sixth. *GCSE:* in 1990, 70% upper fifth gained at least grade C in 8+ subjects; 20% in 5–7; and 10% in 1–4 subjects. *A-levels:* 10% upper sixth passed in 4+ subjects; 60% in 3; 20% in 2; and 10% in 1 subject. 50% took science A-levels; 30% arts/humanities; 20% both. *Computing facilities:* BBC machines; Viglen machines in new business school. IT equipment; 2 word processors in dyslexic unit. *Special provision:* Dyslexic Unit – extra tuition. EFL studies.

European Community *Languages:* French offered: to age 14; GCSE; A-level; non-examined. German offered: to age 14; GCSE; A-level; non-examined. Italian: non-examined. Spanish: non-examined. Language classes for parents, holiday classes in French, German, Italian, Russian and Spanish; also business language classes. *Exchanges:* Regular exchanges for pupils aged 11–18 to France and Germany. *Other:* European Studies offered to pupils aged 11–14. Many Euro-boarders spend 1–2 terms in school. 2 French pupils per age group spend 4–6 weeks in school each year.

Senior pupils' non-academic activities *Music:* 160 learn a musical instrument, 18 to Grade 6 or above, 2 accepted for Music School, 56 in school orchestra, 40 in concert band, 30 in choir, 10 in pop groups; 12 have played with National Children's Orchestra and local orchestras/bands. *Drama and dance:* 40 participate in school productions. 52 take Guildhall School exams. *Art:* 15 take as non-examined subject; 15 take GCSE; 16 A-level. 4 accepted for Art School. 14 belong to photographic club. *Sport:* Rugby, cricket, netball, hockey, tennis, squash, athletics, cross-country, badminton, basketball, table tennis, swimming available. Almost all take non-compulsory sport. 15 take RLSS. 9 represent county/country (rugby, ski-ing, cricket, hockey, athletics). *Other:* 15 take part in local community schemes. 12 have bronze Duke of Edinburgh's Award, 2 have silver and 2 have gold. Other activities include a computer club, chess club and matches, vigorous cycling club, Understanding Industry course for lower sixth each year. Driving lessons available.

Careers 5 part time advisers. Annual average accepted for *arts and humanities degree courses* at universities, 11; polytechnics/colleges, 12. *science and engineering degree courses* at Oxbridge, 3; other universities, 14; medical schools, 2; polytechnics/colleges, 14. *BEd,* 4. *other general training courses,* 5. Average going straight into careers in the armed services, 3; the Church, 1; industry, 4; the City, 1; civil service, 1; music/drama, 2; other, 3.

Uniform School uniform worn except in the sixth.

Houses/prefects Competitive houses. Prefects, head boy/girl, head of house and house prefects – appointed by the Head.
Religion Morning prayers compulsory.
Social Regular exchanges with France and Germany. Meals self service. School shop. No tobacco/alcohol allowed.
Discipline No corporal punishment. Pupils failing to produce homework once might expect a warning.
Boarding Upper sixth have own study bedroom, lower sixth share; about half in dormitories of 6+. Single sex houses of 50, in vertical groups. Resident qualified nurse(s). Central dining room. At least two weekend exeats each term. Visits to the local town allowed with permission.
Alumni association is run by G H Knowles, Hon Secretary, Old Grovian Association, c/o the School.
Former pupils Lord Woolley (NFU); Sir Noel Stockdale (Chairman Asda); Alan Cuckston (harpsichord); Steven Burnhill (rugby international); Kenneth Hind MP.

· *Worksop* ·

Worksop College
Worksop
Nottinghamshire
S80 3AP
Tel 0909 472391

- Pupils 400
- Boys 13–18 (Day/Board/Weekly)
- Girls 13–18 (Day/Board/Weekly)
- Upper sixth 67

- Termly fees £1800 (Day) £2625 (Board/Weekly)
- HMC, Woodard Enquiries/application to the Headmaster

What it's like

Founded in 1890, and the last of the Woodard Church of England schools to be founded personally by Canon Woodard. The college lies in a superb estate of 310 acres next to Sherwood Forest about a mile south of Worksop and overlooking the Clumber and Welbeck estates to which pupils of the college have free access. Its handsome if slightly austere brick buildings in the collegiate style form a compact group in a campus of gardens and lawns. Splendid playing fields lie alongside. Earlier buildings include a fine chapel, a theatre, the great hall and a separate art and music school. There has been much modernisation and additional facilities include a swimming pool, a new assembly hall, another theatre, a CDT centre and laboratories. The boys' houses are in the main college and the girls' houses are nearby in separate buildings. The college is now unusually well equipped. Religious worship and instruction is central to the college's life and the chapel is a central feature of life. All boarders attend services on Sundays; there are midweek services for the whole school and several other voluntary services. A large and well-qualified staff allows a favourable staff:pupil ratio of about 1:9. Close attention is given to pupils at all levels. Academic standards and results are consistently high and many sixth formers go on to degree courses. French and Spanish are offered to A-level. There are regular exchanges with France and Spain and pupils are offered the opportunity to attend a French school during their lower sixth year. Music, drama and art are all strong. There are several choirs, an orchestra, concert band, chamber groups and ensembles. Several plays, involving boys and girls, are put on each year in one or other of the theatres. The art studios are very well equipped and work of a high standard is achieved. The main games are rugby, cricket and hockey; in general there is a wide variety of sports and games including golf, sailing, soccer, archery, swimming, tennis, squash, athletics and clay-pigeon shooting. Some 20–25 clubs and societies cater for most people's needs. The strong CCF contingent, comprising Army, Navy and Air Force sections, is very active in connection with the Duke of Edinburgh's Award Scheme in which the girls also take part. The college has a big commitment to local community and social services in Worksop and Bassetlaw.

School profile

Pupils Age range 13–18, 400 pupils. Main entry age 13. Own prep. *Transfer from maintained schools:* 10–12% main intake, plus minimal number to sixth.

Entrance Common entrance or entry test used. Assisted places. Scholarships, including for art and music and all rounders.

Staff Headmaster R D V Knight, 1 year in post.

Academic work GCSE and A-levels. 15 subjects offered (including A-level general studies). In 1990, 83 pupils in upper fifth, 67 in upper sixth. *GCSE:* in 1990, 23% upper fifth gained at least grade C in 8+ subjects; 66% in 5–7; and 15% in 1–4 subjects. *A-levels:* 59% upper sixth passed in 3 subjects; average number of passes 2.4 per pupil. 30% took science A-levels; 40% arts/humanities; 30% both. *Computing facilities:* Fully equipped laboratory and in all departments. *Special provision:* Link with the Dyslexia Institute.

European Community *Languages:* French offered: to GCSE; A-level. Spanish: GCSE; A-level. 10–25% take GCSE in more than 1 EC language. *Exchanges:* Regular exchanges for pupils aged 14–18 to France and Spain. *Other:* Talks from MEP. French students from a school in Bordeaux spend 3 weeks. Lower sixth have opportunity to attend a French school.

Careers In 1990, 61% leavers went on to degree courses; 5% to art/drama/music colleges; 3% to non-degree courses (eg secretarial, BTEC, motor vehicle); 11% straight into careers (eg banking, armed forces, management, police); 20% other. Of those going on to degree courses, 2% went to Oxbridge, 37% to other universities; 61% to poly/colleges. 6% those going on to higher education went to courses in practical art; 1% in drama/acting; 1% in music; 59% in humanities/social sciences; 2% in medicine; and 31% in science/engineering.

· *Worth* ·

Worth School
Paddockhurst Road
Turners Hill
Crawley
West Sussex
RH10 4SD
Tel 0324 715 207

- Pupils 410
- Boys 9–18 (Board)
- Girls None
- Upper sixth 56

- Termly fees £2850 (Board)
- HMC
Enquiries/application to the Headmaster

What it's like

Founded by Downside Abbey in 1933 as a prep school for Downside. In 1957 Worth was made independent and autonomous and in 1959 the upper school was opened for boys of 13+. By 1964 the school had reached the full age range of 13–18. Worth inherits many of the traditions of Downside but has developed its own life and distinctive spirit. The original buildings consist of a late 19th century country house built by Lord Cowdray which is set in an estate of 500 acres of parkland. Monastery and school are closely connected. Many of the lay staff live in houses on the estate so that, as far as possible, monks, lay staff and boys form one community. A well-equipped, energetic and well-run school, Worth lays considerable stress on religious instruction, worship and prayers; the school is informed by the belief that people's growth in faith and commitment to Christ is the fundamental basis of their education and future careers. A large staff (half a dozen or so are Benedictine monks) permits a staff:pupil ratio of 1:8. Academic standards are high and results consistently good. Each year almost all of the pupils go on to degree courses. It is very strong in voluntary service, drama and art. There is a wide range of sports and games and an excellent variety of clubs and societies which cater for most extra-curricular activities.

School profile

Pupils Total age range 9–18; 410 boarding boys. Senior department 13–18, 315 boys. Main entry ages 9, 13 and a few into sixth. Approx 5% are children of former pupils. Own junior house provides more than 40% of senior intake. *Transfer from maintained schools:* 5% senior intake.

Entrance Common entrance used; own exam for transfer from Worth junior house. Oversubscribed. Sport and musical skills looked for. Parents expected to buy A-level text books; maximum extras, £250. 6–8 scholarships/bursaries, 50–15% of annual fees.

Parents 15+% in armed services; 15+% are doctors, lawyers etc; 15+% in industry or commerce. 60+% live within 30 miles; 20+% live overseas.

Staff Headmaster Father Stephen Ortiger, in post for 8 years. 52 full time staff, 20 part time. Annual turnover 2–4%. Average age 40.

Academic work GCSE and A-levels. 20 GCSE subjects offered; 16 at A-level (no A-level general studies). In 1990, 65 pupils in upper fifth, 56 in upper sixth. *GCSE:* in 1990, 2% upper fifth gained at least grade C in 8+ subjects; 45% in 5–7; and 52% in 1–4 subjects. *A-levels:* 65% upper sixth passed in 3 subjects; 20% in 2; and 15% in 1 subject. 14% took science A-levels; 58% arts/humanities; 28% both. *Computing facilities:* Network of 12 BBC's; 6 IBM compatible computers (286 machines) including a DTP system with laser printer.

European Community *Languages:* French offered: to age 14; GCSE; AS-level; A-level. Italian and Spanish offered: to GCSE; A-level. 10–25% take GCSE in more than 1 EC language. *Exchanges:* Regular exchanges for pupils aged 14–16 to Belgium, France and Spain.

Senior pupils' non-academic activities *Music:* 60+ learn a musical instrument, 4 to Grade 6 or above, 1 accepted for Music School every other year. 60 in school orchestra, 25 in choir (member of RSCM), 10 in school pop group, 18 in string band, 15 in swing band. *Drama and dance:* 70 in school productions. 1 accepted for Drama/Dance School every other year; occasional pupil goes on to work in theatre. *Art:* 20 take as non-examined subject; 45 take GCSE, 15 A-level. 3 accepted for Art School; 15 belong to photographic club. *Sport:* Rugby, football, cricket, tennis, squash, fencing, sailing, judo, karate, athletics, swimming, orienteering, cross-country, weight-lifting, basketball, indoor hockey available. Most take non-compulsory sport. 15 take lifesaving exams. Pupils represent county/country (rugby, cross-country, fencing). *Other:* 200 take part in local community schemes. 70 have bronze Duke of Edinburgh's Award, 45 have silver and 6 gold. 5 enter voluntary schemes after leaving, 25 go with handicapped to Lourdes, two-thirds work with national charities, three-quarters with charities in India. Other activities include a computer club, voluntary service (old/disabled), social and development projects, and a wide range of sporting and academic hobbies and societies.

Careers In 1990, 99% leavers went on to degree courses; 1% other. Of those going on to degree courses, 18% went to Oxbridge; 70% to other universities; 11%

to poly/colleges. 3% those going on to higher education went to courses in practical art; 70% in humanities/social sciences; and 23% in science/engineering.

Uniform School uniform worn throughout.

Houses/prefects Competitive houses. Prefects, head boy, head of house and house prefects – appointed by Head and housemasters.

Religion Sunday Mass compulsory; voluntary weekday house Mass; evening prayers by houses.

Social Plays with girls' schools, debates, choral society, sixth form dances. French exchange, ski-ing, annual Lourdes pilgrimage. Meals self service. School shop. No tobacco allowed; limited alcohol for seniors at school functions.

Discipline No corporal punishment. Pupils failing to produce prep might expect to have to get up early and do it before school, or in detention.

Boarding Most sixth formers have own study bedroom, 10 sixth formers share (with 1 other). Resident qualified nurse; doctor visits regularly. Central dining room. Basic allowance of 3 weekend exeats per term, up to 5 may be earned. Sunday visits to local town allowed (14+).

Alumni association run by Kevin Taggart, c/o the School.

· *Wrekin* ·

Wrekin College	• Pupils 380	• Termly fees
Wellington	• Boys 13–18	£1932 (Day)
Telford	(Day/Board)	£2760 (Board)
Shropshire	• Girls 13–18	• HMC, Allied
TF1 3BG	(Day/Board)	Enquiries/application to
Tel 0952 240131	• Upper sixth 80	the Head Master

What it's like

Founded in 1880, it has a fine campus on an estate of about 100 acres stretching out to the Shropshire Plain and backed by the hills of the Wrekin and Ercall. The well-designed and attractive buildings are well dispersed among lawns and gardens with very fine playing fields close by on the edge of the market town. Modern facilities and accommodation are first rate. A C of E foundation, but interdenominational. Anglican practice and worship is encouraged. The pastoral care system is of a high order. Academic standards are high and results are good. A number of leavers go on to degree courses each year. Music, art and drama departments are very vigorous indeed. Sports and games (there is a wide variety) are an important feature. All take part in some compulsory sport. There have been many county and international representatives. An impressive range of extra-curricular activities. Some commitment to local community services.

School profile

Pupils Age range 13–18; 380 pupils, 70 day (45 boys, 25 girls), 310 boarding (200 boys, 110 girls). Main entry ages 13 and into sixth. Approx 10% are children of former pupils. *Transfer from maintained schools:* 7% main intake, plus 10% to sixth.

Entrance Common entrance and own

exam used. Oversubscribed. No special skills or religious requirements. Parents not expected to buy text books; maximum extras £75. 3 assisted places per year at age 13. 20 scholarships/bursaries, £1600–£600.

Parents 15+% in industry or commerce. 10+% live within 30 miles; up to 10% live overseas.

Staff Head Master J H Arkell. 38 full time staff, 12 part time. Annual turnover 6%. Average age 35.

Academic work GCSE and A-levels. 17 GCSE and A-level subjects offered (no A-level general studies). In 1990, 84 pupils in upper fifth, 80 in upper sixth. *GCSE:* in 1990, 38 upper fifth gained at least grade C in 8+ subjects; 8 in 5–7; and 9 in 1–4 subjects. *A-levels:* 3 upper sixth passed in 4+ subjects; 36 in 3; 23 in 2; and 7 in 1 subject. 9 took science A-levels; 48 arts/humanities; 12 both. *Computing facilities:* 12 Archimedes, 6 opus 4, 4 Amstrad available at all times for word processing. *Special provision:* Dyslexic unit of three; maximum two lessons a week per pupil.

European Community *Languages:* French offered: to GCSE; A-level. German offered: to GCSE; A-level. Spanish offered: to GCSE; or as an extra. 10–25% take GCSE in more than 1 EC language. *Exchanges:* Regular exchanges for pupils aged 14–18 to France and Germany began in 1991 (15 fourth form to sister school in Bordeaux in 1991, Black Forest in 1992; 15 lower sixth to various schools in France and Germany in 1991). *Other:* 2–3 German pupils for 1 or 2 terms in fifth and sixth forms.

Senior pupils' non-academic activities *Music:* 52 learn a musical instrument, 12 to Grade 6 or above; 2 accepted for Music School; 1 plays in pop group beyond school; 28 in school orchestra; 46 in choir; 8 in pop group; 20 in jazz band; 4 go to summer schools. *Drama and dance:* 25 participate in school productions – 3 a year. Drama and dance taught to all junior girls. 1 or 2 a year go on to work in theatre. *Art:* 20 take art as non-examined subject; 30 take GCSE; 30 A-level; 1 pottery; 5 a year on average accepted for Art School; 6 belong to photographic club. Photography

offered to GCSE. *Sport:* Rugby, hockey, cricket, netball, athletics, swimming, squash, fives, fencing, shooting, canoeing, sailing, abseiling, climbing, cross-country, 5-a-side soccer available. Most take non-compulsory sport and all take part in some compulsory sport. 3 pupils represent country at gymnastics; 38 represent county (hockey, rugby, athletics, squash, swimming, fencing). *Other:* 15 take part in local community schemes. 3 have silver Duke of Edinburgh's Award, 1 has gold. Other activities include a computer club, chess club, driving lessons. All juniors take self defence. Many seniors take a course in financial skills (mortgages, hire purchase etc).

Careers In 1990, 60% leavers went on to degree courses; 5% to art/drama/music colleges; 15% to non-degree courses (eg agriculture, HNDs); 9% straight into careers; 8% other. Of those going on to degree courses, 3% went to Oxbridge; 22% to other universities; 35% to poly/colleges. 8% those going on to higher education went to courses in practical art; 70% in humanities/social sciences; and 22% in science/engineering.

Uniform School uniform worn except by girls in sixth.

Houses/prefects Competitive houses. Prefects, head boy and girl, head of house and house prefects – appointed by the Head.

Religion Religious worship.

Social Choral works with several local schools. 4 organised trips abroad at Easter holidays (eg canoe trip up Moselle). Meals self service. School shop. No tobacco allowed; alcohol in supervised sixth form bar.

Discipline No corporal punishment. Pupils failing to produce homework once might expect to do it again; those caught smoking cannabis on the premises could expect expulsion.

Boarding 20% have own study bedroom, 40% share (with one other); 20% are in dormitories of 6+. Single sex houses, of 65, same as competitive houses. Resident qualified nurse and doctor. Central dining room. Pupils can provide and cook own food. 2 overnight exeats and half-term. Visits to the local town allowed.

Alumni association run by M J Joyner, c/o the College.
Former pupils Sir Peter Gadsden (Lord Mayor of London, 1980); Brian Epstein (Beatles manager); Cyril Holmes (Olympic athlete and rugby player); many generals, judges and eminent doctors. Harry Andrews (actor); Noel Murless (Keeper of Queen's racehorses).

· Wroxall Abbey ·

Wroxall Abbey School
Warwick
CV35 7NB
Tel 0926 87220

- Pupils 130
- Boys None
- Girls 7–18 (Day/ Board/Weekly)
- Upper sixth 10

- Termly fees
  £1476 (Day)
  £2450 (Board)
  £2338 (Weekly)
- GSA
  Enquiries/application to the Principal

What it's like

Founded in 1872 in Rugby, at the suggestion of Dr Percival, then headmaster of Rugby. It moved to Wroxall Abbey in 1936 where it is set in some 25 acres of fine grounds and unusually magnificent gardens, formerly the domain of a 12th-century Benedictine Priory, of which the 14th-century Lady Chapel and the ruins of the Chapter House survive. The main building is a striking example of Victorian neo-Gothic, elegantly appointed within. The facilities are good and few schools can enjoy such agreeable and civilized surroundings. The beautiful chapel is the focus of worship, and the principles of the Christian faith (in the Anglican tradition) guide the everyday life of the school, but services tend to be non-denominational. It has all the advantages of a small school and a friendly, informal, happy atmosphere is aimed at. There is an unusually favourable staff:pupil ratio, so much attention can be given to individual girls, not least those who have learning difficulties. A broad, general education is provided and results are creditable. Music is strong and most pupils are involved. Drama is also well supported and plentiful use is made of theatres and arts centres in Birmingham, Warwick, Coventry and Stratford-upon-Avon. Concerts are a regular feature and two or three plays are presented each year. Ballet is also taught. Sports and games (a standard range) are well catered for and the facilities are first-rate. Activities include riding (the school has a long tradition in equestrianism). There are ample clubs and societies, plus keen participation in the Duke of Edinburgh's Award Scheme and in local community services.

School profile

Pupils Total age range 7–18; 130 girls. Senior department 11–18, 150 girls (50 day, 80 boarding). Main entry ages 7, 11 and into sixth. *Transfer from maintained schools:* 33% main senior intake, plus 50% to sixth.
Entrance Common entrance and own exam used. Scholarships and bursaries.
Staff Principal Mrs I D M Iles, in post for 10 years.

Academic work GCSE and A-levels. 15 subjects offered (including A-level general studies). In 1990, 32 pupils in upper fifth, 10 in upper sixth. *GCSE:* in 1990, 42% upper fifth gained at least grade C in 8+ subjects; 58% in 5–7. *A-levels:* 2 upper sixth passed in 3 subjects; 1 in 2; and 3 in 1 subject. 2 took science A-levels; 5 arts/humanities; 3 both. *Computing facilities:* Nimbus network, BBCs and Archimedes A3600s. *Special provision:* Specialist staff give extra help, coaching.

European Community *Languages:* French offered: to age 14; GCSE; AS-level; A-level; Institute of Linguists. German, Italian and Spanish offered to GCSE if sufficient demand. 10–25% take GCSE in more than 1 EC language. *Exchanges:* Regular exchanges for pupils aged 14–18 to France. *Other:* Links with schools in Paris and Lille whose pupils visit for part of summer term; also Italian and Spanish visitors and German students in sixth form.

Careers In 1990, 50% leavers went on to degree courses; 50% to non-degree courses (eg secretarial, travel, tourism). Of those going on to degree courses, 40% went to universities; 60% to poly/colleges. 70% those going on to higher education went to courses in humanities/social sciences; and 30% in science/engineering.

· *Wychwood* ·

Wychwood School
74 Banbury Road
Oxford
OX2 6JR
Tel 0865 57976

- Pupils 160
- Boys None
- Girls 11–18 (Day/Board)
- Upper sixth 20

- Termly fees £1080 (Day) £1820 (Board)
- GSA Enquiries/application to the Headmistress

What it's like

Founded in 1897 it is urban and single site on the Banbury Road half a mile from the middle of Oxford. It comprises four main houses and sundry other buildings; modern facilities are good. Worship is in the Anglican tradition. The school council plays a large part in the daily organisation. The atmosphere is friendly and relaxed. Academic standards are high and a number of sixth formers go on to degree courses. French, German and Italian are offered to A-level and there are regular exchanges with France and Germany. A strong music department (virtually everyone is involved). Drama and art are also strong throughout the school. Full use is made of Oxford's cultural amenities. Adequate sports, games and activities. Some involvement in local community schemes including work experience.

School profile

Pupils Age range 11–18; 160 girls, 80 day, 80 boarding. Main entry ages 11, 12, 14 and into sixth. Approx 20% are children of former pupils. Crescent, Manor and Greycotes schools provide more than 20% of intake. *Transfer from maintained schools:* 20% main intakes.

Entrance Own entrance test used. Not oversubscribed. Interesting children with any special talent looked for at entry; no religious requirements. Parents expected to buy text books for pupils in sixth form; other extras variable. Sixth form bursaries.

Parents 30+% in industry or commerce; 30+% are doctors, lawyers etc. 30+% live within 30 miles; up to 10% live overseas.

Staff Headmistress Mrs M L Duffill. 14 full time staff, 12 part time. Annual turnover 1%. Average age 40.

Academic work GCSE and A-levels. 14 subjects offered (including GCSE photography and A-level general studies). On average, 28 pupils in upper fifth, 20 in upper sixth. *GCSE:* on average, 20 upper fifth gain at least grade C in 8+ subjects; 6 in 6–7; and 2 in 1–5 subjects. *A-levels:* on average, 12 upper sixth pass in 3 subjects;

6 in 2; and 2 in 1 subject. On average 9 take science A-levels; 9 arts/humanities; 2 both. *Computing facilities:* BBC Masters; 2 girls to each computer.

European Community *Languages:* French offered: to age 14; GCSE; A-level. German offered: to age 14; GCSE; A-level. Italian: GCSE; A-level. 10–25% take GCSE in more than 1 EC language. Business studies French combined with A-levels. *Exchanges:* Regular exchanges for pupils aged 14–18 to France and Germany. *Other:* Years 1–2 visit Normandy, years 4–5 to Grenoble and sixth form to Paris.

Senior pupils' non-academic activities *Music:* 145 learn a musical instrument, 25 to Grade 6 or above. 1 accepted for Music School. 50 in school orchestra, 50 in choir, others in chamber groups and take singing lessons; 1 in National Youth Orchestra; 6 in county orchestra; 4 in Thames Vale Orchestra. *Drama and dance:* 50 in school productions eg Shakespeare, Wilde, various musicals. *Art:* 80% take GCSE; 6, A-level. 4 accepted for Art School. 10 belong to photographic class. *Sport:* Badminton, squash, tennis, swimming, netball, hockey available. 25 take non-compulsory sport. 3 represent county/country (tennis, cross-country, swimming). *Other:* 15 take part in local community schemes. Other activities include a computer club, debating society, Christian Union, science, chess and design clubs.

Careers In 1990, 50% leavers went on to degree courses; 30% to art/drama/ music colleges; 20% to non-degree courses. Of those going on to degree courses, 50% went to universities; 50% to poly/colleges. 10% those going on to higher education went to courses in practical art; 20% in music; 30% in humanities/social sciences; and 40% in science/engineering.

Uniform School uniform worn except in the sixth.

Houses/prefects No competitive houses. No prefects but councillors elected by the school. Head girl – appointed by Head. School Council.

Religion Church attendance compulsory in first three years.

Social Theatre, operas, lectures etc organised. Use of the city and university facilities. First and fourth year have week's visit to Normandy. Field trips in UK. Pupils allowed to bring own bike to school in the third year. Meals formal. School tuckshop, opens twice a week. No tobacco/alcohol allowed.

Discipline No corporal punishment. The school has a well-tried and proven system of Majors which the girls promoted and therefore adhere to. A pupil caught drinking, smoking, or going out of school without permission could expect to be sent home immediately.

Boarding Upper sixth have own study bedroom, lower sixth share (2 or 3); all others in dormitories of up to 6. Central dining room. Sixth form can provide and cook own food at specified times. 2 weekend and 4 day exeats each term. Visits to city allowed by fourth form and above.

· *Wycliffe* ·

Wycliffe College
Stonehouse
Gloucestershire
GL10 2JQ
Tel 0453 822432
Fax 0453 827634

- Pupils 312
- Boys 13–18
  (Day/Board)
- Girls 13–18
  (Day/Board)
- Upper sixth 75

- Termly fees
  £2066 (Day)
  £3055 (Board)
- HMC
  Enquiries/application to
  the Headmaster

What it's like

Founded in 1882 by G W Sibly, the first headmaster. It became a public school in 1931, by which time the Sibly family had given it a distinctive character which included vigorous championing of vegetarianism and a 'sturdy Protestant independence'. It enjoys a very fine 60-acre, semi-rural site in the Gloucestershire countryside and is within easy range of Gloucester, Cheltenham, Bath and Bristol. The buildings – some dating from the sixteenth century, and some typically Cotswold – are loosely scattered over a campus which has magnificent gardens and playing fields creating a very healthy environment. Much development has taken place in the last 20 years and the school is very well equipped with a purpose-built science block and computing centre. The junior school is close by on a 27-acre site. Wycliffe is interdenominational and there is considerable emphasis on religious instruction and worship (the fine chapel was built by pupils and members of staff in the 1950s). A well-organised school in which there is much enterprise and energy. The teaching is good and academic results are impressive. Each year many pupils for a school of this size go on to degree courses. French, German and Spanish are offered to A-level. There is much strength in music, drama and art. An excellent range of sports and games and an equally good range of extra-curricular activities. The school has a commitment to local community schemes and a remarkable record in the Duke of Edinburgh's Award Scheme.

School profile

Pupils Age range 13–18; 312 pupils, 136 day (102 boys, 34 girls), 176 boarding (113 boys, 63 girls). Main entry ages 13 and into sixth. Approx 5% are children of former pupils. Wycliffe College Junior School provides more than 30% of intake. *Transfer from maintained schools:* 5% main intake, plus 45% to sixth.

Entrance Common entrance and own scholarship exams used. Musical skills looked for; no religious requirements. Parents not expected to buy text books. 42 assisted places. 45 scholarships, 50–5% of fees.

Parents 15+% are in industry or commerce. 30+% live within 30 miles; 10+% live overseas.

Staff Headmaster A P Millard, in post for 4 years. 35 full time staff, 7 part time. Average age 36.

Academic work GCSE and A-levels. 20 GCSE subjects offered; 10 at AS-level; 17 at A-level (including GCSE drama. Sixth form pupils take a general studies course leading to Diploma in Continuing Education). One year sixth form development course for pupils not wishing to follow A-levels and for pupils from overseas (comprises study for the AEB certificate in further studies; information technology; foreign language skills; management and leadership training and European business experience). In 1990, 56 pupils in upper fifth, 75 in upper sixth. *GCSE:* in 1990, 26 upper fifth gained at least grade C in 8+ subjects; 12 in 5–7;

and 10 in 1–4 subjects. *A-levels:* 4 upper sixth passed in 4+ subjects; 51 in 3; 15 in 2; and 6 in 1 subject. 11 took science A-levels; 42 arts/humanities; 24 both. *Computing facilities:* Excellent purpose-built computing department. Apple Macintosh machines. *Special provision:* Individual EFL lessons; support English, though no specialist dyslexic provision.

European Community *Languages:* French offered: to age 14; GCSE; AS-level; A-level. German offered: to age 14; GCSE; A-level. Spanish offered: to age 14; GCSE; A-level.

Senior pupils' non-academic activities *Music:* 120 learn a musical instrument, 36 to Grade 6 or above, 2 accepted for Music College, 1 for university music course. 35 in school orchestra, 55 in choirs, 30 in concert band, several chamber groups. *Drama and dance:* 60 in school productions, 100 in house plays, 10 in weekly workshops. *Art:* 150 take as non-examined subject, 17 GCSE, 23 A-level. 5 accepted for Art School. *Sport:* Rugby, rowing, soccer, hockey, netball, tennis, cricket, athletics, swimming, badminton, cross-country, basketball, squash and riding available. Several represent county and country (rugby, cross-country, rowing, pentathlon, judo). *Other:* 100 take part in local community schemes. 20 have bronze Duke of Edinburgh's Award, 10 have silver and 5 gold. Scouts (and venture scouts), CCF (Army/RAF), car mechanics, drama, sub-aqua, metalwork, woodwork, electronics, video-making, photography, pottery, debating, Young Enterprise, gymnastics, model-making.

Careers In 1990, 80% leavers went on to degree courses; 5% to art/drama/music colleges; 2% to non-degree courses; 5% straight into careers; 7% other. Of those going on to degree courses, 5% went to Oxbridge, 55% to other universities; 40% to poly/colleges. 8% those going on to higher education went to courses in practical art; 4% in drama/acting; 3% in music; 55% in humanities/social sciences; 5% in medicine; and 25% in science/engineering.

Uniform School uniform worn throughout.

Houses/prefects Competitive houses. Prefects, head boy/girl, head of house and house prefects – appointed by Head.

Religion Worship encouraged. Compulsory daily chapel, Sunday service for boarders. Resident Chaplain.

Social Debates, quizzes with local schools; ski-ing, language, rugby, rowing trips abroad. Day pupils in upper sixth allowed to bring own car/bike/motorbike to school. Meals self service. School shop (stationery, sports equipment, toiletries). No tobacco/alcohol allowed.

Discipline No corporal punishment. Pupils failing to produce homework once might expect extra work period; those caught smoking cannabis on the premises can expect expulsion.

Boarding 25% have own study bedroom, 35% share, 40% in dormitories of 6+. Single sex boarding houses of approximately 45, same as competitive houses. Resident qualified nurse/doctor. Separate house dining rooms. Pupils can provide and cook own food. Exeats allowed except when there is school function. Visits to local town allowed in free time.

Alumni association run by Frank Smith, c/o the College.

Former pupils Jeremy Nicholas and Mike Gwilym (actors); Simon Coombs MP; Air Marshal Sir Michael Graydon; Jon Silkin (poet).

· *Wycombe Abbey* ·

Wycombe Abbey
School
High Wycombe
Buckinghamshire
HP11 1PE
Tel 0494 20381
Fax 0494 873836

- Pupils 490
- Boys None
- Girls 11–18
  (Board)
- Upper sixth 85

- Termly fees
  £3024 (Board)
- GSA
  Enquiries to the
  Admissions Secretary
  Application to the
  Headmistress

What it's like

Founded in 1896, it is near the centre of High Wycombe. The main building is a very large mansion in 160 acres of fine grounds. Exceptionally good modern facilities and comfortable boarding accommodation are provided. Academic standards are high. It is a C of E school with its own chapel. All pupils are required to attend daily prayers and a Sunday service. Scripture lessons are also obligatory. A fine range of sports, games and activities is available. Standards in games, music and drama are high. There is a strong commitment to local community schemes and the school has a promising record in the Duke of Edinburgh's Award Scheme.

School profile

Pupils Age range 11–18; 490 boarding girls. Main entry ages 11, 12, 13 and a few into sixth. Approx 3–5% are children of former pupils. *Transfer from maintained schools:* 2% main intake.

Entrance Common entrance exam used. Special skills are always of interest; no religious requirements. Parents expected to buy some text books; other extras variable. 10 junior, 3 sixth form scholarships/bursaries, $\frac{1}{12}$ to full fees.

Parents 15+% are professional. Up to 10% live within 30 miles; up to 10% are overseas pupils.

Staff Headmistress Mrs J M Goodland, in post 2 years.

Academic work GCSE and A-levels. A-level general studies offered. On average, 85 pupils in upper fifth, 85 in upper sixth. *GCSE:* on average, all pupils in upper fifth pass 7 or more subjects. *A-levels:* all pupils take at least 3 A-levels. 25% take science A-levels; 50% arts/humanities; 25% both. *Computing facilities:* Two fully equipped computer rooms with Nimbus network, 36 terminals.

European Community *Languages:* French offered: to age 14; GCSE; A-level. German offered: to GCSE; A-level.

Italian offered: to GCSE; A-level. Spanish offered: to GCSE; A-level. 50–75% take GCSE in more than 1 EC language. *Exchanges:* Regular exchanges for pupils aged 14–18 to France and Spain.

Senior pupils' non-academic activities *Music:* 368 learn a musical instrument, 60 to Grade 6 or above, 90 in school orchestra, 170 in choir. *Drama and dance:* 200 in school productions; 30 take Grade 6 in ESB, RAD etc. *Art:* 40 take GCSE; 5 A-level; 20 belong to photographic club. *Sport:* Lacrosse, netball, tennis, squash, golf, rounders, fencing, gym, athletics, trampolining available. Most take non-compulsory sport or participate in matches. Approx 12 represent county/country (tennis, lacrosse, squash). *Other:* 80 take part in local community schemes. 50 each year do bronze Duke of Edinburgh's Award, 15–20 do silver and gold. Many involved in fund raising for charities. Other activities include computer clubs, film, dining, cookery and bridge clubs, Caledonian, fine art, debating and play reading societies, driving lessons.

Careers In 1990, 98% leavers went on to degree courses; 2% to art/drama/

music colleges. Of those going on to degree courses, 20% went to Oxbridge; 78% to other universities; 2% to poly/colleges. 4% those going on to higher education went to courses in practical art; 56% in humanities/social sciences; 10% in medicine; and 30% in science/engineering.

Uniform School uniform worn except in upper sixth.

Houses/prefects Competitive houses. Prefects, head girl, head of house and house prefects. School Council.

Religion Religious worship compulsory.

Social Caledonian Society, choir, debating society, public speaking and dining clubs with boys' schools. Annual organised choir trip to Europe, ski-ing, cultural visits. School shop. No tobacco allowed; alcohol only on certain occasions.

Discipline No corporal punishment.

Boarding Pupils divided into different houses of 43.

Former pupils Lord Justice Elizabeth Butler-Sloss; Lady Elspeth Howe (Equal Opportunities).

· *Wynstones* ·

Wynstones
Whaddon
Gloucester
GL4 0UF
Tel 0452 22475

- Pupils 286
- Boys 4–18 (Day/Board/Weekly)
- Girls 4–18 (Day/Board/Weekly)
- Upper sixth 10

- Termly fees
  £1158 (Day)
  £2008 (Board)
  £1765 (Weekly)
- Steiner
  Enquiries/application to the College of Teachers

What it's like

It has an agreeable semi-rural site with well-equipped buildings and gardens. Its programme is based on Rudolf Steiner principles and the education is concerned with the inner developmental stages of the child. In the Kindergarten, the main emphasis is on the development of the will, through play and group activities such as games, songs, verses, stories, artistic and practical work. In the lower school the emphasis is on the education of the heart – the life of feelings – to awaken imagination and a sound social sense. In the upper school the emphasis shifts to the development of clear thinking and the exercise of healthy critical judgement. A few pupils go on to degree courses each year, including Oxbridge. There is much emphasis on musical activity and a good deal of drama and art. A full gym, sports and games programme is available and there are some extra-curricular activities.

School profile

Pupils Total age range 4–18; 286 pupils, 268 day (131 boys, 137 girls), 18 boarding (11 boys, 7 girls). Main entry ages, 6–7 and into the sixth. *Transfer from maintained schools:* 5% intakes over 11.

Entrance Entrance by interview. Sometimes oversubscribed. No special skills or religious requirements. Parents expected to buy text books. No scholarships/bursaries.

Parents 60+% live within 30 miles; up to 10% live overseas.

Staff Head, Chairman of College of Teachers (changes annually). 21 full time staff, 18 part time. Annual turnover 2%. Average age 40.

Academic work GCSE and A-levels. 14 subjects offered (no A-level general studies). In 1990, 13 pupils in upper fifth, 10 in upper sixth. *GCSE:* in 1990, 7 upper fifth gained at least grade C in 5–7 subjects; and 6 in 1–4 subjects. *A-levels:* 5 upper sixth passed in 2 subjects; and 3 in 1 subject. All took arts/humanities A-levels. *Special provision:* Remedial department; EFL course.

European Community *Languages:* French offered: to age 14; GCSE; A-level; and as a non-examined subject. German offered: to age 14; AS-level; and as a non-examined subject. Up to 10% take GCSE in more than 1 EC language. *Exchanges:* Regular exchanges for pupils aged 11–16 to France and Germany. *Other:* Up to 5% pupils are EC nationals (French, German, Spanish). EFL programme included.

Senior pupils' non-academic activities *Music:* 30 learn a musical instrument, 6–8 to Grade 6 or above, 1 accepted for Music School every second year; 27 in school orchestra, all attend choir and regular lessons on appreciation and composition; 5 play in local orchestra. *Drama and dance:* 20 in school productions; 2 take exams. 1 accepted for Drama/Dance School; 3 go on to work in theatre. *Art:* 66 take as non-examined subject; 12 take GCSE; 4, A-level; 1–2 accepted for Art School; 2 belong to eg photographic club. *Sport:* Basketball, tennis, hockey, softball available. 20 take non-compulsory sport. 3 represent county/country (basketball, rugby). *Other:* 5 enter voluntary schemes after leaving; 1 works for national charity. Other activities include woodcraft, lapidary, jewellery, photography, printing; small school farm.

Careers In 1990, 25% leavers went on to degree courses; 20% to art/drama/music colleges; 55% other. Of those going on to degree courses, 33% went to Oxbridge; 66% to other universities. 20% those going on to higher education went to courses in practical art; 20% in drama/acting; 60% in humanities/social sciences.

Uniform School uniform not worn.

Houses/prefects No competitive houses or prefects.

Religion Non-denominational Christian assemblies/festivals.

Social Sporting functions with local schools. Organised trips abroad with other Rudolf Steiner schools. Pupils allowed to bring own car/bike/motorbike/horse to school. Meals self service. No tobacco/alcohol allowed.

Discipline No corporal punishment. Pupils failing to produce homework once might expect to stay in after school. Those caught smoking cannabis on the premises would have no future at Wynstones.

Boarding In local, selected private family homes of school parents.

Alumni association run by Mrs Faith Hall, c/o the School.

y

· *Yarm* ·

Yarm School
The Friarage
Yarm
Cleveland TS15 9EJ
Tel 0642 786023

- Pupils 500
- Boys 7–18 (Day)
- Girls 16–18 (Day)
- Upper sixth 43

- Termly fees
  £982 (Day)
  Enquiries/application to
  the Headmaster's
  Secretary

What it's like

Yarm School is a boys' day grammar school, established in its present form in 1978. The major buildings are located at the Friarage, an 18th-century mansion in 14 acres of pleasant grounds alongside the River Tees. Excellent modern facilities are provided including a new classroom block for English, geography and history. Academic standards are high. Very many leavers go on to degree courses, including Oxbridge. Music, drama and art are given considerable attention and a wide variety of sports and games are played. An extensive array of activities range from debating to rock climbing. The Duke of Edinburgh's Award Scheme attracts many participants.

School profile

Pupils Total age range 7–18; 500 day pupils (470 boys, 30 girls). Senior department 11–18, 430 pupils (400 boys, 30 girls). Main entry ages 7, 10+, 11+, 13+ (boys), and into sixth (boys and girls). *Transfer from maintained schools:* 85% senior intake, plus 90% to sixth.

Entrance Common entrance or own exam used. Usually oversubscribed. No religious requirements. Parents expected to buy some text books in sixth form; lunches (£60) extra. 40 scholarships/ bursaries at all age ranges, up to 33% of fees. 8 assisted places pa.

Parents 15+% in industry or commerce; 15+% are doctors, lawyers, etc.

Staff Headmaster R Neville Tate, in post for 12 years. 44 full time staff, 6 part time. Annual turnover 5%. Average age 39.

Academic work GCSE, AS and A-levels. 21 subjects offered (including business studies, politics, A-level general studies for all sixth). In 1990, 66 pupils in upper fifth, 43 in upper sixth. *GCSE:* in 1990, 45 upper fifth gained at least grade C in 8+ subjects; 15 in 5–7; and 6 in 1–4 subjects. *A-levels:* 33 upper sixth passed in 4+ subjects; 5 in 3; 2 in 2; and 2 in 1 subject. 60% took science A-levels; 35% arts/humanities; 5% both. *Computing facilities:* Main computer room has 22 BBC Archimedes, plus about 20 computers in various laboratories and classrooms. *Special provision:* English as a foreign language.

European Community *Languages:* French offered: to age 14; GCSE; AS-level; A-level. German offered: to age 14; GCSE; AS-level; A-level. Italian offered: to age 14; GCSE. 10–25% take GCSE in more than 1 EC language. *Exchanges:* Regular exchanges for pupils aged 11–18 to France and Germany. *Other:* Few German pupils (age 16–17) spend 1 term in school.

Senior pupils' non-academic activities *Music:* 20% learn a musical instrument, 21 to Grade 6 or above; 9% in 3 school orchestras or bands; 8% in choir; 1 pupil in National Youth Orchestra; 3 in other orchestras; 1 pupil on average accepted for Music School. *Drama and dance:* 10–20% in school productions; 1 pupil on average accepted for Drama/Dance School. *Art:* 60% take art as non-examined subject; 15–20 take GCSE, 4–6 A-level; 2 on average accepted for Art School; 18 belong to eg photographic club. *Sport:* Rugby, hockey, cricket, athletics, rowing, tennis, squash, cross-country available; limited activity in ski-ing, swimming, golf, badminton and 6-a-side football. 80 take non-compulsory sport. 18 represent county (rugby, hockey, cricket, tennis). *Other:* 90+ have bronze Duke of Edinburgh's Award, 30+ have silver and 12+ gold. Other activities include a computer club (junior and senior), CAD and computer graphics clubs, chess (Inter School teams), maths (Inter School contests; 10 gold, 14 silver, 13 bronze in UK Maths Challenge 1991), some rock climbing and expedition work, photography, war games, walking, metalwork, plastics moulding, radio control car club, electronics, debating, cooking, extra-curricular art and design, expedition activity (eg India, Peru).

Careers In 1990, 86% leavers went on to degree courses; 8% to art/drama/music colleges; 2% to non-degree courses; 4% straight into careers (eg army, police). Of those going on to degree courses, 7% went to Oxbridge; 61% to other universities; 32% to poly/colleges. 9% those going on to higher education went to courses in practical art; 35% in humanities/social sciences; 17% in medicine; and 39% in science/engineering.

Uniform School uniform worn, modified in the sixth.

Houses/prefects Competitive houses. Prefects, head of school, head of house and house prefects – appointed by the Head.

Religion One compulsory chapel service per week.

Social Joint concerts and orchestral occasions with local choral society and Polam Hall School. About 8 organised trips abroad each year plus regular exchanges with French and German schools. Sixth form pupils allowed to bring own bike to school. Meals self service. Uniform shop; tuck shop (run as company by pupils). No tobacco/alcohol allowed.

Discipline Corporal punishment by Headmaster only. Pupils failing to produce homework once might expect verbal rebuke.

Alumni association is run by R Stephen, c/o The Friarage, Yarm, Cleveland.

· *Yehudi Menuhin* ·

The Yehudi Menuhin School Stoke d'Abernon Cobham Surrey KT11 3QQ Tel 0932 864739	• Pupils 50 • Boys 8–18 (Board) • Girls 8–18 (Board) • Upper sixth 6	• Termly fees £5453 (Board) Enquiries/application to the Headmaster

What it's like

Founded in 1963 by Sir Yehudi Menuhin, with the help of his colleague and friend Marcel Gazelle to provide the ideal conditions in which musically gifted children might develop their potential to the full. The buildings are sited in 15 acres of delightful gardens and grounds in a semi-rural area. The main building is a Victorian Gothic house dating from 1863. This houses the younger children and contains dining room, kitchen and elegant music rooms. The older pupils are accommodated in the other main building, the White House, which contains the science laboratories and school offices. A modern complex dates from 1973, plus another from 1984. A restored barn became a concert hall in 1971. The school is now very well equipped. In 1973 it was given special status as a centre of education for the performing arts with a direct grant from the DES. This, under the auspices of the Music and Ballet scheme, enabled pupils whose parents are resident in Britain (or who have already studied for three years at the school) to receive financial support in accordance with a means test. Overseas pupils (ie nearly 50% of the school's numbers) are heavily dependent on bursaries and donations. It is international and has an international reputation and has produced many distinguished musicians. There are 26 full-time music staff, plus a dozen academic staff (who are all performing musicians). Much of the teaching is done on a one-to-one, or one-to-two basis. Apart from the music tuition which is provided for stringed instruments and piano, there is a broad general education to a high standard. About half of each day is devoted to musical studies. All pupils get guidance in composition and take part in composers' workshops. To develop body suppleness and good posture, training in the Alexander technique is provided. In addition, all pupils are encouraged to work in a wide variety of media, including painting, ceramics, jewellery and textiles. The grounds are well equipped for leisure activities. Sports and games are regarded as important in a pupil's general development. There is a standard range of these. Overall, the school has a highly civilized creative atmosphere and environment and fulfils the founder's intentions.

School profile

Pupils Total age range 8–18, boys and girls (boarding). Main entry age 8.
Entrance By stringent audition. Pupils must be musically gifted; no religious requirements. Aided pupil scheme applies to school.
Staff Headmaster Nicholas Chisholm.

· *York College* ·

York College for Girls
62 Low Petergate
York
YO1 2HZ
Tel 0904 646421

- Pupils 318
- Boys $3\frac{1}{2}$–8 only (Day)
- Girls $3\frac{1}{2}$–18 (Day)
- Upper sixth 18

- Termly fees £1124 (Day)
- GSA, CSCL
Enquiries/application to the Headmistress

What it's like

Founded in 1908, it is right in the city centre in the shadow of the Minster. Its very attractive buildings incorporate 15th-century, Georgian and Victorian architecture, plus a big modern wing. The junior school is nearby and the playing fields are 7 minutes away. It follows Anglican tradition and worship and keeps close links with the cathedral. A balanced all-round education is provided and academic standards are high. Many sixth formers go on to degree courses each year. It is tremendously strong in music and drama. About 50% of pupils learn an instrument and most are involved at some time or another in dramatic productions. A good range of games and sports is available and there are plenty of activities. There is full commitment to local community schemes. Involvement on such a scale is rare.

School profile

Pupils Total age range $3^1/_2$–18; 318 day pupils (26 boys, 292 girls). Senior department 11–18, 199 girls. Main entry ages 3½ (boys and girls), 11 and into sixth (girls). Approx 2% are children of former pupils. *Transfer from maintained schools:* 50% senior intake, plus 3% to sixth.

Entrance Own entrance exam (11+) used. Not oversubscribed. Anglican school but accepts pupils of all religious persuasions. Parents not expected to buy text books; extras include music, drama etc (£55 per term). 1–3 scholarships/bursaries pa, one-third to full fees.

Parents 15+% in farming.

Staff Headmistress Mrs J L Clare, in post for 9 years. 26 full time staff, 8 part time. Annual turnover 5%. Average age between 30 and 40.

Academic work GCSE and A-levels. 15 subjects offered (including A-level general studies). In 1990, 39 pupils in upper fifth, 18 in upper sixth. *GCSE:* in 1990, 26 upper fifth gained at least grade C in 8+ subjects; 9 in 5–7; and 4 in 1–4 subjects. *A-levels:* 6 upper sixth passed in 4+ subjects; 8 in 3; 2 in 2; and 2 in one subject. 9 took science A-levels; 11, arts/humanities; 6, both. *Computing facilities:* Computer room with 11 computers; maths and geography departments have their own.

European Community *Languages:* French offered: to age 14; GCSE; A-level. German offered: to age 14; GCSE; A-level. Spanish offered: to GCSE. 25–50% take GCSE in more than 1 EC language. *Exchanges:* Regular exchanges for pupils aged 14–18 to France and Germany.

Senior pupils' non-academic activities *Music:* 50% learn a musical instrument. *Drama and dance:* School tries to involve everyone at some time. *Art:* 25% take GCSE. *Sport:* Tennis, rounders, swimming, hockey, badminton, netball, squash, athletics, cross-country, fencing, gymnastics available. Over 50% take non-compulsory sport. 2 or 3 represent county/country at various sports. *Other:* Everyone takes part in local community schemes. Other activities include a computer club, choir, orchestra, chess, art club, drama club, needlework, dance.

Careers In 1990, 84% leavers went on to degree courses; 8% to non-degree courses (eg agriculture); 8% other. Of those going on to degree courses, 9% went to Oxbridge; 91% to other universities. 7% those going on to higher education went to courses in music; 58% in humanities/social sciences; and 34% in science/engineering.

Uniform School uniform worn except in the sixth.

Houses/prefects No houses. No prefects. Head girl and deputy – elected by the staff and sixth form. School Council.

Religion Daily assembly. Termly eucharists in the Minster. Saints Day communion in own chapel.

Social Organised trips abroad and exchange systems. Pupils allowed to bring own bike/motorbike to school. Meals self service. No tobacco/alcohol allowed.

Discipline No corporal punishment. Pupils failing to produce homework once might expect a 'returned lesson' or a disorder mark; more serious offences could expect parental involvement and possible expulsion.

Alumni association run by Mrs G Sharper, Secretary OGA, Manor Garth, Church Lane, Skelton, York.

Former pupils Dame Janet Baker.

· *School Spotter* ·

· *School Spotter* ·

This is a search index listing all the schools by country, county and city based on the full description in the *Schools A–Z*, in particular –

Termly fees
If the fees for full and weekly boarding are the same, only one figure is given.

Financial help
Asst places = assisted places; Schols = scholarships; and LEA or MoD mean that the Local Education Authority or the Ministry of Defence offer grants to eligible pupils.

Religion
That which predominates, not necessarily that from which pupils are exclusively drawn.

Special strengths
Non-academic activities in which the school is strong eg music, which does not imply that the school is, say, a specialised music school.

Special provisions
Provision for, say, dyslexic pupils; it should not be supposed the school specialises in pupils with difficulties.

NB Schools are grouped in areas defined by their postal address. In London, schools with, eg SW post codes are in South London, EC post codes in East London. Please be sure to read the full descriptions of the schools in which you are interested in the *Schools A–Z*.

Name of School	Boys/ Girls/ Co-ed	Day/ Board/ Weekly	Termly fees	Financial help	Intake age/ Prep	Special strengths	Special provisions	Religion	Affiliations

· English Cities ·

BIRMINGHAM/WOLVERHAMPTON

Name of School	Boys/ Girls/ Co-ed	Day/ Board/ Weekly	Termly fees	Financial help	Intake age/ Prep	Special strengths	Special provisions	Religion	Affiliations
Edgbaston High	Girls	Day	£1040	Schols Bursaries	11 Own junior	Music, Art, P.E., Drama, D of E		Non-denom	GSA
Holy Child	Girls	Day Weekly	£1065 £2055	Asst places Schols 4 pa	3, 11	Speech & Drama, Tennis	EFL	RC	GSA
King Edward's (Birmingham Boys)	Boys	Day	£1085	Asst places 280 Schols 20	11, 13, 16			Christian	HMC
King Edward (Birmingham; Girls)	Girls	Day	£980	Asst places 185 Schols 25	11, 16			Non-denom	GSA
Royal (Wolver-hampton)	Co-ed	Day Boarding Weekly	£1220 £2110 £1890	Schols Bursaries	4, 11, 16	CCF, Sport	Some help available	C of E	SHMIS SHA
Tettenhall	Co-ed	Day Boarding	£1410 £2290	Schols	7, 11		EFL	Inter-denom	HMC SHMIS
Wolver-hampton Grammar	Boys Mixed sixth	Day	£1131	Asst places 260	11, 13, 16	Music, Sport		Non-denom	HMC

LIVERPOOL

Name of School	Boys/ Girls/ Co-ed	Day/ Board/ Weekly	Termly fees	Financial help	Intake age/ Prep	Special strengths	Special provisions	Religion	Affiliations
Belvedere	Girls	Day	£908	Asst places 30 pa Schols Bursaries	4, 7, 11	Drama, Music, PE		Non-denom	GSA GPDST
Huyton	Girls	Day Boarding	£1085 £2435	Bursaries Schols	2–18		EFL	C of E	GSA

Name of School	Boys/ Girls/ Co-ed	Day/ Board/ Weekly	Termly fees	Financial help	Intake age/ Prep	Special strengths	Special provisions	Religion	Affiliations
Liverpool College	Boys Mixed Sixth	Day	£1025	Asst places 175 Schols 12	5, 11, 16	Music, Sport, CCF		C of E	HMC
Merchant Taylors' (Crosby)	Boys	Day	£963	Asst places 185 Grants 50	7, 11, 13, 16	Sport, Music, CCF	Dyslexia	Non-denom	HMC
Merchant Taylors' (Girls)	Girls	Day	£963	Asst places 164 Schols 7	4, 11	Music, Sport	Mild dyslexia	Non-denom	GSA
St Edwards (Liverpool)	Co-ed	Day	£935	Asst places 385 Schols 10	11, 16 Own prep	Music, Athletics	Dyslexia, EFL Visual handicaps	RC	HMC
St Mary's (Crosby)	Co-ed	Day	£942	Asst places 45 Bursaries 12 pa	4, 11, 13, 16	Art, Sport		RC	HMC

Name of School	Boys/ Girls/ Co-ed	Day/ Board/ Weekly	Termly fees	Financial help	Intake age/ Prep	Special strengths	Special provisions	Religion	Affiliations
LONDON NORTH									
Channing	Girls	Day	£1340	Schols Bursaries	5, 11, 16			Christian	GSA
Francis Holland (Regent's Park)	Girls	Day	£1212	Asst places 5 pa Schols 3 pa	11, 16	Drama, Art, Music		C of E	GSA
Highgate	Boys	Day Weekly	£1675 £2845	Asst places 35 Schols 11 Bursaries 30	7, 8, 9, 10, 11, 13	Sport, The Arts		C of E	HMC
King Alfred (Hampstead)	Co-ed	Day	£1465	Bursaries (sixth form)	4, 7, 11, 14, 16	Drama, Music, Art	Special Needs	Non-denom	
Mill Hill	Boys Mixed sixth	Day Boarding	£1875 £2850	Asst places 15 pa Schols 12 Bursaries	13, 16 Own junior		Extra English, EFL	Non-denom	HMC

Name of School	Boys/ Girls/ Co-ed	Day/ Board/ Weekly	Termly fees	Financial help	Intake age/ Prep	Special strengths	Special provisions	Religion	Affiliations
South Hampstead High	Girls	Day	£1228	Asst places 18 pa Schols/ Bursaries 1–3 pa	5, 11, 16	Music, Art, Drama		Non-denom	GSA, GPDST
Sylvia Young	Co-ed	Day	£805	LEA	7, 11	Specialist stage school	Remedial	Non-denom	ISAI
University College School	Boys	Day	£1690	Asst places 15 pa Schols Grants Bursaries	7, 9, 11, 13	Music		Non-denom	HMC

LONDON SOUTH

Name of School	Boys/ Girls/ Co-ed	Day/ Board/ Weekly	Termly fees	Financial help	Intake age/ Prep	Special strengths	Special provisions	Religion	Affiliations
Alleyn's	Co-ed	Day	£1490	Asst places 200 Schols 12 pa	11, 13, 16	Music, Drama, Art, Sport		C of E	HMC
Blackheath High	Girls	Day	£1024	Asst places Schols Bursaries	4½, 11		Support offered	Non-denom	GSA, GPDST
Christ's (Blackheath)	Boys	Day Boarding	£930 £1680 £1525	Schols 2	4–18		EFL	Non-denom	ISAI
Colfe's	Boys Mixed sixth	Day	£1125	Asst places 222 Schols 30 pa	7–13, 16	Music, Rugby, Drama	Mild dyslexia	C of E	HMC
Dulwich	Boys	Day Boarding Weekly	£1625 £3250 £3125	Asst places 50 pa Schols 30 pa	8, 9, 11, 13	Drama, Art, Music, Sport		C of E	HMC BSA SHA
Eltham College	Boys Mixed sixth	Day Boarding	£1290 £2724 £2594	Asst places 15 pa Schols 19 pa	7, 8, 11	Art, Music, Sport, Drama		Christian	HMC

Name of School	Boys/ Girls/ Co-ed	Day/ Board/ Weekly	Termly fees	Financial help	Intake age/ Prep	Special strengths	Special provisions	Religion	Affiliations
Emanuel	Boys	Day	£1165	Asst places 322 Schols Bursaries	10, 11, 13, 16	Rowing, Music, Drama		C of E	HMC
Francis Holland (Sloane Square)	Girls	Day	£1296	Schols 5 Bursaries	4, 5, 11			C of E	GSA
James Allen's (JAGS)	Girls	Day	£1340	Asst places 150 Schols 20 pa	11 Own prep	All-round		Non-denom	GSA
King's (Wimbledon)	Boys	Day	£1495	Asst places 8 pa Schols 12 pa	13, 16 Own junior	Sport, Music		C of E	HMC
Lycée	Co-ed	Day	£524		4, 14, 16	Bi/tri- lingualism			
Putney High	Girls	Day	£1224	Asst places 20 pa Schols 10	4, 7, 11	Music		Non-denom	GPDST
St Dunstan's (Catford)	Boys	Day	£1150	Asst places 185 Schols 12 pa	7, 11, 16	Music, Sport	Dyslexia	Christian	HMC
St Paul's (Boys)	Boys	Day Boarding Weekly	£1909 £3040	Asst places 11 pa Schols 24 pa Bursaries	13 Own prep	Music		C of E	HMC
Streatham High	Girls	Day	£1024	Asst places 153 Schols 18 Bursaries	11 Own junior	Music, Drama		Non-denom	GPDST
Sydenham High	Girls	Day	£1027	Ass places 136 Bursaries Schols 21	5, 7, 11, 13, 16	Art, Gym, Fencing	Referral	Non-denom	GSA, GPDST

Name of School	Boys/ Girls/ Co-ed	Day/ Board/ Weekly	Termly fees	Financial help	Intake age/ Prep	Special strengths	Special provisions	Religion	Affiliations
Westminster	Boys Mixed sixth	Day Boarding Weekly	£2130 £3200	Asst places 8 pa Schols 8 pa Bursaries (sixth)	13, 16 Own prep	Music, Art, Sport		C of E	HMC
Wimbledon High	Girls	Day	£1024	Asst places 70 Schols 2 Bursaries	5, 7, 11, 16	Music, Drama	Some	Non-denom	GSA GPDST

LONDON EAST

Name of School	Boys/ Girls/ Co-ed	Day/ Board/ Weekly	Termly fees	Financial help	Intake age/ Prep	Special strengths	Special provisions	Religion	Affiliations
City of London (Boys)	Boys	Day	£1578	Asst places 25 pa Schols 25 pa	10, 11, 13	Sport		Non-denom	HMC
City of London (Girls)	Girls	Day	£1362	Asst places 104 Schols 7 pa	7, 11, 16	Music, Drama, Art, Sport	Extra-mural specialists	Christian	GSA
Forest School	Boys Girls Mixed sixth	Day Boarding Weekly	£1348 £2033	Asst places Schols	7, 11			C of E	HMC
Italia Conti	Co-ed	Day	£1700		9	Drama/ dance specialist		Inter- denom	ISAI

LONDON WEST

Name of School	Boys/ Girls/ Co-ed	Day/ Board/ Weekly	Termly fees	Financial help	Intake age/ Prep	Special strengths	Special provisions	Religion	Affiliations
Arts Educational (London)	Co-ed	Day	£1603	Asst places Schols Bursaries	11	Dance and Drama (specialist school)		Non-denom	ISAI
Ealing College	Boys Mixed sixth	Day	£965	Schols (sixth form)	11, 12, 13, 16		EFL	Non-denom	ISAI
Godolphin & Latymer	Girls	Day	£1400	Asst places 25 pa Schol Bursary	11, 16			Non-denom	GSA

Name of School	Boys/ Girls/ Co-ed	Day/ Board/ Weekly	Termly fees	Financial help	Intake age/ Prep	Special strengths	Special provisions	Religion	Affiliations
Latymer	Boys	Day	£1495	Asst places 50 pa Schols Bursaries	9, 11	Music, Sport		Non-denom	HMC
Notting Hill and Ealing High	Girls	Day	£1228	Asst places Bursaries Schols 3	5, 7, 11	Music, Drama		Non-denom	GSA GPDST
Queen's (London)	Girls	Day Weekly	£1250 £2050	Asst places 70 Schols 18 pa	11, 14, 16	Music, Art		C of E	GSA
St Augustine's (London)	Girls	Day	£755		4, 11	Art		RC	
St Benedict's	Boys Mixed sixth	Day	£1250	Asst places 80 Schols	11, 13, 16 Own junior		Some	RC	HMC
St Paul's (Girls)	Girls	Day	£1512	Foundation awards	11	Music		C of E	GSA
Southbank International	Co-ed	Day	£2200	Schols 24	10	Drama, Art	ESL	Inter-denom	ISAI ECIS

MANCHESTER

Name of School	Boys/ Girls/ Co-ed	Day/ Board/ Weekly	Termly fees	Financial help	Intake age/ Prep	Special strengths	Special provisions	Religion	Affiliations
Chetham's	Co-ed	Day Boarding	£3048 £3937	Aided places 240	11, 16	Music specialist	Limited	Non-denom	HMC
Manchester Grammar	Boys	Day	£1000	Asst places 290 Bursaries	11			Christian	HMC
Manchester Jewish Grammar	Boys	Day	£870	Means tested fees Bursaries	10			Jewish	
William Hulme's	Co-ed	Day	£1030	Asst places 35 pa Schols Bursaries	11, 16	Sport		Non-denom	HMC

Name of School	Boys/ Girls/ Co-ed	Day/ Board/ Weekly	Termly fees	Financial help	Intake age/ Prep	Special strengths	Special provisions	Religion	Affiliations
Withington	Girls	Day	£905	Asst places 70 Bursaries	7–9, 11, 16	Music, Drama, Sport		Non-denom	GSA

· **English Counties** ·

AVON

Name of School	Boys/ Girls/ Co-ed	Day/ Board/ Weekly	Termly fees	Financial help	Intake age/ Prep	Special strengths	Special provisions	Religion	Affiliations
Badminton	Girls	Day Boarding	£1525 £2775	Schols 20	7, 11, 12, 13, 16	Music, Drama, Sport, Art		Inter-denom	GSA ECIS
Bath High	Girls	Day	£908	Asst places Schols	11 Own junior			Non-denom	GSA GPDST
Bristol Cathedral	Boys Mixed sixth	Day	£1100	Asst places 25 pa Schols	10, 16	Music		C of E	HMC CSA
Bristol Grammar	Co-ed	Day	£1096	Asst places 350 Schols 7	7, 11, 13, 16	Music, Sport		Inter-denom	HMC
Clifton	Co-ed	Day Boarding	£2170 £3100	Schols 24	13, 16 Own prep	Music, Art	Jewish House	Christian Jewish	HMC
Clifton High	Girls	Day Boarding Weekly	£1025 £2000 £1900	Asst places 13 Schols 11 pa	3, 7, 10, 11, 16	Music, Drama, Art, Sport	English	Christian	GSA
Colston's (Boys)	Boys Mixed sixth	Day Boarding Weekly	£1325 £2195	Asst places 90 Schols 8	13, 16 Own prep	Sport	Dyslexia	C of E	HMC SHMIS
Colston's (Girls)	Girls	Day	£978	Asst places 150 Schols 60 Bursaries	11	Music		Non-denom	GSA
Downside	Boys Mixed sixth	Day Boarding	£1766 £2760	Schols 10 pa Bursaries	11, 13, 16	EC Links, Music, Sport	EFL, Dyslexia, Physical and visual handicap	RC	HMC

Name of School	Boys/ Girls/ Co-ed	Day/ Board/ Weekly	Termly fees	Financial help	Intake age/ Prep	Special strengths	Special provisions	Religion	Affiliations
Grosvenor High	Co-ed	Day	£775	Schols 1 pa	11 Own junior		Dyslexia, EFL	Christian	ISAI
King Edward's (Bath)	Boys Mixed sixth	Day	£990	Asst places 18 Schols 5 pa	11, 13, 16 Own junior	Music, Drama, Sport, Outdoor pursuits		C of E	HMC
Kingswood	Co-ed	Day Boarding Weekly	£1730 £2660	Asst places 37 Schols 11 pa	11, 13, 16	Art, Sport	Visiting specialists	Methodist	HMC
Monkton Combe	Co-ed	Day Boarding	£2135 £2895	Asst places 10 pa Schols 8 pa Bursaries 8 pa	11, 13, 16 Own junior	Sport, Art, Music, CCF	EFL, Dyslexia	Christian	HMC
Prior Park	Co-ed	Day Boarding	£1432 £2590	Asst places Schols	11, 13, 16 Own prep	Art, Music	English	RC	HMC
Queen Elizabeth's Hospital	Boys	Day Boarding	£998 £1752	Asst places 25 pa Schols 6 pa Bursaries	11, 13	Music, Rugby, Cricket		Christian	HMC
Red Maids'	Girls	Day Boarding	£952 £1904	Asst places 25 pa Schols 5	11	Music, Sport, Creative design	EFL	Non-denom	GSA
Redland High	Girls	Day	£925	Asst places 83 Schols Bursaries	11, 16	Art, Music		Christian	GSA
Royal (Bath)	Girls	Day Boarding	£1957 £3066	Schols 20 Exhibitions	3, 11, 13, 16	Music, Drama, Art, Lacrosse	Special needs dept, EFL	C of E	GSA
Sidcot	Co-ed	Day Boarding Weekly	£1375 £2375	Schols/ Bursaries 30	9, 11, 13	Drama, Music, Art	Dyslexia, EFL	Quaker	SHMIS

Name of School	Boys/ Girls/ Co-ed	Day/ Board/ Weekly	Termly fees	Financial help	Intake age/ Prep	Special strengths	Special provisions	Religion	Affiliations
BEDFORDSHIRE									
Bedford	Boys	Day Boarding	£1835 £2890	Asst places 100 Schols 32 Bursaries	7, 8, 11, 13, 16	Music, Sport, Drama		Christian	HMC
Bedford High	Girls	Day Boarding Weekly	£1323 £2524 £2513	Asst places Bursaries	7, 8, 9, 11, 13, 16			Christian	GSA
Bedford Modern	Boys	Day Boarding	£1020 £1885	Asst places 135 Bursaries	7, 11, 13, 16	Sport, Music, Techno- logy		C of E	HMC
Dame Alice Harpur	Girls	Day	£1086	Bursaries Asst places	11, 13, 16 Own junior			Christian	GSA
BERKSHIRE									
Bearwood	Boys	Day Boarding Weekly	£1550 £2800	Schols Bursaries	11, 12, 13, 16	Music, Sport	Dyslexia, EFL	C of E	SHMIS
Bradfield	Boys Mixed sixth	Day Boarding	£2325 £3100	Asst places 6 Schols 18 pa Bursaries	13, 16	Music, Drama, Sport, CDT		C of E	HMC
Douai	Boys	Day Boarding Weekly	£1640 £2600 £2525	Schols 10 Asst places 5	10, 11, 13	Music, Art, Sport	Dyslexia, EFL	RC & Christian	HMC
Downe House	Girls	Day Boarding	£2115 £2920	Schols	11			C of E	GSA BSA
Eton	Boys	Boarding	£3600	Schols 155 Bursaries 120	13	Music, Sport, Art, Drama		C of E	HMC
Heathfield (Ascot)	Girls	Boarding	£3050		11		EFL	C of E	GSA

Name of School	Boys/ Girls/ Co-ed	Day/ Board/ Weekly	Termly fees	Financial help	Intake age/ Prep	Special strengths	Special provisions	Religion	Affiliations
Leighton Park	Boys Mixed sixth	Day Boarding	£2217 £2953	Schols Bursaries 50	11, 13, 16	Music, Drama, Art, Sport	Extra English, Dyslexia	Quaker	HMC
Licensed Victuallers' (Ascot)	Co-ed	Day Boarding Weekly	£1350 £2400 £2350	Schols 12	5, 7, 11, 16	Art	Special Unit	C of E	ISAI SHMIS
Oratory	Boys	Day Boarding	£2012 £2877	Schols Bursaries	11, 13	Music, Drama, Art	Mild dyslexia	RC	HMC
Pangbourne	Boys	Day Boarding	£1950 £2780	Asst places 5 pa Schols 12 pa	11, 13	CCF, Sport	Dyslexia, EFL	C of E	HMC
Queen Anne's (Caversham)	Girls	Day Boarding Weekly	£1695 £2712	Schols 6 Bursaries	11, 12, 13			C of E	GSA
Reading Blue Coat	Boys Mixed sixth	Day Boarding Weekly	£1310 £2390 £2320	Schols 6 pa	11, 13, 16	CCF, Music, Sport		C of E	SHMIS BSA
St George's (Ascot)	Girls	Day Boarding	£1650 £2950		11, 12			Christian	GSA
St Mary's (Ascot)	Girls	Day Boarding	£1788 £2980	Bursaries	10, 11	Sport, Art, Drama		RC	GSA
Wellington College	Boys Mixed sixth	Day Boarding	£2275 £3125	Asst places 34 Schols 14	13 Own prep	Drama, Music, Art, Sport		C of E	HMC

BUCKINGHAMSHIRE

Name of School	Boys/ Girls/ Co-ed	Day/ Board/ Weekly	Termly fees	Financial help	Intake age/ Prep	Special strengths	Special provisions	Religion	Affiliations
Oakdene	Girls	Day	£1290	Schols 16	4, 8, 11, 12		EFL, Mild dyslexia	C of E	GSA
Pipers Corner	Girls	Day Boarding Weekly	£1235 £2225 £2185	Schols Bursaries	8–14, 16	Drama	EFL	C of E	GSA
St Mary's (Gerrards Cross)	Girls	Day	£1180	Schols 6 pa Bursaries 2	11 Own junior	Drama, Sport	EFL, Dyslexia, Mild handicap	Christian	GSA

Name of School	Boys/ Girls/ Co-ed	Day/ Board/ Weekly	Termly fees	Financial help	Intake age/ Prep	Special strengths	Special provisions	Religion	Affiliations
Stowe	Boys Mixed sixth	Day Boarding	£2282 £3262	Asst places 3 pa (sixth only) Schols, Exhibitions, Bursaries 14 pa	13, 16	Sport, Art, Design	Dyslexia	C of E	HMC SHA Allied
Wycombe Abbey	Girls	Boarding	£3024	Schols 13 pa	11, 12, 13	Sport, Music, Drama		C of E	GSA

CAMBRIDGESHIRE

Name of School	Boys/ Girls/ Co-ed	Day/ Board/ Weekly	Termly fees	Financial help	Intake age/ Prep	Special strengths	Special provisions	Religion	Affiliations
King's (Ely)	Co-ed	Day Boarding Weekly	£1943 £2896 £2826	Schols 50	4, 9, 11, 13, 16	Art, Drama, Music, Games		C of E	HMC
Leys	Boys Mixed sixth	Day Boarding	£2190 £2960	Asst places 12 Schols 18	13, 14, 16	Drama, Art	Dyslexia	Methodist	HMC
Perse (Boys)	Boys	Day Boarding	£1087 £2187	Asst places 57 Bursaries	11, 13 Own prep	Art, Sport		Christian	HMC
Perse (Girls)	Girls	Day	£1048	Asst places 20 pa Bursaries 15 pa	7–11	Music, Art, Sport	Some available	Non-denom	GSA
St Mary's (Cambridge)	Girls	Day Weekly	£891 £1590	Asst places 25 pa	11, 16	Drama, Young Enterprise, Music		RC	GSA

CHANNEL ISLANDS

Name of School	Boys/ Girls/ Co-ed	Day/ Board/ Weekly	Termly fees	Financial help	Intake age/ Prep	Special strengths	Special provisions	Religion	Affiliations
Elizabeth College	Boys	Day Boarding	£645 £1565	Schols	7, 11, 13	Music, Sport		C of E	HMC
Victoria (Jersey)	Boys	Day Boarding Weekly	£477 £2304 £1975	Schols 4 pa	7, 11, 13	Sailing, Shooting	EFL	Christian	HMC

Name of School	Boys/ Girls/ Co-ed	Day/ Board/ Weekly	Termly fees	Financial help	Intake age/ Prep	Special strengths	Special provisions	Religion	Affiliations
CHESHIRE									
Birkenhead	Boys	Day	£865	Asst places 250 Schols 20 pa	4, 11, 13, 16			Christian	HMC
Birkenhead High	Girls	Day	£908	Asst places 40 pa Schols	11, 16 Own junior	Drama, Music, Sport		Christian	GPDST
Cheadle Hulme	Co-ed	Day Boarding	£990 £2160	Asst places 20 Schols/ Bursaries 4	7, 8, 11	Music, Art, Drama			HMC
Grange	Co-ed	Day	£870		4, 11			Christian	ISAI
Hammond	Co-ed	Day Boarding	£870 £2500	LEA	11	Classical ballet specialist		C of E	ISAI
King's (Chester)	Boys	Day	£1205	Asst places 100 Schols	8, 9, 11	Drama, Rowing		C of E	HMC
King's (Maccles- field)	Boys Mixed sixth	Day	£1155	Asst places 35 Schols 5	7–11, 13, 16	Sport, Music	English	C of E	HMC
Mount Carmel	Girls	Day	£865	Asst places Bursaries	11	Music		RC	ISAI
Queen's (Chester)	Girls	Day	£852	Asst places 17 pa Bursaries	4, 8, 11		Some	Christian	GSA, SHA
St Ambrose	Boys	Day	£839	88 Asst places Schols/ Bursaries 10 pa	4, 7, 11	Sport		RC	HMC
St Anselm's	Boys	Day	£774	Asst places 35 pa Schols 2 pa LEA	11 Own prep		For visually handi- capped	RC	HMC

Name of School	Boys/ Girls/ Co-ed	Day/ Board/ Weekly	Termly fees	Financial help	Intake age/ Prep	Special strengths	Special provisions	Religion	Affiliations
S Hilary's (Alderley Edge)	Girls	Day	£1015	Schols Bursaries	4, 11			C of E	GSA Woodard
Wellington (Wirral)	Co-ed	Day	£835	Schols/ Bursaries 5	11, 13			Christian	ISAI
CLEVELAND									
Friends' (Great Ayton)	Co-ed	Day Boarding Weekly	£1058 £2281 £2009	Schols Bursaries	7, 11, 13	Music, Drama, Art	EFL, Dyslexia	Quaker	
Teesside High	Girls	Day	£1038	Sixth form bursaries	5, 7, 11	Music, Sport	EFL	Non-denom	GSA
Yarm	Boys Mixed sixth	Day	£982	Schols 40 8 Asst places pa	7, 10, 11, 13	Hockey, D of E expeditions	EFL	Christian	SHMIS
CORNWALL									
Duchy Grammar	Co-ed	Day Boarding Weekly	£980 £1985 £1825	Schols 6	11 Own junior		EFL, Dyslexia	Christian	ISAI
St Clare's	Girls	Day Boarding Weekly	£1087 £2035 £1899	Schols 4–5 Bursaries	16	Music, Sport	English	C of E	GSA Woodard
Truro High	Girls	Day Boarding Weekly	£1090 £1990 £1957	Asst places 15 pa Schols	11 Own junior	Music, Drama, Sport		C of E	GSA
CUMBRIA									
Austin Friars	Co-ed	Day Boarding	£1025 £1800	Asst places Schols 13	11, 13	Sport	EFL	RC	SHMIS
Casterton	Girls	Day Boarding Weekly	£1504 £2444 £2034	Asst places 43 Schols 48	11 Own junior	Outdoor activities	Mild dyslexia	C of E	GSA

Name of School	Boys/ Girls/ Co-ed	Day/ Board/ Weekly	Termly fees	Financial help	Intake age/ Prep	Special strengths	Special provisions	Religion	Affiliations
Lime House	Co-ed	Day Boarding Weekly	£750 £1750 £1400	Schols 12 pa	4–18	Sport, Drama, Art	Dyslexia, EFL	Christian	ISAI
St Anne's (Winder- mere)	Girls	Day Boarding	£1730 £2530	Schols 13	3, 11, 13, 16	Music, Drama, Art	EFL	Christian	GSA SHMIS Round Square
St Bees	Co-ed	Day Boarding Weekly	£1820 £2600 £2550	Asst places 84 Schols Bursaries	11, 13, 16			C of E	HMC
Sedbergh	Boys	Day Boarding	£2065 £2950	Asst places 26 Schols 75 Bursaries 46	11, 13	Sport, Music		C of E	HMC

DERBYSHIRE

Name of School	Boys/ Girls/ Co-ed	Day/ Board/ Weekly	Termly fees	Financial help	Intake age/ Prep	Special strengths	Special provisions	Religion	Affiliations
Normanton (Buxton)	Co-ed	Day Boarding Weekly	£900 £1950 £1875		10		Dyslexia, ESL	Non-denom	ISAI
Repton	Co-ed	Day Boarding	£2180 £2940	Asst places 41 Schols 18 pa Music awards 4	13 Own prep	Music, Tennis, Sport	Dyslexia	C of E	HMC
St Elphin's	Girls	Day Boarding Weekly	£1395 £2396 £2276	Schols	11 Own junior	Music	EFL, Dyslexia	C of E	GSA SHA

DEVON

Name of School	Boys/ Girls/ Co-ed	Day/ Board/ Weekly	Termly fees	Financial help	Intake age/ Prep	Special strengths	Special provisions	Religion	Affiliations
Blundell's	Boys Mixed sixth	Day Boarding	£1800 £2900	Schols 50+	13, 16	Music, Art, Sport	EFL, Dyslexia	Non-denom	HMC BSA
Edgehill	Girls	Day Boarding Weekly	£1235 £2260 £2040	Asst places 22 pa Schols	3, 11, 13, 16	Music, Sport	Remedial, Dyslexia, EFL	Methodist	GSA

Name of School	Boys/ Girls/ Co-ed	Day/ Board/ Weekly	Termly fees	Financial help	Intake age/ Prep	Special strengths	Special provisions	Religion	Affiliations
Exeter	Boys Mixed sixth	Day Boarding	£995 £1855	Asst places 30 pa Schols/ Bursaries 4 pa	11, 12, 13, 16 Own prep	Music, Drama, Sport		C of E	HMC
Kelly College	Co-ed	Day Boarding Weekly	£1195 £2825 £2700	Schols 17 Exhibitions Bursaries	11, 16			C of E	HMC
Maynard	Girls	Day	£953	Asst places 31 pa Bursaries	7, 10, 11	Sport, Music, Drama		Non-denom	GSA
Mount St Mary's (Exeter)	Girls	Day	£750		11 Own junior	Music, Sport		RC	
St Dunstan's (Plymouth)	Girls	Day Weekly	£995 £1615	Schols 7	4, 9, 11	Netball, Hockey	Some	Christian	GSA
Shebbear	Boys Mixed sixth	Day Boarding	£1195 £2218	Schols Bursaries	7, 11, 13, 16	Art, Ceramics	EFL	Methodist	SHMIS
Stover	Girls	Day Boarding Weekly	£1005 £2000 £1950	Schols 4 pa	11			C of E	GSA
West Buckland	Co-ed	Day Boarding Weekly	£1179 £2171	Asst places 14 pa Schols 6 pa	7, 11, 13, 16	Sport	EFL	C of E	HMC
DORSET									
Bryanston	Co-ed	Boarding	£3250	Schols 20	13, 16	Music, Drama, Art, Sport		Christian	HMC
Clayesmore	Co-ed	Day Boarding	£1960 £2780	Schols 20 pa	13, 16 Own prep	Sport, Music, Drama	Remedial, EFL	C of E	SHMIS
Croft House	Girls	Day Boarding	£1635 £2350	Schols 5 Bursaries	11, 12, 13, 16	Art, Riding, Sport	Individual tuition	C of E	GSA

Name of School	Boys/ Girls/ Co-ed	Day/ Board/ Weekly	Termly fees	Financial help	Intake age/ Prep	Special strengths	Special provisions	Religion	Affiliations
Milton Abbey	Boys	Boarding	£2856	Schols 8 pa	13	Art, Sport, CCF	Remedial, EFL	C of E	SHMIS
St Antony's-Leweston	Girls	Day Boarding	£1575 £2480	Schols	11, 12, 13 Own prep	Music, Drama, Art, Sport	English	RC	GSA BSA
St Mary's (Shaftesbury)	Girls	Day Boarding	£1475 £2355	Schols 4 pa	10, 11	Music		RC	GSA BSA
Sherborne (Boys)	Boys	Day Boarding	£2450 £3200	Schols 17 pa	13	Music, Drama, Sport		C of E	HMC
Sherborne (Girls)	Girls	Day Boarding	£1840 £2760	Schols/ Exhibitions 11	12, 13	Music, Drama, Sport	Mild dyslexia	C of E	GSA BSA
Talbot Heath	Girls	Day	£1325 £2316 £2254	Asst places 140 Schols 4–12 pa Bursaries	8, 11	Sport, Music, Drama	EFL Dyslexia	C of E	GSA, SHA
Wentworth Milton Mount	Girls	Day Boarding Weekly	£1340 £2155	Schols Bursaries	11		Dyslexia, EFL	Non-denom	GSA

DURHAM

Name of School	Boys/ Girls/ Co-ed	Day/ Board/ Weekly	Termly fees	Financial help	Intake age/ Prep	Special strengths	Special provisions	Religion	Affiliations
Barnard Castle	Boys Mixed sixth	Day Boarding	£1167 £1972	Schols Asst places	8, 11, 13, 16	Sport, Music, Outdoor pursuits	Dyslexia, EFL	Christian	HMC
Durham	Boys Mixed sixth	Day Boarding	£1933 £2900	Schols	11, 13, 16	Sport	Dyslexia	C of E	HMC
Durham High	Girls	Day	£860	Bursaries	4, 7, 10, 11, 16			C of E	GSA
Polam Hall	Girls	Day Boarding Weekly	£1010 £2060 £2035	Asst places 5 Schols	4, 9, 11, 13, 16	Music, Drama	Dyslexia, EFL	Christian	GSA

Name of School	Boys/ Girls/ Co-ed	Day/ Board/ Weekly	Termly fees	Financial help	Intake age/ Prep	Special strengths	Special provisions	Religion	Affiliations
ESSEX									
Bancroft's	Co-ed	Day	£1328	Asst places 80 Schols 90 Bursaries 35	7, 11, 16	Sport, Drama, Music		Christian	HMC SHA
Brentwood	Boys Girls Mixed sixth	Day Boarding (Boys)	£1384 £2423	Asst places Bursaries Schols 12 pa	11, 13, 16 Own prep (boys)	Sport, Music, Fencing	EFL	Protestant	HMC
Chigwell	Boys Mixed sixth	Day Boarding Weekly	£1527 £2322 £2198	Asst places 60 Schols 6	7, 11, 16	Music	EFL	C of E	HMC
Felsted	Boys Mixed sixth	Day Boarding	£2390 £3030	Asst places 38 Schols 16 Bursaries	13, 16 Own prep	Music, Sport		C of E	HMC
Friends' (Saffron Walden)	Co-ed	Day Boarding	£1598 £2550	Asst places 80 Schols Bursaries	11, 12, 13, 14, 16			Quaker	SHMIS
New Hall	Girls	Day Boarding	£1745 £2725	Schols Bursaries	11, 12, 13, 14, 16	Music, Drama, Art, Dance	Educational needs, Handicaps	RC	GSA
St Mary's (Colchester)	Girls	Day	£885		4, 11	Drama, Music	Dyslexia, EFL	C of E	GSA
GLOUCESTERSHIRE									
Cheltenham (Boys)	Boys Mixed sixth	Day Boarding	£2370 £3150	Schols Bursaries 20	Dover13 Own junior	Drama, Music, Sport		C of E	HMC
Cheltenham Ladies	Girls	Day Boarding	£1920 £3025	Asst places 5 pa Schols 12 pa	11, 12, 13, 16	Music, Drama, Sport		C of E	GSA
Hatherop Castle	Girls	Day Boarding Weekly	£1075 £2165 £2140	Schols 5 pa	3, 11, 16		Dyslexia, EFL	Christian	ISAI

Name of School	Boys/ Girls/ Co-ed	Day/ Board/ Weekly	Termly fees	Financial help	Intake age/ Prep	Special strengths	Special provisions	Religion	Affiliations
King's (Gloucester)	Co-ed	Day Boarding Weekly	£1359 £2296 £2111	Schols 15 Choristers free	4, 11	Music	Mild dyslexia, EFL	C of E	SHMIS CSA
Rendcomb	Boys Mixed sixth	Boarding	£2970	Asst places Schols 12 Bursaries LEA	11, 13, 16	Drama, Art		Christian	HMC
St Edward's (Cheltenham)	Co-ed	Day	£1273	Schols 11 pa Discretionary awards	4	Sport, Drama	Special needs	RC	ISAI
Westonbirt	Girls	Day Boarding	£1723 £2678	Schols Bursaries	11	Lacrosse, Music	EFL, Individual coaching	C of E	GSA Allied
Wycliffe	Co-ed	Day Boarding	£2066 £3055	Asst places 42 Schols 45	13, 16 Own junior	Art, Music, Sport	EFL	Inter- denom	HMC
Wynstones	Co-ed	Day Boarding Weekly	£1158 £2008 £1765		6	Music, Drama	Remedial, EFL	Non-denom	Steiner

HAMPSHIRE

Name of School	Boys/ Girls/ Co-ed	Day/ Board/ Weekly	Termly fees	Financial help	Intake age/ Prep	Special strengths	Special provisions	Religion	Affiliations
Alton Convent	Girls	Day	£720	Schols	11 Own junior			RC	
Atherley	Girls	Day	£1012	Schols 5–6	4, 11			C of E	GSA SHA CSCL
Bedales	Co-ed	Day Boarding	£2240 £3125	Asst places 5 pa Bursaries	13 Own junior	Music, Drama, Art	Dyslexia	Non-denom	HMC SHMIS
Churcher's	Co-ed	Day Boarding Weekly	£1220 £2260 £2210	Asst places 19 pa Schols/ Bursaries	11, 12, 13	Sport		Non-denom	HMC

Name of School	Boys/ Girls/ Co-ed	Day/ Board/ Weekly	Termly fees	Financial help	Intake age/ Prep	Special strengths	Special provisions	Religion	Affiliations
Embley Park	Boys Mixed sixth	Day Boarding Weekly	£1540 £2355	Schols Bursaries	11, 13, 16	Sport, Small groups	Dyslexia, EFL	C of E	SHA BSA ISAI
Farnborough Hill	Girls	Day	£1063	Asst places 179 Bursaries 21	11		Remedial help	RC	GSA SHA
King Edward (South- ampton)	Boys Mixed sixth	Day	£1100	Asst places 40 pa Schols Bursaries	11, 13, 16			Non-denom	HMC
Lord Wandsworth	Boys Mixed sixth	Day Boarding Weekly	£1836 £2352	Asst places 75 Schols 2 6 Foundation Awards pa	11, 13, 16			Non-denom	HMC
North Foreland Lodge	Girls	Boarding	£2700	Schols 2	11			C of E	GSA
Portsmouth Grammar	Co-ed	Day	£985	Asst places Schols Bursaries	11 Own junior	Music, Art		Non-denom	HMC
Portsmouth High	Girls	Day	£908	Asst places 29 pa Schols 5 pa	11, 14, 16 Own junior	Music, Sport	Mild handicap	Christian	GSA GPDST
Stanbridge Earls	Co-ed	Day Boarding Weekly	£2200 £2950	Schols 10	11, 13	Art, Drama	Remedial unit	C of E	
Winchester	Boys	Day Boarding	£2700 £3600	Asst places 5 pa Schols 15 pa Music Awards 6	13	Music, Rowing		C of E	HMC

HEREFORDSHIRE

Name of School	Boys/ Girls/ Co-ed	Day/ Board/ Weekly	Termly fees	Financial help	Intake age/ Prep	Special strengths	Special provisions	Religion	Affiliations
Hereford Cathedral	Co-ed	Day Boarding	£1095 £1885	Asst places 40 Schols 5	11, 13	Music		C of E	HMC

Name of School	Boys/ Girls/ Co-ed	Day/ Board/ Weekly	Termly fees	Financial help	Intake age/ Prep	Special strengths	Special provisions	Religion	Affiliations
HERTFORDSHIRE									
Aldenham	Boys Mixed sixth	Day Boarding	£1927 £3034	Asst places 35 Schols	13, 16	Sport, Pastoral care		C of E	HMC
Arts Educational (Tring)	Girls	Day Boarding	£1550 £2267 £2610	Grants Asst places 50	10–16	Dance, Drama, Music	English	Inter- denom	
Berkhamsted (Boys)	Boys	Day Boarding Weekly	£1643 £2826	Asst places 5 pa Schols 10–12	7, 10, 13, 16	Sport, Music, D of E, CCF	EFL, Extra English	C of E	HMC
Bishop's Stortford	Boys Mixed sixth	Day Boarding	£1960 £2710	Asst places Schols Awards Bursaries	13, 16 Own prep	Art, Music, Drama		Non-denom	HMC
Haber- dashers' Aske's (Boys)	Boys	Day	£1381	Asst places 35 pa Bursaries 12 pa Schols	7, 11	Music, Drama, Art		Christian	HMC
Haber- dashers' Aske's (Girls)	Girls	Day	£900	Asst places 180 Schols/ Bursaries 10 pa	5, 11	Music, Sport		Christian	GSA
Haileybury	Boys Mixed sixth	Day Boarding	£2150 £3195	Asst places Schols 15 Bursaries	11, 13	Music, Drama, Sport	Mild dyslexia	C of E	HMC
Northfield	Girls	Day	£1155	Schols Bursaries	3, 7, 11	Art, Drama, Pastoral care		Inter- denom	ISAI
Princess Helena	Girls	Day Boarding	£1750 £2480	Schols 4 pa Bursaries	11	Music	EFL	C of E	GSA BSA
Queenswood	Girls	Day Boarding	£1897 £2845	Schols 8 pa	11, 12, 13, 16	Music, Drama, Tennis, Art, Hockey	Dyslexia	Christian	GSA BSA

Name of School	Boys/ Girls/ Co-ed	Day/ Board/ Weekly	Termly fees	Financial help	Intake age/ Prep	Special strengths	Special provisions	Religion	Affiliations
Rickmans- worth Masonic	Girls	Day Boarding Weekly	£1194 £2089 £2053	Bursaries Schols 14	7, 11, 16	Music, Art	Mild dyslexia	C of E	GSA
St Albans	Boys Mixed sixth	Day	£1395	Asst places 150 Schols 2	11, 13, 16	Music	Mild dyslexia	Christian	HMC
St Albans High	Girls	Day	£1125	Asst places 15 pa Schols Bursaries	11 Own prep			C of E	GSA
St Christopher (Letchworth)	Co-ed	Day Boarding	£1550 £2740		2, 9, 11, 16	'Family' school, Drama, Art, Outdoor pursuits	Dyslexia, EFL		
St Edmund's (Ware)	Co-ed	Day Boarding Weekly	£1455 £2264 £2099	Asst places 80 Schols 10	7, 11, 13, 16	Sport	Mild dyslexia	RC	HMC SHA
St Martha's (Hadley Wood)	Girls	Day	£690		11 Own junior			RC	
Sherrards- wood	Co-ed	Day Boarding Weekly	£1125 £2120	Schols 2 pa	4, 11, 16		EFL	C of E	ISAI

ISLE OF WIGHT

Name of School	Boys/ Girls/ Co-ed	Day/ Board/ Weekly	Termly fees	Financial help	Intake age/ Prep	Special strengths	Special provisions	Religion	Affiliations
Bembridge	Co-ed	Day Boarding Weekly	£1195 £2225 £2175	Schols 6 Bursaries	7–11, 13	Art, Craft and practical subjects	Dyslexia, EFL	Non-denom	SHMIS
Ryde	Co-ed	Day Boarding Weekly	£1074 £2145 £2042	Schols 5 pa	9, 11, 13, 16	Art		Christian	HMC SHMIS
Upper Chine	Girls	Day Boarding Weekly	£1180 £2220 £1980	Schols Bursaries	3–6, 10, 11, 12	Drama	Remedial	C of E	GSA

Name of School	Boys/ Girls/ Co-ed	Day/ Board/ Weekly	Termly fees	Financial help	Intake age/ Prep	Special strengths	Special provisions	Religion	Affiliations
KENT									
Ashford	Girls	Day Boarding Weekly	£1299 £2267 £2237	Asst places 41 Schols 6	5, 7, 11, 13	Music, D of E Award	Some help	Non-denom	GSA
Baston	Girls	Day Boarding Weekly	£1025 £1930 £1900	Schols/ bursaries 3	3, 4, 5, 7, 11	Music, Art & Crafts, Sport	EFL	Christian	ISAI
Bedgebury	Girls	Day Boarding	£1600 £2643	Schols 15 pa	3–18	Art, Music, Riding, Sport, Outdoor pursuits	Dyslexia, EFL	C of E	GSA
Benenden	Girls	Boarding	£3150	Schols	11, 12, 13	Drama, Sport, Music	Short-term help	C of E	GSA
Bethany	Co-ed	Day Boarding	£1636 £2556	Schols 10 pa	11, 13	Small family school	Dyslexia	Christian	SHMIS
Bishop Challoner	Boys Mixed sixth	Day	£915	Schols/ Bursaries	4, 11, 16			RC	ISAI
Bromley High	Girls	Day	£1024	Asst places 150 Schols variable	4, 11	Music		Non-denom	GSA GPDST
Cobham Hall	Girls	Day Boarding Weekly	£2140 £3190	Schols 7	11, 12, 13, 16	Art, Drama, European links	Dyslexia, EFL	Inter- denom	GSA Round Square
Combe Bank	Girls	Day	£1300	Schols	3, 11, 12, 13	Music	Dyslexia	RC	GSA
Dover College	Co-ed	Day Boarding Weekly	£1890 £2860 £2750	Asst places 5 pa Schols/ Bursaries 12 pa	11, 13, 16 Own junior		EFL, Dyslexia	C of E	HMC

Name of School	Boys/ Girls/ Co-ed	Day/ Board/ Weekly	Termly fees	Financial help	Intake age/ Prep	Special strengths	Special provisions	Religion	Affiliations
Duke of York's	Boys	Boarding	£266	MoD	11, 13		Only sons of army personnel admitted	C of E	
Farringtons	Girls	Day Boarding Weekly	£1193 £2180 £2095	Bursaries 4 Organ schol 1	3, 5	Music, Art	EFL, Extra coaching	Christian	GSA
Fosse Bank	Girls	Day Boarding Weekly	£965 £1935 £1905	Schols 4	5, 12	Small classes	EFL, Mild learning problems	C of E	
Holy Trinity (Bromley)	Girls	Day	£1046	Schols 3	5, 11, 14			RC	GSA
Kent College (Canterbury)	Co-ed	Day Boarding	£1500 £2678	Asst places Schols Bursaries	7, 11, 13, 16	Music	Dyslexia	Inter- denom	HMC
Kent College (Pembury)	Girls	Day Boarding Weekly	£1470 £2465 £2275	Schols 7	Up to 11, 13, 16	Drama, Music, Swimming	EFL Dyslexia	Inter- denom	GSA
King's (Canterbury)	Co-ed	Day Boarding	£2170 £3100	Awards numerous	13	Art, Music		C of E	HMC
King's (Rochester)	Boys Mixed sixth	Day Boarding Weekly	£1741 £2904	Asst places 54 Schols 83	13, 16	Music, Art, Drama, Sport		C of E	HMC CSA
Nativity School	Girls	Day	£900	Schols	3, 11	Drama	Small group teaching	RC	ISAI
Sacred Heart (Tunbridge Wells)	Girls	Day Boarding Weekly	£1520 £2645	Schols 5 Bursaries	5, 11, 14	Art	EFL	RC	GSA
St Augustine's (Westgate- on-Sea)	Boys	Day Boarding	£1725 £2600	Schols	13, 16 Own prep		EFL	RC	
St Edmund's (Canterbury)	Co-ed	Day Boarding Weekly	£1830 £2975	Schol Bursaries	4, 7, 11, 13, 16	Music		C of E	HMC CSA

Name of School	Boys/ Girls/ Co-ed	Day/ Board/ Weekly	Termly fees	Financial help	Intake age/ Prep	Special strengths	Special provisions	Religion	Affiliations
St Hilary's (Sevenoaks)	Girls	Day	£1275	Schols 12 Bursaries 9	3, 5, 7, 11	Music	Dyslexia	Christian	GSA
Sevenoaks	Co-ed	Day Boarding	£1758 £2895	Asst places 5 pa Schols/ Bursaries 50	11, 13, 16	Rugby, Music, Drama, Tennis, Sailing	Some	Inter- denom	HMC
St Lawrence	Co-ed	Day Boarding Weekly	£1790 £2670	Asst places Schols Bursaries	11, 13 Own junior		EFL	C of E	HMC
Stratford House	Girls	Day	£1150	Schols 6 Bursaries	4, 11, 16	Music, Drama, Art		Christian	GSA
Sutton Valence	Co-ed	Day Boarding Weekly	£1766 £2756	Asst places 15 pa Schols Bursaries	11, 13, 16	Sport, Music, Drama	EFL	C of E	HMC SHA
Tonbridge	Boys	Day Boarding	£2150 £3050	Asst places 3 Schols 25 Bursaries	13	Music, Art, Drama, Sport		C of E	HMC
Walthamstow Hall	Girls	Day Boarding Weekly	£1380 £2545	Asst places 75 Schols 5 pa Bursaries 35 pa	5, 7, 11, 16	Music, Drama	EFL	Inter- denom	GSA
West Heath	Girls	Day Boarding	£1930 £2750	Bursaries	11, 12, 13	Music, Sport		C of E	GSA SHA ISA BSA

LANCASHIRE

Name of School	Boys/ Girls/ Co-ed	Day/ Board/ Weekly	Termly fees	Financial help	Intake age/ Prep	Special strengths	Special provisions	Religion	Affiliations
Arnold	Co-ed	Day Boarding Weekly	£882 £1780 £1652	Asst places 60 Schols 10	5, 7, 11	Music, Drama, Art, Sport	Dyslexia	Christian	HMC
Bolton (Boys)	Boys	Day	£998	Asst places 300 Music bursaries 4	8, 11, 16	Music, Drama, Sport		Christian	HMC

Name of School	Boys/ Girls/ Co-ed	Day/ Board/ Weekly	Termly fees	Financial help	Intake age/ Prep	Special strengths	Special provisions	Religion	Affiliations
Bolton (Girls)	Girls	Day	£998	Asst places 43 pa Bursary	11 Own junior	Music, Art	Access for wheelchairs	Non-denom	GSA
Bury Grammar (Boys)	Boys	Day	£800	Asst places 30 1 Schol pa 1 Bursary	10, 11 Own junior	Sport, Outdoor pursuits		Christian	HMC
Bury Grammar (Girls)	Girls	Day	£800	Asst places 35 1 Schol pa	4, 11	Music, Sport	Yes	Christian	GSA
Hulme Grammar (Boys)	Boys	Day	£880	Asst places 35 pa 6 Schols and Bursaries pa	7, 11, 16	Sport, Music			HMC
Hulme Grammar (Girls)	Girls	Day	£940	Asst places 35 pa Bursaries	7, 11, 16	Sport, Music, D of E		Non-denom	GSA
King Edward (Lytham)	Boys	Day	£784	Asst places 30 pa Schols 2 pa Bursaries 5 pa	11 Own junior			Non-denom	HMC
Kirkham Grammar	Co-ed	Day Boarding	£830 £1520	Asst places 10 pa Schols 10	7, 11	Drama, Sport, Music, Art		Christian	SHMIS
Queen Elizabeth's (Blackburn)	Boys Mixed sixth	Day	£1014	Asst places 273 Schols 20–25	8, 9, 11, 16	Music		Inter- denom	HMC SHA
Queen Mary	Girls	Day	£787	Asst places Schols 1 pa Bursaries 6 pa	11 Own junior	Sport		Non-denom	GSA
Rossall	Co-ed	Day Boarding	£1635 £2876	Asst places 47 Schols 15+ pa Bursaries	11, 13, 16 Own prep	Sport, CCF	Dyslexia, EFL	C of E	HMC

Name of School	Boys/ Girls/ Co-ed	Day/ Board/ Weekly	Termly fees	Financial help	Intake age/ Prep	Special strengths	Special provisions	Religion	Affiliations
Scarisbrick Hall	Co-ed	Day	£665	Schols	3, 4, 7, 11			Non-denom	
Stonyhurst	Boys Mixed sixth	Day Boarding	£1489 £2792	Asst places 26 Schols 12 Bursaries	13, 16	Music, Games, Charitable work		RC	HMC
Westholme	Girls	Day	£890	Asst places Schols 100	4, 8, 11, 16	Public speaking, Drama, Music, Sport	Physical handicap	Christian	GSA

Name of School	Boys/ Girls/ Co-ed	Day/ Board/ Weekly	Termly fees	Financial help	Intake age/ Prep	Special strengths	Special provisions	Religion	Affiliations
Leicester Grammar	Co-ed	Day	£980	Asst places Schols	10, 11, 13	Music		C of E	
Lough- borough Grammar	Boys	Day Boarding Weekly	£1079 £2067 £1708	Asst places 23 pa Schols Bursaries	10, 11, 13, 16	Sport, Art, Music		Non-denom	HMC
Lough- borough High	Girls	Day Weekly	£972 £1578	Asst places Schols Bursaries	11 Own junior			Non-denom	GSA
Oakham	Co-ed	Day Boarding	£1600 £2895	Asst places Schols 35 pa	11, 13, 16	Music, Art, Sport	Some	Christian	HMC
Our Lady's (Lough- borough)	Girls	Day	£780	Asst places	3, 5, 7, 11	Music		RC	
Ratcliffe	Co-ed	Day Boarding Weekly	£1470 £2200	Asst places Schols Bursaries	11, 13, 14, 16 Own prep		EFL	RC	HMC
Uppingham	Boys Mixed sixth	Boarding	£3250	Schols 12+	13, 16	Music		C of E	HMC

Name of School	Boys/ Girls/ Co-ed	Day/ Board/ Weekly	Termly fees	Financial help	Intake age/ Prep	Special strengths	Special provisions	Religion	Affiliations
LINCOLNSHIRE									
St Joseph's (Lincoln)	Girls	Day Boarding	£870 £1795		5, 11	Tennis	EFL	RC & Anglican	GSA
Stamford	Boys	Day Boarding	£980 £1960	Asst places 67 Schols 12 pa	8, 11, 13	Music, Sport, D of E	Dyslexia	C of E	HMC
Stamford High	Girls	Day Boarding Weekly	£980 £1764 £1740	Asst places 15 pa Schols 6 pa	4, 8, 11	Music, Drama, Art, Sport, D of E	Dyslexia	Non-denom	GSA BSA
MIDDLESEX									
Buckingham	Boys Mixed sixth	Day	£1000	Schols 3 (sixth form)	11, 13, 16		Some special help	Christian	ISAI
Hampton	Boys	Day	£1100	Asst places 26 pa Schols 12	11, 13	Music, Art, Sport	English	Non-denom	HMC
Harrow	Boys	Boarding	£3725	Schols 20	13	Art, Sport, Music, CCF		C of E RC Jewish	HMC
Heathfield (Pinner)	Girls	Day	£1024	Schols Bursaries	4, 7, 11	Music, Lacrosse		Inter-denom	GSA GPDST
John Lyon	Boys	Day	£1130	Asst places 118 Schols	11, 13			Christian	HMC
Lady Eleanor Holles	Girls	Day	£1125	Asst places 56 Bursaries Schols	7, 11, 16	Drama, Sport, Music		C of E	GSA
Merchant Taylors' (Northwood)	Boys	Day Boarding	£1680 £2680	Asst places 20 pa Schols 14 Bursaries	11, 13, 16	Pastoral care	Special educational needs	C of E	HMC

Name of School	Boys/ Girls/ Co-ed	Day/ Board/ Weekly	Termly fees	Financial help	Intake age/ Prep	Special strengths	Special provisions	Religion	Affiliations
North London Collegiate	Girls	Day	£1140	Asst places 73 Schols 11 pa Bursaries 77 pa	7, 11, 16	Music, Sport		Non-denom	GSA
Northwood	Girls	Day	£1095	Schols 4 (sixth form)	4, 7, 11, 16	Sport, Drama		Christian	GSA
Purcell	Co-ed	Day Boarding	£2063 £3488	Aided pupils LEA awards Schols	8, 12, 16	Music specialist	EFL	Non-denom	SHMIS NAGC
St David's (Ashford)	Girls Mixed sixth	Day Boarding Weekly	£1250 £2150 £2025	Schols Bursaries	5, 11	Music, Gym- nastics, Drama	Dyslexia, ESL	C of E	GSA
St Helen's	Girls	Day Boarding Weekly	£1145 £2160 £2080	Asst places Schols 5	4, 11, 12, 16	Art, Drama, Sport	Extra English	C of E	GSA BSA

NORFOLK

Name of School	Boys/ Girls/ Co-ed	Day/ Board/ Weekly	Termly fees	Financial help	Intake age/ Prep	Special strengths	Special provisions	Religion	Affiliations
Cawston	Co-ed	Day Boarding Weekly	£1160 £2085 £2045	Schols 5	11, 12, 13	Sport, Expedi- tions	EFL, Dyslexia	C of E	Woodard
Gresham's	Co-ed	Day Boarding	£2075 £2965	Asst places 5 pa Schols 9 pa	13	Sport, Music, D of E	Some remedial	C of E	HMC
Langley	Co-ed	Day Boarding Weekly	£1305 £2485 £1960	Bursaries Schols	11, 12, 13, 16 Own prep		EFL, Dyslexia	Non-denom	SHA
Hethersett Old Hall	Girls	Day Boarding	£1115 £2150	Schols 4–9 pa	8, 11	Drama, Music	Dyslexia, EFL	C of E	GSA ISAI
Norwich	Boys	Day Boarding Weekly	£1075 £1975	Asst places 18 pa Bursaries 8 pa	8, 9, 11, 12, 16	Music, Sport		Non-denom	HMC CSA

Name of School	Boys/ Girls/ Co-ed	Day/ Board/ Weekly	Termly fees	Financial help	Intake age/ Prep	Special strengths	Special provisions	Religion	Affiliations
Norwich High	Girls	Day	£908	Asst places 220 Schols Bursaries	7, 11, 16	Music, Drama, Art, Sport		Non-denom	GSA GPDST
Runton & Sutherland	Girls	Day Boarding Weekly	£925 £1870	Schols Bursaries	3–13, 16	Sport	Extra English	C of E	

NORTHAMPTONSHIRE

Name of School	Boys/ Girls/ Co-ed	Day/ Board/ Weekly	Termly fees	Financial help	Intake age/ Prep	Special strengths	Special provisions	Religion	Affiliations
Laxton	Co-ed	Day	£1125	Schols	11, 13, 16			C of E	
Northampton High	Girls	Day	£1035	Asst places	3, 11			C of E	GSA
Northampton-shire Grammar	Boys	Day	£964	Schols 3 Bursaries 4	11, 13	Music, Rugby	Dyslexia	Christian	ISAI
Oundle	Co-ed	Boarding	£3275	Schols	11, 13	Music, Art, Techno-logy	English	C of E	HMC
Welling-borough	Co-ed	Day Boarding Weekly	£1410 £2320	Asst places 60 Schols 12 Bursaries	13 Own junior	Sport, Music, Drama	Dyslexia, EFL	C of E	HMC

NORTHUMBERLAND

Name of School	Boys/ Girls/ Co-ed	Day/ Board/ Weekly	Termly fees	Financial help	Intake age/ Prep	Special strengths	Special provisions	Religion	Affiliations
Longridge Towers	Co-ed	Day Boarding Weekly	£995 £1990 £1880	Schols 6 pa Bursaries	4, 8, 11, 13, 16	Art, Swimming		Christian	SHA ISAI

NOTTINGHAMSHIRE

Name of School	Boys/ Girls/ Co-ed	Day/ Board/ Weekly	Termly fees	Financial help	Intake age/ Prep	Special strengths	Special provisions	Religion	Affiliations
Nottingham High (Boys)	Boys	Day	£945	Asst places 30 pa Schols 15 pa	11, 16	Music, Sport		Non-denom	HMC

Name of School	Boys/ Girls/ Co-ed	Day/ Board/ Weekly	Termly fees	Financial help	Intake age/ Prep	Special strengths	Special provisions	Religion	Affiliations
Nottingham High (Girls)	Girls	Day	£908	Asst places 35 pa Schols Bursaries	4, 7, 11, 16	Drama, Sport		Non-denom	GSA GPDST
Rodney	Co-ed	Day Boarding Weekly	£695 £1285	Schols (sixth)	9, 11, 13	Drama, Dance	EFL	Christian	ISA
Welbeck	Boys	Boarding	Up to £650	Means tested fees	16	Route to Army Technical Corps		C of E	BSA
Worksop	Co-ed	Day Boarding Weekly	£1800 £2625	Asst places Schols Bursaries	13 Own prep		Dyslexia	C of E	HMC Woodard

OXFORDSHIRE

Name of School	Boys/ Girls/ Co-ed	Day/ Board/ Weekly	Termly fees	Financial help	Intake age/ Prep	Special strengths	Special provisions	Religion	Affiliations
Abingdon	Boys	Day Boarding Weekly	£1277 £2426	Asst places 20 pa Schols 1 Bursaries 15 pa	11, 13, 16	Music, Chess	Dyslexia, EFL	C of E	HMC
Bloxham	Boys Mixed sixth	Day Boarding	£2070 £3000	Asst places Schols Bursaries	13, 16		Dyslexia, EFL	C of E	HMC Woodard
Carmel College	Co-ed	Day Boarding	£2250 £3650 (UK), £4212 (Over-seas)	Asst places 91 Schols 120	11, 16	Art, Music	EFL, Dyslexia	Jewish	SHMIS
Magdalen College School	Boys	Day Boarding	£1114 £2114	Asst places 24 pa Schols 5 pa Bursaries 52	11, 13, 16	Music (Choir school)		C of E	HMC CSA
Our Lady's (Abingdon)	Girls	Day Boarding Weekly	£834 £1884 £1879	Schols	11			RC	ISAI

Name of School	Boys/ Girls/ Co-ed	Day/ Board/ Weekly	Termly fees	Financial help	Intake age/ Prep	Special strengths	Special provisions	Religion	Affiliations
Oxford High	Girls	Day	£908	Schols 6 Asst places 25 pa	9, 11, 16	Music, Art, Sport, D of E	Some available	Non-denom	GPDST
Radley	Boys	Boarding	£3100	Schols/ Exhibitions 20	13	Sport, Music		C of E	HMC
Rye St Antony	Girls	Day Boarding Weekly	£1225 £2180 £2065	Schols	7, 11, 16		Small group Tuition	RC	GSA CCSS
St Edward's (Oxford)	Boys Mixed sixth	Day Boarding	£2350 £3125	Schols Bursaries	13, 16	Music, Drama		Anglican	HMC
St Mary's (Wantage)	Girls	Boarding	£2575	Schols 4	11, 12, 16	Music, Drama, Art	Dyslexia, EFL	C of E	GSA
Shiplake	Boys	Day Boarding	£1885 £2870	Schols 5 Bursaries 2	13	Sport, Art	Dyslexia, Remedial teaching	C of E	SHMIS
Sibford	Co-ed	Day Boarding Weekly	£1332 £2617	Quaker Schols/ Bursaries	7–11, 13, 16	Drama, Art, Music, Theatre, Pre-vocational education	Dyslexia, EFL	Quaker	
Tudor Hall	Girls	Day Boarding	£1690 £2650		11			C of E	GSA
Wychwood	Girls	Day Boarding	£1080 £1820	Bursaries (sixth)	11, 12, 14, 16	Music, Art		C of E	GSA

SHROPSHIRE

Name of School	Boys/ Girls/ Co-ed	Day/ Board/ Weekly	Termly fees	Financial help	Intake age/ Prep	Special strengths	Special provisions	Religion	Affiliations
Adcote	Girls	Day Boarding Weekly	£1275 £2150	Schols	7–14, 16		Dyslexia, EFL	C of E	GSA
Moreton Hall	Girls	Day Boarding	£1815 £2735	Bursaries Schols 5	11, 12, 13	Lacrosse, Art, Drama, Business activities	Learning difficulties	C of E	GSA

Name of School	Boys/ Girls/ Co-ed	Day/ Board/ Weekly	Termly fees	Financial help	Intake age/ Prep	Special strengths	Special provisions	Religion	Affiliations
Oswestry	Co-ed	Day Boarding	£1320 £2225	Schols 10	11, 13, 16	Sport	EFL, Dyslexia	Christian	SHMIS
Shrewsbury	Boys	Day Boarding	£2145 £3040	Schols	13			C of E	HMC
Shrewsbury High	Girls	Day	£908	Asst places 14 pa Schols Bursaries	4, 7, 9, 11			Non-denom	GSA GPDST
Wrekin	Co-ed	Day Boarding	£1932 £2760	Schols 20	13, 16	Sport, Art, Gym- nastics	Dyslexia	C of E	HMC Allied

SOMERSET

Name of School	Boys/ Girls/ Co-ed	Day/ Board/ Weekly	Termly fees	Financial help	Intake age/ Prep	Special strengths	Special provisions	Religion	Affiliations
Bruton (Sunny Hill)	Girls	Day Boarding Weekly	£865 £1580	Asst places 25 Schols 6	8, 11, 13, 16	Hockey, Drama, Music	ESL, Dyslexia	Christian	GSA, BSA
King's (Bruton)	Boys Mixed sixth	Day Boarding	£1995 £2820	Asst places 2 Schols 10	13, 16 Own junior		Dyslexia, EFL	C of E	HMC
King's (Taunton)	Co-ed	Day Boarding	£2150 £2880	Schols 20	13 Own prep	Music, Drama, Art, Sport	EFL	C of E	HMC Woodard
Millfield	Co-ed	Day Boarding	£1860 £3185	Schols 160	13, 16 Own junior	Sport, Music, Art	EFL, Dyslexia Unit	Multi-faith	
Queen's (Taunton)	Co-ed	Day Boarding	£1660 £2540	Asst places 14 pa Schols	12, 13, 16 Own junior	D of E	Dyslexia	Methodist	HMC
Taunton	Co-ed	Day Boarding	£1882 £2933	Asst places 11 pa Schols/ Bursaries 107	3, 7, 11, 13	Sport, D of E	EFL, Mild dyslexia	C of E	HMC GSA
Wellington (Somerset)	Co-ed	Day Boarding	£1045 £1945	Asst places 40 Schols	11	Sport, Music, Art	EFL	C of E	BSA

Name of School	Boys/ Girls/ Co-ed	Day/ Board/ Weekly	Termly fees	Financial help	Intake age/ Prep	Special strengths	Special provisions	Religion	Affiliations
Wells Cathedral	Co-ed	Day Boarding	£1235 £2184	Aided places Asst places 75 Schols	11 Own junior	Music (specialist school), Drama	EFL, Dyslexia	C of E	HMC SHMIS

STAFFORDSHIRE

Abbotsholme	Co-ed	Day Boarding Weekly	£1860 £2790	Schols 8 pa Bursaries	11, 12, 13, 16	Small family school, Art, Music	Dyslexia, EFL	Inter- denom	HMC SHMIS Round square
Denstone	Co-ed	Day Boarding Weekly	£1916 £2690 £2690	Asst places Schols Bursaries	11, 13, 16	Music, Sport, D of E, Drama	Dyslexia	C of E	HMC Woodard
New- castle-under- Lyme	Co-ed	Day	£977	Asst places 73 Schols/ Bursaries 6	8, 11	Music, Drama		Christian	HMC
St Dominics (Brewood)	Girls	Day	£927	Schols 10	3, 11	Drama		RC	
St Dominic's (Stone)	Girls	Day	£695	Bursaries	4, 11	Tennis, Netball, Music	Dyslexia	RC	ISAI CCSS CTF
St Joseph's (Stoke)	Co-ed	Day	£870	Asst places Schols 6	11 Own Junior	Sport		RC	ISAI

SUFFOLK

Culford	Co-ed	Day Boarding	£1531 £2355	Asst places 8 pa Schols 4 pa	8, 11, 13		Dyslexia, EFL	Methodist	HMC
Felixstowe	Girls	Day Boarding	£1650 £2695	Asst places Schols	11, 12 Own junior	Music, Drama, Dance, Art	EFL	C of E	GSA ESHA
Framlingham	Co-ed	Day Boarding	£1523 £2373	Asst places Schols	13 Own junior	Art, Music, Drama	Limited provision	C of E	HMC

Name of School	Boys/ Girls/ Co-ed	Day/ Board/ Weekly	Termly fees	Financial help	Intake age/ Prep	Special strengths	Special provisions	Religion	Affiliations
Ipswich	Boys Mixed sixth	Day Boarding Weekly	£1210 £2060 £2000	Asst places Schols	11 Own prep			C of E	HMC
Ipswich High	Girls	Day	£908	Asst places 29 pa Bursaries Schols 3–4 pa	4, 7, 9, 11, 16	Music, Drama, Art		Non-denom	GSA GPDST
Royal Hospital	Co-ed	Boarding	£1840	Means tested fees for children or grandchildren of seafarers	11, 12, 13, 16	Sport, CCF		Christian	SHMIS
St Felix	Girls	Day Boarding Weekly	£1585 £2563	Asst places Schols	11 Own prep	Music, Design & Techno- logy	Mild dyslexia, EFL	Inter- denom	GSA
St Joseph's (Ipswich)	Boys Mixed sixth	Day Boarding	£1040 £1865	Asst places 75 Schols 8 Bursaries	11 Own prep	Sport	EFL, Dyslexia	RC	
Woodbridge	Co-ed	Day Boarding	£1530 £2510	Asst places 101 Schols 60	11 Own junior			C of E	HMC

SURREY

Name of School	Boys/ Girls/ Co-ed	Day/ Board/ Weekly	Termly fees	Financial help	Intake age/ Prep	Special strengths	Special provisions	Religion	Affiliations
Box Hill	Co-ed	Day Boarding Weekly	£1454 £2596 £2420	Schols Bursaries	11, 12, 13, 16		Dyslexia, ESL	Non-denom	SHMIS Round Square ISAI
Caterham	Boys Mixed sixth	Day Boarding	£1340 £2460	Asst places 20 pa Schols 15 pa Bursaries	8–13, 16	Music, Games, Drama	Dyslexia	United Reformed	HMC
Charterhouse	Boys Mixed sixth	Day Boarding	£2700 £3265	Asst places 5 pa Schols 32 Bursaries	13, 16	Music, Sport, Art		Christian	HMC

Name of School	Boys/ Girls/ Co-ed	Day/ Board/ Weekly	Termly fees	Financial help	Intake age/ Prep	Special strengths	Special provisions	Religion	Affiliations
City of London Freemen's	Co-ed	Day Boarding Weekly	£1593 £2481 £2400	Schols 20 pa Asst places 5 pa Bursaries 25	8,13,16	Music, Sport, D of E		C of E	HMC
Commonweal Lodge	Girls	Day	£1045	Schols/ Bursaries 3 pa	4, 5, 8, 11		EFL, Dyslexia	Christian	GSA
Cranleigh	Boys Mixed sixth	Day Boarding	£2400 £3195	Asst places Schols	13, 16 Own prep	Music, Drama		C of E	HMC
Croham Hurst	Girls	Day	£1030	Schols/ Bursaries 5 Asst places	4, 7, 11		Some for learning difficulties	Christian	GSA
Croydon High	Girls	Day	£1024	Asst places 24 Schols 4	4, 5, 7, 11, 16	Music, Sport		Non-denom	GSA GPDST
Dunottar	Girls	Day	£1150	Schols	5, 8, 11, 16			Non-denom	GSA SHA
Elmhurst	Co-ed	Day Boarding	£1730 £2360		9	Dance specialist		C of E	
Eothen	Girls	Day	£1122	Bursaries	3, 7, 11	Music, Art	EFL, Mild dyslexia	C of E	GSA CSCL
Epsom College	Boys Mixed sixth	Day Boarding Weekly	£2000 £2850 £2800	Asst places 10 Schols 30	13, 16	Art, Music, Sport, Drama		C of E	HMC
Ewell Castle	Boys	Day	£1090	Schols	11, 13		EFL	Non-denom	SHMIS
Frensham Heights	Co-ed	Day Boarding Weekly	£1881 £2992	Schols	11	Small school	Dyselxia	Non-denom	HMC
Greenacre	Girls	Day Boarding Weekly	£1277 £2428 £2319	Schols Bursaries	4, 5, 10, 11		EFL	Christian	GSA
King Edward's (Witley)	Co-ed	Day Boarding	£1652 £2237	Asst places 15 Bursaries Schols	11, 13	Art, Music		C of E	HMC

Name of School	Boys/ Girls/ Co-ed	Day/ Board/ Weekly	Termly fees	Financial help	Intake age/ Prep	Special strengths	Special provisions	Religion	Affiliations
Kingston Grammar	Co-ed	Day	£1255	Asst places Schols Bursaries	10, 11, 13, 16	Hockey, Music, Rowing		Christian	HMC
Marymount	Girls	Day Boarding Weekly	£2000 £4800 £4600	Bursaries	12	Inter- national school	EFL	Non-denom	
Notre Dame (Cobham)	Girls	Day	£1095	Schols 14	11			RC	
Notre Dame (Lingfield)	Girls	Day	£1055	Bursaries 2	3, 11, 12	Music, Sport	Dyslexia, EFL	RC	ISAI
Old Palace	Girls	Day	£933	Asst places 35 pa Schols Bursaries	11 Own junior			C of E	
Parsons Mead	Girls	Day Boarding Weekly	£1150 £2135 £1975	Schols 5+pa Bursaries	3, 8, 11		Extra coaching possible	C of E	GSA
Pierrepont	Co-ed	Day Boarding Weekly	£1517 £2523 £2376	Schols 14 pa	11, 12, 13, 16	CCF, Sailing	EFL, Dyslexia	C of E	SHMIS
Prior's Field	Girls	Day Boarding Weekly	£1495 £2395	Schols 4 pa Bursaries	11, 12, 13	Art		Christian	GSA
Reed's	Boys Mixed sixth	Day Boarding	£1600 £2215	Asst places Schols 10 Bursaries	11, 12, 13, 16	Music, Art, Tennis, Printing	Dyslexia	C of E	HMC
Reigate Grammar	Boys Mixed sixth	Day	£1200	Asst places 20 pa Schols Bursaries	10, 11, 13, 16	Music, Games, Drama		Non-denom	HMC
Royal Ballet	Co-ed	Day Boarding	£2374 £4082	Aided pupils scheme	11	Ballet (specialist school)			
Royal Grammar (Guildford)	Boys	Day	£1365	Schols 20 pa Asst places 25 pa	11, 13	Music, Sport, D of E		C of E	HMC

Name of School	Boys/ Girls/ Co-ed	Day/ Board/ Weekly	Termly fees	Financial help	Intake age/ Prep	Special strengths	Special provisions	Religion	Affiliations
Royal Naval	Girls	Day Boarding Weekly	£1550 £2325	Schols 5 pa	11, 13	Music	Remedial	C of E	GSA
Royal Russell	Co-ed	Day Boarding Weekly	£1305 £2485 £2390	Schols Bursaries	11 Own junior		Dyslexia, EFL	C of E	SHMIS
St Catherine's	Girls	Day Boarding	£1450 £2375	Asst places Schols	11 Own prep			C of E	GSA
St George's (Weybridge)	Boys Mixed sixth	Day	£1640	Asst places 35 Schols 6 pa Bursaries	12, 13, 16 Own prep	Community service, D of E		RC	HMC SHMIS SHA
St John's (Leather-head)	Boys Mixed sixth	Day Boarding Weekly	£1800 £2500	Asst places 6 pa Schols 15+	13, 16		Dyslexia	C of E	HMC
St Maur's	Girls	Day	£1600	Asst places 15 Schols Bursaries	4, 5, 11			RC	
St Teresa's	Girls	Day Boarding Weekly	£1345 £2415	Schols	11, 12, 13 Own junior	Art, Music, Sport, Public speaking	EFL	RC	GSA SHA CCSS
Shaftesbury	Co-ed	Day	£890	Schols 5	5, 10, 11, 13	Drama, Badminton	Individual help available	Christian	
Sir William Perkins's	Girls	Day	£955	Asst places Bursaries/ Schols	11	Music	EFL	Non-denom	GSA
Stowford	Co-ed	Day	£978	Schols	7–14, 16	Art	EFL, Dyslexia	Non-denom	
Surbiton High	Girls	Day	£1130	Asst places Bursaries	5, 10, 11, 16	Art, Music		C of E	GSA CSCL

Name of School	Boys/ Girls/ Co-ed	Day/ Board/ Weekly	Termly fees	Financial help	Intake age/ Prep	Special strengths	Special provisions	Religion	Affiliations
Sutton High	Girls	Day	£1024	Asst places 17 pa Schols 6 pa Bursaries	4, 7, 11	Sport, Music, Drama		Non-denom	GPDST
Tormead	Girls	Day	£1145	Asst places Schols Bursaries	5			Non-denom	GSA
Trinity (Croydon)	Boys	Day	£1254	Asst places 150 Schols Bursaries	10, 11, 13	Music	Dyslexia	Non-denom	HMC
Whitgift	Boys	Day	£1140	Asst places 91 Schols Bursaries	10, 11, 13, 16	Music, Drama		C of E	HMC
Woldingham	Girls	Day Boarding	£1600 £2645	Schols 1	11	Sport, Drama, Music		RC	GSA
Yehudi Menuhin	Co-ed	Boarding	£5453	Aided places	8	Strings and piano (specialist school)			

Name of School	Boys/ Girls/ Co-ed	Day/ Board/ Weekly	Termly fees	Financial help	Intake age/ Prep	Special strengths	Special provisions	Religion	Affiliations
Ardingly	Co-ed	Day Boarding	£2275 £2890	Schols 25 Asst places Clergy Bursaries	7, 11, 13, 16	Music, Drama, Art, Sports	EFL	C of E	HMC Woodard
Battle Abbey	Co-ed	Day Boarding Weekly	£1550 £2520	Schols 2 pa	3, 4, 5, 11, 13	Drama, Art	Dyslexia, Extra English, Learning difficulties	Christian	GSA
Beresford House	Girls	Day Boarding	£1525 £2825	Schols	4, 7, 11		EFL	C of E	GSA

Name of School	Boys/ Girls/ Co-ed	Day/ Board/ Weekly	Termly fees	Financial help	Intake age/ Prep	Special strengths	Special provisions	Religion	Affiliations
Brighton College	Co-ed	Day Boarding Weekly	£1905 £2895 £2600	Asst places 20 Schols 14	13, 16 Own junior	Art, Sport, Music, Drama		C of E	HMC
Burgess Hill	Girls	Day Boarding Weekly	£1259 £2186	Asst places Schols 17 pa	3, 11	Drama, Music, Sport	EFL, Dyslexia	C of E	GSA
Charters-Ancaster	Girls	Day Boarding	£970 £1970	Schols Bursaries	3, 11		Dyslexia	Christian	GSA GPDST
Christ's Hospital	Co-ed	Boarding	Means tested	Hospital endowments for all Asst places	11	Music, Drama, Art	Dyslexia	C of E	HMC
Eastbourne	Boys Mixed sixth	Day Boarding	£2158 £2919	Schols 16 pa	13, 16	Music, Drama, Sport, Art		C of E	HMC
Farlington	Girls	Day Weekly	£1325 £2150	Schols 6 pa	11, 12, 13	Music		C of E	GSA BSA
Hamilton Lodge	Co-ed	Day Boarding	£3660 £4880	LEA	5		Specialist school for the deaf	Non-denom	
Hurstpier-point	Boys	Day Boarding	£2285 £2855	Asst places Schols 20 Bursaries	13 Own junior	Sport, Music		C of E	HMC Woodard
Lancing	Boys Mixed sixth	Day Boarding	£2139 £3009	Schols and Exhibitions 30 pa	13, 16	Music		C of E	HMC Woodard
Lavant House	Girls	Day Boarding Weekly	£1440 £2415	Schols 6	7, 11, 13	Drama, Art, Music, Sports	Dyslexia, EFL	C of E	GSA
Mayfield	Boys	Day Boarding Weekly	£1915 £2835 £2765	Schols Bursaries	11, 13, 16	Sport	EFL, Dyslexia	RC	ISAI
Michael Hall	Co-ed	Day Boarding Weekly	£975 £2250 £2050	Bursaries	4, 6	Art	Remedial EFL	Non-denom	Steiner

Name of School	Boys/ Girls/ Co-ed	Day/ Board/ Weekly	Termly fees	Financial help	Intake age/ Prep	Special strengths	Special provisions	Religion	Affiliations
Micklefield	Girls	Day Boarding Weekly	£1400 £2400 £2250	Schols 4 Bursaries	5, 10, 11		Dyslexia, EFL	Christian	GSA BSA
Moira House	Girls	Day Boarding Weekly	£1802 £2695	Schols 12 pa	11, 12, 13, 16	Sport, Music	Dyslexia, EFL	Christian	GSA BSA
Roedean	Girls	Boarding	£3195	Schols 6	11, 12, 13, 16	Music, Drama, Art, D of E		Christian	GSA
Rosemead	Girls	Day Boarding Weekly	£1445 £2495	Schols 3	4, 11, 13, 16	Drama, Music	EFL	Christian	GSA
St Bede's (Hailsham)	Co-ed	Day Boarding	£1900 £3050	Schols 12	12, 13, 16	Tennis, Art, Music, Drama	EFL, Dyslexia	Non-denom	SHMIS
St Leonards-Mayfield	Girls	Day Boarding Weekly	£1700 £2550 £2525	Schols Bursaries	11, 13	Art, Music, Sport	Dyslexia, EFL	RC	GSA CCSS
S Michaels (Petworth)	Girls	Day Boarding Weekly	£1800 £2730	Schols 4 pa Bursaries	11	Lacrosse	Dyslexia, EFL	C of E	GSA Woodard
Seaford	Boys	Boarding	£2530	Schols 20 pa	11, 13	Art, Music	CDT	C of E	SHMIS
Wadhurst	Boys (ballet only) Girls	Day Boarding Weekly	£1570 £2495 £2445	Schols Bursaries	9, 11, 12, 13	Music, Ballet, Drama	Dyslexia	Inter-denom	GSA
Worth	Boys	Boarding	£2850	Schols 6–8	9, 13	Voluntary service		RC	HMC

TYNE AND WEAR

Name of School	Boys/ Girls/ Co-ed	Day/ Board/ Weekly	Termly fees	Financial help	Intake age/ Prep	Special strengths	Special provisions	Religion	Affiliations
Dame Allan's (Boys)	Boys Mixed sixth	Day	£850	Asst places 23 pa Schols 8 Bursaries	9, 10, 11, 16	Sport		C of E	HMC

Name of School	Boys/ Girls/ Co-ed	Day/ Board/ Weekly	Termly fees	Financial help	Intake age/ Prep	Special strengths	Special provisions	Religion	Affiliations
Dame Allan's (Girls)	Girls Mixed sixth	Day	£850	Asst places 20 Schols 8	9, 10, 11, 16	Sport, Music		C of E	GSA
La Sagesse	Girls	Day	£940	Asst places 171 Schols 6 pa	11 Own junior	Drama, Choir, Industrial/ business links	Dyslexia	RC	GSA
Newcastle Church High	Girls	Day	£900	Asst places Schols/ exhibitions 9	4, 7, 9, 11	Music	EFL	C of E	GSA
Newcastle High	Girls	Day	£908	Asst places Bursaries Schols 4 pa	4, 7, 9, 11, 16	Sport, Music	Dyslexia	Non-denom	GSA GPDST
Royal Grammar (Newcastle)	Boys	Day	£850	Asst places 60 pa	11 Own junior			Non-denom	HMC
Sunderland Church High	Girls Mixed sixth	Day	£1006	Schols 3 pa	11 Own junior	Sport	Extra English	C of E	GSA
Westfield	Girls	Day	£986	Schols 10 pa	3, 11	Sport, Drama	Dyslexia	Christian	GSA

Name of School	Boys/ Girls/ Co-ed	Day/ Board/ Weekly	Termly fees	Financial help	Intake age/ Prep	Special strengths	Special provisions	Religion	Affiliations
King's (Warwick)	Girls	Day	£915	Asst places 220 Schols 9	11 Own prep	Art, Sport, Music		Non-denom	GSA
Kingsley	Girls	Day	£990	Schols 4 pa Asst places 5 pa	3, 8, 11	D of E, Music, Drama	Dyslexia	C of E	GSA
Rugby	Co-ed	Day Boarding	£1865 £3220	Schols 16 pa Foundationer- ships 42	12 (day), 13, 16	Drama, Sport, Art, Music	Extra English, Dyslexia	C of E	HMC

Name of School	Boys/ Girls/ Co-ed	Day/ Board/ Weekly	Termly fees	Financial help	Intake age/ Prep	Special strengths	Special provisions	Religion	Affiliations
Warwick	Boys	Day Boarding Weekly	£1070 £2320 £2170	Asst places 170 Schols 100 Bursaries	7, 11, 13	Sport		C of E	HMC
Wroxall Abbey	Girls	Day Boarding Weekly	£1476 £2450 £2338	Schols Bursaries	7, 11, 16		Dyslexia	C of E	GSA

WILTSHIRE									
Dauntsey's	Co-ed	Day Boarding	£1610 £2600	Asst places 55 Schols Bursaries	11, 13	Music, Art, Sport	EFL, Mild dyslexia	Christian	HMC
Godolphin	Girls	Day Boarding	£1570 £2640	Asst places 5 pa Schols Bursaries	11, 12, 13		Dyslexia	C of E	GSA BSA
Marlborough	Co-ed	Day Boarding	£2610 £3480	Schols Bursaries	13, 16	Music, Art, Sport	Dyslexia	C of E	HMC SHA
St Mary's (Calne)	Girls	Day Boarding	£1620 £2725	Schols 6 Bursaries	11, 12	Sport		C of E	GSA
Stonar	Girls	Day Boarding Weekly	£1315 £2375	Schols 4 pa Bursaries	5, 11, 13	Sport, Music, Riding	Dyslexia, EFL	C of E	GSA
Warminster	Co-ed	Day Boarding Weekly	£1290 £2145	Schols 20	11, 13, 16 Own junior	Drama, Sport	Dyslexia	C of E	SHMIS

WORCESTERSHIRE									
Alice Ottley	Girls	Day	£1252	Asst places Schols	11 Own junior		Extra coaching	C of E	GSA

Name of School	Boys/ Girls/ Co-ed	Day/ Board/ Weekly	Termly fees	Financial help	Intake age/ Prep	Special strengths	Special provisions	Religion	Affiliations
Bromsgrove	Co-ed	Day Boarding	£1564 £2495	Schols Bursaries Asst places 29	8, 11, 13, 16	Drama, Sport, Music	Some available	Christian	HMC
Ellerslie	Girls	Day Boarding	£1735 £2670	Asst places 5 pa Schols 3 pa	11, 12, 13	Drama	Individual tuition available	C of E	GSA BSA
King's (Worcester)	Co-ed	Day Boarding	£1480 £2428	Asst places 34 pa Schols 20	7, 8, 11, 13, 16	Sport, Music, Drama	Mild visual handicaps, EFL	C of E	HMC
Lawnside	Girls	Day Boarding Weekly	£1500 £2620	Schols 5 pa Bursaries	11, 12, 13, 16		Dyslexia, EFL	C of E	GSA
Malvern (Boys)	Boys	Day Boarding	£2235 £3070	Asst places 66 Schols 20	13, 16	Music, Art, Drama	SLD, EFL	C of E	HMC
Malvern (Girls)	Girls	Day Boarding	£1880 £2820	Schols 10 pa	11, 12, 13	Music, Sport, Art		C of E	GSA
Old Swinford Hospital	Boys	Day Boarding Weekly	£825	Schols 12 pa Bursaries	11, 13, 16	D of E, Music	Some special support	C of E	SHMIS
RNIB New College	Co-ed	Day Boarding	Nil Nil	LEA pay fees	11+	Music, Sport	Specialist school for the visually impaired		HMC
Royal Grammar (Worcester)	Boys	Day Weekly	£1092 £1923	Asst places Schols	7–13, 16	Drama, Sport		Non-denom	HMC
St James's & the Abbey	Girls	Day Boarding	£1720 £2580	Schols Bursaries	11		Mild dyslexia, EFL	C of E	GSA

YORKSHIRE

Name of School	Boys/ Girls/ Co-ed	Day/ Board/ Weekly	Termly fees	Financial help	Intake age/ Prep	Special strengths	Special provisions	Religion	Affiliations
Ackworth	Co-ed	Day Boarding	£1232 £2193	Asst places Schols 40	7, 11, 13, 16	Music, Drama, Sport, D of E	EFL	Quaker	SHMIS

Name of School	Boys/ Girls/ Co-ed	Day/ Board/ Weekly	Termly fees	Financial help	Intake age/ Prep	Special strengths	Special provisions	Religion	Affiliations
Ampleforth	Boys	Day Boarding	£2432 £2940	Schols 12–14 Bursaries	10, 13 Own junior	Music, Drama, Art	EFL, Learning difficulties	RC	HMC
Ashville	Co-ed	Day Boarding	£1190 £2189	Schols Bursaries 106	7, 8, 11, 13	Drama, Art, Sport	Dyslexia, EFL	Methodist	HMC
Batley	Boys Mixed sixth	Day	£833	Asst places 251 Schols 5–10 pa	11, 12, 13, 16	Music, D of E, Sport		Christian	HMC
Birkdale	Boys	Day	£1080	Schols 10 pa	11, 16 Own prep	Sport, Music	Dyslexia	Christian	SHA
Bootham	Co-ed	Day Boarding	£1435 £2278	Schols 12 Bursaries Asst places	11, 13, 16		Dyslexia, EFL	Quaker	HMC
Bradford (Boys)	Boys Mixed sixth	Day	£1058	Asst places 35 Schols 5	8–11, 13, 16	IT, Music, Sport		Christian	HMC
Bradford (Girls)	Girls	Day	£1067	Asst places 60 Bursaries Schols	4, 9, 11	Art, Sport, CDT		Christian	GSA
Fulneck (Boys)	Boys	Day Boarding Weekly	£1082 £2097 £1852		7–11, 13	Small classes, Sport	Dyslexia	Moravian	SHMIS
Gateways	Girls	Day	£860	Schols 8	4, 8, 11, 13	Art	Dyslexia	Non-denom	GSA
Giggleswick	Co-ed	Day Boarding	£1890 £2850	Asst places Schols Bursaries	13, 16 Own prep	Music, Sport, Outdoor education, Drama, Art	Dyslexia	C of E	HMC
Harrogate Ladies'	Girls	Day Boarding	£1485 £2230	Asst places 35 Schols 50	11, 12, 13, 16	Music	Dyslexia, ESL	C of E	GSA

Name of School	Boys/ Girls/ Co-ed	Day/ Board/ Weekly	Termly fees	Financial help	Intake age/ Prep	Special strengths	Special provisions	Religion	Affiliations
Hymers	Co-ed	Day	£845	Asst places 135 Bursaries	8, 9, 11, 16	Music, Sport		Christian	HMC
Leeds Grammar	Boys	Day	£1107	Asst places 191 Schols 25 pa	8, 10, 11, 13, 16	Drama, Music		C of E	HMC
Leeds High	Girls	Day	£1043	Asst places 142 Schols 7–10 pa	3, 4, 11			Non-denom	GSA
Mount (York)	Girls	Day Boarding Weekly	£1690 £2540	Asst places Schols Bursaries	11, 12, 13, 14, 16	Music, Art	Dyslexia, EFL	Quaker	GSA
Mount St Mary's (Sheffield)	Co-ed	Day Boarding Weekly	£1460 £2162 £1825	Asst places 55 Schols 10	13 Own prep	Music, Drama, Rugby	EFL, Dyslexia	RC	HMC SHA
Pocklington	Co-ed	Day Boarding	£1112 £2173	Asst places 137 Schols Bursaries	11, 13, 16 Own junior	Music, CDT	EFL, Dyslexia	C of E	HMC
Queen Elizabeth (Wakefield)	Boys	Day	£1007	Asst places 154 Schols 17 pa Bursaries	7, 9, 11, 12, 13, 16	Art, Sport, Music, Drama		Non-denom	HMC
Queen Ethelburga's	Girls	Day Boarding Weekly	£1280 £2135	Schols 8 pa Bursaries	5, 11		Special needs, EFL	C of E	Woodard
Queen Margaret's (York)	Girls	Day Boarding	£1550 £2450	Schols 9	11–13	Art, Sport	Slight academic difficulties	C of E	GSA
Read	Boys Mixed sixth	Day Boarding Weekly	£840 £1700 £1590	Schols 8	8, 11, 13, 16	Art, CCF		C of E	ISAI BSA
Rishworth	Co-ed	Day Boarding Weekly	£1350 £2550 £2220	Schols 8 pa Bursaries	4, 7, 11	Art, Drama	EFL, Dyslexia	C of E	SHMIS

Name of School	Boys/ Girls/ Co-ed	Day/ Board/ Weekly	Termly fees	Financial help	Intake age/ Prep	Special strengths	Special provisions	Religion	Affiliations
St Hilda's (Whitby)	Co-ed	Day Boarding Weekly	£1040 £1890 £1850	Schols 15	2½–11, 13, 16	D of E, Music	Dyslexia, EFL	C of E	ISAI
St Peter's (York)	Co-ed	Day Boarding	£1467 £2521	Asst places 120 Schols 8	13, 16 Own junior	Sport, Music		C of E	HMC
Scarborough	Co-ed	Day Boarding	£1288 £2393	Asst places Schols 15	11 Own junior	Music, Drama	Dyslexia	Christian	SHMIS
Sheffield High	Girls	Day	£1052	Asst places 21 Schols Bursaries	4, 11	Music		Non-denom	GSA GPDST
Silcoates	Boys Mixed sixth	Day Boarding Weekly	£1392 £2491	Bursaries	7, 11, 16	Sport	Dyslexia	United Reformed	HMC SHMIS
Wakefield High	Girls	Day	£995	Asst places Bursaries	11 Own junior			Non-denom	GSA
Woodhouse Grove	Co-ed	Day Boarding	£1245 £2035	Asst places 130 Schols 20 pa	11 Own junior	Music, Sport	Dyslexia, EFL	Methodist	HMC
York College	Girls	Day	£1124	Schols 3 pa	4, 11			C of E	GSA CSCL

· Northern Ireland ·

Name of School	Boys/ Girls/ Co-ed	Day/ Board/ Weekly	Termly fees	Financial help	Intake age/ Prep	Special strengths	Special provisions	Religion	Affiliations
Belfast Academy	Co-ed	Day	£39	LEA	4, 11	Music, Sport, Drama		Non-denom	HMC
Campbell College	Boys	Day Boarding Weekly	£151 £1157	Schols Bursaries LEA	11, 13, 16 Own prep	Music		Non-denom	HMC
Christian Brothers	Boys	Day	Nil		11	Sport, Music, Drama		RC	

Name of School	Boys/ Girls/ Co-ed	Day/ Board/ Weekly	Termly fees	Financial help	Intake age/ Prep	Special strengths	Special provisions	Religion	Affiliations
Coleraine	Boys	Day Boarding	£660 £1480	Bursaries	11, 16	Sport, Techno- logy	EFL	Christian	HMC
Friends' (Lisburn)	Co-ed	Day Boarding Weekly	£636 £1464 £1431	LEA	4, 11, 16	Sport, D of E	EFL, Mild handicaps	Quaker	
Hunterhouse	Girls	Day Boarding Weekly	£615 £1315	Day fees nil for NI residents	11, 14, 16 Own junior	Music		Christian	Voluntary Grammar
Methodist College	Co-ed	Day Boarding	£650 £1419	Schols 10	11, 16	Music		Methodist	HMC
Portora Royal	Co-ed	Day Boarding Weekly	£760 £1560 £1418	Schols 2 pa	11	Rowing		C of E Protestant	HMC
Royal (Belfast)	Boys	Day	£60	Schols	11 Own junior	Drama, Music, Sport, CCF		Non-denom	HMC
Royal (Dungannon)	Co-ed	Day Boarding Weekly	£710 £1460	Schols 7 pa Bursaries 3 pa	4, 11	Sport, Music	EFL		SHMIS
Victoria (Belfast)	Girls	Day Boarding Weekly	£1950 £2700	Schols 2	4, 11	Music, Sport, D of E		Non-denom	

· Scottish Cities ·

EDINBURGH

Name of School	Boys/ Girls/ Co-ed	Day/ Board/ Weekly	Termly fees	Financial help	Intake age/ Prep	Special strengths	Special provisions	Religion	Affiliations
Daniel Stewart's	Boys	Day Boarding	£1012 £1956	Asst places Schols 7	12 Own junior			Non-denom	HMC
Edinburgh Academy	Boys Mixed sixth	Day Boarding Weekly	£1265 £2590 £2545	Asst places 7 pa Schols 5	10, 12 Own junior	Art, Music, Sports	Broad intake, Learning support	Christian	HMC

Name of School	Boys/ Girls/ Co-ed	Day/ Board/ Weekly	Termly fees	Financial help	Intake age/ Prep	Special strengths	Special provisions	Religion	Affiliations
Fettes	Co-ed	Day Boarding	£2095 £3120	Asst places 30 Awards 15 Schols Bursaries	10, 13, 16 Own junior House	Music, Drama, Techno- logy	English	Christian	HMC
George Heriot's	Co-ed	Day	£950	Asst places 234 Schols 29 Foundationers 60	5, 12	Drama, Hockey, Music, Rowing, Rugby	EFL, Dyslexia	Christian	HMC
George Watson's	Co-ed	Day Boarding	£1012 £1956	Asst places 237 Schols/ Bursaries 11	3, 5, 10, 11, 12	Drama, Sport, Music, D of E	Dyslexia, EFL	Christian	HMC
Mary Erskine	Girls	Day Boarding	£1122 £1782	Asst places Schols 4	12 Own junior			Non-denom	GSA
Merchiston	Boys	Day Boarding	£1840 £2860	Asst places 30 Schols	11, 12, 13	Sport, Music, Art, Drama	Extra English	Inter- denom	HMC
Dollar Academy	Co-ed	Day Boarding Weekly	£945 £2095 £1998		12 Own prep		EFL	C of S	HMC BSA SCIS
St George's (Edinburgh)	Girls	Day Boarding	£1050 £2060	Asst places 21 6th form scholarships	5, 9, 10, 11, 16	Sport, Music, Art, Drama		Christian	GSA
St Margaret's (Edinburgh)	Girls	Day Boarding	£1000 £2000	Asst places 54 Schols 5	3, 5, 12	Sport, D of E, Choir	EFL, Dyslexia	Christian	GSA
St Mary's Music	Co-ed	Day Boarding	Apply to school	Schols 12 Means tested aided places	8–11	Music (specialist school)		Christian	CSA

GLASGOW

Name of School	Boys/ Girls/ Co-ed	Day/ Board/ Weekly	Termly fees	Financial help	Intake age/ Prep	Special strengths	Special provisions	Religion	Affiliations
Belmont House	Boys	Day	£895	Asst places 18 pa	3, 5, 12	Sport	Dyslexia	C of S Jewish	

Name of School	Boys/ Girls/ Co-ed	Day/ Board/ Weekly	Termly fees	Financial help	Intake age/ Prep	Special strengths	Special provisions	Religion	Affiliations
Craigholme	Girls	Day	£860	Asst places 20 Bursaries 2–4	5, 12	Music		Christian Jewish	SHA HAS
Fernhill	Girls	Day	£695	Asst places 38	12 Own primary	Music, Chess		RC	
Glasgow Academy	Co-ed	Day	£1025	Asst places 70 Schols	4, 8, 11			Christian	HMC
Glasgow High	Co-ed	Day	£1010	Asst places 38 Schols 2 pa Bursaries 5 pa	4, 10, 11	Sport		Non-denom	HMC
Hutchesons'	Co-ed	Day	£861	Schols Bursaries	4, 9, 12	Music		Christian	HMC
Kelvinside	Boys	Day	£925	Asst places 50 Schols 7 pa	4, 7, 8, 11	Sport	Mild dyslexia	Christian	HMC
Laurel Bank	Girls	Day	£1050	Asst places 50+ pa Schols 8	12 Own junior	Music, Art	Learning support	Christian	GSA
Park	Girls	Day	£981	Asst places 51 Schols 4	5, 12	Art, Athletics	Some special teaching	Christian	GSA
Westbourne	Girls	Day	£1062	Asst places 60 Schols 6	2, 5, 12, 13	Music, Art, Drama		Christian	HAS SCIS

· Scotland (General) ·

Name of School	Boys/ Girls/ Co-ed	Day/ Board/ Weekly	Termly fees	Financial help	Intake age/ Prep	Special strengths	Special provisions	Religion	Affiliations
Albyn	Girls	Day Boarding	£900 £2150	Asst places 22	5, 10, 12	Music, Sport		Non-denom	
St Denis and Cranley	Girls	Day Boarding Weekly	£1055 £2120	Asst places 15 Schols 5 pa Bursaries	5, 9, 12	Drama, Art	EFL, Dyslexia	Christian	GSA

Name of School	Boys/ Girls/ Co-ed	Day/ Board/ Weekly	Termly fees	Financial help	Intake age/ Prep	Special strengths	Special provisions	Religion	Affiliations
Dundee High	Co-ed	Day	£962	Asst places 150 Schols 30	5, 9, 10, 11, 12	Sport, Music, Drama	Dyslexia	Christian	HMC SCIS
Fort Augustus	Boys	Day Boarding Weekly	£1372 £2100 £2000	Asst places 35 Bursaries	12, 14	Small classes, Individual tuition		RC	SCIS
Glenalmond	Boys Mixed sixth	Boarding	£3100	Asst places 36 Schols/ Bursaries 63	12, 13, 16	Sport, Music, Adventurous activities		Episcopalian	HMC
Gordonstoun	Co-ed	Day Boarding	£1860 £2900	Asst places 24 Schols 25 pa Bursaries	13, 16	Music, Drama, Outward Bound, Art, Sport	English	Christian	HMC SHA Round square
Keil	Co-ed	Day Boarding Weekly	£1236 £2169	Asst places 6 pa Schols 6 pa Bursaries 6 pa	10, 11, 12, 13, 16	Sport, Music, Drama	EFL, Dyslexia	Church of Scotland	SHMIS
Kilgraston	Girls	Day Boarding Weekly	£1125 £2185	Asst places Schols Own junior	11, 13, 16	Music, Drama, Art	EFL	RC	GSA SHA BSA HAS
Lomond	Co-ed	Day Boarding Weekly	£928 £1187 £1100	Asst places 44 Schols 15	12	Sport, Traditional music	Specialised help available	Christian	
Loretto	Boys Mixed sixth	Day Boarding	£1966 £2950	Asst places 30 Schols	13, 16	Music, CCF, D of E	Dyslexia, Cystic fibrosis	Interdenom	HMC
Morrison's	Co-ed	Day Boarding	£857 £2225	Asst places 153 Schols/ Bursaries 6	5, 12, 16		ESL	Christian	HMC GSA

Name of School	Boys/ Girls/ Co-ed	Day/ Board/ Weekly	Termly fees	Financial help	Intake age/ Prep	Special strengths	Special provisions	Religion	Affiliations
Queen Victoria	Boys	Boarding	£90	MOD	10	Ceremonial traditions, Pipe band, Highland dancing	Open only to the sons of Scottish service personnel	Non-denom	BSA
Rannoch	Co-ed	Day Boarding	£1490 £2520	Asst places 5 pa Schols 10 pa	10, 11, 12, 13	Art, Sport	Remedial	Christian	SHMIS Round Square
Robert Gordon's	Co-ed	Day Boarding	£913 £2013	Asst places 15 pa Schols 35 pa	5, 9, 11, 16	Sport	EFL	Non-denom	HMC
St Columba's (Kilmacolm)	Co-ed	Day	£936	Asst places 35	3, 11			Christian	SHA HAS
St Leonards	Girls	Day Boarding	£1550 £2950	Asst places 22 Schols/ Bursaries 30	11, 12, 13, 16	Drama, Art, Sport, Music	Dyslexia	Non-denom	GSA
St Margaret's (Aberdeen)	Girls	Day	£836	Asst places 19 Schols 1 pa	3, 11, 12		Dyslexia, Mild visual handicap	Non-denom	GSA, HAS
Strathallan	Co-ed	Day Boarding	£1790 £2550	Asst places 32 Schols 30	10, 11, 12, 13, 16		Remedial English	Inter-denom	HMC
Wellington (Ayr)	Girls	Day Boarding	£1080 £2150	Asst places Bursaries	3, 10, 12	Music, Sport	Some for EFL, Dyslexia	Church of Scotland	GSA

· Wales ·

Name of School	Boys/ Girls/ Co-ed	Day/ Board/ Weekly	Termly fees	Financial help	Intake age/ Prep	Special strengths	Special provisions	Religion	Affiliations
Atlantic College	Co-ed	Boarding	£2750	Schols 170 pa	16	Inter-national environ-ment			United World Colleges
Christ (Brecon)	Boys Mixed sixth	Day Boarding	£1579 £2083	Schols 18 pa Asst places 70	11, 13, 16	Music, Sport	Dyslexia, EFL	Anglican	HMC

Name of School	Boys/ Girls/ Co-ed	Day/ Board/ Weekly	Termly fees	Financial help	Intake age/ Prep	Special strengths	Special provisions	Religion	Affiliations
Howell's (Denbigh)	Girls	Day Boarding	£1564 £2500	Asst places 15 pa Schols/ Bursaries 9 pa	11 Own junior	Music, Art	Dyslexia	Anglican	GSA
Howell's (Llandaff)	Girls	Day Boarding	£908 £1908	Asst places 194 Schols 16	7, 11, 16	Music	English language teaching	Non-denom	GPDST
Llandovery	Co-ed	Day Boarding	£1423 £2181	Asst places 12 pa Schols 10 pa	11, 13, 16	Sport	EFL, Dyslexia	C of W	HMC
Monmouth	Boys	Day Boarding Weekly	£1190 £2033	Asst places 26 pa Schols	6, 11, 13, 16	Sport, Music		C of E	HMC
Penrhos	Girls	Day Boarding Weekly	£1630 £2380	Asst places 12 Schols 5	4, 11, 12, 13	Music, Drama, Art, Outdoor activities	EFL, Dyslexia	Inter- denom	GSA
Rougemont	Co-ed	Day	£1084	Schols 9	3, 4, 11, 16		EFL, Dyslexia	Christian	SHMIS
Rydal	Co-ed	Day Boarding	£1946 £2560	Asst places 10 pa Schols 10 Bursaries	13 Own prep	Music, Art	EFL, Dyslexia	Methodist	HMC
St David's (Brecon)	Girls	Day Boarding Weekly	£586 £1258 £1224	Schols	3, 11	Music, Art	EFL	RC	
St Gerard's	Co-ed	Day	£630	Bursaries	3, 7, 11, 13		EFL, Dyslexia	RC	ISAI